To my wife
ANITA

FOREWORD

by E. Raymond Riegel

Ever since the First Edition of "Industrial Chemistry" appeared in 1928, the aim has been to present in a single volume the numerous chemico-commercial activities which make up industrial chemistry. To quote from the Preface to the First Edition, "Never before has this picture been more fascinating. Change is the order of the day." This is even truer now than it was then, especially since in recent years the physicist has been knocking at the door of the chemist, and our entire viewpoint of the physical world has undergone such profound modifications.

The subject has also expanded greatly. In this new volume, for example, the first chapter deals with the "Economic Aspects of the Chemical Industry," the second chapter with "Industrial Water Supplies and Industrial Waste Disposal." These topics are of present-day importance and were not treated in previous editions. In the third chapter dealing with fuels, natural gas is presented in masterly fashion. The latest developments in rocket and missile propellants are covered. Most important of all, the entire subject of nuclear chemistry, which has burgeoned in recent years, is discussed in this book for the first time.

Not only the subject matter, but the personnel is new. I myself had no part in the selection of the specialists. Each chapter is written by the Editor with the collaboration of authorities entirely of his own choosing. The group of younger scientists have been given a free hand both as to choice of topic and relative lengths of their presentations. The Editor is Dr. James A. Kent, Professor of Chemical Engineering at West Virginia University, Morgantown, West Virginia. One member of the group of collaborators happens to have been a student of mine at the University of Buffalo, I am proud to say. In addition, it was my good fortune to have the support of Gessner G. Hawley, Executive Editor of the Technical Book Division of Reinhold Publishing Corporation.

EDITOR'S PREFACE

The present version of this famous book is being printed thirty-four years after the first edition appeared. Throughout the intervening years Dr. Emil R. Riegel, who originated this work, has done an admirable job of keeping it up to date, and his style and thoroughness have made it a widely used and highly regarded book.

The present author-editor has attempted to prepare the revision in keeping with the high standards set by Dr. Riegel. In a world where everything is spoken of in terms of explosions, the exploding technology of the chemical industry requires an ever-increasing number of words to describe its many facets adequately. Accordingly, to keep this edition within reasonable limits, it was necessary to omit many topics which were covered in earlier editions. Among the missing are cement, metallurgy, leather, electrothermal furnace products, instrumentation, unit operations equipment, and others. Some new subjects have been added, notably, the nuclear industries and pharmaceutical industries. Also, the emphasis in many chapters has been shifted.

The writer wishes to acknowledge the generous support of the many collaborators who made this edition possible. Their cooperation and assistance made the preparation of this work a most satisfying and pleasant experience.

It is impossible in the space available to adequately recognize the efforts of each collaborator. Their names appear in appropriate places in the book.

The editors of technical magazines and publishing houses have been most gracious in granting permission for the reproduction of illustrations, and many industrial concerns contributed drawings and photographs. This assistance is gratefully acknowledged.

Comments and criticisms by readers will be welcome.

JAMES ALBERT KENT

Morgantown, West Virginia
April 3, 1962

PUBLISHER'S PREFACE

In view of the rather special history of this book it seems pertinent for the Publisher to insert a few words of comment. The original volume, which appeared in 1928, was the result of an old friendship between Raymond Riegel and Francis M. Turner, who was at that time in charge of the newly initiated Reinhold technical book program. Indeed, the First Edition of "Industrial Chemistry" was one of a small group of titles which paved the way to the subsequent success and expansion of the Reinhold Book Division. In the last 35 years this work has gone through five large editions, each better organized and more comprehensive than the last. During these years, the author had the encouragement and devoted assistance of his wife, Ethel. Throughout its history the book has been widely adopted for course work in scores of colleges from coast to coast and was for many years one of the leading textbooks in this field. It has also won an established place in the literature of chemical technology, as attested by voluminous correspondence which Dr. Riegel has maintained with industrial chemists throughout the world.

As a result of his long and richly deserved retirement from academic and industrial life, Dr. Riegel decided to turn over the responsibility of carrying on his book to Dr. James A. Kent. The present volume, entitled *"Riegel's Industrial Chemistry,"* though somewhat different in its emphasis and manner of presentation, endeavors to maintain the tradition established by its predecessors. It is the Publisher's earnest hope that it will continue and even increase the distinguished contribution to the literature so capably provided by the first five editions.

CONTENTS

1. ECONOMIC ASPECTS OF THE CHEMICAL INDUSTRY   1
   R. F. Messing, A. D. Little, Inc., Cambridge, Mass.
   J. S. Sconce, Hooker Chemical Co., Niagara Falls, N. Y.
2. INDUSTRIAL WATER SUPPLY AND INDUSTRIAL WASTE
   DISPOSAL   10
   Thomas J. Powers, Dow Industrial Service (Div. of the Dow
   Chemical Co.), Cleveland, Ohio
3. FUELS AND THEIR UTILIZATION   36
   Richard C. Corey, Research Director, Pittsburgh Coal Re-
   search Center, U. S. Dept. of Interior, Bureau of Mines,
   Pittsburgh, Pa.
4. SULFURIC ACID AND SULFUR   66
   E. Raymond Riegel, Professor Emeritus, University of Buffalo
5. SYNTHETIC NITROGEN PRODUCTS   86
   R. V. Green, E. I. du Pont de Nemours & Co., Wilmington,
   Del.
6. MISCELLANEOUS HEAVY CHEMICALS   126
   J. A. Falcone, D. J. Saunders, Allied Chemical Corp.
   D. W. Duncan, Virginia Smelting Co.
7. INDUSTRIAL FERMENTATION PROCESSES   180
   Samuel C. Beesch and Fred W. Tanner, Jr., Chas. Pfizer &
   Co., Brooklyn, N. Y.
8. COAL CARBONIZATION AND RECOVERY OF COAL
   CHEMICALS   221
   Charles C. Russell, Koppers Co., Inc., Pittsburgh, Pa.
   Ganson Taggart, Badger Mfg. Co., Cambridge, Mass.
9. RUBBER   240
   R. L. Bebb, Firestone Tire & Rubber Co., Akron, Ohio
10. SYNTHETIC PLASTICS   274
    Robert W. Jones, Monsanto Chemical Company Plastics
    Div., Springfield, Mass.

11. MAN-MADE TEXTILE FIBERS 349
  R. W. Work, Chemstrand Research Center, Inc. Research
  Triangle Park, N. C.

12. ANIMAL AND VEGETABLE OILS, FATS, AND WAXES 399
  H. G. Kirschenbauer, Colgate-Palmolive Co., New York,
  N. Y.

13. SOAP AND SYNTHETIC DETERGENTS 428
  J. C. Harris, Monsanto Chemical Co., St. Louis, Mo.

14. PETROLEUM AND ITS PRODUCTS; PETROCHEMICALS 478
  A. F. Galli, College of Engineering, West Virginia University, Morgantown, W. Va.

15. INDUSTRIAL CHEMISTRY OF WOOD 523
  Edwin C. Jahn and Frank W. Lorey, College of Forestry,
  Syracuse University, Syracuse, N. Y.

16. SUGAR AND STARCH 601
  Sidney M. Cantor, DCA Food Industries, Inc., New York,
  N. Y.

17. INDUSTRIAL GASES 623
  R. M. Neary, Linde Co., New York, N. Y.

18. PHOSPHATES, PHOSPHORUS, FERTILIZERS, POTASSIUM SALTS,
  NATURAL ORGANIC FERTILIZERS, UREA 649
  Vincent Sauchelli, National Plant Food Institute, Washing-
  ton, D. C.

19. CHEMICAL EXPLOSIVES AND MISSILE PROPELLANTS 674
  Melvin A. Cook, University of Utah, Salt Lake City, Utah
  George F. Huff, Callery Chemical Co.

20. PHARMACEUTICAL INDUSTRIES 708
  John J. Miskel and John E. Carlson, Chas. Pfizer & Co., Inc.,
  Brooklyn, N. Y.

21. INSECTICIDES, FUNGICIDES, HERBICIDES, AND RELATED
  PRODUCTS 732
  E. R. de Ong, Albany, Calif.

22. PIGMENTS, PAINTS, VARNISHES, LACQUERS, PRINTING INKS 755
  Robert F. Toomey, John Carroll University, Cleveland, Ohio

23. DYE APPLICATION, MANUFACTURE OF DYE INTERMEDIATES
  AND DYES 781
  R. A. Brooks, Jackson Laboratory, E. I. du Pont de Nemours
  & Company, Wilmington, Del.

24. THE NUCLEAR INDUSTRY 846
  W. K. Eister, Chemical Technology Div., Oak Ridge
  National Laboratory, Oak Ridge, Tenn.

25. SYNTHETIC ORGANIC CHEMICALS 891
  William H. Haberstroh and Daniel E. Collins, Dow Chemical Company, Midland, Mich.

1

ECONOMIC ASPECTS OF THE CHEMICAL INDUSTRY

In collaboration with R. F. Messing* and J. S. Sconce†

IN CONSIDERING THE PRESENT STATUS of and economic outlook for the chemical industry, the problem of definition becomes immediately apparent. To many, the word "chemicals" refers only to discrete products derived by reactions of elements or compounds, materials which the Bureau of the Census lists as industrial organic or inorganic compounds.

The broader, more frequently used term for classifying the chemical industry is "chemicals and allied products." According to the Bureau of the Census, this term includes:

1. Industrial inorganic chemicals
2. Industrial organic chemicals
3. Drugs and medicines
4. Soaps and related products
5. Paints and allied products
6. Fertilizers
7. Gum and wood chemicals
8. Vegetable and animal oils

* Arthur D. Little, Inc., Cambridge, Mass.
† Hooker Chemical Co., Niagara Falls, N. Y.

9. Miscellaneous chemical products—printing ink, carbon black, explosives, etc.

An even more inclusive term, which embraces most of the industries covered in this text, is "chemical process industries"; this embraces not only the nine categories mentioned above, but also those in which the unit processes are the basis of manufacturing operations, such as petroleum refining, glassmaking, papermaking, and similar fields.

The relative size of these different fields is demonstrated by their sales values as of 1958.

	1958 Sales in Billions of Dollars
Industrial organic and inorganic chemicals	12.2
Chemical and allied products	23.2
Chemical process industries	79.5

Several other methods may be used to classify operations of the chemical industry involving differentiation between raw materials used in chemical manufacture, intermediate materials, or final end products; but for our purpose "chemical process industries" is adequate.

Integration and Diversification

In the past, many chemical companies were organized and prospered by the simple procedure of combining two raw materials and marketing the product. Today, however, under the forces of competition and pressure for higher returns on both sales and invested capital, there has been a tendency for the single level manufacturer to produce a greater percentage of his raw materials and also to process his principal product into end products entering the ultimate consumer field.

In addition to the trend toward integration, many companies wishing (1) to avoid cyclical trends associated with a given industry, (2) to invest available capital in fields that promise adequate returns, and (3) to participate in some of the more dynamic areas of growth in American industry, are becoming increasingly concerned with chemical diversification. The result is a pattern with no clear differentiation between, for example, a petroleum producer, a petrochemical company, and a chemical manufacturer. Petrochemistry is, in fact, one of the best illustrations of this diversification, since many major oil companies have found that opportunities for profitable operation and future growth may be more satisfactorily attained by combining the chemical field with the traditional areas of geological exploration, oil production, refining, and marketing.

Acquisition is one method by which many corporations have chosen to move into related fields involving either integration or diversification. In the manufacture of plastics, for example, producers of the primary plastic or polymer have acquired end-product fabricating operations. Such action permits relatively rapid growth without creating a need for heavy investment in research; it discourages increased production capacity at a time when industry's requirements are amply satisfied by existing facilities; and it provides a means of obtaining management and technical talent associated with the new field without creating a need for extensive training.

Investment Trends

During the past decade the flow of capital into the chemical process industries has been surprisingly great, and investment in chemical and allied products has been a sizeable part of the total.

	Capital Spending in Millions of Dollars (1959)
Chemicals and allied products	$ 1,188
Petroleum refining	692
Pulp and paper	613
Rubber	178
Stone, clay, and glass	542
All chemical process	$ 3,213
All manufacturing	$10,025

The major portion of this investment has been for new plants and equipment with a much smaller portion for modernization of older plants, particularly in fields involving products such as soda ash, chlorine, and sulfuric acid, as well as those for which obsolescence is a significant factor. New methods for the manufacture of products such as ethylene oxide and glycol, dibasic acids, acrylonitrile, and caprolactam have given rise to new plant facilities intended primarily for economic manufacture rather than additional output.

A number of factors influence or direct this flow of capital, briefly:

1. Capacity or overcapacity, determined by existing installations and capital already committed to new installations.
2. Import and export trends influenced by monetary, political, and economic forces.
3. The effect of by-products and undesirable co-products on a long-range economic picture.
4. Process technology changes brought about by research and development, resulting in increased capacity in existing plants, or construction of new plants, thus making existing facilities unprofitable.
5. Conversion of existing equipment and facilities to the manufacture of different products both old and new.

The necessity to observe, predict, and evaluate all these factors is probably the most important responsibility of management in this currently expanding chemical economy.

Important Characteristics of the Chemical Industry

The chemical industry, in general, and particularly the industrial chemical field, have several distinguishing characteristics:

1. Rapid Growth Rate. The rapid growth trend of industrial chemicals and allied products as contrasted with all manufacturing operations, as well as the increasing importance of the chemical industry in this nation's

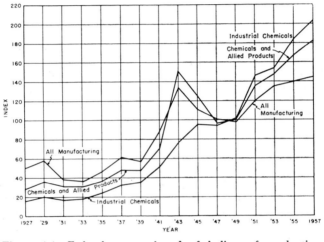

Figure 1.1. Federal reserve board of indices of production (1947–1949 = 100).

economy, is clearly shown in Figure 1.1, a graph of relative Federal reserve board indices of production. So far, there is no indication of a tapering off in the growth of either of these two indices.

Based on a 1935 chemical use index of 100, the Index of Chemical Consumption in *Chemical Engineering* reached an estimated 328 for 1959.[2] The industrial use of chemicals based on the index is given in Table 1.1. A recent article in *Fortune* magazine, which predicts that chemicals will increase from the present 11 per cent of total industrial production to about 15 per cent in 1970, may be some indication of the future of the chemical industry.

2. High Obsolescence and Dependence on Research. The present high sales volume of most major chemical companies, representing new developments over the past fifteen years, demonstrates the significance of research achievement in successful performance in the industry. The total expenditure for research and development in the "chemical and allied products" group is now estimated at $600 million, or slightly less than 3 per cent of the total reported sales. The chemical industry is estimated to support 20 per cent of all the private research undertaken in all fields of industrial activity. New

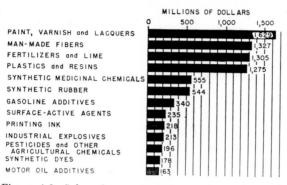

Figure 1.2. Sales of some important end-use chemical groups for 1958. (*Manufacturing Chemists Association*)

products, replacement of natural products, and development of more economic methods of manufacture of chemical materials all constitute important areas of research activity.

3. High Investment and Low Labor Component of Chemical Manufacturing. The chemical industry now ranks among the highest of all industries in capital investment per production worker and per unit of sales realization. Recent estimates of the National Industrial Conference Board indicate that

TABLE 1.1. INDUSTRIAL USE OF CHEMICALS*

	Coal Products	Explosives	Fertilizers	Glass	Iron & Steel	Leather	Paint & Varnish	Paper & Pulp	Petroleum Refining	Plastics	Rayon	Rubber	Textiles	Total
1949	9.6	7.2	52.4	18.1	12.0	4.2	21.9	22.3	21.5	9.6	23.1	4.8	9.2	216
1950	10.3	8.4	54.4	21.7	14.8	4.4	25.8	26.7	22.6	16.0	30.4	6.0	11.4	252
1951	11.2	8.5	56.2	22.3	16.1	4.0	27.2	33.1	25.7	17.3	30.6	6.2	11.5	267
1952	9.9	8.7	59.9	22.2	14.3	4.3	26.7	28.6	25.8	16.9	27.3	6.0	10.5	261
1953	11.9	9.0	58.6	23.3	17.1	4.2	28.1	30.3	27.7	18.6	28.7	6.3	10.6	274
1954	10.3	8.1	60.4	23.6	13.5	3.9	27.2	31.3	27.5	19.1	26.1	5.8	9.7	266
1955	12.1	9.2	65.1	25.4	17.9	4.2	30.4	35.1	29.6	23.1	30.0	7.2	10.4	299
1956	11.2	10.8	68.2	26.0	17.6	4.1	31.9	37.1	31.5	24.3	27.6	6.7	10.3	307
1957	11.3	10.8	67.5	26.7	17.2	4.1	32.1	36.4	31.4	24.5	27.4	6.8	9.6	306
1958	8.0	9.7	67.2	26.7	13.0	4.1	32.1	36.4	29.9	24.7	23.6	6.2	9.2	291
1959[a]	10.0	10.3	79.1	26.5	19.0	4.3	34.4	39.0	30.5	31.6	26.3	7.1	10.2	328

[a] Estimated.

* Source: *Chemical Engineering*, p. 90, Sept. 21, 1959.

the chemical industry accounts for an investment of $27,000 per worker as compared with an average of $13,600 for all manufacturing activity. The chemical industry has always been rather extensively automated, but closed-loop systems of process control will give even higher yields and greater control of manufacturing processes, with correspondingly higher efficiency from the available production force.

Employment in the chemical industry consists not only of process workers who operate the equipment but also of plant-maintenance personnel, and auxiliary workers who handle materials and accounting. The total number of employees in the "chemical and allied products" field has been reported by the Bureau of Labor Statistics as 846,000. This relatively low figure is reflected both in high earning per employee and in low labor cost per unit of finished product. In major chemical companies, labor now accounts for only about 13 per cent of the total manufacturing cost.

4. Stable Pricing. The prices of chemical products in general have not risen as rapidly as the prices of all manufactured products and have been surprisingly stable in their movements, as indicated in the following table.

Wholesale Price Index (Basis 1947–1949 = 100)*

Year	All Manufactured Products	Chemicals and Allied Products	All Industrial Chemicals	Inorganic Industrial Chemicals	Organic Industrial Chemicals
1952	113.2	104.5	115.2	119.4	113.1
1957	125.6	109.5	123.5	138.2	116.3
1958	126.0	110.4	123.5	139.9	115.5
1959 (Dec.)	128.6	110.0	124.0	141.0	115.6

* Source: U. S. Department of Labor, Bureau of Labor Statistics.

This is due partly to more economical manufacturing methods and larger scale production, but it is also the result of strong competition. The relatively fast rise in the inorganic industrial chemical index is the result of increasingly more expensive capital investments in new plants and equipment.

5. Organized Effort for Commercial Development. The chemical industry has been a leader in the utilization of the techniques of market analysis, and has practiced combined industry reporting and statistical evaluation for many years. Others are following this pattern but few have reached the level of the chemical industry.

6. Competition. While many segments of the industry have traditionally been production centered, emphasizing manufacturing rather than sales outlets, marketing processes have assumed greater importance as more companies have entered the field and capacity has been expanded.

In 1958 it was estimated that the chemical industry operated at only 72 per cent capacity; the result was high fixed charges associated with the reduced output since depreciation and many other aspects of cost cannot be reduced in proportion to output. Thus decline in the industry's profits was considerable, proportionately much greater than the change in rate of operation. In 1959 the rate of activity increased to about 80–85 per cent of plant capacity, giving the more efficient companies an opportunity to capitalize on the increased volume and stabilized charges.

A rule of thumb for return on new investment is about 10 per cent after taxes, but this may vary considerably, depending on the proprietary interest of the manufacturer. While it is undoubtedly true that manufacturing know-how regarding many chemical products is widely available, there are still many other categories where process exclusiveness permits a higher rate of return in new facilities.

Impact of the Foreign Chemical Industries[4]

The continued emphasis on expansion of underdeveloped countries and the rising economy of nations recovering from World War II have provided both additional markets and competition for chemical manufacturers. Chemical production in the United States during the war went far ahead of that in most other countries. During this period, United States chemical producers had access to low-cost capital and raw materials while many foreign nations competing in the export field were suffering from the ravages of war.

Recovery in these countries has been rapid, and many foreign chemical companies are in a period of impressive growth. During 1957, total chemical production in the sixteen nations of the Organization for European Economic Cooperation increased 10 per cent, compared with 3.5 per cent in the United States. The importance of foreign producers is apparent from the data in Table 1.2.

Imperial Chemical Industries, Ltd., for example, probably ranks next to du Pont in chemical production, operates over 100 plants in the United Kingdom, and during the period 1948–1958 doubled its output of chemicals. This company is one of Britain's largest exporters and sells over a quarter of its production in 42 countries.

Similar organizations operate in other countries. Montecatini, in Italy, is a leader in research and engineering, having developed processes for plastics and urea fertilizers for which it receives royalties from consumers all over the world. Besides its ammonia process in use in 24 countries, this firm recently announced a new formaldehyde process, developed catalysts for controlling stereospecific polymerization of plastics, and is active in the development of new synthetic rubbers.

In Germany, Badische, Bayer and Hoechst are the chemical leaders. Historically, the German chemical industry has been based on coal and saline deposits. However, petrochemicals figure prominently in the post-war expansion of West Germany; 190 million dollars went for new petrochemical plants during the period 1945–1957 when a total of 4 billion dollars was being invested in its chemical industry. In the United States, Mobay is a joint subsidiary of Monsanto and Bayer, while Badische and Dow hold another joint subsidiary. Still another German company, Chemische Werke Huels, has shown impressive growth, more than doubling its sales to 125 million dollars from 1951 to 1957.

In France, Rhone-Poulenc, Etablissements Kuhlman, Saint Gobain, and Pechiney are the chemical giants. Their products range from pharmaceuticals, cosmetics, and fine organics to plastics and electrochemicals. The

TABLE 1.2. SALES AND CAPITAL EXPENDITURES OF SOME LEADING CHEMICAL FIRMS*
(MILLIONS OF DOLLARS)

	Total Sales		Export Sales		Capital Spending	
	1957	1958	1957	1958	1957	1958
Du Pont	1,964	1,825	163	161	220	231
Imperial Chemical Industries (Gr. Br.)	1,300	1,300	215	207	142	126
Union Carbide (U. S.)	1,395	1,296	98	91	191	144
Farbenfabriken Bayer (W. Ger.)	441	479	183	200	107	70
Badische Anilin & Soda Fabrik (W. Ger.)	430	460	161	170	54	60
Farbwerke Hoechst (W. Ger.)	421	450	136	140		57
Montecatini (Italy)	244	235	70	59(est)	21	36
Rohm & Haas (U. S.)	174	177	21	22(est)	35	13
Canadian Industries (Canada)	143	141	. . .	. . .	16	12
Chemische Werke Huels (W. Ger.)	125	137	44	48	16	18
Sumitomo Chemical (Japan)	80	84	12	12	20	12
Du Pont of Canada (Canada)	73	82	. . .	. . .	15	11
Mitsubishi Chemical Industries (Japan)	50	57	. . .	. . .	35	17
Toyo Koatsu (Japan)	54	57	19	17	2	2

* Source: *Chemical Engineering*, p. 56, June 29, 1959.

commercialization of sulfur from natural gas adds materially to the French chemical economy. During 1958, chemical production in France rose 15 per cent and was expected to go to 40 per cent by 1961.

Similarly, there are flourishing chemical industries in Switzerland, Japan, Belgium, the Netherlands, and other countries, often developing in cooperation with United States firms. Du Pont introduced nylon manufacture in Japan in 1951, and saran, acrylonitrile, and polyesters soon followed. In June, 1960, Japan ranked second only to the United States in synthetic fiber production.[1]

The United States Industry in Foreign Markets[3]

Although a few chemical producers have long been active in foreign markets, most have developed an interest only in recent years. Monsanto and Pfizer, in petrochemicals and pharmaceuticals, respectively, were among the first to undertake foreign expansion. Union Carbide, long engaged in production and sale of electrochemical products abroad, has only recently put its petrochemical potential to work on the foreign scene. A smaller company, Reichhold Chemicals, has a greater geographical spread than any other American chemical firm.

TABLE 1.3. FOREIGN SALES OF SOME AMERICAN
CHEMICAL PRODUCERS *

	Foreign Sales			Foreign Sales	
	Million Dollars	% of Total Sales		Million Dollars	% of Total Sales
Du Pont	161	9	Merck	56	27
Union Carbide	210–280	15–20	American Cyanamid	79[a]	15
Monsanto	172[b]	23	Dow	57[c]	9
Reichhold	55[b]	42	Rohm and Haas	21[c,d]	12
Pfizer	85	39	Olin Mathieson	49[b,d]	8

[a] Not including Canadian sales.
[b] Sales of foreign affiliates only.
[c] Export sales only.
[d] Estimated.
* Source: *Chemical Engineering*. p. 84, May 18, 1959.

European counterparts of American chemical manufacturers have a substantial head start in exploiting the new markets for chemicals around the world. American companies which have appreciable sales abroad are listed in Table 1.3.

This trend toward foreign expansion into the countries with reasonable political stability is expected to increase at an ever growing rate.

REFERENCES

1. *Chem. Eng. News*, **38**, No. 23, 66 (1960).
2. *Chem. Eng.*, **66**, No. 19, 90 (1959).
3. Windisch, R. P., *Chem. Eng.*, **66**, No. 10, 82 (1959).
4. Windisch, R. P., *Chem. Eng.*, **66**, No. 13, 56 (1959).

2

INDUSTRIAL WATER SUPPLY AND INDUSTRIAL WASTE DISPOSAL

In collaboration with Thomas J. Powers*

INDUSTRIAL WATER USES

THE MANUFACTURING INDUSTRIES need water for a great variety of purposes. Whenever locating a new plant or expanding an existing plant it is necessary to study the water demands and make the most economical use of the available water source. A flow diagram should be prepared which shows the relationship of water demand to process material flow. When properly evaluated and engineered, the flow diagram can point up many economies in water use.

Heat Transfer. The largest demand for water in the manufacturing industries is for heat transfer. Wherever heat is to be extracted, water is usually the transfer medium. Condensers, heat exchangers, coolers, refrigeration and air-conditioning equipment, and cooling towers fall under this classification. Large steam-power stations require 800 tons of water per ton of coal consumed to condense exhaust steam.[15] It is not uncommon for a steam-electric generating plant to pump 1,200 millions of gallons of water a day. It is stated that a cooling tower can reduce the water demand of a steam plant from 60 gals/kw-h to 1 gal/kw-h.[13] The cooling tower may

---

* Dow Industrial Service (Division of the Dow Chemical Company), Cleveland, Ohio.

have a 1 per cent loss from evaporation, a 0.2 per cent loss from entrainment and a blowdown of about 0.4 per cent. Thus on a 100 gpm recirculated system the need for make-up from supply might be 16 gpm. One large chemical complex on the Gulf of Mexico pumps 1,440 millions of gallons per day of sea water, most of which is for heat transfer.

Steam. A pound of *steam* requires a pound of water. In the case of electric steam generation, the amount of water required as make-up in the condensate is usually a very small demand. However, where large amounts of process steam or heating steam are used without condensate collection the water use can be very important. One large chemical complex uses over 5 million gallons per day of boiler feed water. A large utility furnishing steam to heat the business section of a city may require several millions of gallons per day for boiler feed.

Raw Material. Water is a *raw material* in the strict sense only when it becomes a part of the product. Thus water is a very important raw material in the beverage industry and the chemical industry. However, water finds many other applications in chemical processing. It is a *reactant* in the manufacture of acetylene from calcium carbide and in the manufacture of phosphoric acid.

The *solvent* uses of water are myriad. Good housekeeping and safety require that floors and equipment be kept clean. Since water is an almost universal solvent this use is common to all industry. Water is also the cheapest liquid available. Impurities in raw materials, intermediate products and final products are often removed by water washing. The solvent action of water on salt is the basis of mining for the production of salt, chlorine and caustic. The rinsing of pickled sheets and galvanized parts is an example of solvent use in the steel industry.

Miscellaneous Uses. Other common industrial water uses are for *material handling* such as sluicing sugar beets from stock pile to factory. Coal is slurried with water and pumped for many miles. Sulphur is mined by melting with hot water. Water handles paper pulp through processing to the paper machines. There are cases where *effluent dilution* requirements may exceed all other needs for water. Here the water requirements are based on restrictive standards on effluent quality.

The use of water for *kinetic energy* is best exemplified by the use of high pressure jets to clean metal parts or tube bundles and to de-bark logs.

Water is also used for *nuclear shielding* or as a moderator in nuclear energy reactors since water itself does not yield any important radioactivities when exposed to a neutron flux.[5]

Sanitary Uses. Every industry must furnish employees with a safe, palatable drinking water. This may be distributed in 5 gallon jugs, piped from a municipal supply, or be a part of the plant water system. Where potable water serves all sanitary fixtures the water needed in an industry is about

15 gallons per person per shift. It is important that the potable water system be engineered so that cross connections to other water systems are rigidly avoided. Potable water for sanitary and process use must meet the standards of the local Health Department. Most Health Departments accept the standards established by the U. S. Public Health Service.

TABLE 2.1. TYPICAL INDUSTRIAL WATER DEMANDS[9]

Industry or Product	Approximate Water Used
Alcohol, industrial	600,000 per 1,000 bu grain
Gunpowder	200,000 gal per ton explosive
Oxygen, liquid	2,000 gal per 1,000 cu ft O_2
Soda ash	15,000 gal per ton 58% Na_2CO_3
Sulfuric acid (contact)	4,000 gal per ton 100% H_2SO_4
Beer	470 gal per bbl beer
Meat packing house	55,000 gal per 100 hog units
Milk receiving and bottling	450 gal per 100 gal milk
Sugar-beet	20,000 gal per ton sugar
Rayon	200,000 gal per ton yarn
Wool scouring and bleaching	40,000 gal per ton goods
Air conditioning	10,000 gal per person per season
Coke by-product	1,500 gal per ton coke
Tannery-leather	16,000 gal per ton hides
Oil refining	77,000 gal per 100 bbl crude
Steel plant	20,000 gal per ton of steel

SOURCES OF WATER FOR INDUSTRY

The primary source of all water supply is rain. The average rainfall on the United States is about 30 inches per year. Approximately 20 inches of this amount is lost by evaporation and transpiration. This leaves some 10 inches to replenish ground water and surface water.

Ground Water. Geologists estimate that ground water, in place, is equivalent to 10 years' precipitation, which is far more than all the country's surface water. It is found in saturated zones of sand, gravel and porous rock. Industry draws heavily on ground water supplies where these are available. Most state geologists and the U. S. Geological Survey have information about the location and yield of the various aquifers. Ground waters are recharged by rain percolating into the ground. Sometimes the recharge is from distant places. Water from a 150-foot-deep well at York, Nebraska, was estimated to have fallen fifty years previously.[13] Water pumped from wells in the Mattaponi formation just east of Williamsburg, Va. is estimated to have been rain which fell on the east side of the Blue Ridge Mountains thousands of years ago.

The extensive use of ground water has caused serious lowering of the ground water table in some areas, notably Long Island, New York, southern California, Texas and Arizona. This is the evident result of withdrawals in excess of recharge. The alluvial deposits near the Ohio and Mississippi rivers furnish tremendous volumes of water for industry in the St. Louis and Cincinnati areas. These aquifers are recharged from the rivers.

Surface Waters. Rivers and lakes supply about three-fourths of the total water pumped for industrial and municipal use. The Great Lakes are said to be the largest reservoirs of fresh surface water in the world. The rivers connecting the Great Lakes are also among the largest in the country. Lake Superior is probably one of the best and largest sources of cool fresh water. Information on the discharge of surface waters is available through the Water Supply Papers published by the U. S. Geological Survey—Surface Water Branch. The early industrial growth of the United States was due in part to the availability of water power and water transportation.

Industry must depend on surface waters for effluent dilution even though an adequate ground water supply is used. The existing quality of the water can restrict the amount of materials it can safely receive and the uses to which it can be put.

Water Quality. In the strict sense absolutely "pure" water is not found in nature. Since water is an almost universal solvent it dissolves gases even when it falls as rain. As soon as it reaches the ground it starts dissolving materials. The impurities dissolved depend on the chemical composition of the rocks and soils contacted. The most common impurity is calcium bicarbonate, formed by the CO_2 which is dissolved in water when it passes over limestone, $CaCO_3$. Water quality is defined by temperature, suspended solids, bacterial count, color, odor and dissolved impurities.

One of the important water-quality determinations is temperature since the total volume required is largely dependent upon temperature. Most deep wells will average close to 55° F while the range of maximum temperature of surface waters in the United States is from 65° to 85° F.

One of the early terms used to express water quality was *hardness*. This refers to the soap-consuming power of the water and is actually measured by the formation of suds with a standard soap solution. Since soaps are the sodium salts of fatty acids such as stearic, palmitic and oleic, they will precipitate as the calcium, magnesium, iron or manganese salts if these ions are present in the water. Waters are broadly classified as "hard" or "soft" but this is arbitrary since in each section of the country we find a different interpretation of these relative terms. Hardness is the total parts per million (ppm) of the calcium as $CaCO_3$ plus the magnesium as $CaCO_3$. (ppm hardness as $CaCO_3$ = (ppm Ca $\times$ 2.497 + ppm Mg $\times$ 4.116).) Waters containing less than 60 ppm hardness are considered "soft" while waters with over 180 ppm can be considered "hard." Iron and manganese salts which may cause product discoloration will also cause hardness but are seldom found in waters in amounts significant to the total hardness.

Hardness is also subclassified as "temporary" or "permanent." "Temporary" hardness is the hardness which can be removed by boiling. The scale in the tea kettle is temporary hardness as $CaCO_3$ which precipitated when bound CO_2 was driven from $Ca(HCO_3)_2$. "Permanent" hardness is hardness which is noncarbonate and is usually $CaCl_2$, $CaSO_4$, $MgCl_2$, or $MgSO_4$.

The *alkalinity* of a water is its acid neutralizing capacity to pH 4.6. Thus carbonate hardness is a part of the total alkalinity. Alkalinity is also expressed in ppm as $CaCO_3$. Alkalinity can be subdivided by titration into caustic, carbonate and bicarbonate. The total alkalinity is determined by titration with acid to methyl orange end point pH 4.6. An identical sample is titrated with acid to the phenolphthalein end point, pH 8.3. This titration gives all the caustic and one-half of the carbonate alkalinity. The

Figure 2.1. Forced draft-cooling tower incorporating biologic waste treatment. (*Courtesy Sun Oil Co.*)

best sources of information on water quality are the state health departments and the U. S. Geological Survey Water Supply Papers. Many handbooks give comparative analyses of ground and surface waters.[9,12]

Re-use of Water. The limitations on water supply in certain areas have forced industry to re-use water many times over. The cooling tower (Fig. 2.1) is a familiar structure where large heat transfer demands exist. The increasing demand for air conditioning has necessitated the installation of cooling towers of various sizes to permit transfer of building heat. The municipal water distribution and sewerage systems could not be expected to accommodate the water required for air conditioning on a once-through basis. As water is re-used it dissolves more substances and through evaporation there is a build-up of dissolved solids. This quality change necessitates discarding or "purging" a portion of the recirculated stream to maintain a constant dissolved solids concentration. The increased dissolved solids and the oxygen saturation require treatment to keep the system operative.

The municipal water supply may be the cheapest water source available if the user can recirculate heat exchange water. Normally a heat exchange and fire protection system can be obtained by an industry from an adequate surface water or well water for less than $30 per million gallons. Due to the distribution system costs and maintenance of minimum pressures a city water is rarely available to industry for less than $60 per million gallons. Treated, recirculated cooling tower water will cost about $30 per million gallons. The economics of using the municipal supply will become apparent only after a careful study of all the cost factors involved.

Sea Water: Brackish Water. Heat exchange is the only important industrial use of sea water or brackish water. The cost of making fresh water from sea water by the most economical method will pay for transporting fresh water for hundreds of miles if necessary. From the research work sponsored by the Saline Water Program of the U. S. Department of the Interior the electrodialysis or charged membrane method stands a fair chance of producing fresh water (1,000 ppm total solids) from sea water (35,000 ppm total solids) at a cost of less than $500 per million gallons.

Stable membranes are now being made which will pass water molecules and positive ions or water molecules and negative ions. By a multiple series arrangement of cells composed of as many as 230 parallel, $\frac{1}{32}$-inch thick membranes ($\frac{1}{8}$-inch apart) between two voltage plates a satisfactory (1,000 ppm solids) water can be produced. It is estimated that the cost of a 1,000 MGD plant to produce water by this method would exceed $390,000,000.[8]

It is reasonable to predict that electrodialysis will permit the use of many brackish waters now unfit for industrial purposes.

PROBLEMS CREATED BY INDUSTRIAL WATER USE

Corrosion. Since water is an almost universal solvent its use will create problems. Perhaps the most costly result of water use is the damage to equipment through corrosion (Fig. 2.2). Basically the corrosion of metal surfaces by water is the result of the solution of the metal. According to the electrolytic theory of corrosion, as iron atoms become positive ions and pass into solution, positive hydrogen ions are plated out.

At anode area

$$Fe - 2e = Fe^{++}$$

At cathode area

$$2H^+ + 2e \rightarrow 2H$$

It is postulated that the hydrogen forms a molecular film on the metal surface and as long as this film is maintained there will be no further corrosion. If dissolved oxygen is present in the water it will react with the hydrogen and remove the protective film. Oxygen also reacts with the iron to form Fe_2O_3 or Fe_3O_4 at temperatures in excess of $100°$ C. These iron oxides will, in turn, form a protective coating on the metal surface if deposited. The erosive effect of high velocity removes these deposits. It can be seen then that corrosion is related to oxygen content of the water. The rate of corrosion is affected by

1. Temperature
2. Dissolved solids
3. Hydrogen-ion concentration
4. Velocity

Corrosion can also be caused by iron bacteria and sulfate-reducing bacteria. These bacteria adhering to metal surfaces release acids which cause localized corrosion.

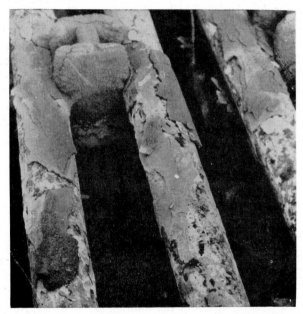

Figure 2.2. Scaled and corroded open-box condenser tubes. (*Courtesy Dow Industrial Service*)

Deposits. The maintenance of process efficiency is often related to water use. Heat transfer surfaces which become coated with deposits will have a reduced transfer capacity. Water flow is also restricted and hot spots in the system may develop, creating localized corrosion and further rapid deposition.

Deposits can result from corrosion, precipitation of dissolved solids, and bacterial growths. Deposits are classified as sludge, scale, biological deposits, and corrosion products. Sludge is soft, non-adhering material, whereas scale is tightly held to the metal surface and will not wash off. Biological deposits are bacterial slimes, fungi or algae which adhere to wetted surfaces and trap materials carried in suspension. Corrosion products which form deposits are not uniformly deposited and form "tubercules" on the metal surfaces. The most common deposit found in water systems is $CaCO_3$. The solubility of $CaCO_3$ at normal water temperatures is approximately 15 ppm; when

Figure 2.3. Calcium carbonate deposited in cast-iron water main. (*Courtesy Dow Industrial Service*)

Figure 2.4. Scale of Fe_2O_3 and $CaCO_3$ in an industrial water line before and after chemical cleaning. (*Courtesy Dow Industrial Service*)

CO_2 is driven off from $Ca(HCO_3)_2$ the resulting $CaCO_3$ will precipitate. Scales have been permitted to grow to the point of almost complete stoppage (Fig. 2.3). In such cases the operation must be shut down to permit chemical or mechanical cleaning (Fig. 2.4). Examination of the chemical analysis of a scale may show the presence of a wide variety of materials such as calcium carbonate, calcium sulfate, silicates, iron carbonates, magnesium hydrate and organic materials. A good analysis of the scale often points the way to corrective measures.

Erosion. High velocity and resulting turbulence in pipes and tubes can cause damage through erosion. Where suspensions exist the impact of these particles can wear away metal surfaces at an increased rate. The erosion of corrosion products also hastens the corrosive action. One of the best examples of erosion is the pumping of dredged materials where the solids separate and move along the bottom half of a pipe line. It is necessary to rotate this pipe quite often to avoid developing leaks along the bottom.

Biological Growths. Slime growths, which may be bacteria, fungi or algae, depending on the location, can affect the efficiency of heat transfer equipment. Biological growths can also contribute to corrosion and cause odors in the water which might restrict usefulness. Flow rates through filters and ion-exchange beds can be seriously retarded by algae and flocculent bacteria.

Pollution. Water pollution affects water quality and water use. In the strict sense industry cannot use water without adding something to it. Waters used for cleaning operations, water passing through a condenser, condensates from cracking operations and recirculated water all pick up impurities in suspension or solution.

Under the common law doctrine of water use every riparian owner is entitled to use as much water as he needs provided he returns it to the stream undiminished in volume and unchanged in quality. The courts have interpreted this into the doctrine of "reasonable use" so that a "reasonable" amount of consumptive use and a "reasonable" change of quality is permitted.

A water may be said to be polluted when its usefulness is impaired. Contamination of water has the connotation of being dangerous to health. Water may become polluted through the addition of "too much" of almost anything.

The more a water is used, the more impurities are added and the more chances for pollution exist. It is reported that the daily withdrawals of water from the Mahoning River in eastern Ohio approach twice the average flow and ten times the low flow of the river. The Ohio River serves 116 communities and 80 major industries. Under conditions such as these the control of waste materials must be restrictive.

The most evident pollutants are floating materials such as oils or scum which adhere to boats and the banks creating bothersome and unsightly conditions. State laws usually restrict the amount of oil in effluents to 10 ppm as measured by chloroform extraction. Restrictions on suspended solids will vary depending on the type of stream. A gravel washing operation can ruin miles of trout stream by depositing colloidal clay on the bottom and smothering the lower forms of aquatic life on which the fish depend for food. Industry can be held liable for the cost of dredging navigable waters where excessive deposition is caused by industrial wastes.[16] Most states will require the removal of settleable solids from the waste stream prior to discharge and the restrictions on the discharge of colloids will become less and less permissive.

Dissolved organic materials demand the most attention. If they are readily metabolized by bacteria they demand oxygen from the water and if they are not readily metabolized they persist for long periods of time and can be traced to drinking water supplies. The anionic detergents based on alkyl benzene sulfonate are not readily metabolized and have caused concern. Phenolics can cause odors, especially if chlorinated, and most states have very strict limits on the discharge of phenolic materials. Further restrictions on odor-producing substances will be inaugurated.

Dissolved inorganic materials increase the total dissolved solids and restrict the usefulness of water by making it more costly to use. Most states require that pH in receiving waters be maintained between 6.5–8.5. This usually requires the neutralization of acids and bases or careful distribution of effluent in the stream to take advantage of the alkalinity of the stream itself.

The effects of water pollution to be avoided are: unsightly oil or scum on water surface, solids deposition to form sludge banks or restrict navigation, oxygen-demanding materials which deplete dissolved oxygen, toxic materials which kill fish or aquatic plants and animals, noticeable color and turbidity, odor-producing substances which flavor fish or drinking water, acidity which depresses the pH.

Every surface water has the ability to receive and dissipate a certain amount of heat, suspended solids, and dissolved inorganic and organic materials without damage to its usefulness. This is known as "self-purification" and involves chemicals, physical and biochemical processes.

WATER TREATMENT

Treatment of a water supply may be necessary to:

1. Make it potable
2. Prevent corrosion, scaling or sliming
3. Permit economic boiler operations
4. Prevent product damage

Potable water is safe for drinking, practically colorless, and palatable. A water may be potable and yet not suitable for many industrial uses. Potable water must meet the standards of the state health departments, most of which accept the standards of the United States Health Service.

It is recommended that physical standards for public acceptance of water be:

1. Turbidity of less than 5 units
2. Color should average less than 15 units
3. Odor threshold should average less than 3
4. The water should have no objectionable taste

The simplest water system is a well system which requires no treatment to make the water potable. The well supply should be tested for chemical

TABLE 2.2. PROPOSED 1961 USPHS DRINKING WATER STANDARDS[10]

	Substance	Limit ppm
Unchanged	Chloride	250
	Chromium (Hexavalent as Cr)	0.05[a]
	Phenol	0.001
	Sulfate	250
	Total Solids	500
Revised	Arsenic (as As)	0.05[a]
	Copper	1.0
	Fluoride (inorganic)	3.0[a,b]
	Lead (as Pb)	0.05[a]
	Iron (as Fe)	0.3
	Manganese (as Mn)	0.1
	Magnesium (as Mg)	50.0
	Selenium (as Se)	0.01
	Zinc (as Zn)	5.0
New	ABS (detergent)	0.5
	Barium (as Ba)	1.0[a]
	Cadmium (as Cd)	0.01[a]
	Cyanide (as HCN)	0.2[a]
	Nitrate (as N)	10.0
	Chloroform-Soluble-Carbon Filter Extract	0.2

[a] Proposed mandatory limits—all others recommended.
[b] Variable depending on average annual temperature.

and bacterial quality and for yield. Pumping tests on wells can establish the well spacing and long-term yield. As a matter of safety most well supplies are disinfected.

Disinfection. This is usually the most important step in making a water potable. It can be accomplished in many ways but the simplest and most economic method has been through the use of chlorine or hypochlorite. Well waters normally require small amounts of chlorine in the range 0.5–1.0 ppm to disinfect since the chlorine demand of a water is dependent upon the amount of organic matter present. The choice between the use of cylinder chlorine and hypochlorite is largely one of economics. Where the demand exceeds 1.5 pounds per day it is usually economic to feed gaseous chlorine from 100–150 pound cylinders. The maximum amount of chlorine which can be removed from a 150-pound cylinder at 70° F is about 40 pounds per day and from a ton cylinder about 400 pounds per day. Demands in excess of these amounts are met by using multiple cylinders or by installing an evaporator. Completely automated chlorination systems are available through several equipment manufacturers.

Dry calcium or sodium hypochlorite [$Ca(ClO)_2$ or $NaClO$] can be purchased in 5-pound cans at 70 per cent available chlorine. One 5-pound can in 40 gallons of water makes approximately a 1 per cent chlorine water solution which may be fed to the water supply through proportioning pumps. These pumps are usually of the diaphragm type which can feed variable quantities of the solution and can be fully automated.

The rapidity with which chlorine acts upon bacteria can be a function of pH. Complete kill in ten minutes might be achieved with 0.2 ppm at pH 6–8 while more than 1.0 ppm residual is required for equivalent kill at pH 10. Other agents for disinfection such as bromine, chlorine dioxide, ozone, ultra-violet light and silver salts have been used but have never been accepted widely.

Filtration. Surface waters for potable supplies usually must be filtered as well as disinfected. New York City does not filter its surface supply, but most of the other surface supplies such as those for Chicago, Detroit, Cleveland, New Orleans, Philadelphia and Los Angeles are filtered. The purpose of filtration is to remove suspended matter which might affect potability or might affect product purity. It is also used following sedimentation and coagulation to remove residual suspensoids. Filtration alone is not economic on waters containing over 30 ppm of suspended solids. Solids content above this figure should be coagulated and removed by settling.

The rapid sand filter (Fig. 2.5) will achieve filter rates of 2.0 gal per min per sq ft of horizontal filter area. Pressure filters with sand media achieve as high as 3.0 gal per sq ft per min. Backwash rates to remove filtered materials vary from 6 to 18 times the flow-through rate. Since backwash water must be filtered water it can be seen that with high suspended solids frequent backwash could result in no production. Normal filter practice limits backwash to 3 per cent of throughput. Some health departments have approved the diatomaceous earth filters which are operated at about 1.0 gal per sq ft per min.[1] Use of these filters provides a large amount of surface in a small area (Fig. 2.6). The precoat required is about $\frac{1}{16}$ inch or 0.1 lb per sq ft. The continuous feed of filter-aid is usually one to three parts per part of turbidity. The advantages of the diatomite filter are low backwash volume (0.25 per cent of throughput), small space requirement, and the ability to filter up to 60 ppm of turbidity. The disadvantages are high pumping costs, necessity for continuous filtering, and the cost of filter aid. The media used to support the precoat is usually a porous stone or a cloth backed by a metal screen.

Coagulation. The precipitation of non-settleable solids in water by chemical addition is termed *coagulation*. Most natural colloids in water carry a negative charge so the object is to add a cationic material which will neutralize or attract these particles to a matrix which will settle rapidly.

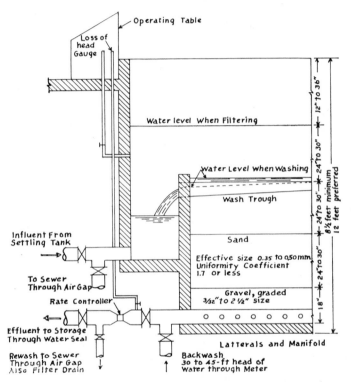

Figure 2.5. Elements of the rapid sand filter. (*Redrawn from Public Works Magazine*)

The common coagulants used in water treatment are $Al_2(SO_4)_3 \cdot 18H_2O$ and $Fe_2(SO_4)_3 \cdot 9H_2O$. If the system is sufficiently alkaline these trivalent ions form insoluble hydrates to which the colloids adhere. The reactions are:

$$Al_2(SO_4)_3 \cdot 18H_2O + 3Ca(HCO_3)_2 \rightarrow$$
$$3CaSO_4 + 2AL(OH)_3\downarrow + 6CO_2 + 18H_2O$$

$$Fe_2(SO_4)_3 \cdot 9H_2O + 3Ca(HCO_3)_2 \rightarrow$$
$$3CaSO_4 + 2Fe(OH)_3\downarrow + 6CO_2 + 9H_2O$$

When treating a water to remove suspensoids by coagulation care must be taken to leave 20–25 ppm alkalinity to prevent corrosion. In some cases it is necessary to add lime for pH control. Organic polymeric materials with long chain molecules such as the polyacrylamids can aid materially in the formation of rapidly settling *flocs*. The formation of flocs from coagulated materials is known as *flocculation*.

Other organic polymeric materials which have been made strongly cationic can be used in place of aluminum or iron salts. The one material then acts to neutralize the colloid charge as well as provide the attachment surface. In special applications it may be necessary to add anionic materials to aid coagulation. The organic polymers can also be made to carry a negative

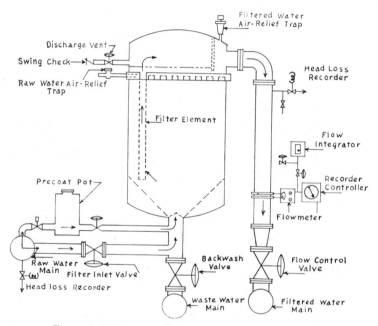

Figure 2.6. Elements of a vertical tube diatomite filter.

charge. The addition of both cationic and anionic materials is known as the "dual system" of coagulation.

Sedimentation. Prior to the filtration of water high in suspended solids or following coagulation for removal of non-settleable solids, it is necessary to use sedimentation tanks or basins where the suspended matter is allowed to settle out. The design of these tanks and basins is dependent upon the materials to be settled. Detention time may vary from two to twelve hours, or more.

Water Softening. In dye application plants, laundries, textile plants, and others, the water used in processing must, as a rule, be soft. If the only available water is hard, it must be treated to remove dissolved calcium and magnesium salts.

The earliest system of softening was the addition of lime to precipitate $CaCO_3$; thus

$$Ca(HCO_3)_2 + Ca(OH)_2 \rightarrow 2CaCO_3\downarrow + 2H_2O$$

Where non-carbonate hardness exists it is necessary to add soda-ash.

$$CaCl_2 + Na_2CO_3 \rightarrow CaCO_3\downarrow + 2NaCl$$

The combined use of lime and soda ash is commonly called the lime-soda process of softening. Where magnesium is present it is necessary to provide excess caustic alkalinity in order to precipitate the magnesium as the hydrate since magnesium carbonate is soluble:

$$MgCl_2 + Na_2CO_3 \rightarrow MgCO_3 + 2NaCl$$

$$MgCO_3 + Ca(OH)_2 \rightarrow Mg(OH)_2\downarrow + CaCO_3\downarrow$$

The lime-soda or caustic-soda softening processes are usually carried out in a sludge-blanket type of precipitator or settler where the sludge is accumulated and freshly treated water is passed up through the pre-precipitated material. This process results in a larger particle size and a more stabilized water. Almost all water-treating equipment companies manufacture equipment to accomplish sludge-blanket contact. The lime-soda process can theoretically achieve a hardnesss of 30 ppm.

Ion Exchange. The production of "zero" hardness water and demineralized water is generally accomplished through the use of ion exchange. This process can be defined as a reversible exchange of ions between a liquid and a solid during which there is no substantial change in the structure of the solid.[6] Although the process was recognized scientifically in 1850 it was not used until 1900. The original materials used were modified natural green sands (glauconite) which had exchange capacities of less than 5000 grains of $CaCO_3$ per cu ft. The name *zeolite* was applied to materials which had exchange properties. The science of manufacturing such materials from organic polymers has progressed rapidly since 1935 so that resins are available today which have exchange capacities of over 40,000 grains of $CaCO_3$ per cu ft.

The major use of ion-exchange resins at the present time is in the field of water treatment. The largest single use in water treatment is the softening of water using cation exchange resins in the sodium cycle. The reactions occurring in the common household water softener are:

Softening

$$Na_2R + Ca^{++} \rightarrow CaR + 2Na^+$$

Regeneration

$$CaR + 2Na^+ \rightarrow Na_2R + Ca^{++}$$
$$\text{(excess)}$$

A more complex procedure is to use the resin in the hydrogen cycle where the positive ions, calcium, magnesium and sodium, are replaced by hydrogen ions. The regenerant in this case is sulfuric or hydrochloric acid. The effluent from the hydrogen cycle is acidic through CO_2 from carbonate alkalinity and other anions. The CO_2 is removed by degasification. The acid water can then be mixed with a sodium cycle effluent to give a low alkalinity "zero" hardness water, or blended with unsoftened water to give the desired degree of alkalinity and hardness. Where completely deionized water is required the hydrogen cycle effluent, with or without degasification, is passed through an acid-absorbing strongly basic anion exchange resin. This system also effectively removes silica.

There have been many designs used to treat water by ion-exchange methods. Most water treatment equipment companies design, manufacture and assemble plants to deliver a specified water based on raw water quality. Completely deionized water systems must compete economically with evaporator systems. Compression distillation is said to produce distilled water at 65 cents per 1000 gal based on 10-cent fuel oil.[5]

Corrosion Prevention. Water treatment to avoid the problems accompanying water use is also accomplished by agents which will inhibit undesirable effects. For example, corrosion could be stopped if a protective molecular film would serve as a barrier to prevent oxygen from contacting the metal surface. Chromates, silicates, amines, polyphosphates, tannins and lignin have been used for this purpose in recirculated water systems. Controlled deposition of calcium carbonate through the addition of lime has also been used. Cathodic protection operates on the principle of maintaining a hydrogen film at the expense of sacrificial anodes or application of direct current.

The precipitation of calcium, magnesium and iron can be prevented by the addition of polyphosphates which form soluble complexes. Sequestering additives are generally too expensive to use on once-through systems unless most of the impurities have been removed by other treatment methods.

Odor Removal. Treatment of water to remove odors may involve aeration, chemical oxidation or adsorption. Chemical oxidation with chlorine in alkaline solution is sometimes called *break-point* chlorination. The amount of chlorine required for disinfection may be only 1.0 ppm while the oxidative chlorination may require as much as 10 ppm, depending on the amount of organic matter in the water. Chlorine dioxide (ClO_2), which is generated by acidifying or chlorinating sodium chlorite, has been very useful in the elimination of chlorophenol odors. Activated carbon is extensively used in large and small water works to adsorb odors from water. Granular activated carbon filters are used by breweries and bottling works to remove chlorine and odors which might affect product palatability. Powdered carbon which can be added as a slurry to water ahead of filtration is popular for odor reduction in municipal water-treatment plants.

Biological Growths. Control of biological growths is usually accomplished by intermittent chlorination of once-through water systems. The addition of chromates for corrosion control will aid in control of slimes and algae in recirculated systems. The Cooling Tower Institute recommends the use of non-oxidizing algaecides—fungicides to prevent aggravating chemical attack of wood.[4] It is also recommended that the pH of recirculated water be kept between 6.0–7.0 and that no more than 1.0 ppm of chlorine be used. There are several formulated biocides on the market to protect wood structures and clean recirculated water systems. It is often necessary to change treatment if growths develop resistance to the chemicals normally used. If chlorination becomes less effective a change to bromine may effectively kill the organism.

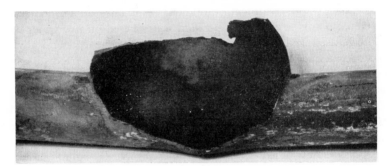

Figure 2.7. Ruptured tube from a superheater. (*Courtesy Dow Industrial Service*)

Boiler Water Treatment. Economic operation of a boiler may require special treatment of the boiler water. As water is evaporated the solids in the boiler water are concentrated. The loosely bound or entrained gases are released to the steam and can corrode boiler plates or tubes at a rapid rate. Deposits in the boiler can cause overheating of the tubes, resulting in bulging or splitting (Fig. 2.7). Complete clogging of boiler tubes can result. The higher the pressure at which a boiler is operated the purer the water make-up must be. Concentration of solids in the boiler above 3,000 ppm might result in "wet" steam. Frequently blow-downs are necessary, with resultant loss of heat.

With low-pressure boilers the hot lime-soda process of water treatment plus internal treatment may suffice. The chemistry of the hot lime-soda process is the same as that of the cold process. However, the reactions proceed faster and since solubilities at near boiling are less, the hot process will achieve as low as 20 ppm hardness. Internal boiler treatment can reduce hardness to "zero" by use of phosphates which precipitate scale-forming materials as insoluble phosphate sludges which are removed with blow-down.

CONTROL AND TREATMENT OF INDUSTRIAL WASTE WATERS

Industrial waste waters must be controlled to preserve the usefulness of the receiving water. The natural industrial approach to this problem is to make every attempt to solve it through process engineering. This begins with a review of housekeeping practices and the elimination of pump packing leaks. The accumulated losses from small leaks can be an important quantity. The waste survey should be designed to obtain enough data to work out a complete material balance. The engineer then studies each loss with the idea of eliminating it. This may involve recirculation, process change, a change of raw material source or a recovery step. Ideally, losses to the water would be reduced so efficiently that capital expenditures for waste treatment are unnecessary. Often the value of contained or recovered materials more than pays for all control costs. Most wet-process industries will find that further waste controls are required.

A clear definition of the effect of residual wastes on the receiving water will point to the most economic solution to the problem. The pollutional characteristics of the wastes must be known in order to apply the proper control method. The questions for which the engineer must find answers for times of least dilution in the receiving water are these: How much does the waste increase suspended solids, dissolved solids, the hardness, the oxygen demand, color, and the odor threshold? What is the effect on pH and dissolved oxygen? Is the waste toxic to marine life? Does the waste react with the water to cause percipitation? Will fish living in the water acquire a taste or odor?

The answers to the above questions will serve as parameters by which the effectiveness of the control method can be measured.

Controlled Discharge. Storage of wastes with controlled discharge is a very practical way to minimize water pollution. This method permits the maximum utilization of the dilution available. It applies to intermittent as well as continuous process wastes and should be used to regulate discharge to a city sewerage system, an industrial sewer leading to a treatment works (Fig. 2.8) or direct discharge to the receiving water.

Storage with controlled discharge has been adopted by the Ohio River Valley Water Sanitation Commission[14] as the only feasible way to control pollution effects from large-volume brine wastes. The Dow Chemical Company, Midland, Michigan has used this system for over 30 years to dispose of a portion of its connate brine wastes (Fig. 2.9). Strong brines are stored during low river-flow months and released during high flow months at carefully computed rates.

Sub-surface Disposal. Very strong wastes which do not lend themselves to economic disposal by any other method may sometimes be handled by sub-

Figure 2.8. 60,000,000-gallon settling and equalization lagoon.
(*Courtesy American Cyanamid Co.*)

Figure 2.9. 145-acre pond for storage of strong brine wastes.
(*Courtesy The Dow Chemical Co.*)

surface disposal. Strong wastes in true solutions such as brines, toxic organic wastes, highly odoriferous waste waters, caustic scrub liquors and radio-active wastes have been disposed in porous formations which contain connate waters not considered commercially usable. The development of a disposal well requires a thorough study of the geology and hydrology of underlying formations and the drilling of a test well to prove capacity. Design of the well must be approved by proper state agencies, usually the State Geologist and the State Health Department. Surface equipment consists of a storage tank, a filter and pumps of proper design to give required pressures. Through proper pumping tests, data may be acquired which will predict the long-term capacity of the formation. Disposal wells now being used in the State of Michigan vary from 900 to 5000 ft in depth. A very deep disposal well (11,000 ft) was drilled in 1961 near Denver, Colorado for disposal of wastes from the Rocky Mountain Arsenal.[2]

Removal of Suspended Solids. The disposal of most industrial wastes by any method usually requires the removal of suspended solids. This is accomplished by detention in settling basins or tanks designed around the character of the solids. As in water treatment, coagulants such as trivalent salts and ionic polymers aid materially in making solids-separation techniques effective. Plain sedimentation, properly designed, can achieve up to 70 per cent removal of suspended matter while the addition of coagulating chemicals can increase this efficiency to as high as 95 per cent. Most waste-treatment settlers are designed with overflow rates of less than 1000 gal per day per sq ft of tank surface. The concentrated slurries from settling tanks or filter backwash is commonly called sludge. Where cheap land is available most industries lagoon these sludges and fill on top of them after long densification periods. With restricted land the sludges are further de-watered through vacuum filters, flotation or centrifugation, and disposed of by land-fill or incineration.

Oxidation. Some organic sludges may lend themselves to *high-pressure oxidation*. The cities of Chicago and Wheeling installed the Zimmerman Process of high-pressure oxidation in 1961.[11] The condition necessary for wet combustion using air is to raise the temperature to 300° C which results in operating pressures in excess of 1500 psi. To be economic the process must carefully exchange heat and recover power when pressure is reduced. Evaluation of disposal methods should also include studies of the economics of *catalytic oxidation* in the vapor phase and *direct burning*. These two methods generally require wastes containing more than 1.0 per cent organic content to be economic.

Destruction of pollutional characteristics through *chemical oxidation* is sometimes the most economical and effective method. A popular example is the destruction of highly toxic cyanide wastes from metal-working plants. The alkaline-chlorination of cyanides is usually a batch process where rinse waters are accumulated and treated with controlled discharge of treated waste. The equations for this process are:

$$2NaCN + 4Na(OH) + 2Cl_2 \rightarrow 2NaCNO + 4 \ aCl + 2H_2O$$
$$2NaCNO + 4Na(OH) + 3Cl_2 \rightarrow 2CO_2 + 6NaCl + N_2 + 2H_2O$$

The alkaline-chlorination method has also been used to destroy toxic or odor-imparting properties of organic chemicals in solution, for example, the chlorophenols. Chlorine dioxide has been used for final threshold treatment of wastes from a phenol-formaldehyde plant.

Biological Treatment. When the organic waste materials can be metabolized by bacteria, they may be disposed of by biological treatment. Anaerobic processes convert carbon sources into protein with the production of CH_4, CO_2, H_2S and NH_3. The aerobic process converts the soluble carbon to insoluble protein, CO_2, H_2O, NO_3 and SO_4. Even with controlled temperature and recirculation the anaerobic process is not considered economic except on strong (3.0 per cent organic) wastes.

Biological oxidation occurs naturally in the receiving water and is a self-purification force which can cause the depletion of the dissolved oxygen if the reoxygenation rate is less than the deoxygenation rate. It is important when considering biological processes for industrial wastes to remember that we are trying to convert an organic material into protein and that nitrogen in the form of ammonia and phosphorous as phosphate are *essential nutrients*. Biological treatment processes are designed to achieve a maximum growth of bacteria in a minimum time. Oxygen must be supplied faster than it is utilized. Temperature control also affects growth rate.

There are two basic methods of achieving biological oxidation. The *trickling filter* is a shallow (3 ft–8 ft) packed column with a distribution and underdrain system designed to permit down-flow of the waste over the packing with sufficient void to simultaneously accommodate air flow. Distribution of the waste over the top of the filter is most effectively accomplished by use of a rotary distributor. Specially formed tiles with slotted tops are laid on a sloped (1.0 per cent) concrete pad so that the waste drains to central collecting channels. Air flow depends on the temperature relationship. If the water is 5° F warmer than the air a definite up-flow results. If the water is 5° F colder than the air the latter will down-flow through the bed.

Bacterial slimes grow on the packing surface. As the water passes over these slime surfaces, there is a transfer of oxygen from the air to the water and then to the slimes. The slimes utilize the organic material in the water to produce more protein, releasing CO_2 and H_2O, oxidizing ammonia to NO_3 and sulfur to SO_4. A trickling filter with $3\frac{1}{2}$-inch stone packing will remove up to 50 lb per day of Biochemical Oxygen Demand (B.O.D.) per 1000 cu ft. Efficiencies are related to hydraulic rate. Overloading a trickling filter can cause such prolific growth that interstices are plugged and aerobic action is stopped. The development of plastic shapes designed to avoid many of the shortcomings of rock packing has created more interest in the packed column type of biological treatment.

The *activated sludge* process has many variations but all of them are fundamentally based on the recycle of preformed, flocculated, settled slimes to incoming wastes in an aeration tank. Aeration is accomplished by many mechanisms, all of which attempt to achieve maximum absorption efficiency in the minimum time while maintaining tank turbulence. Solids concentrations in the aeration tank may vary from 1000 ppm up to 5000 ppm. This process when properly designed can achieve 95 per cent removal of B.O.D. Aeration tanks remove anywhere from 15 to 200 pounds of B.O.D. per day per 1000 cu ft, depending on the waste and oxygen supply.

One of the largest industrial waste-treatment facilities also accepting area sanitary sewage is operated by American Cyanamid Company at Bound Brook, New Jersey (Fig. 2.10). This facility employs almost every treatment technique known; waste equalization, neutralization, lagooning, activated sludge, final clarification and chlorination. The plant was designed for 20 MGD with an average of 43,000 lb per day of oxygen demand. The aeration tanks (Fig. 2.11) provide 24-hour detention. The final clarifiers (Fig. 2.12) provide 2.7 hours detention at an overflow rate of 660 gal per sq ft per day.[3]

An interesting development by Sun Oil Company has been the use of a cooling tower (Fig. 2.1) and the recirculation cooling system as a biological oxidation unit. Selected refinery process waste waters, after preliminary treatment, are used as part of the make-up to an 18,000 gpm recirculated cooling system.* The residual phenolics, sulfides and mercaptans are effectively removed. The bacteria in suspension and on the tower packing and heat-exchange surface have shown no deleterious effects on the wood, steel, or copper.[7] Other methods of utilizing biological oxidation are aeration ponds, spray irrigation and slow sand filters. These methods require an acre of land per 100 pounds of B.O.D. per day. For smaller industries in rural areas use of one of these methods may be most economic provided the waste is readily oxidized and non-toxic.

Chemical Reduction. While anaerobic decomposition of a waste is accomplished by *reduction,* we should examine some of the chemical reductions used to avoid pollution. Hexavalent chromium from plating operations is an extremely toxic ion. The common procedure is to reduce the hexavalent to the trivalent form at pH 2, using SO_2 or ferrous iron. The chromium is then precipitated as the hydroxide with lime. Copper is also a very toxic ion to aquatic life. Copper can be recovered from acid solution by precipitation with H_2S.

Ion-exchange can be used to concentrate impurities but is not economical unless the impurities can be profitably recovered. The recovery of chromium from plating solution has been successfully accomplished by ion-exchange techniques. Ionized organic materials may also lend themselves to profitable recovery by this method. Non-ionized organics in an electrolyte may also be recovered through *ion exclusion,* an operation in which an ion exchange resin is used to separate an electrolyte from a non-electrolyte in a polar sol-

* Patent 2,899,385.

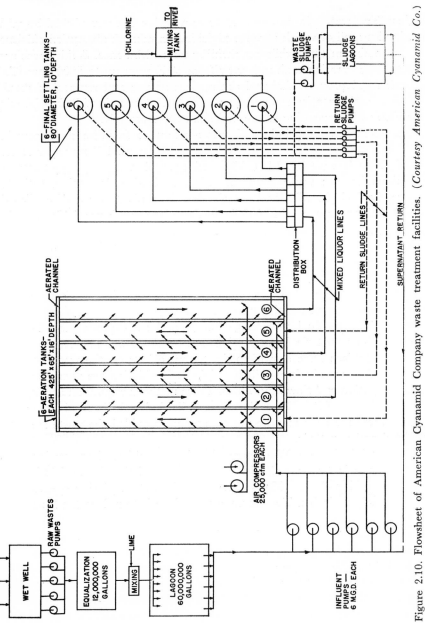

Figure 2.10. Flowsheet of American Cyanamid Company waste treatment facilities. (*Courtesy American Cyanamid Co.*)

Figure 2.11. General view of six aeration tanks in waste treatment plant. Each unit—65 feet wide, 400 feet long, and 16 feet deep—holds 3⅓ million gallons of effluent. (*Courtesy American Cyanamid Co.*)

Figure 2.12. Final settling tanks in waste treatment plant. A mixture of aerated wastes and bacteria is introduced into the center of each unit. Bacteria and other impurities settle to the bottom after which they are returned to the aeration tanks. Purified water is drawn off and chlorinated prior to being returned to the river. (*Courtesy American Cyanamid Co.*)

vent. The resin tends to absorb a non-electrolyte while excluding the electrolyte. Thus the ionized material rapidly passes through the bed while the non-ionized material is held back. Separation is accomplished by alternate water wash and raw feed. Radioactive materials (see Chapter 24) can be removed from water by ion-exchange, concentrated in the resin and disposed of by burial at approved sites. Some of the long-life, high-level radioactive materials in mother liquors are precipitated as hydrates, filtered and immobilized with cement in drums, and buried or disposed of at sea.

Adsorption and Absorption. Adsorption and absorption may be said to be a part of the coagulation and flocculation processes, removing colloidal materials which cause turbidity, color and odors. Activated carbon is not extensively used to adsorb waste materials except as a threshold treatment following the removal of most of the organic constituents by more economic methods.

REFERENCES

1. Bell, G. R., Proc. 14th Annual Water Conference Engineers Society of Western Pennsylvania, 1953.
2. *Chem. Week*, **88**, 1, Jan. 7 (1961).
3. Cherry, A. B., "Biological Treatment of a Complex Chemical Waste," presented at the Southeastern Regional Meeting of the American Chemical Society, Nov., 1959.
4. Cooling Tower Institute Bull. WMS-104, June (1959).
5. DePaul, D. J., "Corrosion and Wear Handbook for Water Cooled Reactors," New York, McGraw-Hill (1957).
6. Dowex: Ion Exchange, The Dow Chemical Company (1959).
7. Elkin, Harold, *et al.*, *Sewage and Industrial Waste*, **28**, 12 (1956).
8. Ellis, C. B., "Fresh Water From the Ocean," New York, Ronald Press (1954).
9. Excerpts from Manual on Industrial Water and Industrial Waste Water, 2nd ed., ASTM (1959).
10. Hopkins, O. C., and Gullans, O., *AWWA J.*, **9**, Sept. (1960).
11. Hurwitz, E., and Dundas, Wm. A., *J. Water Pollution Control Federation*, **32**, 918–29 (1960).
12. Lange, N. A., "Handbook of Chemistry," 9th ed., 800–12, New York, McGraw-Hill (1956).
13. Lynch, R. G., "Our Growing Water Problems," National Wildlife Federation (1959).
14. Ohio River Valley Water Sanitation Commission, 12th Annual Summary (1960).
15. Perry, J. H., "Chemical Engineers Handbook," 3rd ed., 1724, New York, McGraw-Hill (1960).
16. U. S. vs. Republic Steel Corporation *et al.*, 28LW4312, 1960.

SELECTED READING

"Water Treatment for Industrial and Other Uses," E. Nordell, Reinhold, 1961.

"Environmental Sanitation"—Salvato, J. A., Jr., New York, John Wiley & Sons Inc., 1958.

"Biological Treatment of Sewage and Industrial Waste," 2 vols., McCabe and Eckenfelder, Reinhold, 1958.

Manual on Industrial Water and Industrial Waste Water—2nd Edition 1959 ASTM special technical publication No. 148 D.

Cooling Tower Institute Publications—Cooling Tower Institute—1120 West 43rd, Houston 18, Texas.

"Saline Water Conversion," Advances in Chemistry series. No. 27, American Chemical Society, Washington, 1960.

Fresh Water from the Ocean—Cecil B. Ellis—The Ronald Press Company, New York, 1954.

Corrosion, Causes and Prevention—F. N. Speller—McGraw-Hill Book Company. New York—3rd Ed., 1951.

Pollution Abatement Manuals—Manufacturing Chemists' Association—Wahington, D. C.

Manual on Disposal of Refinery Wastes, American Petroleum Institute—1271 Avenue of the Americas, New York 20, New York.

Standard Methods for the Examination of Water Sewage and Industrial Wastes—10th Edition, 1955—American Public Association, Inc., 1790 Broadway, New York 19, New York.

3

FUELS AND THEIR UTILIZATION

In collaboration with Richard C. Corey*

INTRODUCTION

THE PER CAPITA CONSUMPTION of energy used to provide light, heat, and power is closely related to standard of living. Moreover, the rate of growth of a nation's demand for this energy is a reliable index of that nation's technological and economic growth. Historically, the industrial growth of the United States has been based on the development of efficient and diversified means of utilizing coal, petroleum, and natural gas. The carbon and hydrogen in these fuels furnish both thermal energy and a wide variety of chemicals used either as intermediates in manufacturing processes or as products for direct consumption.

Of the four convenient and economic natural sources of energy—coal, petroleum, natural gas and hydroelectric power—the first three are exhaustible, consequently their reserves and rate of consumption are of great concern to any country which depends on them for its economic well being. Hydroelectric energy is renewable, but in so far as the United States is concerned, the need for it and its availability are geographically opposed at the present time.

Energy production from mineral fuels and waterpower in this country for the period 1900 to 1957, in terms of British thermal units, is shown in

*Research Director, Pittsburgh Coal Research Center, U. S. Department of the Interior, Bureau of Mines, Region V, Pittsburgh 13, Pa.

Figure 3.1.[2] The percentage contribution of these energy sources for the same period is shown in Figure 3.2. Although the total energy demand has risen rapidly, the percentage supplied by bituminous coal and lignite has gradually decreased; in 1942 they supplied 52 per cent of the total, and in 1957, 31 per cent. During this same 15-year period the share of energy

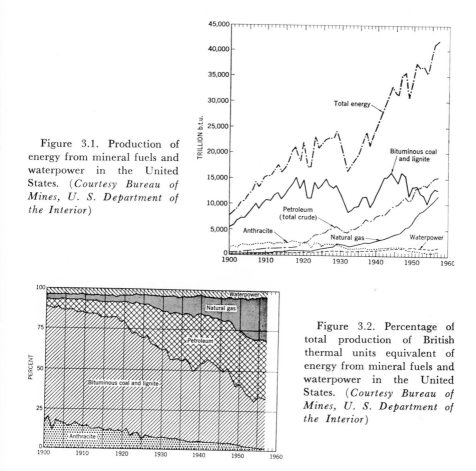

Figure 3.1. Production of energy from mineral fuels and waterpower in the United States. (*Courtesy Bureau of Mines, U. S. Department of the Interior*)

Figure 3.2. Percentage of total production of British thermal units equivalent of energy from mineral fuels and waterpower in the United States. (*Courtesy Bureau of Mines, U. S. Department of the Interior*)

production from both petroleum and natural gas increased from 39 to 64 per cent.

The estimated recoverable reserves of the principal mineral fuels in the United States, and the ratio of the most recent estimate of reserves to production in 1957, are given in Table 3.1. This ratio is useful only for orders of magnitude since the estimates of recoverable reserves are subject to assumptions regarding how much of the coal can be recovered economically. Although the estimated recoverable reserves of petroleum and natural gas have been revised upward many times during the past 25 years, because of increased rates of discoveries it is becoming more difficult and costly to maintain the ratio of reserves to production. In any event, it appears that coal will be a source of mineral-fuel energy long after the reserves of petroleum and natural gas are depleted.

The average fuel prices for 1957 are given in Table 3.2. On the average, coal is the cheapest fuel at the point of consumption, on a Btu basis and for the same combustion efficiency.* However, crude oil or natural gas is cheaper in certain geographical areas.

TABLE 3.1. ESTIMATED RESERVES OF MINERAL FUELS
IN THE UNITED STATES

	Reserves		Ratio of Reserves to 1957 Production
Coal, billion short tons:[1]			
Bituminous coal	1094		
Sub-bituminous coal	373		480*
Lignite	463		
Petroleum, crude, billion bbl	30**	[3]	12
Natural gas, trillion cubic feet	247**	[3]	23

[1] Averitt, Paul, Berryhill, Louise R., and Taylor, Dorothy A., "Coal Resources of the United States," *Geol. Survey Circ.*, **293,** p. 5 (1954).

* Based on estimate that 237 billion tons could be produced at or near present costs.

** Recoverable reserves as of December 31, 1957.

Other sources of energy are sunlight, wind, tidal movements, and the nuclear fission of certain elements. None of these energy sources is currently economic for large-scale uses, but as the need for substitutes for conventional fuels increases because the latter are depleted to the point of being uneconomical or because the nation's energy policies require that they be conserved for purposes which cannot be fulfilled otherwise, nuclear energy, particularly, and solar energy may become dominant factors in the energy pattern of the United States.

COAL AND ITS UTILIZATION

Origin and Classification

Coal originated from the remains of trees, bushes, ferns, mosses, vines, and other forms of plant life which flourished in huge swamps and bogs

* The heating values assumed[2] are: Bituminous coal and lignite, 26.2 million Btu per ton; crude oil, 5.80 million Btu per barrel; residual fuel oil, 6.30 million Btu per barrel; distillate oil, 5.83 million Btu per barrel; natural gas, 1035 Btu per cubic foot. (1 barrel = 42 gallons.)

many millions of years ago during prolonged periods of humid, tropical climate and abundant rainfall. The precursor of coal was peat, which was formed by bacterial and chemical action on heavy accumulations of plant debris, comprising bark, leaves, seeds, spores, various secretions, and the remains of trunks and branches.

TABLE 3.2. COMPARATIVE FUEL PRICES, 1957[2]

Bituminous coal:
    Average wholesale prices, dollars per net ton:

Large domestic sizes, f.o.b. car at mine, to retail dealers	7.45
Domestic stoker, f.o.b. car at mine, to retail dealers	7.00
Screenings for industrial use, f.o.b., car at mine, to industrial consumers	5.56
Metallurgical coal, f.o.b., car at mine, to coke manufacturers	6.64

    Other average prices, dollars per net ton:

Railroad fuel f.o.b. mine	5.53
Average retail price	16.28
Cost of coal at merchant coke ovens	10.76

Anthracite, average sales realization per net ton on shipments to points outside regions, excluding dredge coal, dollars:

Chestnut	13.06
Pea	10.39
Buckwheat No. 1	9.21

Petroleum and petroleum products:

Crude petroleum, average price per barrel at well	3.09
Gasoline, average dealers' net price (excluding taxes) of gasoline in 50 U. S. cities, cents per gallon	16.69

    Residual fuel oil:

No. 6 fuel oil, average of high and low prices in Philadelphia, dollars per barrel (refinery)	3.31
Bunker C, average price for all Gulf ports...........................do	2.85

    Distillate fuel oil:

No. 2 distillate, average of high and low prices at Philadelphia, cents per gallon (refinery)	11.1
No. 2 distillate, average for all Gulf ports..........................do	10.0

Natural gas:

Average United States value, at well...........cents per thousand cubic feet	11.3
Average United States value, at points of consumption..................do	43.1

Exclusion of oxygen from the peat retarded its rate of decay, and the weight of overlying accumulations of plant debris compressed and solidified it. Subsequent flooding of the peat bogs by sea water, and overlying thick mineral sediments resulted in pressures on the peat that started coalification. The extent to which coalification progressed depended on the temperatures and pressures existing during this process, and determined the *rank* of the coal. When the pressure was due mainly to overlying beds of rock, and the prevailing temperature corresponded to a depth of a few hundred feet below the surface, coalification was relatively slow and resulted in *low-rank* coals, such as lignite and sub-bituminous coal. Where rock movements produced much greater temperatures and pressures in the organic masses, the rank increased, producing bituminous and anthracite coal. The significant chemical changes that occur during coalification, from lignite to anthracite, are the decrease in the hydrogen and oxygen content, and the increase in the carbon content.

Coal is a heterogeneous substance, being grossly characterized by layers or bands of glossy and dull constituents. The glossy constituent is called *anthraxylon*, which was formed from woody parts of plants, trunks, limbs, branches, twigs, and roots. The dull constituent consists of finely divided material called *attritus,* which was formed from leaves, pollen, spores, seeds, particles of resin, etc.*

There are four varieties of coal: *common banded* coal, which is predominantly anthraxylon; *splint* coal, which is predominantly attritus; *cannel* coal, which is almost entirely attritus, often rich in spores; and *boghead* coal, which consists largely of the remains of algae.

Table 3.3 gives a classification of coals in the United States according to rank.[1] The main classes are grouped according to certain chemical and physical properties. It will be noted that the factors determining rank, or the degree of coalification, are moisture, volatile matter (material that is volatilized when the coal is heated in the absence of air at a certain temperature and for a certain length of time), fixed carbon (the residue after the loss of volatile matter), heating value, and caking and weathering properties.

An international classification of coals by type, and their application to American coals, was recently developed by the Coal Committee, Economic Commission for Europe, to eliminate confusion in evaluating coals shipped in international trade. Figure 3.3 shows this system of classification. It classifies coals according to their volatile-matter content, calculated on a dry, ash-free (m.a.f.) basis, and results in nine classes of coal.

Since volatile matter is not an entirely suitable parameter for coals containing more than 33 per cent volatile matter, the calorific value on an m.a.f. basis is included as a parameter for such coals. Then the nine classes of coal, based on volatile-matter content and calorific value, are grouped according to their caking properties when the coal is heated rapidly, employing either the free-swelling or the Roga test. These groups are further subgrouped according to coking properties, using either the Audibert-Arnu or the Gray-King test.

A three-figured code number is used to classify a coal. The first figure indicates the *class* of the coal, the second figure the *group*, and the third figure the *subgroup*. The details of its use and the test methods on which it is based have been described.[7]

* In British nomenclature *vitrain* and *clarain* are predominantly anthraxylon, and *durain* is predominantly attritus.

TABLE 3.3. ASTM CLASSIFICATION OF COALS BY RANK[a]

Legend: F.C. = Fixed Carbon   V.M. = Volatile Matter   Btu = British Thermal Units

Class	Group	Limits of Fixed Carbon or Btu Mineral-Matter-Free Basis	Requisite Physical Properties
I. Anthracitic	1. Meta-anthracite	Dry F.C., 98 per cent or more (Dry V.M., 2 per cent or less)	
	2. Anthracite	Dry F.C., 92 per cent or more and less than 98 per cent (Dry V.M., 8 per cent or less and more than 2 per cent)	Non-agglomerating[b]
	3. Semianthracite	Dry F.C., 86 per cent or more and less than 98 per cent (Dry V.M., 14 per cent or less and more than 8 per cent)	
II. Bituminous[d]	1. Low volatile bituminous coal	Dry F.C., 78 per cent or more and less than 86 per cent (Dry V.M., 22 per cent or less and more than 14 per cent)	
	2. Medium volatile bituminous coal	Dry F.C., 69 per cent or more and less than 78 per cent (Dry V.M., 31 per cent or less and more than 22 per cent)	
	3. High volatile A bituminous coal	Dry F.C., less than 69 per cent (Dry V.M., more than 31 per cent); and moist[c] Btu, 14,000[e] or more	
	4. High volatile B bituminous coal	Moist[c] Btu, 13,000 or more and less than 14,000[e]	
	5. High volatile C bituminous coal	Moist Btu, 11,000 or more and less than 13,000[e]	Either agglomerating or non-weathering[f]
III. Sub-bituminous	1. Sub-bituminous A coal	Moist Btu, 11,000 or more and less than 13,000[e]	Both weathering and non-agglomerating

TABLE 3.3. ASTM CLASSIFICATION OF COALS BY RANK[a] (*Continued*)

Class	Group	Limits of Fixed Carbon or Btu Mineral-Matter-Free Basis	Requisite Physical Properties
III. Sub-bituminous (*Continued*)	2. Sub-bituminous B coal	Moist Btu, 9500 or more and less than 11,000[e]	
	3. Sub-bituminous C coal	Moist Btu, 8300 or more and less than 9500[e]	
IV. Lignitic	1. Lignite	Moist Btu, less than 8300	Consolidated
	2. Brown coal	Moist Btu, less than 8300	Unconsolidated

[a] This classification does not include a few coals which have unusual physical and chemical properties and which come within the limits of fixed carbon or Btu of the high-volatile bituminous and sub-bituminous ranks. All these coals either contain less than 48 per cent dry, mineral-matter-free fixed carbon or have more than 15,500 moist, mineral matter-free Btu.

[b] If agglomerating, classify in low-volatile group of the bituminous class.

[c] Moist Btu refers to coal containing its natural bed moisture but not including visible water on the surface of the coal.

[d] It is recognized that there may be noncaking varieties in each group of the bituminous class.

[e] Coals having 69 per cent or more fixed carbon on the dry, mineral-matter-free basis shall be classified according to fixed carbon, regardless of Btu.

[f] There are three varieties of coal in the high-volatile C bituminous coal group, namely, Variety 1, agglomerating and nonweathering; Variety 2, agglomerating and weathering; Variety 3, non-agglomerating and nonweathering.

GROUPS (determined by caking properties)

GROUP NUMBER	ALTERNATIVE GROUP PARAMETERS — Free-swelling index (crucible-swelling number)	ALTERNATIVE GROUP PARAMETERS — Roga index
3	>4	>45
2	2½–4	>20–45
1	1–2	>5–20
0	0–½	0–5

CODE NUMBERS

The first figure of the code number indicates the class of the coal, determined by volatile-matter content up to 33% V. M. and by calorific parameter above 33% V. M.
The second figure indicates the group of coal, determined by caking properties.
The third figure indicates the subgroup, determined by coking properties.

Group	Subgroup	Class 0	Class 1 (A / B)	Class 2	Class 3	Class 4	Class 5	Class 6	Class 7	Class 8	Class 9
3	5					435	535	635			
3	4				334	434	534	634			
3	3				333	433	533	633	733		
3	2				332a / 332b	432	532	632	732	832	
2	3				323	423	523	623	723	823	
2	2				322	422	522	622	722	822	
2	1				321	421	521	621	721	821	
1	2			212	312	412	512	612	712	812	
1	1			211	311	411	511	611	711	811	
0	0		100	200	300	400	500	600	700	800	900

SUBGROUPS (determined by coking properties)

SUBGROUP NUMBER	ALTERNATIVE SUBGROUP PARAMETERS — Dilatometer	ALTERNATIVE SUBGROUP PARAMETERS — Gray-King
5	>140	>G8
4	>50–140	G5–G8
3	>0–50	G1–G4
2	≤0	E–G
3	>0–50	G1–G4
2	≤0	E–G
1	Contraction only	B–D
2	≤0	E–G
1	Contraction only	B–D
0	Nonsoftening	A

As an indication, the following classes have an approximate volatile-matter content of:

Class 6   33–41% volatile matter
     7   33–44%   "   "
     8   35–50%   "   "
     9   42–50%   "   "

CLASSES (Determined by volatile matter up to 33% V. M. and by calorific parameter above 33% V. M.)

CLASS PARAMETERS	0	1 (A / B)	2	3	4	5	6	7	8	9
Volatile matter (dry, ash-free)	0–3	>3–10 (>3–6.5 / >6.5–10)	>10–14	>14–20	>20–28	>28–33	>33	>33	>33	>33
Calorific parameter [a]	—	—	—	—	—	—	>13,950	>12,960–13,950	>10,980–12,960	>10,260–10,980

[a] Gross calorific value on moist, ash-free basis (30 C., 96% relative humidity) B. t. u./lb.

Note: (i) Where the ash content of coal is too high to allow classification according to the present systems, it must be reduced by laboratory float-and-sink method (or any other appropriate means). The specific gravity selected for flotation should allow a maximum yield of coal with 5 to 10 percent of ash.
(ii) 332a....>14–16% V. M.
     332b....>16–20% V. M.

Figure 3.3. International classification of coals by type. (*Courtesy Bureau of Mines, U. S. Department of the Interior*)

Mining Methods

There are two kinds of coal mines: *underground* and *open cut*. In the former, the mining machinery is located inside the mine, and in the latter, outside of the mine. There are three types of underground mines. If the mass of coal can be reached horizontally, say from the side of a hill on a level grade straight to the coal seam, it is called a *drift mine*. If the seam is at a perceptible angle to the entry, it is called a *slope mine*. If the seam must be reached by a vertical shaft from the surface, it is called a *shaft mine*. These types of underground mines are shown diagrammatically in Figure 3.4. Open cut mines, commonly called *strip mines*, are used when the coal is less than 100 feet below the surface. The overlying earth and rock is stripped

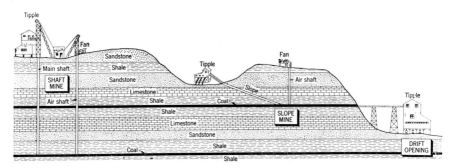

Figure 3.4. Three types of entrances to underground mines—shaft, slope, and drift. (*Courtesy Bureau of Mines, U. S. Department of the Interior*)

away with large earth-moving equipment, or horizontal or vertical holes are bored in the overburden. These are loaded with explosives and fired. The debris is removed mechanically to expose the coal which is then broken with explosives or dug without blasting.

In many strip mines the overburden is so thick that continued stripping becomes economically impractical. Then, augers up to 60 inches in diameter are used to bore horizontal holes 100 to 200 feet into the coal seam. The coal falls from the augers into a conveyor and is elevated into a truck. This type of mining is generally known as high-wall *auger mining*.

Preparation Methods

As-mined coal consists of a wide range of sizes and contains rock slate, pyrites, and other impurities. Since many coal users have rather rigid specifications concerning size and the ash and sulfur content, a comparatively large proportion of mined coal is screened into sizes best suited to its ultimate use, and cleaned to remove various amounts of the impurities before it is sent to the markets. The structure where the coal is received from the mine is called a *tipple;* for anthracite coal it is called a *breaker.* Coal preparation equipment, such as crushers, screens, and cleaning devices, are located in the tipple.

Impurities in coal are denser than the coal itself, hence the coal can be separated from the impurities on the basis of the differences in specific gravity. The most popular mechanical cleaning processes are *jigging* and *dense-medium washing.* Jigging effects separation by inducing pulsations in water in which the coal is suspended. An open-top rectangular box having a perforated bottom, or screen plate, is used. The pulsations are induced through the screen plate by reciprocating devices, causing agitation of the coal-water mixture and separation of the coal according to the specific gravity of the particles. The cleaner or less dense particles rise to the top, overflow the end of the jig and are removed as salable product. The denser particles settle on the screen plate and are withdrawn as refuse.

TABLE 3.4. STATISTICS OF BITUMINOUS COAL AND LIGNITE MINED IN THE UNITED STATES IN 1957[2]

Production, net tons	492,703,916
Method of mining, net tons:	
Underground	368,590,378
Strip	124,108,538
Production per man day, net tons	10.59
Mechanically cleaned, net tons	304,027,194
Percentage of production	61.7

Dense-medium washers employ liquids having a specific gravity intermediate between cleaned coal and refuse; consequently, the former floats and is removed as salable product. Other cleaning devices include launders, classifiers, pneumatic cleaners, and froth-flotation cells.[6] The cleaned coal is dried mechanically or thermally and loaded for transport to the markets.

Salient data concerning mining and preparation of bituminous coal and lignite in the United States are given in Table 3.4. The output per man has risen rapidly because of increased mechanization in the mines.

Composition

Coal is composed chemically of carbon, hydrogen, oxygen, nitrogen, sulfur, and mineral matter (ash). The carbon, hydrogen, sulfur, nitrogen, and ash are determined directly, and the oxygen by difference, by means of an *ultimate analysis* which has been standardized by the American Society for Testing Materials (ASTM). The ultimate analysis is important for calculating material balances in thermal and chemical processes that use coal as a feed material (combustion, carbonization, gasification, hydrogenation, etc.). For certain uses, such as comfort and process heating, steam generation, and coking, it is usually sufficient to know the moisture, volatile matter, fixed carbon, ash, and sulfur contents, and the heating value* of the coal. The *proximate analysis* is used for this purpose. Both types of analyses are described in ASTM[1] and Bureau of Mines publications.[4]

Figure 3.5 shows the proximate analyses, on an ash-free basis, of coals selected to represent the various ranks. Analyses by state, county, and coal bed may be found in several Bureau of Mines publications; Bulletin 446 is a condensed, useful source of this information.

Utilization

The principal uses of coal may be classified broadly as follows:

Combustion to obtain thermal energy for power generation and process heating, including sintering and calcining.

Gasification to obtain industrial gases for heating, chemical reduction, and hydrogenation and synthesis reactions.

Carbonization to convert coal to coke, char, tars, chemicals, and industrial gases.

Raw or processed coal, and coal ash cinders have several miscellaneous uses which will be described later.

Combustion. *Steam Generation for Heat and Power.* The greatest percentage of the coal consumed in the United States is burned in boilers to generate steam for turbo-electric power plants in the electric utility industry. Remarkable advances have been made in the energy efficiency of these plants as a result of improvements in boiler furnaces and turbines. The average heat rate was 0.93 pounds of coal per kilowatt-hour in 1957, 1.31 in 1947 and 1.44 in 1937. Several plants which have recently gone into operation, employing the most modern concepts of steam-generation technology, have heat rates of approximately 0.7 pounds of coal per kilowatt-hour, which corresponds to an over-all plant efficiency of about 37 per cent on the basis of coal with a heating value of 13,100 Btu per pound.

In the early days, boilers were rated by horsepower. One rated horsepower was defined as equivalent to 10 square feet of boiler heating surface. A *developed* horsepower was arbitrarily set as equal to the evaporation of

---

* Heating value, Btu per lb, is the *high-heat value* (HHV), which is the heat of combustion at 20° C and constant volume when the fuel has burned to ash, CO_2 (gas), SO_2 (gas) and H_2O (liquid). The *low-heat value* (LHV) is calculated from the HHV by deducting 1030 Btu for each pound of water derived from a quantity of fuel, including both the water originally present as water and that formed by combustion. The HHV is most often used in the United States. The Dulong formula is quite accurate for calculating the heating value if the ultimate analysis is known.

$$\text{Btu per pound} = 145.4C + 620 \left(H - \frac{O}{8} \right) + 41S$$

C,H,O, and S, are, respectively, the weight percentage of carbon, hydrogen, oxygen, and sulfur in the coal.

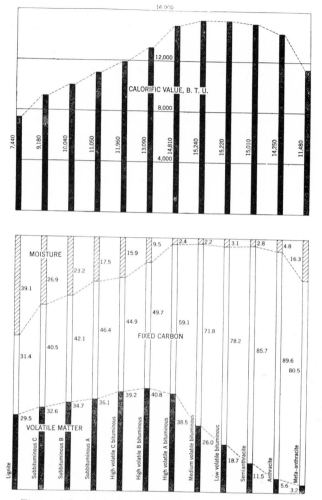

Figure 3.5. Analysis of United States coals selected to represent the various ranks. (*Courtesy Bureau of Mines, U. S. Department of the Interior*)

34.5 pounds of water per hour at 212° F. Later, an equivalent heat unit of 33,480 Btu per hour was adopted. From these definitions, R_b, per cent boiler rating, is obtained:

$$R_b = \frac{w(h - h_w) \times 100}{3348 \times S}$$

where: h = enthalpy of steam at boiler or superheater outlet, Btu/lb
h_w = enthalpy of water at boiler or economizer inlet, Btu/lb
S = boiler heating surface, sq ft

Per cent boiler rating is still used for small boilers and is a relative measure of "size" where furnace-wall cooling and super-heating surfaces are absent or relatively small compared with boiler convection surface.

Utility and industrial boilers have a relatively large amount of heat-transfer surface *other* than boiler convection surface and boiler horsepower and boiler rating are not suitable means of designating boiler output. Almost invariably output is now given in pounds per hour of steam flow at maximum continuous load. Peak or overloads are given as percentages of full load.

The type of fuel-burning equipment used depends on the characteristics of the coal and the amount of steam required. Table 3.5 gives the approxi-

TABLE 3.5. APPROXIMATE RANGE OF CAPACITIES OF VARIOUS
METHODS FOR FIRING COAL IN BOILERS

Type of Firing	Capacity Range, lb steam/hr
Pulverized coal	35,000–3,500,000
Cyclone	200,000–2,000,000
Single retort stoker	1,000– 40,000
Multiple retort stoker	15,000– 150,000
Spreader stoker, dumping grate	1,000– 100,000
Spreader stoker, continuous ash discharge	25,000– 200,000
Chain or traveling grate stoker	25,000– 200,000

mate range of capacities of conventional methods for firing boilers with coal, based on present-day practices for selecting such equipment. Central-station and large industrial power plants favor pulverized-coal-fired and cyclone-fired furnaces because of their inherent flexibility regarding the kind and quality of coal that can be burned, and their comparatively good availability.

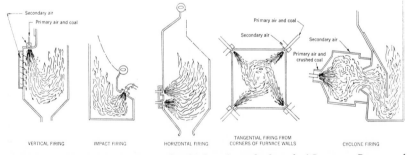

Figure 3.6. Methods of firing pulverized and crushed coal. (*Courtesy Bureau of Mines, U. S. Department of the Interior*)

Figure 3.6 shows, schematically, these methods of firing coal. The cyclone is designed for coal crushed to 95 per cent through a 4-mesh sieve. Details of these types of firing may be obtained from books listed in the Supplementary References.

There are various kinds of industrial and utility boilers, broadly classified as *fire-tube* and *water-tube*. In the former, the hot combustion gases pass through tubes, and heat is transferred to water outside the tubes. The most common and least expensive boiler of this type is the horizontal return tubular (HRT) boiler. However, because of the design and construction of fire-tube boilers, there is a definite limitation to their size and the pressure which they can tolerate. Water-tube boilers may be broadly classified as straight-tube and bent-tube types, the latter having several variations in design and being preferred for applications where higher capacities and steam pressures are required. In both types, heat is transferred by radiation or convection to the outside of the tubes, and water flows inside the tubes as the result of thermal circulation, or in the case of certain bent-tube boilers, as the result of forced circulation. A comparatively new version of the forced-circulation, bent-tube boiler for central-station power plants is the "once-through" type. The feed-water passes progressively through the heating, evaporation, and superheater sections; no drum is used for separating the steam from the boiler water as in other boilers; consequently, the ratio of water circulated in the boiler to steam generated is unity.

Details concerning the design and performance characteristics of the various types of boilers may be found in books listed in the Supplementary References. The data in Table 3.6 approximate the range of steam capacities and pressures for the principal types of boilers.

TABLE 3.6. APPROXIMATE RANGE OF CAPACITIES OF VARIOUS TYPES OF INDUSTRIAL AND UTILITY BOILERS

Type	Capacity, lb steam/hr	Maximum Design Pressure, psig
Fire tube (HRT)	1,000– 15,000	250
Water tube		
straight	15,000– 150,000	2000
bent, 3-drum, low-head	1,000– 35,000	400
2-drum, vertical	1,000– 350,000	1000
special utility[1]	150,000–4,000,000	3000

[1] Designs are available for natural (thermal) or forced circulation, sub- or supercritical pressures, and steam temperatures up to 1150° F.

Sintering and Calcining. Sintering is a process of agglomerating finely-sized fusible materials to obtain a product suitable in size for a particular use. Typical applications of sintering are the production of lightweight aggregate for use in concrete, and of sintered ore for use in blast furnaces. The Dwight Lloyd type of machine, which is widely used to sinter fine materials, is shown schematically in Figure 3.7. The mixture of coal (or coke) and the material to be sintered, which may be pelletized ore or fly-ash from power plants, is fed to the grate and ignited by a gas- or oil-fired hood.

Air is drawn *through* the charge by induced draft, and ignition and burning occur from the top to the bottom of the bed. The quality of the sinter depends mainly on the composition of the mixture, the thickness of the bed, the speed of the grate, and the amount of air drawn through the bed. Usually, the windbox is compartmented to control the amount of air flowing through the bed at certain points.

Lightweight aggregate for concrete is also produced by burning pelletized refuse coal from coal-preparation plants on conventional traveling grates.

A significant amount of coal is consumed annually for calcining to make cement, lime, gypsum, alumina, and magnesia, and for firing ceramic products. Calcining is usually done in rotary kilns, and ceramics are fired in tunnel kilns and muffles. Portland cement requires approximately 75 pounds

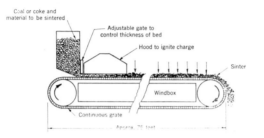

Figure 3.7. Dwight Lloyd stoker for manufacturing sintered products. (*Courtesy Bureau of Mines, U. S. Department of the Interior*)

of coal per barrel, lime 500 pounds of coal per ton, and gypsum 100 pounds of coal per ton.

Gasification. In recent years single-stage processes for the continuous, complete gasification of coal under pressure have been developed, thereby eliminating a separate, intermediate stage of carbonization to obtain coke used for water-gas sets and gas producers. The latter types of gasifiers are not used nearly as extensively at present as they were before abundant supplies of natural gas became available in the United States. On a Btu basis, coke is a comparatively expensive fuel and cannot compete with processes that gasify coal directly and at high pressures.

Gasifiers may be classified on the basis of whether the coal is gasified in lump form on a grate, or in pulverized form in suspension. Intermediate between these is the fluidized bed, which uses a finely-crushed fuel that has little or no caking properties. Examples of these kinds of gasifiers are given below.

1. Coal is retained on a fixed bed and the flow of gases and coal feed may be counter- or cocurrent. The coal must have comparatively low caking characteristics, otherwise the plastic flow of the coal will impede the flow of gases through the bed and the pressure drop will become excessive. The most successful gasifier of this type is the Lurgi generator, which operates with non-caking or weakly caking coal down to $\frac{1}{4}$ inch size and at pressures up to 450 psi. Other fixed-bed gasifiers are the Thyssen-Galocsy, Koppers,

Wellman-Galusha, Power Gas Corporation, and Phillipon. None of these types is used in the United States.

2. Crushed coal is fluidized by passing the reactant gases through it at a velocity high enough to keep the particles in suspended motion but not so high as to cause excessive amounts to be carried from the gasifier. Low-rank coal or a coal that has been processed to reduce its caking characteristics, for example, a char, must be used, otherwise agglomeration of the fuel impairs uniform fluidization and temperature distribution in the bed. The principal example of this type of gasifier is the Winkler (German). Consolidation Coal Company has also developed a mechanism for gasifying char from a low-temperature carbonization process.

3. Pulverized coal is suspended in the gases and the particles either move more or less linearly with the gases or follow a vortex path. Examples of

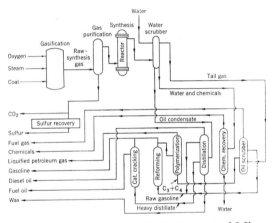

Figure 3.8. Fischer-Tropsch process for synthesis of liquid and gaseous fuels and of chemicals. (*Courtesy Bureau of Mines, U. S. Department of the Interior*)

experimental and industrial gasifiers of this type are: U. S. Bureau of Mines, Koppers-Totzek, Babcock and Wilcox, Texaco, Institute of Gas Technology, Fuels Research Station (British), Panindco, and Wirbelkammer (German). Some of these types operate only at atmospheric pressure, while others go up to 450 psi; some remove the ash dry, and others remove it as molten slag.

If coal is gasified with oxygen and steam (the oxygen burns a fraction of the coal to furnish sufficient heat for the steam-carbon reaction), mixtures of hydrogen and carbon monoxide (synthesis gas) are obtained, the ratio of these constituents depending on operating conditions. Appreciable quantities of methane are produced in the Lurgi generator; practically none occurs in entrained systems (items 2 and 3 above).

Synthesis gas can be converted by catalytic processes to a wide variety of liquids and gaseous hydrocarbons and to oxygenated compounds. The most important catalytic processes are: methane synthesis; the Fischer-Tropsch and the Oxo synthesis; and ammonia synthesis, by mixing the synthesis gas with sufficient nitrogen. The flow sheet in Figure 3.8 illustrates the range of products obtainable from the Fischer-Tropsch synthesis process. By suitable selection of the carbon-hydrogen ratio in the synthesis gas, catalyst, temperature, and pressure, the proportions of the various products can be adjusted as desired.

Because of significant trends in the energy-fuels pattern in the United States, which indicate that sources of methane to supplement the natural-gas reserves will be needed during the next decade, the Bureau of Mines and the Institute of Gas Technology are intensively studying economic and feasible processes for converting synthesis gas from coal to methane.

Synthesis gas from coal is also a source of hydrogen, via the catalytic water-gas shift reaction, $CO + H_2O \rightarrow CO_2 + H_2$. Hydrogen has numerous

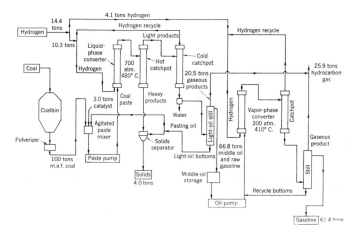

Figure 3.9. Direct hydrogenation of coal to liquid and gaseous fuels and to chemicals. (*Courtesy Bureau of Mines, U. S. Department of the Interior*)

uses in industrial processes, principally ammonia synthesis, direct reduction of ores, and direct hydrogenation of oils, fats, and coal.

Direct Hydrogenation. The direct hydrogenation of coal is a potential source of liquid and gaseous fuels, and of industrial chemicals. The coal-hydrogenation process shown in Figure 3.9 consists of two steps: liquid-phase and vapor-phase hydrogenation. The light oils from the liquid-phase converter are comparatively rich in aromatic hydrocarbons, and contain a large number of different tar acids. The overhead stream from the light-oil still, usually boiling below 620° F, is fed to the vapor-phase converter where it is converted to quality gasoline. The gasoline is rich in aromatics, consequently benzene, toluene, and xylene can be extracted readily with selective solvents. Additional aromatics can be obtained by hydroforming, platforming, or similar processes. The heavy products from the liquid-phase converter and the bottoms from the light-oil still are combined and recycled as pasting oil for the feed to the liquid-phase converter.

The catalysts and operating conditions for both steps in the hydrogenation process determine the kinds of products and their respective yields. Table 3.7 gives the estimated yields from a 30,000 barrel-per-day coal-hydrogenation plant.

Reaction of hydrogen directly with coal at comparatively high temperatures and pressures (hydrogasification) to obtain a substitute for natural gas is in the experimental stage at both the Bureau of Mines and the Institute of Gas Technology.

Direct Reduction with Hydrogen. Because of present-day costs of hydrogen, many important industrial processes amenable to direct reduction with hydrogen, for example, conversion of iron ore directly to iron without a blast furnace, are not economical. If, however, the economy and feasibility of processes for making hydrogen from coal are improved, hydrogen may

TABLE 3.7. ESTIMATED YIELDS FROM A 30,000 BBL/DAY COAL-HYDROGENATION PLANT, BASED ON BITUMINOUS COAL FROM ILLINOIS NO. 6 BED[1]

	Yield, bbl/day
Tar acids (phenols, cresols, xylenols, etc.)	1,380
Aromatics (benzene, toluene, xylene, etc.)	13,490
Motor and aviation gasoline	8,920
Liquefied "petroleum" gases (butane and propane)	7,300

[1] Donath, E. E., "Chemicals from Coal Hydrogenation," American Institute of Mining and Metallurgical Engineers, Gasification and Liquefaction of Coal, pp. 15–27, New York, 1953.

be used extensively for reduction processes; this could result in marked changes in conventional metallurgical practices.

Carbonization. Carbonization of coal yields solids, liquids, and gases having great industrial importance. When coal is heated at a uniformly increasing temperature in the absence of air, moisture is driven off first; at about 400° F, thermal degradation of the coal substance begins, and as the temperature continues to rise, water vapor, carbon dioxide, carbon monoxide, hydrogen, and a wide variety of organic compounds are liberated. The latter range from methane to complex high molecular weight compounds. The relative proportions of all these products at any particular temperature depends largely on the rate of heating and the length of time that the gases and vapors are at the specified temperature. The condensible fractions, other than water, are tars, which may be defined as those compounds that are either liquid or solid when in contact with their respective vapors at atmospheric temperature and pressure.

Coking coals are distinguished by the fact that they begin to soften at approximately 550° F; as the temperature continues to rise the fluidity of the mass reaches a maximum, and finally the mass solidifies to form coke. The gases and vapors evolved during the plastic stage swell the mass, causing the coke to have a porous structure. Noncoking coals do not soften during heating, and the product, generally referred to as char, has little or no characteristic structure and crumbles easily.

Carbonization is divided into three broad classes, based on the final temperature.

High-Temperature Carbonization. Between 1650° and 2100° F, the process is designated as high-temperature carbonization. Slot-type or beehive ovens are used. The quality of the resulting coke depends on careful control of several variables, among which are the kind and the bulk density of the

TABLE 3.8. CHEMICAL BY-PRODUCTS SOLD IN THE UNITED STATES IN 1957, FROM HIGH-TEMPERATURE CARBONIZATION OF COAL[2]

Tar, crude, million gallons	442
Tar derivatives:	
Crude chemical oil, million gallons	27.2
Pitch (soft, medium, and hard), thousand net tons	65.0
Other,[a] value, million dollars	16.9
Ammonia:	
Sulfate, million pounds	1940
Liquor (NH_3 content), million pounds	31.6
Diammonium phosphate, million pounds	79.4
Gas:	
Used under boilers, etc., billion cubic feet	70.6
Used in steel or allied plants, do	528.5
Distributed in city mains, do	50.9
Sold for industrial use, do	37.2
Crude light oil, million gallons	14.6
Light-oil derivatives	
Benzene, all grades, million gallons	173.7
Toluene, all grades, do	37.1
Xylene, all grades, do	10.3
Solvent naphtha, do	6.3
Other light-oil products, do	4.5
Intermediate light oil, do	1.4
Sodium phenolate, do	4.0
Sulfur, million pounds	4.3

[a] Includes creosote oil, cresols, cresylic acid, crude light tar, naphthalene, phenol, pyridine, red oil, road tar, tar paint, topped tar.

coal used, and the rate and duration of heating. Coke for blast furnaces must be strong, to support the burden in the furnace, and must have a high resistance to abrasion.

Some 90 per cent of the 76 million tons of high-temperature coke produced in the United States in 1957 was used in blast furnaces; the remainder was used largely in cupolas, sintering machines, boilers, gas producers, and water-gas generators. The volatile products generally are recovered as tar, light oil, and gas, which are used directly, or as raw materials for making hundreds of commodities. The industrial markets for the by-products of high-temperature carbonization are given in Table 3.8.

Medium-Temperature Carbonization. Between 1200° and 1650° F the process is designated as medium-temperature carbonization. Slot-type ovens are used which have narrower chambers than those used for high-temperature carbonization. This process is employed in Europe but not in the United States.

Low-Temperature Carbonization. Between 950° and 1200° F the process is designated as low-temperature carbonization. A variety of types and designs of retort are used. Until recently, this process was employed primarily to produce smokeless fuel for domestic and industrial markets. "Disco" is such a product. It is made by preheating and oxidizing a mixture of high-volatile bituminous coal and recirculated fines (breeze), which is fed continuously to a revolving, inclined, cylindrical retort, externally and internally heated. Some inleakage of air occurs in the retort and dilutes the carbonization gases. Coke in the form of rough spheres is removed from the retort; two sizes are available, 2 by ¾ inch and +2 inch. The volatile matter averages about 16 per cent. The by-products per ton of coal processed are 15 gallons of tar, and 3,700 cubic feet of gas having a heating value of 375 Btu per cubic foot.

Low-temperature carbonization processes yield more tar per ton of coal than high-temperature processes because there is less thermal decomposition of tar vapors to gases. Low-temperature tars are quite different in chemical composition than the high-temperature variety. Table 3.9 gives some of the differences. Comparing columns 1 and 3, it may be seen that low-temperature carbonization of bituminous coal yields a distillate that is richer in tar acids, and a neutral oil richer in saturated compounds and leaner in aromatic compounds than the high-temperature carbonization of bituminous coal. The higher aromatic content of the neutral oil in high-temperature tar is believed to be due to dehydrogenation of naphthenic compounds and dehydroxylation of certain tar acids caused by the high temperature of the process, compared with that of low-temperature carbonization.

Another significant difference, not indicated in Table 3.9, is that the ring compounds in low-temperature tar are more heavily alkylated, predominantly methyl and ethyl groups, than the ring compounds in high-temperature tar. Again, the difference between the process temperatures appears to be a significant factor, since the extent of dealkylation during hydrocarbon pyrolysis increases with temperature.

High-temperature tars are comparatively uniform in composition, the composition of the coal having no significant effect on that of the by-product tar. Low-temperature tars, however, may differ considerably in composition, depending on the composition of the coal, and the process that is used, which determines both the mode and the time of contact of the tars in the carbonizer.

These facts, together with the increasing use of coal for power generation, the gradual depletion of coking-coal reserves, and the possibilities of using low-temperature tars as a source of chemicals and chemical raw materials, has stimulated considerable interest in low-temperature carbonization in the United States. The ideal process would consist of an integrated power plant and chemical plant, the char being burned in boilers to furnish electric

TABLE 3.9. GENERAL COMPOSITION OF LOW- AND HIGH-TEMPERATURE TARS

	Low-Temperature Tar		High-Temperature Tar
	Bituminous Coal[a]	Lignite Coal[b]	Bituminous Coal[c]
Distillate yield to 300° C, wt %	27	43	21
Residue pitch	66	52	78
Loss	7	5	1
Composition of distillate, vol %			
Tar acids	28	26	14
Tar bases	3	4	6
Neutral oil	69	70	80
Composition of neutral oil, vol %			
Olefins	8	40	12
Aromatics	47	48	85
Saturates	45	12	3
Raw coal analysis			
Proximate analysis, %			
Moisture	1.1	30.4	2.2
Volatiles	33.0	30.6	34.7
Fixed carbon	55.9	29.6	60.7
Ash	11.1	9.4	2.4
Ultimate analysis, %			
Carbon	74.8	43.7	82.5
Hydrogen	4.9	6.5	5.6
Oxygen	6.0	38.2	7.5
Nitrogen	1.6	0.9	1.4
Sulfur	1.6	1.3	0.6
Heating value, Btu/lb	12,877	7,570	14,770

[a] Tar produced from an Alabama high-volatile bituminous coal carbonized at 950° F in a continuous fluidized bed.
[b] Tar produced from a Texas lignite coal carbonized at 900° F in a continuous fluidized bed.
[c] Tar produced from a Virginia high-volatile A bituminous carbonized at 1800° F in a coke oven.

energy for distribution and the tar being processed to obtain salable products.

A fluidized-bed process, developed by the Bureau of Mines[5,8] and installed by the Texas Power and Light Company in Rockdale, Texas, is designed to furnish boiler fuel and tar from lignite.

Miscellaneous Utilization Processes. Solvent extraction, alkaline hydrolysis, and low-temperature oxidation of coal are means of obtaining chemicals from coal. Only solvent extraction, however, has reached the commercial stage. The residual products from the combustion of coal are being utilized to a greater extent every year.

Solvent Extraction. Processes may be grouped into two classes, according to whether the temperature is below or above 650° F. Below 650° F, resins and waxes are extracted from lignite and processed into dielectric enamels and similar materials. Approximately 280 pounds of montan wax has been extracted per ton of lignite. The lignite is extracted further to obtain a humate substance, and the spent lignite is used as a fertilizer filler. Above 650° F, a low-ash carbon suitable for manufacturing electrodes can be obtained by solvent extraction of coal followed by high-temperature carbonization of the extract.

Alkaline Hydrolysis. Low-rank coals, lignite and sub-bituminous, will yield soluble and gaseous products by treatment with relatively strong solutions of alkali between 650° and 800° F. Phenols and fatty acids comprise the soluble fraction and account for approximately 25 per cent of useful yields.

Low-Temperature Oxidation. Treatment of coal with alkali and oxygen at 500° F results in appreciable yields of carboxylic acids which are useful as drilling-mud additives, intermediates for plasticizers, and glyptal-type resins. Commercial use of this process depends on feasible and economic methods for treating the products and the availability of cheap oxygen.

Residual Products from Combustion of Coal. Cinders, stoker ash, and fly ash have many commercial uses. Because of its pozzolanic properties, thousands of tons of fly ash are used annually in the building industry; some 20 to 30 per cent of the portland cement used in concrete may be replaced by fly ash at a considerable saving in costs and improvement in quality of the concrete.[9]

Fly ash and stoker ash are a source of germanium, which is an important element in electronic diodes and transistors. Fly ash from several pulverized coal-fired boilers contained 15 to 60 parts per million (ppm) of germanium; a sample from a cyclone furnace contained 290 ppm.[3] At the present time, however, the recovery of germanium from coal ash cannot compete with its recovery from zinc sulfide concentrates, which contain approximately 100 ppm.

PETROLEUM AND NATURAL GAS AND THEIR UTILIZATION

Petroleum

Origin. Of the numerous theories advanced concerning the origin of petroleum, the one most widely accepted is that it was formed from fatty oils deposited anaerobically and not at high temperatures in old marine sediments. The specific source, or sources, of the fatty oils is not definitely known, but these compounds occur widely and in substantial amounts in marine animal and vegetable life.

The mechanism of the formation of petroleum is complicated by the necessity for explaining its complex chemical composition (normal and branched paraffins, cycloparaffins, aromatics, etc.) within the limitations of all the geological evidence on hand. Theories of the mechanism have included thermal decomposition of fatty oils under pressure, action of alpha radiation on methane or other organic matter, bacterial decomposition of organic debris deposited in marine sediments, and catalytic action of minerals in sedimentary strata on heavy bitumens. No one of these theories, however, can account for all the known physical and chemical characteristics of petroleum. Petroleum was not formed in the pools in which it is found.

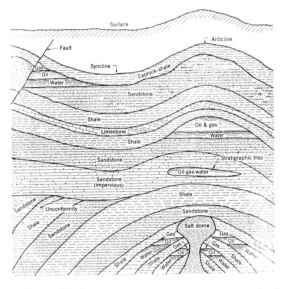

Figure 3.10. Composite geologic cross sections of petroleum traps. (*Courtesy Bureau of Mines, U. S. Department of the Interior*)

Being fluid, it migrated through porous geological strata until a substantial quantity was trapped in or against the higher parts of folds or wrinkles in the earth's crust, called anticlines and domes, or in tilted formations sealed by faults, changes in sedimentation, cementation, and inconformities. These are illustrated in Figure 3.10. When the petroleum oozes from exposed strata or escapes through faults or crevices it may seep to the surface. Some oil fields have been found where seeps have led to closer examination of surface geological features and the drilling of oil wells.

Studies of surface geology and examination of data acquired by geophysical or geochemical prospecting methods sometimes indicate potential sources of petroleum. Wells, some more than 20,000 feet deep, must be drilled to confirm commercially attractive deposits. Gas or water pressure native to oil reservoirs forces the oil into well bores and, if it is high enough, to the surface. Bottom hole pumps lift the oil through pipes in wells when fluids cease to flow to the surface.

Appreciable additional amounts of petroleum can be obtained from energy-depleted fields by secondary recovery methods which involve pumping water or gas into injection wells, according to a definite pattern and schedule, to force the remaining oil to adjacent producing wells.

Composition. The chemical constituents of petroleum are hydrocarbons, oxygen compounds, sulfur compounds, nitrogen compounds, resinous and asphaltic substances, and metallic compounds. Hydrocarbons comprise the largest fraction of these constituents, Pennsylvania crude oils containing as much as 98 per cent, Mid-continent and Gulf crudes 90–95 per cent, and heavy California crudes about 50 per cent.

The hydrocarbons in petroleum are paraffins, cycloparaffins (naphthenes), and aromatics; olefins and other unsaturated compounds are not present. Although all the types of saturated compounds are present in all petroleums, their relative amounts vary considerably in crudes from different sources. For example, Pennsylvania crudes are richest in paraffins, Mid-continent (Texas, Oklahoma, etc.) crudes contain more naphthenes than paraffins, and California crudes are relatively rich in aromatics having a low molecular weight. A comparative method used for distinguishing the various types of crudes is based on these characteristics: *paraffin-base crudes, mixed-base crudes, naphthene-base crudes,* and *aromatic crudes.* Both crudes and petroleum fractions may be characterized by the factor, K, which is defined as the ratio of the cube root of the normal boiling point in degrees Rankine to the specific gravity at 60° F. Approximate values for K are 12.5, 12.0, and 11.5 for Pennsylvania, Mid-Continent, and Gulf crudes, respectively.

The commonly used tests for petroleum and its products are given in an annual publication of the American Society of Testing Materials entitled *ASTM Standards on Petroleum Products and Lubricants,* and in pertinent supplements thereto. These tests include specific gravity, viscosity, flash- and fire-points, pourpoint, water and sediment, carbon residue, smoke point, heating value, ultimate analysis, distillation temperatures, corrosion test for sulfur, aniline point, and octane and cetane numbers.

The paraffin compounds in crudes range from hydrocarbon gases to solid paraffins containing 30 or more carbon atoms. Generally, straight-chain paraffins, or those with little branching, predominate. The cycloparaffins present are cyclopentane, and cyclohexane and their homologs. The aromatics include benzene, toluene, ethylbenzene, all isomeric xylenes, and certain homologs of benzene and naphthalene.

Oxygen compounds in petroleum occur naturally and as the result of oxidation in storage or during use. The naturally-occurring oxygen compounds are present in relatively small quantities, and include certain fatty acids and naphthenic acids. Occasionally, very small amounts of phenols are found.

Sulfur compounds in petroleum are largely combined in the resinous and asphaltic constituents.

The metallic compounds are present in trace quantities and are mainly vanadium and nickel porphyrins.

Consumption.[2] The total demand in 1958 for crude petroleum totaled 2,816 million barrels, an average of 7,700 thousand barrels daily. Domestic production furnished approximately 88 per cent of the total demand, or 6,760 thousand barrels daily, and imported crude oil furnished the remainder. For comparison with these data, the total demand in previous years, in millions of barrels, was 2,974 in 1957, 2,959 in 1956, 2,763 in 1955, 2,570 in 1954, and 2,591 in 1953. During this period, the percentage of the demand furnished by imported oil has steadily increased.

The domestic demand in 1958 for petroleum products, in descending order, was as follows: gasoline, distillate fuel oil, residual fuel oil, miscellaneous uses, kerosene, jet fuels, and lubricants. Gasoline accounted for 48.3 per cent of the demand.

Refining. The refining of petroleum to obtain salable products is one of the most advanced of all chemical engineering techniques, requiring the application of virtually all of the unit operations in present-day use, especially those based upon thermodynamics, material and energy balances, kinetics, and catalysis.

Before crude petroleum is refined, hydrocarbon gases dissolved in it at the pressures existing in the wells are separated by passing the crude through an oil-gas separator, which also effects separation of water and dirt. The gases that are separated are largely methane, ethane, and significant amounts of butane, propane, and heavier hydrocarbons. These are processed to make natural (casing-head) gasoline, liquefied petroleum (LP) gases, and to furnish a substantial amount of natural gas for pipeline distribution.

The crude from the oil-gas separator is sent to a refinery where it is fractionally distilled at atmospheric pressure; this is known as *topping* or *skimming*. The liquids obtained from the various stages of topping are known as *straight-run*, or *primary*, fractions; these may be used without further treatment, or they may be processed in various ways to increase the yield of a specific product or products, as will be described later. Primary untreated fractions are classified as: light gasoline, naphtha, kerosene; light, medium, and heavy gas oils; and topped crude.

The residue or topped crude is further processed in two main ways: *thermal cracking* to obtain gasoline and petroleum coke, and *vacuum or steam distillation* to obtain gas oil, lubricating-oil stock, and asphalt.

It is important to note that refinery flow plans are seldom similar because each crude oil and each market environment dictate the most effective and economic flow plan. However, there are certain basic steps that must be employed. They are described briefly below, in the order which comprises the over-all refinery process.

Thermal and Catalytic Cracking. The heavier straight-run products, such as the gas oils and residual stocks, can be thermally cracked into lighter fractions by heating to about 950° F at pressures in the range of 300–600 psi.

By use of a suitable catalyst, cracking can be accomplished at lower temperature and pressure. Catalytic cracking produces gasoline with a higher octane rating and lower gum-forming tendency than does thermal cracking. In addition, less methane and ethane are produced in catalytic cracking because the catalyst tends to break the larger hydrocarbons from the end. Thermal and catalytic cracking increase the yield and the quality of gasoline and light oil per barrel of crude.

Cracked Product Fractionation. Since the products from cracking operations have a wide boiling range and are in the vapor state, special fractionation procedures are employed to separate the products that are required.

Stabilization and Concentration of Hydrocarbon Gases. This step removes methane, ethane, most of the propane, and some of the butanes from the topped and the cracked gasolines, and makes a gasoline with the desired vapor pressure. At the same time, the hydrocarbon gases are obtained as highly enriched fractions, and are treated as described below.

Polymerization and Alkylation. Light hydrocarbon gases recovered in the stabilization process are partly converted to gasoline by polymerization and alkylation processes. Thus hydrocarbon gases are utilized more advantageously than if they were burned as a refinery fuel. Polymerization produces a larger olefin from the reaction of two olefins; alkylation produces a saturated compound by reaction of an olefin and a paraffin. Use of a catalyst such as sulfuric or phosphoric acid causes polymerization to occur at a lower temperature. The olefin formed may be hydrogenated to yield a more stable paraffin product. Thus "isooctane" is formed by hydrogenation of polymerized isobutylene.

Purification. Except for heavy distillates and fuel oils, the liquid products contain impurities which must be removed before the products can be sold. Some of the common purposes of purification are: to remove certain sulfur compounds, to improve the color, to remove gum-forming compounds, to improve stability towards light, to improve odor, and to reduce corrosiveness. Depending on the product to be treated and the impurities that are present, upgrading can be accomplished by one or more of many chemical treating and extraction processes, by hydrogenation, by absorption of the impurities on certain solids, and by the addition of oxidation inhibitors.

Blending. The market for refinery products requires many different gasolines, naphthas, distillate oils, etc.; consequently the refiner produces basic stocks that can be blended to meet the market requirements. For example, motor gasolines are blended of natural, cracked and reformed gasolines, butanes, light straight-run naphtha, and relatively smaller proportions of polygasoline and alkylate. Aviation gasolines are blends of isopentane, catalytic-cracked gasoline, straight-run gasoline, aromatic distillates, and alkylates. Light fuel oils commonly are blends of kerosene and appropriate light-oil stocks in the proportions necessary to meet a desired specification. However, they may be recovered from the refining process as a separate fraction.

Utilization. At the turn of the century, kerosene was the major commercial product from petroleum. Today thousands of different products have become indispensable to industrial operations, heat and power generation,

TABLE 3.10. SOME BASIC PETROLEUM PRODUCTS

Fuels for power and heating
  Aviation, motor, diesel, jet fuels
  Nos. 1, 2, 4, 5, and 6 fuel oils for burners
Solvents for cleaning, thinning, placticizing
Lubricants
  Automotive: crankcase and transmission oils and greases
  Industrial: engine, turbine, machine oils and greases
Specialty oils
  Machining, heat treating, hydraulic electrical insulation, and heat transfer
Asphalts
  Road building, roofing, and waterproofing
Waxes
  Waterproofing, insulating, and rubber compounding
Pharmaceuticals
  Mineral oils, jellies, and chemicals

TABLE 3.11. PRODUCTION OF REFINERY PRODUCTS
IN THE UNITED STATES, 1958[2]

	Thousand Barrels
Gasoline, natural and refined	1,422,835
Kerosene	110,008
Distillate fuel oil	631,405
Residual fuel oil	363,358
Jet fuel	73,676
Lubricants	51,298
Wax (1 barrel = 280 pounds)	5,252
Coke (5 barrels = 2000 pounds)	37,808
Asphalt (5.5 barrels = 2000 pounds)	89,380
Road oil	5,925
Liquefied gases	57,623

transportation, military operations, and commercial activities. Petroleum products range from such familiar materials as kerosene and gasoline to methyl and ethyl alcohols, which number among the numerous pure compounds (petrochemicals) derived from petroleum. Table 3.10 gives some of the basic products. Table 3.11 gives data for the production in the United States of the principal products. The domestic demand for residual fuel oil exceeded refinery production, consequently the remainder was imported. These two tables indicate the size and complexity of the petroleum industry.

Natural Gas

Natural gas consists predominantly of a mixture of hydrocarbons produced from gas and oil wells. It has excellent combustion characteristics and is used extensively as a fuel for residential, commercial, and industrial uses. It is also an important raw material for the production of a wide variety of chemical products.

Origin and Composition. Like petroleum, natural gas is found in rocks of sedimentary origin, where geological phenomena have trapped it, forming gas reservoirs. In the reservoir natural gas may be "dry," that is, entirely in the gaseous state, or it may be "wet," in which case it is associated with hydrocarbons that are easily separable as liquids by compression, refrigeration, or absorption.

Dry natural gas is mainly methane, but it may contain appreciable amounts of ethane, depending on its geographical source. Typical analyses cannot be given because of the variations in composition with respect to both its source and the age of the wells. It may be said, however, that the methane content of natural gas ranges approximately from 60–95 per cent, and the ethane content from 5–20 per cent. The higher heating value of natural gas ranges from 950 to 1,150 Btu per cubic foot, depending on its composition. Other constituents, present in comparatively small concentrations, are propane, butane, carbon dioxide, and nitrogen.[10] Some sources, especially in the Texas area, contain helium which is separated by the liquefaction of all other components. Trace concentrations of hydrogen sulfide and organic sulfur compounds ("sour" gas) occur in some of the sources.

Treatment of Raw Natural Gas. The most important treatment of natural gas at its source is the removal of salable light liquid hydrocarbons, water, carbon dioxide, and sulfur compounds. Such treatment improves the quality of the natural gas for pipeline transmission and marketing, and recovers certain products having a comparatively high market value, such as natural gasoline, propane, and butane.

The sulfur compounds in natural gas are a significant source of elemental sulfur. When the gas contains more than 1.5 grains of hydrogen sulfide per 100 cubic feet, it is termed "sour" gas. The primary desulfurization treatment is based on liquid-phase absorption of the sulfur compounds in sodium carbonate or phosphate, sodium phenolate, or mono-, di-, or triethanolamine. These processes also remove some of the carbon dioxide in natural gas, which occasionally is present in relatively high concentrations.

Consumption and Utilization. Enormous quantities of natural gas are consumed annually as a fuel for producing heat and power, and to a smaller extent as a raw material for manufacturing numerous chemical products. Six areas in the United States where natural gas is produced are divided, roughly, as (1) Appalachian, (2) Indiana, (3) Mid-continent, (4) Texas, (5) Rocky Mountain, and (6) California. Greatest marketed production is from Texas, about 5,178 billion cubic feet in 1958. Louisiana produced 2,452 billion cubic feet in the same year. Oklahoma, New Mexico, Kansas, and California are the next major sources, each producing between 500 and 1,000 billion cubic feet, and West Virginia, Wyoming, Pennsylvania, and Mississippi each produced between 100 and 500 billion cubic feet in the same year.

In 1958, the consumption of dry natural gas for all purposes was 11,030 billion cubic feet, of which 2,714 billion cubic feet were consumed for residential heating, 872 billion cubic feet for commercial purposes, and 7,174 billion cubic feet for industrial purposes. The manufacture of carbon black consumed about 3 per cent of the gas used for industrial purposes. Large amounts of hydrogen are obtained from the carbon-black process, and by direct reaction of natural gas with steam. Hundreds of intermediate chemicals are made, including ethylene, acetylene, propylene, glycols, toluene, acetic acid, alcohols, and ketones. These intermediates contribute significantly to the production of synthetic rubbers, plastics, resins, insecticides, and solvents.

The hydrocarbons extracted from raw natural gas are mainly propane, butane, and pentane; these are sold as natural gasoline or *casinghead* gasoline, and liquified petroleum (LP) gases. In 1958, some 4.5 billion gallons of natural gasoline, and 6.7 billion gallons of LP gases were produced from natural gas in the United States. These products are used principally for blending in refinery gasoline, heating fuel, synthetic rubber components, and in numerous chemical processes.

Intensive research investigations are being conducted by the U. S. Bureau of Mines and private research organizations to develop economic processes for synthesizing methane from coal. These efforts are the result of steadily rising production and transmission costs of natural gas and of the profound changes that have been taking place in the energy pattern of the United States as the result of population growth, industrial developments, and the declining use of solid fuels for domestic heating.

REFERENCES

1. American Society for Testing Materials, Coal and Coke, Part 8 of 1958 Book of ASTM Standards, pp. 999–1029, Philadelphia, Pa., 1958.
2. Bureau of Mines Minerals Yearbook, Review of the Mineral-Fuel Industries in 1958, Vol. II, 1959.
3. Corey, R. C., Myers, J. W., Schwartz, C. H., Gibson, F. H., and Colbassani, P. J., "Occurrence and Determination of Germanium in Coal Ash from Power Plants," *Bureau of Mines Bull.*, 575, 1959.

4. Fieldner, A. C., and Selvig, W. A., "Methods of Analyzing Coal and Coke," *Bureau of Mines Bull.*, **492**, 1951.

5. Gomez, M., Goodman, J. B., and Parry, V. F., "Low-Temperature Tar from Fluidized Carbonizing Reactors," *Bureau of Mines Report of Investigations*, 5302, 1957.

6. Mitchell, D. R., ed., "Coal Preparation," 2nd Edition, American Institute of Mining and Metallurgical Engineers, New York, 1950.

7. Ode, W. H., and Frederick, W. H., "The International Systems of Hard-Coal Classification and Their Application to American Coals," *Bureau of Mines Report of Investigations*, 5435, 1958.

8. Parry, V. F., Landers, W. S., Wagner, E. O., Goodman, J. B., and Lammers, B. C., "Drying and Carbonizing Fine Coal in Entrained and Fluidized State," *Bureau of Mines Report of Investigations*, 4954, 1953.

9. Russell, H. T., "Future Prospects of Flyash Utilization," *Coal Utilization*, March 1956.

10. Shnidman, L., "Gaseous Fuels," 2nd Edition, American Gas Association, New York, 1954.

SUPPLEMENTARY REFERENCES

American Institute of Mining and Metallurgical Engineers, "Gasification and Liquefaction of Coal," New York, 1953.

Ayers, E., and Scarlott, C. A., "Energy Sources—The Wealth of the World," McGraw-Hill Book Co., Inc., New York, 1952.

The Babcock and Wilcox Company, "Steam—Its Generation and Use," New York, 1955.

Combustion Engineering, Inc., "Combustion Engineering," New York, 1952.

Given, P. H., "The Production of Chemicals from Coal and Petroleum," Review No. 154, *British Coal Utiln. Res. Assoc., Monthly Bull.*, **19**, pp. 589–605 (Dec. 1955).

Glenn, R. A., and Rose, H. J., "The Metallurgical, Chemical, and Other Process Uses of Coal," Bituminous Coal Research, Inc., Pittsburgh, Pa., 1958.

Hoy, H. R., and Wilkins, D. M., "Total Gasification of Coal," Review No. 174, *Brit. Coal Utiln. Res. Assoc., Monthly Bull.*, **22**, pp. 57–110 (Feb.–Mar. 1958).

Kirk, R. E., and Othmer, D. F., Editors, Encyclopedia of Chemical Technology, Vol. 10 (Petroleum), pp. 88–228, Interscience Publishers, Inc., New York, 1953.

Lowry, H. H., ed. Chemistry of Coal Utilization, Vols. I and II, John Wiley and Sons, Inc., New York, 1945.

Lowry, H. H., "Coal as a Future Energy Resource," Address at Energy Resources Conference, Denver, Col., Oct. 15–16, 1958.

Sherman, A., and MacMurphy, A. B., "Facts About Coal," Government Printing Office, Washington, D. C., 1955.

Wilson, P. J., and Wells, J. H., "Coal, Coke, and Coal Chemicals," McGraw-Hill Book Co., Inc., New York, 1950.

"Minerals Facts and Problems," *Bureau of Mines Bull.*, **585** (1960).

4

SULFURIC ACID AND SULFUR

In collaboration with Dr. E. Raymond Riegel*

SULFURIC ACID

SULFURIC ACID, one of the so-called "heavy chemicals," is an oily liquid of relatively low volatility and strong corrosive properties. It has hundreds of uses and has become an important article of commerce because of its low price and its versatility.

Sulfuric acid is the center of much of the chemical industry. It is used in the production of hydrochloric acid, ammonium sulfate, superphosphates for agriculture, the refining of petroleum, in electric storage batteries, in the manufacture of glucose, and in dyeing, textile printing, tanning, paper manufacture, and scores of other industries. The raw materials used in the production of sulfuric acid are common and abundant: the most important is sulfur, either from natural deposits or, to a lesser extent, recovered as a by-product; iron pyrites; and several minor sources. The sulfur or the pyrite ore is burned (smelted) to form sulfur dioxide gas, and the acid is made by oxidizing the sulfur dioxide with air and adding water. Natural sulfur was originally obtained from Sicily and later from Louisiana and Texas; pyrites are widely distributed in the Eastern United States, as well as in parts of Europe.

* Professor Emeritus, University of Buffalo.

Sulfuric acid is made by either the chamber process or the contact process. The former is the older process gradually developed by combining earlier single steps, some of which date from the alchemists of the Middle Ages. In this process, large lead boxes (so large that they may properly be called chambers) are used to react sulfur dioxide with air, oxides of nitrogen, and steam or water in the form of a spray. Until the last twenty-five years the chambers were very large, i.e., 28 by 14 feet in cross section, and as much as 75 feet long. Modern lead chambers are smaller, and to compensate for the

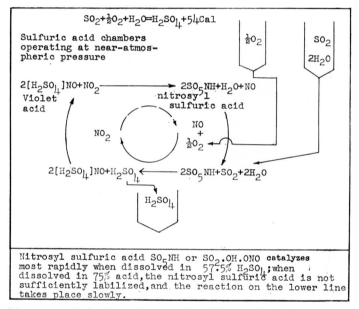

Figure 4.1. Cycle of reactions in the sulfuric acid chambers, when operating at near-atmospheric pressure.

smaller size, the reaction is more intense. The role of the oxides of nitrogen is to transfer the oxygen in the air to the sulfur dioxide so that it forms sulfur trioxide, at the same time acquiring water to form sulfuric acid. SO_2 (sulfur dioxide) $+ \frac{1}{2}O_2 + H_2O$ (water) $= H_2SO_4$ (sulfuric acid). The functions of the intermediate compounds, violet acid and nitrosyl sulfuric acid, are shown in Figure 4.1. The sulfur trioxide (SO_3) is not isolated in the chamber process. Sulfur dioxide, oxygen, the oxides of nitrogen, and water are gases at the reaction temperature, $232°$ F ($111°$ C) in the first and second chamber, for example. The oxides of nitrogen are not consumed in the reaction but are used over and over again; they are a gaseous catalyst. The sulfuric acid produced collects in the bottom of the chambers, whence it is moved to storage or shipping tanks by centrifugal pumps of special metal.

Figure 4.2. A battery of acid pumps, with individual drive, lifting the cooled process acid to the top of the Petersen towers in the manufacture of sulfuric acid.

The principal commercial strengths of chamber acid are:

	% H_2SO_4
50° Bé acid (chamber acid)	62.18
55° Bé acid (chamber acid)	69.65
60° Bé acid (chamber acid, concentrated by heat)	77.67
66° Bé acid (oil of vitriol, concentrated by heat)	93.19

The strength of the acid is determined by a hydrometer test for strengths up to 66° Bé (93.19 per cent H_2SO_4); between 93.19 per cent and just above 100 per cent H_2SO_4, the electrical conductivity is a reliable and convenient method. Between 8 and 56 per cent free SO_3, the oleums may be tested with a hydrometer; below and above these figures, by titration. The oleums are made by the contact process.

Both the chamber process and the contact process are continuous.

There are in the United States 216 sulfuric acid producing plants (1958) of which 70 are chamber process plants, 141 are contact process plants, and 5 operate both processes. In tons of acid produced, the contact process outranks by far the chamber process, as indicated in the table below.

TABLE 4.1. PRODUCTION OF SULFURIC ACID, BY PROCESS*
IN THE UNITED STATES†

Short Tons of 100% H_2SO_4

	Chamber acid	Contact acid	Total	Per cent chamber acid of total
1958	1,741,756	13,538,667	15,950,199	10.83
1957	1,988,303	13,779,922	16,459,608	12.5
1956	2,233,600	13,503,748	16,494,538	13.8

* Bureau of the Census.

† World distribution of sulfuric acid plants is described in detail in Economic Geography of Industrial Materials by Albert S. Carlson, pages 239–246, Reinhold Publishing Corporation, New York, 1956.

Sources of Sulfuric Acid

To the main sources of sulfuric acid, sulfur (brimstone) and iron pyrites, there have been added smelter gases and recovered hydrogen sulfide. In 1954, sulfuric acid made from smelter gases (copper plants, zinc plants) amounted to 885,975 short tons (basis 100 per cent acid).

TABLE 4.2. PERCENTAGE OF TOTAL RAW MATERIALS
FOR SULFURIC ACID (U. S.)

	1951 %
Sulfur (brimstone)	80.0
Pyrites	13.08
Other forms	7.10

TABLE 4.3. PRODUCTION IN THOUSANDS OF LONG TONS
WORLD SULFUR PRODUCTION STATISTICS

	1957	1956
Frasch sulfur	6,514	7,177
Recovered sulfur	1,075	893
Native sulfur rock	470	531

Chamber Process

In order to manufacture sulfuric acid by the chamber process, there are needed: (a) burners for lump ore, rotary shelf burners for fines (granular ore), burners for melted brimstone or recovered sulfur; (b) a Glover tower; (c) a set of chambers preceded by an ammonia burner; (d) a Gay-Lussac tower which may be one tall structure or several shorter ones, interconnected; (e) storage tanks, distributing tanks, and pumps.

The burners for iron pyrite which might be lump burners, rotary shelf burners, or more elaborate modern burners (Figure 4.3) produce a sulfur dioxide gas with about 8 per cent SO_2; some of the oxygen is lost to the iron. The reaction is $4FeS_2 + 11O_2 = 2Fe_2O_3 + 8SO_2$. Once ignited, the combustion proceeds by itself. The heat evolved is considerable. The gas produced from the ore must be freed from the red dust (iron oxide) by means of dust chambers with shelves, coke boxes, Cottrell precipitators, etc., especially when it is to enter a contact process converter. In the purification most of the heat is lost.

Sulfur burners produce a richer gas, such as 10 or 11 per cent SO_2. The burner may be a slowly rotating horizontal cylinder with inlet ports for air

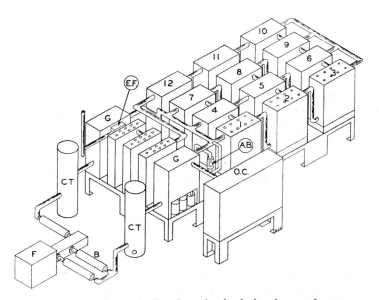

Figure 4.3. An isometric drawing of a lead chamber set for manu-facturing sulfuric acid; not absolutely to scale, but sufficiently so to show the relative sizes. F, sulfur feeder; B, sulfur burner (the sketch shows three burners); CT, combustion towers (to complete combus-tion and to cool the gases); G, Glover towers; between them are the three sections of the Gay-Lussac tower; AB, ammonia burner, between the Glover and chamber 1; OC, outside chamber, added to increase capacity; 1 to 12, lead chambers; EF, exhaust fan, leading to a short exit stack. Note acid-cooling tanks under the Glover. Acid pumps are not shown.

at the feed end, and large outlet ports at the far end. The charge may be solid brimstone which soon melts. The gas passes first to a combustion chamber wherein any sublimed sulfur is given time to oxidize. It then enters the Glover tower where it meets Gay-Lussac acid, that is, nitre gas-rich acid, and water, introduced to liberate the nitre gas. Continuing a description of the chamber process, the effect of the Glover tower is to cool the sulfur gas and to concentrate the acid. A certain amount of new acid is formed in the Glover tower. This latter has silica brick inner walls encased in lead; it is filled with quartz of assorted sizes. Its horizontal cross section is usually square. It may be built in three shorter sections with gas and acid connections which permit functioning on the countercurrent principle.

Leaving the Glover tower the sulfur dioxide gas laden with steam, nitre gas from the Gay-Lussac acid about to be recycled, and with its excess oxygen and its nitrogen, passes the delivery tube from the ammonia burner which furnishes nitrogen oxides in quantities sufficient to make up for the loss in

Figure 4.4. These are the largest units in the world for utilizing (burning) sulfur-bearing ores for the manufacture of sulfuric acid. The two giant ore burners stand over ten stories high and are the first of their type ever built. They are located at the Delaware Works of General Chemical Division, Allied Chemical Corporation, Marcus Hook, Pa. (Note the two figures at lower left)

the tail gas. The gas then enters the chambers. Issuing from the base of the Glover are: the new sulfuric acid made in the tower, the acid which furnishes the nitre gas for recycle, and any acid passed through the tower for concentration. It is the modern practice to pass all the chamber acid through the Glover and thus concentrate it to 60° Bé without expense for heat. The Glover acid is cooled in double-walled lead receiving tanks provided additionally with cooling water coils, from 130° F (54° C) to 60°–70° F (15°–21° C). Acid of this strength is suitable for the absorption of nitre gas in the Gay-Lussac tower, for reactions in chemical plants, and for shipment to customers.

The ammonia burner receives a preheated mixture of 11 per cent NH_3 and air. The burner consists of a well insulated box with stainless steel inlet and high chrome iron outlet. It contains a multi-layer platinum alloy gauze

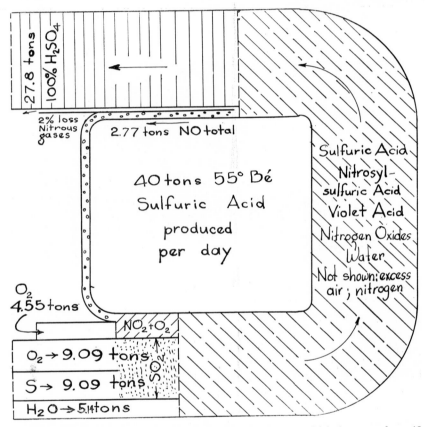

Figure 4.5. Diagram of materials for a chamber plant which is to produce 40 tons of 55° Bé sulfuric acid per day. The relations given are the theoretical ones, inasmuch as most plants almost reach the figures. Water of dilution amounting to 12.2 tons is not included in the diagram.

which is at red heat. Once started, no outside heat is necessary. The intensity of oxidation may be judged visually through a window in the sidewall of the burner. The platinum gradually and steadily fluffs away and must be replaced periodically; its cost is part of the cost of the acid. The reaction is $4NH_3 + 5O_2 = 4NO + 6H_2O$.

The gas travels from chamber to chamber; the reaction continues and acid is made in each chamber. The acid is drawn off by syphons and pumps;

at times, it is allowed to accumulate in the bottom of the chambers. The gas leaving the last chamber ascends the Gay-Lussac tower where it loses its nitre gas to a descending stream of cold 60° Bé acid. All the nitrogen and excess oxygen leave by the tail pipe, carrying with them a small percentage of nitre gas which produces a yellow color.

Among the modifications of the standard chamber process are the following:

The Mills-Packard chambers, introduced in England, are smaller in cubical content; they are truncated cones with the smaller diameter at the top so

Figure 4.6. A view of a Petersen System plant for the manufacture of sulfuric acid. The towers are built of chemical stoneware shapes, reinforced with hoops. The circulated acid is cooled in the return bend coolers, visible in the foreground, and then returned to the top of the towers. It is in the towers that the reaction takes place; in this system, the towers have become the chambers.

that a curtain of water may flow down on the outside of the walls. The chambers are made of lead, supported by an outside steel framework.

The Petersen towers, introduced in Germany, are packed towers; they provide intimate contact between the gases and the acid, enabling the latter to remove the heat of reaction at a fast rate. The acid is cooled in return bends by means of water.

TABLE 4.4. EFFICIENCY OF SULFURIC ACID CHAMBERS SYSTEM
IN TERMS OF REACTION SPACE

Chambers	Cubic feet of space per pound of brimstone burned per 24 hours	Cooled by
Rectangular	7.5–10.0	air
Mills-Packard	2.5– 3.0	water
Anaconda cells, Petersen towers	1.0 and less	cold-acid circulation (acid cooled by water)

Contact Process

In the contact process, a solid catalyst is in contact with the reacting gases. Sulfur dioxide is oxidized to sulfur trioxide. $2SO_2 + O_2 \rightarrow 2SO_3$. The sulfur trioxide is usually absorbed in a sulfuric acid of strength selected to produce 98 per cent acid, or 100 per cent, or the oleums which cointain free sulfur trioxide. On the other hand, for the weaker acids, a dilution step is in order, in which water or a very weak acid is run into a stream of stronger acid. The meeting of sulfur trioxide and water is avoided because they combine explosively.

Figure 4.7. A view in a sulfuric acid contact plant of the standard type, with tray-style converters. The two converters (the two lower vessels at right) and heat exchangers (the taller vessels to the left) are heavily insulated.

It was chiefly because of the demand for 100 per cent H_2SO_4 and for overstrength oleums in the dyestuff manufacturing industry that the contact system prospered, at least at first. In the course of the years since the turn of the century, when it was introduced, it has demonstrated other superiorities: it requires less floor space, requires a lower first cost, furnishes extremely pure acid, and it may be built in large single units having the same characteristics as the smaller ones, that is, it may be scaled up with confidence.

The Badische Anilin and Soda Fabrik developed the first contact mass, which was platinized asbestos. It is made by soaking selected asbestos fibers in a solution of ammonium chlorplatinate, draining, drying, and then heating the yellow mass in a current of air containing sulfur dioxide, when the asbestos turns gray. The heart of the process is the converter which holds the contact mass at a regulated elevated temperature, such as 450° C (842° F).

The presently favored catalyst is vanadium pentoxide on a potassium aluminate-silicate base, or other non-fusible carrier. The mass is shaped in short cylindrical pieces $\frac{1}{4}$ or $\frac{3}{8}$ inch in diameter. The vanadium pentoxide is cheaper and less likely to lose activity through poisoning. A circular bed 4 or 6 inches, or more, in height is formed by carefully heaping the catalyst granules on perforated plates. The entire bed is pervious to gases, in either downward or upward flow. The pressure is essentially atmospheric.*

The catalyst masses best known in the United States and Canada are listed in the table below:

TABLE 4.5. SO$_2$ TO SO$_3$ CATALYST MASSES

	Apparent density of mass	Daily pounds of sulfur as 8 per cent SO$_2$ gas converted per liter of catalyst mass	Appearance
Selden mass V$_2$O$_5$	0.46	5	Light greenish-yellow tablets $\frac{1}{4}''$ diameter
Monsanto mass V$_2$O$_5$	0.56	5	Light green half-cylinders $\frac{3}{8}''$ length

The pellets contain 5.5 per cent vanadium pentoxide, on an average. The carrier is silica, frequently in the form of diatomaceous earth. Potassium aluminate is part of the Selden formulation. The life of the vanadium catalyst is variously given as several years, with $2\frac{1}{2}$ years as average.

The sulfur dioxide gas from the burners, with excess air, at a suitable temperature, and containing a prescribed maximum of moisture, is fed to the catalyst bed held at an elevated temperature. If the gas comes from pyrites, lump ore, fines, or mill tailings, it will have passed through a purifying train where it will also have been cooled. Such cold gas must be preheated before feeding it to the catalyst mass in the converter. However, should the gas come from a sulfur burner, it must be cooled, in a "waste heat" boiler, for example, before sending it to the catalyst mass. If the temperature of the reacting gases and catalyst mass is too high, such as 595° C (1103° F), the

---

* The reaction $2SO_2 + O_2 \rightarrow 2SO_3$ involves a decrease in volume, from 3 to 2, and one would expect that by running the process at a higher pressure, the rate of reaction would be accelerated, and the amount of material would be greater for a given space and contact mass. Yet, as far as is known, all contact processes are run at near-atmospheric pressure, although proposals for, and trials at higher pressures have been made. The explanation probably lies in the slowness of one of the steps, of which the simple reaction given above is but a summation. The rate of diffusion of the incoming sulfur dioxide and oxygen mix to the surface of the catalyst is the slowest step, and it is this step which sets the pace for the reaction as a whole. The sulfur trioxide is strongly absorbed on the surface of the catalyst, and it is through this layer of absorbed sulfur trioxide that the incoming gases must diffuse. Increase in pressure would perhaps raise slightly the speed with which sulfur dioxide and oxygen travel through the sulfur trioxide layer, but the thickness of the latter would probably be increased, thus nullifying the first beneficient effect. [See Discussion by Dr. J. H. Perry of the paper by Dr. Ernst Berl, *Trans. Am. Inst. Chem. Eng.*, **31**, 223 (1935).]

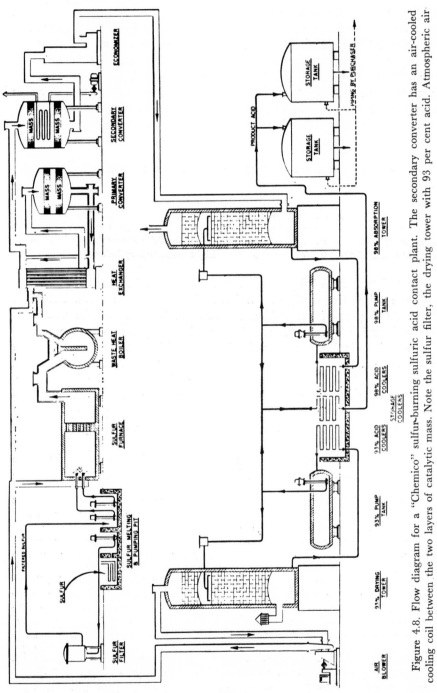

Figure 4.8. Flow diagram for a "Chemico" sulfur-burning sulfuric acid contact plant. The secondary converter has an air-cooled cooling coil between the two layers of catalytic mass. Note the sulfur filter, the drying tower with 93 per cent acid. Atmospheric air enters at the lower left of the drying tower.

reaction $2SO_2 + O_2 \rightarrow 2SO_3$ proceeds very fast, but is incomplete because the reverse reaction, $2SO_3 \rightarrow 2SO_2 + O_2$, begins and produces appreciable amounts of sulfur dioxide. On the other hand, if the temperature is too low, such as 400° C (752° F), the reaction proceeds too slowly. The difficulty is overcome by passing the gas first through an extremely hot bed of catalyst, wherein a rapid, though incomplete, reaction takes place; the gas is then cooled somewhat, and passed through a heavier bed of catalyst mass, wherein the slower reaction, thanks to the longer contact time, can take

Figure 4.9. A new-type Chemico Contact Plant with a 50-ton acid per day capacity, erected outdoors. Visible from right to left: the sulfur spray-type combustion furnace, waste heat boiler, air filter, turbo blower feeding air to the furnace, control house, and acid storage tanks. The tall structure in the background is the quench converter in which the gases are cooled by the direct admission of measured amounts of cold air, with the pipe carrying the gas from the furnace entering near the top. The exit gas plume (on exit stack from P–A Venturi scrubber) is essentially steam, with no acid mist.

place to a considerable degree. A total conversion of 97 per cent is reached and is considered satisfactory.

In some of the new type of contact installations the converter is a single vessel containing two or more beds of catalyst placed over each other, all of the same diameter, but increasing in thickness from the topmost to the lowest one. The sulfur dioxide travels from the top to the bottom.

In the Badische system the excess heat in the gas leaving the first converter was transferred to an incoming colder mixture in tubular heat exchangers before it could enter the second converter. Other constructions since then have provided cooling coils employing air. In the Quench Converter (New Type Chemico) the cooling is achieved by the direct injection of measured amounts of cold air after each stage. This is the quenching feature. The gas entering the converter is made extra high in sulfur dioxide, such as 12 per cent.

The hot sulfur trioxide produced is cooled in a tubular heat exchanger by a stream of cold air, and is absorbed in a 98 per cent sulfuric acid tower. The latter is built of masonry and filled with a checker work of acid-proof bricks preceded by baffles and surmounted by a bed of pebbles. A second level of baffles and pebbles ensures good mixing of the gas and good contact with the descending acid, so that the gas passing to the atmosphere through a stack is exhausted. The absorbing acid is diluted continuously by means of a weaker acid, such as chamber acid, or by means of water in amount sufficient to keep the strength about 98 per cent. A heavy stream of absorbing acid is maintained, and its heat is continuously removed by passing it through cooling pipes laid in water. A weaker acid available at all times in many plants is the effluent from the drying tower; fed in at 93.2 per cent, it is kept over 81.3 per cent.

When oleum is to be made, the oleum tower precedes the 98 per cent acid tower, and receives the gas first. The strength of the oleum is controlled by regulating the amount of acid fed to the tower; the stronger the oleum required, the slower the stream of acid. The gas leaving the oleum tower is still high in SO_3 content, and passes to the 98 per cent acid tower where complete absorption takes place. The oleum leaving the oleum tower is collected separately.

Oleums and "Sulfan"

Oleums are made in a number of strengths, such as 15, 20, 40, 60, and 65 per cent free SO_3 by weight. Their freezing points vary considerably, as shown in Fig. 4.10. What is more, the pure substance, 100 per cent sulfur trioxide, is a white solid which melts without difficulty at $+40°$ C ($104°$ F); however, on standing, it polymerizes to a fibrous solid which on being heated melts with great difficulty, and mainly sublimes. However, there is available a modified 100 per cent oleum, better called a stabilized sulfuric anhydride, which presents none of the difficulties mentioned. In this form it is a liquid and remains one, thanks to the introduction of a stabilizing agent (0.25 per cent). This new material is available in drum lots and in tank-car lots. "Sulfan," the stabilized sulfuric anhydride, is made in the oleum tower and is collected as a warm liquid; the stabilizer is added, and the product remains liquid.

Brimstone and Contact Process

When sulfur in the form of brimstone became available to the sulfuric acid manufacturer, it simplified enormously the plant previously operating on iron pyrites. No longer were the elaborate purification equipment, dust chambers, electrical precipitator, wet tower, wet coke boxes, or dry coke box, required. They still are necessary if the manufacturer chooses to burn pyrites, fines, or lumps, or to operate the Fluosolid system, which is a fluidized bed roaster, or a flash burner in which powdered pyrite is fed into a combustion chamber where it burns very much as powdered bituminous coal burns under a boiler. Some contact systems retain a purification feature, since dust inactivates the contact agent; thus a Monsanto plant overseas has hot gas filters filled with graded silica chips. The method of burning sulfur has variations. Frequently, the brimstone is melted in a preliminary melter; the burner may be a spray burner, in which case filtration of the liquid sulfur is recommended to avoid plugging the nozzle.

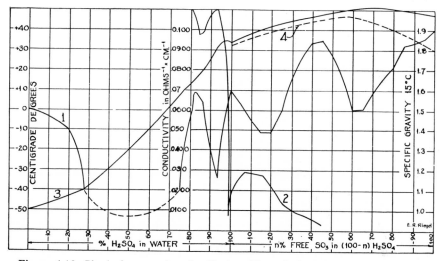

Figure 4.10. Physical properties of sulfuric acids and oleums of various concentrations. 1, melting points (Knietsch); 2, conductivities in reciprocal ohms (Landolt-Börnstein Tabellen); 3, specific gravities at 15° C; 4, specific gravities at 45° C (Knietsch).

The compactness of the contact plant and the relatively low weight of brimstone has permitted the erection of sulfuric acid plants in far off places, for example, the ones at Port Radium on Great Bear Lake and at Gunnar Dock (Fig. 4.11). Bulk sulfur reaches Gunnar Dock on Lake Athabasca from Edmonton in Alberta as follows: 300 miles to Waterways by rail, 200 miles by water down the Athabasca river, and across the lake 164 miles. Even more remarkable is the journey of the sulfur packed in bags and loaded on barges at Waterways where it begins its travel, all by water, to Port Radium on Great Bear Lake, 1335 miles away. The trip is by the Athabasca river, the Slave River, a portion of Great Slave Lake, down the Mackenzie River (460 miles) to Great Bear Lake, with a final 247 miles across the lake to its destination. A year's supply must be moved in the ice-free period which is only three months long. The sulfur is recovered sulfur, from the natural gas fields in British Columbia. The acid-manufacturing plants are contact plants. Gunnar Dock has two Leonard-Monsanto sulfur-burning units with rated capacities of 100 and 65 tons, respectively, of sulfuric acid per day.

Sulfuric Acid Concentrators

In many operations the sulfuric acid functions as a water-remover. The water taken up by the acid may be removed in a concentrator so that the acid, restored to its former higher strength, may be reused. In nitrations, in which mixed acid is generally used, there results a spent acid with very little nitric acid and with its sulfuric acid diluted. In the Chemico drum-type

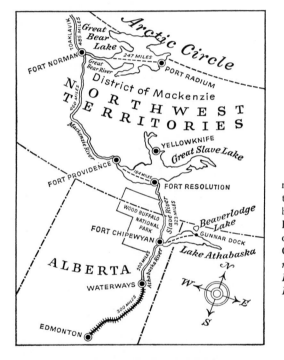

Figure 4.11. Bulk sulfur moves from Waterways, Alberta, to Gunnar Dock, Lake Athabaska, Saskatchewan, on barges. Bagged sulfur is shipped, also on barges, to Port Radium on Great Bear Lake. (*Sketch of map supplied courtesy Link-Belt Company, Chicago 1, Illinois*)

sulfuric acid concentrator, consisting of two acid-proof masonry drum-shaped acid compartments lined with lead, the second drum receives the weak acid; the first drum receives fire gases from an oil burner, and delivers the concentrated acid to cooling coils and then to storage. The gases from the first drum pass just under the surface of the acid in the second drum, causing considerable concentration. The acid from the second drum passes to the first drum for final concentration. The final gases pass to an electrical precipitator and thence to the atmosphere.

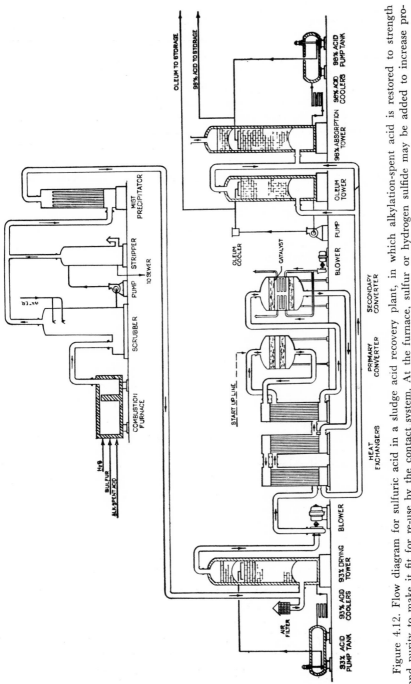

Figure 4.12. Flow diagram for sulfuric acid in a sludge acid recovery plant, in which alkylation-spent acid is restored to strength and purity to make it fit for re-use by the contact system. At the furnace, sulfur or hydrogen sulfide may be added to increase production.

Other devices for concentration are the Chemico Flash-Film Vacuum-type Concentrator, the du Pont falling-film concentrator, the Simonson-Mantius concentrator.

If the acid to be processed is not only diluted but charged with impurities, such as tarry matter from the treatment of petroleum fractions, it has been found advantageous to make sulfur dioxide out of the residual acid in a furnace and re-manufacture (with or without auxiliary sources of sulfur dioxide) sulfuric acid in a vanadium-type converter.

Clean spent acid may be strengthened in two other ways: by the addition of oleum, when it becomes a fortified acid, or, when convenient, by sending it through the absorption tower of a contact plant.

In 1958, the value of a short ton on the basis of 100 per cent H_2SO_4 for total shipments including interplant transfers was $18.18 f.o.b. plant. The

TABLE 4.6. SULFURIC ACID CONSUMED IN THE UNITED STATES (1957) IN THOUSANDS OF NET TONS*

Fertilizer, superphosphate	4,550
Fertilizer, ammonium sulfate	1,600
Chemicals	4,400
Petroleum refining	2,000
Inorganic pigments	1,380
Rayon and film	780
Iron and Steel	1,020
Other metallurgical uses	270
Industrial explosives	450
Textile finishing	30
Miscellaneous	640
	17,120

* Duecker, W. W., and West, J. R.,, "Manufacture of Sulfuric Acid," New York, Reinhold, 1959.

value for commercial shipments for the same year averaged about the same.

The delivered cost of the acid will be higher by transportation and other costs; thus in the year 1954, 47 consuming plants which bought 752,889 tons of sulfuric acid based on 100 per cent H_2SO_4 paid $21.55 per short ton (Bureau of the Census). In that year, the value figure was $19.15 per short ton.

The Anhydrite Process for Manufacturing Sulfuric Acid

The employment of anhydrite [$CaSO_4$], a mineral found in abundance in England, has been considered favorably in England and to a lesser extent in Germany. Heating anhydrite in contact with silica, alumina, or ferric oxide, produces a fair amount of sulfur dioxide. In practice, a well-dried finely-ground mixture in the proper proportions of sand, coal ashes, coke, and anhydrite is fed to a rotary kiln similar to a cement kiln, and heated by oil or pulverized soft coal. The gas leaving the cold end of the furnace contains about 9 per cent sulfur dioxide but almost no oxygen. It passes to purifying equipment and is then mixed with sufficient air for the oxidation of sulfur dioxide to the trioxide. Discharged at the hot end of the kiln is a cement clinker, the important by-product. It will be noted that the anhydrite process requires fuel, while one of the remarkable features of the manufacture of sulfuric acid from sulfur or pyrites is that no fuel is required.[2] In the United Kingdom, the anhydrite as raw material accounted for 6.7 per cent of the sulfuric acid production.

SULFUR

The main sources of elemental sulfur are Sicily and the Louisiana and Texas deposits; sulfur occurs in many other places, however, such as Japan and Mexico. In Sicily, the sulfur occurs mixed with marl and gypsum; it is purified by heating and draining or running off the liquid sulfur; the fuel is sulfur. In the coastal plain of the Gulf of Mexico, a strip of land 225 miles wide is sulfur-bearing; it lies partly in Louisiana, partly in Texas. In 1954, a major sulfur deposit was discovered, by drilling, six miles off the south coast of Louisiana. The sulfur lies at depths of 600 to 1100 feet, and the deposits average 125 feet. It is lifted to the surface by means of the Frasch process. In order to apply it successfully, the sulfur pocket must be covered by a fairly thick and tight cap, for the superheated water (340° F) sent down to melt the sulfur must be kept under 100 pounds gauge pressure. The heated water is forced down 6-inch casings into the deposit; the sulfur melts [melting point 112.8° C (235° F)] and the melted sulfur is forced upward through a 3-inch casing strung inside the outer 6-inch one. A 1-inch pipe inside the 3-inch one carries compressed air (500 pounds) to the liquefied sulfur and, mixing with it, divides it into smaller portions separated by the air, which produces a broken column easier to lift. Not only must sulfur be located, but other conditions must be met before the mining of a given deposit can become a reality. For the production of 1000 tons per day, 2 to 3 million gallons of water are required, a 4000-horsepower boiler plant, fuel, pipelines and bins for receiving the liquid sulfur, and the possible necessity of disposing of "bleed" water from non-producing wells in the same dome. Continuous operation in the Frasch process is essential, for, if interrupted, the liquefied sulfur in the formation congeals and freezes the pipes in each hole. As the liquid sulfur reaches the surface it is delivered to a large vat through discharge pieces which spread the flow. The congealed sulfur forms a huge mass which is broken up for shipment and handled with mechanical loaders. Sulfur produced by the Frasch process is termed Frasch sulfur. In 1954 there were produced 5,514,640 long tons of Frasch sulfur in Texas and Louisiana. In 1956 there were produced in the same two states 6,423,883 long tons of Frasch sulfur, the highest tonnage in recent years. The production dropped in 1957 and again in 1958; in the latter year it amounted to 4,643,243 long tons. Offshore deposits will be tapped and will add to the total Frasch sulfur originating in the United States. Mexican

Frasch sulfur, mined in the Isthmus of Tehuantepec, approached 800,000 tons in 1959.

In the meantime, recovered sulfur is growing; the production in 1954 was 361,107 long tons, containing 359,135 tons of sulfur, and in 1958 it amounted to 641,890 tons containing 640,096 tons of sulfur.[1]

Sulfur is recovered from natural gas, from refinery gases, and coke oven gas. Several processes recover the sulfur as hydrogen sulfide which may be burned, and the SO_2 produced may be made into sulfuric acid. Elemental sulfur is produced by the Thylox, the Ferrox, or the Nickel process. The Thylox process employs a solution of sodium thioarsenate which accepts the sulfur impurity and retains it. In a subsequent step the loaded solution is blown with air, so that part of the sulfur is liberated and comes to the top of the solution; it is skimmed off and filterpressed. At the same time the original compound is reformed and is ready for new absorption. A small part of the sulfur is made into a 35 to 50 per cent paste, a valuable fungicide with its sulfur finely divided. Most of the sulfur is dried, melted, and cast into small bars, properly called brimstone. The reactions are:

$$Na_4As_2S_5O_2 + H_2S \rightarrow Na_4As_2S_6O + H_2O$$
absorbing reaction

$$Na_4As_2S_6O + O \rightarrow Na_4As_2S_5O_2 + S$$
revivifying reaction

In countries without sulfur deposits and without facilities or materials from which recovered sulfur might be obtained, the manufacture of elemental sulfur is the goal of numerous efforts, the most successful of which is the one in Norway, where the Orkla Metal Company manufactures brimstone sulfur from cupri-ferrous pyrites.[3] The pyrites are smelted with coke, quartz, and limestone; a large part of the iron forms a slag, while the copper and other metals combine with some sulfur to form a matte, which is then suitably worked up separately. The gases from the furnace contain gaseous sulfur, sulfurous acid, and carbon disulfide. With the aid of suitable catalysts, these various gaseous compounds are made to react, forming CO_2 and free sulfur. The latter is solidified by condensation and subsequently treated by a nodulizing process, which eliminates dust and produces a granular product. The sulfur is of high purity, entirely free from bituminous matter and seldom contains more than 0.01 per cent ash. A recovery of 85 to 90 per cent of the sulfur and copper content is obtained. Heat recovered in cooling the furnace gases and condensation of the sulfur supplies enough steam to run the entire plant. In 1956, Orkla Grube produced 98,000 tons of elemental sulfur and 14,000 tons of copper matte.

Frasch sulfur is yellow; occasionally it is brown due to an admixture of oil. The yellow brimstone may be crushed, ground, refined, sublimed or made into flowers of sulfur. Air-borne sulfur dust may form an explosive mixture with air.

The average price of sulfur shipped from Frasch mines in 1954 was $26.65 per long ton; in 1957, $24.20, and in 1958, $23.50.

The main use of sulfur is for the manufacture of sulfuric acid. It has, however, other important applications, as shown below.

TABLE 4.7. ESTIMATES OF PRINCIPAL NONACID USES OF SULFUR AND PYRITES IN THE UNITED STATES (1954)

Use	Long Tons
Wood pulp	400,000
Carbon bisulfide	200,000
Other chemicals, dyes	90,000
Insecticides, fungicides	100,000
Rubber	75,000
Other	135,000

Pyrites produced in the United States in 1958 were 974,000 long tons, with sulfur content of 403,000 long tons, and valued at $7,987,000. The world production of pyrites in the same year was 17,650,000 long tons; its sulfur content was 7,400,000 long tons.[1]

There were produced 85,855 short tons of 100 per cent sulfur dioxide in 1958, valued at $44.7 a ton (Bureau of the Census).

REFERENCES

1. *Bureau of Mines Minerals Yearbook* (1958).
2. *Chemistry and Industry,* 771 (Aug. 9, 1952); 1190 (Dec. 6, 1952).
3. *Mineral Resources* (1932–1933).

SUPPLEMENTARY REFERENCES

1. Duecker, Werner W., and West, James R., "Manufacture of Sulfuric Acid," ACS Monograph No. 144, New York, Reinhold Publishing Corp., 1959.
2. Carlson, Emery J., "Sulfonation with Sulfur Trioxide," *Industrial and Engineering Chemistry,* **50,** 276–284 (1958).
3. Bedwell, W. L., "The Production of Sulfuric Acid from Calcium Sulfate," lecture, The Royal Institute of Chemistry, 30 Russell Square, London, W.C.1, 1952.
4. *Chemical and Engineering News,* pp. 38–44 (July 21, 1958).

Other references will be found in the fifth edition of this book, pp. 40–42.

5

SYNTHETIC NITROGEN PRODUCTS

In collaboration with R. V. Green*

NITROGEN FIXATION AND AMMONIA SYNTHESIS

As LONG AGO as 1780 Cavendish caused atmospheric nitrogen and oxygen to combine by means of an electric spark. The first practical large-scale manufacture of a nitrogen compound from atmospheric nitrogen was that of Birkeland and Eyde at Nottoden, Norway, early in this century. In this process air is passed at a rapid rate through an arc spread out to form a flame. Bradley and Lovejoy used the arc method in 1902 at Niagara Falls, but the attempt failed because the arc flame area was too small and the gases were not removed from the reaction chamber fast enough. The Norwegian process benefited from the faults demonstrated in this installation.

The manufacture of synthetic ammonia, tried a little later, succeeded first in the Haber process in which a mixture of nitrogen and hydrogen is passed at a moderately high temperature and under pressure over a contact catalyst, with a partial conversion of the elemental gases to ammonia. Several modifications for making ammonia from the elements have been so successful that this process is now more important than all other synthetic processes combined. Ammonia salts are valuable fertilizers; moreover, if nitric acid is called for, ammonia may be oxidized with atmospheric oxygen, aided by a contact catalyst, so that the synthetic ammonia process

---

* E. I. du Pont de Nemours & Company.

may also produce from atmospheric nitrogen, in an indirect way, what the arc process furnishes directly. In recent years the use of ammonia nitrate and urea as fertilizer materials has established a continuing need for nitrogen as ammonia as well as nitric acid.

An entirely different process for the fixation of atmospheric nitrogen is the calcium cyanamide process which depends on the fact that metallic carbides, particularly calcium carbide, readily absorb nitrogen gas to form the solid cyanamide. This substance is a fertilizer. By further treatment it may be transformed into cyanide, by another into ammonia; but this ammonia is more costly than direct synthetic ammonia. The process was developed by Frank and Caro in Germany during the years 1895 to 1897, and has been introduced in many countries, including the United States and Canada, since that time.

Nitrogen can also be fixed by high-temperature contacting of nitrogen with oxygen in the air. Experimental work on such a process has been undertaken by several investigators and results have been reported in the literature. The concentration of nitric oxides in the product gas has been too low to make the process commercially feasible. If this deficiency could be rectified, the process might become commercially attractive; there would still remain, however, engineering problems associated with the design of the high temperature equipment.

This high temperature nitrogen process operates in the range of 2,000° C, hence materials of construction are critical. The feed to the process is raised to the reaction temperature by means of a pebble preheater which is heated by burning a fuel such as natural gas or fuel oil. Pebble attrition is a serious problem in the operation of the preheater.

Nitrogen may be passed over metals at suitable temperatures to form nitrides which when treated with steam will yield ammonia. The best known process embodying this principle is the Serpek process, introduced in France but not in America, for the manufacture of aluminum nitride.

The various processes with actual or potential value for the fixation of atmospheric nitrogen may be grouped together as follows:

Arc Processes. Air is passed at a rapid rate through a broad or long electric arc. This was the earliest method for fixation of nitrogen and it is reported that the process is still used in Norway or Sweden.

Direct Synthetic Process. Nitrogen is combined with hydrogen to produce ammonia by contacting the two gases over a catalyst at elevated pressure and temperature. The ammonia can then be oxidized with air to produce nitric acid which will combine with additional ammonia to produce ammonium nitrate. The great expenditure of electric energy required by the arc process is avoided; however, energy requirements for compression of the hydrogen-nitrogen mixture are large. In addition, a large expenditure of energy is necessary to produce the hydrogen from either natural gas or water.

In reforming methane with steam the reaction heat is supplied by burning methane with air. In partial combustion some of the methane is burned with oxygen to supply the heat necessary to raise the reactants to the proper temperature. When producing hydrogen from coke or coal and steam, most of the hydrogen is obtained from water. Steam is reacted with carbon to produce carbon monoxide and hydrogen; the carbon monoxide is later reacted with steam to produce carbon dioxide and hydrogen. This is sometimes called the carbon monoxide shift reaction.

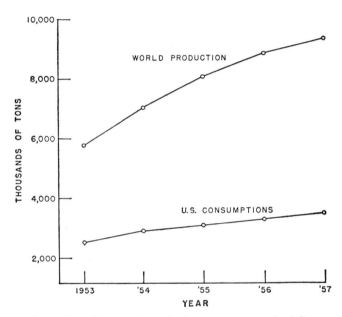

Figure 5.1. Consumption of nitrogen compounds (nitrogen equivalent). [Ruhlman, E. R., *Bureau of Mines Mineral Year-book* (1957).]

Cyanamide Process. This process requires fairly pure nitrogen as well as calcium carbide, a product of the electric furnace. Calcium cyanamide may be used as a fertilizer, or ammonia may be produced by steaming in autoclaves. The latter is rarely done.

Cyanide Process. Nitrogen is passed into a vessel containing an alkali and coal. The products are cyanides and ferrocyanides. This process has no commercial importance at present.

Nitride Process. Nitrogen reacts with certain metals to produce nitrides, such as aluminum nitride, which in turn, when treated with water, yield ammonia.

Fixation of atmospheric nitrogen has been a difficult task because elemental nitrogen is comparatively unreactive. It combines with few other elements, and then only under drastic conditions (elevated temperatures).

Nitrogen Consumption

World consumption of nitrogen is increasing at a rather uniform rate. During the period 1954–57 consumption increased from 3 million tons to 3.6 million tons.[27] It is anticipated that as the benefits of fertilization are fully realized, consumption will increase at a more rapid rate as has happened in the United States following World War II. World consumption of nitrogen and world production are shown in Figure 5.1.[27] Only a fraction of the amount that could be used is now consumed or produced. The rate of application in the United States should double and be about 20 pounds per acre in the next two decades. However, the rate is now 150 pounds per acre in the Netherlands, 84 in Belgium, 46 in West Germany, and 15 in France.

Fertilizer consumption in various countries is given in Table 5.1.[27]

TABLE 5.1. WORLD CONSUMPTION OF FERTILIZER NITROGEN COMPOUNDS (1956–57) *

	1,000 Tons
United States	1,875
Japan	647
West Germany	581
France	444
United Kingdom	343
Italy	295
East Germany	264
Netherlands	209
Spain	186
Korea (South)	172
India	170
Mexico	159
Egypt	136
Denmark	108
Sweden	99

* Nitrogen Compounds, U. S. Bureau of Mines 1957 Yearbook.

Fertilizer consumption in the United States is three times that of the next leading country, Japan. This emphasizes the importance that nitrogen plays in supplying food for the world. To provide adequate food for existing populations in many of these countries consumption of nitrogen would exceed that of the United States. India, with a population of about 400 million as compared to the 160 million in the United States for instance, consumes only 170 thousand tons of fertilizer per year.

Materials consumed as fertilizer in the United States are given in Table 5.2.[16]

TABLE 5.2. NITROGEN CONSUMPTION IN UNITED STATES
(DIRECT APPLICATION MATERIALS)*

	Year (1,000 Tons)			
	1955	1956	1957	1958
Ammonia, Anhydrous	290	344	372	479
Ammonia, Aqua	47	63	77	73
Ammonium Nitrate	375	317	372	377
Ammon um Nitrate—Limestone	74	65	62	55
Ammonium Sulfate	109	87	108	120
Calcium Cyanamide	14	14	10	10
Calcium Nitrate	9	9	8	9
Natural Organics	14	13	13	13
Nitrogen Solutions	38	34	75	100
Phosphate Products	53	57	63	73
Potash Products	2	3	1	2
Sodium Nitrate	99	88	80	70
Urea	31	42	50	45
Others	1	2	1	2
Total	1,157	1,137	1,292	1,428

* Agricultural Research Service, U. S. Department of Agriculture.

Quantities and materials used, as indicated in this table, are for direct application. It is interesting to note that for the three years reported, the largest gains in consumption have been made by anhydrous and aqua ammonia, nitrogen solutions, and urea. Consumption of calcium cyanamide and sodium nitrate have decreased. Urea is of interest since it contains the largest amount of nitrogen per pound for solid fertilizers. The rate of increase of nitrogen consumption was 80 thousand tons per year prior to 1950, and after 1950 the rate of increase has gone up to 200 thousand tons per year.

TABLE 5.2A. CONSUMPTION OF NITROGEN
IN ALL FERTILIZERS (1000 TONS)*

Year	Nitrogen Consumed in All Fertilizer (1000 Tons)
1940	412
1950	1005
1951	1237
1952	1442
1954	1847
1956	1933
1958	2284
1959	2672
1960	2767

* U.S.D.A,

Ammonia Production

The major producers of ammonia in the United States are listed in Table 5.3. In January 1957 there were 41 producers with a total capacity of 4,975 tons per year.[11,32] Capacity for synthetic nitrogen is given in Figure 5.2.[16,17] Prior to World War II the capacity was relatively unchanged. During the

TABLE 5.3. U. S. ANHYDROUS AMMONIA PRODUCERS*

Company	Plant Location
Allied Chemical & Dye	Hopewell, Virginia
	La Platte, Nebraska
	South Point, Ohio
Brea Chemicals	Brea, California
Commercial Solvents	Sterlington, Louisiana
Calumet Nitrogen	Hammond, Indiana
Dow Chemical	Freeport, Texas
	Midland, Michigan
	Pittsburg, California
Du Pont	Niagara Falls, New York
	Belle, West Virginia
Grace Chemical	Memphis, Tennessee
Grand River Chemical (Deere)	Pryor, Oklahoma
Hercules Powder	Pinole, California
	Louisiana, Missouri
Lion Oil (Monsanto)	El Dorado, Arkansas
	Luling, Louisiana
Mississippi Chemical	Yazoo City, Mississippi
Olin Mathieson	Lake Charles, Louisiana
	Niagara Falls, New York
Phillips Chemical	Etter, Texas
	Pasadena, Texas
Shell Chemical	Pittsburg, California
	Ventura, California
Standard Oil of California	Richmond, California
Standard Oil of Ohio	Lima, Ohio
Spencer Chemical	Pittsburg, Kansas
	West Henderson, Kentucky
	Vicksburg, Mississippi
Sun Oil	Marcus Hook, Pennsylvania
Tennessee Valley Authority	Wilson Dam, Alabama

* *Chem. Week*, **80**, 2, 66 (1957).

war the need for explosives caused a sharp increase in the production of nitric acid and hence ammonia. Available nitrogen capacity after the war was diverted to the manufacture of fertilizers. Accordingly, there was a rapid increase in fertilizer consumption. The advantages of fertilizer were therefore emphasized, and productive capacity increased by leaps and bounds. From 1945 to 1951 the number of ammonia producers doubled.

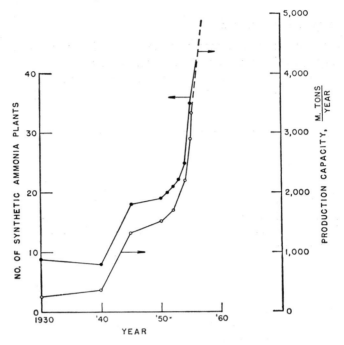

TOTAL NITROGEN CAPACITY IN 1956 – 3,602 M. TONS

Figure 5.2. Capacity for synthetic nitrogen. (*U. S. Department of Agriculture Bull. No. 191*)

Ammonia processes which have been used are indicated in Table 5.4.

TABLE 5.4. AMMONIA PROCESSES

Process	Catalyst	Pressure Atm	Temperature °C	Gas Recycled	Conversion %	H₂ Source
American	Promoted Iron	300	500	Yes	20–30	Natural Gas or Oil
Haber	Promoted Iron	200	550	Yes	8	Coke-Steam
Mont Cenis	Iron Cyanide Complex	100	400	Yes	9–20	
Claude (France)	Promoted Iron	900	650	No	40–85*	Coke Oven Gas
Casale (Italy)	Promoted Iron	750	500	Yes	15–18	
Fauser	Promoted Iron	200	500	Yes	12–23	Electrolytic H₂

* 85 % conversion by using two converters in series.

A promoted iron catalyst is used for all processes with the exception of Mont Cenis. Pressures employed vary from 200 to 900 atmospheres and the temperatures from 400 to 650° C. In general, gas recirculation is used to give good utilization of hydrogen and nitrogen since only 9 to 30 per cent conversion is obtained per pass over the catalyst. The synthesis gas source varies depending on the location. In some instances electrolytic hydrogen is used; in others, hydrogen from petroleum products or natural gas.

Processes[18,25] for producing ammonia from several raw materials are shown in Figures 5.3, 5.4, 5.5, and 5.6. Figure 5.3 illustrates a process that

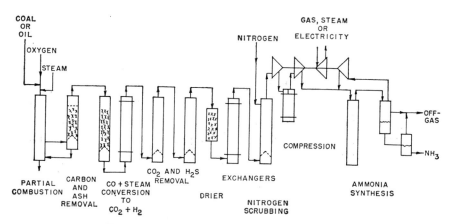

Figure 5.3. Ammonia synthesis from coal or oil.

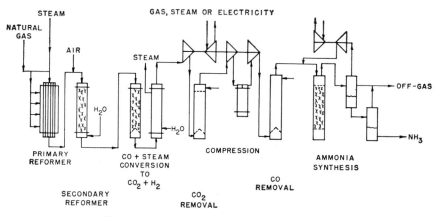

Figure 5.4. Ammonia synthesis via reforming.

employs coal or oil for a raw material. Today the process includes partial combustion of coal followed by carbon and ash removal, carbon monoxide conversion, carbon dioxide and H_2S removal, low temperature scrubbing with liquid nitrogen, and compression for ammonia synthesis.

With natural gas as a raw material, many of the new plants depend on steam reforming to produce hydrogen. In some instances air is bled into a secondary reformer to supply the nitrogen. The carbon monoxide is then reacted with steam to produce hydrogen and carbon dioxide; the latter is removed and the gas compressed. The residual carbon monoxide is removed by scrubbing with a copper ammonium formate solution, and the gas is then fed to the ammonia synthesis unit.

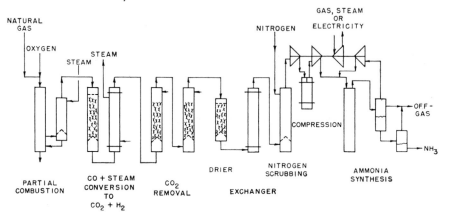

Figure 5.5. Ammonia synthesis via partial combustion.

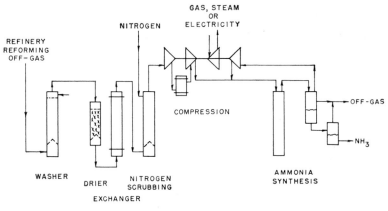

Figure 5.6. Ammonia synthesis from refinery reforming off-gas.

Partial combustion of natural gas with oxygen is a widely used method of producing hydrogen and carbon monoxide. Processes based on this initial step convert the carbon monoxide with steam to carbon dioxide and hydrogen directly after partial combustion. The carbon dioxide is removed; the gas is scrubbed with liquid nitrogen to remove residual carbon monoxide, argon, and methane, and then it is sent to ammonia synthesis.

With the advent of "platforming" of petroleum products to give unsaturated compounds for high test gasoline, large volumes of hydrogen off-gas have been produced.[37] In many instances this hydrogen has been burned to recover the fuel value; however, the petroleum industry has been alert to the advantages of converting this hydrogen to ammonia.

The off-gas from the "platforming" operation frequently will contain over 90 per cent hydrogen. In such cases the processing requirements for ammonia manufacture are greatly reduced. It is only necessary to wash out the higher hydrocarbons, and scrub the gas with liquid nitrogen to remove methane and carbon monoxide for the hydrogen-nitrogen mixture to be ready for ammonia synthesis. This process is demonstrated in Figure 5.6.

For an ammonia plant at a new location where by-product hydrogen is not available, selection of the most economical process will depend to a large extent on the raw material used. Production of hydrogen requires a large amount of energy, hence the energy reserves will dictate the type of process. The data[23] given in Table 5.5 indicate the relative availability of various

TABLE 5.5.* ENERGY RESERVES

	Billion Therms
Natural Gas	2,460
Natural Gas Liquids	250
Crude Petroleum	1,760
Coal	
Bituminous	136,000
Sub-bituminous	35,000
Lignite	31,000
Anthracite	2,000
Oil Shale	72,000
Nuclear	
Fissionable	5,600,000
Fusion	
Solar (U. S. A.)	300,000/Yr

* Data from I.G.T. Chicago News Letter, 1958.

energy sources. It can be seen that the supply of natural gas will suffice for the immediate future. However, the type of raw material that will be consumed subsequently will no doubt depend on the process that is developed for utilization of the available energy.

At the present time the U. S. Bureau of Mines is working on a process for using nuclear fission as a source of energy for producing hydrogen from coal. The Institute of Gas Technology in Chicago has studied the partial combustion of coal as a means of producing synthesis gas as well as a high BTU pipeline gas.

Natural gas is currently the preferred source of hydrogen and energy. Coal is a good source of energy but a poor source of hydrogen. When coal is used the hydrogen must be obtained from water. Nuclear fission will supply abundant energy, but the source of hydrogen is yet to be determined.

Hydrogen Production

A list of processes for producing hydrogen is given in Table 5.6, along with the hydrogen to carbon monoxide ratio of the synthesis gas produced. When synthesis gas is made by the gasification of coke with steam and oxygen, the hydrogen to carbon monoxide ratio is 0.6; with the intermittent gasification of coke with air and steam the synthesis gas has a ratio of 0.9. By using excess steam with the reforming of methane, the hydrogen to carbon monoxide ratio can be increased to as high as 5.[29] Thus by the selection of the proper process, the equipment requirements for conversion of carbon monoxide to hydrogen with steam can be reduced.

TABLE 5.6. SYNTHESIS GAS H_2/CO RATIO

Method of Manufacture	H_2/CO Ratio
Oxygen-Coke-Steam	0.6
Air-Coke-Steam	0.9
Oxygen-Coal-Steam	1.0
Oxygen-Fuel Oil-Steam	1.0
Propane-Steam	1.33
Methane-Oxygen	1.7
Methane-Oxygen-Steam	2.3
Methane-Steam	3.0–5.0

Very often the raw material available, such as natural gas, coal, or oil, will dictate the type of process employed. Table 5.7 gives raw material requirements for the various processes in the production of synthesis gas.

Selection of a process for hydrogen manufacture depends not only on the raw material and its cost, but also on the scale of operation, the purity of the synthesis gas produced, the pressure level of the natural gas, and other carbon monoxide and H_2 requirements.

Today hydrogen is manufactured by four principal processes: (1) steam reforming of natural gas; (2) partial combustion of natural gas or oil with pure oxygen; (3) gasification of coal or coke with air or oxygen and steam; (4) recovery of hydrogen from petroleum refinery gases.

Reforming. The reforming reaction is as follows: $CH_4 + H_2O \rightarrow 3H_2 + CO$. The reaction is endothermic and requires the input of a large amount of heat. The heating gas requirement is about 80 per cent of the process gas requirement. The reaction is carried out at temperatures in the range of 800° C and at pressures ranging from atmospheric up to 175 psig. A catalyst is required.

A reaction furnace usually consists of a number of 2 to 8 inch stainless steel tubes about 10 to 30 feet long, mounted vertically in a refractory-lined furnace. The process gas is fed downward over the catalyst and removed from the bottom of the tubes. The tubes are heated by burners located strategically in the sides of the furnace. Even distribution of heat is essential to ensure uniform temperature distribution throughout the tubes.

During the change from atmospheric temperature to reaction temperature, expansion of the catalyst tubes is considerable, thus provision must be made to allow for this growth. Usually the tubes are suspended by springs, or counterweights are attached to the top of the tube. Feed materials are introduced through flexible tubing.

TABLE 5.7. SYNTHESIS GAS RAW MATERIAL REQUIREMENTS

Method of Manufacture	Requirements per 1,000 CF of $(CO + H_2)$
Air-Coke-Steam	40 lb Coke
	80 lb Steam
	2,200 CF Air
Oxygen-Coke-Steam	30 lb Coke
	300 CF Oxygen
	34 lb Steam
Coal Partial Combustion	37 lb Coal
	350 CF Oxygen
	37 lb Steam
Natural Gas Partial Combustion	360 CF Natural Gas
	260 CF Oxygen
Natural Gas Reforming	425 CF Natural Gas
	60 lb Steam
Propane Reforming	3 gal Propane
	1.67 gal Distillate for Fuel
	380 lb Steam (includes CO shift to CO_2 and H_2 with steam)
Fuel Oil Partial Combustion	20.5 lb Oil
	320 CF O_2
Electrolysis	163 KWH
Steam-Iron	290 lb Steam
	0.3 lb Ore
	206 CF Fuel Gas
	65 lb Coke
Coke Oven Gas	353 lb Coal (excludes $CH_4 + CO$ in coke oven gas which can be converted to H_2)
"Platforming" Off-Gas	84 gal Feed Stock

Steam and natural gas are mixed prior to introduction into the furnace. These materials are preheated to avoid use of the catalyst bed as a preheating section.

Since the nickel catalyst used in the reaction is sensitive to sulfur, the feed materials must be treated for sulfur removal before entering the reaction zone.

The H_2 to carbon monoxide ratio for the product gas is usually about 3; however, this can be increased if additional steam is used in the reaction. This will reduce the demand on the carbon monoxide shift converters which follow after the reformer for production of H_2 from steam and carbon monoxide. Steam is introduced after the reformer before the gas is fed to the carbon monoxide shift converter.

In the shift converters the carbon monoxide reacts with steam over an iron chromite catalyst to produce H_2 and carbon dioxide. The carbon monoxide leakage from this reaction is about 2 per cent. The reaction is exothermic and is unaffected by pressure. Temperature, however, plays an important part in the equilibrium. As the temperature is increased less H_2 is formed. Usually the temperature range is from 350 to 450° C. Temperature is regulated by controlling the ratio of the feed materials or by cooling coils placed in a catalyst zone.

The effluent from the shift converters is cooled in waste heat boilers and by raw water to ambient temperature; then it is ready for final purification.

To introduce nitrogen into the gas for ammonia synthesis a secondary reformer is sometimes used, such as that shown in Figure 5.4. When nitrogen is so supplied the first reformer is operated so CH_4 leakage is about 5 per cent. This gives enough fuel so that when the primary reformer effluent is mixed with air and the mix passed through a secondary reformer, the oxygen combining with the H_2 or CH_4 releases sufficient heat to support the reaction, and nitrogen is introduced to give the desired $3/1$ H_2/N_2 ratio.

Partial Combustion. By burning natural gas with a limited quantity of oxygen, a synthesis gas containing approximately 2 moles of H_2 for each mole of carbon monoxide can be produced.[34] The equation for this reaction is $CH_4 + \frac{1}{2}O_2 \rightarrow CO + 2H_2$. The reaction is exothermic and must be carried out in a refractory-lined or water-cooled vessel. High temperatures favor the formation of carbon monoxide and H_2.[28] Pressure will hinder the reaction; however, normal pressures of 300 p.s.i. do not significantly alter the equilibrium, and a gas of low methane content can be synthesized. If steam is introduced into the reaction the H_2 to carbon monoxide ratio can be increased to over 2. Because of high temperatures involved, for instance, 1,400° C, special care must be observed in processing the gas after the reactor.

Preheating the natural gas and oxygen will reduce the oxygen and natural gas process requirements since the burning of some of the natural gas to carbon dioxide is needed in order to raise the products to their proper temperature. The partial combustion reaction itself is not sufficiently exothermic to raise the products to the desired temperature.

The partial combustion of fuel oil or crude oil is practiced in many areas where natural gas and coal are not available. When using crude oil, care must be taken to provide for removal of sulfur compounds and ash-containing materials in the crude oil. These have been known to damage the refractory and, of course, to introduce sulfur into the product gas. In all partial combustion reactions there is some residual carbon remaining in the product gas. In the case of crude oil or fuel oil partial combustion, the carbon content is much greater and special design considerations are necessary to produce a satisfactory gas.

Nitrogen to produce the proper H_2/N_2 ratio is usually introduced later in the processing sequence.

Coal and Coke Gasification. One of the important processes currently used for the gasification of coal and coke is the Lurgi process, used in South Africa at the "coal to oil" plant and at a number of places in Europe. This process requires the use of coke or a non-caking coal, and the product gas is usually high in methane. The reaction is carried out with a fixed bed of burning coal or coke into which is introduced steam and oxygen. The product gas will contain as impurities sulfur compounds and ungasified carbon, ash, and compared to natural gas partial combustion, large quantities of carbon dioxide. The gas may be further processed by converting the residual methane to carbon monoxide and H_2 by passing the gas over a reformer catalyst with steam.

In the United States, coal has been gasified with steam and oxygen in processes developed by Babcock and Wilcox, E. I. du Pont de Nemours and Company, the Institute of Gas Technology in Chicago, and the U. S. Bureau of Mines. In all these processes pulverized coal is introduced into a refractory zone along with steam and oxygen. Product gas contains H_2 and carbon monoxide and is relatively low in methane compared to the Lurgi process. Again, sulfur compounds in the coal appear in the product gas, and the carbon dioxide content runs much higher than in the gas made by the partial combustion of methane.

Nitrogen may be introduced for ammonia synthesis by using oxygen-enriched air for the gasification.

Hydrogen from Petroleum Gases. Petroleum gases from platforming operations, hydroformers, and butadiene plants are used to recover H_2.[25] The gas from the platformer is particularly rich in H_2, containing as much as 90 to 95 per cent. This gas is usually purified by low temperature fractionation or washing with liquid nitrogen.

Purification. There are several processes for purifying synthesis gas, depending on the source of the gas and the impurity content. Impurities usually present are H_2S, CS_2, COS, ungasified carbon, and residual ash. Other factors which influence the selection of a purification process are H_2 to carbon monoxide ratio and the carbon dioxide content.

If the gas contains large amounts of sulfur it is quite often the practice to remove this sulfur before the carbon monoxide shift operation. There are a number of sulfur removal processes, namely: amine scrubbing, hot potassium carbonate scrubbing, and the Thylox process. Ash and carbon removal must also be carried out before the gas is treated in the carbon monoxide shift converter.

If a gas does not contain large quantities of sulfur and ash the carbon monoxide shift reaction is carried out directly after the synthesis operation. In some instances it is also desirable to remove the carbon dioxide before the shift operation since it has an adverse effect on the carbon monoxide shift equilibrium. Carbon dioxide may be removed by water scrubbing,

Figure 5.7. Synthesis-gas scrubbing equipment—ammonia manufacture. (*Courtesy E. I. du Pont de Nemours and Co.*)

monoethanolamine (MEA) scrubbing, or hot potassium carbonate scrubbing. The preferred process depends to some extent on the local economics and the particular conditions under which the synthesis gas is produced.

After the synthesis gas is purified and the carbon monoxide reacted with steam to give carbon dioxide and H_2, there still remain trace quantities of carbon monoxide, water, and carbon dioxide which must be removed prior to ammonia synthesis. These materials may be removed by caustic drying and nitrogen wash, or scrubbing with copper ammonium carbonate.

CO Shift. Conversion of carbon monoxide to carbon dioxide and H_2 with steam is necessary to make economic use of the raw synthesis gases produced by the foregoing processes. In this operation the following reaction is promoted:

$$CO + H_2O \rightleftarrows CO_2 + H_2$$

The reaction is exothermic; the equilibrium is not affected by pressure, but high temperatures are unfavorable for complete conversion, hence it is necessary to carry out the reaction in the range of 300 to 450° C. With normal amounts of steam this temperature range will give a gas with 1.0 to 3.0 per cent carbon monoxide. The catalyst used for the reaction is usually iron chromite. Although it is sulfur tolerant, to operate with large quantities of sulfur in the feed gas is not economical.

Since the reaction is highly exothermic it is necessary to provide for heat removal by heat transfer surface or by diluting the reactants so that the temperature rise will not be detrimental.

Nitrogen Wash Operation. The last traces of carbon monoxide are removed by liquid nitrogen scrubbing in many of the new plants. In the nitrogen wash operation the gas must be thoroughly dried and the carbon dioxide removed before the gas is cooled to the point where it can be scrubbed with liquid nitrogen. Thus the gas must be put through silica gel driers and a caustic wash step to remove the water and carbon dioxide. At this point the gas can be cooled to liquid nitrogen temperature.

By washing with liquid nitrogen, the carbon monoxide, methane, and argon can be removed. Extensive heat exchange equipment is required to conserve refrigeration and make the process economical. The overhead gases from the wash tower usually contain about 90 per cent hydrogen and 10 per cent nitrogen, thus requiring the addition of more nitrogen to give the required ratio for ammonia synthesis. The gas so produced is very favorable for ammonia synthesis, and the introduction of impurities into the circulating system is held to a minimum.

Copper Ammonium Carbonate Scrubbing. In some instances it is preferable to use copper scrubbing to remove the last traces of carbon monoxide in the ammonia synthesis gas. This process is usually carried out at pressures in the range of 1 to 1.5 thousand psi, one of the intermediate pressures of the high pressure compressors. The copper liquor is circulated counter-current to the synthesis gas, picking up the carbon monoxide as a copper ammonium carbonate-carbon monoxide complex and producing a relatively carbon monoxide-free gas. Methane and argon, however, are not removed; these pass on with the hydrogen to the ammonia synthesis units.

The copper liquor is regenerated by reducing the pressure on the liquid, thus allowing the carbon monoxide complex to decompose. The carbon monoxide is separated from the copper liquor, and the liquid is compressed and recirculated to the scrubbing operation.

Ammonia Synthesis. Ammonia synthesis is carried out at pressures from 3 to 10 thousand psig. The preferred pressure depends largely on the quality of the synthesis gas and specified conditions such as production requirements per converter.

The ammonia reaction is $N_2 + 3H_2 \rightarrow 2NH_3$. The reaction is exothermic. Equilibrium for the reaction is shown in Table 5.8.

TABLE 5.8. PERCENTAGE AMMONIA AT EQUILIBRIUM*
RATIO $H_2/N_2 = 3$

Temperature °C	Pressure (Atm Absolute)						
	1	10	50	100	300	600	1000
200	15.30	50.66	74.38	81.54	89.94	95.37	98.29
300	2.18	14.73	39.41	52.04	70.96	84.21	92.55
350	0.90	7.41	25.23	37.35	59.12	75.62	87.46
400	0.44	3.85	15.27	25.12	47.00	65.20	79.82
500	...	1.21	5.56	10.61	26.44	42.15	57.47
600	...	0.49	2.25	4.52	13.77	23.10	31.43
700	...	...	1.05	2.18	7.28	...	12.87

* Compiled from publications of the Fixed Nitrogen Research Laboratory by Dr. Alfred T. Larson.

As can be seen from this table, a low temperature favors a high percentage of ammonia at equilibrium. However, the rate of reaction at low temperature is so slow that the process is uneconomical at temperatures below about 400° C. Usually a conversion of about 15 to 30 per cent per pass is obtained when the temperature is in the range of 500 to 600° C.

One of the major cost items in the manufacture of ammonia is the power required for compression of the hydrogen-nitrogen mixture to reaction pressure. Design of the compressors is critical from the standpoint of efficiency and economy. The compressibility of gases must be considered when working at pressures of 3 to 10 thousand psi. Compressibility factors for a mixture of 3 hydrogen and 1 nitrogen are available.[24]

The gas composition for ammonia synthesis is also critical, relative to the cost of ammonia. High concentrations of inert materials such as argon or methane will build up in the circulating system and produce a low partial pressure of hydrogen and nitrogen resulting in low conversions to ammonia. In such cases it is necessary to purge these materials from the system and maintain the proper ratio of hydrogen to nitrogen. An excess of either one of these reactants will act as an inert material and lower the effective partial pressure of the controlling component. Again, it would be necessary to purge excessively to restore the desired degree of conversion.

The optimum concentration of inerts will depend on the temperature and pressure of the operation and the concentration of inerts in the make-up gas. The solubilities of argon, methane, hydrogen, and nitrogen in liquid ammonia determine the amounts of these gases which are removed from the system with the liquid ammonia. The designer has some control over this purge. The conditions of synthesis can be selected to give optimum purge rates once solubility, make-up gas composition, and degree of conversion are obtained.

The converter details are critical since the reaction is exothermic and must be carried out at a high temperature. Because of the hydrogen embrittlement of steel at the reaction temperature and pressures involved, it is

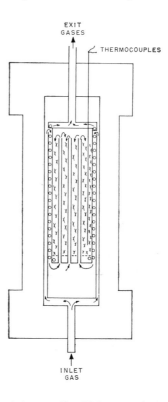

Figure 5.8. Detail of ammonia converter. [Adapted from *Chem. Eng., Progr.*, **48**, No. 9, 468–476 (1952).]

necessary to design the converter so that the retaining wall will be at a low temperature. Figure 5.8 shows the converter detail.[35] Where the temperatures are high, stainless steel and copper are used for construction.

In addition to the care which must be exercised with respect to materials of construction, it is also necessary to design for heat removal. This is usually accomplished by internal heat exchangers in the converter. The incoming gas is heated by the exit gas which is cooled. A temperature rise of about 150° is used in the design of a converter. One of the current circulating systems for ammonia synthesis is shown in Figure 5.9.

All catalysts used for ammonia synthesis are basically reduced iron oxide (Fe_3O_4). The catalyst is prepared by melting relatively pure iron with an electric arc to produce the iron oxides. This material is then mixed with promoters such as potassium, calcium, magnesium, or aluminum. The material is broken up, crushed, and sized for introduction to the converter.

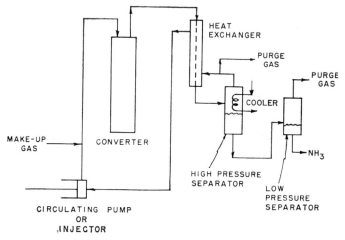

Figure 5.9. Circulating system for ammonia synthesis.

The oxide granules are reduced with hydrogen in the converter to the metallic constituents prior to the production of ammonia.

Uses of Ammonia

The uses for ammonia are given in Table 5.9. By far the greatest consumption is in the manufacture of fertilizers or as direct application for fertilization purposes.

TABLE 5.9. USES OF AMMONIA*

Fertilizers	70%
Industrial	24%
Others	6%

Industrial Uses

Explosives	—Nitrates, Dynamite, Azides
Plastics	—Nitrocellulose, Urea-Formaldehyde, Melamine
Metallurgy	—Bright Annealing of Steel, Dry Reducing Gas
Pulp and Paper	—Ammonium Bisulfite, Melamine
Rubber	—Aniline, Acrylonitrile, Poly-urethanes, Chemical Blowing Agents (for foam rubber)
Textiles	—Nylons, Acrylonitrile, Terphthalates
Foods	—Amino Acids, Sodium Nitrate, Sodium Nitrite, and Nitric Oxides
Drugs	—Vitamins, Nitro-furans
Miscellaneous	—Refrigerant, Detergents, Insecticides, Nitroparaffins, Hydrazine

* Based on data in *Chem. Eng.*, **62**, 11, 280–282 (1955).

NITRIC ACID

Nitric acid has been known since the 13th century. Glauber devised the process based on strong sulfuric acid and sodium nitrate; however, it was Lavoisier who showed that nitric acid contained oxygen, and Cavendish that it could be made from moist air by an electric spark.

In the oldest methods used, Chile saltpeter was reacted with concentrated sulfuric acid in heated cast iron retorts; the evolved nitric acid vapors were condensed and collected in stoneware vessels.

Today nitric acid is made by oxidation of ammonia with air over a precious metal catalyst at atmospheric or higher pressures and at 800 to 950° C.[33] Nitric oxide is formed according to the reaction: $2NH_3 + \frac{5}{2}O_2 = 2NO + 3H_2O$. The nitric oxide is then further oxidized by additional air to give $2NO_2$, which combines with water to give HNO_3 and nitric oxide. The nitric acid processes currently in use are listed in Table 5.10.

TABLE 5.10. NITRIC ACID PROCESSES

	Temperature °C	Pressure	Acid Strength %
Low Pressure Process	800	Atmospheric	50–52
Medium Pressure Process (Montecatini)	850	40 psi	60
Medium Pressure (Kuhlman's)		40 psi	70
High Pressure—Du Pont	950	120 psi	60
"Hoko"-Fauser			98–99
			$+N_2O_4$

Pressures vary from atmospheric to 120 psig. The concentration of nitric acid that can be produced is greater for the high pressure process; however, with the exception of the "Hoko"-Fauser process, only 60 per cent acid can be produced with conventional equipment. If higher strengths are needed a special method of concentration is required.

Nitric acid can also be produced by the high temperature combination of nitrogen with oxygen in the air and by use of radiation.[7] One method which has received considerable attention in recent years is the so-called "Wisconsin" process. Although a 40-ton per day plant was built, it could not compete economically with the conventional ammonia oxidation route.

Nitric acid is generally a light amber liquid; however, the pure acid is colorless, strongly hygroscopic, and corrosive. It is a strong oxidizing acid. It boils at 78.2° C, freezes at —47° C, and forms a constant boiling mixture with water (68 per cent nitric acid by weight) which boils at approximately 122° C at atmospheric pressure.

Production of nitric acid (100 per cent basis) in the United States was 2,698,400 tons in 1958. The largest amount goes into the manufacture of fertilizers (about 74 per cent), but substantial quantities are also used in the explosives industry (16 per cent), in the manufacture of organic chemicals, and in pickling steel.

Processes.[33] Liquid ammonia is vaporized, mixed with preheated air, and introduced into the converter. The ammonia is oxidized to nitric oxide.[31] The equation is as follows: $4NH_3 + 5O_2 \rightarrow 4NO + 6H_2O$. The reaction is exothermic and liberates 216.7 kilocalories. The gases emerging from the converter pass through suitable heat exchangers and coolers where the following reaction takes place: $2NO + O_2 \rightarrow 2NO_2$. This is accompanied by evolution of 26.9 kilocalories.

The gases then pass to the absorber where the nitrogen dioxide combines with water in the absorber to produce nitric acid and nitric oxide. The equation is: $3NO_2 + H_2O \rightarrow 2HNO_3 + NO$. This reaction is exothermic and liberates 32.5 kilocalories. Sufficient air must be present in the absorber to oxidize the nitric oxide as it is liberated when the nitrogen dioxide and water combine.

In the first stage of the process where ammonia and air are mixed, it is important to hold the proper ratio of constituents. Usually a mixture of about 10 per cent ammonia and 90 per cent air is employed. At this point in the process it is important to avoid decomposition of ammonia on the converter walls. Aluminum is superior to mild steel in this respect. At 350° C the rate of decomposition is 300 times faster on mild steel than on aluminum. Ammonia is decomposed 70 times faster on stainless steel than on aluminum.[31] By keeping the preheat temperature low, satisfactory yields can be obtained with mild steel. The temperature level used is below 200° C.

In the reaction which takes place over the catalyst bed, the rate-limiting step is the diffusion of ammonia to the catalyst surfaces. With a high gas rate through the gauze, some of the ammonia will not reach the catalyst surfaces. It reacts with the nitric oxide which is produced to give elemental nitrogen according to the following equation: $4HN_3 + 6NO \rightarrow 5N_2 + 6H_2O$. The linear flow of gas across the catalyst is therefore important and will depend on the arrangement of the catalyst. Linear flow rates of 1 to 3 feet per second have given high efficiency. These rates are for gas at standard temperature and pressure. Without selection of proper flow rates or, conversely, the proper converter size for a given production, inefficient operation may result not only from too high a velocity with the aforementioned yield loss but also from low velocities which would produce gas channels along the walls of the converter.

The catalyst for ammonia oxidation is a platinum-rhodium alloy containing about 10 per cent rhodium. A gauze made of wire 0.003 inch in diameter with about 80 meshes to the inch is used. During the life of the catalyst it becomes polycrystalline in appearance. There is also some weight loss, the effect of which is more pronounced at the higher converter temperatures employed in the pressure process. Accordingly, recovery steps are required for operation at 120-pound pressure. This usually involves periodic cleaning of the converter and heat exchange equipment, and the use of a filter in the gas stream beyond these pieces of equipment.

Absorption. Absorption of nitric oxide takes place in a bubble cap tower into which is added air to oxidize nitric oxide to nitrogen dioxide. The nitrogen dioxide must be absorbed in water to liberate nitric acid and nitric oxide. There are two equilibria as follows: $N_2O_4 = 2NO_2 = 2NO + O_2$. The first of these two equilibria is established relatively quickly; the second more slowly. At 150° the N_2O_4 is almost completely decomposed into nitrogen dioxide. At 500° C the equilibria lies at 25 per cent of nitrogen dioxide and 75 per cent nitric oxide. The formation of nitrogen dioxide from nitric oxide and oxygen is relatively slow at atmospheric pressure, but proceeds quite rapidly under pressure. It is interesting to note too that this reaction has a negative temperature coefficient. The absorber is usually operated at the lowest temperature obtainable with available cooling water, in the temperature range of 10 to 40° C.

The absorption characteristics of nitrogen dioxide in water are of importance in the design of the absorber.[31] There are two factors which determine the strength of the nitric acid in the absorption tower, namely total pressure on the system and gas composition. To increase the strength of nitric acid in equilibrium with a gas of a fixed composition by 10 per cent, it is necessary to raise the pressure about ten fold.

The gas composition also affects concentration of the nitric acid. The degree of oxidation of the nitric oxide to nitrogen dioxide should be as high as possible. Concentrations of nitric acid above 90 per cent are difficult to obtain.

There is some thought that the rate of diffusion of nitrogen dioxide to the liquid surfaces controls the rate of absorption. Some other data, however, indicate that the rate of absorption depends on the rate of chemical reaction of the N_2O_4 with water. Thus diffusion and chemical rate may both be controlling factors in the rate of absorption. Absorption towers are currently designated by empirical methods. A novel tower design has been developed by Etablissements Kuhlman.[4]

The processes for nitric acid manufacture may be described as atmospheric, pressure, and medium pressure. These produce nitric acid in the concentration range of 50 to 60 per cent by weight. Figure 5.10 depicts the pressure process. Nitric acid of greater than 90 per cent strength can be produced by a process such as that shown in Figure 5.11.

Figure 5.12 illustrates the process employed to concentrate nitric acid from 60 to 95 per cent strength by means of a dehydrating agent, in this case magnesium nitrate.

Atmospheric Plant. In an atmospheric plant ammonia efficiency and utilization of the precious metal catalyst is good. Temperature is about

800° C. The mixture to the converter contains about 9.5 to 11 per cent ammonia. Air is preheated by the exit gases from the converter; the gases are then fed through a heat exchanger which cools the reactants before they enter the oxidizer tower. Water is added to the tower in which the

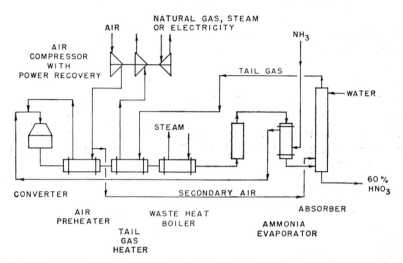

Figure 5.10. Pressure process for nitric acid manufacture via ammonia oxidation. [Adapted from Strelzoff, S., *Chem. Eng.*, **63**, No. 5, 170 (1956).]

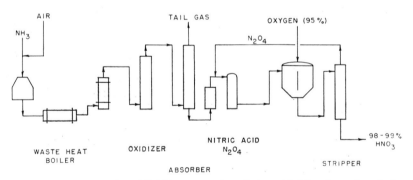

Figure 5.11. Fauser ("HOKO") process for nitric acid. [Based on description in *Chemical Week*, **83**, No. 5, 67 (1958).]

nitric acid solution is circulated. The product is drawn off through a cooler to an acid bleacher and storage. It contains approximately 50 to 52 per cent nitric acid.

Pressure Nitric Acid Plant. In the pressure nitric acid plant the equipment is much smaller, making the investment less. The ammonia content of the feed is about 10 per cent. Temperature is approximately 900° C.

Ammonia and air are mixed ahead of the converter, having been preheated by the product gases. The tail gas from the absorber is preheated by the product gas and then sent to an expansion turbine which supplies power for air compression. Any of the additional power required for air compression is created by natural gas turbine, steam, or electrically driven power units.

To reduce catalyst loss with the pressure nitric acid plant, a catalyst filter is installed after the converter. At 820° C the platinum catalyst requirement is about .03 troy ounce per ton of nitric acid. About ⅔ of this is recovered. The ratio of platinum loss in the pressure plant to that in the atmospheric plant is only 3 or 4 to 1.

Medium Pressure Plant. The medium pressure plant combines the advantages of both the high pressure and low pressure systems. In this process

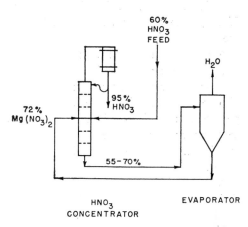

Figure 5.12. Magnesium nitrate process for nitric acid concentration. [*Chem. Trade Journal* (July 11, 1958).]

the converter operates at low pressure, the absorber and cooling system at high pressure. The disadvantages lie in the fact that the gases from the converter must be compressed before going to the absorption tower. For this reason the process has not received wide acceptance.

Table 5.11 gives the requirements per ton of nitric acid for the three processes.[33]

TABLE 5.11. REQUIREMENTS PER TON OF NITRIC ACID*

	NH₃ Tons	Pt Cat. Troy oz	Power† KWH	Steam Credit (Tons)	Water 1000 Gal	Strength	Investment
Atmospheric Plant	.29 −.30	.0025	85–90	1.0	27	45–52	Highest
Pressure	.29 −.294	.005–.01	350	0.8–1.25	30	57–60	Lowest
Combination Pressure	.287–.29	.0025	350	1.0	30	57–60	Intermediate

* Sterlzoff, S., *Chem. Eng.*, **63**, 5, 170 (1956).

† In modern pressure plants, power requirements may be substantially less than shown in the foregoing table because of highly efficient recovery of power from the exhaust gases by means of an expansion turbine.

High Strength Nitric Acid. The Fauser or "Hoko" process for the manufacture of high strength nitric acid is shown in Figure 5.10. In this process the N_2O_4 is produced by using 95 per cent oxygen. The product contains 98 to 99 per cent HNO_3. It is also possible to recover nitrogen tetroxide.[14]

Concentration of Nitric Acid. The 50 to 60 per cent nitric acid made by conventional processes cannot be concentrated by simple distillation because a constant boiling mixture is formed which contains approximately 68 per cent HNO_3 by weight; therefore, it is customary to use a dehydrating agent to aid removal of water. The method most widely used consists of mixing the 60 per cent nitric acid with strong (93 per cent) sulfuric acid, and then passing the mixture through a distillation system from which there is obtained concentrated (95 to 98 per cent) nitric acid and denitrated residual sulfuric acid containing approximately 70 per cent H_2SO_4. The dilute residual sulfuric acid may be reconcentrated for further use.

A recently developed process employs magnesium nitrate as a dehydrating agent.[8] The process is illustrated in Figure 5.12. An aqueous solution containing 72 per cent magnesium nitrate is fed to the middle of a tower which also receives the 60 per cent nitric acid feed. Pure nitric acid of 95 to 98 per cent strength is taken overhead. A solution containing about 55 per cent magnesium nitrate is removed from the base. After reconcentration to 72 per cent the magnesium nitrate is recirculated to the nitric acid tower.

A new Pintsch Bamay process[5a] concentrates nitric acid by using the difference in composition of the nitric acid-water constant boiling mixtures at different pressures. A two column distillation system is employed.

Uses of Nitric Acid. The primary use of nitric acid is in the manufacture of ammonium nitrate for the fertilizer industry.[12] Production of ammonium nitrate has been increasing over the past few years. Ammonium nitrate is second only to anhydrous ammonia as a source of nitrogen for fertilization. Solution fertilizers, many of which contain nitrates, are also growing in importance.

Nitric acid is used in some cases for the acidulation of phosphate rock to produce mixed fertilizers. However, with the return of abundant supplies of sulfuric acid this use for nitric acid has not developed as rapidly as was anticipated.

About 15 per cent of the nitric acid produced is consumed in industrial explosives (see Chapter 19). Approximately 500 thousand tons per year of nitric acid is used for explosives which, in turn, are used in coal mining, quarrying, metal and non-metal mining, heavy construction, and petroleum exploration. Of recent interest in the explosive fields is the use of fertilizer grade ammonium nitrate as an explosive or blasting agent. It is mixed with oil and set off by priming with a high explosive.

Nitric acid has a number of other industrial applications. It is used in pickling stainless steel, in steel refining, and in the manufacture of dyes, plastics, and synthetic fibers. A new use is developing, that of uranium metallurgy. Most of the methods used for recovery of uranium, such as ion exchange and solvent extraction, use nitric acid. Thus with the expansion of the nuclear program nitric acid consumption may increase.

Production of nitric acid in 1957 was 2,800,000 tons or about 75% the installed capacity. The largest producers are Allied Chemical, du Pont, Hercules Powder, Monsanto Chemical, and Spencer Chemical Company.[22a]

AMMONIUM NITRATE

The production of ammonium nitrate[27] in the United States has been increasing at the rate of approximately 140 thousand tons per year. In

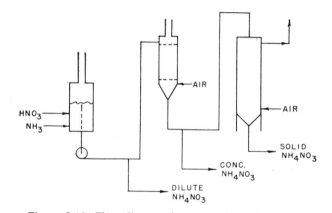

Figure 5.13. Flow diagram for ammonium nitrate manufacture. [Based on description in *Chem. and Eng. News*, **36**, No. 34, 50 (1958).]

1957 the production was approximately 2,561,000 tons. A large part of this is consumed as fertilizer material; however, increasing amounts are being used for explosives and some for the manufacture of nitrous oxide.

The process for ammonium nitrate consists of neutralizing ammonia with nitric acid under controlled conditions. Water is evaporated and the anhydrous or nearly anhydrous solution is prilled or dried to produce solid products[6] (see Figure 5.13).

There are four different crystalline forms of ammonium nitrate. One is stable at $-16°$ C, another at -16 to $32°$ C, a third at 32 to $84°$ C, and the fourth at 84 to $169.6°$ C, the melting point. When dissolved in water the negative heat of solution causes the temperature to drop. When heated, ammonium nitrate decomposes into N_2O and water.

It is important to mention the hazard involved in handling ammonium nitrate. Avoid using concentrated solutions in large amounts at high temperatures; in particular, avoid contamination with organic materials. The Texas City disaster was dramatic proof that organic material and ammonium nitrate decompose with explosive violence. Following a fire under conditions of confinement, an explosion occurred which took almost 600 lives, injured 3,500, and destroyed 33 million dollers worth of property. Ammonium nitrate solutions also exploded with disastrous results.

To prill ammonium nitrate, a solution is evaporated in a vacuum or falling film evaporator until it is almost free of water. The concentration of ammonium nitrate will vary from 95 to 99.95 per cent. The prilling tower itself is about 50 to 100 feet tall depending on the process being used. The concentrated ammonium nitrate solution is fed through sprayformers which break up the stream into small droplets that solidify during the free fall in the tower. In some instances limestone is mixed with ammonium nitrate before prilling; in other cases the prills are coated with limestone dust. A mixture of limestone and ammonium nitrate is known as "Nitro chalk" in the fertilizer industry. Plants that use the 95 per cent ammonium nitrate feed to the prilling tower usually require a drying step before the material can be bagged.

HEXAMETHYLENETETRAMINE[30]

Hexamethylenetetramine or "tetramine" is manufactured in the liquid phase by the following reaction:

$$4NH_3 + 6HCHO \rightarrow (CH_2)_6N_4 + 6H_2O$$

The heat of reaction is equal to 28.2 kilocalories per mole of tetramine.

The reaction mix is controlled at a pH of 7 to 8 at a temperature of 30 to 50° C. Under acidic conditions formic acid, carbon dioxide, and water are produced. At temperatures above 50° C decomposition of the tetramine occurs. Tetramine is produced either by continuous or batch operation. In batch operation cycle times up to 6 to 8 hours have been used, whereas in continuous operation the hold-up may be only 15 to 30 minutes.

Figure 5.14 shows the equipment which is used in the process. Thirty-seven per cent formaldehyde, usually containing less than 2 per cent methanol, is fed along with ammonia to a reactor which is cooled as a result of the solution being circulated through a water-cooled exchanger. The effluent from the reactor is fed to a vacuum evaporator. Here the product is concentrated, and crystals are formed. The slurry is centrifuged, and the crystals washed and discharged to a drier. The mother liquor is recycled to the reaction system; however, a small bleed is necessary to avoid the build-up of impurities in the system.

The mechanism of the reaction is discussed by Baur and Ruetschi.[21] They indicate a one-step trimerization reaction of the third order in which the rate is proportional to the ammonia concentration and the square of the formaldehyde concentration. Boyd and Winkler[1] have indicated a more complex reaction mechanism. The exact mechanism may depend on whether ammonia or formaldehyde is in excess.

The reaction may be carried out at temperatures up to about 50° C. Above this temperature the rate of hexamine decomposition becomes excessive. The degree of conversion is essentially complete after 4 or 5 hours; only minor benefits are obtained by operation for 6 to 8 hours.

The vessels are usually made of stainless steel or aluminum. The heat exchanger for cooling the reaction mixtures is also made of stainless. Crystallization takes place in the evaporator and it is important to note at this

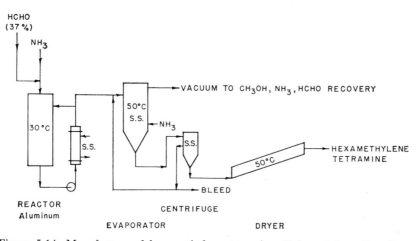

Figure 5.14. Manufacture of hexamethylene tetramine. [Adapted from *Petroleum Refiner*, **37**, No. 9, 351–353 (1958).]

point that hexamine has an inverse solubility. At 25° C 86.7 grams are dissolved in 100 cubic centimeters of water, whereas at 50° C the solubility is only 80 grams per 100 cubic centimeters of water. The continuous addition of a small amount of ammonia during the evaporation step tends to reduce the decomposition of the tetramine during evaporation. If the formaldehyde feed contains methanol then the methanol will be removed from the system along with the ammonia and water from the evaporator. The evaporators are usually made of stainless steel.

In the final drying step the temperature must be held to less than 50° C to avoid decomposition. The over-all yield is good, on the order of 95 to 96 per cent based on the formaldehyde.

Hexamine is used in the production of high explosives. The manufacture of "RDX" came into its own during World War II. By nitrating tetramine a compound with high explosive properties is obtained. Hexamine is also used in resin production as a curing agent. This is its principal use in a peacetime economy. It serves as a methylating agent in the curing of phenol-formaldehyde resins and is used as an accelerator in the rubber industry to prevent vulcanized rubber from blocking. Pharmaceutical applications exist for tetramine and some of its derivatives. It is also being studied as a fungicide in the citrus fruit industry, as an inhibtor of corrosion caused by strong mineral acids, as a shrink-proofing agent in the textile industry, and as an agent to improve color fastness and to give better elasticity to cellulosic fibers.

HYDRAZINE MANUFACTURE[15]

Hydrazine (N_2H_2) is becoming more important as an industrial chemical. Its manufacture involves the following reactions:

$$NaOH + Cl_2 \rightarrow NaOCl + HCl$$
$$NaOCl + 2NH_3 \rightarrow N_2H_4 + NaCl + H_2O$$
$$NH_3 + NaOCl \rightarrow NH_2Cl + NaOH$$
$$NH_2Cl + NaOH + NH_3 \rightarrow N_2H_4 + NaCl + H_2O$$

Side reactions are as follows:

$$2NH_3 + 3NH_2Cl \xrightarrow{Cu^{++}} 3NH_4Cl + N_2$$
$$2NH_2Cl + N_2H_4 \rightarrow 2NH_4Cl + N_2$$

Glue and gelatin are used to prevent these side reactions.

Hydrazine is a colorless liquid and boils at 113.5° C. It has a melting point of 1.4° C and a specific gravity of 1.014 at 15° C. Hydrazine hydrate (H_2NNH_3OH) is obtained by fractional distillation from water. The hydrate boils at 119° C and is still liquid at -40° C. It has a specific gravity of 1.03 at 21° C. Hydrazine forms a sparingly soluble sulfate ($NH_2NH_2H_2SO_4$) and the chloride. Hydrazine is a powerful reducing agent and is very poisonous even through the skin.

The process carried out in the liquid phase is outlined in Figure 5.15. Sodium hydroxide and chlorine are mixed in a cooler-reactor system to produce sodium hypochlorite. Glue is added to this solution as an inhibitor until the mix is viscous; a dilute solution of ammonia (5 to 15 per cent) is added until a mol ratio of $3NH_3$ to 1 hypochlorite is obtained. This mixture forms chloramine which when reacted with anhydrous ammonia in a ratio of 20–30 to 1 produces hydrazine. The temperature reaches 130° C. The effluent from the hydrazine reactor is fed to an ammonia removal still where excess ammonia is taken off overhead. The tails are fed to an evaporator where concentrated sodium chloride is removed. The vapors from the evaporator are dehydrated in three columns. In the first column the hydrazine is dehydrated until the water-hydrazine mixture approaches the hydrate NH_2NH_3OH (65 per cent NH_2NH_2). In the second column aniline is used as a dehydrating agent, the water being removed overhead with the aniline. A third column is required to remove the aniline from the hydrazine; 98 per cent hydrazine is produced. An over-all yield of about 70 per cent is obtained.[9]

Synthesis efficiency is increased by operation with a dilute system, but operating costs increase because of low concentrations.

In some cases anhydrous hydrazine is obtained by dehydrating with 50 per cent caustic. Pressures less than atmospheric are used to reduce decomposition; however, this may permit air leakage and result in decomposition of the hydrazine to nitric oxide, water, and ammonia.

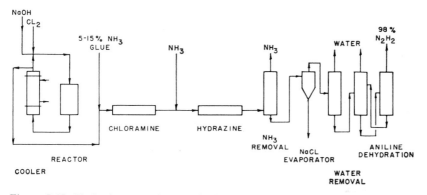

Figure 5.15. Hydrazine manufacture. [Adapted from Chilton, C. H., *Chem. Eng.*, 65, No. 14, 123 (1958).]

Hydrazine is used primarily as a scavenger for oxygen and as a high energy fuel. It is also used in the manufacture of organic chemicals.

UREA

Urea was first synthesized by Wohler in 1828 from ammonia and cyanic acid. It is a colorless crystalline material, soluble in water and in alcohol but not in ether. Urea contains 46 per cent nitrogen, the most of any ordinarily solid fertilizer material. Since it is converted into ammonia and then into nitrates in the soil, it makes a very concentrated form of nitrogen fertilizer. It is also used in resin and plastic manufacture and in the synthesis of organic materials.

Urea can be produced by the hydrolysis of cyanamide (melting point 44° C) according to the equation $CN \cdot NH_2 + H_2O \rightarrow C = O(NH_2)_2$. At 33 to 53 atmospheres urea can also be formed by heating ammonium carbonate. Equilibrium is obtained at 130 to 150° C with a 30 to 45 per cent yield. The common method of manufacture is to combine ammonia and carbon dioxide under pressure to form ammonium carbamate which is then decomposed into urea and water. The unreacted carbon dioxide and ammonia are recovered and recycled to the synthesis operation.

A number of processes available are given in Table 5.12.[10,36]

TABLE 5.12. UREA PROCESSES*

	Du Pont	Pechiney	Montecatini	Inventa	Chemico
Type of Operation	Carbamate Recycled with NH_3 and Water	Carbamate Recycled with Oil	Partial Liquid Recycle	Aqueous Urea Nitrate for NH_3 Recovery	MEA used to Absorb CO_2— NH_3 Recycled
Reactor Conditions:					
Temperature, °C	200	180	180	200	185
Pressure, Atm	400	200	200	200	170
Lining	Silver	Lead	Stainless	Undisclosed	Silver
$NH_3:CO_2:H_2O$	5:1:0.73	2:1:0	3.4:1:0.84	$2^+:1:0$	6:1:0
CO_2 Conversion, %					
In Autoclave	70	50	52	50	76
Total	70	50	88	50	76
NH_3 Conversion, %					
In Autoclave	24	50	32	50	25
Total	24	50	72.5	50	73

*Chem. Week, **75**, 22, 90 (1954).

In the *Du Pont* process the unconverted carbon dioxide and ammonia are recovered and recycled as water solution. The converter, lined with silver, operates at approximately 400 atmospheres and 200° C. Conversion is approximately 70 per cent.

In the *Pechiney* process (Figure 5.16) the reaction takes place in an oil medium later used to return the unconverted ammonia and carbon dioxide

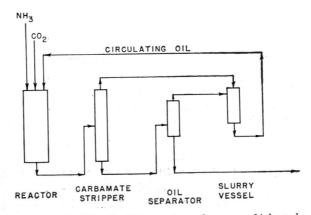

Figure 5.16. The Pechiney process for urea. [Adapted from Tonn, W. H., *Chem. Eng.*, **62**, No. 10, 188 (1955).]

to the converter which is lined with lead and operates at approximately 200 atmospheres and 180° C. Conversion is approximately 50 per cent.

The *Montecatini* process is offered in several modifications—without recycle of the ammonia and carbon dioxide, with partial recycle, or with total recycle (Figure 5.17). In the total recycle process the ammonia and carbon dioxide are recycled with water. In partial recycle the ammonia is used to produce by-product ammonium sulfate or ammonium nitrate. The converter is made of stainless steel, the pressure is approximately 200 atmospheres, and the temperature 180° C. Conversion is about 72 to 72.5 per cent.

The *Inventa* process employs aqueous urea nitrate to recover ammonia without concurrent absorption of the carbon dioxide. The ammonia and

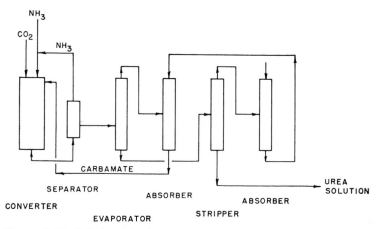

Figure 5.17. Solution recycle process for urea manufacture. [Adapted from Tonn, W. H., *Chem. Eng.*, **62**, No. 10, 187 (1955).]

carbon dioxide are then recompressed and fed with the make-up carbon dioxide and ammonia to the converter. Conversion is in the range of 50 per cent.

In the *Chemico* process the carbamate, carbon dioxide, and ammonia are recycled in a solution to the converter. MEA has been used to absorb the carbon dioxide and separate it from the ammonia. The ammonia is then recycled independently to the converters. Conversion is in the range of 73 per cent.

A new urea synthesis process has been described by Raymond Fanz and Fred Applegath of Lion Oil. The process utilizes carbon monoxide and operates at 30–50 psig. Ammonia, carbon monoxide and sulfur dissolved in methanol are fed to an autoclave. Hydrogen sulfide with unreacted ammonia and carbon monoxide are recycled. The hydrogen sulfide must be oxidized back to sulfur before recycling.[5b]

When combined with superphosphate, urea produces a fertilizer known as "Phosphazote." A salt with calcium nitrate is also recommended as a fertilizer. Combined with formaldehyde, urea gives resins that can be machined. With hydrogen peroxide, urea forms a crystalline additive $[CO(NH_2)_2 \cdot H_2O_2]$ which is employed as a disinfectant and oxidizing agent.

When heated above its melting point urea will dissociate to cyanic acid and NH_3. Cyanic acid will combine with urea to produce "biuret" $(NH_2CONHCONH_2)$, a by-product in the synthesis of urea. At 195° C biuret decomposes to ammonia and cyanic acid which polymerizes to cyanuric acid $[C_3N_3(OH)_3]$ and *ammelide*.

The production of urea has been increasing at a rapid rate.[20] The capacity for 1958 was 623 thousand tons.[13] The principal outlet for urea is in the fertilizer field, not only as a solid fertilizer but also as a liquid in the production of granular materials. This use has tripled since 1949. In some instances urea is combined with formaldehyde to produce a slowly soluble compound which will supply nitrogen to the soil during the entire growing season.

Urea has found acceptance as a protein substitute for ruminant animals. In this application it can efficiently replace about one-third the natural protein in ruminant feeds, but care in formulating must be exercised to optimize the concentration. Urea is toxic in large doses.

Urea formaldehyde, urea furfural formaldehyde, and urea resorcinol form thermosetting resins which are used in molding applications such as radio and TV cabinets, in the treatment of paper and fabrics, and as adhesives for bonding wood. The resins are nearly colorless but opaque, and may be pigmented as desired. They improve crush and crease resistance in textiles, and impart wet strength to paper and paper coatings. A small amount of acid or acid generating catalysts may be added to make the resin set.

Urea is used as an ingredient in softeners for cellulose, cellophane, and wood. It is used to retard end checking of boards during drying. Added to glue, gelatin, and starch, it reduces the viscosity and permits the use of higher concentrations of active materials. Urea is used in the petroleum industry to separate straight chain hydrocarbons by means of crystallization. The separation is effected by the formation of crystalline complexes between urea and a hydrocarbon with a long straight carbon atom chain. Urea is used in the preparation of barbituric acid, caffein, ethyl urea, hydrazine, melamine, guanidine, and sulfamic acid. It is also used in the manufacture of medicinals, in some cosmetic applications and deodorants, and in skin creams to improve the texture.

HYDROGEN CYANIDE

Hydrogen cyanide is a relatively new commercial chemical. It is increasing in importance with the rapid growth of acrylonitrile, used in the manufacture of certain synthetic fibers. Ordinarily hydrogen cyanide is a gas and a very toxic material. It has a melting point of −14° C and can be liquefied by cooling to 26° C. The liquid is colorless. It is soluble in cold water, alcohol, and ether. It forms explosive mixtures with air. The lower limit of flammability is 5.6 per cent and the upper limit 40 per cent.

The material can be manufactured in several ways. One of the earliest methods involves the action of sulfuric acid on sodium cyanide. The process is convenient for small quantities. Sodium cyanide may be produced by reacting sodium carbonate with carbon and nitrogen. The cyanide may also be prepared by reacting sodamide with charcoal. Ammonia and carbon

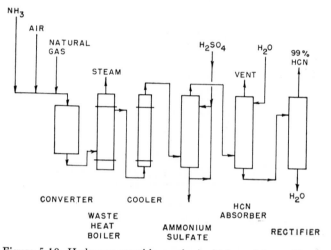

Figure 5.18. Hydrogen cyanide synthesis. [Adapted from *Chem. Eng.*, **62**, No. 9, 289 (1955).]

monoxide may be passed through molten sodium to form sodium cyanide and carbon dioxide.

Hydrogen cyanide may be obtained from hydrogen, nitrogen, and carbon by passing the two gases through an electric arc formed by two carbon electrodes. The conversion is low even at 2,000° C, hence the reaction is not of commercial importance.

Formamide has been dehydrated to produce hydrogen cyanide and water. Today, however, most hydrogen cyanide is produced by the reaction of ammonia with methane and air[26] (Figure 5.18). The reaction will proceed only if sufficient heat is supplied. The air is used to burn methane and produce the heat required for hydrogen cyanide synthesis.

The reaction of methane with ammonia is as follows:

$$CH_4 + NH_3 \rightarrow HCN + 3H_2$$

As indicated by the reaction, the formation of hydrogen cyanide requires the addition of heat—60 kilocalories per mole. In some instances the heat is supplied to the reaction zone through small diameter converter tubes, in which case the converter gases are not diluted with large volumes of nitrogen from the air.

The reaction of methane, air, and ammonia is believed to proceed in accordance with the following equations:[26]

$$NH_3 + O_2 \rightarrow NH_3 \cdot O_2 \rightarrow HNO + H_2O \tag{1}$$
$$HNO + CH_4 \rightarrow HNCH_2 + H_2O \rightarrow HCN + H_2 + H_2O \tag{2}$$

The net result of these two reactions is:

$$NH_3 + O_2 + CH_4 \rightarrow HCN + H_2 + 2H_2O$$

Equation (2) evolves 66 kilocalories per mole. The other reaction is also exothermic and the net effect is 144 kilocalories liberated per mole of hydrogen cyanide produced. Reactions (2) and (3) occur at very high rates below 850° C. Temperatures above 1,100° C are necessary to promote reaction (1) at a significant rate. The feed compositions for the converter are selected to meet the demands of equation (3) which is as follows:

$$NH_3 + CH_4 + 1.5O_2 \rightarrow HCN + 3H_2O + 144 \text{ kilocalories per mole} \tag{3}$$

Some side reactions occur and produce carbon monoxide and hydrogen which are in turn partially consumed by the oxygen to give carbon dioxide and water. The effluent gas normally contains about 6 per cent hydrogen cyanide, 1.6 per cent ammonia, 7.5 per cent H_2, 57 per cent nitrogen, 23 per cent water, and smaller amounts of carbon monoxide, carbon dioxide, CH_4, and O_2.

A catalyst is universally employed. A platinum catalyst may be used; however, it is usually alloyed with 10 to 20 per cent rhodium and deposited on a ceramic material to give it mechanical strength. It may be used as a gauze.

Under conditions of hydrogen cyanide synthesis, platinum alone will volatilize and in some cases recrystallize. Both these phenomena will result in the loss of catalyst. By alloying with rhodium, the catalyst will give satisfactory performance for as long as 4,000 hours.

It is important that the ingredients be properly metered to the system and that foreign materials be removed before the feed enters the catalyst chamber. Oil filters for the NH_3 and dust filters for the air and methane are sometimes used. Phosphorous compounds will deactivate the catalyst and hence must be removed from the feed materials. Short term exposure will not permanently injure the catalyst but long term exposure will result in loss of catalyst activity on a permanent basis. Hydrocarbons will crack to carbon and hydrogen; the carbon will deposit on the catalyst resulting in temporary loss of activity. Unsaturated materials and hydrocarbons with more than 3 carbon atoms are particularly detrimental. Iron rust from pipelines must also be avoided since it is a catalyst poison. Feed materials are usually filtered separately since acidic components in the air react with ammonia to produce solids which might plug the filter screen or the catalyst bed.

The manner of introduction of the feed materials into the reactor zone is important. Extreme precautions may be necessary to distribute the reactants over the catalyst bed. The catalyst shape may be other than flat to ensure proper distribution of the gases.

Gas fed to the converter usually has the following composition:

Ammonia	11 to 12%
Methane	12 to 13%
Air	74 to 78%

In many cases the converters are provided with rupture discs to relieve the pressures which may result from explosions caused by improper control of feed materials.

Ordinarily the converter is started by heating a portion of the gauze electrically or with a torch to reach reaction temperature. The reaction then speads thoughout the gauze as a result of the over-all exothermic reaction.

Approximately 60 to 67 per cent ammonia and 53 per cent methane are converted in a single pass. Higher conversions may be obtained at pressures of 30 to 40 psig. The choice of pressure is influenced more by the recovery system than by the advantages to be gained in the synthesis step.

It is important that the reaction mixture be cooled quickly to avoid cracking of the hydrogen cyanide. Basic materials such as NH_3 promote the polymerization. Accordingly, the gases are introduced into a waste heat boiler where about 6 pounds of steam are produced per pound of hydrogen cyanide. From the waste heat boiler the gases are passed through a cooler and then to an ammonia absorption system. At this point in the process several innovations have been developed. The most common method for removing ammonia is to use sulfuric acid as the absorbent; however, a polyhydroxy-boric acid complex, also used, has one advantage—the ammonia may be recovered for recycle. The bottoms from the scrubbing tower contain an aqueous ammonium sulfate which is processed further to produce solid ammonium sulfate. The overhead gases which are free from ammonia are then absorbed in water prior to purification. The water-hydrogen cyanide mixture is rectified in a final scrubber to produce 99 per cent hydrogen cyanide.

Materials are important in the construction of the equipment. Aluminum has good corrosion resistance to the products of reaction but its strength is lacking above 600° C and it promotes polymerization of hydrogen cyanide in the presence of ammonia and moisture.

Hydrogen cyanide is used principally in the manufacture of acrylonitrile by reaction with acetylene or ethylene oxide, methyl methacrylate, and adiponitrile. Tertiary alkylamines are also obtained by addition of hydrogen cyanide to tertiary olefins followed by hydrolysis of the formamides produced.

ACRYLONITRILE[6]

Acrylonitrile is a colorless liquid with a boiling point of 77.3° C, a melting point of —82° C and a density of 0.806 at 20° C.

The demand for acrylonitrile has increased during the last 10 years.[22] Since 1953 the production has tripled, rising from about 50 to 175 thousand pounds per year. Acrylonitrile production capacity, which exceeds the demand, has been limited to a relatively few producers, among them Union Carbide at Institute, West Virginia; American Cyanamid at Fortier,

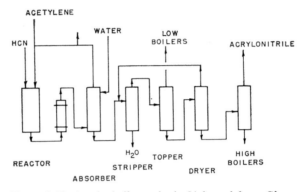

Figure 5.19. Acrylonitrile synthesis. [Adapted from *Chem. Eng.*, **62**, No. 9, 289 (1955).]

Louisiana; Monsanto at Texas City, Texas; B. F. Goodrich at Calvert City, Kentucky. Capacity is approximately 1.7 times that of actual production. The rapid rise in consumption, however, is expected to make use of the current productive capacity within the next few years.

Acrylonitrile is commercially manufactured by reacting hydrogen cyanide with acetylene (Figure 5.19) according to the following reaction:

$$HCN + HC\equiv CH \rightarrow HCH=CHC\equiv N$$

In practice, about 10 moles of acetylene are used per mole of hydrogen cyanide.[2]

Another process for the manufacture of acrylonitrile employs ethylene oxide. In this process hydrogen cyanide is reacted with ethylene oxide to produce the cyanohydrin which, when dehydrated, yields acrylonitrile. The production of acetylene and ethylene oxide are described in Chapters 17 and 25, respectively, and will not be discussed here. It will be mentioned, however, that from standpoints of safety and of yield, care must be taken in handling these materials to avoid loss. Acetylene must be purified before it is introduced into the reaction mixture. The actual combination of hydrogen cyanide and acetylene takes place in a liquid phase at 80° C with an aqueous catalyst containing cuprous chloride. All the hydrogen cyanide reacts, and about 10 per cent of the acetylene. Other products are also formed, such as acetaldehyde, vinyl chloride, methylvinylketone, chloroprene, and condensation polymers. The reactor is usually rubber lined.

Gases from the reactor containing the acrylonitrile, water, by-products, acetylene, and hydrogen cyanide are scrubbed with water to remove the acrylonitrile and unreacted hydrogen cyanide. The solution is then sent to a water stripper where the acrylonitrile is removed overhead. The low boilers are removed in a topping column. The bottoms from the topper are sent to the acrylonitrile dryer which removes the water by azeotropic distillation. Finally, acrylonitrile is recovered in a rectification column, the acrylonitrile being removed overhead, the high boilers from the base of the column.

New processes[5] for acrylonitrile manufacture are being developed. One of these reactions involves combination of acetylene with hydrogen cyanide on a fluidized bed. Another employs crude gas from acetylene manufacture for the manufacture of acrylonitrile. Recently Sohio Chemical Company and du Pont announced plans to manufacture acrylonitrile using propylene.

Acrylonitrile is used in the manfacture of many synthetic fibers. The manufacture of these fibers has increased as well as the number of producers. Acrylonitrile is also used in the manufacture of synthetic nitrile rubber. This material has good oil resistance and hence is used in the manufacture of aircraft and automotive equipment. Acrylonitrile is used in the manufacture of plastics and is copolymerized with such materials as butadiene and styrene. It is also used in preparing insecticides and surface coating resins.[25a]

Cyanoethylation is receiving considerable attention since with cotton it produces a material that is more receptive to dyes, is more resistant to rot, mildew, and bacteria, and has a higher abrasion and stretch resistance.

OTHER NITROGEN COMPOUNDS

Additional nitrogen compounds receiving commercial attention are the nitroparaffins[19,37] and the methylamines. The methylamines are produced by the reaction of methanol with ammonia at 475° C and 250 psi. Primary, secondary, and tertiary amines are produced.[3] These are separated by fractionation. Dimethyl amine is used in the manufacture of dimethyl formamide, a solvent for acrylic fibers.

The nitroparaffins are produced by the Commercial Solvents Corporation by nitration of propane at 400° C and 100 psi. Seventy-five per cent nitric acid is sprayed into the reactor to give a high hydrocarbon-nitric acid ratio. A yield of 40 per cent per pass based on nitric acid is obtained.

By-products such as aldehydes, ketones, acids, alcohols, carbon dioxide, and water are obtained.

Physical properties of the nitroparaffins are given in Table 5.13.

TABLE 5.13. PHYSICAL PROPERTIES OF THE COMMERCIALLY AVAILABLE NITROPARAFFINS*

	Abbreviation	Freezing Point °C	Boiling Point °C 760 mm	Specific Gravity 20/20 °C	Refractive Index 20/D	Flash Point† °F
Nitromethane	NM	−29	101.2	1.139	1.3818	112
Nitroethane	NE	−90	114.0	1.052	1.3916	106
1-Nitropropane	1-NP	−108	131.6	1.003	1.4015	120
2-Nitropropane	2-NP	−93	120.3	0.992	1.3941	103

* *Pet. Ref.*, **35,** 8, 151 (1956).
† Tag open cup.

Nitroalcohols are produced from the nitroparaffins by reaction with formaldehyde. These alcohols are used in the synthesis of amino alcohols which are emulsifying agents for waxes, paints, and cleaners. The chloronitro compounds have insecticidal and fumigant properties.

The nitration of benzene and other aromatic compounds is also becoming more important. These materials are used in the manufacture of aniline, trinitrotoluene (TNT), and dyes. The reactions are controlled by varying the catalyst (H_2SO_4) concentration, the excess HNO_3 present, the temperature, and the pressure. Orientation of the nitro group is predominately in the ortho-para position of toluene. In nitrating alkyl benzenes the size of the alkyl group influences the position of nitration. Di-nitration is more difficult than mono-nitration.

REFERENCES

1. *Can. J. Research,* **B** 25.
2. *Chem. Eng.,* **62,** 288–291 (Sept. 1955).
3. *Chem. Eng.,* **62,** 122 (Nov. 1955).
4. *Chem. Eng.,* **65,** 58 (July 28, 1958).
5. *Chem. Eng.,* **66,** No. 4, 55–57 (Feb. 23, 1959).
5a. *Chem. Eng.,* **67,** No. 8, 94 (1960).
5b. *Chem. Eng.,* **67,** No. 25, 71 (1960).
6. *Chem. & Eng. News,* **36,** No. 34, 50 (Aug. 25, 1958).
7. *Chem. & Eng. News,* **36,** No. 38, 62–64 (Sept. 22, 1958).
8. *Chem. Trade J.,* p. 75 (July 11, 1958).
9. *Chem. Trade J.,* p. 260 (Aug. 1, 1958).
10. *Chem. Week,* **75,** No. 22, 88–92 (Nov. 27, 1954).
11. *Chem. Week,* **80,** 66 (Jan. 12, 1957).

Reading References:

Astle, M. J., "Industrial Organic Nitrogen Compounds," New York, Reinhold Publishing Corp., 1960.

Sauchelli, V., "Chemistry and Technology of Fertilizers," New York, Reinhold Publishing Corp., 1960.

12. *Chem. Week,* **81,** No. 1, 46–47 (July 6, 1957).
13. *Chem. Week,* **83,** No. 1, 58–59 (July 5, 1958).
14. *Chem. Week,* **83,** No. 6, 67–68 (Aug. 2, 1958).
15. Chilton, C. H., *Chem. Eng.,* **65,** No. 14, 120–123 (July 14, 1958).
16. "Consumption of Commercial Fertilizers and 'Primary Plant' Nutrients in the U. S.," U. S. Department of Agriculture (year ending June 30, 1957).
17. "Consumption of Commercial Fertilizers and 'Primary Plant' Nutrients in the U. S.," U. S. Department of Agriculture (year ending June 30, 1956).
18. Duff, B. S., *Chem. Eng. Prog.,* **51,** No. 1, 12-J (Jan. 1955).
19. Hatch, L. F., *Petroleum Refiner,* **35,** No. 8, 147–152 (Aug. 1956).
20. Hatch, L. F., *Petroleum Refiner,* **37,** No. 8, 123 (Aug. 1958).
21. *Helv. Chim. Acta,* **24,** 754 (1951).
22. *Ind. Eng. Chem.,* **51,** No. 1, 25A–27A (Jan. 1959).
22a. *Ind. Eng. Chem.,* **52,** No. 2, 103 (1960).
23. News Letter, Institute of Gas Technology, Vol. X, No. 3 (1958).
24. Perry, J. H., "Chemical Engineers Handbook," p. 208, New York, McGraw-Hill Book Company, Inc., 1941.
25. *Petroleum Processing* (Sept. 1956).
25a. *Pet. Ref.,* **40,** No. 7, 145 (1961).
26. *Refining Engineer,* C-22-C-27 (Feb. 1959).
27. Ruhlman, E. R., "Nitrogen Compounds," Bureau of Mines Mineral Yearbook, 1957.
28. "Selected Values of Properties of Hydrocarbons," A. P. Inst. Research Project 44, National Bureau of Standards.
29. Sherwood, P. W., *Petroleum Processing,* **5,** No. 12, 1308, 1311 (Dec. 1950).
30. Sherwood, P. W., *Petroleum Refiner,* **37,** No. 9, 351–353 (Sept. 1958).
31. Spratt, D. A., *Proceedings of the Fertilizer Society of England,* London (Mar. 25, 1958).
32. "Statistics on Fertilizers and Liming Materials in the U. S.," Bulletin 191, U. S. Department of Agriculture.
33. Strelzoff, S., *Chem. Eng.,* **63,** 170–174 (May 1956).
34. Synthetic Fuels Symposium, A.C.S. (Sept. 12–15, 1955).
35. Thompson, H. L., Guillaumeron, P., and Updegraff, N. C., *Chem. Eng. Prog.,* **48,** No. 9, 468–476 (Sept. 1952).
36. Tonn, W. H., Jr., *Chem. Eng.,* **62,** No. 10, 186–190 (Oct. 1955).
37. Updegraff, N. C., and Mayland, B. J., *Petroleum Refiner,* **33,** No. 12, 156–159 (Dec. 1954).

6

MISCELLANEOUS HEAVY CHEMICALS

In collaboration with Mr. J. A. Falcone,* Dr. D. W. Duncan†
and Dr. D. J. Saunders*

SODIUM CHLORIDE

SODIUM CHLORIDE (common salt, NaCl) occurs in nature in almost unlimited quantities. It is the direct source of such sodium compounds as soda ash, caustic soda, sodium sulfate or salt cake, crystallized sodium sulfate or Glauber salt; indirectly, through soda ash, it furnishes the sodium for sodium phosphate and many other salts. Moreover it is the source of chlorine and of hydrochloric acid. It is these uses which come to the chemist's mind when he thinks of salt; but even without these salt has an imposing list of uses, which place it among the important substances in the economic world. It serves to preserve meat, fish, and hides; it is a necessary article of diet, and as such appears on every table; it is used in dairies to give temperatures below the ice point. Large quantities are used for ice control on streets in the northern states. Salt enables the soap maker to separate the soap from the glycerin lye, and the dye manufacturer to precipitate his products. In addition, salt is an important agent for regeneration of water-softening resins.

The form of salt used in nearly all the chemical industries,‡ in the north-

* Allied Chemical Corporation.
† Virginia Smelting Company.
‡ Except soda ash and chlorine, for which the brine is better adapted.

126

ern part of the United States at any rate, is rock salt, cut from the solid salt deposit by means of a shaft. The shaft mines number 13 in all, distributed as follows: five in Kansas, four in Louisiana, one in Michigan, two in New York, and one in Texas. One of the New York mines is at Retsof, Livingston County; the other is at Myers, Tompkins County. The Michigan mine is near Detroit. The depths of the shafts are 1063 (Retsof), 1950 (Myers) and 1050 (Detroit). The bed of rock salt at Retsof is 18 ft thick, and 9 to 12 ft is being worked at present. The rock is lifted to the mouth of the shaft, crushed and screened to size, without any other operation for purification. The color is a light gray-white, and it is essentially pure (98.5 per cent NaCl).

The shaft of the Avery Salt Company at Avery, La., is 518 ft deep. The quality of the salt runs 99.4 per cent NaCl. There is one place at Avery Island where salt comes within 10 or 12 ft of the surface.

TABLE 6.1. UNITED STATES SALT PRODUCTION IN SHORT TONS, 1959[a]

Manufactured (evaporated) salt	3,977,000
In brine	15,023,000
Rock salt	6,160,000
Total	25,160,000

[a] "Minerals Yearbook," 1960. (Salt production is an all-time high.)

Salt is obtained more frequently by means of water sent down one pipe, and after becoming saturated, brought up by another pipe concentric with the first (partly by hydrostatic pressure), and then pumped to a refining plant. Such artificial brines permit a cheaper operating cost, and are well adapted to soda ash manufacture and particularly to the making of white table salt. Artificial brines are obtained in New York State at Watkins Glen, Silver Springs, Myers, and Tully near Syracuse. Artificial brines are made in Michigan, where natural brines also occur but are of less importance; one field is near Detroit (Wyandotte) and a second one in the center of the State, near Midland. Kansas has many artificial brine wells; West Virginia and Ohio use both. A number of other states produce artificial brines.

In the dry climate of the Western states, salt is found as an outcrop at the surface;* in some of these states this salt is utilized to some extent.

In southern California, as also in Spain and southern France, and other locations, sea water is concentrated in wide basins, by solar evaporation, until the salt deposits; by running off the mother liquors at that point, the bitter magnesium salts are removed. An interesting application of the same method is at Salt Lake, Utah. Of the many salt deposits of the world, those at Stassfurt, Germany, underlying the potassium salt beds, deserve mention because they are several thousand feet thick, compared with 18 feet at

* From the streets of the town of Salina, Sevier County, Utah, outcrops of salt may be seen at the side of the hills; its color is red, and it may be fed to cattle.

Retsof, N. Y.; the stoutest bed in America is one in Kansas, 400 feet thick,[24] while a Texas salt dome is said to be 3000 feet thick.

From the brines, whether artificial or natural, a grade of salt suitable for table and dairy use is made by solar evaporation (in sunny climates), by open-pan evaporation, or by evaporation in vacuum pans, with one pan (single effect) or several pans (double or triple effect); in the latter the steam raised from the salt solution in one pan becomes the heating steam in the next pan. The evaporation of salt solutions offers the difficulty that, as salt is about as soluble in cold as in hot water, cooling a hot strong solution is not enough to form crystals; the water must actually be removed from the hot solution, until the salt drops out for lack of solvent.

The precipitated salt is dried in rotary driers, frequently constructed of Monel metal.

There were 85 plants of 53 companies operating in 1959.

TABLE 6.2. PRODUCTION OF SALT BY METHOD OF MANUFACTURE
(U. S. 1959)

	Short Tons[a]	Approximate Value per Ton
Evaporated salt		
Bulk		
Open pans or grainers	326,000	$29.07
Vacuum pans	2,088,000	21.37
Solar	1,278,000	5.56
Pressed blocks	288,000	23.49
Rock		
Bulk	6,105,000	6.50
Pressed blocks	55,000	25.56
Salt in brine	15,023,000	3.11

[a] "Minerals Yearbook," 1960.

The several states in the production of salt in any form stand as shown in Table 6.3.

TABLE 6.3. SALT SOLD OR USED BY PRODUCERS (U. S. 1959)[a]

	Short Tons	Per Cent of Total
Michigan	4,485,000	18
New York	4,011,000	16
Ohio	2,858,000	11
Louisiana	4,807,000	19
Texas	4,519,000	18
Kansas	1,123,000	4
California	1,388,000	6
West Virginia	811,000	3
Utah	209,000	0.8
Puerto Rico	3,000	0.01
New Mexico	36,000	0.14
Other States	916,000	4
(Nev., Okla., Va., Colo., Ala.)		

[a] "Minerals Yearbook," 1960.

The total world production in 1959 was estimated at over 88,000,000 short tons, of which the United States production was 28 per cent. West Germany produced 3,659,000 short tons of rock salt and 363,000 tons of evaporated salt, in 1959. Other large producers are China, Russia, India, Canada, and France.

SODA ASH, THE COMMERCIAL SODIUM CARBONATE

In the United States, soda ash from salt is made by the ammonia process exclusively; in England, a certain amount, decreasing yearly, is made by the older Leblanc process; but even there, over three-quarters of the total production is by the ammonia process. In France, Belgium, Germany, and other countries, the soda ash made is ammonia soda. To some extent, natural soda is isolated from the accompanying salts; such natural sodas and the ashes of seashore plants were the only source until Leblanc invented his process in the closing years of the eighteenth century.

The ammonia soda is usually called *Solvay soda,* for the successful manufacture, in 1864, by this process is due to Ernest Solvay, a Belgian, and many of the devices still in use were patented by him. The process is based on the fact that when ammonium bicarbonate is added to a saturated solution of common salt, the ammonium salt dissolves and sodium bicarbonate separates as a solid; if filtered, dried, and calcined, it is changed to soda ash, or sodium carbonate, Na_2CO_3:

$$NH_4HCO_3 + NaCl \rightleftarrows NaHCO_3 + NH_4Cl$$
$$2NaHCO_3 + heat \rightarrow Na_2CO_3 + H_2O + CO_2$$

This simple principle proved difficult of application, for ammonia is comparatively expensive, and unless it is all, or nearly all, recovered, the process cannot sustain itself economically. It was the nearly complete recovery of the ammonia which enabled Solvay to defeat the well-established Leblanc soda process.

In practice, a saturated salt solution is treated with ammonia gas, and this solution is then saturated with carbon dioxide; the resulting suspension of sodium bicarbonate in an ammonium chloride solution is filtered, and the sodium bicarbonate is dried and calcined (Figure 6.1.). The ammonium chloride filtrate is treated with lime and steam to recover the ammonia. The danger of losing ammonia in this operation is not great; it is rather in the gas leaving the carbonating vessels and in that leaving the calcining vessel that provision must be made to recover any ammonia which it may contain.

The carbon dioxide is obtained by burning limestone, and this furnishes at the same time the lime necessary for treating the ammonium chloride solution. It is clear that much fuel is required to burn the limestone, to calcine the sodium bicarbonate, and to raise steam for the ammonium chloride still. For the reaction proper, no fuel is required.

The ammonia process has one imperfection, in that the chlorine which common salt furnishes is not recovered, except to a small extent; it passes to waste in the form of a solution of calcium chloride.

Ammoniating the Brine. As a rule, sode ash plants are located near the source of salt; thus the Syracuse, N. Y., plant formerly drew brines from the property, and now that a greater supply is needed, brine from Tully and the neighborhood is piped to Syracuse, about 20 miles away; the

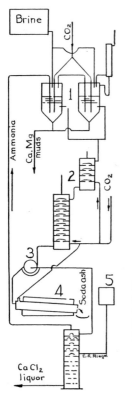

Figure 6.1. Simplified diagrammatic flow sheet for the Solvay ammonia soda process. 1. brine tanks with ammonia absorption; 2. carbonating towers; 3. rotary suction filter; 4. calciner, giving the finished product; 5. milk of lime box for ammonia still below. The ammonia circulates. Lime kiln not shown.

brines flow by gravity. At Wyandotte, Mich., huge deposits of salt are available. The great Dombasle plant in Lorraine, France, was also located there because of the almost limitless supply of salt in the region. Rock salt may be shipped in by rail, which, however, involves extra expense for freight, and rock salt costs more than salt in brine. The brine must be freed from calcium and magnesium salts, which tend to clog the carbonating towers in the later steps. This purification may take place in the same vessels in which the ammonia is absorbed. Such vessels are usually upright cylinders 15 ft high and 12 ft wide, with covers and conical bottoms. Ammonia dissolves in brine with evolution of heat, so that cooling coils containing flowing

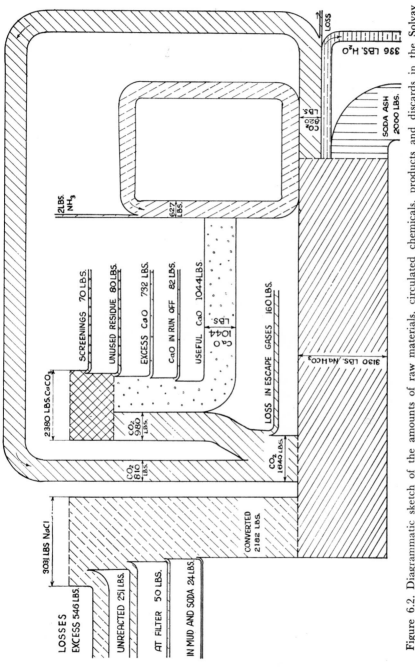

LOSSES

EXCESS 546 LBS.

UNREACTED 251 LBS.

AT FILTER 50 LBS.

IN MUD AND SODA 24 LBS.

3091 LBS. NaCl

2380 LBS. CaCO₃

SCREENINGS 70 LBS.

UNUSED RESIDUE 80 LBS.

EXCESS CaO 732 LBS.

CaO IN RUN OFF 82 LBS.

USEFUL CaO 1044 LBS.

CaO 1044 LBS.

LOSS IN ESCAPE GASES 160 LBS.

CO_2 810 LBS.

CO_2 980 LBS.

CO_2 1640 LBS.

CONVERTED 2182 LBS.

3130 LBS. NaHCO₃

1211 LBS. NH₃

627 LBS.

CO_2 820 LBS.

SODA ASH 2000 LBS.

336 LBS. H_2O

LOSS

Figure 6.2. Diagrammatic sketch of the amounts of raw materials, circulated chemicals, products and discards in the Solvay process for soda ash. The widths of the columns and frames are in proportion to the weight of the materials they represent. (*After Kirchner*)

cold water form part of the absorber. Towers with shelves may also be used, with cooling coils outside.

The brine run into the absorber does not fill it, as space for expansion must be left; as the ammonia gas dissolves, the volume increases. At the same time, the solubility of the salt diminishes; by feeding in dry ammonia gas, thus avoiding moisture which would dilute the brine and disturb the conditions, the desired amount of ammonia may be introduced while the salt content remains at the saturation point for that particular ammonia content. A saturated salt solution at 15° C contains 318 g of NaCl per liter of solution, if no ammonia is present. A solution containing 60 g of ammonia per liter is saturated with respect to salt if it contains 275 g NaCl per liter, also at 15° C. This amount of ammonia requires only 206 g of NaCl for the reaction, so that there is an excess of 69 g of salt (33 per cent); because some ammonia remains as ammonium bicarbonate, since the reaction $NH_4HCO_3 + NaCl \rightleftarrows NaHCO_3 + NH_4Cl$ does not run to completion (to 73 per cent for good operating conditions), the excess salt is really somewhat greater. The excess of salt is desirable, first because it drives the reaction to the right, and secondly, because it diminishes the solubility of the sodium bicarbonate.

A certain amount of carbon dioxide gas is sent into the absorber at the same time, but not enough to form ammonium carbonate; the calcium, most of the magnesium,* and all the iron salts precipitate, and collect in the cone unless the brine has been purified previously. After the proper amount of ammonia has been absorbed, the solution is settled and the clear ammonia-brine is blown by compressed carbon dioxide to the carbonating tower. A loss of ammonia during the treatment of the brine is avoided by connecting the outlet pipe of the absorber to a small tower with shelves, down which a fresh brine solution travels. By using a battery of absorbers, a supply of ammoniated brine is always ready.

There are two sources of carbon dioxide; one is the limestone kiln which furnishes gas containing 35 to 40 per cent CO_2, the rest mainly nitrogen; the other source is the furnace in which the sodium bicarbonate is calcined; its gas may be as high as 95 per cent CO_2. This second portion of the gas may be considered as circulating. In some plants, the two gases are combined in the pump house and no distinction is made.

Carbonating the Ammoniated Brine. In the Solvay system, carbonation is performed in towers with shelves, on the counter-current principle; the

* A magnesium salt content in the brine is not desired, and yet if the amount is small, and it escapes precipitation by the ammonia, which occurs because ammonia is a poor reagent for the purpose, its presence may be an advantage. Magnesia forms glass-like double salts with NaCl, which coat the walls of the apparatus, and prevent the contamination of the soda by iron with its subsequent discoloration. The factory experience is that those plants which occasionally have their soda colored red (unsalable) operate with magnesia-free brine.

brine flows downward, the gas enters at the base and travels upward; the other systems are gradually adopting the towers. Two towers are used in many of the plants, instead of the original single tower; a short first tower, in which enough carbon dioxide is fed into the solution to form neutral ammonium carbonate:

$$2NH_3 + CO_2 + H_2O \rightarrow (NH_4)_2CO_3 \tag{1}$$

In the second, taller tower, enough additional carbon dioxide enters to form the bicarbonate:

$$(NH_4)_2CO_3 + H_2O + CO_2 \rightarrow 2NH_4HCO_3 \tag{2}$$

In other plants, the tower is a single unit, and there are several towers. If there are five, to take an example, four would be actively precipitating bicarbonate; the fifth one would receive the ammoniated brine from the saturators, as well as a moderate flow of lean gas (40 per cent CO_2), delivering at its bottom outlet a clear liquor, carbonated as required by reaction (1). The temperature is allowed to rise, reaching 32 to 40° C [90 to 104° F]. The partly carbonated ammoniated brine is an active solvent for incrustations of bicarbonate, which form in spite of the engineers' skill. This procedure then has as object (1), the partial carbonation of the ammoniated brine, (2), the removal of the crusts. Each tower in turn works four days, and on the fifth, it is rid of all obstructions. From the fifth tower, the clear liquor is divided and fed in equal amount to each one of the four working towers. The flow of brine through the fifth tower is four times faster than its flow through the working or precipitating tower.

On traveling down the working tower, the liquor meets a flow of strong carbon dioxide gas, traveling upward. Reaction (2) takes place, and simultaneously, reaction (3).

$$NH_4HCO_3 + NaCl \rightleftarrows NaHCO_3 + NH_4Cl \tag{3}$$

The temperature rises to 65° C [149° F]; by means of the cooling pipes provided in the lower sections of the tower (see Figure 6.3), the temperature may be lowered. It is essential not to lower it too far, however, for at low temperature the sodium bicarbonate forms in such finely divided form that it cannot be filtered. The temperature of 26 to 27° C [78.8 to 80.6° F] has been found to be right for the production of grains of the proper size.

The tower consists of 28 upper sections, each 15 inches high, surmounting 9 lower sections which are 42 inches high. The material is cast iron. Each upper section has a floor with central opening, over which a dome-shaped piece is supported by three brackets. The rising gas is deflected sidewise by the domes. The lower sections have nests of cooling tubes; for the latter, wrought iron has proved a little more durable than cast iron. Other details may be obtained from Figure 6.3. It may be well to point out that this

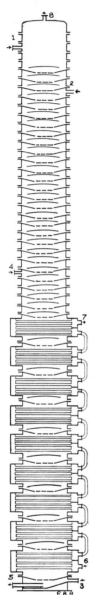

Figure 6.3. A carbonating tower in the ammonia soda process (Solvay); it is 69 feet high and 6 feet in diameter. (*Modeled after Kirchner*)

1. Entry for ammoniated brine, used when the tower is being cleaned.
2. Entry for the ammoniated brine for the regular bicarbonate precipitation.
3. and 4. Carbon dioxide entries.
5. Outlet for the bicarbonate slurries.
6. Cooling water inlet.
7. Cooling water outlet.
8. Escape for uncondensed gases.

tower is not a bubble tower; the rising gas has no liquid seals to overcome; it meets only the rain and foam of the descending liquid or slurry. Each shelf is flushed clean of deposit (within limits) by the descending liquid.

A tower such as that shown in Figure 6.3 has a capacity of 50 tons of finished soda per day.

The brine containing 60 g of ammonia per liter requires 83 g of carbon dioxide to form the neutral carbonate, a part of which is added in the absorbers. For the bicarbonate, an additional 83 g must be added; in fact, a little more is required, for some carbon dioxide passes out unused from the top of the main tower. It carries away some ammonia, which is recovered with part of the carbon dioxide, in a supplementary tower fed with fresh brine.

The carbon dioxide gas enters at the base of the tower under a pressure of 30 lb. As it rises, much of it is absorbed and the pressure drops. At the top of the tower the unabsorbed portion and the inert gas (nitrogen) pass through a supplementary tower where fresh brine removes any ammonia carried out.

The suspension is drawn off from the lowest compartment at frequent intervals, and fed to the trough of a continuous suction filter, of either the drum or the single-disk type. The cake is washed to remove all ammonium chloride; at the same time about 10 per cent of the bicarbonate is also dissolved and lost. In spite of the washing some ammonium bicarbonate is left in the cake, and its ammonia must be recovered; this is easily done, fortunately, for the ammonia passes out with the carbon dioxide on calcining the sodium bicarbonate, and the two gases together are sent to the carbonating tower.

Calcining Sodium Bicarbonate. A great variety of devices is used for calcining the bicarbonate, which is by no means an easy operation. In Europe a covered pan with semicircular cross section and scrapers having a sidewise motion (Thelan pan), with outside firing, is much used. In America, the rotary furnace with horizontal axis, with outside firing or heated by steam coils, is favored; to prevent the forming of insulating crusts on the walls, some of the hot cake just discharged is mixed with the cake to be calcined. The gas is saved in all cases, and forced into the carbonating devices:

$$2NaHCO_3 \rightarrow Na_2CO_3 + H_2O + CO_2$$

The discharged cake is light; for many uses, a denser cake is demanded; by calcining at a higher heat, the density is raised, but the dense soda ash of commerce is made by adding water to the light soda, and recalcining.

An analysis of a good commercial soda ash made by the ammonia soda process follows:

	Per Cent
Na_2CO_3	99.50
NaCl	0.20 to 0.25
Na_2SO_4	0.02
Insoluble	0.02
Moisture	balance

There is a tremendous sale for the bicarbonate to be used for baking powders, but for this purpose, the material must be purified, chiefly of ammonium salts. The crude sodium bicarbonate may be recrystallized, or a solution of soda ash may be carbonated. In 1957, 142,000 tons of refined bicarbonate were produced.

There is also a market for crystallized sodium carbonate, $Na_2CO_3 \cdot 10H_2O$, called sal soda, made by cooling a solution of purified sodium carbonate of the proper concentration.

Ammonia Recovery. The bulk of the ammonia is present as ammonium chloride, NH_4Cl, in the filtrate from the bicarbonate; some ammonia is present as carbonate, carbamate, and bicarbonate. The recovery is performed in a modern ammonia still in which the free ammonia (carbonate, sulfide) is driven off first, and then only is lime added to liberate the fixed ammonia (sulfate, chloride):

$$2NH_4Cl + Ca(OH)_2 \rightarrow 2NH_3 + CaCl_2 + 2H_2O$$

The calcium chloride passes out at the bottom of the still.

The run-off from still or tower contains no ammonia, or only a trace; it is blown by steam pressure to compartment settling tanks, and there settled; the clear liquor is removed, and the semi-solid lime mud carted to the dump.

The ammonium chloride liquor contains about one-third of the original salt (NaCl) unchanged; it is better to waste it than to have a less complete reaction. Part of the calcium chloride formed is wasted; but part of it is made into a concentrated calcium chloride liquor, the "brine" of the refrigerating plants; the diluted solution is also used to sprinkle on dirt roads.* A considerable portion of the calcium chloride formed is evaporated to dryness, and used as stated below under Natural Calcium Chloride.

A lime kiln which allows the recovery of the carbon dioxide is used. The gas from such a kiln contains the fire gases as well as the carbon dioxide from the limestone, and also dust. It is passed through a three-tray box, where it meets running water; the dust deposits, and the gas is cooled. From here it is forced into the carbonating tower.

Natural soda occurring mixed with sodium chloride and sulfate as well as magnesium salts may be isolated by treating the solution with carbon dioxide; sodium bicarbonate precipitates, is filtered off, and calcined to soda ash in horizontal rotary cylinders:†

---

* Calcium chloride is hygroscopic and retains enough moisture to lay the dust.
† The sesquicarbonate of sodium, often mentioned in the literature on natural soda, is $Na_2CO_3 \cdot NaHCO_3 \cdot 2H_2O$, and is also called *trona*.

The production in the United States is given in Table 6.4.

TABLE 6.4. PRODUCTION OF SODA ASH IN THE UNITED STATES[a]

	1958 Short Tons
Soda ash, ammonium soda process	4,896,000
Natural soda ash	735,000

[a] "Chemical Economics Handbook," Stanford University, 1958.

The estimated distribution of soda ash for 1957 is given in Table 6.5.

TABLE 6.5. ESTIMATED DISTRIBUTION OF SODA ASH IN THE UNITED STATES[a]

Consuming Industries	Per Cent (1957)
Glass	30
Caustic, bicarbonate, and other chemicals	37
Pulp and paper	7
Non-ferrous metals	10
Cleansers, soaps, petroleum refining, textiles, miscellaneous	16

[a] Sodium and Sodium Compounds, Mineral Facts and Problems, 1960.

The price of soda ash in 100-lb paper bags, carload lots, in 1959 was $37.00 a ton. The natural soda ash reported was produced from natural trona in Wyoming and from Owens Lake and Searles Lake in California.

Natural Calcium Chloride. The mother liquor from salt crystallization contains mostly calcium and magnesium chloride. Most of it is concentrated to a high salt content, and then *flaked* on a flaking machine. The product is packed in multi-paper bags and serves in the treatment of roads, coal and coke for dust prevention, on tennis courts, for refrigeration, and a variety of other purposes. During 1954–58, 356,000 tons of this calcium-magnesium chloride valued at $18.85 per ton were produced annually from natural brines in the United States.

A portion of by-product calcium chloride in the ammonia soda process is marketed in the form of flakes, and used for similar purposes. In 1957, calcium chloride production, which includes the chloride used in the liquid (solution) form as well as the flakes, estimated from its relation to the soda ash production, came to 536,000 tons.

SALT CAKE

Salt cake, the commercial anhydrous sodium sulfate, was produced originally by the action of sulfuric acid on salt ($NaCl$) in the pot and muffle process; within the last several years, employment of niter cake instead of free acid with the salt, and the roasting of the mixture in mechanical salt-cake furnaces, has rendered the first process obsolete. It was partly to consume the niter cake which at one time glutted the market that the mechanical salt-cake furnace was developed. It has been a brilliant success. As Chilean nitrate came to be used less, and the air oxidation of ammonia for nitric acid replaced it, less niter cake became available. Fortunately, one of the two methods for making concentrated nitric acid from the 65 per cent acid normally produced by the oxidation of ammonia method consists of neutralizing the weak acid with soda ash and evaporating to dryness, which gives synthetic sodium nitrate. The nitrate so obtained takes the place of the earlier Chilean nitrate for the production of concentrated nitric acid, with the now desired niter cake as by-product. The latter is then used for the mechanical salt-cake furnace operation, producing hydrochloric acid and sodium sulfate.

Another way to help matters is to make niter cake from salt and sulfuric acid in cast-iron retorts:

$$NaCl + H_2SO_4 \rightarrow HCl + NaHSO_4$$

Such niter cake, which has never seen niter, may be mixed with salt and fed to the mechanical furnace just as well as true niter cake. The amount of hydrochloric acid produced, let it be noted, is twice as great, and a market must be available for the additional amount. Less salt cake, with respect to the salt used and hydrochloric acid made, is produced when starting with sulfuric acid than when starting with niter cake from the nitric acid still, for this niter cake is already half salt cake.

Finally, a third procedure may be adopted. The mechanical furnace may be fed with salt (NaCl) and sulfuric acid directly, and the mass plowed and heated until the reaction to the sulfate is completed:

$$2NaCl + H_2SO_4 \rightarrow 2HCl + Na_2SO_4$$

In several important installations which have adopted this procedure, the cast-iron muffle floor has a center of acid-resisting bricks, to minimize the corroding effect of the acid.

The Mannheim Mechanical Salt-Cake Furnace

The best known mechanical furnace is the Mannheim. It is an automatic device, with continuous operation; the labor is a minimum; and the labor pulling out the fuming salt cake by hand rakes, a suffocating operation, is rendered unnecessary. When using niter cake, the reaction is:

$$NaCl + NaHSO_4 \rightarrow HCl + Na_2SO_4$$

It takes place to near completion at 650° C (1202° F).

The Mannheim furnace consists of a circular muffle of cast iron, 12 ft in diameter, with bottom and top dish-shaped; the inner height at the circumference is 20 inches, in the center 40 inches. A shaft penetrates it from below and carries four arms, each of which carries two cast-iron plows. The shaft is rotated slowly, 1 revolution in 2 min, by the gear and pinion indicated in Figure 6.4. The mixed salt and niter cake is fed in from the top near the center, and is moved to the circumference by the plows. Plow 8 is wider than the others, and discharges the burned cake (now salt cake) through the opening of the chute. Here the cake accumulates to some

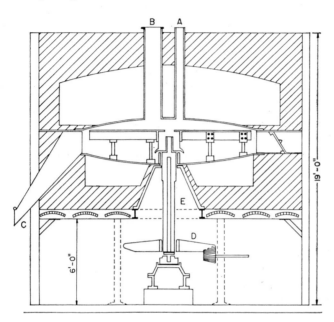

Figure 6.4. Mannheim mechanical salt-cake furnace, with hydrogen chloride as by-product. The charge enters at *A* and is discharged at *C*; the gas passes out at *B*. The eight plows are rotated from below by gear *D*; the shaft may be water cooled at *E*.

extent and is removed in small trucks to the storage bins. The discharge cake is yellow and turns white on cooling.

Some of the details of construction of the muffle will be plain from the illustration; the bottom and top are single castings. The sides consist of twelve curved castings which, when assembled, provide three doors; one of these is over the discharge opening and chute. Each plow differs in length of shank; and each is slightly turned so that the cake is swept outward. The heat is furnished by a small fireplace. The fire gases enter over the muffle, heating the top; then travel to the underside by a passage in the brickwork and heat the lower side; from here they pass out to the chimney. The temperature is registered by a platinum resistance pyrometer placed in a protecting cast-iron tube reaching into the center of the muffle from above.

The salt used is rock salt of the fineness of sand; it may be either purchased in that form, or if coarser, reduced in a swing hammer mill. The niter cake, in pieces 1 ft across or smaller, is fed to a pot crusher or jaw crusher; the product, the size of walnuts, is reduced to a coarse powder in a squirrel-cage disintegrator or a swing hammer mill. Salt and niter cake are carefully mixed in some plants by placing equivalent quantities (250 lb of salt and 700 lb of niter cake, for example) in a rotating cylinder and mixing for 15 min. In other plants merely dumping salt and niter cake alternately into the hopper serving the screw conveyor which brings the cake to the feed pipe of the muffle is found to give sufficient mixing.

The reaction is preceded by a fusion; the niter cake fuses first. The effect of high sulfuric acid on the fusion point of niter cake is not so great as that of the moisture content; 10 per cent moisture lowers the fusion point from 320° F (160° C) for the dry cake with 37 per cent H_2SO_4 to 210° F (99° C); but 10 per cent sulfuric acid added to the dry niter cake has almost no effect on its fusion point.

Temperature and Capacity. The temperature of the muffle is indicated by the pyrometer and is not kept constant, but is increased slightly as the wearing of the plows progresses; it lies between 625° and 675° C. The guide is the daily analysis of the salt cake. A well-burned salt cake should contain 2 per cent or less of NaCl, and 1.5 per cent or less of H_2SO_4; if the cake runs higher in both impurities, the temperature may be increased. Other ways to control the quality are to change the relative proportions of salt and niter cake, and the absolute weight fed in. In the 12-ft diameter muffle, six tons of good cake may be produced per day.

Length of Run. The plows need renewing every two months (approximate figure); the bottom casting may last two years, but one year is considered fair enough; the top casting and the sides will outlast several bottoms. The life of the plows may be lengthened by making the blades of Duriron and bolting them to cast-iron shanks.

Safety Flange. Should a plow become jammed against some foreign object a break may occur in the gears, which would be an expensive accident. This is prevented by fitting the pinion shaft with two flanges working through a pin whose size is just sufficient to carry the load. Any sudden resistance will break it, and at the same time indicate that the obstruction must be removed.

Pot Stills. The niter cake from the nitric acid retorts is supplemented, as already suggested, by the product obtained as still residue when salt is treated with sulfuric acid in the proportions indicated by the reaction:

$$NaCl + H_2SO_4 \rightarrow NaHSO_4 + HCl$$

A mechanical furnace, differing from the Mannheim, which has been installed in American plants is the Laury furnace, a two-stage cylindrical furnace,[16] not unlike the cement furnace, but shorter and stouter.

The production of salt cake in 1959 was 728,000 tons, including the figure for Glauber Salt; refined anhydrous sodium sulfate was 286,000 tons. In 1958 salt cake production amounted to 639,800 tons, refined anhydrous sodium sulfate to 255,100 tons and Glauber Salt, not included in the salt cake figure this time, to 106,100 tons as $Na_2SO_4 \cdot 10H_2O$, a total of 1,001,000 tons. The crude salt cake, in bulk shipments, was quoted at $28.00 in 1959. A considerable tonnage of salt cake is imported.

The uses of sodium sulfate are indicated in Table 6.6.

TABLE 6.6. END USE DISTRIBUTION FOR SODIUM SULFATE[a]

Kraft paper	71%
Detergents	7%
Glass	11%
Other industrial	4%
Dyeing	3%
Sponge	1%
Miscellaneous and export	3%

[a] Chemical Economics Handbook, Stanford Univ., 1958.

The major sources of sodium sulfate in 1957 were: natural brines, 34.5 per cent; viscose rayon, 29 per cent; and Mannheim and Hargreaves processes, 26 per cent.

Synthetic Salt Cake. The stoppage of importations of salt cake from European countries, particularly from Germany, by World War II created a shortage so serious that a synthetic salt cake was manufactured. It consisted of sulfur melted into soda ash, and was made as follows: As the soda ash leaves the calciner and enters a screw conveyor, sulfur in powder form is added. The hot ash melts the sulfur, and the action of the conveyor mixes the two, the sulfur coating the granules of soda ash, and producing a gray mass. This proved just as satisfactory in the kraft paper industry as true salt cake. The production was at a rate of 400 tons a day in 1941.

The Leblanc Process for Soda Ash. In the Leblanc process,* salt is treated with sulfuric acid, giving sodium sulfate and hydrogen chloride; this first step was retained for the manufacture of hydrochloric acid with sodium sulfate as a by-product. The salt cake (sodium sulfate) mixed with

---

* Invented during the period of the French revolution, by Nicholas Leblanc, a physician. The inventor did not receive the promised prize from the government, and his plant suffered from the political upheavals. For a century, civilization has enjoyed abundance of window glass and inexpensive soap, thanks to Leblanc's genius, but he himself died unrewarded, unthanked, in an asylum, by his own hand. See Hou, "Manufacture of Soda," 2nd ed., Chapter 1, New York, Reinhold Publishing Corp., 1942.

limestone and coal is heated in a short rotary furnace, producing the "black ash" which, after leaching with water, gives a solution of sodium carbonate containing also caustic. This solution is evaporated by the waste heat of the black ash furnace, during which process it receives enough carbon dioxide to form all carbonate. The monohydrate $Na_2CO_3 \cdot H_2O$ separates, and is dehydrated completely in reverberatory furnaces. A part of the soda ash was made into caustic soda by treating the solution with lime, so that a lime kiln usually formed a part of the plant. The Leblanc process, even though no longer practiced, is one of the most famous in industrial chemistry. In the course of its development, fundamental engineering principles were recognized and firmly established (the counter-current principle, for example, in the Shanks system of lixiviation).

HYDROCHLORIC ACID

Hydrochloric acid is made (1) from salt, in salt-cake furnaces; (2) by burning electrolytically produced chlorine in excess hydrogen; (3) as by-product from the chlorination of hydrocarbons such as pentane and benzene:

$$C_6H_6 + Cl_2 \rightarrow C_6H_5Cl + HCl$$

A fourth method[12] employs chlorine and steam over heated coke (350° C, 662° F) containing iron compounds as catalysts, or charcoal, to which iron oxide has been added.

$$2H_2O + 2Cl_2 \rightarrow 4HCl + O_2$$

Hydrogen chloride is a gas; on cooling to room temperature, it does not condense to a liquid, as does nitric acid, but must be dissolved in water. The ordinary commercial strength is 20° Bé, at 60° F (15.5° C), containing 32.46 per cent HCl. The system for absorption is essentially the same, whichever method for the production of hydrogen chloride is employed. As an example, the gas from a Mannheim furnace may be taken.

The gas from the Mannheim furnace passes through a 10-inch stoneware line, coated with tar to close the pores, to a short stone box, where it cools further and deposits most of the sulfuric acid which it carries. From the stone box, it passes to S-bend coolers or to Cellarius vessels set in running water; the cold gas then passes to the absorbing towers, where the solution in water or weak acid takes place. Tower No. 3 receives cold water, and delivers at the base a 12° Bé acid, which is warm; before feeding it to No. 2, this acid passes through about 6 lengths of 1-inch glass tubing set in cold water. The cold acid is elevated to the top of No. 2 by a small automatic, hard-rubber-lined elevator, or by a *monte-jus,** a gentle stream

---

* French, juice-raiser.

of air into a 1-inch glass pipe so that it forms gullets of liquid which give a broken column easily pushed up. The acid solution from the base of No. 2 is cooled and fed to No. 1, where its maximum strength is obtained. The acid from No. 1, after cooling, is the 20° Bé acid ready to ship. The daily production of a furnace furnishing 6 tons of salt cake is about 9000 lb of 20° Bé acid.

The towers are made of stoneware, usually in 10 sections, each 30 inches high, and 36 inches in diameter; the packing is coke of carefully selected sizes, or 3-inch spiral rings of stoneware. Three towers are sufficient for

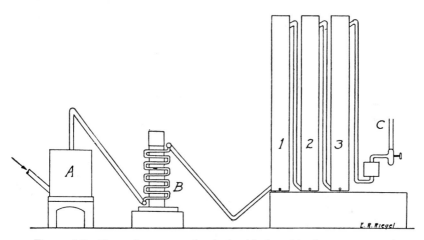

Figure 6.5. Absorption system for hydrochloric acid; the gas enters dry box *A*, then cooler *B*, and the absorbing towers 1, 2, and 3; the exhausted gas passes out at *C*.

complete absorption, but in many plants four are used, and in the summer months, even five.

The gas is pulled through the absorbing system by a fan set at the exit from a third tower (see Figure 6.5). The fan is protected from acid mist by a small coke box, so that a lead-lined fan or even an ordinary steel fan may be used. The suction exerted on the system is so regulated that it is felt at the muffle just enough to prevent the gas from passing around the working doors into the room. The strong gas may also be propelled by a stoneware fan set between the cooler and the first tower.

The stone box is built of sandstones which have been boiled in tar to prevent the acid from penetrating them; the stones are held together by cast-iron corner pieces and rods. The joints are made tight with rubber gaskets, or with asbestos cord smeared with china clay and linseed oil. The cooler may be made of S-bends, stoneware or fused quartz; for one furnace, there would be 5 rows of 4-inch S-bends, of which one is shown in the illustration; these pipes are cooled by a small amount of water trickling over them.

In some installations the towers are supplemented by Cellarius vessels of stoneware, about 46 inches long by 28 inches across, for acid cooling and absorption (see Figure 6.6). The design of this vessel provides for maximum absorption surface to a given total volume of solution. The function of the cooler S-bends may be performed by the Cellarius for gas cooling, of the same dimensions as just stated, but constructed in the opposite sense, so that it holds no liquid. Figure 6.7 indicates the details.

Acid made by method (3) involves the removal of any unchlorinated hydrocarbon present in vapor form, then absorbing hydrogen chloride in water in a continuous system. For the recovery of hydrochloric acid

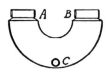

Figure 6.6. Cellarius stoneware vessel for gas cooling; the gas enters at A and leaves at B; the vessel is set in running water with only the bells protruding. C is the outlet for any liquid which may condense.

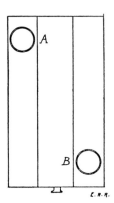

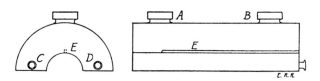

Figure 6.7. Cellarius stoneware vessel for acid cooling and absorption; the gas enters at A and leaves at B; the acid solution enters at C and must travel to the rear of the vessel and then forward again in order to reach the outlet D, because dam E is in the way. The vessel is submerged in water.

obtained as by-product of pentane chlorination, a plant has been described.[9]

Acid made by burning chlorine in hydrogen, with absorption in towers with iron-free packing, is a water-white acid, essentially chemically pure. It more than meets the requirements for the chemist's C. P. acid. A patented method[31] avoids an excess of hydrogen with the consequent necessity of scrubbing the gas to be reworked, by using the undiluted gases in a system closed as to escape gases.

Acid made by method (1) has a pale yellow color; it is shipped in glass carboys of 12-gal capacity, set in a wooden protecting box, or in rubber-lined wooden tanks, four tanks to a flat railroad car, or, in steel tanks lined with sheet rubber. The content of arsenic is usually 0.0002 per cent As_2O_3 in the commercial acid; this low figure is due to the use of contact sulfuric acid which is made from carefully purified sulfur dioxide gas, itself obtained from selected ore or from sulfur. For certain purposes a still purer acid must be furnished; from the pot stills, an acid is made with an arsenic content of 0.00005 per cent As_2O_3.

The production of hydrochloric acid expressed as 100 per cent HCl in 1958 was 848,500 short tons. The 20° Bé acid was quoted at $30.00 a ton; the 22° Bé acid as $35.00 a ton. The relative production by the several methods differs from year to year. At one time, 67 per cent of the total for the year came from the salt-cake furnace, and 33 per cent from chlorine, or as a by-product. There is an interesting relation between the several products involved. In making synthetic HCl, the sodium in the salt is obtained as caustic soda, while by the furnace method, it appears as salt cake. Depending upon market conditions, it may be more desirable to operate in one way instead of the other.

Hydrochloric acid is used to clean steel before galvanizing (dipping in melted zinc), in wire steel plants, in the manufacture of dyes, phenol, plastics, and for a number of minor purposes.

GLAUBER SALT

Glauber Salt ($Na_2SO_4 \cdot 10H_2O$) is a purified salt cake; the Glauber plant is usually adjacent to the salt cake storage bin.

Salt cake is dissolved in hot water, preferably in a circular wooden tank with stirrer. Steam is passed in during the solution to make up for cooling to the air. The solution is made as strong as possible (32° Bé hot), lime is added to neutralize the sulfuric acid invariably present, and to precipitate iron hydroxide and alumina. The liquor is allowed to settle, and the clear portion is run into the crystallizers. The muddy bottom is filter-pressed, and the filtrate sent to the crystallizers.

The latter are usually wooden forms lined with lead, 15 ft long, 6 ft wide, and 2 ft deep. On standing over night, crystals form; the mother liquor is then run off by removing a wooden plug from the outlet in the bottom of the crystallizer, and the crystals are shoveled into low trucks on wheels; these are pushed to one of several openings in the floor, through which the crystals are dumped into the storage bin and shipping room below. The mother liquor is collected in a low tank and pumped into the dissolver, replacing, after being heated, a part of the water.

The crop of crystals in the winter months is greater than in the summer; in fact during hot spells it may happen that no crystals form at all. For this reason, a stock of crystals is accumulated in the winter and spring, and stored in bins closed on all sides. Ventilation must be avoided, for Glauber Salt loses its water of crystallization on exposure to the air.

Glauber Salt is crystallized from an acid liquor to obtain colorless crystals; from a neutral liquor, slightly colored brown crystals form. The composition is:

	Per Cent
$Na_2SO_4, 10H_2O$	97.52
NaCl	0.21
Moisture	2.23
$Fe_2(SO_4)_3$	0.01
$CaSO_4$	0.022
Free acid	0.008

In a few plants, iron crystallizers are used, and the liquor is kept alkaline; this results in a product slightly off color.

Glauber Salt is used extensively in the textile industry; in 1958, 110,000 tons were produced; the market price, averaged between high and low, was $14.50 a ton. Its manufacture is interesting not only because of the high purity obtained but because, by making the first hot solution strong enough, no concentration of any kind is needed. This principle is followed in the chemical industries whenever possible.

SODIUM SILICATE

Sodium silicate is made by fusing together sand and soda ash in the proportions of 100 lb of sand to 52 lb of soda ash. Its formula is somewhat indefinite; it lies between $Na_2O \cdot 3SiO_2$ and $Na_2O \cdot 4SiO_2$. It occurs chiefly as a thick syrup, a water solution of the solid (30° to 40° Bé). Sodium silicate is commonly called *water glass,* because when solid it actually is a glass, and because this glass, unlike lime-soda glass (ordinary window glass) is soluble in water. The melting is performed in large tank furnaces similar to the window-glass furnace. The materials are introduced in batches, at intervals; the product may be drawn off continuously or periodically. A mixture of sodium sulfate and coal may be used instead of part of the soda ash.

As the melt leaves the furnace, a stream of cold water shatters it to fragments; these are dissolved by means of superheated steam in tall, rather narrow steel cylinders with false bottoms,[32] and the resulting liquor clarified.[33] Sodium silicates are sold in solutions which vary from the most viscous, 69° Bé, to thinner ones, reaching finally 22° Bé solutions, adapted for paints. The dry material in the form of a powder is also on the market, and is made by forcing the thick liquor through a very fine opening into a chamber swept by a rapid current of cold air, which carries off the moisture.[13] Because sodium silicate is hygroscopic, powdered sodium sulfate is sometimes incorporated with the solid silicate[34] to prevent caking. In composition, the sodium silicates may be varied from $Na_2O \cdot 2/3SiO_2$, to $Na_2O \cdot 3.9SiO_2$; they differ in alkalinity from pH 13.2 for $Na_2O \cdot 2/3SiO_2$, to pH 10.8 for the $Na_2O \cdot 3.9SiO_2$ silicate measured in 1 per cent solutions. In the concentrated solutions, the pH is not very different. Each of the commercial ratios results in a liquid with special properties, rendering it the proper selection for a specific purpose.

The uses of sodium silicate are surprisingly numerous; it is added in the crutching of soap; it serves to impregnate wood, to weight silk, as a mordant, as a heat-resistant binding agent, to clarify juices and solutions, to render bricks and cements non-porous, as a detergent, and as an adhesive, particularly in making corrugated paper boxes. The 1957 production was 813,800 tons (on the anhydrous basis). Sodium silicate as 40° Bé solution, (drums) carload lots, was $24 a ton in 1959.

BROMINE AND BROMIDES

When the brines from which table and dairy salt is made contain bromides, the bromine may be recovered from the mother liquors. The oldest process, still in use, is to concentrate the mother liquor and to treat it in a stone still (untarred) with sulfuric acid and sodium chlorate (formerly with manganese dioxide); a current of steam carries off the bromine liberated. An earthenware coil receives the mixed steam and bromine and condenses both, by water cooling; two layers collect in the stoneware receiver; the lower one is the dark red, liquid bromine; the upper one, bromine water. They are separated, and the bromine from the water layer may be recovered by blowing with air or natural gas. This lean bromine gas is treated separately; it is passed through a small stoneware tower filled with moist iron filings, and a strong solution of ferric bromide forms, from which the bromine is displaced by chlorine gas. Bromine is a liquid which boils at 63° C (145° F).

In another process the brine is treated directly with chlorine gas; still another process is based on the fact that on electrolyzing a bromide-bearing brine, the bromine is liberated first, the chlorine only later.

Crude bromine is purified from chlorine, its chief impurity, by a redistillation, passing the vapor over iron filings which retain the chlorine.

Bromides are made by saturating caustic soda (for sodium bromide, NaBr) with bromine; a smaller amount of sodium bromate is simultaneously formed

$$6NaOH + 3Br_2 \rightarrow 5NaBr + NaBrO_3 + 3H_2O$$

Bromides are valuable pharmaceuticals; bromine serves in the manufacture of certain dyes as a disinfectant; its irritating and suffocating properties have led to its use as a war gas.

At Wilmington, N. C., bromine is obtained from sea water, which contains 0.0064 per cent (average) of bromine; 1800 gal of sea water must be treated for each pound of bromine obtained. This plant is now the largest American producer. A second plant using sea water as source is the Freeport, Texas plant of the Dow Chemical Company, also a large producer.

Bromine is obtained also at Midland and Saginaw, Michigan, in Ohio, and in West Virginia. A large part of the world's supply formerly came from Stassfurt, Germany. A salt deposit rich in bromides and readily flooded by controlled amounts of sea water occurs in Tunis.

Bromine and bromine in compounds sold or used by producers in the United States during 1957 came to 192,000,000 lb. The price of bromine in 1957 was 23.9 cents a pound. The production figure is seven times that for 1936.

SODIUM SULFIDE

In a modern chemical establishment manufacturing a number of heavy chemicals for the general trade, there is a relation between the various sections, in that the product of one becomes the raw material for the next. Sulfuric acid, the first product, is the only exception; it is made entirely from purchased materials (sulfur or pyrite), or from by-product sulfur dioxide gas from a smelter. The preparation of nitric acid from sulfuric acid and sodium nitrate in retorts is accompanied by the production of niter cake, and this must be supplemented, when necessary, by its manufacture from salt and acid in the pot stills; the niter cake fused with salt gives hydrochloric acid and salt cake (Na_2SO_4). A large amount of salt cake is sold as such; the remainder is heated with coal or coke and made into sodium sulfide, Na_2S. By-products of this are sodium carbonate, Na_2CO_3, and sodium sulfite, Na_2SO_3, which are properly worked up into sodium thiosulfate, $Na_2S_2O_3$, usually called *hypo* from its old name of hyposulfite, now abandoned. Not all sodium sulfide is made from salt cake, for although the latter is the cheapest raw material, furnaces, leaching tanks, and other equipment are required; for small-scale operations, soda ash and sulfur are more suitable. In large plants, caustic soda, chlorine, and soda ash are not usually included, but all those products which require sulfuric acid for their manufacture are part of the plant. Soda ash is usually purchased in considerable quantities, for it serves to make anhydrous bisulfite of soda, $Na_2S_2O_5$, sodium hyposulfite (hydrosulfite), $Na_2S_2O_4$, and, following the older process, sodium thiosulfate, $Na_2S_2O_3 \cdot 5H_2O$; plants for these three products properly belong to an establishment which includes the manufacture of sulfuric acid, because the sulfur dioxide required may be taken from the burner house by simply erecting a pipe line. To complete the description, a power house for steam and electric current generation would be included; also water pumps for cooling, washing, and absorbing water; shipping facilities, and offices.

Sodium sulfide, Na_2S, has become extremely important as a depilatory, in the manufacture of sulfur dyes, and, in solution, as a solvent for the same sulfur dyes. It was formerly produced altogether in the form of crystals, $Na_2S \cdot 9H_2O$, which in the commercial form contained about 30 per cent

Na_2S; the crystals are brown, whereas pure sodium sulfide crystals are colorless. These crystals are still made, but the greater part of the sulfide is now marketed in the form of concentrated sodium sulfide with 60 per cent Na_2S, as solid cakes and lumps, or as flakes (*chips*). The method may be outlined as follows: Salt cake (or roast cake) from the Mannheim furnace mixed with coal is heated in a reverberatory furnace; a melt is produced which is raked out and either dissolved in water at once, or allowed to cool to solid cakes which are later leached with hot water. The solution is made strong enough so that when it is cooled in shallow pans, crystals of

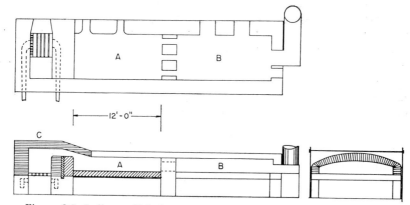

Figure 6.8. Sodium sulfide furnace, reverberatory type; A, reduction hearth; B, preheating chamber. The fireplace and half of the bridge wall are of hard firebricks; C, the hearth of alunite or aluminate bricks.

$Na_2S \cdot 9H_2O$ form. To produce the 60 per cent sulfide, the crystals are melted in special pots and water driven off from the hot liquid; on cooling, a black solid with red fracture forms. Another method is to boil down the first solution after filtering or settling, until the sodium sulfide content is a little above 60 per cent.

Reverberatory Furnace. A reverberatory furnace is shown in Figure 6.8; it is a low arch furnace with a fireplace separated from the hearth by a bridge wall. The fire gases strike the roof over the fireplace and are deflected onto the charge on the hearth; the low arch forces intimate contact between fire gases and charge. From the furnace proper the gases pass to the preheating chamber, of dimensions similar to those of the hearth, and from there to the stack. For a furnace whose hearth is 12 ft long and 8 ft wide, the charge is 1000 lb of salt cake* and 500 lb of coal screenings. Such a

---

* Instead of salt cake, niter cake was formerly used; the escaping sulfuric acid caused a cloud at the top of the stack, which caused much difficulty with municipalities. It was thought that by substituting salt cake, the cloud would vanish; it continued. In this case, it is due to sublimed sodium salts; these may be removed from the stack gases by a Cottrell precipitator.

charge is shoveled into the rear of the preheating chamber, where it is warmed by the outgoing gases for an hour. It is then pushed with a hoe to the working hearth and heated there, with occasional stirring, for another hour, when it is ready to be pulled out. Instead of shoveling in the charge, it may be fed in from an overhead bin through an opening in the arch. Melted sulfide is extremely corrosive, so that the construction of the furnace is a special one. The floor of the hearth consists of alunite or other basic bricks, set upright on their smallest face. These bricks rest on several thicknesses of asbestos paper soaked in silicate of soda solution; such an underlining has been found efficient in preventing the escape of melt. The alunite bricks are placed in a solution of silicate of soda for some hours just before laying. The hearth side of the bridge wall is also lined with alunite bricks, while the fireplace side and the arch over the whole furnace are of ordinary fire bricks. The rear wall is usually lined with a hard firebrick. Such a furnace will last 8 to 12 months, when it must be rebuilt.

In order to insure a high yield the atmosphere in the furnace must be a reducing one; the fire gases should contain one or several per cent carbon monoxide and no oxygen. Such fire gases are obtained by building a deep bed of coal on a fireplace of rather small dimensions, using soft coal and forced draft. The reactions on the hearth are:

$$Na_2SO_4 + 2C \rightarrow Na_2S + 2CO_2$$
$$Na_2SO_4 + 4CO \rightarrow Na_2S + 4CO_2$$

There are several ways in which the melt may be handled on leaving the furnace. A simple and efficient way is to pull the charge into 8 or 10 buggies on wheels, each holding 80 to 100 pounds, so that one man can handle them. Another way is to pull the charge into two steel boxes on low trucks. In either case the melt is allowed to cool; during the cooling of the cakes, some further reduction takes place. The cold cake is broken with a sledge and fed to an edge runner washed by a constant flow of warm water. A solution of sodium sulfide with suspended matter results, which is elevated to a settling tank. In the older plants, the cake is fed to a jaw crusher in the floor, then elevated to one of four leaching tanks which are worked in series; each tank accommodates one day's melt. The fresh melt is wetted with the wash from the melt of the day before, and this wash in turn has first rested on the nearly spent melt of two days before; the fourth tank is being emptied. In this way each melt is leached three times.

A totally different way is to pull the melt into a ladle and to bring it over a dissolving tank with a stirrer. The fluid melt, still hot, is run into the water, which is thereby heated; this operation is extremely noisy. It utilizes a part of the heat of the melt, however, and saves labor, so that it will probably become standard, at least for large plants. The suspension may be settled or filter-pressed using iron wire filter cloth; the press cake is made up with water once more, filter-pressed again, and the filtrate used in the dissolving tank.

The melt in the cakes is 60 to 65 per cent Na_2S; such rich melts flow less easily than melts contaminated with unreduced sulfate or with carbonate.

The sulfide liquor obtained by any of these variations is hot, and of such strength that after it is run into shallow iron pans, crystals deposit over night. The mother liquor contains sulfide, and also sulfate, sulfite, and carbonate; it may be concentrated, when all the salts other than sulfide precipitate, leaving a concentrated solution of sulfide which may usually be crystallized; in some cases it may contain so much silicate that it will not crystallize. The precipitated salts are dissolved in water and the solution used for making thiosulfate. The brown crystals with 30 per cent Na_2S may be sold as such, or they may be placed in iron pots over a fire, melted, and enough water removed to raise the content of Na_2S to 60 per cent. The liquor may be run into concentrating pans directly and evaporated to the higher strength; the difficulty in that case is that the sulfate, carbonate, and similar impurities deposit during the concentration and coat the bottom of the concentrating pans, causing them to become locally overheated, which results in leaks.

The 60 per cent liquor may be run into shallow flat pans, where it solidifies over night; it is then broken and shipped as lumps. There are many other ways to fix the final shape of the product; the best one is to feed a thin layer to a water-cooled rotating drum, actuated by a ratchet; a knife detaches the cake, and the thin strips fall and break into still smaller flakes, called *chip sulfide*.[35] In this form, solution at the consumer's plant is greatly facilitated. The color of chip sulfide is red; like any other form of sulfide it must be stored in air-tight, thin, steel drums; otherwise it turns green because of the formation of sulfate and carbonate.

New Types of Sulfide Furnaces. The old reverberatory furnace is a reliable way to manufacture sulfide, but new types of furnaces are displacing it. The aim of the newer furnaces is to reduce labor to a minimum by a continuous operation, largely automatic. On one of these furnaces, a rotary style[36] is proposed with carbon monoxide gas, prepared in auxiliary vessels, as reducing agent and fuel. Several German proposals are promising also; one[14] involves the use of a Bessemer pear such as is used for making steel, and still another[15] proposes ovens with pendulum or shaking motion. Two blast furnaces have been patented; one proposal[16] allows the melt to solidify; in the other[17] the fluid melt is either tapped at intervals or drawn off continuously. In the latter furnace, as well as in one proposed by H. K. Moore,[37] the fluid melt is dropped at once into a *quench tank*. Finally, studies in the application of the electric furnace to the manufacture of sodium sulfide have been made[5] and were applied commercially in Italy during the war of 1914–18.

The annual production of sodium sulfide, as 100 per cent Na_2S is approximately 20,600 tons. The price in 1957 was $136 a ton. The flakes (60–62 per cent Na_2S) are sold in 440-lb drums.

In 1942, there was developed at Höchst (Germany) a method of producing sodium sulfide (62 per cent Na_2S) directly from sodium polysulfide, by the action of the latter on sodium amalgam:

$$Na_2S_4 + 6Na \rightarrow 4Na_2S[7]$$

The amalgam is produced in the mercury caustic cell; the polysulfide is introduced into the decomposing chamber of the mercury cell. It is necessary to maintain the temperature of the decomposing chamber at 90° C (194° F).

SODIUM THIOSULFATE

Sodium thiosulfate, $Na_2S_2O_3 \cdot 5H_2O$ or *hypo,* is the agent employed in photography for dissolving the unreduced silver salts, and in textile mills as an *antichlor.* It is made in two ways: the first is independent of any other process, and requires soda ash and brimstone; the second makes use of by-product sulfide liquors and is dependent upon a sulfide plant; its sulfur dioxide may be drawn from the burner house of the sulfuric acid plant generally forming part of a large establishment. It is customary in the second kind of plant to have in reserve soda ash and brimstone, so that in case the by-product liquor fails, these materials may be used instead. The same apparatus serves without any change, and burner gas is the source of sulfur dioxide, as before.

The Soda Ash-Brimstone Process. Soda ash is dissolved in hot water and the solution (26° Bé) pumped to a small storage tank at the top of the first of two absorption towers. These are of lead supported on wooden beams, and are filled with hardwood sticks, except in the lower part where a small chamber of hard acid bricks is provided. The nearly spent sulfur gas from the second tower (second with respect to the liquor) enters at the base and meets the descending soda ash solution which absorbs all the remaining sulfur dioxide. The partly gassed liquor from the first tower is elevated to the top of the second tower wherein it meets the sulfur dioxide gas fresh from the burners; the soda ash is completely changed to sodium bisulfite, which runs out through a seal at the base of the tower and is collected in lead-lined receiving tanks.

$$Na_2CO_3 + H_2O + 2SO_2 \rightarrow 2NaHSO_3 + CO_2$$

Figure 6.9 indicates the disposition of the apparatus. The nitrogen, oxygen, and carbon dioxide pass out of the first tower to a small stack.

Sulfur dioxide may be made by burning brimstone in iron pans cooled from below by air, and set in brick work; or, a special patent burner may be installed, such as the Glens Falls (N. Y.) rotary burner, the Chemico spray burner, the Vesuvius burner with shelves, and others. Formerly the bisulfite liquor, with 22 per cent SO_2 content, was an important product; it has been replaced by anhydrous bisulfite of soda, $Na_2S_2O_5$, a powder with 67 per cent SO_2. By means of soda ash, the bisulfite liquor is changed into

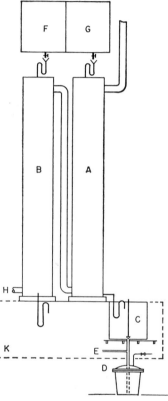

Figure 6.9. A simple plant showing the working principles for making sodium bisulfite solution. Soda ash solution in tank G is fed to the first lead tower, A, where it meets the weak gas from the top of the second lead tower, B. The liquor from A collects in C, is run into the lead-lined cast-iron pot D, used as a blowcase, and forced through E to tank F, from which it is fed to tower B, meeting fresh gas entering at H. The finished liquor collects in the storage tank K. The towers are packed with wooden grids.

neutral sulfite, and this is heated with powdered brimstone* in a brick-lined, cast-iron vessel with a stirrer. A solution of sodium thiosulfate results; it is concentrated hot in a boiler from 36° Bé to 51° Bé. After settling, this liquor is run into lead-lined or steel crystallizers and allowed to cool. When iron crystallizers are used, a crust of the crystals is left on the sides and bottom to avoid contamination.

$$2NaHSO_3 + Na_2CO_3 \rightarrow 2Na_2SO_3 + H_2O + CO_2$$
$$Na_2SO_3 + S \rightarrow Na_2S_2O_3$$

* The crushing of brimstone is not without danger.

After two or more days, the mother liquor is run off, the crystals $Na_2S_2O_3$ $\cdot 5H_2O$ are shoveled to centrifugals which remove adhering mother liquor, washed by a short spraying from a hose, and dumped to a conveyor leading to the interior of a rotating cylindrical steel wire screen. The screen consists of two sizes, a six-mesh half which receives the unassorted crystals, and a three-mesh screen which forms the rear half. The fines drop through the six-mesh wire as the screen slowly rotates; the pea size drops through the three-mesh wire, while the coarser pieces, the "crystal" size, roll off at the far end of the wire. No drying of the crystals is necessary.

A fine crystal product of uniform size called *granulated hypo* is made by cooling the 51° Bé liquor in circular steel pans 10 ft in diameter and 3 ft deep, in which a two-armed scraper slowly revolves while the liquor cools.

Sodium thiosulfate crystals effloresce so readily in air that they must be packed at once in air-tight containers, cartons or paper-lined barrels.

The By-Product Sulfide Liquor Process. The carbonate and sulfite which separate from the sulfide liquor while it is in process of concentration are made up with water; the adhering sulfide is also dissolved. This liquor becomes the raw material for sodium thiosulfate manufacture. In the plants which filter the suspension from quench tanks, and make up the first mud with water again, then filter once more, this second filtrate becomes the raw material for hypo; the first filtrate is essentially sulfide. The most satisfactory relation of the carbonate and sulfide (the sulfide is usually very low) is about 8 per cent Na_2S and 6 per cent Na_2CO_3, when the reaction

$$2Na_2S + Na_2CO_3 + 4SO_2 \rightarrow 3Na_2S_2O_3 + CO_2$$

takes place during the gassing period. An excess of sulfide over this amount must be avoided, as it may lead to a loss of useful materials in the generation of H_2S:

$$Na_2S + SO_2 + H_2O \rightarrow Na_2SO_3 + H_2S$$

Some of this hydrogen sulfide will be changed into sulfur by sulfur dioxide, but it is manifestly cheaper to supply sulfur in the form of brimstone, if any is needed. Technical sodium sulfide always contains some polysulfides, and these supply some sulfur which reacts with such sulfite as may be present in the original liquor. Should the carbonate run high and the sulfur low, brimstone may be added to change the sulfite formed (the bisulfite is avoided*) into thiosulfate.

The sulfide-carbonate liquor may be treated with sulfur dioxide gas, the regular burner gas with 7 per cent SO_2, in towers. Instead of a single passage of the liquor through a rather tall tower, many passages through a

---

* Acidity due to $NaHSO_3$ is detected and measured by a titration with caustic in presence of phenolphthalein; Na_2SO_3 is neutral to phenolphthalein, but alkaline to methyl orange; it is measured, with any carbonate present, by a titration with standard acid, in the presence of methyl orange; $NaHSO_3$ is neutral to methyl orange.

shorter tower may be substituted; these are then called *circulating towers*. The liquor is run into a large tank and pumped at a rapid rate to the top of the tower, which has wooden shelves. As the liquor cascades from shelf to shelf, fresh surfaces are exposed and the absorbing liquid exhausts the gas readily. The gassed liquor at the base of the tower runs back into the original tank. The tower may be 20 ft high, 4 ft in diameter, of steel lined with bricks; the wooden shelves are perhaps 10 inches apart. Each shelf covers only about two-thirds of a circle, and the openings are staggered, so that the liquor changes direction constantly. Two or more towers may be used, the gas passing from one to the other to insure its exhaustion.

After sufficient gassing, the liquor is filter-pressed through cotton duck cloth and concentrated in a steel boiler with a steam chest. The crystallization and further steps are the same as under the soda-ash brimstone process. It will be noted that in normal running the sulfide by-product liquor requires no brimstone addition.

In 1957, there were produced 37,900 tons of sodium thiosulfate, $Na_2S_2O_3 \cdot 5H_2O$, valued at \$90.00 a ton.

SODIUM BISULFITE, ANHYDROUS

The sodium bisulfite of commerce, generally listed as sodium bisulfite, anhydrous, is in reality the anhydride of two molecules of sodium bisulfite, $NaHSO_3$. This anhydride is sodium metabisulfite or sodium pyrosulfite, $Na_2S_2O_5$. Most commercial products contain at least 98 per cent $Na_2S_2O_5$ and approximately 0.5 per cent sodium sulfate, with the remaining 1.5 per cent being largely sodium sulfite, Na_2SO_3. Low moisture content enhances the storage characteristics of the material. The commercial methods[38] for the manufacture of sodium bisulfite, a white crystalline powder, differ in details but generally follow the same principle. The mother liquor from previous batches, saturated with sodium bisulfite, is reinforced with soda ash, converting the dissolved bisulfite to sodium sulfite and forming a suspension of soda ash. Sulfur dioxide gas from a sulfur or pyrite burner is fed into the soda-ash suspension, forming the metabisulfite.

In some processes the absorbers are steel tanks lined with brick. The tanks are 15 ft high and 15 ft in diameter and are equipped with tight-fitting tops of cast iron covered with lead. A hard lead propeller, working through a stuffing box, makes 100 rpm. The gas inlet pipe reaches about one foot below the liquid surface. A 10-inch main brings the gas to the absorbers and three-inch lines (three to each tank) deliver it into the suspension. The gas enters first into the second-stage absorber, is drawn next into the first-stage and is finally withdrawn by a fan and discharged into the air. The propeller shaft is lead covered, as is also the rod carrying the plug valve which closes the discharge hole in the bottom. Countercurrent absorption columns, packed with rings or saddles, can also be used to absorb the sulfur dioxide.

Formation of the crystals of metabisulfite from the saturated solution is promoted by a moderate lowering of the temperature. The crystals are removed by centrifuging, followed by return of the mother liquor to the absorption system. Rapid drying of the crystalline product is important in order to avoid excessive oxidation to sulfate or decomposition with loss of sulfur dioxide.

Processes described in patents indicate that the wet powder can be dried by passing it through a shelf drier having six shelves. Rotating arms move the material from shelf to shelf, dropping it through alternate circumferential and central openings. The shelves are steam heated. So-called flash driers, which give especially rapid drying, can also be used. The function of the drier is merely to remove adhering moisture. The anhydrous bisulfite (or metabisulfite) is produced as such in the reaction during the absorption of sulfur dioxide:

$$Na_2CO_3 + 2SO_2 \rightarrow Na_2S_2O_5 + CO_2$$

By using a building with several stories, the material may be moved by gravity, except for feeding the soda ash to the suspension tank, and lifting the soda-ash suspension to the absorbers. These operate in two stages; the first-stage absorbers, on the top floor, receive the fresh soda-ash suspension and the sulfur dioxide gas which has already passed through the second-stage absorbers. The latter, on the floor below, receive the suspension from the first-stage absorbers by gravity, and the fresh sulfur dioxide from the sulfur or pyrite burners. Here the soda ash is completely transformed to anhydrous bisulfite, and this suspension is fed to the centrifugals on the floor below; the drier is on the ground floor on a level with a railroad car floor.

Anhydrous sodium bisulfite is used in the manufacture of dyes and in their application to fibers, in the leather industry, in the photographic industry, as an antichlor, in the sterilization of casks for beer and similar beverages, for preservation of grass silage and for many other purposes.

The neutral sulfite, Na_2SO_3, can be made by the action of soda ash on sodium bisulfite. It is sold both as the anhydrous form and as crystals, $Na_2SO_3 \cdot 7H_2O$.

The annual United States production of sodium bisulfite, anhydrous may be estimated at about 40 million pounds. The published price of the technical grade (August, 1958) in carload quantities was 5¢ per lb, f.o.b. producing point. The product is shipped in 100-lb net, polyethylene-lined bags and 400-lb net, fiber drums.

SODIUM HYPOSULFITE (HYDROSULFITE)

Sodium hyposulfite, anhydrous $Na_2S_2O_4$, called hydrosulfite in the trade, is a convenient form of the powerful reducer which is used for the reduction of certain dyes. Before its advent in the trade, it had to be prepared as a solution in the textile mills and used at once. Formerly it had to be imported, chiefly from Germany. There are now several manufacturers in the United States. The commercial product, a free-flowing crystalline material, generally analyzes about 93–94 per cent $Na_2S_2O_4$, with varying amounts of the sodium salts of sulfite, chloride and carbonate.

The method of manufacture[25a] includes four steps. (1) Finely divided thermal zinc dust (normally screening 95 per cent through 325 mesh), containing at least 95 per cent metallic zinc, is suspended in water in a lead-lined container provided with cooling coils and a stirrer. Pure sulfur dioxide, best from a tank of liquid sulfur dioxide, now an article of commerce, is led in, fast at first, and more slowly near the end. The temperature is kept below 40° C. The color changes to black, to gray and finally to cream.

$$Zn + 2SO_2 \rightarrow ZnS_2O_4$$

(2) The content of the reactor is transferred to a lead-lined steel tank equipped with a stirrer. A soda ash solution is added, in excess over the amount indicated by the reaction.

$$ZnS_2O_4 + Na_2CO_3 \rightarrow ZnCO_3 + Na_2S_2O_4$$

A basic zinc carbonate is formed and precipitated, while sodium hydrosulfite remains in the alkaline solution. The slurry is filtered on a stationary suction filter. The cake is washed several times, but only the first wash is added to the filtrate. The subsequent wash waters are sent back to the first-stage reactor. (3) The filtrate, containing about 15 per cent $Na_2S_2O_4$, is pumped to a salting-out tank. To this solution is added slowly about 300 g per liter of sodium chloride. Hydrated sodium hydrosulfite, $Na_2S_2O_4 \cdot 2H_2O$ separates in the form of needles. The suspension is agitated and heated rapidly to 60° C and held there until all the crystals have been transformed into crystals of anhydrous sodium hydrosulfite, $Na_2S_2O_4$, a sand-like crystalline powder.* The crystals are allowed to settle, the supernatant liquor is drawn off and hot denatured alcohol is added. (4) The crystals suspended in the alcohol are transferred to a steam-jacketed vacuum drier, the alcohol drawn off after settling, and successive portions of alcohol added and drawn off so that no water remains. By gently heating under vacuum, the adhering alcohol is removed and recovered, leaving the dry crystals.

The annual United States production of sodium hydrosulfite, $Na_2S_2O_4$, may be estimated at about 45 million pounds. The published price (August, 1958) in carload quantities was 23.75¢ per lb, delivered. Sodium hydrosulfite is a yellow label commodity and is shipped in ICC specification drums, usually containing 250 lb net weight.

---

* The transition point of the hydrated salt to the anhydrous form is 52° C.

CAUSTIC SODA AND CHLORINE

Caustic soda, NaOH, a white solid, extremely soluble in water, is made by causticizing soda ash by lime and by the electrolysis of salt, NaCl, in water solution, with the simultaneous production of chlorine and hydrogen.

The Electrochemical Society reported[26] that caustic soda production for 1958 amounted to 4,055,000 tons, a decrease of 6.7 per cent from the 1957 level. The apparent per capita consumption was 44.2 lb compared to 29.9 lb in 1948 and 11.2 lb in 1938. Approximately 1200 tons per day of lime caustic soda was produced during the first eight months of 1958. This represented an increase of about 260 tons per day over the 1957 average and comprises nearly 11 per cent of the total caustic production in 1958. The corresponding figure for 1957 was 7.9 per cent. The Bureau of the Census, after August 31, 1958, is not separating lime soda and electrolytic caustic production figures.

Production of electrolytic caustic exceeded that of lime-soda caustic for the first time in 1940.

Caustic Soda by Causticizing

Soda ash in the form of a 20 per cent solution is treated with milk of lime in slight excess, in a tank fitted with an agitator. The solution is warm (85° C, 185° F). After an hour, the agitator is stopped and the precipitated calcium carbonate settles; the strong (12 per cent NaOH) caustic liquor is decanted. Wash water is run into the agitator, and after some time is allowed to settle out its mud; the clear liquor is run off to the weak liquor tank. The mud is washed once more, yielding the *wash* which is run to the wash water tank. The mud is discharged from the tank; it may be carted to the dump, or it may be filtered and calcined, yielding a lime suitable for further causticizing. The first and second liquors are evaporated to 50 per cent NaOH concentration in single- or multiple-effect evaporators, and if solid caustic is desired, to the final strength of 98 per cent or better in cast-iron pots over a free flame. In many plants, the 12 per cent NaOH liquor is used directly.

It has been found that choosing the concentrations of the reacting liquors as stated gives a good conversion (98 per cent) in the reaction

$$Na_2CO_3 + Ca(OH)_2 \rightleftarrows 2NaOH + CaCO_3$$

and yet does not impose too high a fuel cost for evaporation. The lime is slaked with just enough of the wash to form the hydrate, and then with only as much more as is required to make the milk; so prepared, the rate of settling of the calcium carbonate is 1.5 ft per hr instead of 0.28, when making the milk at once. Using a rotary slaker, the rate of settling becomes 7.81 ft per hr.[25] To utilize all the wash water, solid soda ash and the solid slaked lime may be fed into it.

Instead of batch operation, which the description just given presents, continuous operation may be secured, with classifiers for purifying the milk of lime, and thickeners to hasten the separation of mud from clear liquor. The two best-known systems are the Dorr and the Mount. In the study of the evaporation of the caustic liquor to high strengths, the use of diphenyl vapors around a nickel tube was found promising.[1]

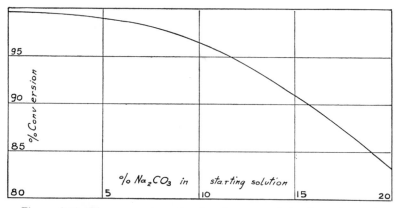

Figure 6.10. The conversion of soda ash to caustic by lime, for various concentrations of the soda ash in the starting liquor. The lime added is $Ca(OH)_2$ with no additional water.

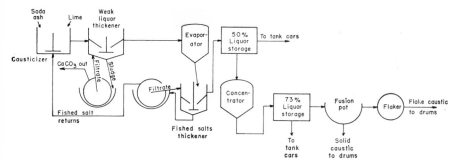

Figure 6.11. A flow diagram for the lime-soda process for making caustic soda. (*Courtesy Columbia-Southern Chemical Corp.*)

An analysis of caustic soda made by causticizing soda ash manufactured by the ammonia soda process, reveals that such caustic has a low chloride content, an important consideration in many uses. The composition is:

	Per Cent
NaOH	98.62
NaCl	0.30
Na_2CO_3	0.90
Na_2SO_4	0.18

Caustic Soda by Electrolysis of Brine

In tonnage, electrolytic caustic soda exceeds that made by causticizing; it represents, moreover, a totally different method of working, namely, the application of an electric current to chemical decompositions and regroupings.

Many cells have been devised in which the decomposition of salt in water solution may be performed. They may be listed under three heads: diaphragm cells; mercury cells; and the bell-jar type, without diaphragm and without mercury. The first diaphragm cell was the Townsend cell, which is represented in modified forms by the Allen-Moore, Nelson, Gibbs, Vorce, Hooker, Dow Bi-polar, and other cells. The original mercury cell was the Castner, also the invention of an American, which is still used in its original form in one plant.

For all cells it is customary to purify the salt solution and to use it as strong as possible, that is, not far from saturated, about 25 per cent NaCl. The manufacture of caustic soda in diaphragm cells, in a few words, involves the preparation and purification of the saturated salt solution; electrolysis of this solution in the cell, wherein half the salt is transformed into caustic; concentration of this mixed solution with separation of the salt as the concentration rises; and final evaporation to anhydrous caustic. For the mercury cells, the procedure is about the same, but the caustic liquor issuing from the cell is free from salt. This is an important advantage if the liquor is to be used as produced; it requires no concentration. The liquor issuing from the diaphragm cell, with as much salt as caustic, could not be used as such for most purposes. For the manufacture of solid caustic, the diaphragm cells produce a final product with 2 per cent NaCl; this small amount sometimes is not objectionable for the important applications of caustic. The great purity in this respect of caustic from mercury cells (0.004 per cent NaCl) does not bring it a premium. The general procedure for bell-jar type cells is similar to that for diaphragm cells.

The decomposition efficiency of cells varies between 50 and 60 per cent. Decomposition efficiency is the ratio of the salt decomposed to the total salt; thus if 6 parts of salt are decomposed into caustic, and 4 parts of salt remain unchanged in the liquor (both determined by titration), the decomposition efficiency is 60 per cent. The decomposition voltage for commercial cells lies between 3.5 and 5, with 4.5 perhaps an average. The theoretical decomposition voltage for NaCl in water solution is 2.25.* The voltage efficiency is the theoretical decomposition voltage divided by the actual decomposition voltage, here $2.25 \div 4.5 \times 100 = 50$ per cent. The actual voltage applied

---

* This value is based on the Gibbs-Helmholtz equation, and takes into account the heats of formation of the substances represented in the equation $NaCl + H_2O \rightarrow NaOH + \frac{1}{2}Cl_2 + \frac{1}{2}H_2$.

will vary with the current density desired, that is, the number of amperes per square unit of surface of electrode; the higher the current density, the higher the voltage necessary. A part of the difference in energy represented by the voltage figures appears as heat; the temperature of the diaphragm cell, for instance, maintains itself at about 60° C. In general, the rough estimate is made that the potential drop for each cell is 5 volts.

The current efficiency, or better, the cathodic current efficiency, varies from 90 to 96 per cent in the best-designed cells, under even running; it may drop to 75 per cent or even less, for a variety of causes. The cathodic current efficiency is the weight of caustic formed divided by the theoretical weight of caustic which the amount of current per hour (ampere hour, independent of voltage) should have formed (1.491 g), multiplied by 100.

The energy efficiency is the product of the voltage efficiency and the current efficiency, here $0.96 \times 0.50 \times 100 = 48$ per cent.

The amount of current required to liberate a gram-equivalent at each pole is the faraday, which is equal to 96,580 coulombs (1 coulomb = 1 ampere-second). One ampere-hour equals 3600 coulombs, so that the amount of material liberated by 1 ampere-hour is:

$$\text{Chlorine } \frac{3600}{96,580} \times 35.46 = 1.3218 \text{ g}$$

$$\text{Caustic } \frac{3600}{96,580} \times 40.01 = 1.4913 \text{ g}$$

The Electrolytic Cell

The two cells in Figure 6.12 show the essential parts of an electrolytic cell. The current, which is always direct current, is said to enter at the anode

Figure 6.12. Cells for the electrolysis of solutions of sodium chloride in water. The chloride ion Cl^-, forms chlorine gas at the anodes, marked A and C; the hydrogen ion, H^+ forms hydrogen gas at the cathodes; the latter are marked B and D. A diaphragm divides the anode brine compartment from the cathode compartment.

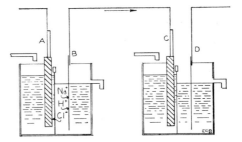

and to leave at the cathode.* In a brine, there are present sodium ions (Na^+) and chloride ions (Cl^-), as well as ions resulting from the ionization of water, i.e., the hydrogen ion (H^+) and the hydroxyl ion (OH^-). After the current is applied, the chloride ions give up their negative charge (one electron) and become yellow chlorine gas, Cl_2. The hydrogen ions acquire an

* It would be more satisfactory to say that electrons enter at the cathode and leave at the anode, but the general custom will be observed.

electron each at the cathode, and form the hydrogen molecule (hydrogen gas). There are many more Na^+ ions than H^+ ions present at any time, but the single potential for hydrogen is lower than that for sodium.* As soon as the hydrogen ions present have deposited, more are formed by ionization of the water molecule, a process which takes place at a rate approaching the speed of light. The Na^+ ions thus remain undisturbed during the action of the current on the brine. The OH^- ions, constantly formed by the ionization of the water, accumulate at a rate which equals that of chlorine ion discharge, so that the Na^+ ions are matched in number by the newly formed OH^- ions. The reaction may be written:

$$Na^+ + Cl^- + H^+ + OH^- \rightarrow Na^+ + \tfrac{1}{2}Cl_2 + \tfrac{1}{2}H_2 + OH^-$$

This is the process which goes on in the diaphragm cell. In the mercury cell, the deposition of hydrogen ions at the mercury cathode does not occur, because the mercury cannot accept them; here, the Na^+ ion functions, by acquiring an electron and dissolving as sodium metal in the mercury. In a second chamber, the amalgam first formed is denuded of its sodium, forming with water Na^+ again, and liberating hydrogen, which in turn leaves an equivalent number of OH^- ions to form the caustic soda in solution:

$$2Na + 2H_2O \rightarrow 2NaOH + H_2$$

Returning to the diaphragm cells, it should be noted that they are so connected that the current leaving at the cathode of one cell enters at the anode of the next. The path of the current lies through the metallic bar to the anode, through the liquid to the cathode opposite, through a metallic connection to the next anode, and so on to the last cathode, which is connected to the terminal at the generator. As it passes through the metal, the current causes no change (no chemical change); but as it goes through the brine, the decomposition takes place. In the Townsend cell, caustic gradually accumulates near the cathode; to prevent it from diffusing toward the anode, a wall may be placed in the cell, forming two compartments. The wall allows slow passage of the solution and free passage to the sodium ions; by keeping the level in the anode chamber higher than in the cathode chamber, the hydrostatic flow is toward the cathode, nullifying the diffusion tendency of the NaOH toward the anode. The permeable wall is usually asbestos fibers supported on an ion screen, and is called the *diaphragm*.

Purification of the Salt Solution

The salt may be in the form of a natural brine, an artificial brine, or rock salt. The purification of the latter includes such steps as may be required

* The deposition potential for H^+ from a solution with pH 7 is about 0.414 volt; even with a hydrogen overvoltage on iron of 0.8 v, the total is only 1.213 v. The single potential for sodium is 2.7146 v in a normal solution of sodium ions, somewhat less in the 4.3 normal solution here. The hydrogen ions therefore deposit first.

for the brines. The salt is conveyed from hopper cars into an underground hopper feeding an inclined belt elevator or bucket elevator by means of which it is raised to the dissolving tank. This is kept filled, and warm water is pumped in at the base and allowed to overflow at the top; during its passage through the salt it becomes saturated. Instead of a wooden tank, a concrete tower may be used. The brine is collected in the treating tank, where sodium carbonate is added in amounts just sufficient to precipitate the calcium and magnesium salts. After settling to remove the coarse suspended particles, the cloudy liquor is decanted periodically into a series of large, wooden or metal settling tanks which function at the same time as storage. The tanks are in series, and the brine overflows very slowly from one to the next, so that they function as catch basins. The solution passing from the last basin is almost clear. It is filter-pressed; but the content of solid is so low that the press need be opened but once a week. Instead of filter-pressing, the brine may be filtered through a sand bed. The filtered salt solution, containing about 25 per cent NaCl, is elevated to a tank above the cells and fed through a constant-level boot to a pipe with side branch for each cell. The method of regulating the amount fed to the cell varies considerably; one of the simpler schemes is to insert a horizontal plate with small orifice in the vertical branch leading to the anode compartment, with a glass sleeve immediately below the orifice plate to permit observation of flow. The size of the orifice determines the rate of flow.

Diaphragm Cells

All diaphragm cells embody the principle of enclosing the anode compartment by a diaphragm, as originally proposed by C. P. Townsend; therefore, they are all referred to as Townsend cells. However, the modified constructions of the later cells have been of the greatest importance; furthermore, they differ from each other radically. It is chiefly for convenience that they are grouped together under the same name. Of these modified Townsend cells, a sub-group would be formed by the Townsend-Baekeland[2] and Hooker cells, which are evidently related. Both have liquor in the cathode compartment, the kerosene in the Townsend-Baekeland cell being replaced by caustic liquor, with a residual salt content, in the Hooker cell.[28] It seems certain that no cell remains in commercial operation with kerosene in the cathode compartment, so that the Hooker cell may be taken as typical of the diaphragm cells which have liquor in the cathode compartment.

The Hooker "S" Cell. The Hooker "S" cell (Figure 6.14) is essentially square in cross section. It consists of a concrete top piece, a concrete bottom piece (set on short legs), and a central steel frame which carries the iron wire mesh forming the multi-fingered cathode.[39] The latter is also the support for the asbestos diaphragm, an unbroken mat formed by plunging the steel cathode into a suspension of 40 lb of asbestos fibers in cell liquor

Figure 6.13. Electrolytic cell room before the installation of cells is complete. Graphite anodes are exposed here. Later, the cathode assembly and concrete cell tops are placed over the anodes. (*Courtesy Hooker Chemical Corp.*)

Figure 6.14. View of Hooker "S" cell with the middle section, the cathode section, in place. (*Courtesy Hooker Chemical Corp.*)

and applying suction to the cathode chamber. The anode is part of the bottom section. It is made of impregnated graphite slabs set in a bitumen-covered lead base plate which receives the current; the slabs reach up from below between the fingers of the cathode, so that every vertical face of the cathode and diaphragm is close to a similar graphite surface. A single broad-faced connection at the cathode of one cell carries the current the short distance to the single stout rod feeding the anode of the next cell. The construction will be clearer after examination of Figure 6.15. The cell, closely

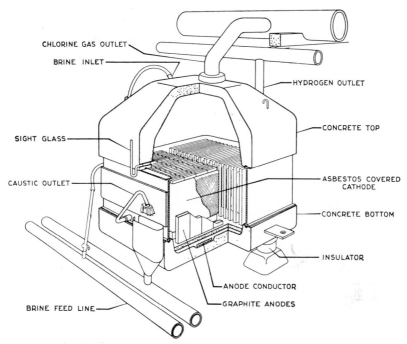

CHLORINE GAS OUTLET

BRINE INLET

HYDROGEN OUTLET

CONCRETE TOP

SIGHT GLASS

CAUSTIC OUTLET

ASBESTOS COVERED CATHODE

CONCRETE BOTTOM

INSULATOR

ANODE CONDUCTOR

GRAPHITE ANODES

BRINE FEED LINE

Figure 6.15. Hooker-type "S-3B" cell. (*Courtesy Hooker Chemical Corp.*)

packed as it is with anode and cathode branches, has a 4-inch central passage for anolyte circulation.

The brine is preheated to 60° C (140° F) and enters the cell in the dome (see sketch); the stream of brine breaks into drops, so that there is no electrical conductivity from the cell to pipes and heaters outside the cell. Its content of salt (NaCl) is 322 g per liter, essentially a saturated solution. The cell works at a temperature of 90° C (194° F). The chlorine gas outlet is in the dome, a stoneware pipe connected to a larger stoneware header. The hydrogen leaves the upper level of the cathode chamber through an iron pipe, insulated by a rubber sleeve coupling. The caustic dribbles out from the lower part of cathode chamber through an adjustable outlet, so that the level of caustic in the chamber can be controlled.

The voltage drop per cell when the cell is new is 3.4 v; as time passes, the anode surfaces become imperfect, and the voltage gradually rises to a final 4.4, when the anode section is renewed. The current density* at the anode for the 7000-amp cell is 0.446 amp per sq in., and at the cathode, 0.377 amp per sq in. The level of the brine may be observed by means of a sight glass; as the cell ages, it rises, producing a higher head, in order to overcome plugging in the diaphragm and maintain a given flow of cathode liquor. The diaphragm is replaced on an average of 4 times per anode run. The life of the anode section is about 365 days. In the 10,500-amp cell,

Figure 6.16. Several of Hooker's latest design Type S-3B electrolytic cells in four rows have a rated daily capacity to produce 110 tons of 50% and 73% liquid caustic soda, 100 tons of chlorine, and 1,000,000 cubic feet of hydrogen. (*Courtesy Hooker Chemicals Limited, Canada*)

the loss of graphite averages about 5½ lb per ton of chlorine produced. The construction of the cell is such as to allow the vertical removal of the upper section and of the cathode section, a feature which saves floor space. As spare sections are always in readiness, a change can be made in a few hours. The energy efficiency is 65 per cent; the ampere efficiency is of the order of 97 per cent.

At the higher temperature of operation,† chlorine is less soluble in the anolyte, and a smaller amount of chlorate forms.

The caustic liquor produced contains on an average 11.3 per cent NaOH, 15 per cent NaCl and 0.1 per cent $NaClO_3$. The gas in the chlorine header

* The current density means the current is amperes per unit surface. An increase in current density requires an increase in voltage.

† The higher the temperature, the less the resistance; higher than 90° C is avoided because of the greater action of the products on the cell walls.

contains on a dry basis, 97.5 per cent Cl_2, 1.4 per cent CO_2, 0.8 per cent O_2, 0.2 per cent H_2 and 0.1 per cent N_2. The hydrogen gas, except for moisture, is essentially pure; it is under a slight positive pressure. The chlorine line is under a slight negative pressure.

The 10,500-amp cell produces 790 lb of caustic (NaOH), 685 lb of chlorine and 3560 cu ft of hydrogen per day.

Nelson Cell. In the Nelson cell, as also in the Allen-Moore, Gibbs, Vorce, and several other cells, the cathode compartment contains no liquor; the caustic solution, with residual salt, runs down the diaphragm and collects at the base. In the Nelson cell, steam is sent into the cathode space to maintain the temperature near 65° C (149° F). The form of the cell is again a narrow rectangular box set up as the Hooker cell is; the Allen-Moore has a similar outside appearance. There is only one row of suspended graphite anodes, and the usual size unit receives 1000 amp; the current density is 50 amp per sq ft, half of that in the Hooker cell. The voltage is lower, averaging 3.7 v. Among other advantages, this cell produces a very pure chlorine; for this reason it was chosen for the installation at Edgewood arsenal during the first World War:[19] 3500 Nelson cells furnished 100 tons of chlorine per day; the anodic ampere efficiency (for chlorine) was 90 per cent; the caustic liquor was maintained 10 to 12 per cent NaOH and 14 to 16 per cent NaCl.

Allen-Moore Cell. The Allen-Moore cell[23] has usually 1700 ampere units, working with a voltage of 3.6; the cathodic current efficiency is maintained at 95 per cent over extended periods. The caustic liquor contains 8 to 10 per cent NaOH and about 12 per cent NaCl. The cell is constructed of concrete and cast-iron sides, and has in general the shape of a narrow rectangular box. The basic principle of the unsubmerged cathode, that is, of using an empty cathode compartment, was first proposed by the designers of the Allen-Moore cell.[29]

The cell described by L. D. Vorce[30] is cylindrical, and is said to furnish more caustic per square foot of floor space than any other cell. Another cylindrical cell used in Canada, and by the United Alkali Company of Great Britain, is the Gibbs cell,[20] patented in 1907.[3] The units are of 1000-amp capacity, requiring 3.6 v; the floor space occupied is small.

The Hargreaves-Bird cell produces sodium carbonate solution. The caustic soda primarily formed is changed to the carbonate at once by carbon dioxide and steam injected into the cathode compartment. The Griesheim cell has magnetic anodes, and solid salt is fed into the anode liquor.

Concentration of the Caustic Liquor

The liquor flowing from the cathode compartment contains both caustic and salt, for the diaphragm cells just discussed. The solution contains about 12 per cent NaOH and 12 per cent NaCl. It is concentrated in a

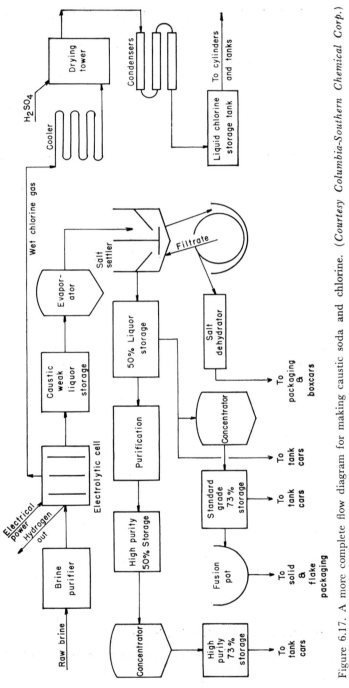

Figure 6.17. A more complete flow diagram for making caustic soda and chlorine. (*Courtesy Columbia-Southern Chemical Corp.*)

double-effect evaporator, for example, and each boiling pen may have its own separator in which the salt is collected as fast as it separates from solution, so that the heating surface in the pan may always be swept by liquor. When a batch of cell liquor has been concentrated to 50 per cent NaOH, only 1 per cent of salt remains in the solution. The suspension from pan and separator is pumped to a settler with Monel wire over a conical base; the salt settles on the wire, the caustic liquor collects in the cone. The liquor passes to cooling tanks, where any salt in suspension is carefully removed by settling. The 50 per cent NaOH liquor is concentrated further in some plants to a 70 per cent concentration in a single vacuum pan heated with

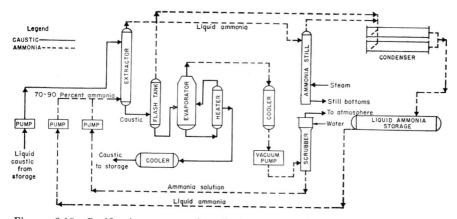

Figure 6.18. Purification process for diaphragm caustic liquor using anhydrous ammonia as extracting medium. (*Courtesy Columbia-Southern Chemical Corp.*)

high-pressure steam. The liquid caustic, which is sold as such, offers several advantages: it may be handled in pipes; no drum containers are necessary; less labor and less fuel are required in its production in comparison with solid caustic; and it is in the form in which the customer applies it. In order to produce anhydrous caustic, the 50 or 70 per cent is boiled down in cast-iron pots heated by an oil fire, until all the water is evaporated. The liquid anhydrous caustic, with perhaps 2 per cent NaCl, is removed from the pots by a centrifugal pump.[20] The liquid caustic is pumped to thin steel drums on low trucks; after cooling, the mass is solid. The weight of a "solid" caustic drum is generally 700 lb net. The anhydrous caustic is also produced in flake form by use of a rotary drum flaker and Hummer screen to obtain desired size. It is packaged in 400 lb drums. More recently, some anhydrous caustic soda manufacturers have achieved success in packaging the flake product in 100-lb polyethylene lined multi-wall bags. The use of bags is more economical since they cost less than the drums and are more easily handled.

The salt in the settlers is washed a number of times by liquors of decreasing caustic content; it is made up to a soft mush and pumped to the dissolver, re-entering the system with the raw salt solution.

More and more evaporators are being equipped with nickel tubes, and also with nickel-clad walls wherever they come into contact with caustic liquors. In some recent installations for the manufacture of anhydrous caustic soda, the liquor is evaporated to the anhydrous state continuously with shell and tube heat exchangers. The tubes in such an exchanger are made of Inconel and the heat transfer agent is either hot gas, molten salt or "Dowtherm" (diphenyl and diphenyl oxide). Product quality, cost and safety favor the continuous process for manufacture of anhydrous caustic soda over the old direct-fired batch-pot method.

For use in making viscose rayon, a caustic soda with a low chloride content, such as 0.15 per cent NaCl on the 100 per cent basis, is required. The excess NaCl in the caustic liquor from diaphragm cells may be reduced in one of several ways: (1) Hydrates such as $NaOH \cdot 3.5H_2O$ and $NaOH \cdot 2H_2O$ may be crystallized in jacketed crystallizers with agitators, and the crystals filtered off; the liquor carries away the bulk of the sodium chloride. (2) A triple salt may be formed by adding sodium sulfate, which binds NaCl as $NaOH \cdot NaCl \cdot Na_2SO_4$, insoluble in 35 per cent caustic solution, and on filtering removes it.[18] (3) Liquid ammonia may be used for the extraction of NaCl and the small amount of sodium chlorate, $NaClO_3$, present.[8] In general, there is no difficulty in selling caustic from diaphragm cells.

The Mercury Cell

In the mercury cell working on brine, the cathode consists of mercury, and the anode of graphite. There is no diaphragm. The salt in solution is decomposed, the sodium ion accepting an electron and forming a sodium metal ion, which dissolves in the mercury.

The chlorine is liberated, as before, in the form of a yellow gas. These events take place in one of the chambers of the cell, the electrolyzing chamber. The amalgam is then transferred, by tilting the cell, by pumping, or in other ways, to the denuding chamber containing water, where the sodium metal reacts to form hydrogen gas and a solution of caustic

$$2Na + 2H_2O \rightarrow 2NaOH + H_2$$

In the original form of the Castner cell,[10] the removal of the amalgam to the denuding chamber is by tilting, about once a minute, through a distance of one-half inch. The cell consists of a low box with three long chambers; each of the two electrolyzing compartments has a graphite anode and mercury cathode; an iron grid on legs rests over the amalgam layer. The longitudinal partitions reach into grooves which the mercury seals, but past which it can travel on tilting. Other details are: rich brine enters the electrolyzing compartment, and depleted brine leaves it; the denuding chamber receives water, while the caustic solution leaves it. The units are 1000-amp units, the voltage being about 4; a liquor containing 50 per cent NaOH is generally obtained. Further concentration of the caustic, when performed, is greatly simplified by the absence of salt.

In the United States, the mercury cells now installed are the Sorensen, I.C.I.-Wyandotte, Solvay et Cie, De Nora, and Hochst-Uhde. Mercury cells

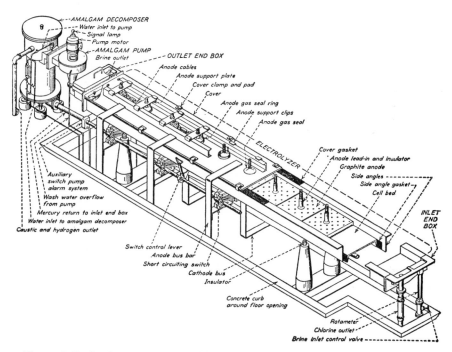

Figure 6.19. Stationary mercury cell with electrolyzing chamber separate from decomposing chamber. (Courtesy Mathieson Chemical Corp.) [*Reproduced from Chemical Engineering*, **54**, (1947) by permission.]

have been in favor with many European countries for many years and consequently many developments and improvements in mercury-cell technology have resulted. Today, some cells, depending on cathodic and anodic surface, are known to operate as high as 200,000 amp. The drum-type vertical mercury cell (also I. G. Farben) in various large sizes runs as high as 40,000 amp. In the latter cell,[6] the cathode is a steel drum with 5 circular disks, which turn in an appropriate space with the anodes as walls (upper part). The speed of rotation is 7 rpm. The lower part of the drum contains mercury, through which the cathode disks travel in the lower half of their path. The steel cathode becomes coated with mercury, which accepts the discharged sodium, carrying it into the basin of mercury where it distributes itself as a dilute amalgam. The amalgam is pumped into the decomposer where water reacts with the sodium, giving caustic and hydrogen; the mercury then returns to the cell.

A mercury cell,[11] installed at Arvida, in Quebec, Canada, is operating successfully. It has a long, narrow electrolyzing chamber; the amalgam passes to a smaller, tower-type, cylindrical decomposer where pure water is fed in to make caustic solutions containing up to 50 per cent very pure NaOH. A pump functions between the electrolyzer and decomposer.

Mercury and diaphragm cells have been compared from time to time, with mercury cells winning most favor. However, the advantages offered by mercury cells are far from clear and are often negated by disadvantages. Their superiority in producing low-chloride content caustic soda is un-challenged.

Typical mercury-cell caustic contains 0.002–0.001 per cent of sodium chloride, compared with about 1 per cent in the product from diaphragm cells. The latter may be reduced to 0.16 per cent when purified. Although the rayon trade must have low chloride material, most users don't need it.

The use of mercury cells is held back partly by the fact that they are not available from U. S. firms. Olin Mathieson and Dow Chemical Company have developed their own mercury cells within the past few years. An Italian firm, De Nora, has had the greatest impact on the U. S. mercury cell picture.

Regardless of inroads made by mercury cells, diaphragm cells maintain an important position. The latter cells are limited to about 30,000 amp in size and require more numerous parts and connections than mercury cells. It would seem that mercury cells will find greatest use in larger installations. It is probable that diaphragm cells will retain the bulk of electrolytic-cell chlorine and caustic for at least the next several years.

The Bell-Jar Type Cell. In the Billiter cell,[4] the graphite anode is suspended in a bell-like housing, from which the chlorine is drawn off; the cathode consists of a number of iron rods slightly inclined from the horizontal; each rod is surrounded by a tight asbestos tube. At the edge of the jar, the rods and tubes rise upward; as the hydrogen is evolved along the rods, it travels upward, carrying with it the caustic liquor, which is delivered to a small receiving chamber in each cell, from which it is sent to the evaporators. The brine entry into the bell is such that the flow is toward the cathode, and as the caustic is carried out as fast as formed, it does not interfere with the passage of the current.

The estimated distribution of caustic soda and chlorine is given in Table 6.7.

TABLE 6.7. CHLORINE—CAUSTIC SODA END-USE PATTERN 1957*

Chlorine[a]	%	Caustic Soda[b]	%
Miscellaneous chemicals	83.0	Miscellaneous chemicals	30.6
Pulp and paper	13.0	Rayon and film	16.9
Others	4.0	Pulp and paper	8.3
		Metallurgical	7.5
		Export	6.8
		Petroleum refining	6.3
		Lye and cleansers	4.5
		Textiles	3.7
		Soap	1.6
		Others	13.8
Total	100.0	Total	100.0

* Report of the Chlor-Alkali Committee of the Industrial Electrolytic Division of the Electrochemical Society for the year 1958.
[a] *Chemical Week*, March 7, 1959, p. 116 (for more detailed breakdown, see "Chemical Week," May 26, 1956).
[b] *Chemical Week*, Jan. 18, 1958, p. 76.

By-Products of Electrolytic Caustic Soda

Hydrogen from the cathode chamber and chlorine from the anode chamber are the by-products of electrolytic caustic soda. In a chemical center such as Niagara Falls, N. Y., any surplus is sold to other industries and the demand is sufficient to justify a hydrogen pipe distribution system. The chlorine may be burned in an excess of hydrogen to give extremely pure synthetic hydrogen chloride, which, dissolved in water, gives hydrochloric acid. A submerged combustion burner has been described.[22] The hydrogen is largely used in catalytic hydrogenation or as fuel. The chlorine, how-ever, is the more important by-product of the two; it is produced at an ever-increasing rate.

TABLE 6.8. SOURCES OF CHLORINE*

	1957		1958 (preliminary)	
	Tons	%	Tons	%
Cl_2 equiv. of NaOH	3,549,000	89.9	3,235,000	89.9
Cl_2 equiv. of KOH	48,000	1.2	44,000	1.2
Cl_2 equiv. of Na	205,000	5.2	170,000	4.7
Cl_2 equiv. (other sources)	146,000	3.7†	151,000	4.2
Cl_2 total gas produced	3,948,000	100.0	3,600,000	100.0

* Report of the Chlor-Alkali Committee of the Industrial Electrolytic Division of the Electrochemical Society for the year 1958.
† By difference.

The chlorine is produced mainly in electrolyses of brine of magnesium chloride, and of fused salt (NaCl). Several thousand tons stem from the nitrosyl chloride process, and from the electrolysis of potassium chloride.

There are market conditions which alter the relation between caustic soda and chlorine, so that the first product of the cell is more truly chlorine, while the caustic is the by-product.

Liquid Chlorine. Gaseous chlorine is easily changed to an amber liquid; this circumstance has extended its usefulness considerably over that of the gas. At $0°$ C ($32°$ F), a pressure slightly over 39 lb will cause liquefaction; at $-20°$ C ($-4°$ F), slightly over 12 lb is needed; at $-33.5°$ C ($-28.5°$ F), only a little over atmospheric pressure is required. A temperature of $-20°$ C may be obtained with an ammonia refrigerating system, brine or gas, while $-40°$ C ($-40°$ F) is obtained by a carbon dioxide system.

The chlorine gas leaves the anode or electrolyzer portion of the cell warm and moist. In such a condition, the wet gas can be handled only in pipes and equipment impervious to its acidic attack. Leakage of hydrogen, or production of hydrogen in the electrolyzer portion of the cell is guarded against carefully because the two gases, chlorine and hydrogen, are explosive over a very wide range of concentrations. The chlorine gas passes along pipes of stoneware, rubber or saran-lined steel, or polyvinyl chloride (PVC) to a cooling tower where the moisture content of the raw gas is reduced by cooling. Cold water is used as the coolant, passing countercurrent to the warm moist gas from the cells. The gas is then dried by passing countercurrent to a stream of strong sulfuric acid. Once the gas is cooled and dried it can be handled in steel pipes or equipment. The gas next reaches a Nash Hytor compressor whose multibladed impeller works in sulfuric acid held in an elliptical casting. For each revolution, there are two compressions and two expansions of the working fluid caused by the shape of the casing; the alternate compression and expansion move the gas. Pressures up to 60 lb are developed with these compressors. The compressed gas is passed through steel pipes to a liquefying unit where it is subjected to cold surface temperatures which cause it to liquefy at the existing pressure in the system. Many systems exist for liquefying chlorine, the most common today being carbon dioxide double pipe coils, or shell and tube heat exchangers using Freon and Genetron refrigerants. The gaseous chlorine liquefies at a rapid rate, and is piped to a steel storage tank. Any of the less compressible gases present as impurities, such as hydrogen, carbon dioxide and air, are vented to bleach chambers or special absorbers.

Chlorine gas may also be compressed in reciprocating compressors to either a low pressure (relatively), requiring refrigeration for liquefaction, or higher pressure with moderate cooling.

Nitrosyl Process. A non-electrolytic chlorine process is in successful operation thanks to skillful engineering, and to the relative inexpensiveness of synthetic nitric acid. The over-all operation consists of reacting concentrated nitric acid with salt (NaCl) to produce sodium nitrate and chlorine. Nitrosyl chloride, NOCl, is also a product of the first reaction, and it may be utilized with the aid of nitrous acid, itself produced by means of a portion of the nitrosyl chloride. Important reactions are:

$$3NaCl + 4HNO_3 \rightarrow 3NaNO_3 + Cl_2 + NOCl + 2H_2O$$
$$NOCl + H_2O \rightarrow HNO_2 + HCl$$
$$2NOCl + 3HNO_2 + 3O_2 + H_2O \rightarrow 5HNO_3 + Cl_2$$

The nitrosyl chloride, a gas above 22° F (—5° C), is also in increasing demand for use as such, and is marketed, in part, as a liquefied gas under pressure.

A second non-electrolytic process for chlorine is a modern version of the Deacon process, in which oxygen (tonnage oxygen), instead of air, with an improved copper chloride catalyst, is employed. Hydrogen chloride is oxidized to chlorine and water at a temperature of 650° C (1202° F).

A third process well investigated during the war, involving the action of sulfur trioxide upon salt, and another which rests upon the decomposition of chlorosulfonic acid, have not become established commercially. Both the two latter processes have one of their difficulties in common, the separation of chlorine from an equimolar mixture of sulfur dioxide and itself.[21]

Shipping Liquid Chlorine. Liquid chlorine is shipped in 50- and 100-lb steel cylinders and in 1-ton steel containers of which 15 are placed on a specially equipped railroad flatcar. In addition to these containers which are usually purchased by consumers of small amounts of chlorine, liquid chlorine is shipped in single-unit tank cars of 16, 30 and 55 net-ton capacity. Moreover, liquid chlorine is also shipped in barges along inland waterways. Such barges have capacities up to 640 net tons liquid chlorine. A barge is equipped with four or six tanks to hold the chlorine. A recent innovation is the shipment of liquid chlorine by tank truck. This truck is of special design and has a carrying capacity of 16 net tons liquid chlorine. The use of such special equipment for truck hauling of liquid chlorine poses its own unique problems. Consequently, it is too early to determine any trend from railroad to tank truck shipment. Many chlorine-producing installations also pipe liquid or gaseous chlorine to other plant units for various chlorination operations. Pumps of special design are used in many installations to move liquid chlorine from one part of a plant to another.

The 1-ton unit is very convenient for making the bleach at the pulp or other mill, because the required quantity of milk of lime may be prepared and all the chlorine in the cylinder allowed to pass in without danger of wasting any. Calcium hypochlorite, $Ca(OCl)_2$, and calcium chloride, $CaCl_2$, are formed. All containers have one or two internal pipes, so that either the gas or the liquid may be drawn. If the gas is drawn, heat must be supplied to make up for the heat of vaporization, or else the process is very slow. It is more convenient and simple to use the liquid, mixing it directly with the milk of lime in a small mixing chamber;[40] in that way the process of vaporization uses a part of the heat of reaction of chlorine on lime. In summer, this is important in keeping the temperature of the mixture below 40° C; above that point the calcium hypochlorite is unstable.*

For the chlorination of municipal water supplies, and for any other chlorination away from the manufacturing plant, chlorine in the liquid form is preferred. It serves mainly indirectly in the manufacture of a host of chlorine compounds which are essential for the effective prosecution of a war. During World War II, all chlorine production was under Government allocation. Besides helping to maintain healthful water supplies, chlorine is used for fire extinguishers (CCl_4), solvents and degreasing agents, and for bleaching textiles, paper, and many other products.

Gaseous Chlorine and Bleach. Chlorine gas at the generating plant is used, without compression to the liquid, to make *bleach*, and for the chlorination of organic substances such as benzene, toluene, pentane, and others.

Bleaching powder is the product of the interaction of chlorine gas and hydrated lime:

$$Ca(OH)_2 + Cl_2 \rightarrow CaOCl_2 + H_2O$$

The chloride of lime so formed, when dissolved in water, gives equal molecular parts of calcium chloride, which as far as bleaching is concerned, is useless, and calcium hypochlorite, which retains the total bleaching power of the original material

$$2CaOCl_2 \text{ dissolved} \rightarrow CaCl_2 + Ca(OCl)_2$$

Chloride of lime or "bleach" must not be confused with calcium hypochlorite.

The chlorine absorption is performed either in a series of low-ceiling brick chambers, or in patent shelf absorbers which require little space. In either case the countercurrent principle is applied, the fresh gas meeting the richest bleach; the lean gas, the new hydrated lime. The bleach so prepared has been displaced to a considerable degree (1) by liquid chlorine, in mills and factories, (2) by calcium hypochlorite, $Ca(OCl)_2$, a stable material of high test, whereas ordinary bleach spoils after several months, and has a low test (35 per cent available chlorine). Available chlorine means chlorine evolved on addition of acid; 35 per cent available chlorine is a material which has the effectiveness of 35 parts of liquid chlorine. Pure calcium hypochlorite, by the laboratory test applied to all bleaching agents, rates 100 per cent available chlorine.†

* The bleaching solution used in pulp and paper mills is 6° Bé and contains 30 g of available chlorine to the liter.

† The test for available chlorine in bleaching powder consists of acidifying in the presence of potassium iodide. The iodide liberated is titrated. It may be liberated by Cl, but also by oxygen.

Calcium hypochlorite contains 99.7 per cent available chlorine, yet only 50 per cent

High Test Hypochlorite (H.T.H.). Calcium hypochlorite, $Ca(OCl)_2$, essentially free from any other material, in the crystal form, is stable, and efforts to produce it in bulk have been earnest and successful.

One method for its manufacture is the chlorination of a lime slurry followed by the salting out of calcium hypochlorite by means of common salt (NaCl). No organic solvent requiring later recovery is needed. The product may be made essentially 100 per cent $Ca(OCl)_2$, but an additional operation is then required, so that the material actually marketed is 75 per cent $Ca(OCl)_2$. It is therefore twice as strong as ordinary bleach; also it does not spoil on standing, it is not hygroscopic, and when it is made up with water the solution is practically clear.

The latest and most successful method for making high test hypochlorite (H.T.H.) is the formation of the triple salt $Ca(OCl)_2 \cdot NaOCl \cdot NaCl \cdot 12H_2O$ and its subsequent reaction with calcium chloride. The triple salt is made as follows: 40 parts NaOH, 37 parts $Ca(OH)_2$ and 100 parts water are chlorinated at a temperature below 16° C (60.8° F), such as 10° C (50° F). This reaction is:

(a) $4NaOH + Ca(OH)_2 + 3Cl_2 + 9H_2O \rightarrow$
$$Ca(OCl)_2 \cdot NaOCl \cdot NaCl \cdot 12H_2O + 2NaCl$$

The comparatively large hexagonal crystals—the triple salt—separate and are centrifuged. In the meantime a special calcium chloride is prepared by chlorinating a milk of lime in these proportions: 74 parts $Ca(OH)_2$, 213 parts water, 71 parts chlorine; the temperature is held at 25° C (77° F);

(b) $2Ca(OH)_2 + 2Cl_2 \rightarrow Ca(OCl)_2 + CaCl_2 + 2H_2O$

Next, this solution is cooled to 10° C (50° F), the centrifugal crystals are added in the proportion required by the reaction:

(c) $2NaOCl + CaCl_2 \rightarrow 2NaCl + Ca(OCl)_2$

and the suspension is agitated with paddles. On warming to 16° C (60.8° F), reaction (c) takes place and the whole sets to a rigid mass.

---

total chlorine; it is evident that a change in the method of designating the strength of bleaches is desirable. The most logical way would be to state the content of calcium hypochlorite, and this would also be the easiest, for it happens that numerically the "available chlorine" present is almost the same as the calcium hypochlorite content. The chlorine equivalent for calcium hypochlorite is shown by the reactions:

$$Ca(OCl)_2 + H_2SO_4 \rightarrow CaSO_4 + 2HOCl$$
$$2HOCl + 4HI \rightarrow 2H_2O + 4I + 2HCl, \text{ and } 4I \text{ are equivalent to } 4Cl$$

Bleaching was explained formerly as oxidation; today it would be said to be the taking of electrons. A substance which yields fragments (ions) which take up electrons is an oxidizing agent. Measured in that way, oxygen as well as chlorine is a bleaching agent, a fact already well known in an empirical way.

The triple salt $Ca(OCl)_2 \cdot NaOCl \cdot NaCl \cdot 12H_2O$ becomes $1\frac{1}{2}Ca(OCl)_2 \cdot 2H_2O$, the dihydrate, 2NaCl and water. After drying in the vacuum, a material testing 65 to 70 per cent $Ca(OCl)_2$ results. Such calcium hypochlorite as accompanied the calcium chloride is just that much more product. The NaCl content from (c) is not removed.

There are other high-test hypochlorites of calcium on the market, as for example Perchloron.

Sodium chlorite,[27] $NaClO_2$, is a commercial chemical which, combined with chlorine or hypochlorite, gives certain advantages in bleaching paper pulp. It also finds use in connection with the bleaching and finishing of cotton, rayon and Celanese.

REFERENCES

1. Badger, W. L., *et al.*, *Am. Inst. Chem. Eng.*, **24**, 56 (1930).
2. Baekeland, L., *Electrochemical and Metallurgical Industry*, **5**, 209 (1907).
3. British Patent 28,147.
4. British Patent 11,693 (1910).
5. *Chem. Abstracts*, **15**, 3423 (1921).
6. *Chem. Eng.*, **53**, 113 (1946).
7. *Chem. Industries*, **61**, 49 (1947).
8. *Chem. Met. Eng.*, **51**, 119 (August 1944).
9. Clark, L. H., *Ind. Eng. Chem.*, **22**, 439 (1930).
10. *Electrochem. Ind.*, **1**, 11 (1902).
11. Gardiner, W. C., *Chem. Eng.*, **54**, 108 (1947).
12. German Patent 427,539 (1926).
13. German Patent 249,222.
14. German Patent 388,545.
15. German Patent 389,238.
16. German Patent 255,029.
17. German Patent 273,878.
18. German Patent 522,676; U. S. Patents 1,888,886 and 1,998,471.
19. Green, S. M., *Chem. Met. Eng.*, **21**, 17 (1919).
20. *Ind. Eng. Chem.*, **16**, 1056–7 (1924).
21. Johnstone, H. F., *Chem. Eng. Progress*, **44**, 657 (1948).
22. Maude, A. H., *Chem. Eng. Progress*, **44**, 179 (1948).
23. Mitchell, F. H., *Chem. Met. Eng.*, **21**, 370 (1919).
24. Phalen, W. C., *Dept. Interior Bull.* No. 146, 124 (1917).
25. Piper, W. E., *Am. Inst. Chem. Eng.*, **24**, 1 (1930).
25a. Pratt, L. A., *Chem. Met. Eng.*, **31**, 11 (1924).
26. Report of the Chlor-Alkali Committee of the Industrial Electrolytic Division for the year 1958, The Electrochemical Society.
27. Taylor, M. C., *et al.*, *Ind. Eng. Chem.*, **32**, 899 (1940).
28. *Trans. Am. Inst. Chem. Eng.*, **13**, *I*, 55–60 (1920).
29. *Trans. Am. Inst. Chem. Eng.*, **13**, *I*, 11 (1920).
30. *Trans. Am. Inst. Chem. Eng.*, **13**, *I*, 47 (1920).
31. U. S. Patent 1,414,762.
32. U. S. Patent 1,385,595.
33. U. S. Patent 1,132,640.
34. U. S. Patent 1,139,741.

35. U. S. Patent 915,633.
36. U. S. Patent 1,397,497.
37. U. S. Patent 1,130,317.
38. U. S. Patents 1,099,177; 1,084,436; 1,023,179.
39. U. S. Patents 1,862,244; 1,865,152.
40. U. S. Patent 1,481,106.

READING REFERENCES

"The manufacture of soda," T. P. Hou, 2nd ed., New York, Reinhold Publishing Corp., 1942.

Kaufman, D. W., "Sodium Chloride," New York, Reinhold Publishing Corp., 1960.

"Salt-making on the Great Salt Lake," Thomas B. Brighton, *J. Chem. Educ.*, **9**, 407 (1932).

"California desert soda," G. Ross Robertson, *Ind. Eng. Chem.*, **23**, 478 (1931).

"Synthetic hydrogen chloride," Aylmer H. Maude, *Chem. Eng. Progress*, **44**, 179 (1948).

"Absorption and purification of hydrogen chloride from chlorination of hydrocarbons," C. F. Oldershaw, L. Simenson, T. Brown and F. Radcliffe, *Chem. Eng. Progress*, **43**, 371 (1947).

"The story of the Hooker cell," by K. E. Stuart, T. L. B. Lyster, and R. L. Murray, *Chem. Met. Eng.*, **45**, 354–8 (1938).

"Diaphragm vs. amalgam cells" (for chlorine-caustic production), Robert B. MacMullin, *Chemical Ind.*, **61**, 41 (1947).

"New mercury cell makes its bow," W. C. Gardiner, *Chem. Eng.*, **54**, 108 (1947).

"Synthetic hydrogen chloride," Aylmer H. Maude, *Chem. Eng. Prog.*, **44**, 179 (1948).

"Caustic purification by liquid-liquid extraction," H. C. Twiehaus and N. J. Ehlers, *Chem. Ind.*, **63**, 230 (1948).

7

INDUSTRIAL FERMENTATION PROCESSES

In collaboration with Samuel C. Beesch and Fred W. Tanner, Jr.*

INTRODUCTION

FROM TIME IMMEMORIAL, one of the processes which depends on the existence and growth of microorganisms has been utilized, namely, that of alcoholic fermentation of grape juice and fruit juices. Its exact nature remained a mystery until Louis Pasteur discovered, isolated, and classified the several kinds of organisms. He succeeded in demonstrating that fermentation and bacterial disturbances in general are not due to spontaneously generated plant organisms, but to organisms which already exist elsewhere and which are carried in by air currents, on the skin of the fruit, or in other ways. In the century since Pasteur's recognition of the significant role of microorganisms, knowledge of their capabilities has gradually evolved into a flourishing branch of the chemical industry.

Industrial fermentation processes may be best described as that portion of biological science which deals with the possible utilization of microorganisms in processes in which their activity becomes of industrial significance.

Bacteria, yeasts, molds, and actinomycetes are utilized to produce a variety of foods and industrial and medicinal chemicals, many of which cannot

* Chas. Pfizer and Co.

be obtained from other sources. The industry is not static; it faces intense competition from the synthetic chemist, and in fact has gradually changed its products from the rather simple carbon compounds to relatively large molecules, with complex stereochemical and structural characteristics. Ethanol, butanol, and acetone, and some other products produced by fermentation prior to World War II, are now supplied more economically by the petroleum industry. Their place in the fermentation picture is now occupied by many important medicinals including vitamins, antibiotics, and steroids, unknown a decade ago. At the same time, several useful organic acids of fermentation origin have become established. Fermentation citric acid has displaced the acid made from cull fruit, and new acids such as itaconic, kojic, and gluconic are finding industrial applications.

One of the newest applications of microorganisms is in the manufacture of certain steroid hormones, where selected microorganisms yield chemical reactions which can be duplicated by the organic chemist only with great difficulty.

A treatment of industrial fermentation processes involves, of necessity, the use of terms which are in general not familiar to the chemist and chemical engineer. The following discussion should help to define some of the terms used throughout this chapter.

The Microorganism

Microorganisms are found in both plant and animal kingdoms. For the fermentation industry useful members are confined to lower forms of plant life (chorophyll-free) and comprise bacteria, fungi, yeasts, and actinomyces.

All are named by a binomial system according to rules of botanical nomenclature. The first word designates the major group, the second, the particular type or subgroup.

Bacteria are unicellular organisms which multiply by fission. Each cell divides every 20–30 minutes under optimum conditions. Cells may be nearly spherical (coccus) or rod-shaped (Bacterium, Bacillus). Some are characterized by the formation of chains (Streptococcus), but usually the cells grow as separate entities. The average cell length varies from 2–6 microns long, the width being half or less the length (1 micron = .001 mm). Bacteria are classified according to their morphological and physiological characteristics. Among the various reactions are motility, spore formation, and ability to use various sugars for growth. A comprehensive compilation of the characteristics of bacteria and their botanical classification is periodically issued in "Bergey's Manual for Determinative Bacteriology."

Fungi comprise two large groups of microorganisms in the family Eumycetes. These microorganisms normally grow as a filamentous structure known as mycelium (or hyphae). Those with non-septate hyphae are in the sub-family Phycomycetes; those with septate mycelium are in the sub-family Mycomycetes. Though the diameters of hyphae are usually only a fraction of a micron, their lengths may extend to centimeters. Within these groups, they are further subdivided on the basis of modes of spore formation. However, many do not form true spores and are placed in the *Fungi Imperfecti.*

Yeasts are generally distinguished from fungi by their ability to grow as individual cells, either spherical or ellipsoidal, usually 1–5 microns in width and from 1–9 microns in length. They possess a thick membrane or cell wall. Yeasts usually multiply by budding. The true yeasts form ascospores, although non-sporulating yeasts are also found among the *Fungi Imperfecti.*

Standing midway between the true bacteria and the more complex fungi are the *Actinomycetes,* a group which is extremely difficult to classify. They

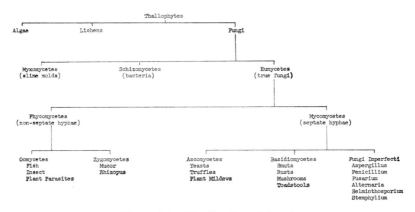

Figure 7.1. Classification of fungi.

are characterized by a delicate mycelium, septate hyphae, and generally show branching. The mycelium frequently fragments into rod- and coccal-like forms.

The general classification of fungi is shown in Figure 7.1.

Microbial Nutrition

The growth and multiplication of microorganisms, like higher plants and animals, depend on proper nutrition. The fundamental food elements necessary for higher forms of life are also required by microorganisms. They include carbohydrate, protein or nitrogen sources, trace metals, vitamins, etc. Some microorganisms possess amazing synthetic abilities; when supplied with relatively simple substrates, such as glucose, inorganic nitrogen, and metal salts, they produce all of the required amino acids and proteins of their cellular structures, the host of complex enzyme systems, and growth (as measured by reproduction) is rapid and satisfactory. Some microbial strains, however, are unable to synthesize one or more essential components of their metabolic systems and these must be supplied in the substrate. Studies of these metabolic deficiencies have led to the discovery of several members of the vitamin B complex and have permitted elucidation of the roles of many biochemical intermediates. One can generalize that those organisms capable of growing rapidly on very simple substrates are endowed with the most prolific synthetic systems and, conversely, the nutritionally fastidious cell is less versatile.

Carbohydrates supply energy for the cells metabolic system, and serve as a source of carbon for its cellular needs. In general, glucose is the fundamental sugar. Disaccharides such as sucrose, maltose, etc., are usually (but not always) hydrolyzed by appropriate enzymes to monosaccharides. Thus maltose is hydrolyzed to 2 moles of glucose. Higher sugars are frequently suitable substrates. Many microorganisms can utilize the various complex carbohydrates, such as starch, while some organisms utilize pentoses.

Carbohydrates frequently represent a substantial portion of the substrate cost so that cheap sources are attractive. Blackstrap molasses, which usually contains about 50 per cent fermentable carbohydrate, is the most abundant low cost source. Invert or hi-test molasses may contain more than 70 per cent fermentable carbohydrate. Beet molasses is also used. Glucose and xylose are found in sulfite liquor now used for feed yeast manufacture in some European countries and the United States.

Nitrogen sources range from simple inorganic ions (NH_4^+, NO_3^-) and urea to proteolytically digested proteins of plant and animal origin. Although growth is satisfactory with the simple nitrogen sources, it is not unusual to obtain improved yields of fermentation products from the more complex materials. Corn steep liquor (a by-product of starch manufacture by the corn wet-milling industry) is almost universally used in penicillin fermentations. Soybean meal is commonly used in *Streptomyces* fermentations for antibiotic production. Corn meal may supply both carbohydrates and nitrogen. The diversity of usable materials depends on the ingenuity of the research worker, availability of the material, and its relative cost. By-products of the processing of agricultural commodities are commonly used.

Metals are frequently required in trace amounts. These usually enter cellular metabolism as components of coenzymes. Natural materials often contain sufficient trace metals to satisfy the requirements. In fermentations producing organic acids, $CaCO_3$ is frequently employed for maintaining the pH in the most productive range by forming calcium salts of the sugar acids. Calcium ions probably serve also in a more fundamental nutritional capacity. Calcium salts of organic acids have limited water solubility and their precipitation in the fermentation medium may increase the problems of product recovery. In such instances, more soluble salts are formed by intermittent neutralizations with NaOH or NH₄OH solutions. These compounds may be introduced automatically if the fermentors are equipped with the proper type of pH control equipment.

Accessory growth factors are required by some organisms not capable of growing on simple inorganic substrates. These are usually resolved into known members of the vitamin B complex (thiamin, riboflavin, pyridoxine, etc.), perhaps some specific amino acids, and even "unidentified growth factors." Material such as corn steep liquor, dried yeast, and oil seed meals furnish good sources of these growth requirements.

Intermediary metabolism of microorganisms is a fascinating study of the mechanisms involved in the release of energy from food. The general principles established for microorganisms are applicable to all forms of life. The classical glucose dissimulation pathways depicted by the Embden-Meyerhoff scheme, coupled with the equally classical Krebs "citric acid cycle," explain the accumulation of such fermentation products as ethanol, butanol, and acetone, and acids such as acetic, fumaric, and citric. Gluconic acid results from an oxidation of glucose by the enzyme "glucose oxidase."

Intermediary metabolism involves a long series of one-step reactions, each mediated by a specific biological catalyst (enzyme). The products of one reaction serve as substrates for the succeeding reaction. If a particular enzyme is missing or inoperable, intermediary products accumulate, and it is this particular feature which explains the production of most fermentation products.

On the other hand, useful complex molecules such as antibiotics result from unexplained syntheses accomplished by the respective microorganisms. The biosynthesis of penicillin has been shown to involve cystine, 1-valine, etc.

Fermentation as a Unit Process

Rather than discuss the methodology and problems of each commercial fermentation, this space can better be devoted to a more general discussion of the principles of fermentation as a unit process. The various steps are similar to those employed in the more common chemical synthesis processes, except for the fact that a biological system is involved. Raw materials for the various fermentation processes are similar, the particular product being dependent on selection of the proper organism. The environment surrounding the organism during the fermentation markedly influences product yields. Finally, the fermentation products must be isolated from the aqueous medium.

The products of the fermentation industry vary widely. Some have a structure very similar to the principal raw material (substrate), while others are quite complex and have no structural relationship to the substrate. Furthermore, fermentation yields may represent nearly stoichiometric conversions of substrate to product, or the product may occur in the broth in minute quantities, measured in parts per million.

Five basic prerequisites of a good fermentation have been suggested:

1. A microorganism must form a useful product. The microorganism must be readily propagated, and must maintain uniform biological and biochemical characteristics to give consistent yields.

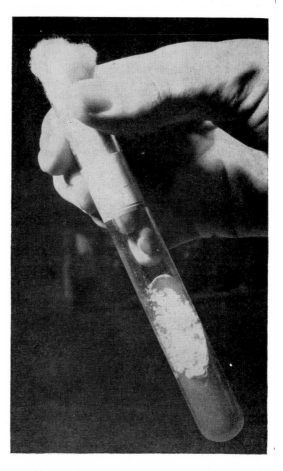

Figure 7.2. An agar slant containing growth of a pure culture of a selected microorganism. (*Courtesy Chas. Pfizer and Co.*)

2. Economically attractive raw materials in good supply and predictably uniform in composition must be available.

3. Acceptable yields must be based on economics.

4. A rapid fermentation time is desirable.

5. The product should be easy to recover and purify.

The microorganism is the heart of the whole synthetic process. It must produce the desired product, preferably with a minimum of by-products. Microbiologists have examined the fermentation products of thousands of cultures isolated from natural habitats, usually soil. From these have been selected strains producing the desired products.

In the laboratory it is generally most convenient to propagate the microorganism on a solid medium. These comprise water-soluble sugars or plant or animal tissue extracts to which a non-nutritive polysaccharide material called agar (manufactured from certain seaweeds) is added. Agar liquefies at 45–50° C and solidifies when cooled to 40° C. The hot medium is placed in test tubes, plugged with cotton, and sterilized by heating under steam pressure (15 psi or 121° C) for 15–30 minutes. During cooling, the tube is tilted to form a "slant" with considerable surface for growth of a microorganism. The same material is also used for culturing microorganisms in flat-bottomed, round, Petri dishes. Viable cultures are maintained on the slants, and stored in refrigerators after good growth is attained.

Preservation of the stock culture is imperative, and should permit long storage with a minimum of effort on the part of laboratory personnel. For instance, viable cells or spores can be maintained in a sterile dry state by lyophilization. Cell or spore suspensions are frozen and the water removed by sublimation, after which the glass tubes are sealed with an oxygen flame. Under these conditions the cells are dormant, but are readily regenerated by transfer to a suitable liquid or solid culture medium. Some spores are easily maintained for long periods of time suspended in sterile dry sand or soil.

Culture improvement is always desirable, either to obtain greater yields or faster fermentations. Since there is a natural tendency for some variation to arise, improvements are sometimes attained through single cell isolations from the mass population of a culture. However, it is recognized that fermentation processes are gene controlled and substantial yield improvements are frequently attained by destruction of certain genes. Gene destruction is accomplished by ultraviolet or X-ray irradiation of cell or spore suspensions, or culturing in the presence of mutagenic substances such as the nitrogen mustards, morpholine, camphor, etc.

All these problems are within the scope of the microbiologist responsible for at least the laboratory phases of the process.

The Medium. It is axiomatic that the medium shall be as cheap as possible, consistent with yields and the product. Raw materials should, if possible, be available year round, be stable, and not require unusual storage conditions. Since the formulated liquid medium must be sterilized, most conveniently by steam under pressure, heat-labile culture medium ingredients create special handling problems.

Yields. As in chemical synthesis, yields or concentration of product in the final fermentation liquor can vary inversely with the market value. Some products (organic acids) may be produced in broth concentrations of 150 grams per liter (perhaps 90 per cent stoichiometric yield from glucose) whereas others, such as antibiotics and some vitamins, are present in concentrations of hundreds of parts per million (1 ppm = 1 microgram/ml). At the low extreme is vitamin B_{12}, which occurs in broths in yields ranging from less than 1 ppm to a few ppm.

Fermentation Rate. The length of time devoted to fermentation is dependent on the productive capacity of the microorganism. Alcohol fermentations by yeasts are generally complete in 50-60 hours; other fermentations

Figure 7.3. Shake flasks containing a *streptomyces* culture. One flask has sterile medium, the other contains medium with a well grown-out microorganism. (*Courtesy Chas. Pfizer and Co.*)

may be shorter or longer. The longer the fermentation cycle, the greater the risk of contamination with an undesirable microorganism. Antibiotic fermentations have the advantage of producing a substance inhibitory to at least some segments of the microbial population. Fermentations which operate at low pH's are also less susceptible to contamination.

Product Stability and Isolation

Chemical compounds vary considerably in stability, and fermentation chemicals cover the whole range. Ease of recovery is also dependent on solubility factors. Some are precipitated as calcium or barium salts (organic acids), some are solvent extracted from the medium (penicillin), others may be adsorbed on ion-exchange resins (streptomycin). Distillation is used for the volatile solvents (ethanol, butanol, acetone).

FERMENTATION

The main fermentation operation methodology depends on the physiological properties of the particular microorganism. Some bacteria are anaerobes, that is, they require no oxygen; in fact the butanol-acetone-producing bacteria *Clostridium acetobutylicum* grows poorly in the presence of oxygen. Yeasts produce ethanol under anaerobic conditions, but in the presence of adequate oxygen the alcohol is further metabolized to water and CO_2 with a resultant increase in yeast crop.

Anaerobic Fermentations

The anaerobic fermentation is a comparatively simple operation. The sterile medium contained in a sterile fermentor is inoculated with the appropriate organism. The organism multiplies rapidly and the "fermentation" is established. In both the important anaerobic fermentations, ethanol by the yeast *Saccharomyces cerevisiae* and butanol-acetone by the bacterium *Clostridium acetobutylicum*, substantial quantities of CO_2, and CO_2 and H_2, respectively, are produced. These must be suitably vented from the fermentor and may be recovered as by-products. In the butanol plants, the gases from one fermentor may be used in the head space of a new fermentation to exclude atmospheric oxygen.

Alcohol Fermentation. Beverage and industrial ethanol (95 per cent ethanol) are produced by yeast fermentations, though the latter is rapidly being displaced by ethanol produced from petroleum. Industrial alcohol is itself a raw material for chemicals; it is also a solvent. It is not subject to the federal alcohol tax. In order to prevent the diversion of industrial alcohol to potable uses, it is "denatured" by the addition of some material which cannot be separated by any physical or chemical process and which renders the alcohol so treated unfit for use as a beverage. Many different formulas are authorized by the government, so that the industrial user may select the particular formula which will have least effect on his particular process. Under the supervision of federal inspectors, chemical processes which require pure industrial ethyl alcohol may be operated.

The fermentation may be conducted on nearly any carbohydrate-rich substrate. Molasses, which is the final mother syrup in the crystallization of sucrose or table sugar, is preferred because of cost and ease of handling. Blackstrap molasses is a viscous liquid containing 50 per cent fermentable carbohydrate. It is diluted to 10–14 per cent sugar, ammonium salts are added to relieve a nutritional deficiency, and it is adjusted to about pH 5–6. The medium is pasteurized, cooled and inoculated. Grain fermentations require additional pretreatment since yeast cannot metabolize starch. The grain (usually corn) is ground, heated in an aqueous slurry to gelatinize or solubilize the starch, cooled to about 145° F, and treated with malt (germinated, dried barley) which is rich in the starch hydrolyzing enzyme diastase, principally beta-amylase. More recently, a fungal amylase produced by *Aspergillus niger* has found favor in some plants. The enzyme system converts the starch to the disaccharide maltose which is readily

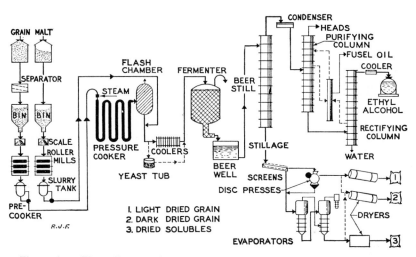

Figure 7.4. Flow diagram for the manufacture of industrial alcohol (ethyl alcohol 95 per cent) by fermentation of grain. (*Based on a sketch in Manufacturing Process Guide for Am. Inst. Chem. Eng. Tour, 1947, Joseph E. Seagram and Sons, Louisville, Ky.*)

fermented by the yeast. The final "beer" contains 5.5–8 per cent alcohol by volume, which is recovered by distillation, and other products including fusel oil, higher alcohols (of which isoamyl alcohol is the principal one), glycerin, and a small amount of organic acids.

The efficiency of alcohol fermentations may be compared to the classical Gay-Lussac equation:

$$C_6H_{12}O_6 \rightarrow 2C_2H_5OH + 2CO_2\uparrow \qquad \Delta H: 31,200 \text{ cal}$$

which predicts that 0.51 pound ethanol shall be produced from each pound of glucose. Note that considerable heat is evolved during the fermentation; this is dissipated by appropriate cooling coils in the fermentor. A flow diagram for the manufacture of industrial alcohol is given in Figure 7.4.

Butanol-Acetone. The history of the butanol-acetone fermentation has been fully compiled by several authors (see Beesch and Underkofler and Hickey) and need not be repeated here. It also represents the first commercial fermentation process requiring aseptic techniques.

The fermentation was an outgrowth of the need for acetone for the manufacture of the explosive cordite during World War I. Butanol was an unwanted by-product. However, with the development of the fast-drying automobile lacquers in the 1920's, large quantities of butanol esters were needed as solvents, and butanol became the principal product. This was indeed fortunate since the fermentation yields roughly 2 parts butanol to 1 part acetone.

The first strains of *Clostridium acetobutylicum* discovered were starch fermenting types; thus grains such as corn were the principal media ingredients. By the 1930's some butanol and especially acetone were being produced by chemical synthesis, and the fermentation industry faced economic difficulties. This problem was finally solved by the discovery of molasses fermenting strains, and the industry thrived until the end of World War II. Petrochemical processes have since dominated.

In the grain fermentation process, 8–10 per cent corn mashes were fermented (corn contains 70–72 per cent starch, dry basis). Fermentation yields were on the order of 29–32 grams mixed solvents per 100 grams starch used, with solvent ratios of approximately 60-30-10 (butanol-acetone-ethanol, respectively). The organisms possessed good diastatic activity, thus malting was not required. The cooked sterile corn meal suspension was aseptically transferred to sterile fermentors, inoculated, and incubated for about 65 hours at 37° C, after which the solvents were recovered by distillation. The aqueous residue (slop or stillage) was concentrated in multiple effect evaporators and drum dried for uses in animal and poultry feeds.

With the advent of molasses fermenting strains of *Clostridium*, more rapid fermentations were attained (40–48 hr) and the solvents produced contained as much as 65–75 per cent butanol, principally at the expense of ethanol.

After distillation of the solvents, valuable by-product feeds are obtained by drying the stillage. With proper control of the soluble iron level in the medium (1–3 ppm), the grain fermenting clostridia produce significant amounts of riboflavin (vitamin B_2) which increase the value of the feed products. Lesser amounts of riboflavin are found in molasses stillage. Fermentation sources of riboflavin are more fully discussed elsewhere in this chapter.

The butanol-acetone fermentations are conducted in large scale equipment; fermentation of 50,000 to 500,000 gallons capacity is commonly used. A photograph of an installation for propagating bacteria for butanol fermentation is shown in Figure 7.5.

Aerobic Fermentations

With the development of aerobic fermentations, the industry was able to produce a wide array of new products, most of which are not in serious competition with chemical synthesis. New and improved techniques and better equipment were required; new production problems were encountered and solved. This is partially explained by the fact that more fastidious conditions must be maintained.

Aerobic fermentations, as the name implies, require the use of substantial amounts of oxygen (from air). Aerobic microorganisms fail to proliferate

Figure 7.5. 800-gallon bacteria—propagation tanks for butyl alcohol fermentation; one tank furnishes the right amount of culture for one 50,000-gallon fermentation tank. (*Courtesy Commercial Solvents Corp., Terre Haute, Ind.*)

in anaerobic systems and the limited oxygen solubility of air in water (7 ppm at 37° C) prevents the initial absorption of sufficient dissolved oxygen to satisfy the continued requirements of the organisms. In the laboratory, aerobic or at least semi-aerobic conditions in the medium can be attained by using a thin layer of liquid medium in an Erlenmeyer or Fernbach flask. The microorganism usually grows on the surface as air diffuses into the medium. Absorption may be further increased by shaker culture methods wherein the flasks are incubated on appropriate reciprocal or rotary platforms.

In large scale fermentations these conditions are obtained in a number of ways. The first is simply a scale-up of the shallow liquid method, or the pan method. A sterilized medium is placed in the shallow pans and inoculated with the appropriate organism which establishes itself as a skin over the surface of the medium. The pans are stacked in cabinets in such a way that sterile air may be forced over their surface to provide an oxygen rich atmosphere and to sweep away CO_2 and other gases which might be produced by the fermentation. The obvious disadvantages are the considerable manual labor and equipment involved.

A modification of this method has been used for the microbial production of certain useful enzymes from molds such as *Aspergillus oryzae*. A moist solid medium, essentially moist bran, is placed on the trays and inoculated. The bran may be stirred or mixed occasionally, but the general methodology remains. The desired enzymes are extracted from the final fermented solids, and the extract is processed to a stable liquid enzyme concentrate or dry powder.

In vinegar generators the bacterium *Acetobacter aceti* grows as a heavy slime on the surface of wood chips in a packed tower. The dilute alcohol solution trickles over the surface, countercurrent to a stream of air. By recycling, a complete oxidation is attained. Edible acetic acid or vinegar, by law, must be of biological origin.

By far the most practical method is the so-called "deep tank" or "submerged aerobic" fermentation and it is universally used except for a few special situations. In this method, continuous aeration of the medium, with adequate agitation, permits luxurious growth of the microorganism throughout the medium. Fermentation rates are more rapid by this method than by others, less manpower is required, and large scale equipment may be employed. These advantages, however, have accompanying problems. Sterile air in large volumes is required since it is customary to inject into the medium $\frac{1}{4}$ to 1 volume of air per volume of medium per minute. The air must be finely dispersed so that a large surface area is available for the transfer of oxygen to the surrounding medium. Fermentors are frequently equipped at the bottom with coils or crossed pipes in which a large number of small holes have been drilled (spargers). Mechanical stirrers may be provided above the air spargers. The air droplets rise through the height of the medium and out the exhaust vents of the tanks. Coalescence of the droplets is undesirable, but little can be done to prevent it.

Sterile air is commonly produced by passing compressed air through sterile filters packed with glass wool or carbon. In such filters microorganisms are removed from the air, presumably by electrostatic and inertial impaction forces. The bulk density, fiber or particle diameter, and fiber distribution all contribute to filtration efficiency. Unfortunately, 99.9 per cent efficiency is not sufficient since a few cells, once passed through the filter and into the fermentation medium, can rapidly multiply and create a serious problem.

Mechanical agitators introduce additional problems. The packing gland where the agitator shaft enters the vessel must be more than liquid proof—it must be sterilized with the vessel and must remain sterile throughout the fermentation cycle. Some plants find it advantageous to equip such packing glands with a "steam seal," a means of maintaining a sterilized environment for the gland. This, however, accelerates thermal decomposition of the packing material. With small equipment, agitators are usually top entry; in large fermentors they may be side entry. Some recent European plants have installed bottom entry agitators. Sometimes aeration alone provides sufficient agitation.

Microbial contamination problems are more prevalent in aerobic fermentations than in anaerobic. Most microorganisms are aerobes, with all degrees of nutritional requirements. Thus there is seldom a lack of organisms capable of thriving on the production medium. Likewise, it is not uncommon to encounter contaminants which multiply as rapidly as the desired culture; competition always produces an undesirable effect on the wanted organism.

Introducing large volumes of air into a fermenting system frequently induces foaming. Antifoam agents such as sterile vegetable or animal fats (soybean or lard oil), or synthetic defoamers such as some of the liquid silicones, are commonly used. The fats are frequently metabolized and so must be added intermittently throughout the fermentation cycle. A satisfactory defoamer must be non-toxic to the microorganism, stable to heat for sterilizing purposes, and must not interfere with the recovery methods.

FERMENTATION EQUIPMENT

As in other branches of the chemical industry, a properly equipped laboratory must be provided to support the production department. Its services include the usual analytical work to indicate the progress of the process. However, a fermentation laboratory performs several other necessary services, chiefly that of maintaining the valuable stock cultures and preparation of inoculum for the production plant. Microbiological processes must be scaled up stepwise from a test-tube scale. The laboratory, under aseptic conditions, prepares a pure culture of actively growing organism. This is done in a properly designed container from which the organism can be transferred to a small inoculum tank (1–10 per cent by volume used as inoculum in each step). The inoculum tank contains a previously sterilized and cooled medium, suitable for the microorganism. Depending on the size of the final fermentation volume, the microorganism is scaled up through one or more successive inoculum stages.

Besides the usual glassware common to laboratories, a fermentation laboratory is equipped with a steam autoclave, dry heat ovens for sterilizing glassware, incubators, culture shakers, etc. Sterile rooms are usually employed for transferring the growing organism from stock cultures to inoculum propagation vessels.

Production Equipment

The production plant is equipped with a battery of fermentation tanks, and auxiliary tanks used for propagating the inoculum. There is no standardization of equipment, since each manufacturer adopts equipment based on

Figure 7.6. A pilot-plant scale fermentor. (*Courtesy Chas. Pfizer and Co.*)

past experience. Usually, the inoculum fermentors are scaled in the range 5–10 per cent of the volume of the production fermentors. It is not unusual to have more than one size inoculum tank; the smallest may receive an inoculum from the laboratory and, after suitable growth has been attained, this in turn may be used to propagate a larger inoculum batch. Thus the scale up is step-wise, and each production fermentor can be traced back to the culture laboratory.

The size and design of fermentors probably vary a good deal throughout the industry. Fermentors of 500,000 gallons capacity have been used for ethanol and butanol-acetone fermentations; many companies have reported using 20,000 gallon fermentors for antibiotics fermentations. Fermentor construction may be of carbon steel, stainless steel, stainless-steel clad, or carbon steel with a relatively stable organic polymer coating. Others have been glass-lined or constructed of nickel alloys (Inconel) or aluminum. Probably stainless steel is the material of choice since it tends to minimize corrosion problems and the deleterious metal toxicities to the microorganism.

Figure 7.7. Some commercial-sized fermentors. (*Courtesy Chas. Pfizer and Co.*)

Virtually all are pressure vessels, capable of withstanding 20 psi steam pressure for sterilization purposes.

The fermentor requires certain auxiliary equipment. After sterilization it must be cooled to the optimum temperature of the microorganism to be used. This is usually in the range 25–37° C, but may be as high at 55° C in the case of certain thermophilic (heat-loving) organisms. In actual operation the smaller size tanks may be used for batch sterilization of the medium and, after cooling, operated as the fermentor. With large tanks, the sterile fermentor receives, through sterile pipelines, a previously sterilized and cooled medium. Because considerable carbohydrate is metabolized, fermentations are exothermic and heat must be removed during the more vigorous phases. For instance, in some antibiotic fermentations as much as 20 Btu per hour per gallon are given off. Cooling is accomplished with internal coils, jackets, or "film cooling" (running water over the outside of the tank).

Media Sterilization

Sterilization implies the destruction of all forms of life in the medium. Heat is the most effective and economic method. Vegetative cells, especially of bacteria, are less heat resistant than spores. Generally, 10–30 minutes at 120° C renders any medium sterile, but one must correct for slow heat penetration rates under certain conditions. The rate of attaining sterility also depends on the microbial population; quantitative death curves are conveniently expressed as logarithmic functions.

In commercial practice media are sterilized by vigorous heating in batch or continuous systems. Two types of batch processes are found. In one, the fermentor itself is used as the batch "cooker." The liquid medium is raised to the boiling point by steam, either injected (ingredient concentrations adjusted for condensate dilution) or in coils, with suitable vents open to displace air; then, with vents closed, the temperature is raised to 121° C (15 psi) for 1 hour. In the second method, a separate batch "cooker" is used, and the sterile medium is transferred through sterile lines to a sterile fermentor.

In continuous sterilization, a heat exchanger may be used, but usually direct injection steam raises the temperature instantaneously, the medium then passing through an insulated pipe system ("retention tubes") followed by a cooling section (heat exchanger) to adjust it to the desired fermentation temperature. This is probably the preferred method; it is flexible with regard to time and temperature, fairly accurately controlled (important for heat-labile media), and economic in its use of steam and cooling water.

The Fermentation

For the main fermentation operation three basic processes have been proposed:

1. Batch fermentation
2. Continuous fermentation (single vessel system)
3. Continuous fermentation (multiple-vessel system)

In commercial practice, only batch operations are used. Most of the theoretical advantages of the continuous fermentations are discounted by the extreme difficulties inherent in maintaining a pure culture system when large volumes of fermenting broths are handled. Continuous fermentations also require a microbial culture which does not deteriorate as successive generations of cells are produced, a requirement that cannot be fulfilled readily.

Fermentation times are those required for attaining the most economic product concentration. Rates of product formation vary during the cycle. At first, a "lag phase" is encountered during which the inoculum is multiplying to attain a maximum cell count. Near the end of this phase, the product begins to accumulate, and a phase of product formation is then established. A third phase, one of declining productivity, eventually arises as a result of factors such as substrate exhaustion, accumulation of substances toxic to the organism, culture deterioration, etc.

Factors Influencing Yields

1. For peak efficiency, the environment of the microorganism must be optimum. The substrate must be selected for its nutritional value. Many microorganisms produce organic acids during carbohydrate metabolism, even though these acids are not the prime desired product. Each microorganism has a limited pH range for maximum yields. Various buffers are employed to control pH; $CaCO_3$ is undoubtedly the most widely used. Intermittent addition of mineral acids or bases such as lime, $NaOH$, NH_3, NH_4OH, etc. are not uncommon. It is possible for medium ingredients to be balanced to permit controlled utilization so that the remaining ions stabilize the pH.

2. Temperature control within 1–2° F is desirable. High temperatures are particularly destructive to the culture; low temperatures usually only depress the rate. Thus cooling capacity must be adequate for the short period of maximum heat of combustion (metabolism). Lesser amounts of heat arise from mechanical stirrers, etc.

3. Aerobic fermentations require adequate aeration with efficient mixing to facilitate maintenance of desired dissolved oxygen levels. Actual measurements of dissolved oxygen in a dynamic system such as a fermenting substrate are difficult. However, these measurements and their proper interpretation could have a marked influence on equipment design and fermentation technique.

4. Temperature and time of sterilization of the media may influence yields. Such treatment may produce toxic substances in the medium or destroy labile unidentified nutrient factors.

5. Size of inoculum frequently influences ultimate yields. No ready explanation can be offered, but through experience it is well established that maximum yields in some fermentations, for example, riboflavin production by *Eremothecium ashbyi* and *Ashbya gossypii*, are attained with young, small inocula (1 per cent). In others, 10–20 per cent inocula are preferred.

ANTIBIOTICS

The science of microbiology was established 100 years ago by the French chemist, Louis Pasteur. Among his many contributions should be mentioned the discovery of the existence of microscopic forms of life. Yeasts were established as the cause of the alcohol fermentation of wine. He later established pathogenic bacteria as the cause of many infectious diseases and even recognized viruses as causative agents of other infections.

Shortly before World War II another significant role of microorganisms began to emerge. Alexander Fleming, an English bacteriologist, is credited with first suggesting that the product of one microorganism might be used to inhibit the growth of another. Fleming observed that a chance contaminant (a Penicillium mold) clearly prevented the growth of a pathogenic *Staphylococcus* he was culturing in a Petri dish. Fleming succeeded in establishing some of the simple properties of the mold product, penicillin, and published his results in 1929. Nearly a decade later, another group of English biochemists undertook to further examine the phenomenon in the course of a broad research program for better chemotherapeutic agents. Florey, Chain, Heatley, and Abraham, of Oxford University, succeeded in isolating a small quantity of penicillin concentrate and by 1941 unequivocally demonstrated its potential usefulness in *Staphylococcus* septicemia. British government officials recognized its possible usefulness in military medicine, but could not further develop the discovery because of the serious war conditions then prevailing. The research was brought to the attention of government and industry in the United States, with the result that an international government-industry research program was established to produce the remarkable chemotherapeutic agent. Success of this program established a new class of powerful therapeutic agents, the antibiotics, which have revolutionized medical practice. Thus the product of one microorganism is used to combat an infection caused by another. To supply the huge amounts of antibiotics needed in modern medicine, the fermentation industry, too, has undergone a virtual revolution.

Since the early 1940's an intensive search for new and useful antibiotics has been in progress throughout the world. Researchers have succeeded in at least partially describing nearly 500 antibiotic substances from microorganisms. Most are only of academic interest because of inherent toxic properties or lack of clinical effectiveness. Less than two dozen of these have been of chemotherapeutic value.

Penicillin

The original mold observed and preserved by Fleming was a strain of *Penicillium notatum*, a common laboratory contaminant. Later, cultures of *Penicillium chrysogenum* were found to be better producers of penicillin, and the present industrial strains have been derived from this species. The original strains produced the antibiotic only by surface fermentation methods and in very low yields, a few ppm. Gradually, improved media and the eventual discovery of strains productive under submerged aerobic fermentation conditions led to dramatic yield increases which made commercial production a reality. Subsequent improvements, principally in culture selection and mutation to more productive strains, further improved yields until today broths often contain 5000 units/ml (1667 units = 1 mg potassium penicillin G). With improved production have come dramatic price

Figure 7.8. Two methods of qualitative determination of antibiotic activity. The test broth is absorbed on filter-paper discs in the left-hand Petri dish. The disc is placed on a nutrient agar and six different test microorganisms are streaked against the disc. Those test organisms sensitive to the antibiotic have an inhibition zone near the disc. Right-hand plates and discs are placed on agar medium pre-seeded with test organism. Clear zone denotes inhibition or presence of antibiotic. (*Courtesy Chas. Pfizer and Co.*)

reductions. For instance, a 100,000 unit vial of penicillin had a wholesale price in 1943 of $20.00. In 1952, the same vial had a wholesale value of as little as $0.13. Table 7.1 indicates that the annual production of penicillin in recent years has reached tonnage quantities.

The original *P. chrysogenum* strains produced large amounts of unwanted yellow pigments which were difficult to remove from the recovered penicillin. Today, non-pigmented mutants, a strain known in the industry as Wisconsin 49-133 (or progeny therefrom), are universally employed. Fermentation is effected by the submerged aerobic process outlined earlier in this chapter. The desired culture is propagated from a laboratory stock in small flasks and transferred to plant inoculum tanks. After 24 hours these are used to

TABLE 7.1. UNITED STATES PRODUCTION, SALES, AND DOLLAR VALUE OF SOME FERMENTATION PRODUCTS[a]

Fermentation Product	Year	Production, lb	Sales, lb	Dollar Value
Penicillin (including salts)	1951	625,000	487,000	$137,517,000
	1952	671,000	588,000	82,655,000
	1953	753,000	708,000	57,752,000
	1954	631,000	427,000	53,030,000
	1955	455,000	445,000	43,980,000
	1956	631,000	593,000	63,529,000
	1957	694,000	601,000	66,294,000
	1958	516 000	491 000	60,321,000
	1959	567,000	489,000	57,343,000
Streptomycin	1951	39,000	36,000	6,051,000
	1952	50,000	51,000	4,876,000
	1953	125,000	104,000	10,785,000
	1954	141,000	75,000	5,497,000
	1955	154,000	99,000	5,127,000
	1956	130,000	147,000	5,604,000
	1957	198,000	169,000	6,786,000
	1958	179,000	166,000	5,797,000
	1959	281,000	240,000	5,388,000
Dihydrostreptomycin	1951	315,000	264,000	40,703,000
	1952	337,000	301,000	34,213,000
	1953	305,000	297,000	24,547,000
	1954	446,000	286,000	19,476,000
	1955	369,000	332,000	16,318,000
	1956	492,000	431,000	18,198,000
	1957	582,000	462,000	20,039,000
	1958	561,000	465,000	17,877,000
	1959	470,000	492,000	13,721,000
All others (including broad spectrum antibiotics)	1951	307,000	268,000	132,787,000
	1952	425,000	391,000	144,829,000
	1953	441,000	354,000	136,880,000
	1954	597,000	461,000	156,278,000
	1955	579,000	480,000	171,745,000
	1956	697,000	552,000	178,051,000
	1957	869,000	729,000	222,093,000
	1958	1,314,000	730,000	213,469,000
	1959	932,000	787,000	234,121,000
Antibiotics for feed supplements food preservation crop spraying	1951	236,000	196,000	17,532,000
	1952	258,000	172,000	16,962,000
	1953	434,000	391,000	19,423,000
	1954	479,000	562,000	25,871,000
	1955	520,000	553,000	26,105,000
	1956	779,000	683,000	28,108,000
	1957	870,000	795,000	31,307,000
	1958	903,000	1,053,000	39,722,000
	1959	1,400,000	1,100,000	39,200,000

TABLE 7.1. UNITED STATES PRODUCTION, SALES, AND DOLLAR
VALUE OF SOME FERMENTATION PRODUCTS[a] (*Continued*)

Fermentation Product	Year	Production, lb	Sales, lb	Dollar Value
Total antibiotics for human or veterinary use	1951	1,286,000	1,055,000	317,058,000
	1952	1,487,000	1,321,000	266,574,000
	1953	1,630,000	1,467,000	231,484,000
	1954	1,837,000	1,263,000	240,128,000
	1955	1,572,000	1,367,000	242,372,000
	1956	1,967,000	1,737,000	271,371,000
	1957	2,373,000	1,986,000	323,546,000
	1958	2,612,000	1,882,000	304,700,000
	1959	2,295,000	2,042,000	318,188,000
Riboflavin for human or veterinary use *	1951	245,000	168,000	8,622,000
	1952	236,000	141,000	7,505,000
	1953	266,000	192,000	7,673,000
	1954	278,000	187,000	6,100,000
	1955	311,000	218,000	6,414,000
	1956	370,000	245,000	5,321,000
	1957	405,000	320,000	5,613,000
	1958	228 000	180,000	2,546.000
	1959	430,000	355,000	4,489,000
Vitamin B_{12}	1951	84	48	11,044,000
	1952	94	61	5,599,000
	1953	387	191	14,270,000
	1954	422	292	18,894,000
	1955	488	357	20,614,000
	1956	655	450	22,640,000
	1957	790	537	21,869,000
	1958	848	575	18,223,000
	1959	938	729	13,100,000

[a] Source: U. S. Tariff Commission, Washington, D. C.
*Human use only.

inoculate larger fermentors which contain a typical production medium composed of:

	Grams per 1000 Ml
Corn steep liquor	30
Lactose	30
Glucose	5.0
$NaNO_3$	3.0
$MgSO_4$	0.25
$ZnSO_4$	0.044
Phenyl acetamide (precursor)	0.05
$CaCO_3$	3.0

The medium is usually sterilized batch-wise or by means of a retention tube, cooled to 24° C, and inoculated. The time of fermentation may vary from 60–100 hours. Sterile air is blown through the tank, usually at a rate of one volume per volume per minute.

When penicillin concentration reaches its peak potency, as determined by microbiological or chemical assays, the broth is clarified by means of rotary vacuum filters. The penicillin, being acidic, is extracted from the aqueous phase into a solvent such as methyl isobutyl ketone or amyl acetate, at a pH of 2.5 by means of a continuous countercurrent extractor, such as a Podbielniak. The penicillin extract is then re-extracted with an aqueous alkaline solution or a buffer at a pH of 6.5–7.0. A 90 per cent recovery is made at this step. The aqueous solution is chilled, acidified, and extracted

Figure 7.9. Commercial broths are usually filtered on rotary precoat filters. Antibiotics are then recovered from the clear filtrates. (*Courtesy Chas. Pfizer and Co.*)

again with a solvent such as ether, chloroform, etc. The solvent extract is then re-extracted into water at a pH of 6.5–7.0 by titration with a solution of base. The base used depends on which salt of penicillin is desired. The popular forms are sodium or potassium salts. A typical flow sheet for antibiotic recovery is shown in Figure 7.10.

Table 7.2 gives the structural formula of the penicillins. As is indicated, several closely related compounds are known. In fact, the early impure product contained a mixture of these types. The crystalline product of commerce is penicillin G, which is a phenylacetyl acid amide of the common nucleus. Phenylacetic acid or some of its derivatives are used as precursors in the fermentation medium to enhance penicillin G synthesis and suppress the production of the less desirable forms.

In recent years, a more stable product, penicillin V, has attracted commercial attention. In this instance, phenoxy acetic acid serves as the precursor.

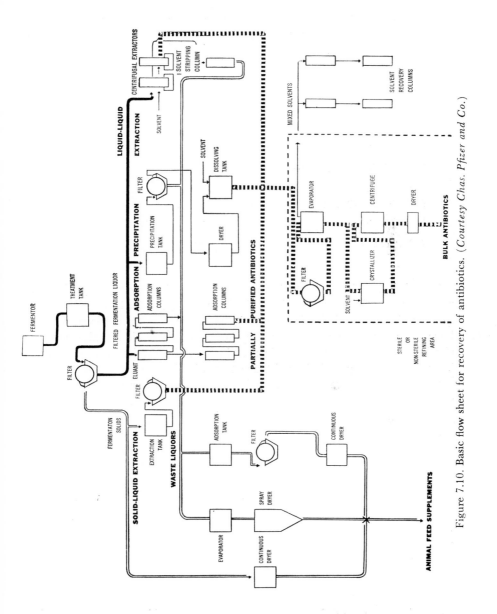

Figure 7.10. Basic flow sheet for recovery of antibiotics. (*Courtesy Chas. Pfizer and Co.*)

TABLE 7.2. STRUCTURAL FORMULA OF PENICILLINS

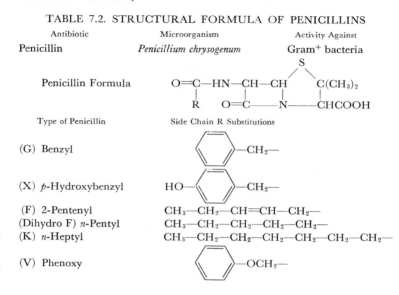

Antibiotic	Microorganism	Activity Against
Penicillin	*Penicillium chrysogenum*	Gram$^+$ bacteria

Type of Penicillin	Side Chain R Substitutions
(G) Benzyl	
(X) *p*-Hydroxybenzyl	
(F) 2-Pentenyl	CH_3—CH_2—CH=CH—CH_2—
(Dihydro F) *n*-Pentyl	CH_3—CH_2—CH_2—CH_2—CH_2—
(K) *n*-Heptyl	CH_3—CH_2—CH_2—CH_2—CH_2—CH_2—CH_2—
(V) Phenoxy	

Chemists and biochemists have recently found economical methods of removing the phenylacetyl side chain from penicillin G, leaving intact the nucleus, 6-aminopenicillanic acid. A large number of "synthetic penicillins" have been made by chemically coupling new side chains in the hopes of altering the range of therapeutic usefulness of the fundamental unit. Such improvements may include resistance to penicillinase (an enzyme found in penicillin-resistant Staphylococci) which inactivates the compound by opening the β-lactam ring. Others may have greatly enhanced activity against gram-negative bacteria.

Some *Cephalosporium* (*Emericellopsis*) strains produce synnematin which is now known to be a penicillin with an α-aminoadipyl side chain. Cephalosporin C has the same side chain with a 6-membered ring (α-aminoadipyl-7-aminocephalosporanic acid). These latter natural compounds are of interest because the biosynthesis of penicillin by Penicillia has been shown to involve the intermediate formation of a tripeptide, α-aminoadipyl-cystienyl-valine, with cyclization of the latter two amino acids to form the 6-aminopenicillanic acid moiety. Replacement of the aminoadipyl moiety with a phenylacetyl moiety produces penicillin G.

Streptomycin

The second major antibiotic introduced to the medical profession was streptomycin, discovered by Waksman and associates at Rutgers University in 1944. It was particularly useful because it was inhibitory to a large group of pathogenic bacteria unaffected by penicillin, namely, gram-negative bacteria and *M. tuberculosis*. Streptomycin also was significant as the first useful antibiotic from the group of microorganisms known as the *Actinomycetes*. This group has since proved to be a prolific source of antibiotics.

Streptomycin is produced by strains of *Streptomyces griseus* when cultivated by submerged aerobic conditions at 27–29° C on media comprising starch or sugar, soybean meal and certain inorganic salts. Yields up to 5000 mcg/ml have been reported in 50–90 hours.

Streptomycin finds wide use as a chemotherapeutic agent; production is shown in Table 7.1.

Chemically, streptomycin is an organic base, not extractable with water immiscible solvents. Commercially, it is recovered from the broth filtrates by ion-exchange methods, eluted as the mineral acid salt and further processed to pure white powder, usually the sulfate.

As is common with such powerful drugs, their use is sometimes complicated by attendant side reactions.

By catalytic hydrogenation, streptomycin is converted to dihydrostreptomycin. This compound has properties similar to streptomycin, but has a somewhat modified quantitative toxicity response.

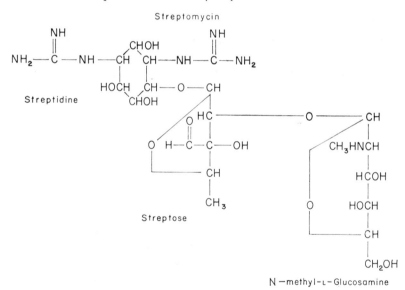

Streptomycin has also been used to treat plant diseases. It is absorbed and stored by the plant leaf. Since it is not removed by rainfall, the antibiotic within the leaf acts as a reservoir of protective agent against infection. It is particularly effective against blights.

Chloramphenicol

Following the discovery of streptomycin, attention was centered on the *Actinomycetes* as possible sources of new antibiotics. This resulted in the discovery of many more antibiotics, some of which have attained major importance. The first of these newer drugs, chloramphenicol (trade marked "Chloromycetin"), was discovered in 1947 by a group of researchers at Parke Davis and Company.

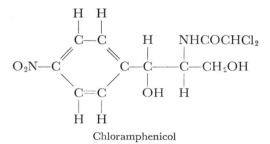

Chloramphenicol

The antibiotic was first produced by an aerobic fermentation using *Streptomyces venezuelae*. This antibiotic, in spite of its stereospecific structure, can also be produced by chemical synthesis involving some 30 steps, and it is believed that a major portion of the drug is produced in this manner.

This important antibiotic attracted immediate interest because it was the first "broad-spectrum" antibiotic, effective against many diseases caused by gram positive and gram negative bacteria as well as against infections caused by Rickettsiae.

The Tetracycline Group

In 1948 another broad-spectrum antibiotic, chlortetracycline ("Aureomycin"), was announced from the Lederle Laboratories, Division of American Cyanamid Company. This antibiotic is produced by *Streptomyces aureofaciens* when grown under submerged aerobic conditions on media composed of sugar, corn steep liquor, and mineral salts. The crystalline compound has a golden yellow color, which suggested the trade name.

The following year a second related antibiotic, oxytetracycline ("Terramycin"), a product of *Streptomyces rimosus*, was announced by Chas. Pfizer & Company, Inc. It also is a yellow substance, chemically and biologically similar to chlortetracycline. Independent research by both companies eventually led to the disclosure of the structure of these two important chemotherapeutic agents; this has been regarded as one of the brilliant achievements of modern organic chemistry.

Both compounds may be regarded as derivatives of a nucleus known as tetracycline. Thus chlortetracycline contains a chlorine atom in the 7-position (R_2 below), whereas oxytetracycline contains a hydroxyl group in the 5-position (R_1 below). The parent compound was synthesized by catalytic hydrogenation of chlortetracycline, which displaced the chlorine atom with a hydrogen atom.

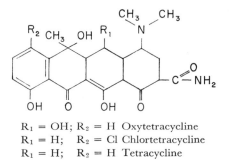

$R_1 = OH; R_2 = H$ Oxytetracycline
$R_1 = H; \quad R_2 = Cl$ Chlortetracycline
$R_1 = H; \quad R_2 = H$ Tetracycline

Tetracycline, together with chlortetracycline, can also be produced by *S. aureofaciens* fermentations under special conditions, i.e., chloride starvation or special strains of the organism which fail to halogenate efficiently.

Tetracycline possesses the many chemotherapeutic qualities of chlortetracycline and oxytetracycline, and is currently the largest selling broad-spectrum antibiotic.

Erythromycin

From the broths of a fermentation carried out by *Streptomyces erythreus,* workers of Eli Lilly and Company obtained a new antibiotic known as erythromycin (Erythrocin, Ilotycin) in 1952. It was produced by submerged aerobic fermentation of soybean meal, corn steep liquor medium.

This antibiotic is the most useful in combating infections caused by strains resistant to penicillin. It is effective against infections caused by gram positive bacteria and Rickettsiae.

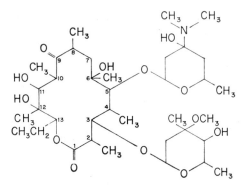

The structure of erythromycin has recently been determined. This is one of several antibiotics in a group, for which Woodward coined the term "macrolide." Essentially, the compound comprises a sugar cladinose, an aminosugar desosamine, and a 14-membered lactone.

Oleandomycin

A second macrolide antibiotic, oleandomycin, produced by *Streptomyces antibioticus,* is also being used to combat some infections resistant to the other agents. The structure is incomplete, but it contains two sugar units, one an aminosugar, and a large lactone.

Other Antibiotics

There are several antibiotics which have proved useful in special situations. Of these, bacitracin and polymyxin are used topically. Both are polypeptides. Bacitracin, a product of *Bacillus licheniformis,* is sometimes used systematically, though it is not absorbed orally. Polymyxin, produced by *Bacillus polymyxa,* is a novel peptide containing a new amino acid, diaminobutyric. Neomycin, from *Streptomyces fradiae,* proved to be too toxic for its original intended use, tuberculosis, but it is useful for treatment of topical infections.

VITAMINS

Another important area of microbial biosynthesis is the production of vitamins.

Riboflavin

Riboflavin was first produced microbiologically by species of the genus *Clostridium,* anaerobic bacteria used for the microbial production of acetone and butyl alcohol. Riboflavin was purely a by-product and was found in the dried stillage residues in amounts ranging from 40–70 mcg per gram of dried residue. Further research developed improvements, adaptable only to the fermentation of cereal, grains, and milk products, by *Clostridium acetobutylicum* to yield residues containing as high as 7000 mcg per gram. This was effected principally by reducing the iron content of the medium to 1–3 ppm, and fermenting in stainless steel, aluminum, or other iron-free tanks.

Later investigations disclosed that riboflavin could be produced by species of a yeast, *Candida flareri* and *C. guilliermondi,* when grown under aerobic conditions in a medium containing a fermentable sugar, an assimilable source of nitrogen, biotin, and less than 10 mcg of iron per 100 ml of medium. Yields as high as 200 mcg per ml were obtained.

Other studies on a fungus, *Eremothecium ashbyii,* and a closely related organism known as *Ashbya gossypii* resulted in the production of much larger amounts of riboflavin. An aerobic process was used in which iron content was not critical. Today, riboflavin is produced in large amounts by the fermentation industry using either the *Eremothecium* or *Ashbya* strains. Yields as high as 5000 mcg per ml are now common.

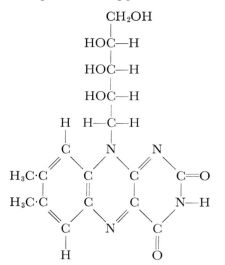

Riboflavin: Vitamin B_2

Concurrently with the development of a fermentation process, synthetic means of producing riboflavin were discovered; however the microorganism can effect its production with such efficiency and economy that the bulk of current production stems from the microbiological process. For many purposes the latter method of manufacturing possesses a distinct advantage, for if the vitamin is to be used in animal feeds it can be recovered as a crude concentrate from the medium, which is then used in proportion to its vitamin content.

Vitamin B_{12}

The microbiological production of vitamin B_{12}, or cyanocobalamin, arose from an interesting sequence of events. For many years liver extract was used to check cases of pernicious anemia. Investigators at Merck and Company discovered that crystalline extracts made from liver contained the highly active compound responsible for the therapeutic action. Identity with the anti-anemia factor in liver was established and the compound was called vitamin B_{12}. Later it was found that spent liquors from the streptomycin and other antibiotic fermentations contained appreciable quantities of vitamin B_{12}. Further investigations resulted in separate fermentations for the production of vitamin B_{12}, using selected strains of *Actinomycetes* and bacteria. Subsequent investigations disclosed that dried sewage residues from the activated sludge process also contained vitamin B_{12}. Today vitamin B_{12} is obtained from various antibiotic fermentation broths, separate fermentations using strains of selected *Streptomyces*, or *Propionobacterium*. Some feed-grade concentrates are recovered from dried sewage.

The isolation of vitamin B_{12} from fermentation media, where it is normally present in parts per million, is a brilliant achievement on the part of the chemist and the chemical engineer. Vitamin B_{12} is an exceedingly active compound biologically and is extremely expensive; the present price is $139.00 per gram of U.S.P. material.

ORGANIC ACIDS

The microbiological production of organic acids represents one of the earlier areas of fermentation, necessary for the accumulation of information which made possible the large scale production of antibiotics and other mircobial products of more recent date.

Citric Acid

Citric acid is one of the most important organic acids used in foods, beverages, and pharmaceuticals. During the past few years it has also become important as an organic intermediate.

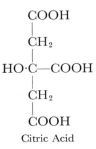

Citric Acid

Citric acid was first isolated from lemon juice in 1784 by Scheele. In 1917 Currie, of the U. S. Department of Agriculture, found citric acid could be produced microbiologically by using *Aspergillus niger* grown on a sugar, mineral salts solution. Since then, many other microorganisms have been shown to produce citric acid; however, *A. niger* has always given the best result in industrial production. Citric acid may be fermented either by using shallow pans or by employing a submerged or deep fermentation process with aeration.

Sucrose in the form of cane or beet molasses is the principal sugar source used. A 12–20 per cent sugar solution is normally used along with mineral supplements. The duration of shallow pan fermentation is 7–10 days at 26–28° C. Submerged fermentation periods are shorter but yields are less. On shallow pans, yields on the sugar used may be 90–95 per cent, while the submerged process normally runs 75–85 per cent. The citric acid is recovered as the calcium salt and treated with sulfuric acid to precipitate calcium sulfate, which is removed. Citric acid crystallizes upon concentrating the resulting solution. Some oxalic acid is recovered as a by-product of the citric fermentation process.

Lactic Acid

The production of lactic acid by bacterial fermentation of carbohydrates

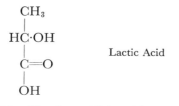

Lactic Acid

was first noted in 1847 by Blondeau. This acid was first commercially produced by fermentation in 1881 and the industry has since continued to be a very important one. Lactic acid exists in three isomeric forms; levo, dextro, and meso. The predominance of a particular isomer is a function of the bacteria used. Normally the industry uses the *Lactobacillus* strains at a high temperature (40–50° C). This facilitates maintaining sterility, since few contaminants will survive this temperature. Many sources of carbohydrates can be used as raw material, including hydrolyzed starches, glucose, molasses, lactose, and sulfite waste liquors. However, recovery difficulties make it most advantageous to start with a refined substrate such as commercial glucose. If a novel recovery method were available, lactic acid would be supplied at lower costs and would probably command more interest chemically. All acid of commerce is in the *dl-* inactive form. The *Lactobacillus delbrueckii* fermentation normally produces the *d-* form, but recemization occurs during the recovery-concentration step. The pH of the fermentation is maintained at neutrality by the continuous addition of calcium carbonate or hydroxide, and the resultant acid is isolated as the calcium salt which is insoluble in water and precipitates as the fermentation proceeds. Yields as high as 90 per cent on the basis of sugar fermented are obtained.

Lactic acid is used in food industries for fruit beverages, etc., in the tanning of leather, and in the textile and pharmaceutical industries.

Gluconic Acid

Gluconic acid is produced by the oxidation of the aldehyde grouping of glucose.

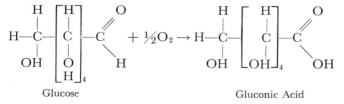

Glucose   Gluconic Acid

Gluconic acid may be prepared from glucose by oxidation with a hypochlorite solution, by electrolysis of a solution of sugar containing a measured amount of bromide, or by fermentation of glucose by molds or bacteria. The latter method is now preferred, from an economic standpoint. The most important microorganisms used are *Aspergillus niger,* and *Acetobacter suboxydans* grown on a glucose salt solution in deep tank fermentation. Yields as high as 90 per cent on the sugar consumed have been reported. Gluconic acid is marketed in the form of several crystalline metal salts, 50 per cent aqueous acid, and the delta-lactone. Calcium gluconate is frequently used as a nutritional calcium source because of its solubility. The sequestering properties of sodium gluconate, particularly for Ca^{++} and heavy metal ions in strong caustic solution, make it useful in cleaning operations.

Acetic Acid

Acetic acid in the form of vinegar (by law, 5 per cent acetic acid) is a widely used food adjunct. Vinegar is produced by the oxidation of ethanol by bacteria of the *Acetobacter* genus. In the food industry many vinegar types are classified on the basis of the source of alcohol. Most vinegar is made from apple cider; a yeast converts the sugar to ethanol and the acetification is accomplished by *Acetobacter aceti* strains.

$$C_6H_{12}O_6 + \text{yeast} \rightarrow 2C_2H_5OH + 2CO_2\uparrow$$
$$C_2H_5OH + O_2 + Acetobacter\ aceti \rightarrow CH_3COOH + H_2O$$

Ethanol may also be converted into acetic acid by catalytic oxidation at high temperatures, but synthetic acid cannot be used in foods.

Itaconic Acid

Itaconic acid is an unsaturated dibasic acid which may be used for the preparation of resins or surface active agents, or in the manufacture of synthetic organic chemical compounds. Its esters may be polymerized.

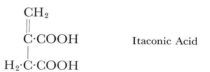

Itaconic Acid

Itaconic acid may be produced by either a shallow pan or a deep tank fermentation process by growing *Aspergillus terreus* or *A. itaconicus* on lactose or glucose salts media. The fermentation of 20–25 per cent glucose concentrations gives yields equivalent to 50 per cent of the sugar consumed.

Kojic Acid

Kojic acid was first discovered in Japan in 1907 by Saito; it was a by-product of the fermentation of steamed rice by *Aspergillus oryzae.* Various other investigators have found that numerous species of *Aspergillus* and some *Acetobacter* bacterial strains produce kojic acid. In 1955 it was first produced on a commercial scale by a fermentation process. Kojic acid is an acid weaker than carbonic. It is reactive at every position and forms a number of products.

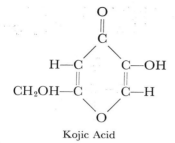

Kojic Acid

Fumaric Acid

Fumaric acid, an unsaturated acid, is produced by several species of mold, principally of the genus *Rhizopus*. Other genera such as *Mucor, Cunninghamella,* and *Circinella* also have the ability to produce fumaric acid from starches, molasses, and sugars. Yields of 40–50 per cent (of the sugar consumed) to fumaric acid have been reported. Fumaric acid is used as an antioxidant, a substitute for tartaric acid in beverages, and in the manufacture of polyhydric alcohols and synthetic resins.

$$HO_2CCH$$
$$\|$$
$$HCCO_2H$$

Fumaric Acid

In the future, fumaric acid will probably be produced by synthetic methods. A significant increase in synthetic capacity has been announced.

OTHER KETOGENIC FERMENTATIONS

Sorbose

Sorbose fermentation, the first bacterial ketogenic fermentation discovered, is one of the simplest. L-Sorbose is produced from the polyhydric alcohol sorbitol by the action of several species of bacteria of the genus *Acetobacter*. Sorbitol is made by the catalytic hydrogenation of glucose. The most commonly used microorganism is *Acetobacter suboxydans*. Since this organism is very sensitive to nickel ions, it is important that the medium and fermentor be free of nickel. The medium normally consists of 100–200 grams per liter sorbitol, 2.5 grams per liter corn steep liquor and antifoam such as soybean oil. The medium is sterilized and cooled to 30–35° C, where about 2.5 per cent inoculum is added. The tank is aerated and sometimes stirred. Yields of 80–90 per cent of the sugar used are commonly obtained in 20–30 hours.

The only commercial use of L-sorbose is in the manufacture of ascorbic acid (vitamin C). The chemical steps in the conversion of sorbose to ascorbic acid involve the preparation of the diacetone derivative which is then oxidized; the acetone groups are removed and the resultant 2-keto-L-gluconic acid is isomerized to the enediol with ring closure. This concept of using combined microbiological and chemical conversions has recently been applied with commercial success to the preparation of new steroid drugs.

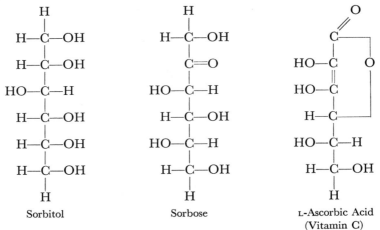

Sorbitol   Sorbose   L-Ascorbic Acid
(Vitamin C)

2-Ketogluconic Acid

2-Ketogluconic acid may be produced by a bacterial fermentation involving various strains of *Acetobacter* and *Pseudomonas*. Selected strains of *Pseudomonas fluorescens* have been reported as giving the highest yields (up to 70 per cent) when glucose or gluconate is used in the medium in highly aerated processes. *d*-Gluconic acid is an intermediate in the oxidation of glucose to 2-ketogluconic acid. 2-Ketogluconic acid is structurally related to both gluconic acid and glucosone, and may be derived from both by oxidation. The 2-ketogluconic acid is recovered as the calcium salt. The principal use of 2-ketogluconic acid is as an intermediate in the preparation of D-araboascorbic acid (iso-ascorbic acid).

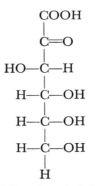

d-2-Ketogluconic Acid

2,3-Butanediol (2,3-Butylene Glycol)

Several species of bacteria such as *Bacillus polymyxa, B. subtilis, Pseudomonas hydrophila,* and *Serratia marcescens* are capable of producing 2,3-butanediol by fermentation. 2,3-Butanediol has considerable industrial value since it can be converted into 2,3-butadiene, a substance used in the production of buna rubber. As a result, a great deal of work has been done on the microbiological production of this product in the United States, Canada, and various European countries, with a resultant process that is technically feasible but not widely used. 2,3-Butanediol exists in three optical isomers. the dextro, levo, and meso forms. *B. polymyxa* produces the pure *l*-isomer, *B. subtilis,* a mixture of levo and meso isomers, and *Serratia marcescens* predominantly meso with a small amount of the dextro form.

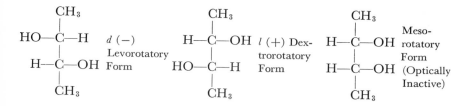

Various sugar sources, such as glucose, sucrose, starches, wood hydrolysates, etc., have been fermented with various strains of bacteria, giving yields up to 40 per cent of the hexose used.

In addition to its possible use in buna rubber, 2,3-butanediol is also used as a solvent for dyes, and in the manufacture of phthalic anhydride. Under controlled conditions the product may be diacetyl instead of the diol. Diacetyl is used in small quantities as a butter flavor.

AMINO ACIDS

Within recent years, the possibility of commercially producing amino acids by fermentation methods has become a reality. These processes have the advantage of producing the natural stereo isomer.

L-Lysine can be produced via a dual fermentation process. It is well established that *Escherichia coli* synthesizes its own lysine requirements by converting carbohydrate to diaminopimelic acid (DAP). Decarboxylation results in lysine. An industrial fermentation employs an *E. coli* mutant which accumulates substantial diaminopimelic acid in the culture medium. This mutant is devoid of diaminopimelic acid decarboxylase. After maximum DAP yields are attained, a second organism, such as another *E. coli* strain or *Aerobacter aerogenes,* is used as a source of DAP-decarboxylase resulting in L-lysine.

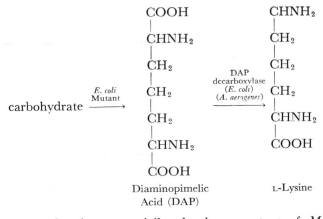

Diaminopimelic   L-Lysine
Acid (DAP)

L-Lysine is produced commercially also by a mutant of *Micrococcus glutamicus* (classification doubtful; variously identified as *Corynebacterium* or *Brevibacterium*) which converts glucose to L-lysine in large quantities. As much as 25 per cent weight yields have been reported from glucose (10 per cent in culture medium).

As indicated by the original name, the parent culture produces large amounts of *l*-glutamic acid; yields of more than 35 grams per liter from approximately 100 grams of glucose have been reported. The amino acid is marketed as monosodium glutamate, a food flavor adjunct. Besides the lysine-producing mutant, others have been developed which produce good yields of L-ornithine, L-valine, L-alanine, L-phenylalanine, and L-homoserine. Markets for these latter amino acids have not developed.

STEROID TRANSFORMATIONS

As one peruses biochemical literature dealing with the activities of micro-organisms, it becomes apparent that many reactions are effected which cannot easily be duplicated by classical chemical methods. Some of the very useful ones have established a vigorous branch of the pharmaceutical industry. Chemical and biochemical reactions have been joined to convert relatively inexpensive raw materials into powerful chemotherapeutics which have brought dramatic changes in the treatment of severe chronic inflammatory diseases. Bacteria, filamentous fungi, streptomycetes, and even protozoa, produce the useful enzymes, but the filamentous fungi are the most versatile.

With the discovery that cortisone might be useful in the treatment of arthritis, and the final elucidation of its structure by the brilliant work of Kendall, production of the chemotherapeutic attracted attention. Purely chemical routes of synthesis from bile acids gradually developed. Another route, probably more widely employed, utilized biochemical reactions in part of the process.

Microorganisms are known to perform a variety of transformations of the steroid nucleus, principally hydroxylation, dehydrogenation, hydrogenation, epoxidation, perhaps direct ketone formation, and even cleavage of the side chain at carbon atom 17.

Steroid transformations are conducted somewhat differently from the usual fermentations. The selected microorganism is propagated in the fermentor until a good cellular mass is attained (usually aerobically). Then an appropriate steroid substrate is added as a solution or well dispersed suspension in a nontoxic organic solvent. The enzymatic reaction proceeds until the maximum product and minimum substrate are attained. Paper chromatographic methods are almost exclusively used for following the progress of the reaction.

Several reviews on microbial steroid transformation, listed in the references at the end of this chapter, may be consulted for more detailed information.

THE BREWING INDUSTRY

Beer is made by boiling, in the presence of hops, certain extractable materials contained in malted barley and other grains, and then fermenting this brew by the addition of brewers' yeast. The methods employed by various breweries in the preparation of beers and ales differ in important details, yet are sufficiently similar to be represented by the practice in a typical brewery in upper New York State.

The capacity of the plant is 600,000 barrels per year (1 barrel-31 gallons). The raw materials are rice, corn grits (both oil-free), wheat flakes, soybean (optional), malt, hops, and some others in smaller quantities. Besides these, pure yeast and an abundance of water are required for making the beverage itself and for cooling. The corn grits, which must be free from germ, and the rice, for example, are taken in quantities sufficient to furnish 30 to 40 per cent of the required starch, while enough malt is added to furnish the remainder. After passing cleaners and crushing rolls, the rice and the corn, made up with water, and with the addition of some malt, are heated in a pressure cooker with an agitator under 5 pounds of pressure for 45–60 minutes. The action is primarily the liquefaction of the starch. The main portion of the malt, made up with water, is placed in the mash tub, which is just like the cooker, and thoroughly mixed at a temperature between 100 and 120° F, then it is allowed to rest. During the rest period the proteolytic enzymes begin to degrade the malt and other proteins into soluble forms. After this period the contents of the cooker are added; these raise the temperature to 149–158° F, at which point the material is held for conversion. The temperature is then raised to 167° F, high enough to arrest the action of the conversion. The purpose of mashing is first to extract from the malt its starch and ferments, including the diastase, which changes the starch to sugars during the conversion period. The material next passes to the Lauter tub the bottom of which has slots; through these the clear liquor, or wort, passes while the arms of the agitator turn slowly. "Sparge water" in spray form is introduced to exhaust the material on the screen. The wort is run into the boiling kettle, a jacketed copper kettle with capacity, in this plant, of 450 barrels. During the period of boiling, which lasts 2½–3 hours, the hops are added at fixed intervals. While in the kettle,

TABLE 7.3. TYPICAL ANALYSES OF BREWERY PRODUCTS

	Lager Beer	Ale
Appearance on arrival	Clear	Clear
Color	5.75° Lovibond	6.0° Lovibond
Odor	Pure	Mildly aromatic
Taste	Pure, somewhat full-bodied, good hop flavor	Pure, vinous, good hop flavor
Foam-keeping capacity	Good	Good
Specific gravity	1.01598	1.01399
Saccharometer indication	4.07° Plato	3.57° Plato
Alcohol, by weight	3.80%	4.20%
Alcohol, by volume	4.89%	5.40%
Extract	5.79%	5.49%
Sugar	1.63%	1.54%
Dextrin	2.52%	2.23%
Unconverted starch	None	None
Acidity as lactic	0.16%	0.16%
Protein	0.40%	0.42%
Heavy metals	None	None
pH value	4.60	4.30
Carbon dioxide, 2 bottles	0.48%, 0.48%	0.45%, 0.45%
Original gravity	13.1° Plato	13.6° Plato
Real degree of fermentation	55.8%	59.6%
Apparent degree of fermentation	68.9%	73.8%
Chilling test, clarity (absolute turbidity) on 2 bottles chilled 24 hours in ice pack	a.—0.0029. b.—0.0030	a.—0.0028. b.—0.0028

the enzymes are destroyed, the hop "bitter" is extracted, undesirable proteins are coagulated, other proteins are precipitated by the tannin in the hops, and the whole is sterilized by the heat. There is also a concentration of about 10 per cent. Next the material is strained to remove all solids, especially the spent hops, and the clear liquor, after settling for a while in the hot wort tank, is run over coolers, such as the Baudelot; from there it goes to fermentors, which may be of wood, glass-lined steel, or aluminum, where the yeast is added (e.g., ¾ pound liquid yeast per barrel). The fermentations last 7–10 days, after which the beer is run through a cooler into glass-lined storage tanks which in this plant have a capacity of 60,000 barrels. Here some 5–15 per cent of beer in high state of fermentation is added to the fully fermented beer and allowed to work out; as it ferments it provides the carbonation, since the tank is sealed to a pressure of 6–8 pounds. The beer absorbs the carbon dioxide. After a period of a week or more the beer is filtered through a mass filter under pressure; it is re-carbonated sufficiently while passing through the pump, at a temperature of 32° F, to bring the carbon dioxide content to 0.48 per cent in the final beer, and the product is bottled or barreled. The carbonation may be performed entirely by pumping sterile carbon dioxide into the cooled beer from the fermentors. The bottled beer is pasteurized at 140° F (60° C) after capping.

REFERENCES

General

1. Prescott, S. C., and Dunn, C. G., "Industrial Microbiology," 3rd Edition, N. Y., McGraw-Hill Book Co., 1959.
2. "Pilot Plant Techniques of Submerged Fermentation," Edited by E. B. Chain, Rendiconti Istituto Superiore di Sanita, Fondazione Emanuele, Paterno, Rome, Italy, 1954.
3. Federal Trade Commission, "Economic Report on Antibiotic Manufacture," Superintendent of Documents, Washington 25, D. C., 1958.
4. "Industrial Fermentation," Vols. I and II, Edited by L. A. Underkofler and R. J. Hickey, New York, Chemical Publishing Co., Inc., 1954.
5. "Biochemical Engineering," Edited by R. Steel, London, Heywood and Co., Ltd., 1958.
6. Nilsson, E., *Utilization of Agricultural Products by Microbial Fermentation,* **IVA,** 28, 117 (1957).
7. Foster, J. W., "Chemical Activities of Fungi," New York, Academic Press Inc., 1949.
8. Raper, K. B., "Microbes: Man's Mighty Midgets," *J. Botany,* **48,** 55 (1957).
9. "Bergey's Manual of Determinative Bacteriology," Baltimore, Md., The Williams and Wilkins Co.
10. Whitmarsh, J. M., "British Fermentation Industries," Pitman & Sons, Ltd., 1958.

Annual Review of Fermentation

1. Silcox, H. E., and Lee, S. B., *Ind. Eng. Chem.,* **40,** 1602 (1948).
2. Lee, S. B., *Ind. Eng. Chem.,* **41,** 1868 (1949).
3. Lee, S. B., *Ind. Eng. Chem.,* **42,** 1672 (1950).
4. Lee, S. B., *Ind. Eng. Chem.,* **43,** 1948 (1951).
5. Perlman, D., Brown, W. E., and Lee, S. B., *Ind. Eng. Chem.,* **44,** 1966 (1952).
6. Perlman, D., Tempel, A. E., Jr., and Brown, W. E., *Ind. Eng. Chem.,* **45,** 1944 (1953).
7. Perlman, D., and Kroll, C. L., *Ind. Eng. Chem.,* **46,** 1809 (1954).
8. Beesch, S. C., and Shull, G. M., *Ind. Eng. Chem.,* **47,** 1857 (1955).
9. Beesch, S. C., and Shull, G. M., *Ind. Eng. Chem.,* **48,** 1585 (1956).
10. Beesch, S. C., and Shull, G. M., *Ind. Eng. Chem.,* **49,** 1491 (1957).
11. Beesch, S. C., and Tanner, F. W., Jr., *Ind. Eng. Chem.,* **50,** 1341 (1958).
12. Beesch, S. C., and Tanner, F. W., Jr., *Ind. Eng. Chem.,* **51,** 1086 (1959).

Acetone-Butanol

1. Beesch, S. C., "Acetone Butanol Fermentation of Starches," *Applied Microbiology*, **1**, 85 (1953).
2. Beesch, S. C., "Acetone Butanol Fermentation of Sugars," *Ind. Eng. Chem.*, **44**, 1677 (1952).

Antibiotics

1. Ross, G., The Production of Antibiotics, *Brit. Chem. Eng.*, **3**, 8 (1958).
2. Herold, M., *Antibotika, Deutscher Verlag der Wissenschaften*, Berlin, 1956.
3. Antibiotics Annual, Yearly since 1953, Edited by H. Welch and F. Marti-Ibanez, Medical Encyclopedia, Inc., N. Y., Years 1953–1954, 1954–1955, 1955–1956, 1956–1957, 1957–1958, 1959–1960.
4. Florey, H. W., *et al.*, "Antibiotics," N. Y., Oxford Press, 1949.
5. Waksman, S. A., and Lechevalier, H. A., "Actinomycetes and Their Antibiotics," Baltimore, Md., Williams and Wilkins, 1953.
6. Demain, A. L., "The Mechanism of Penicillin Biosynthesis," in Advances in Applied Microbiology, Ed. by W. W. Umbreit, Academic Press, **1**, 23–47 (1959).

Alcohol-Yeasts and Brewing

1. "The Chemistry and Biology of Yeasts," A. H. Cook, Editor, New York, Academic Press, Inc., 1958.
2. Kretzschmar, H., "Hefe und Alkohol," Springer-Verlag, Berlin, Germany, 1955.
3. "Yeasts," W. Roman, Editor, W. Junk, The Hague, 1956.
4. DeClerck, J., "Textbook of Brewing," London, Chapman-Hall, 1957.
5. Adult, R. G., and Hudson, E. J., "Brewing, Malting, and Allied Processes," Inst. Brewing, London, 1956.

Amino Acids

1. Kinoshita, S., "The Production of Amino Acids by Fermentation Processes," in Advances in Applied Microbiology, Ed. by W. W. Umbreit, Academic Press, **1**, 201–214 (1959).

Steroids

1. Shull, G. M., *Trans. N. Y. Acad. Sci.*, **19**, II, 147–172 (1956).
2. Visher, E., and Wettstein, A., *Advances in Enzymology*, **20**, 237–282 (1958).
3. Peterson, D. H., in S. A. Waksman, ed., "Perspective and Horizons in Microbiology," New Brunswick, p. 121, 1955.
4. Fried, J., *et al.*, *Recent Prog. in Hormone Research*, **11**, 149 (1955).
5. Eppstein, S. H., *et al.*, *Vitamins and Hormones*, **14**, 359 (1956).

Miscellaneous

1. Gaden, E. L., Jr., "Biochemical Processing," *Chem. Eng.*, p. 237 (May 1957).
2. Raper, K. B., and Thom, C., "A Manual of the Aspergilli," Baltimore, Md., Williams and Wilkins Co., 1945.
3. Raper, K. B., and Thom, C., "A Manual of the Penicillia," Baltimore, Md., Williams and Wilkins Co., 1949.
4. Tanner, F. W., Jr., and Beesch, S. C., "Antibiotics and Plant Diseases," *Advances in Enzymology*, **20**, 383–406 (1958).

8

COAL CARBONIZATION AND RECOVERY
OF COAL CHEMICALS

In collaboration with Charles C. Russell* and Ganson Taggart†

COAL HANDLING AND CARBONIZATION

THE POSSESSION of coal fields by a nation is an asset that can lead to industrial prosperity. The production of steel is a prerequisite to industrialization of undeveloped countries, and steel production is still tied to adequate sources of carbon. The countries that have supplies of coking coals together with iron ore have grown most rapidly in industrial development. Chemicals derived from coal carbonization add to the development and wealth.

Coal carbonization in the United States is economically tied to the steel industry; until the supplies of natural gas are exhausted, coal will not be a source of city gas.

The demands for chemicals such as ammonia, benzene and toluene, once derived only from coal, have grown so rapidly that petroleum and natural gas, together with atmospheric nitrogen are important raw materials for these products. In nations lacking petroleum or natural gas, chemical technology has developed methods for the production of synthetic oils and chemicals from coal.

* Koppers Company, Inc., Pittsburgh, Pa.
† Badger Manufacturing Company, Cambridge, Mass.

The chief use of coal is as a fuel, as described in Chapter 3, but about 20 per cent of the coal produced in the United States is carbonized in coke ovens. The bituminous class of coals will form coke, but anthracite, subbituminous, lignite and peat do not. When bituminous coals are heated in the absence of air they fuse; as the temperature is raised higher, volatile products are evolved, leaving a solid cellular residue of carbon, together with the mineral matter of the coal. The carbon residue produced by heating bituminous coal in coke ovens is the coke of commerce and the volatile products recovered in the chemical recovery oven process consist of gas, tar, ammonia, benzene, toluene, xylol, and other products. Beehive coke ovens, which were developed before the chemical recovery oven process, produce only coke and all of the volatile products are wasted to the atmosphere except the portion that is burned in the process. Under present day conditions, approximately 3 per cent of the coke produced in the United States is made in beehive ovens. Actually, the amount of beehive coke produced varies from year to year depending on the total demand for coke. When the steel industry is operating at high capacity, more beehive coke is made. In 1959, there were 74 chemical recovery coke oven plants having a total of 15,993 ovens and 45 beehive coke oven plants having a total of 7,448 ovens.[4]

Coke is most generally made from a mixture of bituminous coals, blended in selected proportions of each type, to produce the quality desired. The blast furnace for producing pig iron requires a hard, strong coke having a size consist between $\frac{3}{4}$ and 4 inches and resistant to breakage and abrasion. More than 90% of the coke produced in the United States is now used in making pig iron. Other important uses for coke include foundries, various industries including CO_2 manufacture and water-gas production, and residential heating. In 1959 the coal carbonized in chemical recovery coke ovens amounted to 77,722,900 tons having an average value of $9.88 per ton. From this amount of coal, 54,789,000 tons of coke were produced, having an average value of $17.82 per ton and 3,710,900 tons of breeze. Breeze is a coke that is too small to use in the blast furnace and is generally burned for steam raising or for sintering fine iron-ore. The yield of usable coke amounts to about 70 per cent of the coal carbonized.

Coal for carbonization is carefully selected and prepared for charging into the coke ovens. Two or more coals are generally blended, one a high-volatile coal and the other a low-volatile coal. Medium-volatile coal is sometimes used. The low-volatile coal is usually 15 per cent to 25 per cent of the mixture and the proportion is carefully controlled because this type of coal has the property of developing high pressure against the coke oven wall which can cause distortion or serious damage to the brickwork. Coke oven plants maintain a quantity of coal in storage but, since coals lose their coking properties by oxidation in storage, it is necessary to continually remove and replace the stocked coal so that it is not in the stock pile for more than about 6 months. It is also necessary to keep each type of coal in a separate storage pile. In the coal preparation plant, each coal is first broken to about minus 1 inch size in a Bradford Breaker or roll crusher. Each type of broken coal is placed in a mixer bin and the various types of coal are proportioned by withdrawing them from the bottom of the mixer bin onto a slow moving belt, using a gate to regulate the height of the coal on the belt. After blending, the combined coals pass through a hammer mill where they are pulverized to about 80% minus $\frac{1}{8}$ inch. This method of coal preparation is used where high-volatile and low-volatile coals are blended. However, when only high-volatile coal is carbonized, relatively coarse coal is sometimes sent to the ovens. After pulverization, the coal is sent to a bin over the coke ovens from which it is withdrawn into a charging car for charging into the coke ovens.

Each coke oven has three or four holes in the top through which the coal is charged. The coal is generally weighed in the charging car so that each oven receives the same amount of coal; in some cases the coal is charged by volume. The control of the bulk density of the coal in the ovens has become an important consideration and this is done by controlling the moisture content and by adding very small amounts of a light petroleum oil. Since uniformity of heating of the ovens has an important bearing on the quality of the coke produced, it is essential that the bulk density of the charge be uniform throughout the charge and from oven to oven. Coke ovens are charged and pushed on a regular schedule. At the end of the coking period the doors are removed mechanically and the coke is pushed out by the ram of a pusher machine.

Due to the recent very rapid increase in the utilization of natural gas, the distribution of gas produced from coal for city use is rapidly disappearing. This includes not only the gas made by the carbonization of coal in retorts and coke ovens, but also water-gas made from coke.

Chemical Recovery Coke Ovens. Chemical recovery coke ovens are narrow vertical chambers built of silica brick and arranged in groups called batteries. The ovens are about 40 feet long, 12 to 15 feet high, and average 14 to 18 inches wide. The width of the ovens tapers from one end to the other to facilitate the pushing of coke from the oven. In the walls between each oven are flues in which gas is burned to supply the heat for carbonization. A battery may contain from 25 to 85 coke ovens. Each oven will contain from 12 to 18 tons of coal, and 12 to 18 hours are required to complete the carbonization. The temperature in the flues lies between 2000 and 2650° F (1093–1454° C); the temperature at the oven side of the wall is 1700 to 2100° F (927–1149° C), and the coke will average 1600 to 2000° F (871–1094° C). These are the temperatures found in general practice for high temperature carbonization. Low-temperature carbonization, which is carried out to a very small extent, will be discussed later. Each end of the coke oven is closed with a door. In the older ovens the doors were sealed with mud, but modern ovens are equipped with self-sealing doors.

Below the coke ovens are the regenerator chambers filled with checker-brick. These are heated by the combustion gases from the flues for a period before the system is reversed to heat the air prior to meeting the gas in the flues where combustion takes place. The regenerators are so arranged that half of them are heating the air for combustion while the other half are receiving heat from the waste combustion gases. A reversal takes place about every half hour. In some cases where the heating gas is lean, for example, producer gas or blast furnace gas, regenerators are arranged to heat both the gas and the air.

The red-hot coke is caught in a car and taken to a quenching station where it is cooled with a water spray. After quenching, the coke is deposited on a sloping wharf where it cools further and is then run off onto a conveyor belt and taken to a screening station to be separated into various sizes. Recovery of the heat from the coke as it leaves the coke oven has been an intriguing engineering problem that has never been successfully solved. Dry quenching plants have been designed and a few have been constructed, but so far the overall result has not been satisfactory.

The type of coke ovens in use in the United States are: Koppers, Koppers-Becker (Fig. 8.1), Wilputte, Semet-Solvay, Otto, and Simon-Carves.

RECOVERY OF COAL CHEMICALS

The volatile products leave the coke oven through an opening at the top of one end of the oven (in some cases there is an opening at each end) and pass through stand-pipes to the collecting main. The purpose of the stand-pipes is to afford a means of sealing off the oven from the collecting main so that the oven can be opened prior to pushing out the coke. There is a cap at the top of the stand-pipe and a liquid seal in the goose-neck which prevents escape of the gas in the collecting main. The collecting main is equipped with sprays to effect the first cooling of the gases and much of the tar is condensed. From the collecting main, which is maintained under a slight pressure (about 10 millimeters water-gauge), the gases pass through a pressure control valve into a suction main to the primary cooler. The condensate, together with spray liquor, leaves the collecting main through pipes and goes to a separating or hot-drain tank where the tar is separated from the weak ammonia liquor. The primary coolers may be either the indirect tubular type or the direct contact type. In the latter, cooled ammonia liquor is sprayed over grid-filled towers. The coolers cool the gas further and condense water vapor and more tar. The gas passes from the coolers through a gas pump which is usually a turbine driven exhauster type of apparatus. From this point the gas is under pressure. A large part of the tar mist remaining in the gas is removed by these high

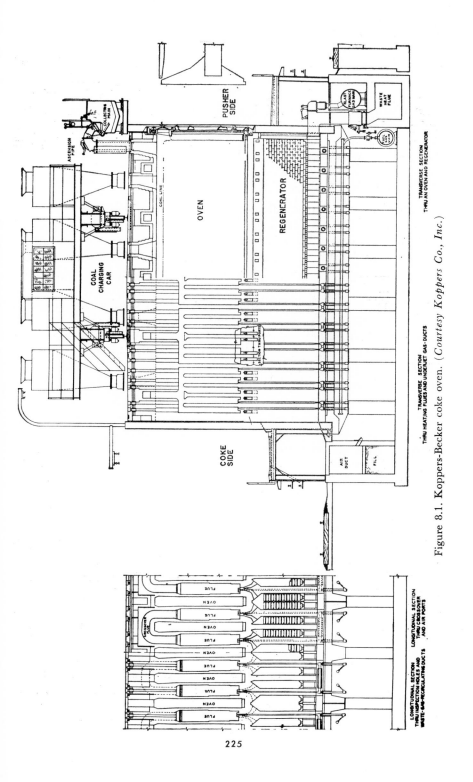

PUSHER SIDE

COAL CHARGING CAR

ASCENSION PIPE

COLLECTING MAIN

OVEN

COAL LINE

REGENERATOR

COKE SIDE

AIR DUCT

FILL

BLAST FURNACE GAS MAIN

WASTE HEAT FLUE

FUEL GAS LINE

TRANSVERSE SECTION
THRU AN OVEN AND REGENERATOR

TRANSVERSE SECTION
THRU HEATING FLUES AND UNDERJET GAS-DUCTS

FLUE

OVEN

FLUE

OVEN

FLUE

OVEN

FLUE

OVEN

FLUE

OVEN

FLUE

CROSSOVER FLUE

LONGITUDINAL SECTION
THRU INSPECTION HOLES AND
WASTE-GAS-RECIRCULATING DUCTS

LONGITUDINAL SECTION
THRU CROSSOVER
AND AIR PORTS

Figure 8.1. Koppers-Becker coke oven. (*Courtesy Koppers Co., Inc.*)

225

speed exhausters, but for removal of the final traces of tar, the gas is passed through an electrostatic precipitator. These are typical apparatus in which a high voltage is imposed on electrodes in the form of steel rods hanging in tubes which are part of the shell and grounded. Tar collects on the electrodes and drips into the bottom collecting section. Following the precipitator, the gas passes through a reheater to raise the dew point, and thence to the ammonia recovery section.

Ammonia Recovery

Ammonia is most commonly recovered as ammonium sulfate. In order to recover all the ammonia as the sulfate, the portion that is contained in the weak ammonia liquor is recovered by steam distilling the weak liquor in the ammonia still (see Ammonia Distillation). The steam-ammonia vapors from this still are added to the gas stream leaving the reheater as it enters the saturator. There are two types of saturators. In the older type, the gas bubbles through a bath which is a saturated solution of ammonium sulfate containing about 5 per cent sulfuric acid. The ammonium sulfate precipitates in the form of crystals and these crystals together with the mother-liquor are pumped to a collecting box at the top of the saturator. After drawing the mother-liquor from the crystals, the salt is put into a centrifuge. The relatively dry crystals are then removed to storage for bagging and shipment. A continuous centrifuge may be used, in which case the mother-liquor and salt are continuously circulated to the centrifuge and the mother liquor returned to the saturator.

Several types of low differential saturators have been designed for the purpose of reducing the pressure drop of the saturator and increasing the size of the crystals. These are frequently constructed of stainless steel. Larger crystals result from a sufficient residence time in the bath to permit growth of the crystals. Recently, several coke oven plants have been recovering the ammonia in the form of either mono- or di-ammonium phosphate.

A small amount of concentrated ammonia liquor containing 20% NH_3 is produced by passing the vapors from the ammonia still through a dephlegmator and condenser. The phenol in the ammonia still waste is removed by contacting it with light oil which extracts the phenol. The phenol is removed from the light oil by reaction with caustic soda to form sodium phenolate. Recovery of the tar acids becomes a credit against the cost of the phenol removal. Dephenolization is described in detail in a later section.

After the gas has been treated for ammonia recovery, it is passed through a final cooler and then conducted to the light-oil scrubbers where a scrubbing oil (light petroleum oil) flowing countercurrent to the gas removes benzene, toluene, xylene and naphthalene. The benzolized oil is steam distilled to remove and separate the light-oils. The scrubbing oil is cooled and returned to the light oil scrubbers. The light oil is fractionated into crude

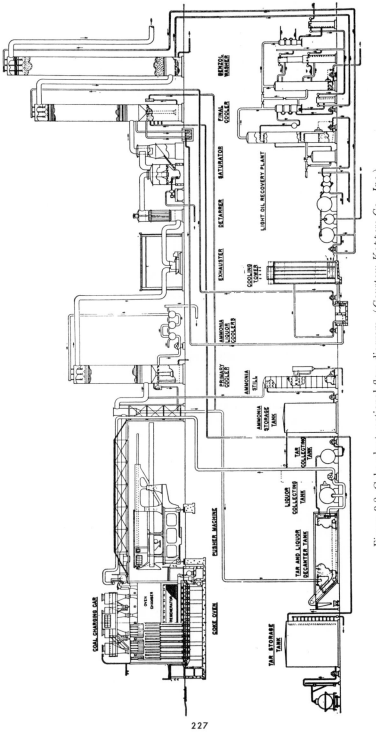

Figure 8.2. Coke plant sectional flow diagram. (*Courtesy Koppers Co., Inc.*)

227

fractions, which are washed with concentrated sulfuric acid and neutralized with caustic soda. Each fraction is then distilled to obtain the pure products, benzene and toluene. The demand for sulfur-free benzene and toluene for the chemical industry has led to the introduction of a high pressure hydrogenation process to remove thiophene and other impurities.

Yield. The amounts of gas, coke, and other materials obtained from one ton of coal vary with the kind of coal used. The following tabulation, taken from the Minerals Yearbook, is representative since the quantities do not change very much from year to year:

Materials Produced per Ton of Coal in 1959

Gas	10,350 cu ft
Coke (excluding "breeze")	1,404 lb
Tar	8.41 gal
Ammonium sulfate	18.7 lb
Light oil	2.81 gal

Liquid Purification. The gas which has now been stripped of its useful chemicals still contains H_2S as an impurity. Because of the introduction of natural gas for city use, substantially all coke oven gas is now used in the steel mills. Removal of sulfur is important for that purpose and the liquid purification processes are most generally used. Final clean-up with iron oxide boxes is not generally practiced. The liquid purification process involves the scrubbing of gas with a solution of sodium carbonate. This removes most of the hydrogen sulfide and hydrogen cyanide. Following the scrubbing operation, the fouled sodium carbonate solution may be treated by several processes. In the simplest method the fouled liquor is pumped to the top of a second tower where it meets an upward moving blast of air which drives out the hydrogen sulfide. The air passing out of the tower with the H_2S may be exhausted to the atmosphere, but it is preferably conducted to the boilerhouse where it is used as part of the combustion air under the grates.

Instead of driving out the H_2S as such and wasting it, the sulfur may be covered in elemental forms by one of several processes. The Thylox process,[3] most comonly used, uses a solution of sodium carbonate to which has been added arsenic oxide. In a subsequent step, the fouled solution is blown with air so that part of the sulfur is liberated, rises to the top, and is skimmed off and filtered. The solution is reactivated by the air and returned to the absorbing tower. The sulfur, which is extremely finely divided, is valuable as a fungicide.

$$Na_4As_2S_5O_2 + H_2S \rightarrow Na_4As_2S_6O + H_2O$$

absorbing reaction

$$Na_4As_2S_6O + \tfrac{1}{2}O_2 \rightarrow Na_4As_2S_5O_2 + S$$

revivifying reaction

In still another type of process, the H_2S recovered is burned in a sulfuric acid plant and the HCN can be liquified or recovered as NaCN. In the Koppers Hot Actification sulfur recovery process, the solution of sodium carbonate is regenerated by boiling the solution under a vacuum. The absorbed impurities, again mainly hydrogen sulfide, are liberated in a concentrated form, and may be conveniently converted into sulfuric acid in amounts generally sufficient for the ammonium sulfate produced in the plant, and for other process requirements. The installation on Neville

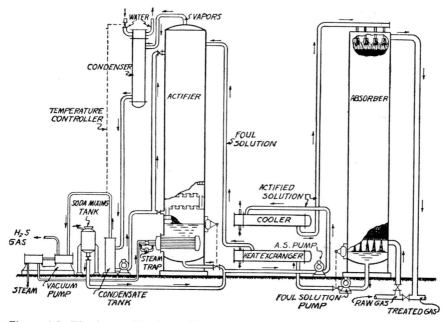

Figure 8.3. The hot actification sulfur recovery process for the purification of coke oven gas and similar gas.

Island (Pittsburgh) shown in Figure 8.3 can treat 22,000,000 cubic feet of gas per day and recover approximately 7 tons of hydrogen sulfide during the same period—enough to produce nearly 20 tons of 66° Bé sulfuric acid.

Modern Practice in Coal Tar Processing

Coal tar is produced by the destructive distillation of soft coal and is a byproduct in the production of coke. In Europe a large quantity of tar is produced in horizontal and vertical retorts as well as coke ovens. In the United States, most of the tar is produced in coke ovens. Tar characteristics are determined by type of coal, type of equipment used for destructive distillation, and by coking temperatures. The major differences in United

States tars can be explained by variations in coking temperatures. At high coking temperatures, tars are highly aromatic, have a relatively high naphthalene content, a low tar acid content, and a high specific gravity. At low temperatures, tars have little if any naphthalene, a high tar acid content, a low specific gravity, and a substantial concentration of paraffinic material. Two general types of tar are produced in the United States.

High-temperature tar is produced at coking temperatures of 1000° C to 1200° C. Most of the tar made in the United States is of this type.

TABLE 8.1. THE UNITED STATES PRODUCTION OF TAR AND TAR PRODUCTS FOR 1959*

		Value per Unit
Tar	669,018,000 gal	
Crude Light Oil	213,036,000 gal	$0.15
Intermediate Light Oil	2,986,000 gal	0.18
Light Oil Distillates		
Benzene		
Tar Distillers & Coke Oven Operators	138,329,000 gal	0.29
Toluene		
Tar Distillers & Coke Oven Operators	30,000,634 gal	0.21
Xylene		
Tar Distillers & Coke Oven Operators	8,008,000 gal	0.28
Solvent Naphtha		
Tar Distillers & Coke Oven Operators	7,834,000 gal	0.26
All Other Light Oil Distillates		
Tar Distillers & Coke Oven Operators	6,370,000 gal	0.18
Pyridine Crude Bases (dry basis)	808,000 gal	1.03
Naphthalene 76–79° C Melt. Pt.	381,024,000 lb	0.05
Crude Tar Acid Oils	21,745,000 gal	0.21
Creosote Oils	90,437,000 gal	0.21
Tar, Road	66,108,000 gal	0.18
for other uses	28,798,000 gal	0.21
Pitch of Tar		
Soft and Medium	909,000 tons	42.01
Hard	619,000 tons	42.82

* United States Tariff Commission, "Synthetic Organic Chemicals," United States Production and Sales—1959.

Tar yield will be about 10 gallons per ton of coke and will contain approximately 10% naphthalene and 2% tar acids. (These tar acids are also known as cresylic acids and include phenol, o, m, and p-creosol, xylenols, and other higher-boiling materials of this type.) Specific gravity at 60/60° F of high temperature tar is usually between 1.18 and 1.23. During periods of low coke demand, industrial practice is to keep all ovens operating, with coke produced on an extended time cycle at a lower temperature. This is done to avoid the high cost of shutting down ovens and results in a tar whose characteristics shift towards those of low-temperature tar.

Low-temperature tar is produced at coking temperatures between 500 to 750° C and accounts for a very small percentage of the tar produced in the United States. It contains substantially no naphthalene, approximately 10% tar acids, and a relatively large quantity of paraffinic material.

In most coke plants, there are two primary points at which the coal tar is condensed and recovered. Sixty-five to seventy-five per cent of the tar is condensed in a large pipe referred to as a collecting main where water is sprayed in to reduce temperature to a little above 200° F. This material contains the highest boiling fractions and will normally contain between seven and nine per cent naphthalene. It has a high specific gravity. The remaining 25 to 35% of the tar is removed in primary coolers and electrical precipitators, will contain between 25 and 30% naphthalene, and have a lower specific gravity. These tars may be processed either separately or as a combination stream. If a company wishes to make electrode pitch for the aluminum industry, this is most easily done by processing the heavy tar from the collecting mains. Production of pitch best suited for some other uses can be done by processing the light or primary cooler tar separately.

In processing tar, it was formerly the aim of the tar distiller to produce as much oil as possible with a minimum quantity of pitch. The greatly increased demand for pitch has reversed this situation so that tar distillers now strive for a maximum production of pitch consistent with a high recovery of naphthalene.

The processing of tar has been carried out in many different ways. The methods which are usually used will be described below along with some interesting commercial variations. Tar is first distilled to obtain separate fractions such as light oil, tar acid oil (phenol, cresol, etc.), creosote oil, and pitch. This distillation was formerly carried out in batch stills and there are still a few of these in operation today. Most of the tar processed in the United States at the present time is fractionated in continuous distillation units.

Tar Processing. To illustrate modern processing methods, three modern tar distillation units will be described.

In one continuous unit, tar feed is preheated first by heat exchange and then in the convection section of an oil fired heater and flashed into a dehydration column. Water and light oil are removed at the top of this column and then separated by decantation. The balance of the tar is heated to a high temperature in the radiant section of the oil-fired heater and flashed into the main fractionating column which operates under vacuum. Solvent naphtha, tar acids, and cumerone-indene resins are removed in the overhead fraction with crude naphthalene and creosote cuts being withdrawn at two separate points on the side of the column. Pitch of the desired melting point is withdrawn continuously from the base of the column. Figure 8.4 is a closeup view of the heart of this plant. The main fractionation tower with its multiple side draw streams stands in the center with the smaller dehydration tower to the right. This plant is designed to process both light (primary cooler) and heavy tars and to produce pitches of widely different melting points.

Another continuous distillation unit designed to process tar which has a high concentration of naphthalene and very few tar acids operates as

Figure 8.4. Continuous tar distillation unit. (*Courtesy Badger Manufacturing Co.*)

follows: Tar feed is heated in a fired heater and then flashed, with the vapor fed to a vacuum dehydration column and the bottoms sent to a second flash system. The pitch product is removed from the base of this second flash system with the overhead vapor going to creosote blending. Solvent naphtha and water are removed from the overhead of the dehydration column and separated by decantation. The bottoms from the dehydration column are pumped to an atmospheric distillation tower where naphthalene is produced as an overhead product, light creosote removed as a sidedraw cut near the base, with the bottoms reflashed for separation of creosote oil from heavy ends.

Another modern tar plant, shown in Figure 8.5, is located at U. S. Steel's Clairton works. The plant is made up of two identical multiple column distillation units. As can be seen in the picture, these units are located on either side of a common stack. The tar is first heated to convert the contained water to steam which is flashed off and condensed. The dehydrated tar then goes to a two-stage flash drum where the more volatile components are separated from the pitch which flows continuously from the base of the

Figure 8.5. Continuous tar distillation unit. (*Courtesy U. S. Steel News*)

flash drum. The flashed vapors are condensed and pumped to multiple fractionating columns working in series. Each column is designed to remove a different fraction from the tar. In each succeeding column, the material is heated to a progressively higher temperature so that tar components of increasingly higher boiling points will vaporize and can be removed as distilled products.

Special problems of corrosion and erosion are encountered in the processing of tar due to the presence of solid particles, water, ammonium chloride, and other chemicals which can cause severe corrosion when concentrated. The newer plants have incorporated techniques which minimize these difficulties. Recent practice has been to use newer types of fractionating trays which give better fractionation at considerably lower pressure drops.

Refining Tar Fractions. The refining of the various tar fractions constitutes an important industry because it furnishes the raw materials for many other products. The processes are as follows:

1. The light oil from the tar distillation is combined with the main light oil stream from the gas scrubbers. Past practice has been to acid wash this material and then fractionate it into its main components (benzene, toluene, xylene, and higher-boiling liquids). The demand in recent years for chemicals

Figure 8.6. Modern light oil plant. (*Courtesy Badger Manufacturing Co.*)

of very high purity has led to the development of improved processing methods to reduce the paraffinic and sulfur impurities which the acid washing process does not completely remove. The first modern light oil processing plant in the United States was built for the Jones & Laughlin Steel Corporation and is shown in Figure 8.6. This comprises a hydrodesulfurization unit for removal of sulfur impurities by hydrogenating the light oil at an elevated temperature and pressure. The sulfur impurities are converted to hydrogen sulfide which is then stripped out of the light oil. The light oil is then sent to an aromatics extraction unit where paraffinic impurities are removed from the aromatics by liquid-liquid extraction. In Figure 8.6 the desulfurization reactors and stripper are located on the left and the aromatics extraction unit is in the center.

2. In the past, the tar acid oil has been caustic washed for removal of tar acids. After separation of the neutralized tar acids in a water solution, they are recovered by "springing," either by acidulation with sulfuric acid or with carbon dioxide. Modern methods of tar acid removal include solvent extraction with dual solvents such as methanol and pentane.

3. After removal of the tar acids, the pyridine bases may be removed by acidification and decantation. Pyridine bases are then recovered from this acid solution by neutralization and distillation.

Figure 8.7. Naphthalene distillation plant. (*Courtesy Badger Manufacturing Co.*)

4. The oil remaining after removal of tar acids is commonly referred to in the United States as "neutral oil." This stream contains most of the naphthalene which was produced in the coke ovens and which is one of the most valuable constituents of coal tar. Naphthalene is recovered from this oil by either distillation, crystallization, or a combination of these two methods. Most crystallization processes now in use result in a recovery of only 50 to 75% of the naphthalene. This is true of the "hot pressed" naphthalene widely produced in Europe. Recovery of over 90% of the naphthalene is normal practice in modern distillation plants. Shown in Figure 8.7 is one of the world's largest naphthalene distillation plants.

5. The creosote may be withdrawn from the tar distillation unit as one fraction or several fractions. In the latter case, these streams would be

referred to as light, middle, and heavy creosote. United States demand for creosote is not great and it is therefore usually difficult to dispose of in this country. Intensive research work has been done on upgrading the creosote stream to obtain more valuable products. No significant results have been published as yet.

6. Numerous grades of pitch can be produced. Two major United States classifications are roofing pitch which has a 65° C melting point, and electrode pitch for the aluminum industry which normally requires a melt point of 110 to 115° C. In electrolysis of aluminum, the anodes are composed of carbon particles cemented together with coal tar pitch. Approximately 0.6 to 0.7 lb of anode is consumed for each pound of aluminum produced. The electrode pitch has to have a high free carbon content (C_1-carbon which is measured as the benzene insoluble material, and C_2-carbon which is measured as quinoline insoluble material). The high free carbon content is obtained by either distilling a heavy tar which already contains sufficient free carbon or else the pitch can be thermally treated to produce a high free carbon content.

In the decade from 1950 to 1960, the dependence on the coke oven industry for aromatic chemicals has ended, since the petrochemical industry is now the major source of these materials. This is illustrated by the following table.

	1960 Capacity[1,2]	
	Coke Oven Industry	Petrochemical Industry
Benzene, Million Gal	203	369
Toluene, Million Gal	43	326
Xylenes, Million Gal	12	308
Naphthalene—Million Lb	642	(450) *

* Capacity under construction.

Ammonia Distillation. The ammonia still shown in Figure 8.8 liberates ammonia gas in two distinct steps. The upper part of the tall vessel, to the right in Figure 8.8, is a six-plate tower, each plate having caps and run-down pipes. The liquor to be distilled is fed in at the top plate; the free ammonia is driven out by heat alone. Free ammonia is that which is combined as ammonium hydroxide, sulfide and carbonate. At the last plate, a liquor collects which has no free ammonia, but still contains fixed ammonia, that which is combined as sulfate or chloride, which must be treated with lime in order to liberate the ammonia gas. This liquor runs through by-pass 2 (see Figure 8.8) to the lower part of the taller vessel, where milk of lime is sent in. Liquor and lime mix thoroughly by the time they reach the over-flow to the fixed leg, where they travel downward over plates with caps and through the run-down pipes to the waste pipe 7. A strong flow of steam enters near the base of the fixed leg, driving out the ammonia completely; the latter passes upward into the free still and with the ammonia from that

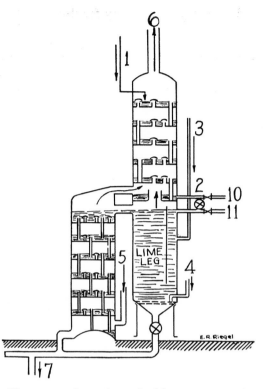

Figure 8.8. Operation of ammonia still with continuous operation. 1, liquor inlet into free still; 2, by-pass to lime leg or mixing vessel, receiving lime at 3 and steam at 4; the milky suspension overflows to the fixed leg, receiving steam at 5; 6, ammonia vapors outlet; 7, waste pipe to sewer.

still, passes through a dephlegmator to the saturators, where ammonium sulfate is produced.

The reactions with lime are:

$$2NH_4Cl + Ca(OH)_2 \rightarrow 2NH_3 + CaCl_2 + 2H_2O$$
$$(NH_4)_2SO_4 + Ca(OH)_2 \rightarrow 2NH_3 + CaSO_4 + 2H_2O$$

In the free still, they are:

$$(NH_4)_2S \rightarrow 2NH_3 + H_2S; \quad (NH_4)_2CO_3 \rightarrow 2NH_3 + CO_2 + H_2O$$

and several others in small proportion.

In regular coke-oven practice, the ammonia still receives only a small part of the total ammonia in any form; the bulk of the ammonia from the coal passes directly to the saturators while still in the coke-oven gas, as stated under Ammonia Recovery. It is the increment in the ammonia liquor used as cooling spray which is sent to the still, together with the water layer from the condensate in secondary coolers.

A certain amount of gas liquor will always have to be distilled to recover ammonia because of the large quantity of water vapor released by the coke ovens (approximately 200 lb per ton of coal). When this vapor is cooled and condensed, it absorbs a fraction of the ammonia.

A process which has been used extensively in industry for de-phenolizing waste ammonia liquor is shown in Figure 8.9. The process consists of removing the phenol from the waste liquor by counter current liquid-liquid extraction with a solvent such as light oil or benzene. The phenol is removed from the solvent stream by liquid-liquid extraction with an aqueous caustic solution. The sodium phenolate thus formed is then converted to phenol by "springing" with either carbon dioxide or an acid such as sulfuric.

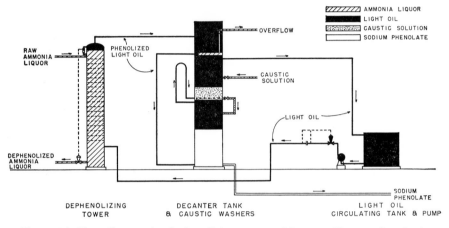

Figure 8.9. Flow diagram for dephenolizing process. (*Courtesy Koppers Co., Inc.*)

Some newer de-phenolization methods have been developed which use improved solvents. Several recent commercial installations use a bacteriological treatment to oxidize the phenols to chemical compounds which are not objectionable.

Low-Temperature Carbonization

Low-temperature carbonization consists of heating coal or lignite to a temperature in the range of 930–1380° F (500–750° C). There have been many processes developed for low-temperature carbonization, but not more than two or three have been successful. The advantages claimed for the processes involve a much higher tar yield and a more combustible solid fuel. Due to the low temperature, however, static processes require a much longer coking time that reduces plant capacity. Using the fluidized process, the time of coking is much shorter, but coking coals must be pretreated to destroy the caking properties of the coal. There are only two salable products of low-temperature carbonization, coke and tar, since the gas produced is just about sufficient to supply heat for the process. The tar is quite different in composition from that of high temperature carbonization and contains appreciable quantities of aliphatic compounds and substituted tar acids. Much work has been done to develop valuable products, but the over-all value of the tar is much less than high-temperature tar. For the present, the low-temperature processes are of small industrial importance in the United States.

Underground Gasification

The underground gasification of coal has received attention both in Europe and the United States. This process is said to have some value in recovery of energy from coal seams that are too thin to mine. It was proposed that underground gasification could supply synthesis gas. Large scale investigations have been undertaken in Alabama and also in Kansas with fair results. The coal in the seam is ignited and a limited volume of air admitted; combustion and distillation take place at the same time and the gases and vapors produced are carried out through a shaft and collected.

REFERENCES

1. *Chem. and Eng. News,* **118,** Mar. 20 (1961).
2. *Chem. and Eng. News,* **140,** Mar. 27 (1961).
3. Gollmar, H. A., *Ind. Eng. Chem.,* **26,** 130 (1934).
4. Minerals Yearbook, Vol. II (1959).

READING REFERENCES

"Chemistry of Coal Utilization," H. H. Lowry, John Wiley & Sons, Inc., New York (1945), 2 vols.

"Coal, coke and coal chemicals," Philip J. Wilson, Jr., New York, McGraw-Hill Book Co., Inc., 1950.

"Encyclopedia of chemical technology," vol. 13, 614–631, Interscience Encyclopedia, Inc., 1954.

"Gas-Coke and By-Product Making Properties of American Coals and Their Determination," A. C. Fieldner and J. D. Davis, American Gas Association, N. Y. (1934), Monograph No. 5.

"Low-temperature carbonization," David Brownlie, *Ind. Eng. Chem.,* **19,** 39 (1927), and preceding eight articles.

"Methods, apparatus used in determining the gas, coke, and by-product making properties of American coals," A. C. Fieldner, J. D. Davis, R. Thiessen, E. B. Kester, and W. A. Selvig, *Bur. Mines Bull.* **No. 344,** 1931. This bulletin contains 18 micrographs of thin sections of coal, showing microspores and macrospores.

"Selection of Coals for the Manufacture of Coke," Charles C. Russell, American Gas Association Proceedings (1947).

"The distillation of coal tar," John M. Weiss, *J. Soc. Chem. Ind.,* **51,** 219 (1932).

"The technology of low temperature carbonization," Frank M. Gentry, Baltimore, Williams and Wilkins Co., 1928.

9

RUBBER

In collaboration with Dr. R. L. Bebb*

INTRODUCTION

PRIOR TO WORLD WAR II, the word "rubber" referred primarily to natural rubber in all applications. As war became imminent and the supply of natural rubber less certain, synthetic rubber assumed an important role, and "rubber" acquired a more general meaning. Since the development of the synthetic rubber industry, sponsored by the government during World War II, synthetic rubber has become an important raw material.

There are several types of synthetic rubber. The first to become commercially available in the United States was Thiokol (1930), and the next, neoprene (1931). Both are still produced commercially. The next important synthetic rubber, the all-purpose type made from butadiene and styrene, represents the bulk of the raw rubber produced in the United States during the war years under the designation GR-S. Specific purpose synthetic rubbers such as butyl rubber, the silicones, Hypalon, nitrile rubber, and the polyurethane elastomers, augment the general-purpose types.

The relative consumption of synthetic and natural rubber in the United States is indicated in Figure 9.1. Importation of Hevea or natural rubber dropped suddenly in 1942, the deficiency being supplied by the synthetic rubber industry during the war years. Reserves of Hevea permitted a comparatively even rate of consumption. Reclaimed rubber, both natural and

* The Firestone Tire & Rubber Company.

synthetic, contributed a sizeable total to the United States rubber raw material reserve during the war.

Production curves and prices for the butadiene-styrene type are charted in Figure 9.2. The relatively steady price of synthetic rubber tended to stabilize the price of the natural product. After the Korean War the price of natural rubber rose from 15 to approximately 75 cents per pound, and synthetic rubber replaced much of the natural rubber then in use. As the price of natural rubber again decreased in 1954 to 20 cents a pound, many

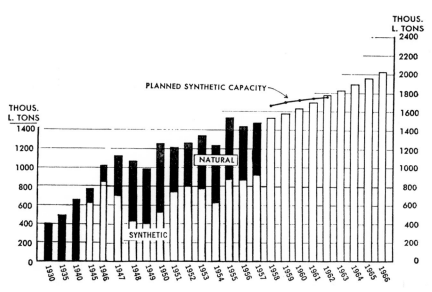

Figure 9.1. United States new rubber consumption. (USDC and RMA)

consumers changed from the synthetic to the natural product. Since that time a fairly free interchange of the two products has been made, depending on the price of each.

Prior to World War II work was begun by several rubber and petroleum companies on the development of the butadiene-styrene general-purpose type of synthetic rubber (GR-S). When the United States actively entered the war, these companies entered into research, development, and production contracts with the government, and for the period from December 1941 to April 1955 conducted, under government sponsorship, closely coordinated programs in which open exchange of background and experience was encouraged. Without close cooperation the success of the synthetic rubber program would have been almost impossible; that it did succeed is evidenced by the production curve of synthetic rubber and the stability of the price of both synthetic and natural rubber. Although decisions had to be made rapidly so that construction of the plants could be started, many authorities were brought into the program and moves made only after the problems had been given due consideration.

Exit of the government from the production of synthetic rubber was planned under the laws by which the emergency program was set up. After

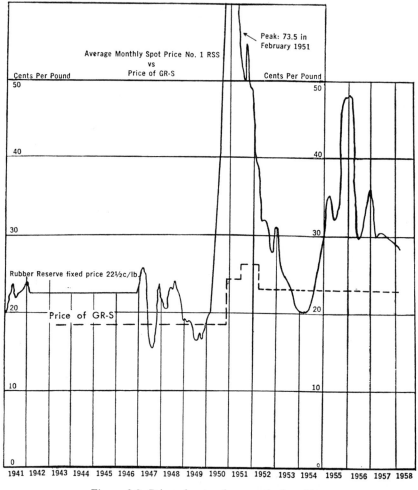

Figure 9.2. Price of natural *vs.* synthetic rubber.

advertising the sale of plants and considering the bids, the government sold the plants to private companies who, in turn, were required to maintain the plants so that synthetic rubber of the GR-S type could be immediately produced in the event of an emergency. Production capacity for producing monomers and rubber has increased considerably under private operation.

The growth of plants under private operation is indicated in Table 9.1.

TABLE 9.1. PRODUCTION CAPACITIES BUTADIENE-STYRENE RUBBERS

Thousand LT Gross

	May 1, 1955	Dec. 31, 1957	Dec. 31, 1960 (est)
ASRC†	44.0	68.5	75.0
Copolymer	49.0	75.0	133.0
Firestone	129.6	231.1	251.5
General		40.0	54.0
Goodrich-Gulf	95.0	232.0	272.5
Goodyear	146.5	255.6	270.0
Phillips	69.4	111.0	121.5
Shell	94.0	126.0	104.0
Texas-U. S.	88.0	127.0	156.0
U. S. Rubber	22.0	30.0	32.0
United Rubber	62.0	69.8	69.8
All Others		5.3	20.3
TOTALS	799.7	1371.3	1559.6

* Compiled from information in the 4th report of the Attorney General on competition in the synthetic rubber industry, July 1, 1959.

† American Synthetic Rubber Corporation.

The following are some important dates in the history of synthetic rubber:

1860 Isolation of isoprene from pyrolyzate of natural rubber, and polymerization to elastomer. Williams, *Proc. Roy. Soc.*, **10**, 616 (1860).

1863 Preparation of butadiene (by pyrolysis of amyl alcohol). Caventou, *Ann.*, **127**, 93 (1863).

1884 Isoprene from turpentine, an independent source of monomer. Tilden, *Chem. Soc.*, **45**, 411 (1884).

1912 First emulsion polymerization patent (German) 254,672 (1912). Isoprene in egg albumen solution.

1915 So-called "methyl" rubber produced in Germany for emergency use.

1930 Thiokol, an organic polysulfide elastomer with resistance to solvents and oils, introduced.

1931 Neoprene (orginally DuPrene), an elastomeric polymer of 2-chlorobutadiene-1,3 with resistance to solvents, introduced.

1933 Buna S, a butadiene styrene elastomer, introduced in Germany.

1936 Buna N, an oil-resistant butadiene-acrylonitrile copolymer, introduced in Germany.

1939 Mercaptan-persulfate emulsion recipe for butadiene-styrene copolymers, later adapted for GR-S production as the "Mutual Recipe," French Patent 843,903, July 12, 1939.

1940 Butyl rubber, characterized by very low permeability to gases, introduced.
1942 GR-S (hot rubber) production begun in the United States. (G. R. stands for "government rubber.")
1944 Silicone elastomers with retention of elastomeric properties over a wide range of temperature introduced.
1946 Polyurethane elastomers prepared by diisocyanate coupling of dihydroxy compounds introduced in Germany.
1947 Cold rubber (41° F) production begun in the United States.
1951 Oil-extended rubber production begun in the United States.
1954–55 Synthesis of *cis*-polyisoprene (synthetic natural rubber) announced. Also known as "Coral" or "Natsyn" rubber.
1955 Purchase of government-owned synthetic rubber plants by private industry, and beginning of expansion of production capacity.

This chapter will include a description of the routes for manufacturing synthetic rubbers, and of the production of natural rubber, the preparation of monomers used in the synthetic rubber industry, and the compounding and curing of rubbers in general.

SYNTHETIC RUBBERS

Butadiene-Styrene Copolymers

$$C_6H_5CH{=}CH_2$$
Styrene

A highly simplified flow sheet for the preparation of butadiene-styrene synthetic rubber is shown in Figure 9.3.

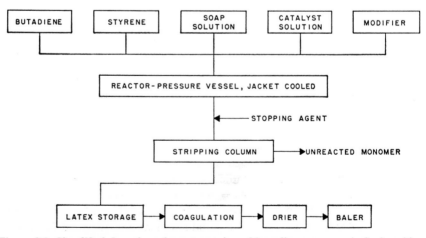

Figure 9.3. Simplified flow sheet for preparation of butadiene-styrene synthetic rubber.

The formula adopted on March 26, 1942 by the Technical Advisory Committee of Rubber Reserve for the preparation of "hot" rubber is as follows: [13,15]

	Parts Per 100 Monomer
Butadiene	75
Styrene	25
Water	180
Soap	5.0
Lorol Mercaptan (n-$C_{12}H_{25}SH$)	0.50
Potassium Persulfate	0.30
Polymerization Temperature	50° C
Time	12 hours
Conversion	75%

The object of the polymerization is to form rubbery polymers of butadiene and styrene of a desired molecular weight. The polymerization is initiated by potassium persulfate, and the molecular weight is regulated by a mercaptan. The role of the mercaptan in this polymerization is particularly important since its type and concentration regulates the molecular weight of the polymer and determines its processing characteristics. Chemical reactions occurring in hot (50° C) emulsion polymerization are given below:

(1) $K_2S_2O_8$ + $C_{12}H_{25}SH$ → $C_{12}H_{25}S\cdot$ Generation of
    Potassium   Dodecyl   Mercaptyl   free radicals
    persulfate   mercaptan   free radical

(2) $C_{12}H_{25}S\cdot$ + $CH_2{=}CHCH{=}CH_2$ → $C_{12}H_{25}SCH_2CH{=}CHCH_2\cdot$ Initiation
              Butadiene   Monomer free radical

(3) $C_{12}H_{25}SCH_2CH{=}CHCH_2\cdot$ +
   $n(CH_2{=}CHCH{=}CH_2)$ → $C_{12}H_{25}S(CH_2CH{=}CHCH_2)_{n+1}\cdot$ Propagation
   Butadiene   Homopolymer radical
   and/or
   $m(C_6H_5CH{=}CH_2)$ → $C_{12}H_{25}S(CH_2CH{=}CHCH_2)(CH_2CH)_m\cdot$
   Styrene   Copolymer radical |
                                                C_6H_5

(4) $C_{12}H_{25}S(CH_2CH{=}CHCH_2)_{n+1}\cdot$ + $C_{12}H_{25}SH$ →
                    $C_{12}H_{25}S(CH_2CH{=}CHCH_2)_{n+1}H$ Termination
                                  Polymer   and chain
                                                    transfer
                                              + $C_{12}H_{25}S\cdot$

The polymerization reactors are designed to withstand pressures over 100 psig. The temperature of the reactants is adjusted to the desired level by controlling the temperature in the reactor jacket or in the internal coils.

The reactors vary in size from 3700 gallons in the early plants to over 5000 gallons. They are either constructed of stainless steel or glass-lined or clad with stainless steel to minimize iron contamination; they are jacketed and agitated. Different types of agitators have been used for the rubber plants;

their selection depends considerably on the type of mercaptan used, since the efficiency of the mercaptan action is affected by the type and rate of agitation. In a hot polymerization the pressure within the reactor may reach 70 psig, dropping to about 40 psig at approximately 70 per cent conversion of the monomer.

The reactors are usually located in a chain and may be equipped for either batch or continuous operation. In the batch route butadiene, styrene, soap solution, catalyst, and modifier are charged directly into the reactor. In the continuous operation the various ingredients are metered into the bottom of the first reactor, out the top, and into the bottom of the second reactor. This process is repeated throughout the chain, the extent of polymerization being followed by total solids measurement.

During polymerization the hydrocarbons are emulsified in the soap solution; a portion is dissolved in the soap micelles where polymerization is initiated. As polymerization proceeds the soap micelle loses importance and the balance of the reaction takes place in the polymer-monomer particles.[18] Butadiene and styrene do not enter the polymer at the same rate. In a 75/25 charge the initial polymer contains 17.2 per cent styrene, whereas at 80 per cent conversion the polymer contains 21.2 per cent styrene and at total conversion, 25.0 per cent.

At the desired conversion, polymerization is stopped by the addition of a material such as hydroquinone which destroys the catalyst and arrests further polymerization. At this stage the rubber is contained in a milky stable suspension known as latex. Before being used as such, or coagulated to isolate the rubber, the latex must be stripped of unreacted monomers. This is done in two steps, butadiene being removed with a compressor and styrene by vacuum steam distillation.

An antioxidant must be added before the latex is coagulated, to prevent deterioration of the rubber during drying, storage, and processing. One material frequently used is phenyl-beta-naphthyl amine, about 1.25 per cent being added as a suspension on the dry rubber. The latex is then coagulated with an acidified brine solution or an acid-glue mixture, or by means of an aluminum sulfate solution. One practice involves creaming the latex with concentrated brine and adding it to an agitated vessel along with dilute acid until the particle size of the crumb reaches the desired value. The fatty acids are released from the soap on the surface of the copolymer particles and large porous crumb aggregates are formed. The crumbs pass over a vibrating screen or an Oliver filter to remove the serum. The rubber is again reslurried, washed, and filtered. It then passes over a continuous belt dryer where it is dried at the lowest possible temperature in the shortest time. The dried rubber is pressed into 75-pound bales for shipment.

The finished butadiene-styrene rubber contains fatty acids, rosin acids, antioxidants, moisture, and some inorganic materials, mainly sodium chloride.

Since termination of the government program, many types of hot rubber have been introduced to the trade for different uses. These have represented variations in butadiene-styrene ratios, changes in plasticity, changes in conversion, and changes in antioxidant and methods of coagulation. Important objectives have been improvements in properties, processing characteristics, and color.

Cold Rubber

Throughout the government program there was a persistent belief that a better rubber could be made at lower polymerization temperatures. Efforts to activate the hot recipe were not particularly successful, and the polymerization times were long at temperatures lower than 50° C (122° F). In the early part of the program a number of revised recipes were proposed, but these did not reduce the polymerization temperature substantially below 30° C. There was no major improvement in the quality of this rubber over that of a normal hot control.

The successful development of ways to accelerate polymerization at low temperatures centered around the "Redox" system which was developed independently in Germany, Great Britain, and the United States. The Redox system involves the presence of an oxidizing agent, usually a peroxide or hydroperoxide, a reducing agent, and a soluble salt of a metal capable of existing in several states of oxidation.

Chemical reactions in cold (5° C) emulsion polymerization are:

(1) $\quad$ ROOH $\quad + \quad$ Fe^{++} $\quad \rightarrow \quad$ RO· $\quad +$ Fe^{+++} $\quad$ Generation of
$\quad$ Diisopropylbenzene $\quad$ Ferrous ion $\quad$ Peroxyl $\qquad\qquad$ free radicals
$\quad$ hydroperoxide $\qquad\qquad\qquad$ free radical

(2) RO· $+$ CH$_2$=CHCH=CH$_2$ $\rightarrow$ ROCH$_2$CH=CHCH$_2$· $\quad$ Initiation
$\qquad\qquad$ Butadiene

(3) ROCH$_2$CH=CHCH$_2$· $+$
$\qquad$ n(CH$_2$=CHCH=CH$_2$) $\rightarrow$ RO(CH$_2$CH=CHCH$_2$)$_{n+1}$· $\quad$ Propagation
$\qquad$ Butadiene $\qquad\qquad\qquad$ Homopolymer radical
$\qquad$ and/or
$\qquad$ m(C$_6$H$_5$CH=CH$_2$) $\rightarrow$ RO(CH$_2$CH=CHCH$_2$)(CH$_2$CHC$_6$H$_5$)$_m$·
$\qquad\qquad\qquad\qquad$ Copolymer radical

(4) RO(CH$_2$CH=CHCH$_2$)$_{n+1}$· $+$ RSH $\rightarrow$
$\qquad\qquad$ RO(CH$_2$CH=CHCH$_2$)$_{n+1}$H $\quad$ Termination
$\qquad\qquad$ Polymer

At the end of the war it was learned that the Germans had developed a system using benzoyl peroxide as the oxidizing agent and sugars as the reducing agent. Good rubbers were produced from these systems in the United States, but polymerization characteristics were considered unsatisfactory. The German process was therefore modified in the United States by the introduction of hydroperoxides and by the replacement of sugar with amines. A recent recipe for use at 5° C is as follows:

	Parts per 100 Monomer[25]
Butadiene	71.5
Styrene	28.5
Water	200
Mixed *tert*. Mercaptans	0.125–0.15
Potassium Fatty Acid Soap	4.7
Daxad-11	0.1
KCl	0.5
FeSO$_4$·7H$_2$O	0.004
Sodium Formaldehyde Sulfoxylate (SFS)	0.0228
Ethylene Diamine Tetraacetic Acid (Sequestrene AA)	0.0246
NaOH	0.0024
Sodium Dimethyl Dithiocarbamate (SDD) Stopping Agent	0.10

With the introduction of cold polymerization, it was found that the physical properties of synthetic polymers, and the wear characteristics of tires made from them, were superior to those of hot rubbers (Figure 9.4). As a

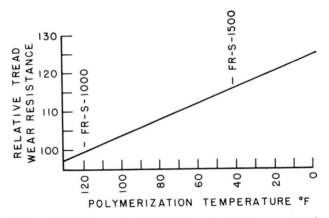

Figure 9.4. Effect of polymerization temperature on tread wear resistance. [Sjothun, *Rubber Age,* **74** (1953).]

consequence, the synthetic rubber program moved increasingly toward cold rubbers. Variations of the polymerization recipe resulted in smoother polymerization rates, better reaction times, and more reproducible performance.

The production equipment used for cold polymerization is similar to that used for hot rubber manufacture except for provision for cooling the reactors with a refrigerant in jackets or in coils within the reactor.

Latex

Since Hevea latex was used extensively before the war, it was logical that synthetic rubber latices should be used as far as possible in similar applications. As in the case of dry rubbers, hot latices were used first despite limitations arising from their generally low film strength. With the introduction of the cold polymerization system, latices more nearly like Hevea latex were introduced for use in the foam rubber industry.

Oil-Extended Rubber

It was known throughout the government synthetic rubber program that high Mooney polymers showed improved wear (Figure 9.5); the difficulty

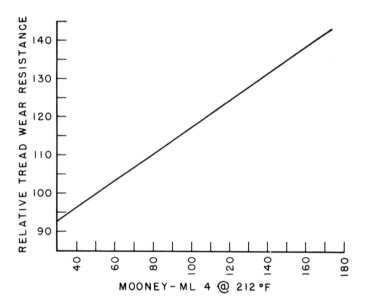

Figure 9.5. Effect of Mooney viscosity on relative tread wear resistance. [Sjothun, *Rubber Age*, **74** (1953).]

arose from the fact that rubbers of high molecular weight and high Mooney plasticities were extremely difficult to process. Hence the practice of mixing high Mooney (120 ML/4 or higher) base polymer with a petroleum oil (usually 25 to 37.5 parts per 100 parts of polymer). The oil may be added to the latex, on a mill, or in a Banbury.

While carbon black may be incorporated into synthetic rubber at the producing plant with conventional dry mixing equipment such as Banbury mixers, it may also be dispersed in the latex before coagulation. Some of the advantages of black masterbatches are minimized need for heavy power-consuming equipment for incorporation, better dispersion of the black, factory cleanliness, and shorter mixing time for rubber stocks.

Butyl Rubber[41]

Butyl rubber is a copolymer of isobutylene with about 3 per cent isoprene. Its polymerization differs considerably from that of butadiene-styrene copolymers. In this case the monomers are polymerized in a solvent containing the dissolved catalyst at polymerization temperatures near $-150°$ F. The catalyst, aluminum chloride, is added as a dilute solution in methyl chloride. As polymerization proceeds, the polymer precipitates and the resultant slurry overflows into an agitated hot water tank. Unreacted monomer flashes off for recovery by drying and condensation. As in the preparation of butadiene-styrene polymers, an antioxidant is added to prevent deterioration during drying and storage. The crumb is passed through a tunnel dryer at 200 to 350° F to remove most of the water; then it is fed into an extruder and onto rubber mills. It is removed continuously to a suitable packaging machine.

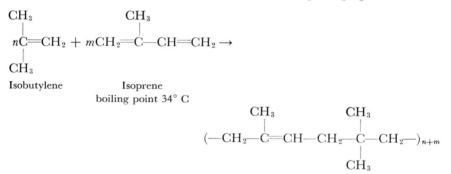

Isobutylene   Isoprene
                  boiling point 34° C

Butyl rubber

Butyl rubber resembles natural rubber in appearance; it is unsaturated and can be vulcanized, but cannot be made into hard rubber because of an extremely low (3 per cent) unsaturation. Butyl rubber does not pass through a latex stage as do butadiene-styrene copolymers. Butyl rubber dispersions may have been prepared indirectly by dissolving the rubber in a solvent, dispersing the solution, and subsequently removing the solvent to leave a dispersion of butyl rubber in water. Since butyl rubber is the least permeable to gases of all rubbers, much of it is consumed in the manufacture of inner tubes for automobile tires. It is also of considerable value in making air bags for curing tires where repeated exposure to high temperatures would greatly shorten the life of normal rubbers.

A somewhat similar polymer known as "Vistanex," a polymer of isobutylene without the addition of isoprene, was developed in Germany. Its range of plasticity varied from a soft sticky gum to tough elastic materials, depending on the degree of polymerization. Unable to be vulcanized, it was mixed with other rubbers for tire treads, for electrical insulation of high voltage wires, for tapes, and for many other special purposes. The seal strength of wax wrappings for frozen foods was found to be improved by blending Vistanex with the coating wax.

Butadiene-Acrylonitrile Copolymers

Butadiene-acrylonitrile copolymers are produced in much the same way as is butadiene-styrene rubber. Because this rubber was not made under government operation there are many trade names for its various types. Each supplier offers a range of plasticities and acrylonitrile contents, thereby achieving considerable variation in oil resistance. Some are stabilized with discoloring antioxidants; others contain light–stable materials for use in special applications.

$$n\mathrm{CH_2}{=}\mathrm{CH} + m\mathrm{CH_2}{=}\mathrm{CH{-}CH}{=}\mathrm{CH_2} \rightarrow$$

$$\underset{\mathrm{CN}}{|}$$

Acrylonitrile   Butadiene

$$(-\mathrm{CH_2{-}CH}{=}\mathrm{CH{-}CH_2{-}CH_2{-}CH}-)_{n+m}$$

$$\underset{\mathrm{CN}}{|}$$

Butadiene-acrylonitrile polymer

The outstanding characteristics of the acrylonitrile rubbers are their resistance to oils, fats, and solvents in general, and their performance at high and low temperatures $(-70$ to $300°$ F$)$.

Since these rubbers are unsaturated, as are the butadiene-styrene rubbers, they may be used for hard rubber by incorporating sufficient sulfur in the classical compounding routes. Latices of butadiene-acrylonitrile copolymers may be used for making foam rubber products as well as special purpose papers.

Neoprene[14,41]

The manufacture of chloroprene $(\mathrm{CH_2}{=}\mathrm{CCl{-}CH}{=}\mathrm{CH_2})$ starts with the conversion of acetylene to monovinylacetylene[26] by polymerization of the acetylene in the presence of an aqueous catalyst solution of cuprous chloride and ammonium chloride. The off-gas is cooled to $-70°$ C to condense the vinyl acetylene $(\mathrm{CH}{\equiv}\mathrm{C{\cdot}CH}{=}\mathrm{CH_2}$, boiling point $5°$ C$)$ while the excess acetylene is recycled. The condensate is distilled in a column; the overhead is pure vinylacetylene while the bottoms contain divinyl-acetylene. One object is to sweep the reactants through the catalyzing solution to avoid the formation of undue amounts of divinylacetylene. Mono-vinylacetylene is then converted to chloroprene by reaction with hydrogen chloride in the presence of a cuprous chloride solution.[7]

The polymerization of chloroprene to neoprene has been described by Walker and Mochel.[27]

	Parts per 100 Monomer
Chloroprene	100
N-Wood rosin	4
Sulfur	0.6 } Dissolved in the monomer
Water	150
Sodium hydroxide	0.8
Sodium salt of naphthalene sulfonic acid—formaldehyde condensation product	0.7
Potassium persulfate	0.2–1.0

The specific gravity change of the contents of the reactor during polymerization is large enough for the conversion to be followed by measuring the gravity. At the desired conversion tetramethylthiuram disulfide is introduced to stop polymerization; the latex is ready for removal of unreacted chloroprene and coagulation. The stripping is done by vacuum steam distillation.

One method for isolating neoprene from the latex involves freezing.[45] Acetic acid is added to the alkaline latex just short of coagulation. The sensitized latex is then passed over the surface of a large brine cooled drum where a sheet is frozen and the rubber is coagulated. The rubber is removed from the drum, washed with water, passed through squeeze rolls, and dried in air at 120° C. The dried film is gathered into ropes and cut into short lengths for bagging and use. The finished rubber has a specific gravity of 1.23.

There are a number of different types of neoprene polymers available. These are sulfur-modified polymers (GN,GNR,GRT) which can be cured by the addition of metal oxides alone. The non-modified types (W and WRT) require accelerators as well as the metal oxides. For vulcanization the neoprene rubbers are usually compounded with light-calcined magnesia and zinc oxide; cross-linking occurs at the 1,2-addition sections. The cured strength may reach 4000 psi with an elongation of 900 per cent, and a 600 per cent modulus value near 1000 psi.

Neoprene is both stable to oxidation and flame resistant; it swells only moderately in oils and chemicals, and has good retention of properties in the swollen state. It has been used in wire insulation, cable jackets, gaskets for aliphatic liquids, belts for power transmission, and conveyor belt covers, especially where oil and heat are encountered. Since it is available as a latex, there are many applications where its unusual properties are an advantage.

The differences between the various synthetic rubbers have been summarized in Table 9.2.

Silicone Rubbers

Silicone rubbers differ from those previously described in that their chains consist of alternate atoms of silicon and oxygen, with no carbon atoms.

TABLE 9.2. RELATIVE PROPERTIES OF NATURAL AND SYNTHETIC RUBBER*

Property	Natural Rubber	Grade R GR-S or Buna S	Butyl	Grade SA Thiokol (GR-P)	Grade SB Nitrile (Buna N)	Grade SC Neoprene (GR-M)	Grade T Silicone
Composition	...	Butadiene-Styrene	Isobutylene-Isoprene	Organic Polysulfide	Butadiene-Acrylonitrile	Chloroprene	Polysiloxane Polymer
Tensile Strength (psi)							
Pure Gum	Over 3000	Below 1000	Over 1500	...	Below 1000	Over 3000	Below 1500
Black Load Stocks	Over 3000	Over 2000	Over 2000	...	Over 2000	Over 3000	...
Hardness Range (Shore Durom A)	30–90	40–90	40–75	35–80	40–95	40–95	40–85
Specific Gravity (Base Material)	0.93	0.94	0.92	1.34	1.00	1.23	...
Tear Resistance	Good	Fair	Good	Poor	Fair	Good	Poor
Abrasion Resistance	Excellent	Good to Excellent	Good	Poor	Good	Excellent	Poor
Solvent Resistance							
Aliphatic hydrocarbons	Poor	Poor	Poor	Excellent	Excellent	Good	Poor
Aromatic hydrocarbons	Poor	Poor	Poor	Good	Good	Fair	Poor
Acid Resistance							
Dilute	Fair to Good	Fair to Good	Excellent	Fair	Good	Excellent	Excellent
Concentrated	Fair to Good	Fair to Good	Excellent	Fair	Good	Good	Fair
Oxygenated Solvents (ketones, etc.)	Good	Good	Good	Good	Poor	Poor	Fair
Permeability to Gasses	Fair	Fair	Very Low	Low	Fair	Low	Fair
Oil and Gasoline Resistance	Poor	Poor	Poor	Excellent	Excellent	Good	Fair
Animal and Vegetable-Oil Resistance	Poor to Good	Poor to Good	Excellent	Excellent	Excellent	Good	Fair
Oxidation	Good	Good	Excellent	Good	Good	Excellent	Excellent
Sunlight Aging	Poor	Poor	Very Good	Good	Poor	Very Good	Excellent
Heat Aging	Good	Very Good	Excellent	Fair	Excellent	Excellent	Outstanding

TABLE 9.2. RELATIVE PROPERTIES OF NATURAL AND SYNTHETIC RUBBER * (Continued)

Property	Natural Rubber	Grade R GR-S or Buna S	Butyl	Grade SA Thiokol (GR-P)	Grade SB Nitrile (Buna N)	Grade SC Neoprene (GR-M)	Grade T Silicone
Resistance to Swelling in Lubricating Oil	Poor	Poor	Poor	Excellent	Very Good	Good	Fair
Resistance to Water Absorption	Very Good	Good to Very Good	Very Good	Fair	Fair to Good	Good	Good
Resistance to Lacquer Solvents	Poor	Poor	Poor	Good	Fair	Poor	Poor
Flame Resistance	Poor	Poor	Poor	Poor	Poor	Good	Fair
Cold Resistance	Excellent	Excellent	Good	Fair	Good	Good	Excellent
Heat Resistance	Good	Excellent	Excellent	Poor	Excellent	Excellent	Excellent
Ozone Resistance	Fair	Fair	Excellent	Excellent	Fair	Excellent	Excellent
Rebound							
Cold	Excellent	Good	Bad	Fair	Good	Very Good	Excellent
Hot	Excellent	Good	Very Good	Fair	Good	Very Good	Excellent
Dielectric Strength	Excellent	Excellent	Excellent	Fair	Poor	Good	Good
Electrical Insulation	Good to Excellent	Good to Excellent	Good to Excellent	Fair to Good	Poor	Fair to Good	Excellent
Compression Set	Good	Good	Fair	Poor	Good	Fair to Good	Fair
Vulcanizing Properties	Excellent	Excellent	Good	Fair	Excellent	Excellent	…
Adhesion to Metals	Excellent	Excellent	Good	Poor	Excellent	Excellent	…
Adhesion to Fabric	Excellent	Good	Good	Fair	Good	Excellent	…

* Krause, R. A. Machine Design, April 19, p. 129 (1956) (by Permission).

Although work on the preparation of the silicone polymers was started in the Corning Research Laboratories, the General Electric Company initiated a program at about the same time, and in 1945 both companies announced the development of silicone rubber.

Most of the silicone rubbers are derived from dimethyldichlorosilane, but variations include a partial substitution of other groups, such as the phenyl for the methyl radical, and the preparation of polymers containing vinyl or allyl radicals.

Dimethyldichlorosilane (boiling point 70° C) is prepared by passing methyl chloride over powdered silicon with copper catalysts at 275 to 375° F. The general reaction is,

$$2CH_3Cl + Si \rightarrow (CH_3)_2SiCl_2$$

The conversion of dimethyldichlorosilane into the polymer follows by the addition of water and subsequent hydrolysis in the presence of small proportions of iron chloride, sulfuric acid, or sodium hydroxide. These catalysts must be washed out of the polymer. Low polymeric materials are removed by distillation.

$$R_2SiCl_2 + 2H_2O \rightarrow R_2Si(OH)_2 + 2HCl$$
$$nR_2Si(OH)_2 \rightarrow HO(SiR_2O)_nH + (n - 1)H_2O$$

Silicone rubbers are useful in a remarkably wide range of temperatures —from −130 to 550° F. Although their tensile strengths are low, other properties compensate. One advantage is the fact that the rubbers are white and can be used for the preparation of light-colored stocks. They are not attacked by ozone and have good electrical properties. Swelling in oils is relatively low, and they are affected by very few chemicals.

Silicone rubbers are generally vulcanized by the addition of a peroxide such as di-*tert*-butyl peroxide or dicumyl peroxide. Oxides of certain metals such as lead and zinc accelerate vulcanization; silica, titania, ferric oxide, and alumina are good fillers.[24,32]

"Hypalon"

This elastomer, recently introduced by the E. I. duPont de Nemours Company, is a chlorosulfonated polyethylene prepared by the action of chlorine on a suitable polyethylene in the presence of sulfur dioxide. The polymer ultimately contains 26 to 29 per cent chlorine and 1.3 to 1.7 per cent sulfur in the form of sulfonyl chloride radicals. These groups become part of the cross-linking reaction during vulcanization.

"Hypalon" is mixed in a normal manner on rubber-mixing equipment without the necessity of breakdown. The material can be calendered and extruded in the usual way and can be colored. No reinforcement by the addition of carbon black is reported. Vulcanizates of Hypalon have fair to good oil resistance, outstanding heat resistance up to 300° F, and good abrasion resistance. The resistance to strong chemicals is such that tubes of Hypalon may be used for handling concentrated sulfuric acid. It is a flame-resistant polymer.

NATURAL RUBBER

Rubber is found in varying amounts in many plants throughout the world. Although others have been used in time of war, only two sources are at present commercially important. The first is the *Hevea brasiliensis,* a tree native to Brazil but now grown throughout the tropics in plantations, and the *Kok Saghys,* a dandelion grown as a biennial in Russia.

Rubber occurs in plants as a milky latex. The dry product is obtained by a process known as coagulation, during which the latex is destabilized by the addition of acids or salts.

Hevea brasiliensis was found growing wild in the tropics of Brazil and was taken into the Far East by the British. Vast natural rubber plantations have grown from this beginning (see Table 9.3). Stock from carefully

TABLE 9.3. SHIPMENTS OF NATURAL RUBBER FROM PRODUCING
COUNTRIES—1960*

	Long Tons
Indonesia	629,808
Malaya	710,485
Thailand	167,165
Vietnam and Cambodia	111,924
Ceylon	97,277
Sarawak	49,658
India	24,794
Other Asia & Oceanic	40,250 (est)
Africa	140,500 (est)
Brazil	22,733
Other Latin Am.	7,000 (est)
Total	2,002,500 (est)

*Taken from Rubber Statistical Bulletin, International Rubber Study Group.

selected trees giving high yields were grafted onto ordinary seedlings to produce a family of descendants from a single tree known as a "clone," and production was improved from an average of 250 to 500 pounds per acre to more than 2000 pounds per acre.

As new seedlings develop in the plantation nursery they are arranged in regular plantings around a collecting house. After the trees are six years old a program is established for tapping them and collecting the latex. In the Hevea brasiliensis the latex occurs in tiny ducts or tubes found under the bark and just outside the green cambium or growing layer. Each morning a diagonal cut just deep enough to produce the latex is made with a special knife. The liquid is collected in a small cup at the bottom of the diagonal cut. When the cut is first made a small amount of preservative is placed in the cup to prevent coagulation. During the several hours before the latex stops flowing a tree will yield about 100 cubic centimeters of normal solids (30 to 40 per cent) latex. This is strained in the collecting station to remove dirt and bark, and treated with more preservative. Then it is transferred to a central factory where it is centrifuged or coagulated.

Because latex is very sensitive to bacterial action, an adequate preservative must be added to protect it from the time it leaves the tree until it is used. Dilute ammonia is commonly used despite its volatility. It does not kill bacteria but reduces their growth. Some plantations use a small amount of formaldehyde to sterilize the latex, following up with ammonia before shipment. Still other producers use Santobrite (sodium pentachlorophenate) at approximately 0.3 per cent based on the latex along with 0.1 per cent ammonia to produce a latex with especially good keeping qualities.[43]

Latex

The natural latex used in commerce is concentrated at the plantations from 30 to 40 per cent solids to about 62 to 68 per cent according to one of four general processes: centrifuging, creaming, evaporating, and electro-decanting.

The *centrifuge* is used to produce most of the concentrated latex of industry. Its success depends on the difference in specific gravities between the rubber and the serum; rubber has a gravity of 0.91 and the serum, 1.02. In this case a special centrifuge separates a cream from a low solids skim containing about 10 per cent solids. The cream fraction is further stabilized by the addition of preservatives and adjusted to correct solids for shipment. Special concentrates for applications requiring low water absorption and high dielectric properties have also been developed by diluting and recentrifuging.

In the *creaming* process a small quantity of a gum such as ammonium alginate, gum tragacanth, or Irish moss is added to produce a reversible agglomeration of the rubber particles. With increased size and slower Brownian movement, the particles cream and a higher solids fraction can be removed from the top. Creamed latices, like centrifuged latices, have lost the major water soluble impurities with the removal of the serum. These latices are therefore of particular value where a low level of impurities is desirable.

Concentration by *evaporation*, although one of the earliest commercial routes, is no longer of primary importance. It requires the addition of stabilizers, alkalis, and soap to the latex. Concentration is effected in a rotating drum in which a smaller rolling drum furnishes additional evaporation and agitates the latex. This route differs from the two previously described in that all ingredients in the original latex plus any additives introduced for stability remain in the finished product. The non-rubber ingredients in the evaporated latex may amount to 6 to 7 per cent. Since latex concentrated by this method can reach as much as 75 per cent solids it is of use in special applications.

The *electrodecantation* method[36] is used to a limited extent. The latex is added to a rectangular tank with an electrode at each end and many grooves, about 1 centimeter apart, in which are placed sheets of regenerated cellophane. When an electric current is applied, particles build up on the cellophane and float to the top as a cream. Fresh latex is added continuously at about the mid-point of the tank to displace the cream from the top of the cell. Latex of 60 to 62 per cent concentration has been produced by this process.

Dry Rubber

The latex is transferred from the collecting station to the factory, stabilized with more preservative such as sodium sulfite if necessary, diluted to about 15 per cent, and coagulated by the addition of dilute formic or acetic acid. In this process the fine particles of rubber agglomerate to large masses. These are transferred to washing and dewatering mills. In the manufacture of "pale crepe" rubber, the material is washed thoroughly before it is dried in a hot oven. In the preparation of "smoked sheets," the freshly coagulated rubber is not washed but dewatered in mills with even-speed rolls, and the wet sheets are dried in wood smoke. The slow smoking process produces a brown rubber which resists deterioration by mold and bacteria. In addition to pale crepe and smoked sheets, plantations produce a number of different grades of rubber including bark, earth scrap, and factory salvage.

The following table, based on an analysis of 35 samples of smoked sheets and 102 samples of pale crepe, gives some idea of the impurities present in both types of rubber.[11]

	Smoked Sheet (Average) %	Pale Crepe (Average) %
Moisture	0.61	0.42
Acetone Extract	2.89	2.88
Protein (N × 6.25)	2.82	2.82
Ash	0.38	0.30
Rubber Hydrocarbon (by difference)	93.30	93.58

The acetone extract fraction contains fatty acids, sterols, and esters. The fatty acids have an important effect on vulcanization; the sterols and esters are believed[33] to contain the natural antioxidants which protect the rubber during processing and storage. The protein fraction has an important effect on the vulcanization rate of the natural rubber. If the coagulum deteriorates during drying or if putrefaction has occurred prior to coagulation, cure rates will vary from lot to lot. The ash content in natural rubber is generally not important unless it is found to contain copper and manganese. These particular elements catalyze oxidation of the rubber and subsequent deterioration. Since these elements are concentrated in the bark of the tree it is important to remove the bark from the latex as soon as possible.

Grades of natural rubber have been established by the Rubber Manufacturers Association[34,43] in an effort to classify the various rubbers produced throughout the world.

POLYMER STRUCTURE

A review of the chemical and physical methods for determining the structure of synthetic rubbers may be found in Reference 41.

The complexity of polymer structure is best illustrated by the polymerization of isoprene. This monomer is capable of polymerizing through 1, 4-addition in a *cis-, trans-,* head-to-tail, and head-to-head arrangement, as well as by configuration 1,2-, and 3,4-:

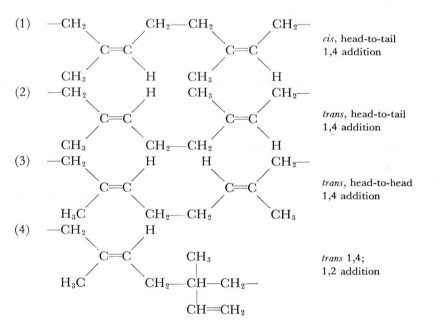

Since about 1955 considerable work has been published on stereospecific catalysts capable of producing polymers with larger amounts of *cis*-addition. In order to define more completely the complexity of these polymers, Professor Natta of Milan, Italy has coined the words *atactic, isotactic,* and *syndiotactic.* A polymer with an ordered arrangement like that of (1) is an isotactic polymer; a polymer with a random arrangement of any sort is an atactic polymer. With the recently developed anionic polymerization catalysts it is possible to produce polymers with a regular spiral arrangement of atoms along the chain. These may further be divided into spirals toward the right and toward the left. This class of compounds represents an isotactic arrangement. If, however, the polymer chain is made up of alternating right and left spirals, the polymer is a *syndiotactic* configuration. Examples of the latter type are currently found in polypropylene, polyethylene, and polystyrene.

In the case of polymers based on diene monomers, the structure is determined by: (1) the nature of the monomer or mixture of monomers selected; (2) the conversion—in the case of a single monomer feed, chain branching or crosslinking may occur at the higher conversion, while in copolymerization the two monomers may enter at different rates; (3) the mechanism of polymerization, whether free radical or ionic; (4) the nature of the catalyst involved; and (5) the temperature of polymerization.

SYNTHETIC NATURAL RUBBER

In preparing butadiene-styrene polymers during World War II, it was recognized that the products were not true duplicates of natural rubbers. Although Hevea is composed of units of isoprene, an emulsion polyisoprene in no way duplicates the high gum tensile strength and many of the properties of natural rubber. Furthermore, emulsion diene polymers are composed primarily of *trans*-diene units, whereas natural rubber is largely the *cis*-1,4-polyisoprene. In the latter case the regular arrangement of molecules permits natural rubber to crystallize during extension;[12,30] butadiene-styrene polymers show no comparable tendency to crystallize.

In November 1955 the Firestone Tire and Rubber Company announced the successful synthesis of a *cis*-1,4-polyisoprene supported by tire test results. This polymer, known as Coral rubber,[37] was prepared by the polymerization of isoprene catalyzed by powdered lithium. The catalyst was made by melting the metal in petroleum jelly and agitating the product in a special high speed stirrer to produce a fine dispersion of lithium. A stirrer speed of 18,000 revolutions per minute for about twenty minutes at 200° C was selected to produce a 35 per cent dispersion of lithium having a mean diameter of 20 microns.

A reactor was charged with 100 parts of pure dry isoprene and 0.1 part lithium. After an induction period at 30 to 40° C the charge thickened and became solid toward the end of the polymerization. The catalyst was decomposed with isopropyl alcohol and the rubber was stabilized with a suitable antioxidant. The polymer was washed, then dried at 50° C.

Lithium was reported to be specific in its effect; other alkali metals gave mixtures of *cis*- and *trans*-polymers.

Tests have been reported[1,2] in which 100 per cent Coral rubber was used in truck tires. The heat build-up during service at 50 miles per hour was identical to that of natural rubber. Carcass stocks gave satisfactory performance and the polymer was considered a satisfactory substitute for natural rubber.

In November 1955 B. F. Goodrich Company reviewed for the American Chemical Society the structure and properties of cis-polyisoprene polymerized according to information supplied by Dr. Karl Ziegler. From the infrared absorption spectra, X-ray diffraction patterns, and second-order transition temperatures, the synthetic polymer was considered substantially the same as natural rubber.

Polyisoprenes require antioxidants as do the emulsion butadiene-styrene copolymers. Since fatty acid is not present in the final polymer, it is necessary to compensate by adjustments in the compounding recipe. Physical tests in the laboratory for pure gum, body and tread stocks indicate that the polymer and Hevea are virtually identical.[20]

According to a Belgian patent[16] of Goodrich-Gulf Chemicals Company, cis-1,4-polyisoprene and mixtures of cis- with trans-1,4-polyisoprene may be prepared by control of a catalyst consisting of a reaction product of an alkylaluminum with titanium tetrachloride in a hydrocarbon medium. A cis-polymer is obtained if the mole ratio of Ti to Al is 1; in the mole ratio 1.5 to 3, a trans-polymer results.

In 1955 the Goodyear Tire and Rubber Company disclosed the preparation of cis-1,4-polyisoprene[9] in which triethylaluminum was used as a catalyst together with a co-catalyst. The infrared spectrum was comparable to that of Hevea rubber.

A description of the pilot plant for the preparation of cis-polyisoprene has been given by the Goodyear Tire and Rubber Company.[42]

The heart of the system consists of two 500-gallon stainless steel autoclaves set up for interchangeable operation. The turbine type agitators are driven by 10 horsepower motors; they move a material which shows a viscosity as high as 100,000 centipoises at a solids content of 15 per cent.

Extremely pure isoprene and a hydrocarbon solvent are involved in this process. Special precautions are required since oxygen and certain unsaturated compounds are severe catalyst poisons. Both isoprene and the solvent are distilled, mixed, and passed through a silica gel or alumina dryer. They are pumped through the dehydrating bed into the reactor where the catalyst is added. The temperature is controlled with water or brine in the reactor jacket at a polymerization temperature of 50° C. In this system lower temperatures give higher molecular weight polymers.

At about 7 per cent solids the contents of the reactor become viscous and temperature control difficult. The final solids of the cement is reported as being about 25 per cent. At this stage the cement is extremely viscous.

At the end of polymerization the cement is pumped to a tank where catalysts can be deactivated and the necessary antioxidant added. The cement is then heated and transferred to an extruder dryer. In this equipment the solvent is vaporized for recovery and re-use. The product as extruded contains less than 1 per cent volatile material; the rubber is packaged into 50-pound bales.

The catalyst for the polymerization consists of two parts. Triisobutylaluminum, spontaneously flammable, must be handled carefully. It should be mixed with the correct proportion of a second component in storage cylinders and pressured into the reactor.

As in the case of the manufacture of butadiene, gas chromatography has been used to trace the purity of the monomer.

Cis-polybutadiene, a recent development in the field of stereospecific polymers, is reported to be of value as an extender for natural rubber. Compounds show high rebound and low heat build-up, characteristics which make *cis*-polybutadiene valuable for truck and bus tire manufacture.[8] It is assumed that stereospecific polybutadiene is made by a solvent polymerization process similar to that used for *cis*-polyisoprene—a hydrocarbon solvent such as kerosene and a lithium or alkylaluminum catalyst.

RUBBER TECHNOLOGY

The commercial application of raw natural and synthetic rubber is very limited. Since raw polymers are plastic and soluble their uses are restricted to adhesives and sealants, for example, friction tape, electrical tape, etc.

When rubber is mixed with sulfur and heated, vulcanization occurs. The rubber changes from a plastic material to a strong elastic substance which is tack-free, abrasion resistant, and no longer readily soluble in common solvents.

For Hevea and the butadiene-based polymers, sulfur is the normal vulcanizing, or curing agent; however, a material with a high sulfur content such as an organic polysulfide (tetramethylthiuram disulfide, alkylphenol disulfides, and aliphatic polysulfides) may be substituted. A new class of curing agent is found among the organic peroxides, such as di-*tert*-butyl and dicumyl peroxides.

Some synthetic rubbers, such as neoprene and copolymers containing methacrylic acid, possess functional groups through which cross-linking may occur without a sulfur cure. In the case of neoprene, zinc oxide and magnesium oxide are the normal curing agents; with butyl rubber, alkylphenol-formaldehyde resins serve the purpose. Otherwise the cure depends on reaction with sulfur or sulfur-containing agents.

The type and concentration of the various ingredients to be added in the development of a rubber stock depend on the properties desired in the finished product. The purpose of the stock will determine the preferred kind of rubber and compounding recipe.

The primary ingredient is sulfur. Although it may be used alone, vulcanization may be shortened by adding accelerators. These are usually selected from the aldehyde amines, guanidines, thiazoles, or the ultra-accelerators ordinarily derived from dithiocarbamic acid. The usual concentration of these materials is in the range of 0.1 to 1.5 parts per 100 parts of rubber.

In the development of a usable compounding recipe, activators such as zinc oxide and fatty acids (stearic, to solubilize the zinc) are often added. The concentration of these materials ranges from 1 to 5 per cent and 0.5 to 4 per cent, respectively. The rubber compound ordinarily contains an antioxidant to improve the aging of the product. These are often selected from secondary aromatic amines or substituted phenols depending on whether the rubber is to be used in a light or a dark-colored application, respectively.

Because "pure gum" products containing the ingredients listed above are not suitable for applications such as tires, reinforcing agents must be added to the stock. Selected for economy and for development of optimum performance, these are normally carbon blacks, inorganic fillers, or reinforcing resins. The many different types of carbon black available for the manufacture of black stocks vary in particle size and in their effect on the properties of rubber stocks. Proper choice of a black or reinforcing pigment is possible only after careful study of available materials.

Stock Preparation

The operations involved in preparing stocks of Hevea or butadiene-styrene rubbers may involve some of the following: breakdown in an oven, a plasticator, or on open-roll mills (in the case of natural rubber); batch mixing in a mill or a Banbury; warm-up on a mill or Banbury if the stock has been allowed to cool during storage; calendering for preparation of sheet skim coating, or frictioning onto fabric to produce stocks or plies of the desired dimensions; extrusion, for treads, onto wires, over hose carcasses; building into green tires, shoes, and hose.

Natural rubber differs from the synthetic butadiene-styrene types in its greater tendency to soften during milling. For this reason the synthetic rubbers are manufactured to a low plasticity suitable for subsequent processing in the factory. The natural product is prepared by mill mastication at as low a temperature as is practical, normally around 200° F but at least below 270° F; in a plasticator the rubber may be heated as far as 350° F for breakdown.

The rubber mills used in preparing stocks consist of two parallel steel rolls which vary in size from 6 to 10-inch models in the laboratory to 84 and 120-inch mills in the factory. The selection of surfaces, roll speed, and ratio of speed of the two rolls depends on the particular types of rubber being handled.

The Banbury mixer is an enclosed machine containing two water-cooled rotors operating in a water-cooled chamber.[31] The Banbury must be of such a size that the batch will completely fill the mixing chamber. Advances in the design of the Banbury mixer now permit a mixing time of 8 minutes or less.

After the Banburys, the stocks are fed to a three- or four-roll calender used for three types of work: frictioning, skim coating, and sheeting (Figure 9.6). Fabric is frictioned when it is passed over Roll C with Roll B running

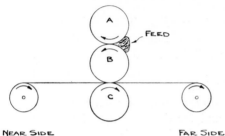

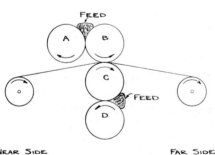

Figure 9.6. Diagrams of a three- and a four-roll calender.

at a higher speed, the rubber compound being wiped into the fabric. Skim coating is a similar operation but the speed of Roll B is the same as that of Roll C, so that a film of rubber is pressed into the fabric. For sheeting, Roll C is lowered and a cotton liner is used; the sheet of rubber formed between Rolls A and B is led into the liner in which it is wrapped. Fabric used for manufacturing tire plies is usually dipped, before it is fed into the calender, in a bath containing either a latex-casein compound or a latex-resorcinol-formaldehyde mixture to improve adhesion of the rubber and threads.

Automobile Tires and Tubes

One of the most important applications of all rubbers is tires. Because of the increased demand for speed and endurance in modern vehicles, it has been necessary to design rubber compounds and build tires with these factors in mind. Tires must be designed to withstand heavy loads and high speeds for long periods; the body of the tires must be able to withstand severe shocks and must not show excessive heat build-up.

Tires are built up on a flat drum with successive plies of fabric (Figure 9.7), friction-coated, and cut on a bias. "Beads" of wire imbedded in rubber

Figure 9.7. A modern tire building drum. (*Courtesy Firestone Tire and Rubber Co.*)

are attached at the edge of the fabric to anchor the tire to the rim of the wheel. The beads may be further protected by chafing strips. The center of the tire is protected by "breaker strips" topped by a slab of highly abrasion-resistant stock comprising the tread. The last part added to the tire is a side wall compounded for white or black, and for maximum resistance to ozone deterioration and curb chafing.

Because of the high temperatures at which tires must operate on passenger cars, trucks and buses, considerable attention has been given to polymers which generate less heat as well as to replacements for cotton fabric which tends to lose strength and fail at higher temperatures. Rayon and nylon cords are finding application for high speed operation.

Tires from the flat drum are shaped around an air bag in a mold for vulcanization or "curing" (Figure 9.8). In modern watchcase molds, the green tire is cured by means of steam in the jacket of the mold; steam and air are introduced into the air bag to expand the tire into the mold. The mold is heated for a specified time at a definite temperature to produce an optimum state of cure throughout the tire. The heat is then shut off, the

Figure 9.8. Tire curing equipment. (*Courtesy Firestone Tire and Rubber Co.*)

internal pressure released, the mold opened, and the tire removed for final inspection.

Mechanical Rubber Goods

This term is applied to the large class of rubber products including hose, belts, gaskets, and molded, extruded, and compounded items for use in the automotive, industrial, household, and appliance fields. These may be made from either natural or synthetic rubber, or mixtures, depending on whether the stocks are expected to show oil resistance or some particular characteristic of aging, abrasion resistance, etc. Since price is often of importance in the manufacture of mechanical rubber goods, these stocks may include more filler than those used for tires.

In applications in the automotive field, mechanical rubber goods must withstand oil and heat, and must supply a high degree of resilience. They are therefore frequently manufactured from neoprene or butadiene-acrylonitrile polymers.

Hard rubber may be made from natural or synthetic rubber by increasing the amount of sulfur to 30 or 35 parts per 100 of polymer. Hard rubber stocks may contain extenders such as hard rubber dust, coal dust, carbon black, or inorganic pigments.

Self-Sealing Fuel Tanks

During World War II, fuel tanks made from synthetic rubber were of considerable value to fighter planes. They were constructed of multiple layers of rubber and fabric with a butadiene-acrylonitrile lining designed for resistance to the material to be contained in the tank. The liner was surrounded by alternating layers of sealant and fabric to achieve the desired thickness. When the resistant liner was punctured, the unvulcanized rubber stock outside swelled in contact with the fuel. For successful performance the hole must seal within an extremely short time.

Latex Products

Latex concentrated to about 60 per cent solids compounded with the same ingredients used in a dry rubber stock may be used to make dipped goods such as balloons and gloves. They may be built up from natural rubber latex or from neoprene latex; less success has been achieved with butadiene-styrene latices because of the low gum tensile strengths of these polymers. Molds are dipped in the concentrated latex several times to build up a coating which is ultimately cured and removed.

The production of *foamed rubber* from concentrated latex of both the natural and synthetic types is an important business. The concentrated latex is compounded with the necessary ingredients plus soap to aid in the foaming process. The latex is then beaten into a foam, fed into a mold, and gelled. Sodium silicofluoride is added during the beating. The sponge may be cured in the mold.

BUTADIENE MANUFACTURE

Butadiene (CH_2=CH—CH=CH_2) has been identified as the product of thermal cracking of a wide variety of organic substances. Its commercial production involves one of the following routes:

(1) Thermal cracking of hydrocarbons of C_4 or greater
(2) Catalytic dehydrogenation of butenes
(3) Catalytic dehydrogenation of *n*-butane
(4) Dehydrochlorination of chlorinated butanes
(5) Catalytic treatment of ethyl alcohol and ethanol-acetaldehyde mixtures

(6) Aldol condensation of acetaldehyde followed by conversion of aldol to butadiene

(7) Reaction of acetylene and formaldehyde to 2-butyne-1,3-diol followed by hydrogenation and dehydration

In 1939 only one commercial producer of butadiene was listed; by 1941 five manufacturers were using different routes, including recovery from refinery streams.

At the initiation of the government program in 1941 it was necessary that a large volume of butadiene be immediately available. "Quickie" plants were started to recover butadiene from refinery streams as a fast temporary solution. A review of the long range routes showed that the alcohol-based plants could be put into production rapidly but that the petroleum routes would ultimately be cheaper.

The following table compares production of butadiene from petroleum and alcohol. The alcohol route was important at the beginning of World War II and again during the Korean War, but it lost favor during the time when maximum production was less urgent.

In the *thermal cracking* route, the one used for the "quickie" program, butadiene may be recovered from an existing refinery stream, or a plant may be designed for cracking a gasoline fraction.[19] The feed must be carefully selected for optimum production; the preferred material used for feed is reported to be cyclohexane. The butadiene yield is about 3.5 weight per cent of the naphtha cracked. This process requires a cyclic operation in a lined, baffled furnace. Economy of production depends on the recovery of non-butadiene products, essential if this route is to compete with other processes.

TABLE 9.4. PRODUCTION OF BUTADIENE*

	Thousands of Short Tons		
	Petroleum	Alcohols	Total
1940	0.2	0.0	0.2
1942	12.1	0.0	12.1
1943	49.3	129.7	179.0
1944	244.5	361.7	606.2
1945	389.9	233.4	623.3
1950	302.4	2.7	305.1
1951	482.9	128.3	611.2
1952	406.6	146.6	553.2
1953	526.9	49.2	576.1
1954	404.4	0.0	404.4
1955	703.2	2.5	705.7
1956	738.4	16.6	755.0

* Synthetic Organic Chemicals—U. S. Production and Sales, U. S. Tariff Commission and Schedule 1, March 31, 1952, Synthetic Rubber Div., Reconstruction Finance Corporation.

Catalytic dehydrogenation of n-butylenes depends on the fractionation of refinery gases to produce a cut of normal C_4 olefins. Extractive distillation is used for this purpose.[6,17] Furfural or acetone is added to the butane-butene stream to alter the relative volatilities of the components so that separation can be effected more easily. The butanes are taken overhead; butylene dissolved in the solvent is removed at the bottom and separated by distillation. Isobutylene must be removed for efficient production of butadiene since this material is inert in the cracking step and concentrates in the recycle. Removal may be achieved by sulfuric acid polymerization to produce diisobutylene or higher polymers which may, in turn, be used for high octane gasoline.

Catalyst 1707, used initially in all plants for cracking butylene, contains a complex mixture of magnesium, copper, iron, and potassium compounds. The butylene feed is diluted with steam to prevent the formation of carbon on the catalyst surface.[23] Catalyst 105, used later for this dehydrogenation, contains iron, chromium, and potassium.[29]

The reactors are designed to supply heat at a temperature of 1150 to 1250° F. The feed must be exposed at a low partial pressure for a short contact time, and facilities must be arranged for regenerating the deactivated catalysts. The original reactors[35] have been revised for operation with some of the more recent catalysts.

Another catalyst is Dow Type B, calcium nickel phosphate stabilized with 2 per cent chromium oxides.[5,29] Butadiene selectivities of 90 mole per cent at 35 per cent conversion of the butene compare with 70 per cent for catalyst 105 at the same conversion level. The Dow B catalyst requires frequent regeneration with an air-steam mixture and needs a steam to hydrocarbon feed of about 20 to 1. This particular route produces as much as 4 per cent acetone based on the butadiene.

The *butane dehydrogenation* route[40] combines two operations in a one-step production of butadiene from butane. During the government operation Phillips used a two-step process, dehydrogenating the butane in fixed beds contained in heated tubes. An 80 per cent yield of butenes resulted at a 30 to 40 per cent conversion per pass using 1 to 2 psig and 1100° F inlet temperature. The reactors operated one hour on stream and one hour on regeneration using a flue gas mixture containing 2 to 3 per cent oxygen. The butenes were dehydrogenated by the same method previously described.

A direct route for producing butadiene (used in the conversion of butane) is based on a regeneration operation[44] in which a chromia-alumina catalyst is employed at low temperatures and pressures. The system is operated on a cycling basis during which the feed stream is cracked for a short period (10 minutes). The catalyst chamber is then evacuated, given an air blow to bring the catalyst back to operating temperatures, and evacuated to complete the cycle.

In the *Lebedev process*[4,38] ethanol is fed into a converter containing metal oxides capable of effecting simultaneous dehydrogenation and dehydration. Recycling of non-butadiene components gives yields of 60 per cent of the theoretical. This process uses an Al_2O_3-ZnO or MgO-CoO catalyst. No United States plant has used this process.

The *Ostromislenski process* feeds an ethanol-acetaldehyde mixture over copper-containing catalysts or silica gel containing tantalum oxide.[10,21,22,28,39] Part of the ethanol is converted to acetaldehyde by dehydrogenation over a copper catalyst at temperatures above 200° C and atmospheric pressure. Ethanol and acetaldehyde are then mixed at about 3 to 1 mole ratios. The catalyst gradually becomes covered with carbon and must be burned off periodically to restore its activity.

The products of this cracking reaction are simpler than those derived from the petroleum cracking processes. They consist primarily of ethylene, propylene, butadiene, unchanged starting materials, and some oxygenated by-products. The butadiene fraction containing 96 per cent butadiene is refined in an extractive distillation by treatment with β,β' dichloroethyl ether ("Chlorex"). The resulting purity is at least 98.5 per cent.

Butadiene, regardless of the method of preparation, is sensitive to polymerization. Unless it is to be used immediately, an inhibitor such as tertiary butyl catechol must be added to avoid spontaneous polymerization. The inhibitor may be removed in the polymerizing plant by either distillation or a caustic wash.

STYRENE MANUFACTURE[3]

The most important route for preparing styrene involves the preparation of ethyl benzene and its dehydrogenation to styrene. The reactions are as follows:

(1)
$$C_6H_6 + CH_2{=}CH_2 \xrightarrow{AlCl_3} C_6H_5CH_2{-}CH_3$$
Benzene   Ethylene   Ethylbenzene

(2)
$$C_6H_5CH_2{-}CH_3 \longrightarrow C_6H_5CH{=}CH_2 + H_2$$
Styrene

Ethyl Benzene. The reactor, a vertical vessel lined with acid-resisting bricks, contains the reaction mixture to a depth of about 35 feet. Ethylene, added at the bottom of the column, causes circulation of the liquid. The reactor is cooled by means of an overhead condenser and a flow of cold water on the outside of the shell to maintain the temperature at 95° C. Pressure within the reactor is 5 pounds per square inch or less. Aluminum chloride and some ethyl chloride are added continuously throughout the process to make up for the catalyst depletion. The ethylene-benzene ratio is controlled at 0.58 moles ethylene per mole of benzene.

The tendency for polyethylated derivatives to be produced during the process is suppressed by the recirculation of polyethylbenzene. Since moisture in the feed would increase the aluminum chloride requirements, special precautions are taken to make sure that the feed is anhydrous. Both fresh and recovered benzene are dried in an azeotropic distillation.

The reactor is operated in a continuous manner; crude ethylbenzene is withdrawn from the top, cooled, and decanted from a lower layer consisting of an aluminum complex-hydrocarbon mixture that can be recovered to conserve catalyst. The crude ethylbenzene is washed with caustic soda and fed to a stripping column to separate ethylbenzene and benzene from the higher polyethylbenzenes. The reactor overhead consisting of ethylbenzene and benzene is again distilled, washed in caustic, and dried over a bed of caustic. The ethylbenzene purity at this stage is 99.5 per cent.

The dehydrogenation of ethylbenzene to styrene is an endothermic reaction requiring the presence of superheated steam which acts as an inert gas diluent. A solid catalyst is used. Since reaction (2) runs, from left to right, with an increase in volume, a decrease in partial pressure would favor higher yields; consequently, a steam (2.6 pounds) -ethylbenzene (1 pound) mix is used to permit cracking under reduced partial pressure. This reduces the partial pressure of the reactants to 0.1 atmosphere and shifts the equilibrium so that a theoretical conversion of 70 to 80 per cent is possible. The superheated steam functions in two ways: it supplies the heat of reaction; it keeps the catalyst clean by reacting with any deposited carbon. The catalyst increases the reaction rate for this temperature to a satisfactory level with a minimum of outside reaction.

The reactor consists of an insulated brick chamber containing the catalyst in granule form. The catalyst (see 1707 from the butadiene section) was found to work satisfactorily for this process and was used extensively during the war period. About 90 per cent of the steam is raised to 383° C by heat exchange with product vapors, then to 710° C in a superheating furnace. The remainder of the steam is mixed with the ethylbenzene charge at 160° C and raised to 520° C by heat exchange with product vapors (ahead of the steam). The two streams meet in concentric inlet tubes, mix thoroughly, and enter the catalyst chamber. The base of the reactor is held at 630° C. The outgoing vapors are cooled by a heat exchanger, a spray-type desuperheater, and finally a condenser. The condensate is steam, ethylbenzene, styrene, benzene, toluene, and tar. Conversion with fresh catalyst is approximately 37 per cent. Vent gas contains hydrogen, carbon monoxide, carbon dioxide, methane, and others. The life of the catalyst operating uninterruptedly is a year or so.

In the styrene finishing step pure styrene is isolated from the crude condensate, containing approximately 37 per cent styrene, by distillation at reduced pressure in the presence of elemental sulfur as a polymerization inhibitor. The small differential in boiling points between ethylbenzene (132.62° C) and styrene (145° C) necessitates a 70 plate tower which may, if desired, be divided into two columns operating in series. The bottoms of the styrene may pass to two batch finishing stills with packed towers, operating under vacuum, where styrene is the overhead and tar and sulfur are the raffinate. The styrene, 99.7 per cent pure, is cooled and stabilized by the addition of 10 to 15 parts per million of *tert*-butyl-catechol inhibitor.

The over-all yield, benzene to styrene, is 88 to 92 per cent as is the ethylene to styrene yield.

REFERENCES

1. Alliger, G., Willis, J. M., Smith, W. A., and Allen, J. J., *Mech. Eng.*, 1098–1102 (1956).
2. Alliger, G., Willis, J. M., Smith, W. A., and Allen, J. J., *Rubber World,* **134,** 549–59 (1956).
3. Boundy, R. H., Boyer, R. F., and Stoesser, S. M., "Styrene," New York, Reinhold Publishing Corp., 1952.
4. British Intelligence Objectives Subcommittee Report No. 1060 (1947).
5. Britton, E. C., Dietzler, A. J., and Noddings, C. R., *Ind. Eng. Chem.,* **43,** 2871–4 (1951).
6. Buell, C. K., and Boatright, R. G., *Ind. Eng. Chem.,* **39,** 695–705 (1947).
7. Carothers, W. H., Williams, Ira, Collins, A. M., and Kirby, J. E., *J. Am. Chem. Soc.,* **53,** 4203–25 (1931).
8. *Chem. Eng. News,* **37,** 23 (1959).
9. *Chem. Eng. News,* **33,** 4518 (1955).
10. Corson, B. B., Jones, H. E., Welling, C. E., Hinckley, J. A., and Stahly, E. E., *Ind. Eng. Chem.,* **42,** 359–73 (1950).
11. Davis, C. C., Editor, "Chemistry and Technology of Rubber," New York Reinhold Publishing Corp., 1937.
12. D'Ianni, J. D., *Eng. Chem.,* **40,** 253–6 (1948).
13. Dunbrook, R. F., *India Rubber World,* **117,** 203–7 (1947).
14. E. I. du Pont de Nemours Co., "The Neoprenes," Wilmington, Delaware.
15. Fryling, C. F., Private Communication (March 26, 1942).
16. Goodrich-Gulf, Belgian Patent 543,292 (1956).
17. Happel, J., Cornell, P. W., Eastman, DuB., Fowle, M. J., Porter, C. A., and Schutte, A. H., *Trans. Am. Inst. Chem. Eng.,* **42,** 189–214, 1001–7 (1946).
18. Harkins, W. D., *J. Am. Chem. Soc.,* **69,** 1428–44 (1947).
19. Heilman, H. H., *Petroleum World,* **44,** No. 3, 51–5 (1947).
20. Horne, S. E., Jr., Kiehl, J. P., Shipman, J. J., Folt, V. L., Gibbs, C. F., Willson, E. A., Newton, E. B., and Reinhart, M. A., *Ind. Eng. Chem.,* **48,** 784–91 (1956).
21. Jones, H. E., Stahly, E. E., and Corson, B. B., *J. Am. Chem. Soc.,* **71,** 1822–8 (1949).
22. Kampmeyer, P. M., and Stahly, E. E., *Ind. Eng. Chem.,* **41,** 550–5 (1949).
23. Kearby, K. K., *Ind. Eng. Chem.,* **42,** 295–30 (1950).
24. McGregor, R. R., "Silicones and their Uses," New York, McGraw-Hill Book Company, Inc., 1954.
25. Mitchell, J. M., Enbree, W. H., and MacFarlane, R. B., *Ind. Eng. Chem.,* **48,** 345–8 (1956).
26. Nieuwland, J. A., Calcott, W. S., Downing, F. B., and Carter, A. S., *J. Am. Chem. Soc.,* **53,** 4197–4202 (1931).
27. "Proceedings Second Rubber Technical Conference," 69–78 (1948).

28. Quattlebaum, W. M., Toussaint, W. J., Jr., and Dunn, J. T., *J. Am. Chem. Soc.,* **69,** 593–9 (1947).
29. Reilly, P. M., *Chemistry in Can.,* **5,** No. 3, 25–9 (1953).
30. Richardson, W. S., and Sacher, A., *J. Polymer Sci.,* **10,** 353–70 (1953).
31. Riegel, E. R., "Industrial Chemistry," New York, Reinhold Publishing Corp., 1942.
32. Rochow, E. G., "Introduction to the Chemistry of Silicones," 2nd Ed., New York, John Wiley and Sons, Inc., 1951.
33. *Rubber Chem. and Technol.,* **7,** 633 (1934).
34. Rubber Manufacturers Assoc. Inc., N. Y., "Type Description and Packing Specifications for Natural Rubber," Revised Dec. 1954.
35. Russell, R. P., Murphree, E. V., and Asbury, W. C., *Trans. Am. Inst. Chem. Engrs.,* **42,** 1–14 (1946).
36. "Semperit" Oesterreichisch-Amerikanische Gummiwerke A.-G. (to Metallgesellschaft A.-G.), British Patent 459,972 (Jan. 19, 1937).
37. Stavely, F. W., *et al., Ind. Eng. Chem.,* **48,** 778–83 (1956).
38. Talalay, A., and Talalay, L., *Rubber Chem. Tech.,* **15,** 403–29 (1942).
39. Toussaint, W. J., Dunn, J. T., and Jackson, D. R., *Ind. Eng. Chem.,* **39,** 120 (1947).
40. Watson, C. C., Newton, F., McCausland, J. W., McGrew, E. H., and Kassel, L. S., *Trans. Am. Inst. Chem. Eng.,* **40,** 309–15 (1944).
41. Whitby, G. S., Davis, C. C., and Dunbrook, R. F., Editors, "Synthetic Rubber," John Wiley and Sons, Inc., 1954.
42. Winchester, C. T., *Ind. Eng. Chem.,* **51,** 19 (1959).
43. Winspear, George G., "Vanderbilt Latex Handbook," R. T. Vanderbilt Co., N.Y., 1954.
44. Womeldorph, D. E., Stevenson, D. H., and Friedman, L., *Am. Petroleum Inst.* (May 14, 1958).
45. Youker, M. A., *Chem. Eng. Progr.,* **43,** No. 8, 391 (1947).

10

SYNTHETIC PLASTICS

In collaboration with Mr. Robert W. Jones*

INTRODUCTION

THE WORD "PLASTIC" was originally used as an adjective to denote a degree of mobility or formability. In the 1909 edition of "Webster's International Dictionary," the noun was not listed. Shortly thereafter, with the introduction of "Bakelite" by Dr. Baekeland, the word was often used as a noun, most frequently referring to "Bakelite," "Celluloid," and casein plastics. Now it is most commonly used as a noun.

The American Society for Testing Materials (D 833-55T) has defined a plastic as "a material that contains as an essential ingredient an organic substance of large molecular weight, is solid in its finished state, and, at some stage in its manufacture or in its processing into finished articles, can be shaped by flow." According to this definition, synthetic fibers, all rubbers, and even bread doughs are plastics, but glass is not. Those who insist that glass is a plastic omit "organic substance" as part of the definition. In this chapter, synthetic fibers (Chapter 11), regenerated cellulose, i.e., rayon, cellophane (Chapter 15), rubber (Chapter 9), glass, those materials used exclusively in surface coatings (Chapter 22) and, of course, bread dough will not be considered.†

* Monsanto Chemical Company, Plastics Division, Springfield, Mass.

† Except in connection with production statistics where the United States Department of Commerce chooses to include as plastics all synthetic resins used as surface coatings.

274

The word "resin" is an old one derived from the Latin *resina* and the Greek *rhetine*. Originally it referred to natural exudates (or their fossil remains) of vegetable origin. The ancient Egyptians used such materials to help preserve their mummies.[52] Frankincense and myrrh, the Wise Men's gifts to the infant Jesus, are both natural resins. There are many such natural products: accroide, congo, rosin, copal, dammar, sandarac, elemi, kauri, manila, mastic, batu, pontianak, and shellac. Today they are used principally in surface coatings or as binders and adhesives. When identified as "synthetic" (the adjective is frequently omitted for brevity), the current meaning of "resin" in the plastics industry is "that base substance of high molecular weight" before it has been mixed with colorants, fillers, plasticizers,* lubricants and/or stabilizers to make a finished commercial plastic molding powder.† In the surface coatings industry, similarly, resin refers to the base binding material of high molecular weight before it has been formulated into a paint, varnish, or enamel.

VIEWPOINT OF THE INDUSTRIAL DESIGNER

Plastics may be classified in many ways. The industrial designer uses conventional physical properties to characterize plastics, e.g., density, tensile strength, impact strength, modulus of elasticity, creep rates, etc. These, however, are not enough. Price, fabricating costs, electrical characteristics, colorability, other appearance factors, and chemical resistance frequently determine the selection of a particular plastic in preference to other plastics or other materials.

For information about specific properties of various plastics, consult Table 10.1, "Modern Plastics Encyclopedia Issue," "Technical Data Book on Plastics, 1957" by the Manufacturing Chemists' Association, and SPI Handbook of Plastics (Reinhold).

Testing plastics is a highly specialized art which has been developed primarily through the efforts of the members of the American Society for Testing Materials. Plastics are usually excellent electrical insulators; electrical properties must be measured over a wide range of electrical and climatic conditions. Few plastics obey Hooke's Law; many types creep even at very low temperatures and stresses. Specialized stress-strain testing machinery has been developed which permits extensive variations in temperature and rate of loading. Coloring versatility and simplicity are prime factors

---

* A plasticizer is a material ordinarily (though not necessarily) of lower molecular weight that makes the plastic more flexible (lower elastic modulus); hopefully it should improve impact strength without increasing creep or lowering ultimate strength markedly.

† The term "powder" is a misnomer. Most commercial molding powder is in the form of granules or pellets which provide high bulk density, good flow, and other desirable handling characteristics.

in many plastics markets. Tests for color reproducibility and stability are becoming established in the industry.

VIEWPOINT OF THE FABRICATOR

Not only must the fabricator keep in mind the industrial designer and consumer; he must also consider the types of equipment required and the behavior of the plastics in relation to this equipment. Plastics are divided into thermosetting and thermoplastic materials. Thermosetting resins require

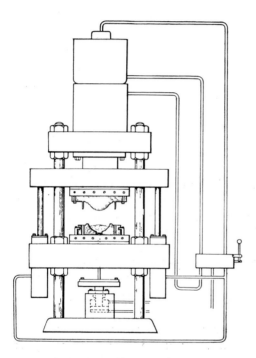

Figure 10.1. A simple compression mold and press charged with molding powder. (*Redfarn, C. A., "A Guide to Plastics," London, Cliffe and Sons, Ltd., 1958, by permission*)

a compression molding (or transfer molding) machine (Figures 10.1 and 10.2). Thermoplastics may be molded in a compression molding machine or in the faster, more economical injection molding machine (Figure 10.3). The concept of maintaining a stable thermoplastic material in a fluid state and squirting it under pressure into a cooler mold was first developed in the middle 1920's by Dr. Arthur Eichengum and the German firm of Eckert and Ziegler.[82] It was not until the late 1930's that successful automatic machines were used in the United States. Once a thermally stable material became commercially available, development of the injection molding machine followed logically. The first such commercial plastic was cellulose acetate, introduced in 1933.

If sheets, rods, tubes, or profiles of various lengths are desired, thermoplastics can be conveniently extruded (Figure 10.4). Many thermoplastics are calendered into films or sheets (Figures 10.5 and 10.6). When processing any thermoplastic material in such equipment, the fundamental considerations are heat transfer, rheology, mixing, and dispersing.

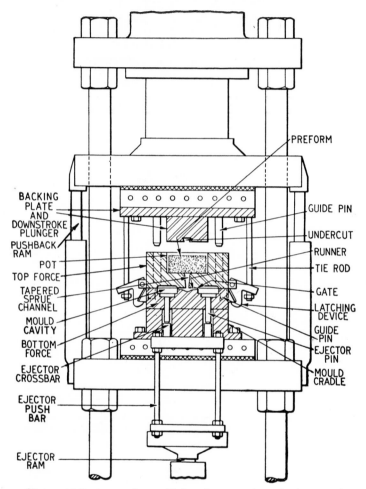

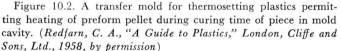

Figure 10.2. A transfer mold for thermosetting plastics permitting heating of preform pellet during curing time of piece in mold cavity. (*Redfarn, C. A., "A Guide to Plastics," London, Cliffe and Sons, Ltd., 1958, by permission*)

The chemical structure of a thermosetting plastic is altered by heat, and products are formed which cannot be resoftened. Thermosetting plastics cannot be used in injection molding machines and extruders since these machines contain spaces where hot molten plastic may remain for indefinite lengths of time, thus causing varying levels of cure and possibly set-up in the

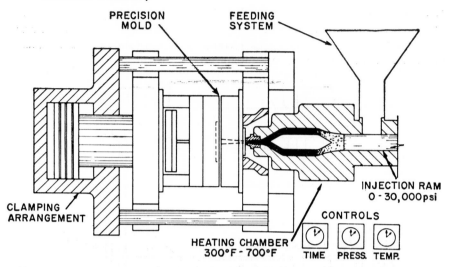

Figure 10.3. Components of an injection molding machine. (*Bernhardt, E. C., "Processing of Thermoplastic Materials," Copyright by the Society of Plastics Engineers, Inc., 1959, Reinhold Publishing Corp., New York*) (*by permission*)

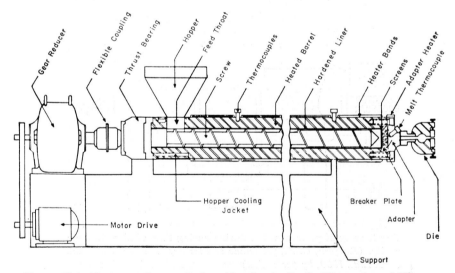

Figure 10.4. Elements of an extruder. (*Bernhardt, E. C., "Processing of Thermoplastic Materials," copyright by The Society of Plastics Engineers, Inc., 1959, Reinhold Publishing Corp., New York*) (*by permission*)

in relating these measurements to gross physical properties, e.g., tensile strength, impact strength, elongation, solubility, etc. However, although the physical chemist has explained a great deal, much remains to be done in

Figure 10.7. Growing crystallites in a melt of polystyrene especially polymerized to give mostly *cis* addition. (*Courtesy Monsanto Chemical Co.*)

this field; it is still necessary to synthesize and test a new polymer before its properties can be known.

VIEWPOINT OF THE ORGANIC CHEMIST

The organic chemist, usually interested in describing chemical reactions and their resulting products, ignored much of polymer chemistry for a long time. The traditional organic chemist of the nineteenth century regarded the uncrystallizable "tars" that formed from certain reactions as unsuccessful experiments, since the objective was the preparation of crystals whose physical chemistry was better understood. The progeny of the polymeric "gunks" which the nineteenth and early twentieth century chemist threw away in disgust today constitute the largest tonnage market for synthetic organic materials.*

* To make this statement precisely true, fuels must be excepted and the colorants, plasticizers, lubricants, stabilizers, and solvents utilized by the plastics, rubber, synthetic fibers, and synthetic surface coatings industries must be included. However, world usage of purified or chemically modified cellulose, about 5 billion tons annually, need not be included as synthetic high polymers if, likewise, it is not called "synthetic."

Now with better methods of characterizing the molecular structure of polymers, the modern organic chemist has developed well understood syntheses for many polymers and has logical mechanisms which explain vast bodies of data. The inventor of nylon, Wallace Hume Carothers,[12] beginning in 1929, showed that the reaction mechanisms and the thermodynamic equilibria ordinarily associated with reactive organic groups were not altered merely because these groups were attached to large rather than small molecules. This vital concept removed the mystery from polymer synthesis and funneled the vast knowledge of organic chemistry into the polymer field, resulting, in the early 1930's, in the dramatic development of new polymers.

Carothers defined two types of polymers: (1) *Addition polymers* are those like polyethylene in which the monomer units, on polymerizing, do not completely rupture a chemical bond but, in the usual case, utilize the π bonding electrons in a double bond to form the new bond between monomers. Most addition polymers are obtained from monomers containing carbon-carbon double bonds, e.g., vinyl monomers, $H_2C{=}CHR$, vinylidene monomers $H_2C{=}CR_2$, or diene monomers $H_2C{=}CR{-}CH{=}CH_2$, but commercial addition polymers are also made from $CH_2{=}O$ and $CF_2{=}CF_2$. (2) *Condensation polymers* are those wherein chemical bonds between atoms completely rupture during polymerization, causing formation of low molecular weight fragments, frequently water. By using pure materials and by forcing the reactions to completion through removal of the low molecular weight fragment, many varieties of high polymers can be made from multifunctional organic molecules, e.g., organic acids and amines (nylon), organic acids and alcohols (polyesters such as "Dacron" and "Mylar") (Chapter 11), as well as alkyd paints (Chapter 22), organic aldehydes, and phenols or amines. Catalysts vary depending on the nature of the functional organic group. Usually Lewis acids or bases are required.

Some reactions do not fit neatly into either the addition or condensation polymer classification but are, nonetheless, usually considered condensation polymers, e.g., reactions between a diisocyanate and a glycol to form a polyurethane,

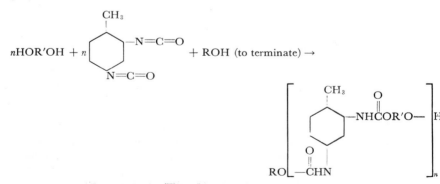

or ring opening reactions such as the formation of nylon 6 from ε-caprolactam,

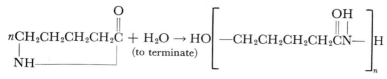

In addition to the large number of vinyl and vinylidene monomers which form addition polymers, and the even larger number of difunctional and multifunctional organic chemicals which form condensation polymers, the combination of various addition monomers into addition copolymers, and mixtures of condensation reactants form literally millions of combinations. Also, by adding monomers to previously formed polymers, e.g., adding styrene to a synthetic rubber, graft polymers* with unusual properties can be formed; this is done commercially for polyvinylchloride copolymers, polystyrenes, and polymethylmethacrylates possessing high impact strength. Also, variations in the molecular weight, molecular-weight distribution, amount of chain branching and crosslinking, molding or forming conditions, types and amounts of plasticizers, stabilizers, colorants, and fillers further increases the possibilities for various material specifications to astronomical levels. Table 10.1 gives a very brief summary of the principal plastics and the monomers from which they are made.

Addition polymerization may be initiated by free radicals or ions. At the present time free radical polymerization is commercially the most important, although the discovery that polymer properties can be greatly influenced by the degree of stereoregularity is currently creating great interest in ionic polymerization. Free radicals can be generated by the action of ultraviolet light, X-rays, and high energy particles. They are commercially produced for industrial polymerizations by heat, peroxides, oxygen, and diazo compounds. The polymerization propagates itself by a chain reaction mechanism, i.e., when a free radical and a monomer molecule react a new free radical is formed, the reacting monomer unit capturing the odd electron and becom-

---

* Graft polymers are a special type of copolymer and resemble block polymers, e.g.,

—ABAABBBABAAA—, —AAAAAABBBBBBBB—, —AAAAAAAAAAAA—
Random copolymer   Block polymer   B   B   B
                                         B   B   B
                                         B   B   B
                                         B   B   B
                                         B   B   B
                                         B   B   B
                                         | B   B
                                               | |

Graft polymer

TABLE 10.1. BASIC COMMERCIAL PLASTICS

Descriptive Name	Chemical Structure of Monomers	Outstanding and/or Typical Properties or Uses*	Thermosetting, Thermoplastic, or Casting	Commercial Methods of Manufacture
VINYL POLYMERS Polyethylene	H₂C=CH₂ (ethylene)	Excellent electrical properties. Good impact strength. Excellent colorability but translucent in thick sections. Good chemical resistance. Used in film, moldings, wire insulation, pipe, paper coating, and flexible bottles. Available in flexible and semi-rigid forms only. Film widely used in packaging.	Thermoplastic	(a) Solvent-nonsolvent to low conversion; "emulsion" to higher conversion at high pressure. (b) Solvent-nonsolvent with Ziegler solid catalysts at low pressure. (c) Solvent with solid catalysts at low pressure (Phillips process).
Polypropylene	CH₃CH=CH₂ (propylene)	Lowest density of any plastic. Fair to good impact. Fair rigidity and dimensional stability. Excellent colorability. Translucent in thick sections. Good chemical resistance. Properties vary widely with degree of crystallinity.	Thermoplastic	Ziegler catalyst. See Text.
Polyvinyl chloride and copolymers with vinyl acetate and vinylidene chloride (**"Vinylite"**)	ClCH=CH₂ (vinyl chloride)	Good electrical properties and flame resistance with proper plasticizers. Rigid as polymerized—made flexible with plasticizers. Good impact strength especially in polyblends. Good chemical resistance. Requires heat stabilizers. Many diverse uses	Thermoplastic	(a) Suspension (b) Solvent-non-solvent. (c) Emulsion used primarily for surface coatings, textile and paper treating, and "Plastisols".

284

Polymer	Structure	Properties	Type	Polymerization
Polyvinylidene chloride, always as a copolymer with vinyl chloride	$\underset{H}{\overset{H}{>}}C=C\underset{Cl}{\overset{Cl}{<}}$ $\underset{H}{\overset{H}{>}}C=C\underset{H}{\overset{Cl}{<}}$	Very low moisture vapor transmission. Good chemical resistance. Self-extinguishing flame resistance. Used in pipe linings, film.	Thermo-plastic	(a) Suspension polymerization (b) Emulsion
Polystyrene; also copolymerized with -methyl styrene and vinyl toluenes to improve heat resistance	$\underset{H}{\overset{H}{>}}C=C\underset{H}{\overset{C_6H_5}{<}}$	Excellent color, transparency, rigidity, dimensional stability, electrical properties, molding speeds. Used principally in moldings; also in phonograph records and rigid foams.	Thermo-plastic	(a) Mass (polymer soluble in monomer) (b) Suspension (c) Emulsion used principally for surface coatings and polishes.
Polystyrene-based graft and/or polyblend polymers with styrene/butadiene copolymer synthetic rubbers	$\underset{H}{\overset{H}{>}}C=C\underset{H}{\overset{C_6H_5}{<}}$ $H_2C=CH-CH=CH_2$	Excellent rigidity, dimensional stability, molding speeds. Good impact strength. Good colorability in opaques. Used extensively in moldings and for extruded sheet which is then vacuum formed. Packaging is large market.	Thermo-plastic	(a) Mass (b) Emulsion
Styrene/acrylonitrile copolymer grafted or polyblended to butadiene/acrylonitrile rubber	$\underset{H}{\overset{H}{>}}C=C\underset{H}{\overset{C_6H_5}{<}}$ $H_2C=CH-CH=CH_2$ $CH_2=CHCN$	Outstanding impact. Good chemical resistance. Good weatherability. Fair colorability in opaques. Used in pipe, moldings, extruded sheet.	Thermo-plastic	Emulsion
Styrene/acrylonitrile copolymer	$\underset{H}{\overset{H}{>}}C=C\underset{H}{\overset{C_6H_5}{<}}$ $CH_2=CHCN$	Better chemical resistance, crazing resistance, weatherability, impact strength than polystyrene. Good colorability including transparents. Used in moldings, film.	Thermo-plastic	Solution

285

TABLE 10.1. BASIC COMMERCIAL PLASTICS (Continued)

Descriptive Name	Chemical Structure of Monomers	Outstanding and/or Typical Properties or Uses*	Thermosetting, Thermoplastic, or Casting	Commercial Methods of Manufacture
Polymethylmethacrylate ("Plexiglass")	*(structural formula of methyl methacrylate monomer)*	**Excellent color, transparency, rigidity, dimensional stability, outdoor stability.** Good impact strength. Used in moldings and as **heavy sheeting. High impact graft** copolymers available.	**Thermoplastic and Casting**	(a) Suspension (b) Casting between **glass for transparent sheeting**
Polyesters	*(structural formula)* HOROH	Used with glass cloth or fibers to achieve very high tensile and flexural strengths approaching those of steel. Used to make laminates in aircraft, boats, furniture. Some potting of electrical components. Some compression **and** low pressure molding.	Thermosetting or **casting**	See Text
Polyvinyl butyral	*(structural formula)* $CH_3CH_2CH_2C{=}O$	Primarily used for safety glass interlayer. Has excellent adhesion to glass. Excellent ultraviolet light resistance in absence of air.	Thermoplastic	See Text

286

Polymer	Structure	Properties	Type	Process
Polychlorotrifluoro-ethylene ("Kel-F")	Cl, F / F, F on $C=C$	Excellent resistance to chemicals. Used as gasketing, packing, and corrosion resistant coatings.	Thermo-plastic	(a) Emulsion (b) Solvent-non-solvent
Polytetrafluoro-ethylene ("Teflon")	F, F / F, F on $C=C$	Excellent resistance to chemicals. Used as gasketing, packing, and corrosion resistant coatings. Attacked only by alkali metals and hot strong bases.	Fuse slowly under high pressure and 450–500° F	Emulsion

CONDENSATION POLYMERS

Polymer	Structure	Properties	Type	Process
Phenol-formaldehyde ("Bakelite")	OH (ring); $H-\overset{O}{\underset{}{C}}-H$	Good electrical properties with proper formulation. High heat resistance. Good to excellent impact and tensile strengths. Very slow to essentially no burning rate depending on filler. Acid resistant. Used for moldings particularly for industrial and electrical applications where its poor colorability is not important. Used extensively for decorative laminate backing.	Thermo-setting and Casting	See Text
Nylon 66	$HOC(CH_2)_4COH$; $NH_2(CH_2)_6NH_2$	Excellent wear resistance, tensile, and impact strengths. Low coefficient of friction. High heat distortion temperature. Self-extinguishing to fire. Used for gears, rolls, and other moving parts.	Thermo-plastic	See Chapter 11

287

TABLE 10.1. BASIC COMMERCIAL PLASTICS (Continued)

Descriptive Name	Chemical Structure of Monomers	Outstanding and/or Typical Properies or Uses*	Thermosetting, Thermoplasic, or Casting	Commercial Methods of Manufacture
ε-Caprolactam (nylon 6)	(ring structure: CH_2–CH_2–CH_2–CH_2–C(=O)–N–H)	Properties very similar to nylon 66.	Thermoplastic	See Chapter 11
Melamine-formaldehyde	(triazine ring: H_2N-C, N, C–NH_2, N, C, N, NH_2) $CH_2{=}O$	Excellent hardness abrasion resistance, flame resistance, heat resistance. Good colorability in opaques, stain resistance, electrical properties. Used in laminates. Used with alkyd surface coatings and for adhesives.	Thermosetting	See Text
Urea-formaldehyde	$H_2N\overset{O}{\underset{}{C}}NH_2$, $CH_2{=}O$	Similar to melamine but poorer alkali resistance, crazing resistance, heat resistance, dimensional stability. Also poorer wear and hardness. Used in adhesives.	Thermosetting	See Text
Epoxy	(bisphenol structure with OH, CH_3–C–CH_3, HO); CH_2—$CHCH_2Cl$; amines, organic anhydrides	Outstanding adhesion to metals. Good chemical resistance. Fair to excellent impact in flexible formulations. Glass laminates have excellent tensile and flexural strengths plus good chemical and outdoor resistance if properly formulated. Widely used in surface coatings and adhesives.	Thermosetting and Casting	See Text

288

Name	Structure	Properties and Uses	Type	Mechanism
Ethylene glycol-terephthalic acid ("Mylar")	HOCH$_2$CH$_2$OH HOC(=O)–⬡–C(=O)OH	Outstanding toughness and tear strength in films. Also widely used in fibers. (See Chapter 11.)	Thermoplastic	See Text
Silicones	(CH$_3$)$_2$SiCl$_2$ ⬡(SiCl$_2$)$_2$ (see text)	Outstanding heat resistance. Unusual solubilities give anti-foam and water-repellent properties. Used for insulating varnish on electric motors, for high temperature rubbers, greases, and lubricants, for high temperature glass laminating, to increase adhesion of polyesters to glass fibers, and a multitude of other specialty uses most of which are not "plastic" applications in the strict sense.	Thermosetting in plastic applications	See Text
Polyurethanes	CH$_3$–⬡(N=C=O)(N=C=O) HOCRC(=O)OH (see text) HOROH	Best properties as rubbers with excellent wear resistance. Widely used as flexible foams; also for rigid foams and surface coating applications.	Thermosetting	See Text
Delrin	H–C(=O)–H	Excellent abrasion resistance. Tough. Excellent colorability in opaques only. Good chemical resistance. Excellent dimensional stability.	Thermoplastics	Ionic solvent-non-solvent (probably a fast chain reaction mechanism like vinyl polymers).

TABLE 10.1. BASIC COMMERCIAL PLASTICS (Continued)

Descriptive Name	Chemical Structure of Monomers	Outstanding and/or Typical Properties or Uses*	Thermosetting, Thermoplastic, or Casting	Commercial Methods of Manufacture
Penton	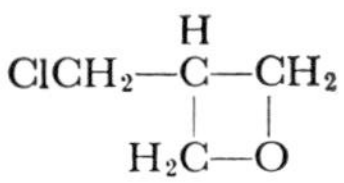 $ClCH_2-\overset{\overset{H}{\mid}}{\underset{\underset{O}{\mid}}{C}}-CH_2$ (see text)	**Best** chemical resistance of easily molded rigid polymers. **Self-extinguishing to fire.**	Thermo-plastic	**Ionic solvent-non-solvent**
Polycarbonates	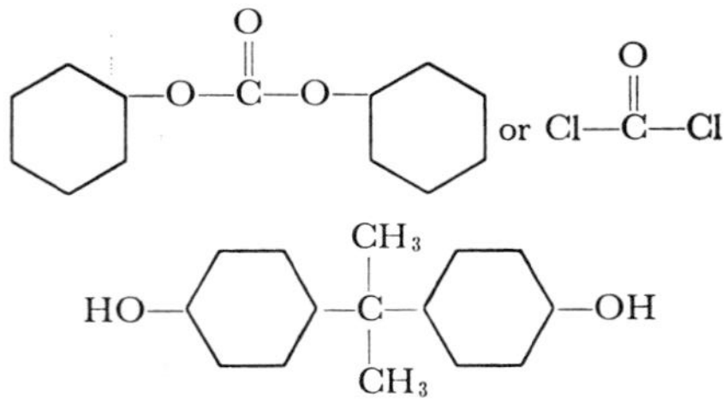 (structure)	Excellent impact, dimensional stability at high temperatures, colorability. Good electrical properties. **Self-extinguishing.**	Thermo-plastic	See Text
CELLULOSIC PLASTICS **Cellulose acetate**	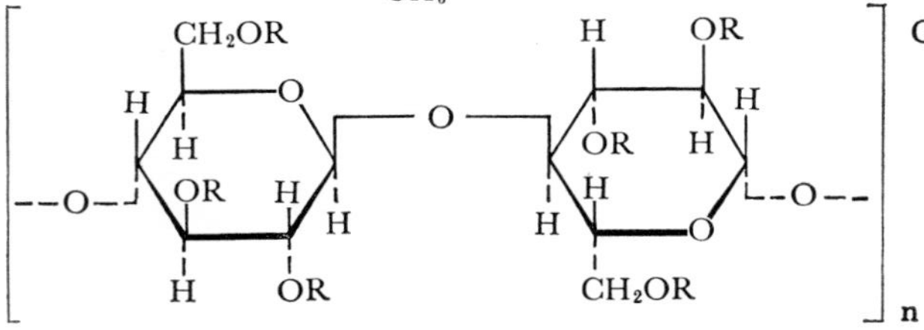 (structure)	Good impact strength. Good transparency. Excellent colorability. Fair outdoor stability. Slow to self-extinguishing burning rate. Requires plasticizers to form. Used for photographic film and moldings.	Thermo-plastic	**See Text**

n = 50–100

$R = -\overset{\overset{O}{\mid\mid}}{C}-CH_3$ (2.2–2.3 R's per ring)

290

Cellulose nitrate	n = 250 R = NO$_2$ (1.9–20 R's per ring)	Outstanding impact strength. Uses as plastic declining.	See Text	See Text
Cellulose acetate butyrate	R = —C—CH$_3$ (1 per ring) ‖ O R' = —CCH$_2$CH$_2$CH$_3$ (1.7 per ring) ‖ O	Similar to cellulose acetate with better dimensional stability and weatherability. Used for pipe, telephone housings, moldings.	Thermo-plastic	See Text
Ethyl cellulose	n = 250 R = —CH$_2$CH$_3$	Outstanding impact of all cellulosics, otherwise similar.	Thermo-plastic	See Text

*Within each class of polymer the properties can be widely varied depending on the plasticizer, copolymer type and the ratio of filler and stabilizer in the basic formulation, particularly in condensation polymers, etc. The properties given are only the outstanding and characteristic ones.

291

ing an initiating free radical itself. By such a mechanism polymer molecules with thousands of monomeric units are generated in a few seconds or less; the monomers are normally linked together in a head-to-tail fashion. If the chain reaction is stopped by the combination of two growing chains or by an initiating radical colliding with the end of a growing chain rather than with a monomer molecule (this is unlikely), both ends of the polymer chains will contain initiator fragments. Chain transfer agents used to control molecular weight, e.g., mercaptans and halogenated aliphatic hydrocarbons, may also terminate a growing chain by splitting into two radical fragments, one terminating the growing chain and the other behaving as a free radical initiator. Disproportionation, i.e., the rearrangement of the polymeric free radical into a more stable configuration, usually with the formation of a double bond, is possible. Also, chain terminators or inhibitors such as quinones, oxygen, sulfur, and amines, may stop a growing chain by forming stable adducts with the initiator and/or polymeric free radical. Early chemists were plagued with the question of what stops the chain; this still is a difficult problem to solve quantitatively for any particular polymerization scheme.

Ionic catalysis of vinyl and diene monomers is a very old art. Matthews[55] in England and Harris[41] in Germany discovered simultaneously, in 1910, that metallic sodium would polymerize butadiene. Yet little commercialization was achieved until very recently. Then around 1952 Karl Ziegler, who had been working in the field of metal-organic compounds for nearly 30 years, discovered that aluminum trialkyls complexed with $TiCl_4$ would polymerize ethylene to high molecular weight at low pressures.[31] At about the same time John Hogan and Robert Banks of Phillips Petroleum discovered that certain hexavalent chromium oxides on silica or aluminum gel would polymerize ethylene to commercial polymers. Shortly thereafter G. Natta and co-workers in Italy discovered that modified "Ziegler catalyst" would cause "stereospecific" propagation* of the growing chain for α-olefins. Other ionic catalysts have been found to influence chain configuration, particularly in dienes.

Polymer molecules possessing a regular structure appear to crystallize readily, producing unusual properties, i.e., they are higher melting, more rigid, stronger, and less soluble than their non-crystalline stereo-irregular counterparts.

This new field has excited great commercial and scientific interest. To date *cis*-polypropylene, *cis*-polyisoprene, and *cis*-polybutadiene have been produced for sale, but crystalline polystyrene, methyl methacrylate, 3-methyl-1-butene, and several methyl penetenes and methyl hexenes have all been produced in the laboratory. Greater commercialization seems certain in the

---

* Natta's modified Ziegler catalyst forbids *trans* addition of an incoming α-olefin molecule; hence all *cis*-polymer is produced.[12]

future. Although the commercial art has not yet been disclosed too extensively in the United States, several hundred Belgian, German, and Italian patents have been issued.

In contrast to the general nature of catalysis of addition polymerization, condensation polymerization utilizes the acid or base catalyst appropriate to the organic groups involved. Some pairs of groups require no catalyst at all. No chain reaction mechanism occurs, and the molecules gradually increase in size as the polymerization proceeds. If trifunctional or higher functional molecules are present, crosslinking will occur, leading first to gelation and eventually to complete hardening.

VIEWPOINT OF THE CHEMICAL ENGINEER

The chemical engineer looks at plastics first of all from the viewpoint of unit processes, unit operations, and fundamental principles of manufacture. The successful commercial development of low cost processes is the contribution of the chemical engineer. These processes will be discussed in more detail later.

The chemical engineer in the plastic industry has a few unique problems which he does not have to the same degree in other branches of his industry. These problems stem from the fact that polymers are not economically purified, i.e., the separation operations of distillation, extraction, adsorption, etc., are not commercially practical methods for isolating good polymeric molecules from undesirable ones. Ordinarily, all polymeric molecules produced by a particular polymerization scheme will end up in the final product sent to the customer. This means that any changes in the polymerization process will be reflected in the properties of the final product. The process engineer in the plastics industry must be completely aware of polymerization mechanisms, kinetics, and quality evaluation schemes. In addition, he must appreciate that tests for "quality" cannot be simple or definitive; variations in the process due to scale-up or modifications made for economic gain may alter "quality" irrevocably in subtle ways not always measurable by simple routine control tests.

VIEWPOINT OF THE ECONOMIST

The plastics industry began a period of rapid growth in the late 1930's and is continuing to expand. (See Figure 10.8 and Tables 10.2 and 10.3.) In 1955 production was more than ten times what it was in 1940 or five times the growth rate of the United States industry as a whole for the corresponding period.

There is much speculation as to when the industry will begin to slow down to a more mature growth curve. Some of the older plastics such as phenol-formaldehyde, urea-formaldehyde, cellulose derivatives, and polystyrene have much slower growth curves and in some cases have even lost ground to new-

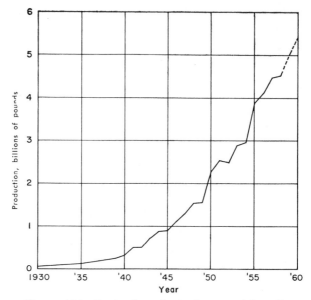

Figure 10.8. Production of plastics materials. (*From U. S. Department of Commerce data, including Std. Ind. Class 2821 and cellulosics*)

comers like polyethylene which is still expanding rapidly, 350 million pounds being manufactured in the United States in 1955 with over one and a quarter billion pounds estimated for 1960.

MANUFACTURING PROCESSES

The number of manufacturing processes for polymers is nearly as diverse as the number of polymers, but it is possible to classify them as follows:

A. Addition polymerization processes
1. Mass
2. Emulsion
3. Suspension
4. Solvent
5. Solvent/non-solvent

B. Condensation polymerization processes
C. Ring opening and other "addition" polymerization processes in which polymer grows in a manner other than a chain reaction.

Addition Polymerization

Addition polymerization has evolved along many paths to solve the major engineering problem of removing the large heat of polymerization, e.g., 12–26 kg cal/mole of vinyl monomer.[*,74] For polyethylene this amounts to

* The difference in energy between a "standard" carbon-carbon double bond and two single bonds is about 16 kg cal. Variations from this level are due to substituents.

TABLE 10.2. PRODUCTION IN 1957 OF SYNTHETIC PLASTICS AND RESIN MATERIALS (DRY BASIS[1]) IN THE UNITED STATES *

Material	Production, 1,000 pounds	$ Value/pound[3]	Per cent of total $ value of all plastics
Grand total	4,474,227	$0.35	
Polyethylene	707,500	0.32	14.2
Polyvinylchloride and copolymers	689,456	0.29	12.5
Styrene resins including copolymers, polyesters for protective coatings only, ion exchange resins, styrene-butadiene latices, etc.	673,325	0.30	12.7
Phenolic and other tar acid resins[4]	532,306	0.27	9.0
Phthalic alkyd and other alkyd resins[5]	523,019	0.35	11.5
Conmarone-indene and petroleum polymer resins	286,144	0.10	1.8
Urea resins	237,907	0.23	3.4
Cellulose plastic materials (not for textiles or regenerated cellulose sheet, i.e., cellophane)	146,112	0.52[6]	4.8
Melamine resins	111,170	0.46	3.2
Polyester resins for laminates, molding and casting	96,232	0.40	2.4
Rosin, terprene and tall oil resins	55,004	0.23	0.8
Epoxy resins	46,702	0.70	2.1
Silicone resins	3,375	3.03	6.4
All vinyl resins not listed above[7]	197,050	0.51	6.3
All benzenoid plastics and resins not listed above[8]	6,548	0.54	0.2
All plastics and resins not elsewhere listed[9]	162,377	0.84	8.6

Total production   4,474,227,000 lb
Total value $1,590,000,000

* Compiled from a preliminary report by U. S. Department of Commerce, August 1958 [2]

1. Dry basis is defined as the total weight of materials including resin, plasticizers, fillers, extenders, colors, and stabilizers as sold by base resin supplier, and excluding water, solvents, and other liquid diluents. Many other fillers, plasticizers, extenders, colors, etc., are added by the purchaser in processing the goods to finished products.
2. Contains all materials listed under U. S. Dept. of Commerce Std. Ind. Class. #2821. This class includes resins for surface coatings, adhesives, binders, sizes, ion exchange resins, non-vulcanizable rubbers, etc., but excludes all cellulose-based fibers, regenerated cellulose sheet (cellophane), synthetic fibers, vulcanizable rubbers. This definition is slightly broader than the one given earlier but it is necessary to permit standardized comparison with prior years.
3. Calculated on rounded figures.
4. Much of this is not molding powder but goes into surface coatings, adhesives, binders, etc.
5. Almost entirely used in surface coatings.
6. Estimated from prices quoted in *Chem. Eng. News Price Supplement*, October 6, 1958.
7. Includes polyvinylacetate (used principally in surface coatings and adhesives), polyvinylidenechloride, polyvinylalcohol, polyvinylbutyral, polyvinylformal, and copolymers of vinyl chloride containing less than 50 per cent vinyl chloride.
8. Includes data for aniline-formaldehyde, toluenesulfonamide, etc.
9. Includes data for methylmethacrylate, nylon, other polyamides, etc.

more than 1500 Btu pound, or a temperature rise of over 2000° F under adiabatic reaction conditions. Such temperature changes are intolerable, causing complete breakdown. For example, carbonization occurs for ethylene under high pressure at about 600–700° F. In addition, the temperature at which polymerization occurs is an important factor in determining such

TABLE 10.3.[1] WORLD GROWTH IN PLASTICS[2] PRODUCTION, MILLIONS OF POUNDS

Country	1938	1950	1954	1956
United States	130	2,280	2,951	4,124
Germany†	148	287	801	1,221
Great Britain	66	348	611	688
Japan	33	42	170	335
U.S.S.R.*	. . .	60–70	200–220	320–340
France	29	73	187	287
Italy	9	51	172	243
Canada*	. . .	. . .	150	220
Others*	25	148–158	342–252	546–566
Total	440	3289–3309	5584–5614	7984–8024

[1] Taken from: Wittmeyer, H., and Theurer, A., "World Trade Statistics," in "Modern Plastics Encyclopedia," p. 34, 1959, Plastics Catalog Corp., Bristol, Conn.
[2] Not including regenerated cellulose.
* Estimated.
† Includes West and East Germany for 1950 and later.

TABLE 10.4.[1] WORLD PRODUCTION OF PLASTIC[2] MATERIALS, 1956

	Millions of Pounds	%
Vinyls[3]	1520–1760	19–22
Phenolics	1200–1440	15–18
Alkyds[4]	1120–1280	14–16
Styrene polymers and copolymers	800–960	10–12
Polyethylene	800–960	10–12
Aminos	720–880	9–11
Acrylics	320–420	3–4
Others	1600–400	20–5

[1] Taken from: Wittmeyer, H., and Theurer, A., "World Trade Statistics," in "Modern Plastics Encyclopedia," p. 34, 1959, Plastics Catalog Corp., Bristol, Conn.
[2] Not including regenerated cellulose (cellophane).
[3] Mostly polyvinylchloride and copolymers.
[4] Used in surface coatings.

quality factors as molecular weight, chain branching, color, stability, etc. Commercial reaction temperatures range from −130° F for isobutylene, to 360–520° F for high pressure polyethylene. For monomers that are solvents for their polymers, extreme viscosities are reached at low conversions, e.g., 100,000–200,000 centipoise is the viscosity of 30 per cent converted styrene syrups at the polymerizing temperature of 190–195° F. For polymers which will precipitate from their monomers (polyvinylchloride, polyacrylonitrile), unstirrable slurries result at 25–35 per cent conversion. The thermal conductivity of such organic materials is very low—less than most common insulating materials—and thus magnifies the already difficult heat transfer problem. Unusual methods are required to solve this problem peculiar to the polymer industry.

Mass Polymerization

The term mass or bulk polymerization, as used here, refers only to monomers which dissolve their polymers (styrene, methylmethacrylate) and not those from which the polymers precipitate (vinyl chloride, vinylidene chloride, acrylonitrile). Mass polymerization is the method frequently used in the laboratory to study a new monomer and its copolymers; no extra variables are introduced and the heat removal problem is trivial provided thin (10–25 mm) glass tubing is used. However, scaling-up such a process in a practical manner presents tremendous problems. Only polystyrene is commercially manufactured today by a pure mass polymerization process.*

In the middle 1930's Badische Anilin in Germany developed a continuous process for manufacturing polystyrene which is still used in at least Germany and Italy.[24] The process consists of polymerizing styrene monomer to 30–33 per cent in stirred jacketed kettles at about 190–195° F and then feeding this viscous syrup to the top of a vertical jacketed tower, about 30 inches in diameter by 19 feet long, containing a few temperature regulating coils. This tower is operated at atmospheric pressure and is not quite full; thus temperatures are prevented from rising much above the boiling point of styrene monomer (293° F) until high conversions are attained, at which point temperatures rise to about 400° F. Molten polystyrene is pumped from the bottom of the towers at a rate of about 900 lb/hr by means of screw extruders. The molten strands from the extruder are cooled and then cut into transparent granules or pellets.

In the United States the degree of temperature control attained in the German tower process has not been adequate to achieve optimum quality and versatility; equipment has been devised[2,3,4,84] which will control the reaction temperatures more effectively to higher conversions than in the German tower process. Most of these processes utilize slowly revolving screws or paddles which gently agitate the viscous polymerizing syrup, thereby aiding heat transfer. To reach very low monomer contents, devolatilization is achieved under high (29" of Hg) vacuum using vented twin screw extruders or similar devices.[3]

Polymethylmethacrylate is mass polymerized to make sheets utilizing plate glass as the mold material.[76] Also, certain allyl resins containing some tri-

---

* Methylmethacrylate and "allyl" casting resin syrups are cast and polymerized in thin sections by a pure mass process, but these processes, though practiced commercially on a small scale for speciality items, will not produce molding powder economically. Methylmethacrylate molding powder is made via a suspension process.

functional molecules for crosslinking are mass polymerized to encase or "pot" electrical components. The volume manufactured by these latter processes is very small.

Emulsion Polymerization

Emulsion polymerization, in the modern sense, is polymerization of a hydrophobic monomer, water, a water-soluble free radical initiator, and an emulsifying agent which drastically lowers the interfacial tension between the water and monomer phases, e.g., soaps, alkyl sulfates, aryl alkyl sulfonates, etc. Gentle agitation is required, at least in the beginning, to keep the large initial monomer droplets well distributed, but the particle size of the final latex particle is not appreciably influenced by the intensity of agitation. The result is a stable latex of small polymer spheres much smaller than the initial monomer droplets and usually between 0.01 and 1.0 microns in diameter (Figure 10.9).

Emulsion polymerization was first attempted with natural gums and other hydrophilic protective colloids in an effort to duplicate natural rubber. Though patented in 1913, these methods were neither practical nor reproducible. Then in 1927, Dinsmore,[22] and Luther and Heuck[51] in Germany tried to make synthetic rubber from normal soaps and surface active agents. Later on Luther and Heuck used water-soluble initiators. Much of the development and study of emulsion technology was spurred by the need, just prior to and during World War II, for synthetic rubber, first in Germany and then in the United States.

Emulsion polymerization has a rather complicated mechanism different from that of the mass or suspension process. Briefly, the emulsifier promotes the solubility of monomer (and sometimes the initiator*) in the water phase where initiation first occurs. Depending on the concentration of the emulsifier in the water phase,† the newly formed radical either collects sufficient emulsifier to form a new particle or, because of its polar initiator end group, acts like a "radical soap" and migrates to the interface of existing emulsion particles. In most emulsion polymerizations much of the polymerization occurs in the monomer-swollen emulsion particles where the growing radicals are somewhat less mobile and incapable of reacting with radicals in neighboring particles. The net result is a severe reduction in the rate at which the radicals can combine to stop chain growth. Hence both molecular

---

* Many initiators are completely water soluble; others, like cumene hydroperoxide, are only partially water soluble. The argument, almost semantic, about whether the emulsifier micelles, the emulsifier-monomer-initiator domains, or "the water phase" is the true site of initiation will not be discussed here.

† After a few particles have formed they begin to drain the emulsifier from the water phase to the surface of these particles. The concentration in the water phase, therefore, is constantly changing.

weight and reaction rate are significantly increased. Such features of polymer structure as amount of branching, type of crosslinking (micro-gel), etc. also differ from those obtained by other polymerization mechanisms.

Modern emulsion polymerization solves the major problem of heat transfer admirably. Rapid polymerization rates may be obtained at precisely defined low temperatures while high molecular weights are maintained, particularly when "redox" catalyst systems are utilized.[9] Also, the use of water-

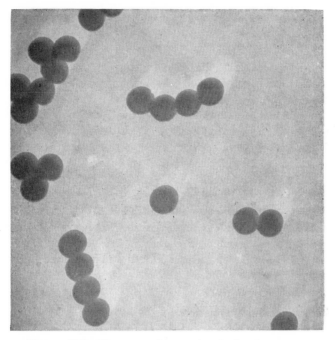

Figure 10.9. Electron micrograph of the famous mono-disperse Dow latex frequently used for routine calibration of electron microscopes. (*Courtesy Monsanto Chemical Co.*)

soluble catalysts frequently promotes stability of the latex particles which are much smaller than those obtained by dispersion of monomer through intensive mixing. Continuous polymerization is possible in tubular reactors, in towers, or in a series of agitated reactors.

In spite of its many advantages, however, emulsion polymerization has not been used extensively to make solid plastics.* Since it is commercially impractical to remove the emulsifying agents completely, emulsion-produced polymers are poorer in haze, color, heat stability, and electrical properties than products made by other processes. Also, some water-soluble initiators

* It is important to distinguish between plastics, rubbers, resins for surface coatings, and synthetic fibers; the latter three industries utilize emulsion technology extensively, the rubber industry almost exclusively, at the present time.

such as potassium persulfate make comparatively unstable chain end groups for at least vinyl chloride and vinylidene chloride polymers. In addition, the cost of obtaining a dry-pelleted polymer from a latex is considerably higher than for mass or suspension polymer. First the emulsion must be coagulated. This may be accomplished in many ways: by adding acid or other electrolytes, by vigorous mixing, by ultrasonics, through freezing, by forcing through jets, etc. The coagulated crumb will ordinarily contain most of the water originally present in the latex, e.g., from 40–65 per cent water. This water is not on the surface but must slowly diffuse out through the polymer. Drying is therefore slow and expensive. After drying, the crumb (or sometimes powder) must be densified into pellets. Drum drying[24] and spray drying (commercially used for polyvinylchloride plastisols) achieve coagulation and drying in a single step but both of these methods are comparatively expensive.

Latices commercially processed to plastics include: polyvinylchloride plastisol resin (produced by spray drying latex); "Kralastic," "Cycolac," and "Lustran," styrene/acrylonitrile graft polyblends with synthetic rubbers; "Teflon" (polytetrafluoroethylene); and, possibly, "Kel-F" (polytrifluorochloroethylene). Many other latices are produced in large volume to be sold as such for use in formulations for surface coatings, textile finishes, adhesives, paper binders and coatings, waxes and polishes, etc.

Emulsion polymerization equipment is almost always glass-lined because plating or scaling of polymer on metals is frequently very severe. In the laboratory, tumbling 6 ounce soft-drink bottles may be used for pressures up to 150 psig.*

Suspension Polymerization

For a long time suspension and emulsion polymerization were considered synonymous. Then Mark and Hohenstein[53] pointed out the characteristics which today serve to separate the two processes: emulsion polymerization utilizes comparatively low molecular weight substances of high surface activity for emulsifiers, i..e., substances which markedly lower the interfacial tension; suspension polymerization, on the other hand, requires finely-

---

* Permission should be obtained from the appropriate company for such use, and the bottles should be kept segregated.

† Protective colloids are water-soluble substances of great molecular weight. They usually contain amounts of hydrophobic groups sufficient to cause them to locate preferentially at the oil-water interface; however, the interfacial tension is not markedly lowered by the great molecular weight. Water-soluble polymers that have been utilized for suspension polymerization include gelatin, natural water-soluble gums (usually polysaccharides), polyvinyl pyrrolidone, polyvinylalcohol, sulfonated polystyrene, polyacrylic acid and its salts, polymethacrylic acid and its salts, and many others.

divided solids or a protective colloid† which, though they locate themselves preferentially at the interface, do not greatly lower the surface tension. In the emulsion process, initiation of polymerization begins in the continuous water phase; in suspension polymerization the catalyst is soluble in the monomer phase and initiation begins there. The most apparent physical effect resulting from these essential differences is the much larger polymer particle produced by suspension polymerization, e.g., suspended particles usually range between 50 and 2,000 microns (about 0.002–0.08 inch) in

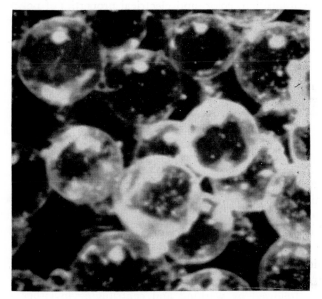

Figure 10.10. Polystyrene beads. (*Courtesy Monsanto Chemical Co.*)

diameter, while most emulsion particles range between 0.01 and 1.0 micron (Figure 10.10). The large suspension particles are easily separated from the water phase, whereas the smaller emulsion particles are separated with much more difficulty. Also, the importance of agitation differs for the two systems. In emulsion polymerization a certain minimum level of agitation is required to break up the pure monomer phase, but after this minimum level is attained agitation may vary greatly up to the point where it causes coagulation of the emulsion particles; agitation does not ordinarily affect particle size or particle-size distribution as it does in suspension polymerization.

Many types of finely divided solids, frequently combined with protective colloids or very small quantities of low molecular weight surface-active agents, have been used as suspending agents: commercial tricalcium phosphate (hydroxy apatite), specially precipitated barium sulfate, calcium oxalate, bentonite clay, aluminum hydroxide, etc.

The use of an oil-soluble catalyst gives reaction kinetics and mechanisms essentially identical to mass polymerization rather than emulsion polymerization. Reaction rates are therefore slower in the former than in emulsion polymerizations aiming for the same molecular weight product.

Suspension polymerization is of great importance in the plastics industry. It not only solves the heat transfer problem but also permits simple and complete separation of the polymer from water and suspending agents. Haze, water absorption, color, and electrical properties of polymer made by a good suspension process will essentially equal those of polymer made by a laboratory or commercial mass process.

A typical formulation[35] for batch suspension polymerization is:

	Parts
Deionized and deaerated water	68
Styrene monomer (deoxygenated)	100
Hydroxy apatite	0.77
Dodecylbenzene sulfonate	0.00256
Benzoyl peroxide	0.204

Diffusion at the beginning is sufficiently rapid so that the order of charging is not significant. The polymerization cycle is a functon of temperature and varies from $6\frac{1}{2}$ hours at 194° F to $3\frac{1}{2}$ hours at 239° F. Following completion of the reaction period the charge is cooled to 185° F and transferred to a slurry hold tank.

If a solid suspending agent is used it must be dissolved after polymerization. For example, HCl is used to dissolve hydroxy apatite (tricalcium phosphate), followed by washing and centrifuging in either a continuous or batch centrifuge. From the centrifuge the nearly dried beads (3–10 per cent moisture) are fed to a suitable dryer, e.g., a rotary cocurrent air, counter-current steam tube, rotary vacuum, etc. (Figures 10.11, 10.12, and 10.13). From the dryer the beads are mixed with colorants, stabilizers, plasticizers (if polyvinylchloride), etc.; melted in a Banbury mixer or an extruder; extruded, cooled, and finally chopped into pellets for bagging as a molding powder.

Plastic molding powders that are commercially made via a suspension process include:

(a) Polymethylmethacrylate
(b) Polystyrene
(c) Polyvinylidene chloride/vinylchloride copolymer
(d) Polyvinylchloride and copolymers
(e) Polyvinylacetate

Commercial suspension processes are (as far as is known) all batch, but there are no technical reasons preventing development of continuous processes. The batch reactors are glass-lined to avert polymer scaling problems similar to those which occur in emulsion processes. The difficulties of commercially obtaining a "clean" bead with no contamination or agglomeration are treated by Tromsdorff.[77] In polyvinylchloride polymerization a further difficulty is that of obtaining a porous bead that will soak up plasticizer rapidly and uniformly in subsequent processing. The commercial art

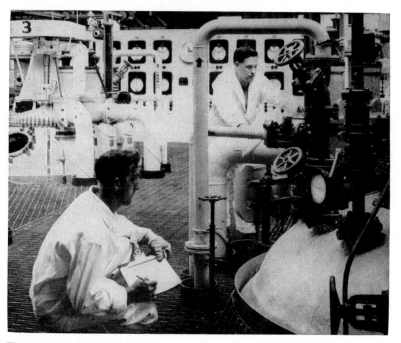

Figure 10.11. Polyvinylchloride suspension polymerizers. (*Courtesy Monsanto Chemical Co.*)

of suspension polmerization is complicated and many details have not been disclosed. The complete suspending agent recipe is the most important part of the process, although agitation also plays a vital role.

Solution Polymerization. Addition-type polymerization carried out in a solvent which will dissolve the monomer, the polymer, and the polymerization catalyst, is termed solution polymerization. Polymerization of pure monomers that dissolve their polymers is solution polymerization provided the polymerization is halted at a low enough conversion to maintain a reasonable level of fluidity. The eventual high viscosity levels of complete bulk polymerization are avoided in solution polymerization and heat transfer

Figure 10.12. Laboratory suspension polymerizer. (*Courtesy Monsanto Chemical Co.*)

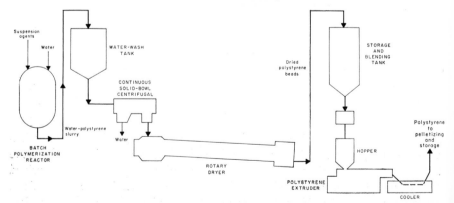

Figure 10.13. Flow sheet for polystyrene by a suspension process. [*Chemical Engineering*, **65**, 100–1 (Dec. 1, 1958).]

is greatly facilitated. By proper adjustment of reaction temperature and pressure, reflux of monomer or solvent may remove heat. (Because of the high molecular weight of polymers, boiling elevation is insignificant until high per cent conversions by weight are reached.)

Solution polymerization will generally slow down the reaction rate and lower the molecular weight, particularly when free radical initiators are used. Depending on the polymer, such effects may be commercially desirable or undesirable. In some instances the rate at which monomer will graft onto preformed polymer molecules can be lessened; this leads to lower levels of chain branching and crosslinking.

Solution polymerization, however, has been used sparingly in the plastics industry, primarily because most of the polymers marketed to date have been successfully polymerized by the more economical mass and suspension processes. The cost of solvent removal and recovery may be appreciable. Machinery that can successfully and economically devolatilize a solvent from a polymer is not yet standardized. Although vacuum drum driers will do the job they are extremely costly for the rates attainable. Twin-screw extruders have been commercially utilized, and multiple-vented single screw extruders are being marketed. High vacuum, i.e., greater than 29" of Hg, is usually required. Production rates are slow because of the slow diffusion rates in polymers.

A solution process for making styrene/acrylonitrile copolymer and other copolymers of styrene[39,40,45] which probably is being utilized for commercial production of styrene/acrylonitrile has been disclosed. (Styrene/α-methyl styrene is probably also made commercially by a similar process, but here the solvent is merely the monomer.) For styrene/acrylonitrile copolymers, ethylbenzene or toluene at 30 per cent concentration by weight are the preferred solvents; they ensure a balance between reaction rate and chain transfer, i.e., reaction rates and molecular weights are both lowered to commercially desirable levels. The process is a continuous one with the reactant (70/30 styrene/acrylonitrile) and solvent being fed to a recycling loop of a 20 per cent by weight polymer solution maintained at 300° F by a heat exchanger. The reaction rate under these conditions is 27 per cent/hr. A form of a twin screw extruder called the "Plastruder"[37,38] recovers the solvent and the unreacted monomer for recycle to the reactor.

Solution polymerizations of the addition type using ionic catalysis have been studied in the laboratory without notable commercial success as yet. Cationic catalysts, e.g., $AlCl_3$, HF, are used extensively to polymerize olefins in the petroleum industry (Chapter 14). Also, many tons of petroleum resins and asphaltic polymers are produced using cationic catalysts, e.g., concentrated sulfuric acid, aluminum halides, ferric chloride, boron halides.[1,26,65] To describe all these resins and their manufacture is beyond the scope of this chapter.

Solvent-Nonsolvent Polymerization (Precipitation Polymerization)

Some polymers are insoluble in their monomers, e.g., polymers of vinyl chloride, vinylidene chloride, acrylonitrile, chlorotrifluoroethylene, ethylene (at least at lower temperatures and pressures), etc. If polymerization is initiated in the pure monomers a polymeric precipitate forms. Sometimes other solvents are added to increase or decrease solubility of the monomer in the solid polymer. Surprisingly, with free radical catalysts, molecular weights are frequently much higher in such systems than in nearly equivalent homogeneous systems. The reason for this molecular weight effect is probably similar to the reason for emulsion polymers having higher molecular weight, i.e., initiation occurs primarily in the continuous phase so that each precipitated particle is likely to have only one growing radical to which fresh monomer can readily diffuse, while other polymeric radicals cannot. Termination by combination of two polymeric radicals, therefore, is infrequent because of the relative immobility of the growing chains, even if two precipitated particles should fuse.

Chain termination mechanisms have not been explored in detail for any particular system, but chain transfer to monomer, to the polymeric chain, to the solvent, or to a chain transfer agent are possibilities as is disproportionation or termination by catalysts, inhibitors, or retarders. If chain transfer to polymer is possible as it is to polyvinylchloride, branched structures develop.

Solvent-nonsolvent polymerization was the method selected for preparing the vinylchloride/vinylacetate copolymers ("Vinylites") first commercially introduced in 1935. Their initial patents[23,71] have expired, but none of the many other manufacturers of vinylchloride polymers and copolymers in the United States utilize a similar process. Except for a very few patents, little has been disclosed. The material is polymerized at moderate temperatures, 30–70° C, and moderate pressures of 80–140 psig using reactive free radical catalysts (acetyl benzoyl peroxide or many types of aliphatic acid peroxides). At about 20–30 per cent conversion, the polymer slurry becomes too thick to agitate and the vinylchloride monomer, which is a gas at normal temperature and pressure, must be recovered by flash drying or other methods. A recent French process[5] employs a ball mill to fluidize the polymer and aid heat removal in the thick pasty polymerizing mass. Conversions of 80–85 per cent are claimed.

Recently, polyoxymethylene (polymerized formaldehyde) has been commercially developed utilizing basic ionic catalysts such as quaternary ammonium bases, trialkyl amines of high molecular weight, and trialkyl phosphines.[78] Thoroughly dried hydrocarbon solvents which do not dissolve the polymer are used, e.g., hexane, cyclohexane, and toluene. Pure formaldehyde completely free of water and acids must be used to obtain polymer of high molecular weight with reasonably narrow molecular weight distribution and good thermal stability. After polymerization is completed the polymer is stabilized by acetylating the end groups at high temperatures, 700° F, with acetic anhydride in the presence of pyridine or an alkali acetate as a catalyst.[25]

A continuous low temperature (32° F) solvent-nonsolvent process has been described[60,70,95] for polytrifluorochloroethylene ("Kel-F"). The reactive, free radical catalyst, *bis*-trichloroacetyl peroxide dissolved in trichlorofluoromethane, is added continuously to a stirred, jacketed, stainless steel reactor along with the monomer. The polymer is separated from the slurry in monomer and trichlorofluoromethane by means of a continuous filter or centrifuge and then further dried in a vacuum drier to remove all the remaining monomer. The unreacted monomer and diluent is recycled to the reactor with a portion being sent to a repurification distillation column.

Condensation Polymerization

Generalizations concerning processes and equipment for the various commercial condensation polymerizations would be meaningless. These subjects will be treated in the following sections where each type of condensation polymer is discussed separately.

CONDENSATION POLYMERS

Phenol-Formaldehyde Resins

It is not surprising that the first completely synthetic plastic was made from the common and highly reactive multifunctional chemicals, phenol and formaldehyde. As early as 1870 Baeyer in Germany observed the reactions between phenol and formaldehyde and characterized the phenol alcohols formed. Around the turn of the century Delair, Smith, and Leback attempted to utilize the resinous reaction products for shellac substitutes. Beginning in the early 1900's Dr. Leo Baekeland discovered that useful moldings could be made if the final stages of the reaction were carried out under heat and pressure, preferably in the presence of a suitable filler, e.g., sawdust, wood flour, cotton cloth, etc. Since that time phenolic resins have become the "work-horse" of the plastics industry, being used in electrical components, insulating varnishes, industrial laminates, binders, etc.

The chemistry of this complex reaction is, even today, not completely understood. When crosslinked structures of large size are formed, isolation and characterization of these structures is very difficult. Much investigation has been done, however, and a great deal is known—so much, in fact, that the brief description given below suffers from oversimplification.

The first step in the reactions is the formation of phenol alcohols under the influence of either acids or bases.

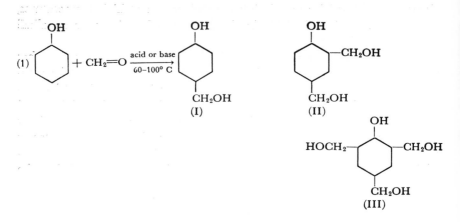

Next, these phenol alcohols condense in a complex manner. Using acid catalysts the following reactions are favored.

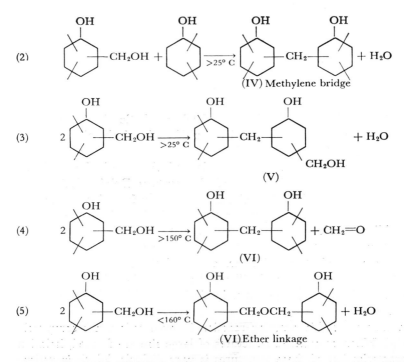

Reactions (2) and (3) with the benzene nucleus proceed quickly with acid catalysts even at temperatures below the point where phenol alcohols form rapidly. Hence, under acid-catalyzed conditions unreacted phenol alcohols cannot ordinarily be isolated, but are intermediates. Reaction (5), though catalyzed by weakly acidic conditions, is slower than Reactions (2) and (3) and occurs, therefore, at neutral pH's and/or when all of the *ortho* and *para* positions on the phenol nuclei are occupied by alcoholic or unreactive groups. At high temperatures (around 160° C) the ether becomes unstable, losing formaldehyde and reverting to methylene bridges [Reaction (4)].

With basic catalysts Reaction (5) is slow at the high pH's used commercially. The condensation reactions (2), (3), and (4) will take place but at a much slower rate than under acid catalysis; also, at a surprisingly low concentration of strong base, further amounts of base do not increase the rates of these reactions. The formation of phenol alcohols [Reaction (1)] is strongly catalyzed, permitting isolation of pure or partially condensed alcohols, since the condensation reactions are not as strongly catalyzed.

Commercial equipment for the above reactions usually includes jacketed anchor-agitated steel or stainless-steel kettles equipped with vacuum reflux condensers, although scraped wall heat exchangers might be used for a continuous process.

Two major types of commercial molding powders are based on either one- or two-stage resins. One-stage resins are made with basic catalysts, e.g., 1 to 2 parts $Ca(OH)_2$ to 100 parts phenol, and with a formaldehyde/phenol mole ratio between 1.1 and 1.5. Formalin or paraformaldehyde* may be used to supply the formaldehyde. Phenol alcohols may be formed in a few minutes at 200–212° F or in a few hours at 150–165° F, depending on the heat exchange capacity of the reaction equipment, the catalyst concentration, and the type of resin desired. After most of the formaldehyde has combined with the phenol, the water is removed and condensation continued under 27–29 inches of Hg vacuum at 160–180° F. When the desired level of condensation is reached the entire contents of the kettle must be cooled uniformly and rapidly to ensure a uniform degree of polymerization. One commercial method involved dumping the entire contents onto a large steel cooling floor through which cold water flows. After cooling, the resin is ground to a fine powder and blended about half and half with wood flour or other fillers and colorants plus small quantities of mold release agents and/or cure accelerators (MgO, CaO). This blend is then densified and fused on hot mill rolls, cooled, and ground into molding powder (Figure 10.14).

One-stage resins, though still manufactured, are not as important for

---

* Formalin, which is a 37% solution of formaldehyde in water, was formerly almost always used but, with the advent of cheap solid paraformaldehyde (a solid polymer of formaldehyde) from natural gas, it is frequently used to increase capacity and save on subsequent dehydrating costs.

molding powders as two-stage resins (novalaks) which usually have superior flow characteristics. The polymerization equipment used for two-stage resins is essentially the same as that used for one-stage resins although acid resistant kettles are preferred.

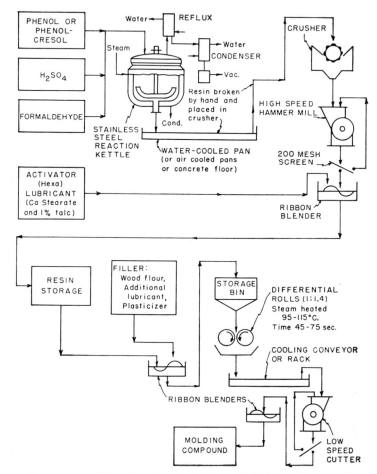

Figure 10.14. Flow sheet for phenol-formaldehyde molding powders. (Winding, C. C. and Hasche, R. L., "Plastics, Theory and Practice," *Courtesy of McGraw-Hill Book Co.*)

The first stage of a two-stage resin may be prepared as follows:

One hundred parts of phenol and 0.5 part of concentrated H_2SO_4 are charged into an anchor-agitated stainless-steel reaction vessel equipped with a reflux condenser. The charge is heated at 100° C and 69 parts (0.8 mole CH_2O/mole of phenol) of 37 per cent formalin added at a rate compatible with the heat exchange capacity of the reflux condenser. After all the formalin has been added the charge is refluxed for an additional 30 minutes and dehydration is begun by switching the condensate flow from reflux to a distillate receiver. Vacuum is applied as the boiling point begins to rise until a vacuum of 28 inches of mercury and temperature of 215° F are reached, corresponding to approximately 4 per cent free phenol in the final resin. The charge is neutralized with lime and dumped to a cooling floor. The solid resin is then ground into a fine powder.

The large heat of reaction[*,46] and the rapid rate of condensation under acid conditions makes the above procedure desirable for safety reasons. The resulting resin is thermoplastic and is termed a novalak. To make a thermosetting molding powder, hexamethylenetetramine† crystals (about 10 to 15 parts/100 parts of novalak resin) are blended with wood flour, colorants, mold release agents, and cure accelerators using a fifty/fifty ratio of total resin including "hexa" to total fillers. After blending, the resin is fused on hot mill rolls, cooled, and ground into a molding powder in a manner similar to the method used for one-stage resins.

To explain the final cure of one- and two-stage resins, a highly reactive quinone methide is postulated as an intermediate which combines to form complex condensed rings of red or brown color. These quinone methides may also explain the reaction of phenolic resins with the double bonds in rosin, in drying oils, in rubber, and in other addition-type monomers. Addition polymerization with rosin and drying oils has been used extensively to increase the oil solubility of phenolic resin varnishes.

To explain the reaction of hexa, the following principal reactions are postulated:

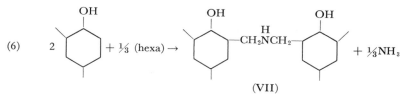

$$(6) \quad 2 \quad \text{(phenol)} + \tfrac{1}{3} \text{ (hexa)} \rightarrow \text{(VII)} + \tfrac{1}{3}NH_3$$

(VII)

* For the complete condensation of formaldehyde to form a methylene bridge structure plus liquid water, about 21 kcal/mole of formaldehyde are released. This can be split into 4.1 kcal/mole for the formation of the phenol alcohol and 16.9 kcal/mole for the formation of the methylene bridges [Reaction (2)].

† Commonly called "hexa," it is the nearly instantaneous reaction product of ammonia and formaldehyde,

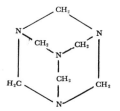

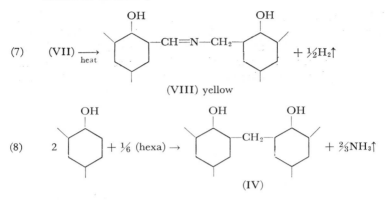

(7)   (VII) $\xrightarrow{\text{heat}}$ ... $+\frac{1}{2}H_2\uparrow$

(VIII) yellow

(8)   2 ... $+\frac{1}{6}$ (hexa) $\rightarrow$ ... $+\frac{2}{3}NH_3\uparrow$

(IV)

Many more reactions during curing have been proposed which undoubtedly do occur to some extent. Several authors[13,54,56,75] have given excellent summaries of experimental evidence for the above and other possible reactions.

Aminoplast Resins

Urea was known to react with formaldehyde as early as 1884, but commercial molding powers were not developed until 1926. As in the case of phenolic resins, commercial development preceded an understanding of the basic chemistry involved. Again, this is primarily due to the difficulty of characterizing complicated crosslinked structures. The following equations oversimplify a very complex picture:[21,44,89,90]

(1)
$$CH_2=O + H_2N\overset{\overset{\displaystyle O}{\|}}{C}NH_2 \rightleftarrows H_2N\overset{\overset{\displaystyle O}{\|}}{C}N\overset{\displaystyle H}{}CH_2OH \quad (I)$$

$$\uparrow\downarrow\ +CH_2=O$$

$$HOCH_2N\overset{\displaystyle H}{}\overset{\overset{\displaystyle O}{\|}}{C}N\overset{\displaystyle H}{}CH_2OH \quad (II)$$

$$\uparrow\downarrow\ +CH_2=O$$

$$(HOCH_2)_2N\overset{\overset{\displaystyle O}{\|}}{C}N\overset{\displaystyle H}{}CH_2OH \quad (III)$$

Reaction (1) is catalyzed by base or acid and is an equilibrium type. Under commercial conditions very little trimethylolurea is formed. If acid catalysts are used the methylolureas cannot be isolated since further condensation occurs as follows:

(2)
$$\left[\ -\overset{\overset{\displaystyle OR'}{\|}}{C}N\overset{\displaystyle |}{}CH_2OH + H_2N\overset{\overset{\displaystyle OR'}{\|}}{C}N-\ \right] \rightarrow \left[\ -\overset{\overset{\displaystyle OR'}{\|}}{C}N\overset{\displaystyle |}{}CH_2N\overset{\overset{\displaystyle OR'}{\|}}{C}\overset{\displaystyle H}{}N-\ \right] + H_2O$$

(IV)

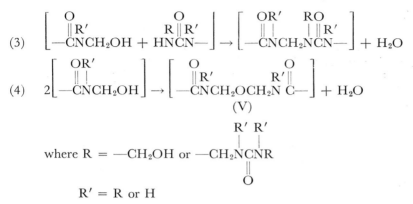

$$(3) \quad \left[\begin{array}{cc} \overset{O}{\underset{||}{C}}\overset{R'}{N}CH_2OH + & \overset{O}{\underset{||}{H}N}\overset{R'}{C}N- \end{array} \right] \rightarrow \left[\begin{array}{cc} \overset{OR'}{\underset{||}{C}N}CH_2\overset{RO}{\underset{||}{N}C}N- \end{array} \right] + H_2O$$

$$(4) \quad 2\left[\begin{array}{c} \overset{OR'}{\underset{||}{C}N}CH_2OH \end{array} \right] \rightarrow \left[\begin{array}{cc} \overset{O}{\underset{||}{C}N}CH_2OCH_2N \overset{O}{\underset{||}{C}}- \end{array} \right] + H_2O$$

$$(V)$$

where $R = -CH_2OH$ or $-CH_2\overset{\begin{array}{cc}R' & R'\\ | & |\end{array}}{N}\underset{\underset{O}{||}}{C}NR$

$$R' = R \text{ or } H$$

With equal concentrations of possible reaction sites, Reaction (2) with an unsubstituted amide hydrogen to form methylene bridges (IV) and Reaction (4) to form ether linkages (V) are favored over Reaction (3) with a substituted amide hydrogen to form methylene bridges. Under basic conditions Reactions (3) and (4) are not favored and Reaction (2) will proceed very slowly.

At the higher temperatures and acid conditions which exist during molding, the ether linkages are unstable, breaking to form methylene bridges and formaldehyde. For this reason low formaldehyde/urea ratios of about 1.5 are used in molding power or laminating resins to minimize ether formation and subsequent shrinkage and cracking during molding or after long use.

Melamine was an expensive laboratory curiosity until about 1939. Low cost commercial manufacture was then stimulated when the outstanding properties of melamine resins were discovered (Table 10.1).

Melamine has the following structure. The possibility of many resonating configurations account for its excellent thermal stability.

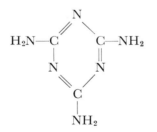

The chemistry of the condensation of melamine with formaldehyde is analogous to that of urea, with the following exceptions:

1. Six reactive hydrogen atoms exist, three of which are the highly reactive unsubstituted amide* type.

* The $-NH_2$ groups in melamine behave even more like amide groups than do the $-NH_2$ groups in urea.

2. The reactivity of these hydrogens is greater than that for urea, and methylene bridges are formed readily under basic conditions.

3. Since the melamine molecule contains three highly reactive sites it can more readily form crosslinked structures than urea with only two highly reactive sites, e.g., formaldehyde/melamine ratios for molding and laminating resin are usually 2.5 compared to 1.5 for urea.

4. The methylolmelamines are much more resistant to dissociation into formaldehyde and melamine. The hexamethylol compound is readily formed, and the di- and trimethylol compounds do not dissociate rapidly.

The equipment and processing steps for the preparation of melamine and urea resins are very similar to those described earlier for phenolic resins. Corrosion resistant equipment is used to retain the excellent color inherent in these resins.[63] Although water may be removed by simple vacuum distillation as it is for phenolic resins, spray drying is frequently the method employed. If the laminates or molding powders are made at the resin manufacturing site, impregnating the laminating paper or the molding powder filler with the wet resin is most economical; drying at atmospheric pressure in tunnel or tray driers follows. The dried impregnated sheets or molding powders are then completely cured under heat and pressure as are phenolic molding powders. The spray-dried, low molecular weight resins used for laminates are redissolved in water and alcohol to make an impregnating solution. Fillers are ordinarily highly refined α-cellulose and cotton fibers which retain the excellent color inherent in the base resins. Paper with a natural high wet strength is used for laminates.

The adhesive, textile, paper treating, and surface coating industries comprise a slightly larger market for aminoplast resins than do the molding powder and laminating markets. To ensure compatibility with surface coatings, butyl ethers are usually formed with butanol, using higher formaldehyde ratios to increase ether formation. Other nitrogen-containing chemicals used in aminoplast formulations include dicyandiamide, substituted melamines, cyclic ethylene urea, and thiourea.

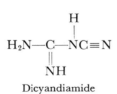

Dicyandiamide

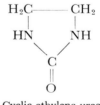

Cyclic ethylene urea

Polycarbonates

Condensation polymers need not be thermosetting. Nylon, nylon 6 (polymer of ϵ-caprolactam), "Dacron" fiber, or "Mylar" film (ethylene glycolterephthalic acid polymer) all are thermoplastic and are used for plastic applications. However, these materials are primarily known for their excellent properties as fibers and are therefore discussed in Chapter 11.

Polycarbonates are new plastics (General Electric's trade name is "Lexan") which have the generic formula,

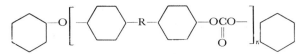

As yet only the compounds where R is $\diagup C(CH_3)_2$ have been marketed, but a large number have been studied.[79,88]

Two methods of manufacture are used: *ester interchange* and *phosgenation*.

Ester Interchange. A slight excess of diphenyl carbonate made from phosgene and phenol is reacted with bisphenol A, first at temperatures of 400–450° F and 20–30 mm of Hg pressure until 80 to 90 per cent of the phenol formed during the condensation is removed.

Diphenyl carbonate   Bisphenol A

Then the temperature must be raised to as high as 575° F and the pressure reduced to 1 mm Hg or less to complete the condensation and attain a high molecular weight. Because of the extremely high melt viscosity of this resin, special types of equipment such as vacuum mill rolls are required to obtain a high molecular weight product.

Phosgenation. Phosgene can be reacted directly with bisphenol A either in a pyridine containing solvent or in a two-phase water-oil system made by mixing water, water-soluble bases, inert solvent, and reactants. The pyridine or caustic serves to catalyze the reaction and react with the hydrochloric acid formed. The solvent renders the polymer molecules sufficiently mobile so that complete reaction is possible. Benzene, toluene, methylene chloride, and trichloroethylene have been used successfully. After polymerization is complete the polymer must be separated from the mixture. The commercial methods for achieving this separation have not been disclosed.

Epoxy Resins

Epoxy resins, commercially introduced at the end of World War II, reached a capacity of 35 million pounds in 1957 and may reach 60 million pounds in 1960. At present most are used in surface coatings, but applications are growing rapidly for potting electrical components, and in laminates and castings, particularly for metal-forming tools. Perhaps the most unique property is exceptional adhesion to metals; thus epoxies rather than metal rivets are used to apply the outer skin of aluminum on high speed aircraft.

The reactive "epoxy" group $-OCH_2\overset{O}{\overset{\diagup\diagdown}{CH-CH_2}}$* was first used in resin chemistry by the Germans in the late 1930's. In the United States Pierre Castan, a Swiss chemist, obtained the first patent.[14] Later, S. O. Greenlee of Devoe and Raynolds, the large paint manufacturer, greatly extended and developed the use of epoxies.[34] Still later, chemists from Shell Development, interested in extending markets for propylene derivatives such as epichloro-hydrin, $ClCH_2\overset{O}{\overset{\diagup\diagdown}{CH-CH_2}}$, became active in this field.[92]

Most epoxies are based on the glycidyl ether resulting from the condensation of bisphenol A and epichlorohydrin, and may be represented by the formulas:

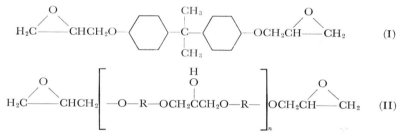

(I)

(II)

where for most commercial resins and $n = 1$ to 8 and

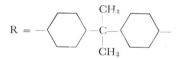

The reaction scheme by which these *bis*-glycidyl ethers are produced is discussed in greater detail by Skeist,[81] Lee and Neville,[50] and Coderre;[19] a brief summary follows:

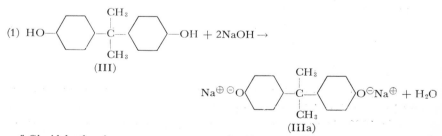

* Glycidyl ether is a more correct term since epoxy groups without oxygen on the α carbon atom do not have the same reaction characteristics as glycidyl ether groups. However, in resin chemistry the term epoxy is synonymous with glycidyl ether and will be so used here.

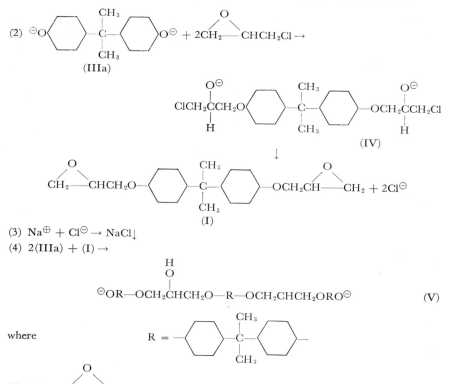

(2) $\ominus$O... C ... O$\ominus$ + 2CH$_2$—CHCH$_2$Cl →
(IIIa)

ClCH$_2$CCH$_2$O... C ... —OCH$_2$CCH$_2$Cl
(IV)

↓

CH$_2$—CHCH$_2$O... C ... —OCH$_2$CH——CH$_2$ + 2Cl$^\ominus$
(I)

(3) Na$^\oplus$ + Cl$^\ominus$ → NaCl↓

(4) 2(IIIa) + (I) →

$^\ominus$OR—OCH$_2$CHCH$_2$O—R—OCH$_2$CHCH$_2$ORO$^\ominus$ (V)

where   R = ... C ...

(5) (V) + CH$_2$—CHCH$_2$Cl → higher molecular weight analogs of (IV) and (I).

Reaction (1) in the above requires a small amount of water (about 1 per cent) to permit formation of the ionized species (IIIa). Reaction (2) to form the chlorohydrin (IV) is slow compared to the formation of the epoxy from the chlorohydrin and to the formation of salt [Reaction (3)]. If an excess of base or water is present the epichlorohydrin and the epoxy group in the resin (I) will undergo reaction to the glycol. The rate of addition of base must be adjusted to the rate at which Reaction (2) occurs if optimum basicity is to be maintained. Also, to make the monomeric *bis*-epoxy (I), an excess of epichlorohydrin will favor Reaction (2) over Reaction (4). The above principles are embodied in the following preparation[50] of a nearly pure monomeric *bis*-epoxy resin (I).

"A reaction vessel fitted with a heater, stirrer, thermometer, and distilling head having a separator providing return to the reactor of lower layer was charged with a solution containing a mole ratio of epichlorohydrin to bisphenol of 10:1. The solution was heated to about 100° C and maintained at this temperature during addition of 1.90 moles of sodium hydroxide per mole of the bisphenol, the caustic being introduced as a 40 per cent aqueous solution. Water and epichlorohydrin distilled from the reaction mixture was condensed in the head, and only the epichlorohydrin layer returned to the reaction mixture. The rate of addition of caustic and rate of distilling kept the temperature at about 100° C so that the reaction mixture contained about 1.5 per cent water, the addition taking approximately 2 hours. Upon completing the caustic addition the bulk of the unreacted epichlorohydrin was distilled from the reaction mixture followed by application of vacuum to a pressure of 1 mm Hg and 160° C to remove residual epichlorohydrin. The residue consisting of ether product and salt was cooled and to it was added an equal weight based on the ether of methyl isobutyl ketone along with three times this weight of water. The mixture was agitated at about 25° C and then allowed to separate into two phases. The brine phase containing about 9.5 per cent salt was removed and discarded. The organic phase with ether product containing about 1.0 per cent chlorine was then contacted with an equal weight of 5 per cent aqueous sodium hydroxide solution, and the mixture was agitated for an hour at about 80° C. This quantity of excess caustic amounted to about 8.9 times that needed to react with the organically bound chlorine [Product IV in the reaction scheme preceeding] in the ether product. The mixture was next cooled to about 50° C and the aqueous phase separated. The organic phase was then agitated with about half an equal weight of 2 per cent aqueous solution of sodium dihydrogen phosphate at about 25° C to neutralize any residual sodium hydroxide. After separation of phases the methyl isobutyl ketone was distilled from the organic phase, first up to a temperature of 160° C under atmospheric pressure, then down to a pressure of about 1 mm Hg at the same temperature. The resulting diglycidyl ether of bisphenol [Product I above] was a pale yellow liquid which analyzed as containing 0.25 per cent chlorine and 0.521 epoxy equivalents per 100 grams, and had a molecular weight of 355. The product had high reactivity with added bisphenol, giving 100 per cent reaction when heated at 190° C for 6 hours with an added 35.6 per cent bisphenol."[64]

An alternate method of removing salt from the *bis*-epoxy monomer involves filtering it, then washing the filter cake with isopropanol to recover the adhering resin, and finally distilling the isopropanol from the filter cake wash.

If higher molecular weight solid epoxy ethers are desired, as is the case in surface coatings, lower mole ratios of epichlorohydrin to bisphenol A, e.g., 1.2 to 2.0, are used. Also, less caustic catalyst is required per mole of bisphenol A since this is partially consumed by the condensation reaction (4) which does not destroy the caustic catalyst through formation of NaCl. For these higher molecular weight resins, salt is ordinarily removed by stirring the resins with water that is above the melting point of the resin, then decanting off the salt layer. Washing is repeated with hot water until the resin reaches a neutral pH.

Equipment for preparing base epoxy resin is similar to that used for phenolics and aminoplasts, i.e., batch operations are performed in an anchor-agitated kettle which has a vacuum reflux condenser. The high temperatures (400° F) required for alkyds are not necessary, but corrosion-resistant material is usually used to maintain a good level of color.

Besides bisphenol A, other polyhydroxyl molecules are used for commercial base resins, e.g., glycerol and novalac (phenol/formaldehyde) resins; however, at present bisphenol A is by far the principal polyol. Other epoxy materials which have been used in specific formulations include butadiene dioxide, the dioxide of vinyl cyclohexene, styrene oxide, and an epoxidized Diels-Alder condensation product (see below) of butadiene and crotonaldehyde.

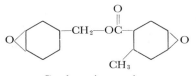

Condensation product

Epoxy groups may be introduced into olefins by means of the newly perfected peracetic acid epoxidation process,[66] valuable in manufacturing epoxy plasticizers from unsaturated natural oils (e.g., soybean oil). The epoxy group acts as a heat stabilizer for vinyl chloride resins and also promotes resin compatibility.

The base *bis*-epoxy resins are very stable, requiring catalysts and/or co-reactants, e.g., amines, organic acid anhydrides, boron trifluorides-tertiary amine complexes, to effect cure.

In the curing reactions no volatile products* are evolved; thus shrinkage strains, which cause problems in other thermosetting condensations where volatile products are evolved during the final curing operations, are minimized. The lack of volatiles during cure and the inherent stability of most of the bonds in the cured epoxy, plus the high softening point imparted by the aromatic groups, account for many of the desirable properties of epoxy materials. The ester bond formed with acid anhydride catalysts is the weakest with respect to caustic or water hydrolysis while the heat distortion temperature of aliphatic amine hardened resins is frequently lower than acid hardened resins, not because of bond rupture but because of the flexibility of the aliphatic crosslinkages.

The secondary amine first formed when using amine co-reactants is even more reactive than the original primary amine, giving an autocatalytic effect to the reaction rate even if temperatures are held constant. In addition, a large amount of heat of reaction is produced, on the order of 20–25

---

* Although no volatile products result, the catalysts themselves are sometimes volatile. At the high temperatures reached in the exotherm with amine co-reactants, many of the amines are quite volatile, causing toxicity and odor as well as foaming. Also, BF_3 is a toxic gas and poses similar problems.

Kg cal/mole of condensing epoxide group. For liquid resins with a large number of epoxy groups per unit weight, adiabatic temperature rises of 350° F or more are easily possible in either thick laminates or potting molds. Many amines, particularly those aliphatic amines partially reacted with ethylene oxide or bisphenol A to decrease the dermatitis frequently caused by amines, will react with epoxy groups even at room temperature, giving handling times (i.e., "pot lives") as short as 15 minutes in some cases. To solve the short pot life problem, automatic two fluid metering devices have been developed. Aliphatic amine hardeners used commercially include ethylene diamine, diethylenetriamine, triethylene tetramine, and their partially hydroxy-ethylated partially cyanoethylated or glycidyl ether counterparts. Commercially important aromatic amines are m-phenylenediamine, 4,4'-methyl-enedianiline, 4,4'-diaminodiphenyl sulfone. The aromatic groups increase the softening temperature of the cured resin.

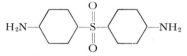

4,4'-Diaminodiphenyl sulfone

The polymerization catalyzed by tertiary amines is believed to be a true chain reaction type of addition polymerization, but the length of the chain is probably very low. The reaction is sensitive, and the presence of alcohols such as the secondary alcohol in the epoxy-base resins, containing more than one bisphenol A molecule, water, etc., though accelerating the reaction will cause chain transfer; the molecular weight is thereby drastically lowered, and the properties of the cured resin are significantly altered. One commercial tertiary amine, 2,4,6 tris-(dimethylaminomethyl) phenol, is commonly used, however. In addition, this polymerization reaction undoubtedly occurs with the tertiary amine formed by epoxide condensation with primary and secondary amines, accounting for greater than stoichiometric yields from many amines, particularly piperdine.

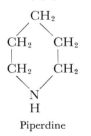

Piperdine

The amine hardeners discussed so far give resins with high softening temperatures but also with poor impact resistance. To improve impact strength and flexibility, multifunctional amines having long flexible aliphatic chains between the amino groups are used, e.g., hexamethylenediamine and mixed diamines derived from fatty acids. Similar products are the so-called poly-amides ("Versamids"), the reaction product of aliphatic polyamines, e.g., diethylenetetramine and the di-acid obtained via a Diels-Alder dimerization of unsaturated fatty acids (e.g., linoleic isomers). Another means of impart-ing flexibility to the cured resin is to include a Thiokol "liquid polymer" which has a structure similar to $HS(CH_2CH_2OCH_2CH_2SS)_nCH_2CH_2$-$OCH_2CH_2SH$. In the presence of amine hardeners the mercaptan groups will react with epoxy groups incorporating the flexible "rubber" chain into the molecule.

Acid anhydrides react with the epoxy group to form ester linkages. These reactions are only mildly exothermic and do not cause the "exotherm" problems associated with amine hardeners. Also, the acid conditions catalyze formation of ethers between the secondary alcohol in (V) and other epoxy groups; therefore less than stoichiometric quantities of acids are frequently used to achieve cure. Ether formation is believed not to occur under the basic conditions existing in amine curing. Pot lives of acid anhydride-catalyzed formulations are very long at room temperatures, but higher temperature curing or baking ovens are necessary to effect cure (300–400° F $vs.$ 150–250° F for amine catalysts). Commercial acid anhydrides are classified as solids, liquids, or chlorinated derivatives. The solids include phthalic anhydride, hexahydrophthalic anhydride, and pyromellitic dianhydride.

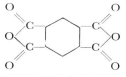

Pyromellitic dianhydride

The liquids include dodecinyl succinic anhydride and a methylated maleic adduct of phthalic anhydride ("Methyl Nadic Anhydride"). To give flame resistance, chlorinated anhydrides include dichloromaleic anhydride and hexachloroendomethylenetetrahydrophthalic anhydride.

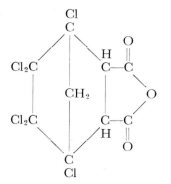

Hexachloroendomethylenetetrahydrophthalic anhydride

The diversity of chemicals used during curing and the complexity of the curing reactions explain why those who use epoxies (in contrast to many other plastics) frequently have an independent chemical laboratory directed by a competent industrial chemist or chemical engineer.

Polyester Resins

In the plastics industry the term *polyesters* has a far narrower connotation than is chemically implied. In the plastics field a polyester is ordinarily the base resin consisting of a liquid unsaturated polyester plus a vinyl-type monomer; this liquid mixture is capable of reacting to form infusible cross-linked solids under the influence of catalysts and/or heat. Such polyesters (in the strict chemical sense) as polyethylene glycol-terephthalic acid and alkyds for paints (Chapter 22) are not polyesters in the plastics industry.

Polyesters are used primarily in rigid laminates, moldings, or castings and are almost always reinforced with glass cloth or glass fibers. They were developed during World War II and were first used very successfully in self-sealing gas tanks containing a rubber liner. When pierced by a bullet, metals splay or "flower" and prevent the rubber tank liner from swelling shut and closing the hole. Polyester laminates do not splay and therefore allow the rubber liner to close the hole. When reinforced with glass, their high flexural strength is outstanding, approaching that of metals.

Maleic anhydride is the principal unsaturated dibasic acid used in the polyester although fumaric acid is also used in limited amounts.

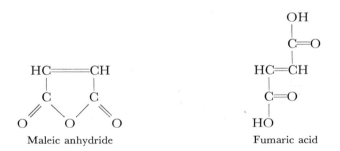

Maleic anhydride   Fumaric acid

Uniquely among ordinary unsaturated monomers, the double bond in maleic anhydride, its acid, its esters, and similar α,β carboxyl substituted olefins will not undergo homogeneous polymerization even at high temperatures but will copolymerize rapidly with a wide variety of vinyl monomers at even faster rates than these monomers will homopolymerize. It is because of this peculiar property of maleic anhydride that polyesters are prepared by first making (at the necessarily high temperatures) a linear low-viscosity gel-free polyester containing several double bonds per molecule and then mixing this unsaturated polyester with a vinyl type monomer, usually styrene, which, under the influence of catalysts and/or heat, will crosslink the polyester molecules to form a rigid infusible polymer.

The difunctional alcohol ethylene glycol is frequently used for the co-reactant but it is supplemented with propylene glycol, diethylene glycol, or dipropylene glycol to decrease the tendency for the liquid resin to crystallize and to increase the flexibility of the cured resin.

To promote compatibility with the styrene monomer used to crosslink the polyester, phthalic anhydride is incorporated into the polyester backbone in mole ratios with maleic anhydride of from 1:1.5 to 1:1. Besides giving compatibility with styrene, phthalic anhydride imparts some flexibility to the cured resin and lowers the cost. Adipic acid, because of its long flexible aliphatic carbon chain, is used to promote a high degree of flexibility.

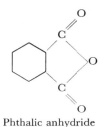

$$\underset{\text{Adipic acid}}{HO\overset{O}{\overset{\|}{C}}(CH_2)_4\overset{O}{\overset{\|}{C}}OH}$$

Phthalic anhydride

Styrene is by far the most common crosslinking agent and is usually added to the base polyester by the manufacturer of the polyester. To ensure that most of the maleic unsaturated groups are reacted and optimum strength is achieved, an excess of styrene must be used (30–40 per cent is the average) because the styrene monomer will polymerize not only with an active maleic radical but also with an active styrene radical; maleic radicals, however, will react only with styrene monomer. Low temperatures favor the maleic-styrene reaction while high temperatures favor the styrene-styrene reaction, accounting for the advantages frequently found in initial low temperature cures.

Besides styrene, many other vinyl monomers may be used to develop special properties, e.g., triallylcyanurate to promote heat resistance, diallylphthalate to reduce volatility during cure, acrylic acid ester to promote flexibility via internal plasticization and to impart improved weatherability.

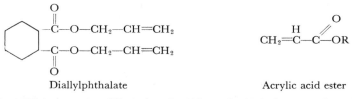

Diallylphthalate   Acrylic acid ester

In addition to the difunctional acids and alcohols, monofunctional acids and alcohols may be added in small amounts to limit polyester molecular weight. Allyl alcohol has been used to give additional unsaturation for sub-sequent crosslinking.

The properties of polyesters depend on the nature of the reactants. High levels of crosslinking and high percentages of aromatic rings promote hard-ness, rigidity, strength, and brittleness. Lower levels of crosslinking (less maleic anhydride) and long flexible aliphatic chains impart flexibility and some impact strength. Larger polyester molecules promote some strength although this effect has a definite upper limit which is reached at a moderate molecular weight. The above brief picture illustrates how complicated and varied the formulation of polyesters can be; this accounts for the more than 300 formulations available in the United States and the 37 formulations offered by one supplier alone. For a more complete picture see Reference 6.

As an example[6] the preparation of a particular polyester might be carried out in a jacketed stainless steel reaction vessel equipped with an agitator, and a reflux condenser followed by a total condenser. The charge is 5 moles of maleic anhydride, 3 moles of phthalic anhydride, 4 moles of ethylene glycol, and 4 moles of diethylene glycol. The temperature is raised to 375° C until an acid number* of 60–65 is obtained, meanwhile maintaining an

---

* Acid number is the number of milligrams of potassium hydroxide necessary to neutralize the free acid in one gram of sample. Since each free carboxyl group represents, on the average, one molecule, the number average molecular weight of the resin, Mn, is given by the following:[30]

$$Mn = \frac{1000 \times 56}{\text{Acid Number}}$$

If, as has been experimentally verified for a number of resins, the reaction rate is independent of molecular size, then the weight average molecular weight, Mw, is given by:[30]

$$Mw = Mn \left[2 - \frac{(\text{Molecular Weight of Structural Unit})(\text{Acid Number})}{(1000) \times (56)} \right]$$

which for the above resin reduces to

$$Mw = \frac{56,000}{\text{Acid Number}} \left[2 - \frac{\text{Acid Number}}{307} \right]$$

Since the mole fraction of maleic groups in the structural unit of the above resin is only $\frac{5}{8}$, the average number of maleic groups per molecule (based on a weight average molecular weight) is

$$\text{Average Number of Maleic Groups} = \frac{\frac{5}{8} Mw}{\text{Molecular Weight of Structural Unit}}$$

which for the above resin is equal to

$$\left[\frac{192}{\text{Acid Number}} \right] \left[2 - \frac{\text{Acid Number}}{307} \right]$$

For an acid number of 60 the weight average molecular weight is 1680 and the aver-age number of maleic groups based on this weight average molecular weight is 5.75. Polyesters before crosslinking are not "giant" molecules at all.

inert atmosphere. The inert purge gas (CO_2 or N_2) is introduced through a submerged sparger. In addition to excluding oxygen, which discolors the resin, it aids in removing the water formed during the condensation reaction. The temperature is then raised and held at 440° C until the acid number is 45–50 or until a Gardner-Holt* viscosity of N to Q is reached when 100

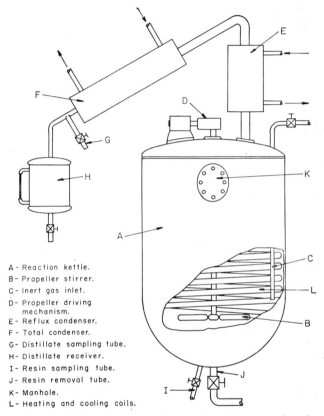

A- Reaction kettle.
B- Propeller stirrer.
C- Inert gas inlet.
D- Propeller driving mechanism.
E- Reflux condenser.
F- Total condenser.
G- Distillate sampling tube.
H- Distillate receiver.
I- Resin sampling tube.
J- Resin removal tube.
K- Manhole.
L- Heating and cooling coils.

Figure 10.15. Equipment for condensation reaction in manufacture of polyester resins. (*Bjorkstein Research Laboratories, Inc., "Polyesters and their Applications," New York, Reinhold Publishing Corp., 1956*)

parts of polyester are combined with 50 parts of styrene. When the reaction is completed (about 5 hours total time) the reaction mass is cooled to 300° F and mixed with 6.5 moles of styrene containing *para-t*-butyl catechol inhib-

* Gardner-Holt viscosities are widely used in the surface coating industry and are obtained by comparing the time it takes for a standard bubble of air to rise in a sample tube with the time it takes for a similar bubble to rise in a set of standard tubes identified by letters. N to Q Gardner-Holt corresponds roughly to 3.40 to 4.35 poise at 77° F.

itor (0.02 per cent of final mixture), the temperature during mixing being maintained at about 100° F. The mixture is cooled to 70° F and pumped to drums or tank cars.

Many catalysts, most of which are free radical generators, have been proposed to cure the resins. Benzoyl peroxide, mixed with 50 per cent dibutyl phthalate to facilitate mixing with the resin, is most frequently use for hot cures (those above 125° F) at levels of 1 to 2 per cent, while methylethyl ketone peroxide, as a 60 per cent solution in dimethyl phthalate, is sometimes used for lower temperature cures, particularly combined with such paint "driers" as cobalt napthenate. Sometimes combinations of these lower temperature catalysts plus a much higher temperature catalyst, e.g., ditertiary butyl peroxide (active beginning at about 235° F) and dicumyl peroxide (active beginning at about 225° F), may be used for composite cures leading to improved properties.

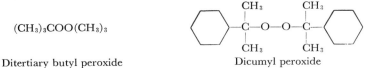

$(CH_3)_3COO(CH_3)_3$

Ditertiary butyl peroxide

Dicumyl peroxide

Promoters (amines) are sometimes used to lower the temperatures at which the catalysts become effective. Many other catalyst systems are used.

In addition to free radicals, some cure is possible by further condensing the polyester itself, utilizing acids or bases which will catalyze esterification, e.g., calcium hydroxide, barium hydroxide, para-toluene sulfonic acid.

The properties, e.g., filament size, type of weave, etc., of the laminating material (almost always glass fibers or glass cloth) is as important to the final properties of the cured laminate or casting as the resin. To ensure a good bond between resin and glass, the starch lubricants, necessary during weaving, must be burned off; adhesive coatings such as special vinyl silicones are also used.

POLYETHYLENE POLYMERIZATION PROCESSES

Polyethylene polymerization processes are too unique to be fitted into the previous classifications.

Polyethylene has had a spectacular rate of growth. From early exploratory investigations by English chemists in 1933–35 (8 grams of polymer were finally made in December, 1935) and initial limited production during World War II for specialty electronics work, production has increased rapidly since the end of World War II, with more than a billion pounds forecast for 1960 in the United States alone. The current annual capacity is more than the cumulative total of all plastics produced in all the years prior to 1935.

High Pressure Process

In 1933 a group of chemists at the British company, Imperial Chemical Industries, using new high pressure laboratory equipment designed by Professor Michels at Amsterdam University, explored the effect of high pressure on polymerization and other reactions. When benzaldehyde underwent a pressure of 1400 atmospheres at 170° C, using ethylene to produce the pressure, a waxy polymer was produced on the walls of the vessel. This was found to be a polymer of ethylene rather than of benzaldehyde. Repeating the experiment with pure ethylene resulted in an explosive reaction which discouraged further experiments with ethylene until 1935. Repeating the experiments with "pure" ethylene in December, 1935, 8 grams of polymer were produced in an 80 cc autoclave because of an almost miraculous combination of events; a small leak developed at 180° C and the ethylene used to repressurize the autoclave must have contained a very small but precisely proper quantity of oxygen. It took several months to explain the success of the above experiment.*

Polyethylene is currently produced by two basically different processes, a high pressure process employing free radical catalysts and a low pressure process employing solid ionic catalysts. The high pressure process, which was chronologically first, produces polymer with more branches on the chain, a lower level of crystallinity, and a lower density. Since the early patents[28] very little has been disclosed about the details of the high pressure process except for an extensive list of patents by duPont[36,68,97] primarily covering a continuous, versatile water-emulsion process using benzene as a solubilizing agent for the polymer. The following is a patent example which may resemble commercial practice:[49]

"A silver-lined steel reaction vessel is charged with 10 parts of water and 1 part of benzene. The vessel is closed, an internal mechanical stirrer put in motion, and ethylene injected at a pressure such that at the reaction temperature of 200 to 220° C, to which the vessel is heated, the pressure is approximately 1000 atmospheres.

As soon as the reaction commences, from the bottom of the reaction vessel a liquid phase comprising a mixture of polymer, water and benzene is continuously withdrawn and passed into a separating vessel maintained at a lower pressure and temperature than that of the reaction vessel.

From the top of the separating vessel, unreacted ethylene is conducted, together with additional benzene and water, to the reaction vessel for further reaction. The water in the liquid phase remaining in the separating vessel, together with benzene in admixture therewith may be recirculated to the reaction zone after removal therefrom of its polymer content.

* This account of the early history of the development of polyethylene has been condensed from J. C. Swallow's[86] entertaining account of the exploratory work which led to the discovery of polyethylene.

The ethylene employed has an oxygen content of approximately 30 parts per million. The water and benzene ratios, based upon the ethylene introduced, are maintained at 4 parts of water and 0.4 parts of benzene per part of ethylene introduced."

Note that no emulsifying agent is used. Instead of silver-lined steel, normal 18-8 chromium nickel austenitic stainless steels have proved satisfactory.[96] The details of the highly special agitation system, required to operate continuously at 1000 atmospheres or more, have never been disclosed.

The above scheme solves the heat transfer problem presented by ethylene polymerization.* By feeding cold water, benzene and ethylene to the hot reactor, the cold feed streams absorb considerable portions of the heat of polymerization, permitting higher conversions per pass. Also, compression of cold liquid ethylene below the critical point is claimed[33] to minimize contamination from compressor lubricants. Disadvantages of the above process include the problems of separating the benzene and water from the product and of separating the water from the recycle ethylene stream to avoid formation of solid ethylene hydrates.

As an alternative to using a stirred reactor, the mixture of benzene, water, and ethylene may be fed through high pressure tubes which are either jacketed or immersed in a suitable heat transfer fluid, e.g.,

"A stainless steel tube of $\frac{3}{16}$ inch internal diameter and 40 feet in length is charged with 6 parts of water and 0.35 part of benzene. Under 1000 atmospheres pressure, ethylene containing 90 parts oxygen per million is constantly introduced into the inlet end of the reaction vessel together with 0.35 part of benzene and 6 parts of water per part of ethylene introduced. The tubular reaction vessel is maintained at a temperature ranging from 160 to 225° C preferably being submerged in a boiling liquid the operating temperature of which is determined by the pressure on the boiling liquid system.

A product draw-off valve at the converter exit lets down directly into an atmospheric pressure separator from which the gas and liquid are continuously drawn and the solid polymerization product is cleaned out hourly. The gas feed return to the inlet of the tube is controlled by the setting of a draw-off valve electrically heated to prevent freezing and to provide smooth, sure operation.

The solid polymerization product obtained according to this example . . . is found to have highly improved characteristics, such as elongation (as high as 500 per cent) tensile strength at break (1200–2500 pounds per square inch) and flex resistance."[97]

---

* As mentioned before, the heat transfer problem is tremendous when ethylene is polymerized in massive high pressure equipment which must have not only thick sections but also high throughputs in order to be economic. The heat of polymerization is approximately 1400–1500 Btu/lb and the specific heat of ethylene about 0.6–0.7 Btu/lb (°F) at polymerizing temperatures and pressures. Temperatures of 600–650° F may decompose ethylene explosively at high pressures into carbon and hydrogen. Therefore, if adiabatic polymerization is assumed with ethylene entering at 350° F, only about 10 per cent conversion is permissible in an adiabatic tubular reactor.

The "mass" tubular process is similar; however, it utilizes no diluent or second phase to help achieve good heat transfer. Very little has been disclosed about this process. The latest patent gives details only about a laboratory apparatus in which flow surges were purposely generated, presumably to agitate the two-phase system* believed to be present:

"In a small continuous experimental polymerization apparatus, a series of runs was made in which ethylene containing free oxygen was subjected to polymerization to make polyethylene. The letdown valve was controlled manually. In the first ten runs irregular and severe pressure drops occurred, temperature control was poor, most of the runs were terminated by explosions, and the products were severely contaminated with carbon black. In the eleventh run the pressure was deliberately dropped at timed intervals. Procedure was as follows: A standard operating pressure of 25,000 pounds per square inch was used. The let-down valve was rapidly opened by hand and pressure allowed to drop approximately 1500 pounds per square inch after which the valve was closed. The pressure was then allowed to build up until it reached the standard operating pressure of 25,000 pounds per square inch; then a period of 5 seconds was allowed to elapse during which the pressure was maintained at that value by automatic control of the pump. At the end of the 5 seconds the valve was again opened and the cycle repeated. Process conditions were: oxygen content 100 parts per million, dwell time 11 minutes, temperature approximately 240° C. As a result of operating in this manner, process control was good, polyethylene was produced in a conversion of 25 weight per cent, and no carbon black was made nor did any explosion occur."[72]

Normal conversions per pass are reported to lie in the range of 15–25 per cent. To separate this large quantity of ethylene from the polymer, the pressure may be lowered directly to atmospheric, but this highly irreversible process is very wasteful of compressor energy—a major production cost item. By putting in at least one separator operating at moderate pressures (100–300 atmospheres), considerable savings are possible in recompression costs. If the pressures are too high, considerable low molecular weight polyethylene may remain dissolved in the recycle ethylene, causing recompression problems. From the final atmospheric pressure separation pot, polyethylene still molten may be removed by means of gear pumps, screw pumps, or extruders. Further blending of the base resin with colorants, lubricants, stabilizers, etc. may then be made in Banburys or extruders, followed by chopping or cutting to pelleted molding powder.

A stirred continuous autoclave may also be used as a polymerizer. As in the benzene-water process, sensible heat (or really its absence) in the cold

* Some data have been presented[43,48] which show that low molecular weight polyethylenes will dissolve in high density ethylene gas above its critical temperature. Hence, in a tubular reactor two phases probably are present, one a higher molecular weight molten polyethylene containing large amounts of dissolved ethylene, and the other "gaseous" ethylene, above its critical temperature, in which some lower molecular weight polyethylenes are dissolved.

feed serves to aid the attainment of high conversions. No details of this reactor have been disclosed.

Low Pressure Polymerization

There were three separate and independent developments of low pressure polymerization methods for ethylene. Around 1953 Karl Ziegler[98] in Germany discovered the unusual synergistic effect of $TiCl_4$ in the presence of aluminum tri- or dialkyls. At about the same time John Hogan and Robert Banks at Phillips Petroleum[42] discovered that chromium salts deposited on conventional cracking catalysts* and oxidized with air at high temperatures to produce hexavalent chromium oxide would polymerize ethylene to high molecular weight. Even earlier, Standard Oil of Indiana found several catalyst systems, notably nickel oxide on charcoal partially reduced with hydrogen and molybdena-alumina activated by hydrogenation. The Standard Oil process has not yet reached large scale commercial development. Each of these processes has been described in a bewildering number of variations in the patent literature, particularly the foreign patent literature, to date. It is not clear what is preferred commercial practice; hence, although an attempt will be made to describe the probable commercial conditions used in these processes, this attempt may miss the mark considerably.

Ziegler catalysts are the reaction products of trialkyl aluminum and $TiCl_4$. The precise chemical nature of these unstable complexes has not been precisely determined. It is known that the aluminum alkyl first reduces the $TiCl_4$ to the "β" crystalline form of $TiCl_3$. The alkyl aluminum chloride formed by this reaction complexes with the $TiCl_3$ as does additional "unoxidized" aluminum trialkyl. Al/Ti mole ratios are ordinarily around 2.0. A simplified explanation of the polymerization mechanism is that coordinate Al-Ti linkages on particular sites in the $TiCl_3$ crystal activate the corresponding $\overset{\oplus}{A}l$-$\overset{\ominus}{C}$ bonds. Ethylene monomer then feeds into this activated $\overset{\oplus}{A}l$-$\overset{\ominus}{C}$ bond making a new alkyl aluminum with increased molecular weight. Reaction is completed when an active hydrogen-containing molecule, e.g., an alcohol, severs the bond and terminates the polymer.

$$\begin{array}{l} \quad R'' \\ \leftarrow Al(CH_2\!-\!CH_2)_nR + 3R'OH \rightarrow \\ \uparrow R'' \\ \mid \qquad\qquad\qquad\qquad Al(OR')_3 + 2R''H + H(CH_2\!-\!CH_2)_nR \\ \rule{1.2cm}{0.4pt}\text{low energy coordinate linkage to } TiCl_3, R'' = \text{alkyl or Cl.} \end{array}$$

To make high molecular weight polymer, such active hydrogen compounds as acids, water, and alcohol must be rigorously excluded. An inert

* Microspheroidol $90SiO_2/10Al_2O_3$ of large pore size and small surface area are preferred.

aliphatic hydrocarbon (e.g., hexane, refined kerosene, isooctane, cyclohexane) is the usual reaction medium.

Maximum polymer content of the slurry ranges from 20 to 30 per cent depending on the solvent, temperature, and reaction system used. Catalyst efficiency depends primarily on (1) the purity of the solvent and the reactants, and (2) the temperature and other factors affecting molecular weight. Efficiencies as high as 12,000 pounds of polymer per pound mole of aluminum trialkyl have been reported,[61] keeping the cost of the expensive trialkyl aluminum-$TiCl_4$ catalyst within reason.

Separation of the catalyst from the polymer is essential to good heat stability and is achieved by a complicated procedure. First, excess solvent is wrung out with a centrifuge. The polymer cake is then successively extracted as a slurry in a higher alcohol (C_4 or above) to remove the catalysts. Finally the alcohol is removed by steam distillation; drying follows. The dried fluffy powder must then be densified, stabilized against heat and light, colored, lubricated, etc., to make a molding powder. These last steps ordinarily are performed simultaneously in an extruder or Banbury.

The Phillips Petroleum process uses a "hexavalent" chromium oxide deposited on a microspheroidal commercial cracking catalyst support, e.g., a $90SiO_2/10Al_2O_3$ silica gel catalyst with large pore size and small surface area. The catalyst may be made by slurrying the support with an equal weight of a 0.78 molar $Cr(NO_3)_3$ and 0.78 molar $Sr(NO_3)_2$ water solution, filtering off the excess solution, drying the catalyst, and finally activating the catalyst by heating at 950° F while passing thoroughly dry air through the catalyst at a space velocity of 300 reciprocal hours.[42]

The flow sheet in Figure 10.16 illustrates the over-all polymerization process. A catalyst slurry in the cyclohexane solvent is fed along with the ethylene into a stirred moderate pressure (200–300 psig) 4000 gallon steel autoclave.[93] The preferred proportions of the reactants have not been disclosed but hourly rates to a 4000 gallon continuous reactor may be 2500 pounds of ethylene, 25 pounds of catalyst, 22,500 pounds of cyclohexane. Reaction temperatures are probably in the range of 275–300° F. Higher pressures corresponding to higher ethylene concentrations produce higher molecular weights while lower temperatures produce lower molecular weight products. From the reactors the solution of polymer in cyclohexane, catalyst, and the very small amount of unreacted ethylene are fed into specially developed continuous pressure centrifuges[91] of the sloped-internal-disc type which remove the catalyst as a slurry through fine discharge nozzles. The catalyst is washed with hot cyclohexane to recover the polyethylene and fed to a second centrifuge which sends the washed catalyst to the catalyst regeneration plant and recycles the wash liquor to the main centrifuge. From the main centrifuge the polymer solution is fed to a water precipitator which precipitates the polymer and steam distills the cyclohexane solvent and any unreacted ethylene. From the precipitators polymer is separated from the bulk of the water by flotation and then dried in a rotary steam-tube drier.[93] After drying, the polymer dust is blended with colorants, stabilizers, etc. and densified into pellets by extruders.

The Standard Oil process has not yet reached full commercial development. Many patents have been issued covering two different catalyst systems. One catalyst consists of a nickel-salt deposited on charcoal, oxidized to the oxide at 500° F and then activated by reduction with hydrogen at

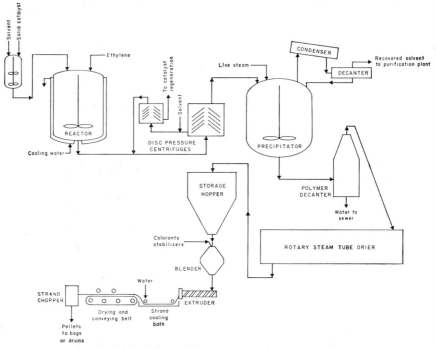

Figure 10.16. Phillips low-pressure polyethylene process.

392–500° F. The other is an 8 per cent molybdena-on-alumina catalyst calcined at 807–898° F.[87] Xylene is reported to be used as the solvent, and the process, after the polymerization stage, probably resembles the Phillips more than the Ziegler process since no simple extraction step is known for the catalysts which undoubtedly must be filtered or centrifuged off from a hot polymer solution.

CELLULOSE DERIVATIVES

Cellulose is the most common naturally occurring high polymer of organic chemical nature. The cell walls of nearly all plants consist of cellulose.*

* Native cellulose may contain some rings other than the "glucose" (or more

Throughout the world, over 900 billion pounds of cellulose are converted annually to paper products, regenerated cellulose (rayon and cellophane), and cellulose-based plastics, with less than 0.3 per cent utilized in the plastics industry.

Although cellulose is a linear molecule, heating below its charring temperature will not soften it sufficiently to permit plastic flow. The cause for this behavior is believed to be the strong hydrogen bonds between neighboring molecules forming highly stable crystalline structures with regular lattice spacings. To solubilize or fluidize the molecule, the crystalline structure is broken up by substituting various groups at the hydroxyl groups of the cellulose. The xanthate group, —OCSNa, and the cuprammonium complex
$$\overset{\text{S}}{\overset{\|}{}}$$
are used commercially to temporarily dissolve cellulose in caustic solutions for eventual regeneration to rayon or cellophane. More permanent substitution is achieved with organic acid groups, ether groups, and inorganic acid groups. Cellulose acetate, propionate, acetate-butyrate, and nitrate are commercial plastics, as is the ethyl ether of cellulose.

Sulfuric acid aids nitration (1) by forming cellulose sulfate which causes the fibers to swell rapidly; (2) by complexing with the water formed, thus forcing nitration to a high level. Since only about 1.9–2.0 of the three hydroxyls available in a "glucose" ring are substituted for plastic applications, more water is used in the nitrating acid than in the preparation of guncotton, e.g., a suitable nitrating acid for plastics consists of 61 per cent H_2SO_4, 21 per cent HNO_3 and 18 per cent H_2O. After nitration at low temperatures (75–85° F) to minimize acid cleavage of the "glucose" rings which lowers the molecular weight and impairs impact strength, the spent

---

properly, anhydro-β-D-glucopyranose) ring, but such portions of the "cellulose" chain are considered anomolous and "pure" cellulose usually means the following,

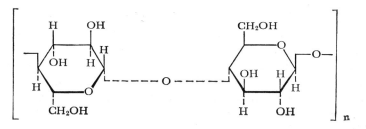

where the end groups in the naturally occurring product, though somewhat uncertain, are believed to consist equally of reducing end groups and nonreducing end groups in cellulose which has undergone hydrolytic chain cleavage to lower the molecular weight. These end groups are sometimes acidic in nature, presumably because of oxidation.

acid is centrifuged off; the centrifuged fibers are washed thoroughly and boiled in water which is periodically drained off and replaced. This boiling, which takes from 10 to 60 hours, removes the sulfate groups that cause product instability. After boiling, the fibers are bleached with 1 per cent chlorine and treated with Na_2SO_3. To remove the water the wet fibers are pressed tightly together and alcohol is percolated through the pressed cake. The alcohol-wet cake (30 per cent alcohol by weight) is then charged to a powerful mixer together with 26 per cent camphor to plasticize the polymer.

The alcohol, as well as the camphor, fluidizes the polymer, permitting extrusion or other forming operations to be carried out in comparative safety. After forming, the alcohol is removed by very slow aging or drying to minimize distortion. During all the above processes prior to the final aging, it is essential that the nitrated cellulose be kept wet with water or alcohol since serious fires can easily be started by slight frictional heating. Because of the necessity for final aging and because of great sensitivity to heat degradation, nitrocellulose is not a thermoplastic in the ordinary sense; however, neither is it a thermosetting plastic.

To make the acetate (or propionate or butyrate), the purified alpha-cellulose pulp [usually obtained by the sulfite process from wood (Chapter 15)] is shredded and mixed with acetic acid to wet and swell the fibers. This mixture is then fed to the acetylation reactor where sulfuric acid catalyst (1 per cent cellulose), methylene chloride solvent (or more acetic acid as solvent), and acetic anhydride are added. Acetylation is done at moderate temperatures, e.g., 90–120° F, to minimize acid cleavage. Following acetylation, wet acetic acid is added to remove the sulfate ester groups and to de-esterify the cellulose to the desired level. During the acetylation process the fibers dissolve in the solvents. This requires precipitation in water and subsequent milling to make a flake and to squeeze out most of the acid and water. The flake is then washed with water in a countercurrent band filter; centrifuging, drying, and blending follow (Figure 10.17). To make a molding powder the flake is rapidly cold mixed with a plasticizer but not homogeneously blended. The mix is then fed to a set of hot mill rolls where colorants are added; the plasticizer is then homogeneously mixed. The mill-rolled sheet is diced to molding powder pellets. Alternatively, the flake and the plasticizer containing dispersed colorants are fed continuously to a heated extruder which homogenizes the mixture and forms strands which are subsequently cooled and chopped into molding powder. To make the mixed acetate-butyrate* or acetate-propionate, butyric acid or propionic acid is added to the acetylating mixture.

Ethyl cellulose for plastic purposes usually contains 2.3–2.5 ether groups per "glucose" ring. It is made by reacting cellulose under alkaline conditions

---

* Usually about 1.7 butyryl and 1.0 acetyl groups are substituted per "glucose" ring.

in the presence of water and ethyl chloride. By-products are ethyl alcohol and ethyl ether formed via hydrolysis of the ethyl chloride.

Following the reaction, the reaction mass is mixed and simultaneously precipitated and atomized to fine granules; a special two-fluid spray nozzle is used in which the "gaseous" fluid stream is steam.

The polymer spray is contained in a precipitating tank where the volatile benzene, ethyl chloride, ethyl ether, and ethyl alcohol are steam distilled off. After precipitation the polymer is centrifuged, washed with hot water, and bleached with dilute sodium hypochlorite (pH 10.5–11.3 at 175° F); another centrifuging and washing follow. Stabilization (deashing) is achieved with a dilute acetic acid rinse (pH 4–4.2) and a final centrifuging and water rinsing; this is followed by drying in a countercurrent rotary steam tube or a concurrent rotary hot air drier. The dried crumb

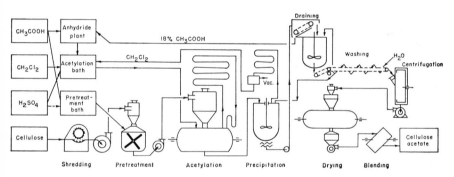

Figure 10.17. Manufacture of cellulose acetate by the methylene dichloride method. (*After Ranby, B. G., and Rydholm, S. A., "Cellulose and Cellulose Derivatives," in "Polymer Processes," New York, Interscience Publishers, Inc., copyright 1956*)

is then mixed with colorants, stabilizers, and plasticizers, and extruded to strands which are chopped into molding powder pellets.

The above is but a brief description of the cellulosic plastics; Ott and Spurlin,[62] and others[11,58,69] give more complete accounts.

OTHER PLASTICS

Besides the plastics already discussed, there are several others that are used either in small amounts as plastics or extensively for applications other than plastics as narrowly defined in this chapter.

Casein plastics, made by hardening the milk or rennet protein, casein, with formaldehyde,[84] are used to make buttons. The dyeability of the polymer permits interesting color effects, but cost plus the lack of any other outstanding properties has limited the use of this plastic almost solely to buttons.

Polyvinylbutyral is used for the interlayer of safety glass. Although for this purpose it is the best plastic on the market, it has few other uses. Its formula may be represented by:

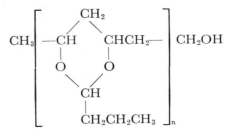

although some acetyl groups and alcohol groups are also present. It is made by polymerizing vinyl acetate, $CH_2{=}CHOCCH_3$, either in suspension or solution with free radical catalysts, by hydrolysis with sulfuric acid in an alcoholic solution to yield polyvinylalcohol and then acetal formation with butyraldehyde using a mineral acid catalyst.[16] *Polyvinyl acetate* is used extensively for coatings, textile and paper finishes, and adhesives. *Polyvinylalcohol* also has a large specialty market. *Polyvinylformal* is made by a similar process for use as an insulating varnish.

Silicone plastics are very well known and much publicized. They may be represented by the generic formula,

$$R'\left[\begin{array}{c} R \\ -SiO- \\ R \end{array}\right]_n R'$$

where R is usually $-CH_3$ or $-\langle\bigcirc\rangle$. They are produced from the corresponding diorgano silicon chlorides, R_2SiCl_2, plus water and acid or base condensation catalysts. A very small amount of the triorgano substituted silicon chloride will terminate the chain and control molecular weight. Branching and eventual crosslinking may be achieved by using the monoorgano silicon chloride $RSiCl_3$ or by adding oxidizing agents to oxidize the methyl groups (e.g., benzoyl peroxide) as in the vulcanizing of silicone rubbers. Allyl groups have been utilized to permit vinyl-type crosslinking to occur with free radical generating catalysts. Depending on the conditions, oils, heat hardenable resins, or rubbers may be formed. Silicones are used commercially for surface coating enamels (particularly in electrical applications), for stable rubbers, for lubricating oils and greases with extraordinarily low variations of viscosity with temperature, and for specialty uses, e.g., mold release agents, anti-foam agents, water repellents, polyester-glass bonding agents, etc. Their use in special heat stable moldings, castings, and laminates is minimal, hence they are minor industrial plastics.

Although they were manufactured in Germany during and since World War II, *polyurethanes* are developing rapidly in the United States. They are used to some extent in rigid foams and laminates, but the largest markets are in flexible (rubbery) foams and surface coatings. They are the cross-linked product formed when tolylene diisocyanates (2,4, and 2,6 isomers) are reacted with a linear polymer, usually liquid, containing two or more active hydrogen atoms per molecule, e.g., polyesters with either alcohols or acid groups on the ends of the molecule and polyethers with alcohol groups on the end of the molecules. Two methods are used for producing foam: [75] (1) The "one-shot" process involves simultaneous mixing of all reactants, catalyst, and additives. The reactions begin at once; foaming is complete in a couple of minutes but several hours may be required to complete the cure. (2) In the "prepolymer" method the isocyanate and polymer are reacted to produce a prepolymer. This product is foamed later by reaction with water. The molecular weight is increased during foaming. Typical reactions for the second method are:

(1) $2R(C{=}N{=}O) + HOR'OH \rightarrow$

$$O{=}C{=}N{-}R{-}N{-}\overset{\overset{O}{\|}}{C}{-}O{-}R'{-}O{-}\overset{\overset{O}{\|}}{C}{-}N{-}R{-}N{=}C{=}O \quad \text{"Propolymer"}$$

(2) $n \text{ (Prepolymer)} + nH_2O \rightarrow \left[{-}NCN{-}R{-}NCO{-}R'{-}OCN{-}R{-} \right]_n + nCO_2$

Besides the large industry engaged in manufacturing base resins, a sizeable synthetic organic chemical industry is based on plasticizers for these resins. Over 442,000,000 pounds of plasticizers were made in 1957. These materials impart flexibility and formability to many polymers, particularly those based on vinyl chloride and cellulose. Chemically they are frequently aliphatic esters (usually C_4 or higher) of dibasic acids, e.g., phthalic, adipic, azelaic, and sebacic. Expoxidized unsaturated natural esters (soybean oil) and similar epoxidized unsaturated esters are increasing in importance. Phosphate esters, polyester resins, and aromatic hydrocarbons of high molecular weight are also common.

The list of commercial polymeric materials is growing rapidly despite the fact that each new product must compete with the properties and prices of existing polymers. The perfect polymer for all plastic applications is an impossibility. A plastic that is resistant to high temperatures yet is heat-sealable and readily molded at low temperatures, that has excellent outdoor stability but is transparent, that has excellent hardness and abrasion resistance, yet is strong and tough, that may be either rigid or flexible as desired, that is an excellent electrical insulator but also dissipates static charge at a high rate, and that is resistant to all chemicals yet can form solution coatings—such a plastic exists only in salesmen's dreams and chemists' nightmares.

RAW MATERIALS

Phenol

Phenol is obtained by many routes, the earliest being caustic extraction from the heavy coal tar obtained when coal is heated to make coke and producer gas (Chapter 8). Now most phenol in this country is made by one of four synthetic methods.[67]

Sulfonation Process. Benzene obtained from coal tar or by the catalytic cyclizing of petroleum fractions is sulfonated with sulfuric acid; sodium hydroxide fusion of the sodium benzene sulfonate follows.

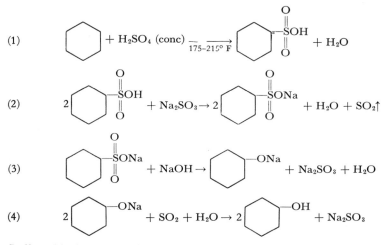

(1)

(2)

(3)

(4)

Sodium bisulfite salt is a by-product of this reaction.[47]

Chlorination (Dow) Process. Chlorobenzene is hydrolyzed directly to sodium phenate which, when reacted with HCl, yields phenol.

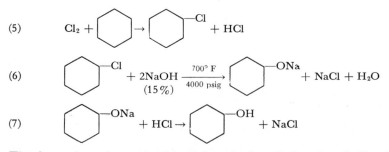

(5)

(6)

(7)

The formation of considerable diphenyl ether during the alkaline hydrolysis [Reaction (6)] is prevented by recycling a substantial part of this product, which remains in the organic layer, along with unreacted chlorobenzene.

Raschig Process. Direct hydrolysis is achieved with water; no by-product is produced.

(8)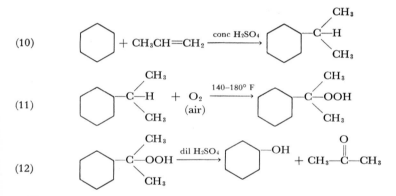

The over-all yield is about 1 lb phenol and 0.1 lb dichlorobenzene per lb of benzene.

Cumene Process. Cumene is oxidized to the hydroperoxide and then cleaved by sulfuric acid to produce phenol and acetone.

Phenol and acetone are condensed to make bisphenol A which is used in epoxides and polycarbonates.

(13)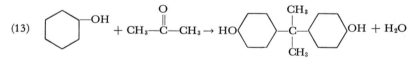

Stearic factors cause the 4,4 compound to be made almost exclusively.

Styrene

Styrene was a rare chemical until the Germans, just prior to World War II, discovered its usefulness in manufacturing synthetic rubber. At about the same time interest arose in the pure polymer.

Styrene is usually made by alkylating benzene with ethylene using Friedel-Craft catalysts, e.g., $AlCl_3$.

(14)

The ethyl benzene, diluted with steam to reduce its partial pressure and to improve its thermodynamic equilibrium, is then cracked over a catalyst to styrene.

(15)

$$\text{C}_6\text{H}_5\text{—CH}_2\text{CH}_3 \xrightarrow[\text{1175° F}]{\text{Al}_2\text{O}_3 \text{ (or Fe}_2\text{O}_3\text{)}} \text{C}_6\text{H}_5\text{—CH=CH}_2 + \text{H}_2$$

Because of the closeness of their boiling points,[8] the styrene formed must be separated from the unconverted ethyl benzene by careful vacuum distillation. A new process for obtaining pure ethyl benzene has recently been developed in which is used the mixed xylene fraction obtained when petroleum naptha is converted to aromatics with a platinum catalyst. (See Platforming in Chapter 14.) The separation of ethyl benzene (boiling point 136.2° C) and paraxylene (boiling point 138.5° C) is accomplished using a 350-plate distillation column which is, necessarily, split into three 200-foot columns.[18]

Vinyl Chloride

Vinyl chloride is prepared by two methods.[10,29] Acetylene plus HCl over an activated mercuric chloride catalyst:

(16)
$$\text{HCl} + \text{HC}\equiv\text{CH} \xrightarrow[\substack{\text{CoCl}_3\cdot 4\text{HgCl}_2 \\ \text{on charcoal}}]{\text{212° F}} \text{CH}_2\text{=CHCl}$$

Dehydrochloronation of ethylene dichloride:

(17)
$$\text{CH}_2\text{=CH}_2 + \text{Cl}_2 \rightarrow \text{CH}_2\text{ClCH}_2\text{Cl}$$

(18)
$$\text{CH}_2\text{ClCH}_2\text{Cl} \xrightarrow[\substack{\text{10–20 atm} \\ \text{O}_2, \text{Cl}_2, \text{ or CCl}_4 \text{ catalyst}}]{\text{925–1125° F}} \text{CH}_2\text{=CHCl} + \text{HCl}$$

Vinylidene chloride is prepared by reacting 1,1,2-trichloroethane with caustic solutions.[32]

(19) $2\text{CH}_2\text{ClCHCl}_2 + \text{Ca(OH)}_2 \xrightarrow{\text{195° F}} 2\text{CH}_2\text{=CCl}_2 + \text{CaCl}_2 + \text{H}_2\text{O}$

Trichloroethane may be prepared by reacting ethylene with chlorine gas in the presence of metal catalysts, e.g., copper, antimony, iron, or manganese.[20]

(20) $\text{CH}_2\text{=CH}_2 + 2\text{Cl}_2 \xrightarrow{\text{80–140° F}} \text{CH}_2\text{ClCHCl}_2 + \text{HCl}$

Formaldehyde

Formaldehyde is ordinarily prepared by the catalytic air oxidation of methanol.[90]

(21) $$CH_2OH + \tfrac{1}{2}O_2 \xrightarrow[\text{Ag catalyst}]{1400°\ F} CH_2{=}O + H_2O$$
(air)

In the above process, air, methanol, and steam in a weight ratio of approximately 4:2:1.4 are fed into the hot catalyst bed and then quickly quenched to halt further oxidation. Instead of a pure silver catalyst, a Fe_2O_3/MO_3 (1:5 weight ratio) catalyst, either unsupported or on a silicon carbide support, has recently been used, permitting lower temperatures of 600–700° F and lessening the problems of excessive oxidation. A higher ratio of air to methanol (10:1) is required to achieve complete conversion in a single pass.[17,80]

A newer method for making formaldehyde involves the partial air (or oxygen) oxidation of propane and butane to a complex mixture of methanol, formaldehyde, acetadehyde, acetone, and higher alcohols. The original patent for this process described heating butane (1 part) to 300° F, mixing it with air (5 parts) and steam (34 parts) at 750° F under 300–400 psig pressure for a reaction time of about 1 second, and then quenching the mixture with water to below 300° F.[7,90] This mixture must undergo a complex series of fractionations and extractions to ensure pure products.

Hexamethylene tetramine, a derivative of formaldehyde, is used to cure two-stage phenolic resins. It is made by the nearly instantaneous reaction of ammonia and formaldehyde. The speed of this reaction is truly remarkable considering the complexity of the final product.[57]

(22) $4NH_3 + 6CH_2{=}O \rightarrow$

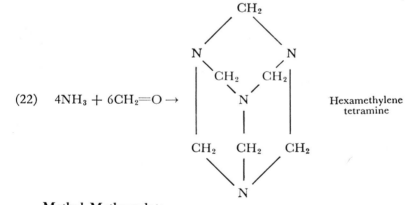

Hexamethylene tetramine

Methyl Methacrylate

The following reaction scheme is used:[73]

(23) $$CH_3{-}\overset{\overset{\displaystyle O}{\|}}{C}{-}CH_3 + NaC{\equiv}N + H_2O \rightarrow CH_3{-}\underset{\underset{\displaystyle CN}{|}}{\overset{\overset{\displaystyle OH}{|}}{C}}{-}CH_3 + NaOH$$

$$(24) \quad 2CH_3\overset{\displaystyle OH}{\underset{\displaystyle CN}{C}}CH_3 + H_2SO_4 \text{ (dil)} \rightarrow (CH_2\overset{\displaystyle O}{=}\underset{\displaystyle CH_3}{C}CNH_2)_2 \cdot H_2SO_4 + H_2O$$

$$(25) \quad (CH_2\overset{\displaystyle O}{=}\underset{\displaystyle CH_3}{C}CNH_2)_2 \cdot H_2SO_4 + 2CH_3OH \rightarrow$$

$$2CH_2\overset{\displaystyle O}{=}\underset{\displaystyle CH_3}{C}COCH_3 + (NH_4)_2SO_4$$

Now HCN is used to make acetone cyanohydrin, the HCN being produced by the high temperature catalyzed reaction of pure oxygen, ammonia, and methane.[59]

$$(26) \qquad \tfrac{3}{2}O_2 + NH_3 + CH_4 \xrightarrow[\text{2600° F}]{\text{Pt-Rh catalyst}} HCN + 3H_2O$$

HCN may also be produced by the acidification of sodium cyanide manufactured by the Castner Process.

$$(27) \qquad Na + C + NH_3 \xrightarrow{\text{1500° F}} NaCN + \tfrac{3}{2}H_2$$

$$(28) \qquad 2NaCN + H_2SO_4 \rightarrow Na_2SO_4 + 2HCN$$

Urea

Urea is produced commercially by synthesis from ammonia and carbon dioxide.

$$(29) \qquad 2NH_3 + CO_2 \rightarrow NH_2\overset{\displaystyle O}{C}NH_2 + H_2O$$

This over-all reaction can be broken down into two reversible reactions:

$$(30) \quad 2NH_3 + CO_2 \rightleftarrows NH_2\text{—}\overset{\displaystyle O}{C}\text{—}ONH_4 \text{ (ammonium carbamate)}$$

$$(31) \quad NH_2\text{—}\overset{\displaystyle O}{C}\text{—}ONH_4 \rightleftarrows NH_2\text{—}\overset{\displaystyle O}{C}\text{—}NH_2 + H_2O$$

There are four commercial schemes for accomplishing the above.[94] If the unreacted ammonia can be used and the unreacted carbon dioxide wasted or utilized, a once-through process is possible. Recycling the unreacted ammonia and carbon dioxide may cause formation of the solid ammonium carbamate in the compressors and lines. Three ways to avoid this are:

(1) Dissolve the gases in sufficient water to dissolve any solid ammonium carbamate. This necessitates the use of higher temperature, pressure, and ammonia concentrations to compensate for the unfavorable equilibrium resulting from the extra water. The higher temperature requires the use of silver-lined equipment to avoid corrosion. This process is known as the solution recycle process and is used by duPont. Most newer plants use method (2) or (3) below.

(2) Slurry the reactants and recycle stream in an inert mineral oil which keeps the solid ammonium carbamate crystals dispersed and pumpable. This process is known as the Pechiney oil-slurry process:

(3) Absorb one of the two off gases in a suitable solvent. The Inventa process uses urea nitrate to absorb the ammonia; the Chemico process uses monoethanolamine to absorb the carbon dioxide; the Montecatini process presumably uses an undisclosed solvent to extract one of the two gases.

Melamine

Melamine is a modern example of how the discovery of attractive end uses can cause an organic chemical to change from an exotic, commercially unavailable chemical to a tonnage low cost one. Prior to 1939 melamine, when available, sold for several dollars a pound; in March 1959 its price was 30 cents per pound.

Melamine is obtained commercially from calcium carbide, starting with the preparation of calcium cyanamide.

(32) $$CaC_2 + N_2 \xrightarrow{2000° \text{ F}} CaNC{\equiv}N + C$$

Calcium cyanamide is extracted with water to form the acid salt, and lime which is filtered off. Then the water solution of calcium acid cyanamide is adjusted to a pH of 9.6 with sulfuric acid and heated to 167° F; sulfuric acid is added to maintain the 9.6 pH as the reaction proceeds. When the reaction is completed the precipitated calcium sulfate is filtered off and the filtrate cooled to precipitate the dicyandiamide which may be recrystallized from water if high purity is desired. Vacuum is preferred to dry the "dicy" if conversion to melamine is undesirable.[89]

(33) $$2CaNC{\equiv}N + 2H_2O \rightarrow Ca(HNC{\equiv}N)_2 + Ca(OH)_2$$

(34) $$Ca(HNC{\equiv}N)_2 + H_2SO_4 \xrightarrow{pH \ 9.6} CaSO_4 + NH_2C\underset{\underset{NH}{\|}}{-}N{-}C{\equiv}N$$

To convert the "dicy" to melamine, provision must be made to remove the heat of reaction, 372 Btu/pound of melamine. This is achieved by reacting slowly at moderate temperatures in an alcoholic solution, e.g., isopropanol at 350–450° F. The alcohol either dissolves the melamine or maintains it as a stirrable slurry from which heat may be removed directly or by reflux. Excess ammonia is added to prevent the diamination of melamine to undesirable products, behavior which occurs rapidly above 400° F. An alternate method of removing the heat of polymerization involves charging an excess of ammonia and venting it off as the reaction progresses, thereby removing the heat of reaction as sensible heat.

(35)

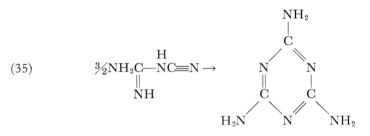

Maleic and Phthalic Anhydride

Both of these products are produced by very similar catalytic oxidations, phthalic anhydride from napthalene and maleic anhydride from benzene.[15,83]

(36)

(37)

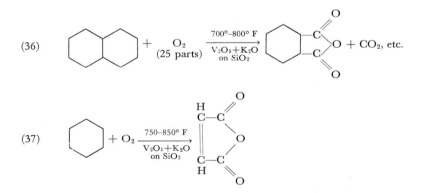

A cooling medium of mercury or a molten equimolecular mixture of $NaNO_3$ and KNO_3 surrounds the catalyst tubes. In the phthalic anhydride process 8–10 per cent maleic anhydride is also produced and must be carefully removed.

An alternate method for manufacturing phthalic anhydride involves a similar oxidation of ortho xylene, obtained by "platforming" petroleum (Chapter 14).

Other Monomers

Ethylene manufacture is described in Chapter 14. For polymerization purposes this monomer must be especially purified.[27]

Vinyl acetate and acrylonit.ile are used very little in plastics as the term is defined in this chapter. They are manufactured in a manner similar to vinyl chloride, by reacting acetylene with the corresponding acid in the presence of suitable catalysts.

Acrylate esters are frequently used to make copolymers, particularly for use in surface coating, paper, textile treating, adhesives, and polishes. They are made by reacting acetylene, an alcohol, and carbon monoxide in the presence of nickel carbonyl and hydrochloric acid according to the following idealized equation:

$$(38) \qquad CH{\equiv}CH + ROH + CO \xrightarrow[\text{HCl}]{\text{Ni(CO)}_4} CH_2{=}CHCOR \quad \overset{\text{O}}{\underset{\|}{}}$$

The reaction is much more complex than this simple equation.[73]

REFERENCES

1. Abraham, H., "Asphalts and Allied Substances," 5th Ed., New York, D. Van Nostrand Co., Inc., 1945.
2. Allen, I., et al. (to the Union Carbide Co.), U. S. Patent 2,496,653 (Feb. 1952).
3. Allen, I., et al. (to the Union Carbide Co.), U. S. Patent 2,614,910 (Oct. 1952).
4. Amos, K. E., et al. (to the Dow Chemical Co.), U. S. Patent 2,530,409 (May 1948).
5. Baeyaert, A. E. M., U. S. Patent 2,715,117 (Aug. 1955); U. S. Patent 2,856,272 (Oct. 1958) (Saint-Gobain, France).
6. Bjorksten Research Laboratories, Inc., "Polyesters and Their Applications," New York, Reinhold Publishing Corp., 1956.
7. Bludworth, J. E. (to Celanese Corp.), U. S. Patent 2,128,908 (Sept. 1938).
8. Boundy, R. H., and Boyer, R. F., "Styrene," New York, Reinhold Publishing Corp., 1952.
9. Bovey, F. A., Kolthaff, I. M., Modulin, A. I., and Mechon, E. J., "Emulsion Polymerization," pp. 71–93, New York, Interscience Publishers, Inc., 1955.
10. Boyd, T. (to Monsanto Chemical Co.), U. S. Patent 2,446,123 (July 1948).
11. Bracken, W. O., "Encyclopedia of Chemical Technology," Kirk, R. E., and Othmer, D. F., Editors, "Cellulose Plastics," Vol. III, pp. 391–411, Interscience Publishers, Inc., 1949.
12. Carothers, W. H., "Collected Papers," Mark, H., and Whitby, G. S., Editors, New York, Interscience Publishers, Inc., 1940.
13. Carswell, T. S., "Phenoplasts," New York, Interscience Publishers, Inc., 1947.
14. Castan, Pierre, et al., U. S. Patent 2,324,483 (July 1943); 2,444,333; 2,458,796; 2,637,715 (Ciba).
15. Chem. Eng., 60, 238 (July 1953).
16. Chem. Eng., 61, 346 (Feb. 1954).

17. *Chem. Eng.,* **61**, 109 (Nov. 1954).
18. Chilton, Ch. H., *Chem. Eng.,* **65**, 98 (Dec. 1958).
19. Coderre, R. A., "Encyclopedia of Chemical Technology," Kirk, R. E., and Othmer, D. F., Editors, "Epoxy Resins," Vol. I (Supplement), pp. 312–329, New York, Interscience Publishers, Inc., 1957.
20. Conway, J., "1,1,2-Trichloroethane," in "Encyclopedia of Chemical Technology," Kirk, R. E., and Othmer, D. F., Editors, Vol. III, p. 765, New York, Interscience Publishers, Inc., 1949.
21. DeJong, J. I., DeJonge, J. I., *Rec. trav. chim.,* **71**, 643 (1952); **72, 88,** 653, 1027 (1953); **73,** 139 (1953).
22. Dinsmore, R. P. (to the Goodyear Co.), U. S. Patent 1,732,795 (Oct. 22, 1929; filed Sept. 13, 1927).
23. Douglas, S. D. (to the Union Carbide Co.), U. S. Patent 2,075,429.
24. Dunlop, R. D., and Reese, F. E., *Ind. Eng. Chem.,* **40**, 654 (1948).
25. E. I. duPont Co., British Patent 770,717 (April 1955).
26. Ellis, C., "The Chemistry of Synthetic Resins," pp. 123–141; 201, 231, New York, Reinhold Publishing Corp., 1935.
27. Fair, J. R., Bolles, W. L., Nisbet, W. R., Kniel, L., McGarry, R. J., Reitmeier, R. E., Fleming, H. W., Davison, J. W., Hays, G. E., Swanson, W. M., and Watkins, C. H., *Chem. Eng. Prog.,* **54**, 39–56 (1958).
28. Fawcett, E. W., Gibson, R. D., Perrin, W., Paton, J. G., and Williams, E. G., British Patent 471,590 (Sept. 1937) (I.C.I.); U. S. Patent 2,153,553 (April 1939); U. S. Patent 2,188,465 (June 1940).
29. Firestone Co., U. S. Patent 2,755,315 (July 1956); Farbwerke Hoecht, U. S. Patent 2,724,006 (Nov. 1955).
30. Flory, P. J., "Principles of Polymer Chemistry," Ithaca, Cornell University Press, 1953.
31. Gaylord, N. G., and Mark, A., "Linear and Stereospecific Addition Polymers," New York, Interscience Publishers, Inc., 1959.
32. Gray, D. R., "Vinylidene Chloride," in "Encyclopedia of Chemical Technology," Kirk, R. E., and Othmer, D. F., Editors, Vol. XIV, p. 736, New York, Interscience Publishers, Inc., 1955.
33. Greenewalt, C. H. (to the E. I. duPont Co.), U. S. Patent 2,388,138 (Oct. 1945).
34. Greenlee, S. O., *et al.,* U. S. Patent 2,456,408 (Dec. 1948); 2,503,726; 2,510,-885–6; 2,511,913; 2,512,996; 2,521,911–12; 2,528,359–60; 2,538,072; 2,558,949; 2,581,464; 2,582,985; 2,589,245; 2,592,560; 2,615,007–8; 2,694,694; 2,698,315; 2,712,000; 2,717,885 (to Devoe and Raynolds).
35. Grim, J. M. (to the Koppers Co.), U. S. Patent 2,715,118 (Aug. 1955).
36. Hanford, W. E., and Sargent, D. E., "Reactions of Organic Gases Under Pressure," in Gilman's "Organic Chemistry," Vol. IV, pp. 1024–1042, New York, John Wiley and Sons, Inc., 1953.
37. Hanson, A. W., Heston, A. L., and Buecken, H. E. (to the Dow Chemical Co.), U. S. Patent 2,519,834 (1950).
38. Hanson, A. W. (to the Dow Chemical Co.), U. S. Patent 2,488,198 (1949).
39. Hanson, A. W. (to the Dow Chemical Co.), U. S. Patent 2,769,804 (Nov. 1956).
40. Hanson, A. W., and Zimmerman, R. L., *Chem. Eng. News,* **77** (1957).
41. Harries, C., *Ann.,* **383**, 213 (1911).
42. Hogan, J. P., and Banks, R. L. (to Phillips Petroleum), U. S. Patent 2,825,721 (March 1958).

This observation may be regarded as the beginning of the idea of man-made fibers. Yet almost two hundred years elapsed before this concept was realized by Andemars, who drew fibers from a solution of cellulose nitrate containing some rubber; and only after considerable development and the passage of a generation did Chardonnet's patent (1885) open the door for commercialization of man-made fibers. During the last years of the nineteenth century and the beginning of the twentieth, progress was so rapid

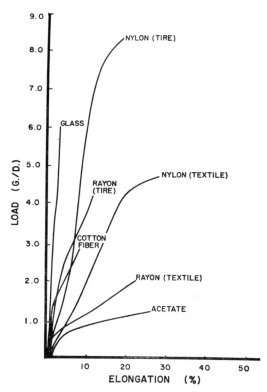

Figure 11.1. Load-elongation curves of some man-made fibers.

that volume increased from 100 pounds per day in 1891 to over 2 million pounds in 1910 of the fiber known then as artificial silk and since named "rayon." Although in the United States its production had risen to about 150 million pounds by the time the revised first edition of this book was published (1933), its future was still so unpredictable that the following statement was made: "the artificial silk industry may therefore be regarded as supplementing worm silk production rather than rivaling it." That edition also mentioned that worm silk importation into the United States in 1931 totaled almost 90 million pounds. It is with this background in mind that the development and production of man-made fibers should be examined.

VOLUME OF PRODUCTION*

Figure 11.2 compares population growth with the production of "silk-like" man-made fibers and the consumption of silk in the United States. The use of rayon and nylon in tire cord has not been included in order that trends in clothing and household goods may be seen more clearly. It may be noted that in competition with rayon and acetate, silk declined

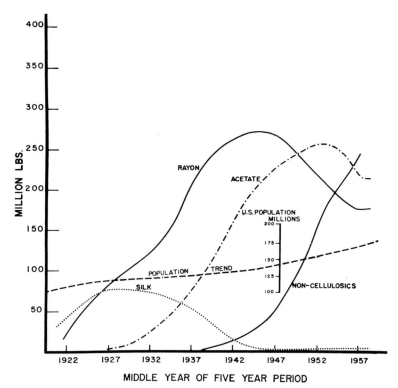

Figure 11.2. Production of silk-like man-made fibers compared with consumption of silk and population growth in the United States.

seriously even before World War II and the advent of nylon had undermined its importance as a major continuous filament yarn. Just as acetate in part replaced rayon and essentially halted its expansion, so did the noncellulosics affect both. It is possible that the advent of triacetate and the use of acetate tow in cigarette filters reversed the over-all trend of this material.†

* Developed from data contained in various issues of the monthly "Textile Organon" published by the Textile Economics Bureau, Inc., New York, N. Y.

† Since there is only one manufacturer of cellulose triacetate, all information on its production is hidden by making it a part of the economic data on secondary acetate fibers. It is impossible, therefore, to clearly define the situation at present.

In regard to tire cord, as late as 1951 cotton comprised about 40 per cent of the total output of approximately half a billion pounds, and nylon was at a negliglible level of 4 million pounds. In 1960, cotton had all but disappeared; nylon represented about 37 per cent of the total (on a pound basis), a dramatic change considering that only about 0.8 pound of nylon is needed to replace 1.0 pound of rayon.

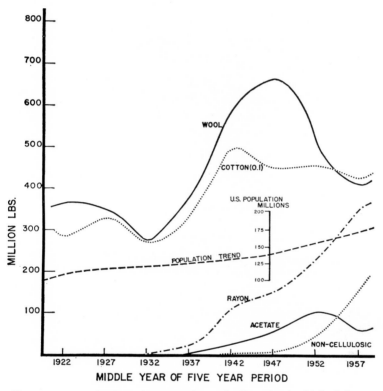

Figure 11.3. Production of man-made staple fibers in the United States compared with consumption of wool and cotton.

Figure 11.3 illustrates the production of man-made staple fibers in the United States as compared with the consumption of wool and cotton. Despite an initially rapid expansion, acetate could not compete with the non-cellulosics. Rayon, however, was not so adversely affected. The use of rayon in the manufacture of tufted carpets in the early 1950's explains its continued growth. Wool and cotton consumption shows considerable fluctuation, especially during the war years, but the over-all trend is counter to the population increase in the United States.

World production of man-made fibers exhibits a somewhat different situation (Figure 11.4). Although here, too, the output of non-cellulosics has risen with great rapidity, there is less competition in the total market with rayon and acetate. The production of filament rayon and acetate has leveled off (not shown in Figure 11.4) but staple continues to expand. The natural fibers, wool, and cotton, less affected, continue to increase in usage.

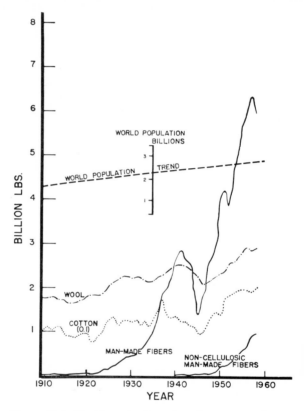

Figure 11.4. World production of wool, cotton, and man-made fibers compared with population trends.

When compared with population trends it appears that the over-all demand resulting from an improved standard of living still dominates international fiber markets.

A presentation of exact information about consumption of raw materials, chemical reactions, reagents used, and efficiencies of operations in the manufacture of man-made fibers would undoubtedly contribute to a better understanding of the economics involved. There are several factors which prevent such a presentation, however. When the chemical aspects of manufacture are not obvious, the details are never released, and efficiencies are always closely guarded secrets. Nonetheless, a considerable degree of public knowledge has developed concerning the older fibers. Secrecy is maintained despite the fact that chemical engineering knowledge available in most large chemical concerns permits an almost complete appraisal of a competitor's activities.

In general, the cost of the original raw material may have very little bearing on the selling price of the final fiber; rather, the complexity of the

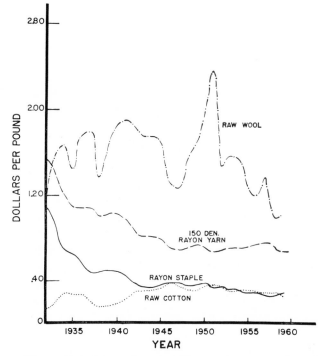

Figure 11.5. Prices of natural fibers and rayon staple and filament yarn (corrected for changes in Wholesale Price Index).

processes involved in conversion determines the cost. As a process becomes older, research minimizes this complexity; with simplification, there may be rapid drops in plant cost. These are reflected in the selling price, with little or no variation in the cost of raw materials having occurred. A comparison of rayon and nylon will serve as illustration. "Chemical cellulose" for rayon was priced at 9 to 10 cents per pound when rayon staple was selling at about 31 to 35 cents per pound. On the other hand, benzene at $4\frac{1}{2}$ cents per pound becomes adipic acid at 32 cents and finally nylon fiber at well over a dollar per pound. The great difference in the ratio of raw material cost to selling price of fibers lies in the intermediate manufacturing operations rather than profit considerations. Figure 11.5 illustrates the drop in prices (corrected for changes in the Wholesale Price Index; all commodities 1947–1949 = 100) of rayon staple and filament yarn over long periods as well as their relative stability in recent years as compared with the more volatile natural fibers. The great importance of man-made fibers in the chemical industry and in the over-all economy of the United States becomes apparent when the volume of production of these materials is considered (Figure 11.2) and compared with the market value of even the least expensive of them (Figure 11.5).

RAYON

Chemical Manufacture

Rayon, the first of the man-made fibers, depends on natural polymer cellulose for its raw material. In the early days the main source of raw material was cotton linters, the short fibers left on the cotton seed after the lint was removed for use in textiles. This was natural since linters, a relatively pure source of cellulose, were readily available and inexpensive, and the non-cellulosic portions could be removed without excessively drastic treatment. The combination of improved technologies for purifying cellulose derived from wood, and the shortage of cotton linters brought about during World War II when they were used for cellulose nitrate, resulted in the present situation: a ratio of 99 per cent wood pulp to 1 per cent cotton linters.

Whatever the source, cellulose or "pulp" is now received by the manufacturer in sheet form, 20 by 30 inches not unlike a thick unbacked blotter. In the manufacture of this pulp,[3] impurities are removed, special care being given to traces of metallic elements such as manganese, which affect the manufacturing process and the quality of the final product. Thus uniformity in cellulose sheets meets a very high standard.

When wood is the raw material its purification involves drastic chemical action at elevated temperatures, and it is not surprising that degradation occurs which reduces substantially the originally very high molecular weight of the cellulose. This breakdown is essential, but it also results in a wide distribution of molecular weights which vary in solubility characteristics. Cellulose which is not soluble in the 17 to 18 per cent aqueous solution of caustic used in rayon manufacture is known as alpha cellulose. The beta and gamma fractions of lower molecular weight are soluble and are lost. The composition of the pulp is therefore aimed at as high an alpha content as is economically feasible. An average level is 87 per cent.

In the manufacture of rayon it is the usual practice to begin "blending" at the first step which involves batch steeping the pulp. Further blending proceeds throughout succeeding steps. The warehouse supply of pulp consists of numerous shipments from the pulp source or, preferabley, sources. In making up the batches, a few sheets are taken from each of several shipments received from various vendors, the ratio being so predetermined that all units of the stock are used, and every exhausted shipment is replaced by a new one. This serves two purposes. It prevents a slight varia-

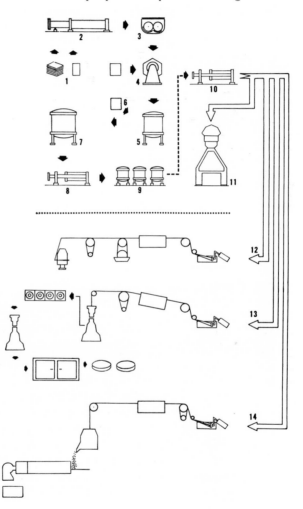

Figure 11.6. Flow diagram for manufacture of viscose rayon. 1. Cellulose sheets and caustic soda 2. Steeping press 3. Shredder 4. Xanthating churn 5. Dissolver 6. Supply 7. Ripener 8. Filtration 9. Deaeration 10. Filtration 11. Continuous process 12. Tire cord 13. Pot spinning 14. Staple spinning

tion in a single pulp lot from affecting unduly any given volume of production, and it provides a moving average so that changes in time are reduced to a minimum.

The cellulose sheets are loaded into a combination steeping bath and press, which is slowly filled with a solution of 17 to 18 per cent caustic, in which they remain for about 1 hour. In the steeping, the alpha cellulose is converted into alkali or "soda" cellulose;[8] at the same time, the caustic solution removes the beta and gamma celluloses (also called hemi celluloses) which are too low in molecular weight to be used in the final rayon fiber. The exact chemical composition of the soda cellulose is not known,

Figure 11.7. Rayon plant of American Viscose Corporation at Front Royal, Virginia. (*Courtesy American Viscose Corp.*)

Figure 11.8. Steeping bath for cellulose sheets. (*Courtesy American Viscose Corp.*)

but there is evidence that one mole of NaOH is associated with two anhydro-glucose units in the polymer chain.

$(C_6H_{10}O_5)_n$ (cellulose) $+ 18\%$ aqueous NaOH $\rightarrow [(C_6H_{10}O_5)_2 \cdot NaOH]_n$ (swollen, insoluble, soda cellulose I) $+$ soluble soda celluloses from β and γ celluloses

The excess caustic solution is removed by forcing the sheets between press plates with a hydraulic ram. Even after this operation the sheets remain in a highly swollen condition and retain from 2.7 to 3.0 parts of the alkali solution. The spent steeping solution is pumped to dialyzers which separate and recover the caustic from the organic material.

Following removal of the solution, the sheets of soda cellulose are discharged into a shredder. Blending is again accomplished by mixing the charges from two or more steeping presses in a single shredder where the already soft sheets are torn into small pieces or crumbs; cooling is provided to prevent thermal degradation. Shredding is controlled to produce crumbs that are open and fluffy, and that will allow air to penetrate the mass readily; this is essential in aging.

Soda cellulose is aged by holding it at a constant temperature in perforated containers so that air can contact all the material. The oxygen in the air produces uniform aging and reduction in molecular weight, and an increase in the carboxyl groups present. The target of aging is a molecule large enough to produce satisfactory strength in the final rayon but low enough in weight so that the viscosity of the solution used in spinning will be neither excessively high at the desired concentration nor require reduction of the concentration to an uneconomically low point. The aging proceeds for periods up to several days, although the tendency is to speed up the operation. A combination of experience and constant quality control testing guarantees that the material will reach the correct point for conversion to cellulose xanthate.

Cellulose xanthate is obtained by mixing the aged soda cellulose with 30 to 35 per cent by weight of carbon disulfide in a vapor tight xanthating churn.

$$[(C_6H_{10}O_5)_2 \cdot NaOH]_n + CS_2 \text{ (30–40\% based on weight of cellulose in}$$

soda cellulose) $\rightarrow (C_6H_{10}O_5)_n[C_6H_7O_2(OH)_x(O-\underset{\underset{S}{\parallel}}{C}-S \cdot Na^+)_{3-x}]_m$ or,

for simplicity, (cellulose $-O-\underset{\underset{S}{\parallel}}{C}-SNa$)

Cellulose xanthate is an addition product of the two, and its solubility in a dilute solution of sodium hydroxide—a characteristic discovered by Cross and Bevan in 1892—makes the spinning of rayon possible. It is a yellow solid; when dissolved in a dilute solution of alkali it becomes a viscous honey-colored liquid, hence the word "viscose." At this stage the viscous solution contains about 7.25 per cent cellulose as xanthate in about a 6.5 per cent solution of sodium hydroxide.

If regular or, to use the industry term, "bright" rayon is desired, the solution is ready for filtration, aging, deaeration, and spinning. But only in the days of "artificial silk" did the shiny fiber alone satisfy the market. After a few years a dull appearing fiber was also demanded. At first, fine droplets of oil in the filaments were used to produce dullness until it was discovered that titanium dioxide pigment, having a particle size smaller than one micron in diameter, was even more satisfactory. It has since become the universal delusterant for all man-made fibers.

The usual practice has been to add this pigment when mixing the cellulose xanthate into the dilute solution of caustic. However, it must be realized that not only bright and dull, but also semi-dull fiber is needed, and the demand for each of the three kinds of rayon varies from time to time. Cleaning or flushing equipment, made necessary by change-overs, involves additional costs and makes desirable the development of a process which would inject pigment as far along toward the spinning as is possible.

When the "dope dyeing" of rayon (the use of colored pigments in the fiber) became important, it was no longer possible in all cases to make the final spinning solution during the process of dissolving the xanthate. ("Dope dyeing" will be discussed in greater detail under another heading; it is sufficient to point out here that a large volume of this type of rayon is manufactured and is of considerable importance.) Moreover, in recent years chemicals other than pigments have had to be added in order to obtain a rayon different from the simple material which was the standard product in the early days of the industry. In order to produce rayon of different physical properties, the rate of precipitation and regeneration of the cellulose is modified by the addition of various chemicals to the spinning bath.[9]

From the standpoint of chemical processing it is obvious that pigments and other chemicals may be added when the cellulose xanthate is dissolved in dilute caustic solution, or at any time up to the moment before it enters the jet prior to being extruded. To keep the operations as flexible as possible the additives should be injected at the last possible moment so that when a change-over is desired there will be a minimum amount of equipment to be cleaned. On the other hand, the farther along in the operation that additives are placed into the stream the greater the problem of obtaining uniformity in an extremely viscous medium, and the greater the difficulty in maintaining exact control of proportions before the viscous solution is passed forward and spun. Furthermore, all insoluble additives must be of extremely small particle size, and all injected slurries must be freed of agglomerates by pre-filtration; if not, the viscous solution containing the additives must be filtered. Each manufacturer of viscose rayon develops his own particular conditions for making additions, depending on a multitude of factors not the least of which is investment in equipment. All manufacturers must face the universal necessity of filtering the solution, with or without pigments or other additives, so that all impurities and agglomerates are removed which might block the holes in the spinnerette. Such filtration is carried out in plate and frame filter presses.

Although it was known in the years following the discovery by Cross and Bevan that viscose solution could be used in the preparation of regenerated cellulose, the conversion of this solution into useful fibers was not possible until the discovery that the solution required aging until "ripe." Ripening is the first part of the actual chemical decomposition of cellulose xanthate which, if allowed to proceed unhampered, would result in the gelation of the viscose solution.

$$\text{Cellulose} -\text{O}-\underset{\underset{\text{S}}{\|}}{\text{C}}-\text{SNa} \overset{H_2O}{\rightleftarrows} \text{Cellulose} -\text{O}\underset{\underset{\text{S}}{\|}}{\text{C}}-\text{SH} + \text{NaOH} \overset{H_2O}{\rightleftarrows}$$

$$\text{Cellulose} + \text{HO}\underset{\underset{\text{S}}{\|}}{\text{C}}-\text{SH} \rightarrow \text{Cellulose} + CS_2 + H_2O$$

Experience has taught the manufacturer the correct time and conditions for his aging operation, but the requirement of aging itself demands that the entire process be so planned that the viscose solution will arrive at the jet possessing, as nearly as possible, the optimum age to produce fibers having the desired characteristics. One step in the over-all aging operation involves the removal by vacuum of residual, mechanically-held air. It should be mentioned that so inevitable is decomposition of cellulose xanthate and consequent gelation of the contents of pipes and tanks, that all viscose rayon plants must be prepared to pump in-process viscose solutions to the sewer, purging them with dilute caustic solution in the event of a long delay in spinning.

Wet Spinning

Spinning a viscose solution into rayon fibers (wet spinning) is the oldest of the three methods of making man-made fibers. In this method the polymer is dissolved in either an aqueous solution or an organic solvent and, after appropriate filtrations, is forced through fine holes in the face of the spinnerette or jet. The pressure necessary for this extrusion is supplied by a gear pump which also acts as a metering device; the solution is moved through a final or "candle" filter before is emerges from the holes of the spinnerette. There is immediate contact between these tiny streams and the liquid or "wet" bath in which the spinnerette is immersed. As the bath solution makes contact with the stream of material extruded from the holes, chemical or physical changes take place. These changes whether of lesser or greater complexity (usually the latter), convert the solution of high molecular weight linear polymer first to a gel structure and then to a fiber.

As the first and still primary example of wet spinning, the formation of rayon fibers from viscose solution constitutes an extremely complex physical and chemical phenomenon. The spinning bath usually contains 1 to 5 per cent zinc sulfate and 7 to 10 per cent sulfuric acid, as well as an active surface agent without which minute deposits will form around the holes in the spinnerette. Sodium sulfate (15 to 22 per cent) is present, formed by the reactions, and as sulfuric acid is depleted and sodium sulfate concentration builds up, an appropriate replenishment of the acid is required.

Figure 11.9. Wet spinning of viscose solution into rayon fibers. (*Courtesy American Viscose Corp.*)

There is precipitation of the organic material as the sulfuric acid in the spinning bath neutralizes the sodium hydroxide in the viscose solution; at the same time, chemical decomposition of the cellulose xanthate takes place to regenerate the cellulose. The gel-like structure, the first state through which the material passes, is not capable of supporting itself outside the spinning bath. As it travels through the bath, however, it quickly becomes transformed into a fiber that can be drawn from the spinning bath and that can support itself in subsequent operations. The reactions between the bath and the forming fiber are paramount in determining the characteristics of the final product; it is for this reason that additives (previously mentioned) may be used so as to control both the rate of gelation and regeneration. In this manner the arrangement of the cellulose molecules may be controlled to produce the structural order desired.[9]

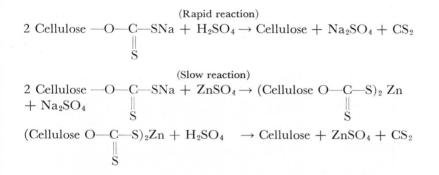

Because of hydraulic drag, stretching occurs in the bath and also in a separate step after the yarn leaves the bath. In both cases the linear molecules of cellulose are oriented from random positions to positions more parallel to the yarn axis. If a rayon tire cord is to be the final product the fibers must be severely stretched to produce high orientation of the molecules, this being the basis of the tire cord's high strength and ability to withstand stretching. For regular textile fibers such high strengths are not desired, and the spinning and stretching operations are controlled to produce rayon of lower strength and greater stretchability under stress. In order to stretch the yarn uniformly during the manufacturing process, two sets of paired rollers or "godets" are employed which operate at different rotational speeds. The yarn is passed around the first godet several times to prevent slippage and is supplied to the stretching area at a constant speed. A second godet moves it forward at a more rapid rate, also without slippage. Spinning speeds are on the order of 100 meters per minute, but these may vary with both the size of the yarn and the process used.

Spinning conditions, composition of the spinning bath, and additives to the viscose solution determine the physical characterstics of the rayon, its ability to resist swelling in water, and its strength characteristics in the wet state as compared with those of the dry material. Not only must the chemical composition of the spinning bath be carefully controlled; the temperature must be carefully regulated at a selected point, somewhere in the range of 40 to 60° C, to ensure those precipitation and regeneration conditions essential to the manufacture of viscose rayon having preferred properties.

After the precipitating bath has reacted chemically with the viscose solution to regenerate the cellulose, and all the raw rayon fiber has been formed, the subsequent steps must be controlled so that differences in treat-

ment are minimized; otherwise such sensitive properties as "dye acceptance" will be affected and appearance will vary. Minute traces of
suspended sulfur resulting from the chemical decomposition of cellulose
xanthate must be removed by washing with a solution of sodium sulphide.
It is expedient to bleach the newly formed fibers with hypochlorite to improve their whiteness; an "anti-chlor" follows. The chemicals present
originally and those used to purify the fibers must be removed by washing.

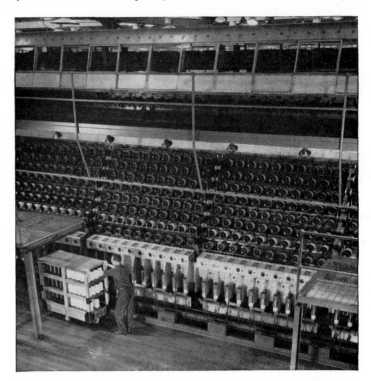

Figure 11.10. Equipment for continuous spinning process. (*Courtesy
Industrial Rayon Corp.*)

As a final step a small amount of lubricant must be placed on the filaments to reduce friction in subsequent textile operations.

There are several processes for spinning and purifying rayon. One of the
most common involves the formation of packages of yarn, each weighing
several pounds, for separate treatment. After it has been passed upward out
of the spinning bath and stretched to the desired degree, the yarn is fed
downward vertically into a rapidly rotating can-like container called a
spinning pot or "Topham" box (after the man who invented it in 1900).
It is thrown outward to the wall of the pot by centrifugal force and
gradually builds up like a cake. This cake is firm, although it must be

handled with care, and is sufficiently permeable to aqueous solutions to permit purification.

In another method of package spinning the yarn is wound onto a mandrel from the side, thus necessitating an increase in the speed of the drive, as the diameter of the yarn build-up increases, to maintain a constant delivery speed. With this process the yarn may be purified and dried before delivery to the package, or it may be wound wet and the packages handled in much the same manner as those produced by pot spinning. In any of these systems the spinning and stretching, as well as subsequent steps, may involve separate baths.

Figure 11.11. A continuous process reel. (*Courtesy Industrial Rayon Corp.*)

The first continuous process of spinning textile grade rayon yarn merits particular mention from the standpoint of industrial chemistry: applying continuous chemical processing techniques resulted in a rayon of extremely high uniformity and quality.

This method employs "advancing reels" which make it possible for the yarn to dwell for a sufficient length of time on each, thus allowing the several chemical operations to take place in a relatively small area. Operation of the advancing reels depends on the situation existing when the shafts of a pair of cyclindrical rolls are oriented slightly askew. Yarn led onto the end of one these and then around the pair will progress toward the other end with every pass, the rate of traversing and therefore the number of warps being determined by the degree of skewness. The same result may be obtained by using a pair of circularly arranged digitating set of fingers called advancing reels, the axes of which are also slightly askew.

Nitro, Cuprammonium, and Cellulose Acetate Processes for Rayon

Nitrocellulose. Although nitro cellulose was spun and regenerated into cellulose in the early days of the rayon industry, it is several years since this process has been used commercially, and today it is only of historical interest.

Cuprammonium Cellulose. Cellulose forms a soluble complex with copper salts and ammonia. Thus, when cellulose is added to an ammonical solution of copper sulfate which also contains sodium hydroxide, it dissolves to form a viscous blue solution and in this form it is known as cuprammonium cellulose. When used in determining the viscosity of cellulose as a measure of its molecular weight, it has been called "Schweizer solution." The principles on which the chemical and spinning steps of this process are based are the same as those for the viscose process. Cellulose is dissolved, in this case in a solution containing ammonia, copper sulfate, and sodium hydroxide. The cellulose-cuprammonium complex has had several formulae ascribed to it. One of these is:

$$CuSO_4 + 2NaOH + \text{excess } NH_3 + H_2O \rightarrow$$
$$Cu(NH_3)_4(OH)_2 + 2Na^+ + NH_4^+ + SO_4^= + OH^-$$
$$(C_6H_{10}O_5)_n(\text{cellulose}) + NaOH \underset{\xrightarrow{H_2O}}{\longleftarrow} (C_6H_8O_5)_n^{--} + 2\overset{+}{Na}$$

Using only two anhydro glucose units in a cellulose molecule, for purposes of illustration,

$$2(C_6H_8\overset{--}{O_5}) + [Cu(NH_3)_4](OH)_2 + \overset{++}{Cu} + SO_4^= + 4\overset{+}{Na} \rightarrow$$
$$[(C_6H_8O_5)_2Cu]\cdot[Cu(NH_3)_4] + 4\overset{+}{Na} + SO_4^= + 2\overset{-}{OH}$$

It appears that an equilibrium exchange may exist between the cupric and sodium ions.

Unlike the viscose solution, the cuprammonium solution need not be aged and will not precipitate spontaneously on standing except after long periods. It is, however, sensitive to light and oxygen.

The cuprammonium solution must be filtered before spinning. Precipitation occurs when the tiny streams passing through the holes of the spinnerette make contact with the large excess of water; an acid solution is required only to remove the last traces of copper salt and ammonia from the precipitated filaments. In the manufacture of cuprammonium rayon, a continuous process was developed following the original single package method. In this process a large number of strands or "ends," to use the textile term, are spun and then passed as a sheet through the purification and washing baths, dried, and then wound in parallel around a large spool or "beam."

A greater drawing occurs in the spinning bath in the cuprammonium process than in the viscose, without producing excessively high strength and low elongation. Although this rayon has never been manufactured in a volume even approaching that produced by the viscose method, these finer filament yarns continue to have a specialized market.

Cellulose Acetate. The conversion of cellulose to cellulose acetate is still another method of making this high molecular weight polymer soluble. (The manufacture of cellulose acetate will be described in a later section.) A solution of the acetate in acetone may be wet spun, but since the compound is considerably more stable chemically than either cellulose xanthate or the cuprammonium complex, the regeneration of cellulose is not as easily accomplished. It is preferable to spin the cellulose acetate and then saponify it in a separate operation.[1]

For wet spinning, acetate should be soluble in acetone and insoluble in water, and the solvent should transfer easily from the solution to water when the two are brought into contact. The rate at which the transfer takes place may be controlled so that the period during which a plastic state exists (this corresponds to the gel state in the viscose operation) will be sufficiently long to allow stretching. This stretching operation (like the corresponding step in the manufacture of rayon tire yarn) produces a fiber in which cellulose acetate molecules are highly oriented. The result is filaments with high strength and resistance to elongating forces. Cellulose acetate is saponified back to cellulose in a caustic solution containing a relatively large amount of sodium acetate. Under such conditions disorientation does not take place, and a regenerated cellulose yarn of extremely high strength is produced.

$$[C_6H_7O_2(OH)_{.65}(CH_3\overset{O}{\overset{\|}{C}}\!-\!O)_{2.35}]_n + NaOH \xrightarrow[\text{H}_2\text{O}]{\text{CH}_3\text{COONa}}$$
$$\text{Cellulose} + CH_3COONa + H_2O$$

TEXTILE OPERATIONS

After the filament rayon fiber has been spun and chemically purified, much of it passes through what are known as "textile operations" before it is ready to be knitted or woven. Since these steps of twisting and packaging or beaming are common to the manufacture of all man-made fibers, it is advisable to review briefly the background and processes.

Rayon, the first man-made fiber, had not only to compete in an established field, but also to break into a conservative industry. The cotton, wool, worsted, and linen systems of converting fibers to yarns were well established and their products universally accepted. Silk was the only continuous filament yarn, and products made from it were expensive and had prestige value. This offered a tempting market for rayon. Thus the new product entered as a silk competitor and became known as "artificial silk."

When making yarn it was customary to twist the silk filaments in order to increase the strength and prevent the breaking of a single filament from pushing back to form a fuzz ball. Rayon, since it is weaker than silk and the individual filaments are smaller, required the same or even more twisting. In pot spinning the twists were two to three per inch at the start; in package spinning, none. Experience proved that both the degree of twisting and the size of the package desired by the weaver or knitter varied according to the final application.

These operations could have been carried out in the same plant where the yarn was spun, but the existence of silk "throwsters" (from the Anglo-Saxon *"thrāwan,"* to twist or revolve) made this unnecessary. As the rayon industry developed, the amount of yarn twisted in the producing plant and by throwsters was the result of many factors. Over the years the trend was to use less twist and to place, instead, several thousand parallel ends directly on a "beam," to form a package weighing as much as 300 to 400 pounds. Such a beam was shipped directly to a weaving or knitting mill. The advent of stronger rayons, as well as other strong fibers, and the diminishing market for crepe fabrics which required highly twisted yarns, accelerated the trend away from twisting.

In all twisting and packaging operations the yarn makes contact with guide surfaces and tensioning devices, often at very high speeds. To reduce friction it is necessary to add a lubricant as a protective coating for the filaments. This is generally true of all man-made fibers, and it is customary to apply the lubricant or "spinning finish" or "spinning lubricant" as early in the manufacturing process as possible.

Spun Yarn

After rayon became established in the textile industry where it could be used as a silk-like fiber, steps were taken to develop it as a staple fiber for use in cotton-like or wool-like fabrics (see Figures 11.2 and 11.3). The fiber was cut into lengths the same as those of cotton and wool. For producing short pieces it was first necessary to secure a large tow containing several hundred thousand parallel filaments which could be chopped into the desired lengths. The viscose rayon process is eminently suited to the production of such tows. The pressure required to force the solution through the holes is so low that neither heavy metal nor reinforcement of the jet face is necessary to prevent bulging and large spinnerettes containing several thousand holes can be used. Furthermore, the spinning bath succeeds in making contact with all the filaments uniformly. As a result, the spinning of viscose rayon tow is very similar in principle to the production of individual smaller yarns.

Since cotton and wool have crimps, machinery for their processing was designed to operate best with crimped fibers. Thus rayon had to have similar lengths and crimps to adapt to such equipment. The crimp, that is, several deformations from straightness per inch, may be produced in rayon either "chemically" or mechanically. In the former case the precipitation-stretching step in spinning is carried out so that the skin and core of the individual filaments are radially non-uniform and constantly changing over very short lengths along the filaments. Since the skin and core differ in sensitivity to moisture, a situation occurs which is not unlike the thermal effect on a bimetallic strip, with consequent distortion of the filaments. Mechanical crimp is produced by feeding the tow between two wheels, which in turn force it into a chamber already tightly filled with tow. As soon as the tow leaves the nip of the feeding wheels it is forced against the compacted material ahead of it, and the straight filaments collapse immediately. As the mass of material is pressed forward it becomes tightly compacted in the distorted condition and remains that way until it escapes through a pressure loaded door at the opposite end of the chamber.

Crimped tow is passed to a cutter where it is divided into uniform lengths, the more frequent being $1\frac{9}{16}$, 2, $2\frac{1}{2}$, and 3 inches. It may be dried as tow, or wet crimped, cut, and dried as staple fiber. The final step is baling for shipment.

CELLULOSE ACETATE

Historical

Cellulose acetate was long known as a chemical compound before its potential use as a plastic or fiber forming material was recognized. The presence of hydroxyl groups had made it possible to prepare cellulose esters from various organic acids, although the chemistry of these materials was not clear. Now it is known that cellulose consists of a long molecular chain of beta anhydro glucose units, each of which carries three hydroxyl groups— one primary, the other two secondary. The formula for cellulose (already noted) is $[C_6H_7O_2(OH)_3]_n$; when this is fully esterfied a tri-ester results. It was learned earlier that whereas cellulose tri-acetate is soluble only in chlorinated solvents, a product obtained by partial hydrolysis of the tri-ester to a "secondary" ester (having about 2.35 acetyl groups per anhydro glucose unit) was easily soluble in acetone containing a small amount of water. Many other cellulose esters have been prepared, but only acetate has been commercialized successfully as a man-made fiber. Propionates and butyrates, and mixtures of one or both, with acetate have plastic applications.

Cellulose nitrate, a well-known material, was used to "dope" the fabric wings of fighter planes in World War I to render them taut and impermeable to air. With the advent of tracer bullets these aircraft were dubbed "flaming coffins," and the need for large scale production of the less flammable secondary cellulose acetate became imperative. Thus at the end of the war the brothers Camille and Henri Dreyfus found themselves in possession of a large factory and a product having no apparent usefulness. Necessity being the mother of invention, they not only developed a method

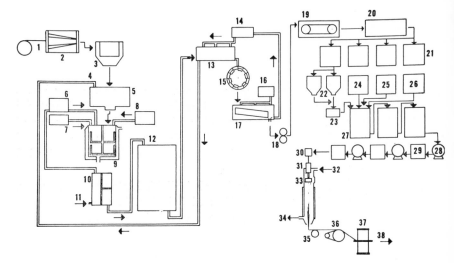

Figure 11.12. Flow diagram for manufacture of cellulose acetate yarn. 1. Wood pulp 2. Attrition mill 3. Cyclone 4. 35% HAc 5. Pretreater 6. Mg acetate solution 7. Pre-cooled acetylation mix 8. H_2SO_4 9. Acetylator 10. Ripener 11. Steam 12. Blendor 13. Precipitator 14. Dilute HAc 15. Hammer mill 16. H_2O 17. Rotary screen washer 18. Squeeze rolls 19. Drying oven 20. Blendor 21. Storage bins 22. Silos 23. Weigh bins 24. Acetone 25. Wood pulp 26. Pigment 27. Mixers 28. Hold tanks 29. Filter press 30. Pump 31. Filter 32. Air 33. Jet 34. Acetone recovery 35. Oiling wheel 36. Feed roll 37. Bobbin 38. Inspection

for spinning cellulose acetate into a fiber, they also sponsored the research which resulted in new dyestuffs and a salable textile product.

Manufacture of Secondary Cellulose Acetate

Cellulose acetate was made originally from purified cotton linters but this raw material has been entirely replaced by wood pulp. Other raw materials used in the manufacture of cellulose acetate are acetic acid, acetic anhydride, and sulfuric acid. Acetic acid and acetic anhydride, organic materials, have been produced by the petrochemical industry for many years, although the initial sources were natural.

The manufacture of cellulose acetate is a batch operation; the "charge" of cellulose is of the order of 800 to 1500 pounds. It is pretreated with about one-third its weight of acetic acid and a very necessary amount of moisture, about 6 per cent of its weight. If it is too dry at the time of use, more water must be added to the acetic acid. The pretreatment swells the cellulose and makes it "accessible" to the esterifying mixture.

Although there has been much discussion of the chemistry of the acetylation of cellulose, it is now generally agreed that the sulfuric acid is not a "catalyst" in the normal sense of the word, but rather that it reacts with the cellulose to form a sulfo-ester. The acetic anhydride is the reactant which provides the acetate groups for esterification. The acetylation mixture consists of the product from the anhydride recovery unit, which is 60 per cent acetic acid and 40 per cent acetic anhydride, in an amount 5 to 10 per cent

Figure 11.13. Process vessel for acetylation of cellulose. (*Courtesy Celanese Fibers Co.*)

above the stoichiometric requirement, to which has been added 10 to 14 per cent sulfuric acid based on the weight of cellulose used. The reaction is exothermic and requires that the heat be dissipated. Since acetic acid freezes at slightly below room temperature, it is possible to control the reaction.

In preparing for acetylation, the liquid reactants are cooled to a point where the acetic acid crystallizes, the heat of crystallization being removed by an appropriate cooling system. When a temperature of about 0° C is reached, the slush of acetic acid crystals in the acetic anhydride-sulfuric acid mixture is pumped to the acetylizer, a brine cooled mixer of heavy construction. This may be either a unit equipped with sigma blades on horizontal axes or a tank carrying a vertically mounted stirrer. The pretreated cellulose is dropped in from the pretreating unit located above. The extreme heat developed at the start of the reaction melts the acetic acid and prevents a dangerous rise in temperature which would degrade the molecular weight of the cellulose chain. As the reaction proceeds, brine in the jacket of the acetylizer provides additional cooling.

Cellulose + $(CH_3CO)_2O$ + H_2SO_4 (10–15% based on weight of cellulose)

$$\xrightarrow[\text{Anhydrous}]{\text{CH}_3\text{COOH}} [C_6H_7O_2(OSO_3H)_{.2}(CH_3COO)_{2.8}]_n$$

The reaction product is a cellulose sulfo-acetate of uncertain chemical composition insofar as the substitution of primary and secondary hydroxyls are concerned, but it appears that complete substitution takes place. This compound is soluble in the acetylation mixture; as it is formed and dissolved, new surfaces of the cellulose are presented to the reagents. One variation of this procedure makes use of methylene chloride, rather than an excess of acetic acid in the reaction mixture. This chemical is used both to dissipate the heat by refluxing (boiling point, 40.2° C) and to dissolve the cellulose ester as it is formed. As the reaction proceeds, the temperature is allowed to rise. Since the cellulose is a natural product obtained from many sources it varies slightly in composition and the end of the reaction cannot be exactly predicted; the disappearance of fibers as determined by microscopic examination is therefore the only means of following its progress.

During the acetylation operation a certain amount of chain fission takes place in the cellulose molecule. This is to ensure that the viscosity of the cellulose acetate spinning solution will be as low as possible for ease of handling but high enough to produce fibers with the preferred physical characteristics. The temperature of the reaction controls both rate of acetylation and molecular weight degradation. By carefully regulating the temperature, acetylation can be carried to completion in less time than is needed to reduce the molecular weight to the target value. The final adjustment to this target can then be made easily by continued stirring at a constant temperature.

The next step in the manufacture of cellulose acetate is "ripening," the objective of which is to convert the tri-ester, that is, the "primary" cellulose acetate, to a "secondary" acetate having an average of about 2.35 acetyl and no sulfo groups per anhydro glucose unit. While still in the acetylizer, sufficient water is added to react with the excess acetic anhydride and start the hydrolysis of the ester. Usually the water is used as a solution of sodium or magnesium acetate to increase the pH and promote the hydrolysis. In the early years of the industry, ripening was allowed to proceed slowly at room temperature for a period of over 24 hours. More recently the trend is to raise the temperature to about 70 to 80° C by direct injection of steam to speed the reaction.[16] Although this introduces additional water, the total amount is far below the point where insolubility occurs; with constant stirring, hydrolysis, first of the sulfo and then of the acetate groups, is relatively homogeneous. Hydrolysis is continued until the desired "acetyl value" is obtained. (This is not the acetyl value of the ester, but rather the amount of acetic acid which 100 units of the ester will produce after complete hydrolysis.) The usual level for cellulose acetate used in the manufacture of fibers is 54.0 to 55.0. When this value is reached, an aqueous solution of magnesium or sodium acetate is added to cool the batch and stop the hydrolysis. The batch is then ready for precipitation.

$$[C_6H_7O_2(OSO_3H)_{.2}(CH_3COO)_{2.8}]_n + (CH_3COO)_2Mg \xrightarrow{\text{aqueous conc. } CH_3COOH}$$
$$[C_6H_7O_2(OH)_{.65}(CH_3COO)_{2.35}]_n + MgSO_4$$

The regeneration of sulfuric acid and the presence of magnesium ions in a concentrated solution of acetic acid results in the formation of magnesium sulfate which subsequently may be crystallized, with cooling, in a long needle-like form. These crystals may be used as a "filter aid" if it is desirable to filter the solution of secondary cellulose acetate in the diluted acetic acid solution to remove any unacetylated fibers and other impurities.

The solution is carried to the verge of precipitation by adding dilute acetic acid. It is then flooded with more dilute acetic acid and mixed vigorously, so that the cellulose acetate comes out as a "flake" rather than a gelatinous mass or a fine powder. This flake is then washed by standard counter current methods to remove the last traces of acid, and dried in a suitable commercially available dryer.

Manufacture of Cellulose Triacetate

When completely acetylated cellulose rather than the secondary ester is the desired product, the reaction must be carried out with perchloric acid rather than sulfuric acid as catalyst. In the presence of 1 per cent perchloric acid a mixture of acetic acid and acetic anhydride converts a previously "pretreated" cellulose to triacetate without changing the morphology of the fibers. If methylene chloride rather than an excess of acetic acid is present in the acetylation mixture, a solution is obtained. However it is not imperative to secure an ester with no hydroxyl groups whatsoever in order to obtain a fiber which will behave in essentially the same way as the triester. It is possible to use about 1 per cent sulfuric acid instead of perchloric acid. When the sulfoacetate obtained from such a reaction is hydrolyzed so that only the sulfo ester groups are removed, the resulting product has an acetyl value of about 61.0 to 61.5 instead of the theoretical 62.5 of the triacetate. The preparation, hydrolysis, precipitation, and washing of "triacetate" are in all other respects similar to the corresponding steps in the manufacture of the more common secondary acetate.

Acid Recovery. In the manufacture of every pound of cellulose acetate about 4 pounds of acetic acid are produced in 30 to 35 per cent aqueous solution. Needless to say, every attempt is made to move the more dilute solutions counter current to the main product so as to concentrate them. For example, as already mentioned, acid dope is diluted and precipitation flooded with previously obtained dilute acid rather than water.

The accumulated acid contains a small amount of suspended "fines" and some dissolved cellulose esters of low acetyl value and molecular weight. To remove the former the acid is passed slowly through settling tanks. Then it is mixed with organic solvents, for example, a mixture of ethyl acetate and benzene,[10] which concentrate the acid in the organic layer and allows

Figure 11.14. Recovery of acetic acid. (*Courtesy Celanese Fibers Co.*)

decantation. Distillation separates acid and solvent, and concentrates the former to the glacial grade for conversion to the anhydride.

To produce acetic anhydride from the acid, the latter is dehydrated to ketene and reacted with acetic acid using a phosphate catalyst at 500° C or above in a tubular furnace.[11]

$$CH_3COOH \xrightarrow[\text{catalyst}]{\text{heat}} H_2O + CH_2{=}C{=}O$$
$$CH_2{=}C{=}O + CH_3COOH \rightarrow (CH_3CO)_2O$$

Both the dehydration and reaction may be carried out in separate steps, or they may be allowed to take place with the products quenched so as to prevent the water produced from reacting with the anhydride. In the latter operation the mixture of unreacted acid, water and anhydride is fed directly to a still which yields dilute acetic acid overhead and an anhydride-acetic acid mixture at the bottom. Conditions are so controlled that the raffinate is about 40 per cent anhydride and 60 per cent acetic acid. As already mentioned, this is the desired ratio for acetylation of cellulose.

Blending of Flake. As in the manufacture of viscose, the products of batch operations are blended to promote uniformity in the manufacture of cellulose acetate, since it has not been found possible to manufacture a consistently uniform product. Although a blend of different celluloses is selected in the beginning, the pretreatment, acetylation, and ripening are batch operations with little or no mixing. Before precipitation, a holding tank provides opportunity for mixing; then precipitation, washing, and drying—all continuous—promote uniformity. The dried cellulose acetate flake moves to holding bins for analysis: moisture content, acetyl value, and viscosity are especially important. The results of the analyses determine what further blending is necessary to obtain a uniform product; rather elaborate facilities are used to select, weigh, and mix the flake. After blending and mixing portions of selected batches, the lot is air conveyed to large storage bins or "silos" which are filled from the center of the top and emptied from the center of the bottom, thus bringing about further mixing.

Spinning Cellulose Acetate

Although cellulose acetate was dissolved originally in acetone containing a small amount of water in large rotating drum-like mixers, the more recent method is a continuous operation. The acetone is metered into a vertical tank equipped with a stirrer, and the cellulose acetate flake and filter aid are weighed in an automatic hopper; all operations are controlled by proportioning methods common to the chemical industry. The ratio of materials is about 25 per cent cellulose acetate, 4 per cent water, less than 1 per cent ground wood pulp as a filter aid, and the remainder acetone. The mixture moves forward through two or three stages at the rate at which it is used, the length of time being determined by experiment. After solution is complete, filtration is carried out in batteries of plate and frame filter presses in which the filter medium may be any of the several highly open-type pulps, rather than blotter-type cellulose sheets. Passage is usually in series through two or three presses.

Much of the cellulose acetate is delustered by the addition of titanium dioxide pigment. From the standpoint of thorough dispersing and mixing it is desirable to add the pigment as early as possible in the dissolving and mixing operation; this creates problems of cleaning, however, and reduces the flexibility of the equipment. On the other hand, injecting a slurry of pigment as far along toward the spinning jet as possible reduces the cleaning problem but accentuates the necessity for thorough mixing, careful filtration, and strict quality control. Each manufacturer must make compromises according to his particular needs.

Between each (and after the last) filtration, the dope goes to storage tanks which serve to remove bubbles; in this case vacuum is not necessary. From storage it is pumped to a header located at the top of each spinning machine; then it is directed to a series of metering gear pumps, one for each jet (spinnerette). Since the holes in the cellulose acetate spinning jet are smaller (0.03 to 0.05 mm) than the holes in the corresponding viscose jets, great care must be taken with the final filtration. An additional filter is placed in the fixture to which the jet is fastened for the removal of any small particles that may have passed through the large filters. Another filter is placed in the jet assembly over the top of the jet itself.

The dope is heated (in some cases above the boiling point of acetone, 56.5° C) before it enters the jet assembly to lower its viscosity and thus reduce the pressure required to extrude it, and to supply some of the heat required for evaporating the acetone solvent. Heat may be produced in a thermostatically controlled preheater or in the cabinet itself by including the final filter and jet assembly.

The jet is stainless steel, and because the filaments must be heated and prevented from sticking together, and space must be allowed for the escape of acetone vapor, the holes must be kept farther apart than those of the spinnerettes used for wet spinning. As the hot solution of cellulose acetate in acetone emerges from the jet into the spinning cabinet, an instantaneous loss of acetone takes place from the surface of the filaments which tend to form a solid skin over the still liquid or plastic interior. A current of air, either in the direction of the filaments or counter current to them, heats the filaments and removes the vaporized acetone.

The cabinet through which the yarn passes vertically downward must be long enough to allow sufficient acetone to diffuse outward and evaporate from the surfaces of the filaments so that the latter will not stick to the first surface contacted nor fuse to each other. The temperature of the air in the cabinet, the rate of flow, the length of the cabinet, the size and number of filaments, and the rate of travel all are interrelated in the spinning process. Since it is desirable to increase spinning speeds to the limit of the equipment, the tendency has been to construct longer spinning cabinets as each new plant is built. Present spinning speeds are of the order of 500 to 600 meters per minute, measured as the yarn emerges from the cabinet.

The spinning of cellulose acetate illustrates one of three possible spinning methods, that is, "dry" spinning. Having come after the development of viscose rayon manufacture, which had been named "wet" spinning, the absence of water and its replacement by heated air was logic enough for the use of the contrasting word. Other dry spinning operations follow essentially the same pattern. For example, the dry spinning of cellulose triacetate is identical to the process used for the older and more familiar secondary acetate except that the acetone solvent must be replaced by a chlorinated hydrocarbon such as methylene chloride. The solubility is improved by the addition of a small amount of methanol (5 to 15 per cent).

The acetate or triacetate yarn may emerge from the cabinet through an opening on the side near the bottom after passing over a deflecting pin, or it may be brought out of the bottom directly below the spinning jet. In either case it makes contact with an applicator which provides the lubricant required to reduce both friction and static formation in subsequent operations. With its surface lubricated, the yarn passes around a "feed" roll which determines the rate of withdrawal from the spinning cabinet. It then passes from the feed roll to any desired packaging device.

Unlike the packaging of rayon yarn, cellulose acetates are either "ring" spun or wound onto a package called a "disc," "zero twist," or "cam wound." In the ring spun package the yarn carries a slight twist of less than one turn per inch, but it requires a relatively expensive bobbin. Since the trend is toward less twisting, much acetate yarn is "beamed" in the producers plant after little or no twisting, the heavy beams being shipped directly to knitters or weavers.

Solvent Recovery. The air containing the acetone vapor is drawn out of the spinning cabinet and passed through beds of activated carbon which sorb the organic solvent. To recover the acetone it is steamed and separated from the water by distillation. Efficiency of recovery is about 95 per cent, and about 3 pounds of acetone are recovered per pound of cellulose acetate yarn. The recovery of methylene chloride and methanol from the manufacture of cellulose triacetate follows the same general procedure.

Dope Dyed Yarn. Colored pigments or dyestuffs may be added to the spinning solution so that the yarn will be colored as it is spun, thus eliminating the necessity of dying the final fabric. Although methods of dope dyeing may differ in detail depending on the fiber and process used, certain essentials are the same throughout. For example, when using titanium dioxide a compromise must be made on the basis of two competing needs. Complete mixing, uniformity, and filtration require that the addition be made early in the operation; minimal cleaning problems during change overs require just the opposite. This problem is much more difficult to solve when colored pigments are involved since the demands for colors are determined by ever-changing style trends. A manufacturer may plan a long run of a given color, arranging the changes from color to color so that the differences in successive runs will be negligible. This might, for example, include a series of blues ranging from pastel to navy; but such is not always possible. There exists two solutions.

If a manufacturer must produce a multitude of colors in relatively small amounts, it is desirable to pre-mix individual batches of spinning dope, each batch being pre-tested on a small scale to ensure that the desired color will be produced exactly. Facilities must be provided to allow each batch of colored dope to be cut into the system very close to the spinning operation in order to minimize pipe cleaning. Permanent piping must be flushed with solvent or the new batch of colored dope; some of the equipment may be disassembled for mechanical cleaning after each change of color.

Another method of producing spun dyed yarn involves using a group of "master" dopes of such color versatility that injected by appropriate pro-portioning pumps into a mixer located near the spinning operation they will produce the final desired color. The advantages of such an operation are obvious; the disadvantage lies in the textile industry's demand for an in-finite number of colors. No small group of pigments known will produce final colors of every desired variety.

PROTEINS

As previously mentioned, the use of naturally existing polymers to pro-duce fibers has had a long history. In the case of cellulose the results were fabulously successful. An initial investment of $930,000 produced net profits of $354,000,000 in 24 years for one rayon company.[6] On the other hand, another family of natural polymers—proteins—has thus far resulted in failure or at best very limited production.

These regenerated proteins are obtained from milk (casein), soya beans, corn, and peanuts. More or less complex chemical separation and purifica-tion processes are required to isolate them from the parent materials. They may be dissolved in aqueous solutions of caustic, and wet spun to form fibers which usually require further chemical treatment as, for example, with formaldehyde. This reduces the tendency to swell or dissolve in subsequent wet processing operations or final applications. These fibers are charac-terized by wool-like feel, low strength, and ease of dyeing. Nevertheless, for economic and other reasons they have not been able to compete successfully with either wool (after which they were modeled) or man-made fibers.

NYLON

Historical. Nylon was the first direct product of the technological break-through achieved by W. H. Carothers of E. I. duPont de Nemours & Com-pany. Until he began his classic research on high polymers, the manufacture of man-made fibers was based on natural linear polymers. Such materials included rayon, cellulose acetate, and the proteins. His research showed that chemicals of low molecular weight could be reacted to form polymers of high molecular weight. By selecting reactants to produce molecules having great length as compared with cross section, that is, linear molecules, fiber-forming polymers are obtained. With this discovery the man-made fiber in-dustry entered a new and dramatic era.

The word "nylon" was established as a generic name for polyamides, one class of the new high molecular weight linear polymers. The first of these,

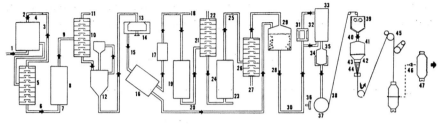

Figure 11.15. Flow diagram for manufacture of nylon. 1. Air 2. Cyclohexane from petroleum 3. Reactor 4. Recycle cyclohexane 5. Still 6. Cyclohexanol cyclohexanone 7. HNO₃ 8. Converter 9. Adipic acid solution 10. Still 11. Impurities 12. Crystallizer 13. Centrifuge 14. Impurities 15. Adipic acid crystals 16. Drier 17. Vaporizer 18. NH₃ 19. Converter 20. Crude adiponitrile 21. Still 22. Impurities 23. H₂ 24. Converter 25. Crude diamine 26. Still 27. Impurities 28. Nylon salt solution 29. Reactor 30. Stabilizer 31. Calandria 32. Evaporator 33. XS water 34. Autoclave 35. Delustrant 36. Water sprays 37. Casting wheel 38. Polymer ribbon 39. Grinder 40. Polymer flake 41. Spinning machine 42. Heating cells 43. Spinnerette 44. Air 45. Drawtwisting 46. Inspection 47. Nylon bobbin

Figure 11.16. Nylon plant, the Chemstrand Corporation, Pensacola, Florida. (*Courtesy The Chemstrand Corp.*)

and the one still produced in the largest volume, is "nylon 66" or poly-hexamethylene adipamide. Numbers are used with the word "nylon" to indicate the carbon atoms in the constituents, in this case hexamethylene-diamine and adipic acid.

Manufacture

To emphasize the fact that it does not depend on a naturally occurring polymer as a source of raw material, nylon has often been called a "truly synthetic fiber." To start the synthesis, benzene, secured as a by-product from the coking of coal, may be hydrogenated to cyclohexane,

$$C_6H_6 + 3H_2 \xrightarrow{\text{catalyst*}} C_6H_{12}$$

* U. S. Patent 2,373,501 mentions a Ni-Al catalyst, 180 to 250° C and 150 to 900 psi of hydrogen.

or the cyclohexane may be obtained from petroleum. The next step is oxidation to a cyclohexanol-cyclohexanone mixture by means of air.

$$x \; C_6H_{12} + O_2 \; (air) \xrightarrow{\text{catalyst*}} y \; C_6H_{11}OH + z \; C_6H_{11}O$$

In turn, this mixture is oxidized by nitric acid to adipic acid.

$$C_6H_{11}OH + C_6H_{11}O + HNO_3 \xrightarrow{\text{catalyst*}} (CH_2)_4(COOH)_2$$

Adipic acid so obtained is both a reactant for the production of nylon and the source of raw material for hexamethylene diamine, the other reactant. The adipic acid is first converted to adiponitrile by ammonolysis and then to hexamethylenediamine by hydrogenation.

$$(CH_2)_4(COOH)_2 + NH_3 \xrightarrow{\text{catalyst†}} (CH_2)_4(CN)_2 + H_2O$$
$$(CH_2)_4(CN)_2 + H_2 \xrightarrow{\text{catalyst‡}} (CH_2)_6(NH_2)_2$$

Another approach is through the series of compounds furfural, furane, cyclo tetra methylene oxide, 1-4 dichlorobutane, and adiponitrile. The furfural is obtained from oat hulls and corn cobs.

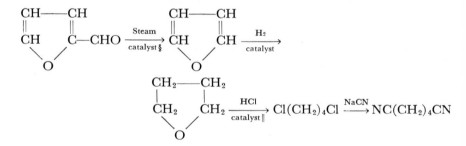

* U. S. Patent 2,439,513 mentions silver oxide, a vanadium compound, and a trace of copper as a catalyst, 75 to 175° C and 50 to 250 psi for the air oxidation and ammonium metavanadate plus freshly dissolved copper as catalyst; 50 to 150° C and 15 to 500 psi for the nitric acid oxidation. U. S. Patent 2,557,282 mentions cobalt naphthenate as catalyst, 50 to 170° C and 750 to 3750 psi for the air oxidation and ammonium vanadate plus freshly dissolved copper as a catalyst for the nitric acid oxidation.

† U. S. Patent 2,144,340 mentions silica gel as catalyst, 320 to 400° C.

‡ U. S. Patent 2,166,151 mentions nickel in the presence of ammonia, 120° C and 1500 to 2000 psi.

§ U. S. Patent 2,374,149 mentions the use of mixed chromites of Zn and Mn or Zn, Fe and steam at temperatures above 200° C.

‖ U. S. Patent 2,491,834 mentions the use of an amine salt catalyst in a liquid phase at 60 to 100° C.

Or 1-4 butadiene, obtained from petroleum, may be used as a starting raw material to make the adiponitrile via 1-4 dichloro-2-butene and 1-4 dicyano 2-butene.

$$CH_2{=}CHCH{=}CH_2 \xrightarrow{\text{Cl}_2*} ClCH{=}CHCH_2CH_2Cl$$
$$\xrightarrow[\text{catalyst}\dagger]{\text{HCN}} NC{-}CH{=}CHCH_2CH_2CN \xrightarrow[\text{catalyst}\ddagger]{\text{H}_2} NC(CH_2)_4CN$$

When hexamethylenediamine and adipic acid are mixed in a 1 to 1 molar ratio solution, the so-called "nylon salt" hexamethylenediammonium-adipate, the direct progenitor of the polymer, is precipitated. After preparing the nylon salt, it is polymerized to obtain a material of the desired molecular weight. It is heated to about 280° C while being stirred in an autoclave for 2 to 3 hours; a shorter holding period follows, and the process is finished off at 300° C. An inert atmosphere is maintained above the melt to prevent oxidation and discoloration; the water produced is vented. The molecular weight must be raised to a level high enough to provide a fiber-forming material, yet no higher. If it is too high its corresponding viscosity in the subsequent spinning operation will require the use of both high temperatures and pressures to make it flow. Accordingly, a small amount of acetic acid is added to terminate the long chain molecules by reaction with the terminal amino groups.

The polymerized product is an extremely insoluble material and must be melt spun (see below). Therefore, should a delustered fiber be desired it is necessary to add the titanium dioxide pigment to the polymerization batch before that reaction occurs. For ease of handling, the batch of nylon polymer is extruded from the autoclave to form a thin ribbon which is easily broken into chips after rapid cooling.

Nylon 6 and Nylon 11

Nylon 6 is made from caprolactam, nylon 11 from omega amino un-decanoic acid. The former is known as "Perlon" in Europe where it was developed.[4] Commercially it is the more important of the two materials; production has been started recently in the United States.

Manufacture. Like nylon 66, nylon 6 uses benzene as raw material, converted through previously mentioned steps to cyclohexanone. This compound is in turn converted to the oxime by reaction with hydroxylamine, and the cyclohexanoneoxime is made into caprolactam by the Beckmann rearrangement.

---

* U. S. Patent 2,369,117.

† U. S. Patent 2,477,674 mentions the use of a cuprous halide catalyst in a non-alkaline medium, at 100 to 150° C under the pressure developed by the reactants.

‡ U. S. Patent 2,532,311 mentions the use of a Pd catalyst at 250 to 300° C at 1 to 5 atmospheres of hydrogen.

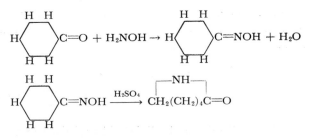

After purification, the lactam is polymerized by heating at elevated temperatures in an inert atmosphere. During self-condensation the ring structure of the lactam is opened so that the monomer acts like epsilon aminocaproic acid. Unlike nylon 66, polymerization of caprolactam is never complete; the polymer remains in equilibrium with a small amount of monomer. Like nylon 66, nylon 6 is extruded in ribbon-like form, quenched, and broken into flake for subsequent spinning.

Castor oil is the source of raw material for nylon 11. It is decomposed by heating at 300° C to produce undecylinic acid which, in turn, is converted first to omega bromo-undecanoic acid by treatment with hydrogen bromide in the presence of a catalyst, then to omega amino-undecanoic acid by reaction with ammonia.

$CH_3(CH_2)_5CHOHCH_2CH=CH(CH_2)_7COOH$ (as glyceryl ricinoleate)

$\xrightarrow[\text{vacuum}]{\text{heated in}} CH_2=CH(CH_2)_8COOH$ (undecylinic acid) $+ CH_3(CH_2)_5CHO$

$CH_2=CH(CH_2)_8COOH + HBr \xrightarrow{\text{catalyst}} BrCH_2(CH_2)_9COOH \xrightarrow{NH_3}$

$H_2N(CH_2)_{10}COOH$

Melt Spinning. Because of its extremely low solubility in low boiling, and inexpensive organic solvents, nylon 66 required a new technique for converting solid polymer into fibers, hence the development of melt spinning, the third basic method for manufacturing man-made fibers. The following description refers essentially to nylon 66 since that was the first and is still the largest single item so produced; but the method applies, in general, to all melt-spun man-made fibers.

In melt spinning nylon,[7] the chips (pre-dried if necessary) are fed into a chamber where they can be held in contact with an inert atmosphere. They rest on a melting grid the holes of which are small enough to permit passage of molten nylon only. In contact with the hot grid the polymer melts and drips into a pool where it becomes the supply for the usual gear-type metering pump. It is moved forward at the desired rate and pressure for passage through the filter and jet. The filter consists of metal screening and graded sand so arranged that the finest sand is at the bottom. After being filtered the molten polymer is extruded through the small holes in the jet. It is necessary to maintain the temperature of the pool, pump, filter, jet assembly, and jet somewhat above 255 to 265° C (the melting range of nylon 66).

Subsequent melt spinning procedures have been modeled after the method used for nylon 66. Changes have been incorporated to adapt the equipment to the different physical characteristics of other materials and, as might be expected of any batch chemical operation or otherwise discontinuous system,

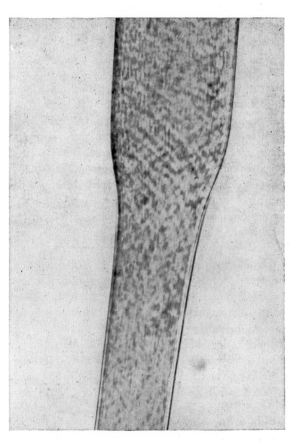

Figure 11.17. "Necking down" of nylon at point of drawing. (× 1000)

the manufacturers of nylon and melt-spun fibers have tended to develop a process which is continuous from polymerization to extrusion of the molten polymer at the jet.

When the extruded fibers emerge from the jet face into the relatively cool spinning chamber, rapid solidification takes place. In the case of those polymers which expand lengthwise by sorption of moisture from the air or some other source, this moisture must be supplied either by steam or by a wet surface before the fibers are wound onto a package. If this is not done, lengthwise expansion will produce a soft package of yarn commercially unacceptable. After solidification, an antistatic lubricant is applied to prevent static formation and to reduce friction in subsequent textile operations. Great care must be used in conveying the freshly spun yarn from the spinning chamber to the yarn package since it is easily "drawn." Drawing must be done as a separate operation under carefully controlled conditions to ensure uniformity.

When "staple" fiber is the desired product in a melt spinning operation, both the size of the jet and the number of holes are increased. The output of a group of jets is combined into a tow which, after drawing, is cut into short lengths.

Cold Drawing. It was learned early that the fibers made from polyamides and other high molecular weight linear polymers could be extended to about four times their original length with very little effort, their resistance to extension thereby being increased as well. It was discovered that during this high extension the entire length of fiber did not extend uniformly as the cross section decreased. Rather, a "necking down" occurred at one of several points, and when all the length under tension had passed through this phenomenon, a fiber of high strength was obtained. It was also found that more than one necking down in a given length of fiber caused discontinuity at the point where two came together. Accordingly, the cold drawing operation is aimed at forcing it to occur at a single point as the yarn advances from the supply package to the take-up package.

Cold drawing consists essentially of removing the yarn from the package prepared in the melt spinning operation and feeding it forward at a uniform, controlled rate under low tension. It is passed around a pulley or roller which determines the supply rate and prevents slippage; then it is wrapped several times around a stationary snubbing pin. From there it goes to a second roller which rotates faster than the supply roller to produce the desired amount of stretch, usually about 400 per cent. The necking down or drawing occurs at the snubbing pin. In the case of nylon 6, drawing may be effected satisfactorily without the yarn being passed around a snubbing pin.

In the drawing operation the long molecules of polymer, randomly positioned in the molten polymer extruded from the jet and solidified in the same random configurations in the freshly spun fiber, are so oriented that their lengthwise dimensions tend to be parallel with the long axis of the fiber. It is this orientation which converts the fiber having low resistance to stress into one of high strength.

By controlling the amount of drawing as well as the conditions under which this operation takes place, it is possible to vary the amount of orientation. A minimal amount is preferable in the manufacture of nylon for textile applications where elongation of considerable magnitude and low modulus or stiffness rather than high strength is required. On the other hand, strength and high modulus are at a premium when nylon is to be used

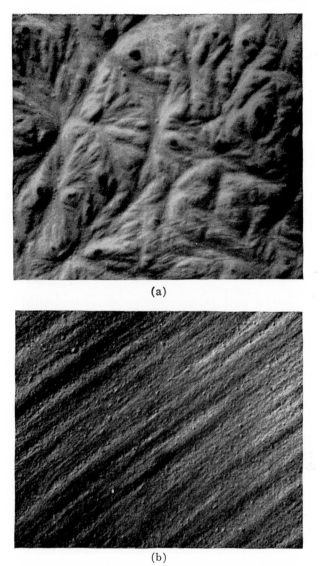

(a)

(b)

Figure 11.18. Electron micrograph of a) undrawn nylon;
b) drawn nylon. ($\times$ 42,000)

in tire cord. High resistance to elongation is imperative if the tire is not to
"grow" under conditions of use. In this connection it should be noted that
nylon tire cord that has been produced by twisting the original tire yarn
and plying the ends of these twisted yarns together is hot stretched just
before use at the tire plant to increase strength and reduces the tendency
to elongate under stress even more.

POLYESTERS

Historical

Just as the original work of Carothers regarding polyamides inspired research which resulted in the development of nylon 6 in Germany, so did the same stimulus result in Whinfield and Dixon's discovery of polyesters in England.[2] These men found that a synthetic linear polyester could be produced by condensing ethylene glycol and terephthalic acid, and that a fiber having valuable properties could be made from this polymer. Unlike nylon, this material has not been popularized under its generic name, polyester. Rather, the commercial fiber produced in England by Imperial Chemical Industries, Ltd. was named Terylene®, and the corresponding material in the United States has been called Dacron® by E. I. duPont de Nemours and Co.

Manufacture

When the development of polyethylene glycol terephthalate occurred, ethylene glycol was already being produced in large amounts from ethylene, a by-product of petroleum cracking. Synthesization is by oxidation of ethylene to ethylene oxide and subsequent hydration to ethylene glycol

$$CH_2{=}CH_2 + O_2 \rightarrow \overset{\displaystyle O}{\overset{\diagup\quad\diagdown}{CH_2{-}CH_2}} \xrightarrow{H_2O} HOCH_2CH_2OH$$

or via ethylene chlorohydrin

$$CH_2{=}CH_2 + HClO \rightarrow HOCH_2CH_2Cl \xrightarrow[NaHCO_3]{H_2O}$$
$$HOCH_2CH_2OH + NaCl + CO_2$$

On the other hand, although the orthophthalic acid, or rather its anhydride, had long been produced in enormous amounts for use in the manufacture of alkyd resins, the para derivative was less well known and not available on a large scale. The synthesis is a straightforward one, however, from para-xylene oxidized to terephthalic acid by means of nitric acid.

Unfortunately terephthalic acid is not easily purified to the high degree necessary in the manufacture of a polymer that is to be converted to white yarn. For this reason terephthalic acid is converted to dimethyl terephthalate which, after purification, is reacted with ethylene glycol to form the linear fiber-forming polymer.

Polyester is spun by equipment and in a manner not very different from the process used for nylon, already described.

Polyesters are drawn differently from nylon because they tend to crystallize. They are therefore hot drawn, the ratio being somewhat higher than that used for polyamides. Both may be drawn to varying degrees, however, to produce a range of tenacities, moduli, and breaking elongations. The fiber with low tenacity and high elongation is used for textile purposes; that with high tenacity and correspondingly low elongation is used for industrial applications.

HEAT SETTING

The ability of fibers to be "set" is not characteristic of man-made fibers only. Aided in many cases by the presence of starch, cotton fabrics may be ironed; the sharp crease in trousers has been commonplace for generations. However, when fabrics made from natural fibers are set by the application of heat and moisture, much of the effect is lost by washing or exposure to high relative humidity. With the development of nylon and the more recent man-made fibers (e.g., polyesters) came a more durable kind of setting. When these fibers, in fabric form, are exposed to elevated temperatures either in the dry condition or in the presence of water vapor, "heat setting," which depends on not only the temperature used but also the duration of the exposure, occurs. Thus a few seconds at 230° C will produce the same results as exposure for a considerably longer period at 50 to 75 degrees lower. The permanency of the setting, that is, the ability of a fabric to return after distortion to its original configuration even after drastic exposure to moisture and raised temperatures, is a function of the severity of heat setting. A compromise is again necessary since the higher the heat setting temperature the greater the danger of thermo-degradation and discoloration of the fabric.

TEXTURED YARNS

Fundamentally, the manufacture of "textured" yarns is closely related to the heat setting of fabrics, the only difference lying in the fact that the individual filaments or the bundle of filaments in textured yarns are distorted and then heat set. In some instances the objective is to distort the fibers in a more or less random way; at other times a regular pattern is desirable.

The first commercially successful textured yarn was produced by twisting nylon 66 more than the normal amount, heat setting it as a full package of yarn, and then untwisting through zero and applying a small amount of twist in the opposite direction. When such yarn is knitted or woven into fabric, the filaments tend to return to the spiral configuration in which they were originally heat set. This in turn converts the smooth flat fabric into a "stretch" fabric and gives the surface a textured appearance.

Forcing yarn into a heated tube by means of "nip" rolls so that it becomes highly crimped is another means of giving it texture. The yarn is held in this distorted condition while heat is applied to set it. After removal from the heated zone the yarn will tend to remain randomly distorted, with the individual filaments being bent at high angles, and extremely short lengths occurring between the bends. After being knitted or woven under tension into flat fabrics, these fibers tend to regain distortion, thereby giving the fabric a textured surface.

With fabrics made from textured yarns, whether the yarn has been produced by heating in the twisted or in the crimped condition, the final garment may be heat treated to stabilize the fabric in a desired geometric configuration. There are a number of variations of the texturing process; these, combined with heat setting, impart considerable versatility to the final product. Carpets are a significant market for such fibers since texture is one of their most outstanding characteristics. This versatility is important to the successful use and expanded development of nylon and polyester yarns.

ACRYLICS

Polymer Manufacture

Acrylic fibers are spun from polymers that are made from monomers of which a minimum is 85 per cent acrylonitrile. This compound is made from hydrogen cyanide and ethylene oxide through the intermediate of ethylene cyanohydrin

$$\overset{\displaystyle O}{\overset{\displaystyle \diagup\!\diagdown}{CH_2CH_2}} + HCN \rightarrow HOCH_2CH_2CN \xrightarrow[-H_2O]{catalyst} CH_2{=}CHCN$$

It may be made directly from acetylene and hydrogen cyanide

$$CH{\equiv}CH + HCN \rightarrow CH_2{=}CHCN$$

More recently, it has been reported to be made from propylene, ammonia, and air

$$CH_2{=}CHCH_3 + NH_3 + O_2 \text{ (air)} \xrightarrow[<500° C]{catalyst*} CH_2{=}CHCN + CO$$
$$+ CO_2 + CH_3CN + HCN$$

Pure acrylonitrile may polymerize at room temperature to polyacrylonitrile (PAN), a compound which, unlike polyamides and polyesters, does not melt at elevated temperatures but only softens and finally discolors and decomposes, and which is not soluble in inexpensive low boiling organic

* U. S. Patent 2,904,580 mentions bismuth, tin and antimony salts of phosphomolybdic and molybdic acids, and bismuth phosphotungstate, 425 to 510° C and atmospheric pressure or slightly above.

solvents. Since fibers made from it resist the dyeing operations commonly used in the textile industry, the usual practice is to modify it by copolymerization with other monomers, e.g., vinyl acetate, vinyl chloride, styrene, isobutylene, acrylic esters, acrylamide, and vinyl pyridine. The choice of

Figure 11.19. Acrilan plant, The Chemstrand Corporation. (*Courtesy The Chemstrand Corp.*)

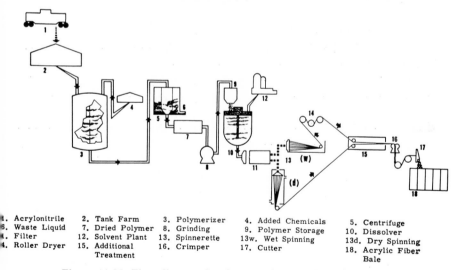

1. Acrylonitrile	2. Tank Farm	3. Polymerizer	4. Added Chemicals	5. Centrifuge
6. Waste Liquid	7. Dried Polymer	8. Grinding	9. Polymer Storage	10. Dissolver
4. Filter	12. Solvent Plant	13. Spinnerette	13w. Wet Spinning	13d. Dry Spinning
4. Roller Dryer	15. Additional Treatment	16. Crimper	17. Cutter	18. Acrylic Fiber Bale

Figure 11.20. Flow diagram for the manufacture of acrylic fiber.

modifier depends on the characteristics which a given manufacturer considers to be important in a fiber, the availability and cost of raw materials in his particular area of production, and the patent situation.

In copolymerizing acrylonitrile with another monomer, conditions must be so controlled that the reaction produces a polymer having the desired chain construction and length. Generally the reaction takes place in the presence of substances capable of producing free radicals. In addition, certain trace metals which have been found to increase reaction rates offer a means of controlling chain length. After an induction period the polymerization of acrylonitrile is rapid and gives off a considerable amount of heat, making bulk polymerization difficult to control. Since the polymer is not soluble in the monomer, a thick paste is formed which makes heat removal difficult. Conducting the polymerization in the presence of a large amount of water is a convenient method and the one most generally used. The polymer then forms a slurry, and the water provides a means for removing the heat from the site of the reaction. Moreover, most of the common redox catalyst systems are water soluble. Polymerization may involve either a batch or a continuous method ranging from a pipeline or moving batch type of operation to a simple batch overflow.

In the standard batch method the monomer and catalyst solutions are fed slowly into an agitated vessel containing a quantity of water. The heat of reaction is removed either by circulating cooling water through the jacket surrounding the vessel or by operating the reaction mixture at reflux temperature and eliminating the heat through the condenser water. The monomer and catalyst feeds are stopped when the reaction vessel is full, and the reaction mixture is allowed to continue to polymerize until there is a small amount of monomer present in the reaction mixture. Then the slurry is dumped from the reaction vessel, filtered, and dried.

In the moving batch or pipeline operation the raw materials are metered into one end of the pipe and polymerization proceeds as the mixture moves forward. The resulting polymer slurry emerges from the other end. This method requires exceedingly careful control of feed ratios and temperatures to maintain consistent polymer quality.

In the continuous overflow method, rather than stopping the monomer and catalyst feed when the reaction vessel is full, the slurry is simply allowed to overflow; the solids are removed by filtration and dried. The filtrate contains a larger amount of unreacted monomer which is recovered, after the catalyst is destroyed to prevent further polymerization, by steam distillation. The dried polymer, however produced, is the raw material from which fibers are spun.

Spinning

As already mentioned, polyacrylonitrile softens at elevated temperatures, and thermal decomposition starts before the molten state is reached. The same is true of its copolymers. Accordingly, melt spinning is impossible; spinning must be done from a solution of the polymer. Both dry and wet spinning are carried out in current commercial operations.

The principles which apply to either the wet or dry spinning of acrylics are essentially the same as those already described for rayon and acetate, respectively. The polymer must be completely dissolved in solvent and the solution filtrated for removal of any impurities which would cause jet blockage. Because acrylic polymers are not soluble in common non-polar solvents,[15] polar substances such as dimethyl formamide,[14] or solutions of inorganic salts[13] such as zinc chloride-calcium chloride mixtures[17] are

Figure 11.21. Spinning Acrilan tow. (*Courtesy The Chemstrand Corp.*)

required. Only wet spinning is possible with the latter. The details of spinning acrylic fibers by either wet or dry methods have not yet been described in the literature. Dimethyl formamide boils at 152.8° C and possesses a vapor pressure of 3.7 millimeters at 25° C as compared with acetone (used in dry spinning) which has a vapor pressure of 228.2 millimeters at 25° C. Unlike acetone which requires an activated carbon system for recovery, dimethyl formamide may be condensed directly from the air stream.

Acrylics, like rayon, require stretching either during spinning or immediately after fiber formation in order to obtain the desired characteristics of modulus, breaking tenacity, and breaking elongation. These same properties are influenced by spinning speed, temperature of the drying air if dry spun, or temperature and composition of the bath if wet spun.

In the 1940's and early '50's the tendency was to stretch considerably to produce fibers with high breaking tenacities and correspondingly low breaking elongations. Recently, breaking tenacity has centered around 2.5 grams per denier. However, because of the versatility of acrylic fibers, it is possible to obtain breaking tenacities and elongations over a broad range. It is also possible to vary the conditions of manufacture so that the product obtained has either dimensional stability in boiling water or relatively high shrinkage. When a mixture of dimensionally stable and unstable fibers are blended in a spun yarn and that yarn is used in the manufacture of fabric, the fabric will be dimensionally unstable. This is desirable for many applications. When such a fabric is dyed in boiling water, contraction and deformation of the fibers result in a tighter and thicker material with increased coverage and volume.

GRAFT POLYMERS

It is generally agreed that a "perfect" fiber which would fulfill the requirements of all applications is not obtainable since the characteristics required of one product may be diametrically opposite to those required of another. The ability of various vinyl derivatives to polymerize in pure form and, more importantly, to copolymerize with each other, makes possible a large number of fiber-forming materials with a wide variety of properties. The recent development of techniques for producing block and graft polymers has made the potential number almost limitless, offering particular promise in filling the gaps among mixed polymers and copolymers. At the same time, a complexity of chemical composition results. The ratios of monomers used become subordinated to the physical structure obtained and the process used. Neither the physical structure of the polymer molecules nor the process of manufacturing them is easily determined by examination of a fiber or study of its characteristics. Both are secrets closely guarded by the manufacturer.

A polymer which contains only identical repeating units, that is, a homopolymer, may produce a fiber with certain desired physical characteristics, such as high melting point, good strength, excellent elastic recovery from deformation, and the like. These properties are closely related to the structure of the linear polymer molecules. Inclusion by copolymerization of a second kind of monomer unit in the polymer chain in random position will radically affect such properties. If the homopolymer does not contain adequate dye sites it may be difficult or even impossible to use existing dye methods or equipment. However, if molecules having dye sites are grafted as occasional side chains onto the linear homopolymer to produce a graft polymer, dyeability may be obtained without substantially changing valuable physical properties. For example, the homopolymer secured by polymerizing an olefin is a hydrocarbon that possesses neither active sites for the attachment of dye molecules nor groups which tend to attach water molecules by hydrogen bonding. Thus selected side chains may be grafted for dyeability, an essential of any fiber in the apparel field.

The replacement of hydroxyls by acetyl groups in the cellulose homopolymer illustrates the effects of side chains. Although cellulose acetate is not a graft polymer in the true sense of the word, it may be considered an extreme form and may serve as an excellent example. Cellulose triacetate is soluble in chlorinated hydrocarbons (e.g., methylene chloride). The secondary acetate with about 2.4 acetyl groups per anhydroglucose units is soluble in acetone, and its solution possesses a minimum viscosity when 6 to 7 per cent water is present in the acetone. As the number of acetyl groups is decreased the amount of water in the acetone must be correspondingly increased to retain solubility. Finally an acetate is obtained which is water soluble. Further decrease of acetyl groups renders it insoluble in water as is the fully regenerated cellulose. Although both cellulose and cellulose acetate are easily dyed, direct dyes that are substantive to the former only stain the latter, whereas dispersed dyes act in a reverse manner.

In preparing graft polymers, similar selective behavior characteristics may be engineered into the material. Two approaches are used: a potentially chemically reactive group may be included in the main polymer chain; a few of the homopolymer units may be chemically or physically activated.

When dimethyl terephthalate and ethylene glycol are polymerized by condensation to produce the polyester, polyethylene terephthalate, a small amount of dimethyl terephthalate containing a potentially reactive group that does not react in the condensation itself may be added. Where "X" is about 10 to 40 and "A" is a reactive group that can be used to attach a side chain to the polymer chain at intervals equal to the length of $X + 1$ units, the repeating unit will be

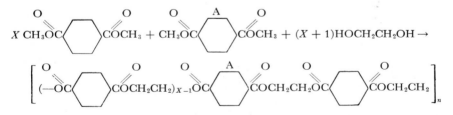

Similar results may be obtained from homopolymers modified by copolymerization with small amounts of a second component carrying a potentially reactive atom or group.

On the other hand, the homopolymer may be activated either by chemical or physical means. A monomer or polymer may be reacted with a chemically activated carbon atom in the main polymer chain to start the building of a side chain at that point. For example, polystyrene may be activated with a peroxide, a side chain being built from vinyl monomers. Or physical sources such as the gamma rays from Co^{60}, electrons from a Van de Graaf accelerator, or ultraviolet radiation may be used to form free radicals and bring about the formation of side chains on polymers.

VINYL FIBERS

Acrylics have already been defined as those fibers which employ a minimum of 85 per cent acrylonitrile in preparing the polymer from which the fibers are spun. At least two fibers reputed to contain less than this amount of acrylonitrile are in commercial production in the United States.

"Dynel"* has been mentioned as a copolymer of vinyl chloride and acrylonitrile in about the ratio of 60 to 40. It is dry spun from acetone and hot drawn. The vinyl chloride contributes both chemical resistance and nonflammability but it lowers the softening point to such an extent that normal household ironing conditions may prove harmful.

"Verel"† is reported to have about a 50 to 50 ratio of vinylidene chloride and acrylonitrile, with perhaps a small amount of a third component to contribute a higher moisture regain. Its properties, however, suggest that it is a graft polymer rather than a straight copolymer. It is dry spun from acetone. A new entry into the fiber field, it has become a minor blending fiber used in carpets.

Polyvinyl chloride and the chlorinated product are wet spun. These materials, used principally for blending purposes, have had greater success in Europe than in the United States. Their tendency to shrink at elevated temperatures has limited their applications. On the other hand, shrinkage has made them useful in novelty fabrics and felted structures. Chemical inertness has resulted in the development of a number of industrial applications for polyvinyl chloride fibers.

"Vinyon,"‡ a copolymer of vinyl chloride and vinyl acetate in the ratio 88 to 12, deserves special mention; although it is still produced in relatively small quantities, it is one of the first "fully synthetic" fibers. Developed about 1933, it was first produced in 1939 as a dry spun, wet-stretched fiber. Made into staple, it has become a specialty fiber used for bonding purposes.

"Saran"§ is a copolymer of vinylidene chloride and vinyl chloride, perhaps with a small amount of acrylonitrile present. A ratio of 85 to 13 to 2 has been suggested. It is melt spun and cold drawn into filaments commonly called "monofilaments," larger than those used in clothing fabrics. Because of its chemical and abrasion resistance, and ability to withstand weathering, "Saran" monofilaments are used for heavy fabrics in the chemical industry, in outdoor furniture, and in upholstery for seats in public transportation.

* Registered trademark, Union Carbide Chemicals Company.
† Registered trademark, Eastman Chemical Products, Inc.
‡ Registered trademark, Union Carbide Chemicals Company.
§ Registered trademark, Dow Chemical Company.

"Vinylon"* reached a production level of about forty million pounds in Japan in 1959 and has been introduced into the United States as vinal fiber. A shortage of most raw materials, including petroleum, natural gas, and cellulose, combined with the availability of electric power favors the production of this material in Japan. Acetylene made from calcium carbide is converted to vinyl acetate which, following polymerization, is saponified to polyvinyl alcohol.

$$CH{\equiv}CH + CH_3C{\overset{O}{\diagup}}{-}OH \rightarrow CH_2{=}CH{-}O{\overset{O}{\diagdown}}CCH_3$$

$$CH_2{=}CHO{-}{\overset{O}{\diagdown}}CCH_3 \xrightarrow[\text{catalyst}]{\text{heat}} ({-}CH_2CH{-}O{\overset{O}{\diagdown}}CCH_3{-})_n \xrightarrow[\text{H}_2\text{O}]{\text{catalyst}}$$

$$({-}CH_2CHOH{-})_n$$

This is soluble in hot water, and the solution so obtained is wet spun into a coagulating bath consisting of a concentrated solution of sodium sulfate. The fibers are heat treated to provide temporary stabilization so that they may be converted to the formal derivative by treatment with aqueous formaldehyde.

$$({-}CH_2CHOH{-})_n \xrightarrow[\text{heat}]{\text{CH}_2\text{O}} \text{to produce a polymer chain which probably}$$

possesses the unchanged groups, $-CH_2CHOH-$, the hemi-acetal groups, $-CH_2CHOCH_2OH$, the crosslinking acetal groups,

and the cyclic acetal groups,

$$-CH_2CHCH_2 \qquad CH-.$$
$$\diagdown OCH_2O \diagup$$

This final product resists hydrolysis up to the boiling point of water. The bulk has been made in staple form. Thus far it has been difficult to make the continuous filament material sufficiently uniform to obtain level dyeing fabrics. This has limited the use of the continuous filament form to industrial applications. No doubt further research will solve the problems relating to dyeing. The development of extremely strong "Vinylon" yarns may lead to increasingly important applications.

POLYTETRAFLUOROETHYLENE

"Teflon"† is unique in that it is not soluble in any known solvent and will not melt below about 400° C, at which point it is not stable enough to allow

---

* Registered trademark, Kurashiki Rayon Company.
† Registered trademark, E. I. duPont de Nemours & Company.

spinning. Such a combination would seem to pose an impossible problem. Research into the fundamental characteristics of this polymer, however, revealed that the submicroscopic particles precipitated from the polymerization reaction were about 100 times as long as they were thick. When a thin stream of a suspension of polytetrafluorethylene is extruded and the dispersion broken, the particles line up to form a discrete filament which possesses sufficient strength to allow transportation to a sintering operation. The fiber so obtained has an adequate tenacity (1.5 grams per denier) for ordinary textile handling, knitting, and weaving.

The chemical inertness and thermal stability of this material is so great that in spite of its extremely high price ($6.60 per pound in 1961) it is used in chemical operations where drastic conditions exist and no other organic fiber is suitable.

GLASS

The use of glass fibers in the textile industry has increased rapidly in recent years. First developed on a commercial scale in the late 1930's, production rose to only about 8 million pounds in 1949. By 1959 however, the output had reached almost 150 million pounds per year. In regard to this last figure it should be noted that because of its high specific gravity, about twice as many pounds of glass fibers are required per yard of fabric as organic materials.

Glass is melt spun, but because it retains considerable strength even in the molten state, it is drawn out of orifices in a jet rather than extruded by means of pressure on the melt. The speed is very high, and the filaments are generally much finer than those of organic polymers.

Because of its nonflammability, glass fiber is used in industrial and electrical insulating, and for drapery and decorative fabrics in homes and public buildings. The combination of high strength and modulus, perfect elasticity, and chemical inertness makes glass fiber a good reinforcing medium in plastics. It is used for thermal insulation in the form of batting.

POLYOLEFINS

Polyethylene has been melt spun and cold drawn as monofilaments for some years. However, the discovery of the "low pressure" variety with its higher softening point, and the spur of activity in the entire field of polyolefins, has increased interest enormously. Even low pressure polyethylene is limited to specialized uses since its softening point (120° C) precludes use where household ironing is required. Since the corresponding isotactic polypropylene has a melting range of 165° to 175° C, considerably nearer the temperatures of electric irons, it appears this material will quickly replace the otherwise similar polyethylene.

Four companies in the United States have announced their intentions to produce polypropylene fibers. Two or three companies outside the United States are, or soon will be, producing this fiber. In view of the cheap raw material from petroleum refining, low specific gravity (less than 1.00), and excellent strength, it is to be expected that the current problems of poor dyeability, waxy hand, and slow relief of applied stress will almost certainly be solved.

Research on the polymerization of ethylene and propylene to form stereo regulated polymers has stimulated corresponding investigations of many other vinyl-type monomers. Although this work is still in its early stages and more effort will be required before the results can be applied to the field of industrial chemistry, it is not too early to report that progress is being made in the desired direction. Raised melting points is one characteristic which is being improved; it may be assumed that this new area of investigation will provide unexpected contributions.

SUGGESTED FURTHER READING

For an excellent and recent treatment of the subject of man-made fibers, the reader is referred to "Man-Made Fibres" by R. W. Moncrieff, 3rd ed., New York, John Wiley & Sons, Inc., 1957, reprinted with additions, 1959.

Both man-made and natural fibers are covered in "Textile Fibers," Herbert R. Mauersberger, editor, sixth edition, New York, John Wiley & Sons, Inc., 1954.

The Marburg Lecture, "Textile Fibers, An Engineering Approach to an Understanding of their Properties and Utilization," given by H. D. Smith before the ASTM and published in the ASTM Proceedings, 1944, is considered a classic.

There are a number of books covering specialized aspects of fibers.

Other Reference Books for the Advanced Student

1. Hague, Douglas C., "The Economics of Man-made Fibres," London, Gerald Duckworth and Co., Ltd., 1957.

2. Harris, Milton, "Handbook of Textile Fibers," 1st ed., Washington, D. C., Harris Research Laboratories, Inc., 1954.

3. Hartsuch, Bruce E., "Introduction to Textile Chemistry," New York, John Wiley & Sons, Inc., 1950.

4. Hermans, P. H., "Physics and Chemistry of Cellulose Fibres," New York, Elsevier Publishing Company, Inc., 1949.

4a. Hill, Rowland, ed., "Fibres from Synthetic Polymers," New York, Elsevier Publishing Company, Inc., 1953.

5. Kaswell, Ernest R., "Textile Fibers, Yarns, and Fabrics," New York, Reinhold Publishing Corporation, 1953.

6. Meredith, R., ed., "The Mechanical Properties of Textile Fibres," Amsterdam, North Holland Publishing Company, 1956.

7. Woods, H. J., "Physics of Fibres," London, The Institute of Physics, 1955.

8. Weber, F., and Martina, A., "Die neuzeitlichen Textilveredlungsverfahren der Kunstfasern," Vienna, Springer-Verlag, I, 1951; Erganzungsband, 1954.

9. McFarlane, Samuel B., ed., "Technology of Synthetic Fibers," New York, Fairchild Publications, Inc., 1953.

REFERENCES

1. Bradshaw, W. H., and Denyes, R. O., "Spinning of Filamentary Materials," U. S. Patent 2,732,586.
2. British Patent 578,079.
3. Calkin, John B., ed., "Modern Pulp and Paper Making," 3rd ed., New York, Reinhold Publishing Corporation, 1957.
4. German Patent 748,253.
5. Mark, H., and Whitby, G. S., "Collected Papers of W. H. Carothers," New York, Interscience Publishers, Inc., 1940.
6. Markham, J. W., "Competition in the Rayon Industry," 16, Boston, Harvard University Press, 1952.
7. Mersereau, H. C., *Can. Chem. Process Ind.*, **29**, 808–813 (1945).
8. Ott, Emil, ed., "Cellulose and Cellulose Derivatives," 2nd ed., Part II, 825–863, Interscience Publishers, Inc., 1954.
9. Smith, D. K., "High Strength Regenerated Cellulose Fibres," *Textile Research J.*, **29**, 32–40 (1959).
10. Smith, L. H., ed., "Synthetic Fiber Developments in Germany," 375 *et seq.*, Textile Research Institute, 1946.
11. Ibid, 388, 394.
12. "Development of Some Man-Made Fibres," Textile Institute, Manchester, England, 1952.
13. U. S. Patent 2,140,921.
14. U. S. Patent 2,404,713.
15. U. S. Patent 2,404,723.
16. U. S. Patent 2,539,586.
17. U. S. Patent 2,882,253.

12

ANIMAL AND VEGETABLE OILS, FATS, AND WAXES

In collaboration with H. G. Kirschenbauer*

FATTY ACIDS

THE ANIMAL AND VEGETABLE OILS, fats, and waxes are esters of organic acids belonging to the fatty acid series, so called because of their presence in fats. An ester is formed by the combination of an alcohol and an acid, with the elimination of water. The animal and vegetable oils and fats are glycerin (really, glycerol) esters of a wide variety of fatty acids in which the glycerin is the alcohol; the waxes are esters of the same kind of acids and an alcohol other than glycerin. The fatty acids belong chiefly to three or four subdivisions: to the saturated series (stearic acid), to the oleic series (unsaturated, lacking two hydrogen atoms), or to more unsaturated series lacking four and more hydrogen atoms.

The glycerides of the saturated series melt higher than those of the oleic series. A fat is rich in glycerol-stearate and has some glycero-oleate admixed; an oil is rich in glycero-oleate and lean in glycero-stearate. Among the glycerides of the saturated acids, however, a further consideration must be made. One molecule of glycerin requires three molecules of acid to form an ester. If the three acid residues are the same, the fat is rather hard; thus glycero-tristearate, called stearin for short, melts at 72° C. If the three acid

* Colgate-Palmolive Company.

residues are unlike, the fat has a lower melting point; thus glycero-distearate-monopalmitate melts at 63° C.

$$
\begin{array}{cccc}
CH_2\text{—}OH & & CH_2\text{—}O\text{—}OCH_{35}C_{17} & \\
| & & | & \\
CH\text{—}OH & + \ 3C_{17}H_{35}COOH \rightarrow & CH\text{—}O\text{—}OCH_{35}C_{17} & + \ 3H_2O \\
| & & | & \\
CH_2\text{—}OH & & CH_2\text{—}O\text{—}OCH_{35}C_{17} & \\
\text{Glycerin} & \text{Stearic acid} & \text{Glyceryl-tristearate} & \\
\text{(an alcohol)} & & \text{(an ester)} &
\end{array}
$$

Each oil and fat contains a number of different fatty acids, sometimes as many as ten, six or more being the rule; this makes the study of the composition of an oil difficult enough. The complications of mixed esters such as glycero-distearate-monopalmitate increase the difficulty still more; it is therefore not surprising that there are some oils and fats the compositions of which have not been fully determined.

The study of the composition of oils and fats is based on a knowledge of the constituent fatty acids, a number of which are listed in Table 12.1 with the names of oils and fats in which they occur. The latter are merely examples, for each fatty acid occurs in a large number of oils and fats.

The fats belong to the broad class of lipids and have been classified as simple, compound, and derived lipids. The compound lipids include the phospholipids, such as lecithin and cephalin. The simple lipids comprise the fats and waxes. These occur together with fats, usually in minor amounts, and other important compounds. These include the fat-soluble vitamins A, E, D and K, cholesterol, other alcohols, and certain hydrocarbons. Most of these are contained in the "unsaponifiable" fraction of fats and oils.

Vegetable fats and oils occur predominantly in seeds and the flesh of some fruits (olive and palm), but they are also found in the roots, branches, stems, and leaves of plants. In some seeds, for instance in most cereals, the fat occurs almost exclusively in the germ. Fats are also produced by certain bacteria, molds, and yeasts. The important animal fat depots are subcutaneous tissue, abdominal cavity, liver, and intermuscular connective tissue. The bones (bone grease), and particularly the feet and skin bones of cattle (neat's foot oil) and other animals, also contain appreciable amounts of fat. The mechanism of fat formation in the plant is not yet known. Fat in the animal body may originate from ingested fat, from carbohydrate, and also from protein in a manner not fully understood. There is evidence indicating that the highly unsaturated fatty acids, linolenic and linoleic, cannot be synthesized by the body. Because of their importance to the animal body, these acids are known as the essential fatty acids. Fats are digested by the action of the bile with the assistance of enzymes. Because of the strongly acid nature of the gastric juice, no appreciable digestion of the fats takes place in the stomach. Hydrolysis of fats, therefore, takes place in the small intestine by the combined action of the bile and the pancreatic enzyme steapsin. Inside the intestinal walls, fatty acids and glycerol recombine and are carried by the lymph fluid into the blood stream. As nutritional agents, the fats liberate more than twice the amount of calories per weight unit than proteins or carbohydrates.

The important procedures of commercial production of fats are rendering, pressing, and solvent extraction. In the rendering process, the fat is recovered by heating the fat-containing tissue. Rendering is applied almost exclusively to the production of animal fats and oils. Fat recovery by pressing is generally applied in the production of vegetable fats and oils, with the exception of palm oil which is obtained by methods similar to rendering. The two important variations of pressing which have been practiced are: (1) batch methods by application of hydraulic or other presses, and (2) continuous production using expellers. In many instances, such as the production of soya oil, solvent extraction is used extensively.

The purification of crude fats and oils to remove suspended, dispersed, and dissolved foreign matter which show up as free fatty acids, color, odor, and saturated glycerides, is accomplished by a variety of methods. In some instances only one or two of the purification steps are applied; in others, as, for example, in the production of salad oils, all of them may be employed. Removal of finely dispersed or colloidally dissolved matter includes elimination of meal, protein, and carbohydrate matter, as well as water. It may be done by gravity-settling or centrifuging, often after the oil has been heated. Free fatty acids are usually deacidified or removed by adding an aqueous solution of caustic soda or sodium carbonate to the heated fat charge. The aqueous soap phase, also known as foots or soap stock, which is formed during the treatment, is separated by gravity-settling or centrifuging. It contains undesirable impurities often present in the crude fats.

Adsorbents are generally used for the removal of coloring constituents. These include fuller's earth, activated clays, and charcoals. The adsorbents are added in finely pulverized form to the heated oil charge with good agitation and preferably in the absence of air. For the removal of the "spent bleach" the charge is finally pumped through filter presses. For inedible fats, a chemical bleach is often used, with oxidizing or, to a lesser extent, reducing agents. Adsorbent bleaching removes some of the odoriferous constituents of the treated fats, but usually not to a satisfactory degree. Deodorization equipment has therefore been developed in which the odor-causing volatile constituents are extensively steam-distilled from the heated fat charge using a relatively high vacuum. Such a unit is shown in Figure 12.1. Basically, the deodorizer consists of a tower containing several sections. The oil enters the top section of the tower where it is deaerated by heating to 300°–320° F under an absolute pressure of 6 mm Hg. From here it flows down to the next section where it is heated to 460°–490° F, thence downward

TABLE 12.1. SOME IMPORTANT FATTY ACIDS

SATURATED FATTY ACIDS

Number of carbon atoms	Systematic name	Common name	Melting point, °C	Boiling* point, °C	Methyl esters* bp, °C	Occurrence
4	Butanoic	Butyric	−7.9	162	...	Some milk fats
6	Hexanoic	Caproic	−3.2	206	15/2	Milk fats. Small amounts in Palmae seed fats
8	Octanoic	Caprylic	16.3	239	45/2	Palmae seed fats. Milk fats
10	Decanoic	Capric	31.3	269	77/2	Palmae seed fats. Milk fats. Sperm head oil
12	Dodecanoic	Lauric	43.9	130/1	100/2	Seed fats of Lauraceae, Palmae. Milk fats. (Coconut oil 50%)
14	Tetradecanoic	Myristic	54.4	149/1	114/1	Myristicaceae, Irvingia seed fats. Minor amounts in most fats
16	Hexadecanoic	Palmitic	62.9	167/1	136/1	In nearly all fats. (Palmoil 40%)
18	Octadecanoic	Stearic	69.6	184/1	156/1	Widely distributed
20	Eicosanoic	Arachidic	75.4	204/1	...	Minor amounts in Leguminosae seed fats. (Rambutan tallow 35%)
22	Docosanoic	Behenic	80.0	...	...	Minor amounts in various seed fats. (Ben seed oil 6%)
24	Tetracosanoic	Lignoceric	84.2	...	...	Minor amounts in various seed fats. (Peanut oil 1%)
26	Hexacosanoic	Cerotic	87.7	...	...	In plant waxes, seldom in fats
28	Octacosanoic	Montanic	90.9	...	...	Beeswax and other waxes
30	Triacontanoic	Melissic	93.6	...	...	Beeswax and various other waxes.

UNSATURATED FATTY ACIDS, ONE DOUBLE BOND

10	9-Decenoic	Caproleic	...	142–8/15	115–6/12	Milk fats of the ruminants
12	9-Dodecenoic	...	...	...	...	Milk fats of the ruminants
14	9-Tetradecenoic	Myristoleic	...	...	108–109/1	Seed fat of Pycnanthus Kombo (23%). Whale oil, depot fats. Milk fats of the ruminants
16	9-Hexadecenoic	Palmitoleic	−0.5 to 0.5	...	134–5/1	In nearly every fat, often in small amounts. (Marine oils 15–20%)
18	6-Octadecenoic	Petroselinic	30–33	208–210/10	...	Umbelliferae and Araliacae. (Parsley seed oil 75%)
18	9-Octadecenoic	Oleic	16.3	153/0.1	152.5/1	Most common of all acids. Probably 40% of total fatty acids. (Almond oil 77%). (Olive oil 75%)
18	11-Octadecenoic	Vaccenic	39.5 (trans)	...	...	In small amounts in certain animal depot and milk fats
20	9-Eicosenoic	Gadoleic	23.5	...	...	Marine oils
20	11-Eicosenoic	Gondoic	...	...	...	Marine oils
22	11-Docosenoic	Cetoleic	...	...	...	Marine oils
22	13-Docosenoic	Erucic	33.5	241–3/5	169–170/1	Tropaeolaceae and Cruciferae. (Rape oil 50%)
24	15-Tetracosenoic	Selacholeic (Nervonic)	40.0–42.5	...	...	Many Elasmobranch fish. Brain cerebrosides
26	17-Hexacosenoic	Ximenic	...	...	...	Ximenia seed oils. Tallow wood oil
30	21-Triacontenoic	Lumequic	...	...	...	Seed fat of Ximenia americana (5%)

TABLE 12.1. (Continued)

Number of carbon atoms	Systematic name	Common name	Melting point, °C	Boiling point, °C	Methyl esters bp, °C	Occurrence
UNSATURATED FATTY ACIDS, 2 DOUBLE BONDS						
10	2,4-Decadienoic	Stillingic	...	...	...	Stillingia oil (5%)
18	9,12-Octadecadienoic	Linoleic	−5.	202/1.4	149.5/1	Widely distributed. (Cottonseed oil 45%)
20	11,14-Eicosadienoic	...	...	...	...	Brain phosphatides
22	13,16-Docosadienoic	...	...	...	...	Rape oil
UNSATURATED FATTY ACIDS, 3 DOUBLE BONDS						
16	6,10,14-Hexadecatrienoic	Hiragonic	...	180–190/15	...	Sardine oil
18	6,9,12-Octadecatrienoic	...	...	...	...	Some seed fats of the Evening-Primrose Family
18	9,12,15-Octadecatrienoic	Linolenic	−11	157–158/0.001 0.002	184/4	Many drying oils. (Linseed oil 35–65%)
20	5,8,11-Eicosatrienoic	...	...	...	...	Brain phosphatides
20	8,11,14-Eicosatrienoic	...	...	...	...	Liver oil of a shark species
22	7,10,13-Docosatrienoic	...	...	...	...	Brain phosphatides
UNSATURATED FATTY ACIDS, 4 AND MORE DOUBLE BONDS						
16	4,8,11,14 or 4,9,12,15-Hexadecatetraenoic	...	...	...	...	Sardine oil
16	6,9,12,15-Hexadecatetraenoic	...	...	...	...	South African Pilchard oil

UNSATURATED FATTY ACIDS, 4 AND MORE DOUBLE BONDS (Continued)

18	4,8,12,15-Octadecatetraenoic	Moroctic	...	...	...	Sardine oil
20	5,8,11,14-Eicosatetraenoic	Arachidonic	−49.5	...	...	Adrenal, brain and liver phosphatides. Small quantities in many animal fats
20	8,11,14,17-Eicosatetraenoic	...	...	...	...	Brain and liver phosphatides
20	5,8,11,14,17-Eicosapentaenoic	...	...	...	...	Brain lipides
22	4,7,10,13-Docosatetraenoic	...	...	...	...	Brain phosphatides
22	4,10,13,16-Docosatetraenoic	...	...	...	...	Organ phosphatides
22	7,10,13,16-Docosatetraenoic	...	...	...	...	Brain phosphatides
22	4,7,10,13,16-Docosapentaenoic	...	...	...	...	Brain phosphatides
22	7,10,13,16,19-Docosapentaenoic	...	...	...	...	Brain phosphatides
22	Docosapentaenoic-Docosahexaenoic mixture (Position of double bonds uncertain)	Clupanodonic	...	...	160–175/1	Sardine oil
22	4,7,10,13,16,19-Docosahexaenoic	...	...	...	...	Brain phosphatides
24	4,8,12,15,18,21-Tetracosahexaenoic	Nisinic	...	...	...	Sardine oil

TABLE 12.1. (Continued)

Number of carbon atoms	Systematic name	Common name	Melting point, °C	Boiling point, °C	Methyl esters bp, °C	Occurrence
UNSATURATED FATTY ACIDS, CONJUGATED DOUBLE BONDS						
18	cis 9, trans 11, trans 13-Octadecatrienoic	Eleostearic (alpha)	49	235/12	...	Rosaceae and Euphorbiaceae. [Tung (China Wood) oil 72–82%]
18	cis 9, trans 11, cis 13-Octadecatrienoic	Punicic (alpha)	44	...	...	Pomegranate seed oil (72%) and snake gourd oil
18	18-Hydroxy, cis 9, trans 11, trans 13-Octadecatrienoic	Kamlolenic (alpha)	77–78	...	...	Euphorbiaceae. (Kamala oil 59%)
18	4-keto, cis 9, trans 11, trans 13-Octadecatrienoic	Licanic (alpha)	75	...	...	Rosaceae. (Oiticica oil 75%)
18	9,11,13,15-Octadecatetraenoic	Parinaric (alpha)	86	...	...	Rosaceae and Balsaminaceae. (Seed fat of Parinarium laurinum 56%)
SUBSTITUTED UNSATURATED FATTY ACIDS, HYDROXY OR EPOXY GROUP						
18	12-Hydroxy-9-Octadecenoic	Ricinoleic	5.5	...	...	Euphorbiaceae. Oleaceae (Castor oil 91–94%)
18	9-Hydroxy-12-Octadecenoic	...	...	...	...	Apocynaceae. (Seed oils of strophantus genus 7–14%)
18	12,13-Epoxy-9-Octadecenoic	Vernolic	...	...	...	Compositae. Euphorbiaceae. (Seed fat of Vernonia anthelmintica 70%)

No.	Systematic name	Common name				Occurrence
18	6-Octadecynoic	Tariric	50.5	...	...	Simarubaceae. Several species of the genus. Picramnia sow 90%
18	11-Octadecen-9-ynoic	Ximenynic (Santalbic)	...	...	...	Olacaceae—Santalaceae and Santalum species (40–95%)
18	17-Octadecen-9,11 Diynoic	Isanic (Erythrogenic)	...	...	...	Olacaceae, Isano oil (principal acid)

BRANCHED-CHAIN FATTY ACIDS

No.	Systematic name	Common name				Occurrence
5	3-Methylbutanoic	Isovaleric	−51.0	177	...	Dolphin and porpoise depot fats
19	10-Methylstearic	Tuberculostearic	11	...	...	Lipide of tubercle bacillus
16	11-(2-Cyclopentenyl)-Hendecanoic	Hydnocarpic	60.5	...	203/20	Hydnocarpus seed fats
18	13-(2-Cyclopentenyl)-Tridecanoic	Chaulmoogric	68.5	...	227/20	Hydnocarpus seed fats
18	13-(2-Cyclopentenyl)-6-Tridecenoic	Gorlic	6.0	...	219/12	Hydnocarpus seed fats

Hydnocarpic: $R \cdot (CH_2)_{10} \cdot COOH$
Chaulmoogric: $R \cdot (CH_2)_{12} \cdot COOH$
Gorlic: $R \cdot (CH_2)_6 \cdot CH : CH \cdot (CH_2)_4 \cdot COOH$

$$R = \begin{array}{c} CH = CH \\ | \qquad \quad CH- \\ CH_2 - CH_2 \end{array}$$

to the initial deodorizing section—a series of trays where it flows counter-current to stripping steam. This section is also maintained at 6 mm Hg. Next, the oil flows down to a soaking section where certain reactions occur which are important in preventing reversion of the oils. Final deodorization is conducted under vacuum on another series of stripping trays located below the soaking section. The deodorized oil is cooled, filtered, and sent to receiving tanks. "Winterizing" is carried out for the partial removal of

Figure 12.1. A large con-
tinuous fatty-oil deodorizer.
(*Courtesy Blaw-Knox Co.*)

saturated glycerides. Some oils, such as cottonseed oil, which are clear and completely liquid in summer, are converted into milky-looking products of undesirable appearance and consistency because of precipitation of saturated glycerides at winter temperatures. To eliminate this, salad oils and certain glyceride lubricating oils are "winterized" by slow-chilling in suitable tanks. After the oils have been kept for a considerable time at a suitable low temperature, the crystallized glycerides are separated from the liquid oil in a refrigerated chill room with the aid of filter presses.

The commercial conversion of glycerides into free fatty acids and glycerin has been termed "fat splitting." The processes in use are almost exclusively of a hydrolytic nature, and the presence of water is therefore essential. At ordinary temperature, water and oil are poorly soluble in each other, and hydrolysis proceeds extremely slowly. Catalytic agents greatly accelerate the rate of reaction and therefore have found extensive application. At temperatures above 200° C the solubility of water in fatty oils and fatty acids is increased to an extent that allows hydrolysis to proceed quite rapidly, even in the absence of catalysts, and it is at these high temperatures that the continuous countercurrent splitters operate. The mixtures of fatty acids obtained by the splitting of various fats are often fractionated by distillation, crystallization, or solvent extraction. If it is desirable to separate acids of different chain length, for example, lauric acid from palmitic acid, fractional distillation may be employed. If, on the other hand, acids are to be separated that have the same chain length, such as stearic, oleic, and linoleic, each of which has 18 carbon atoms but are distinguished by the degree of unsaturation, fractional crystallization or solvent extraction must be used.

The refined fats are further processed and often considerably modified in the various fat industries. The three principal consumers of fats and oils are the edible fat, soap and detergent, and paint and varnish industries. The chief chemical modification process in the edible industry is hydrogenation, where liquid oils, such as soya or cottonseed oils, are partially hydrogenated and converted into solid shortenings or margarine materials. The soap industry's principal modification is conversion of the fatty glycerides into soap with the release of an important by-product, glycerin. The paint and varnish industry processes suitable oils into paints, varnishes, and other protective coatings so formulated and treated that they will "dry" satisfactorily on use. This hardening process consists of oxidation and polymerization.

There are many other methods of processing and modifying fats and oils; a few are mentioned here. Esterification of fatty acids is commercially important, e.g., in the production of partial esters of polyvalent alcohols. Ester interchange or directed interesterification is employed to rearrange the distribution of the fatty acid radicals of certain glycerides to adapt their physical properties to specific uses. Oxidation of unsaturated fatty acids may produce hydroxy acids or may split the chain with the formation of shorter chain mono- or dicarboxylic acids. Epoxidation of unsaturated acids has recently become a commercial practice; for instance, epoxidized soya bean oil is now produced and used as a plasticizer for certain resins. Sulfonation of castor oil and other suitable oils has been practiced for many years in the production of Turkey Red oils. For the production of modern detergents, fatty alcohols as well as monoglycerides have been sulfated on a large scale. The fatty alcohols used in these sulfation reactions are produced in large tonnage from fats or oils by high temperature catalytic reduction, or by reduction with metallic sodium and short chain alcohols.

The most important vegetable oils are cottonseed, linseed, soybean, olive, corn, peanut, rape, coconut, palm, and castor. The method of extraction is similar for all. The fruit or seed, after cleaning by sieving and blowing, or by hand selection, is crushed and first cold-pressed for the highest grade, then pressed warm for technical grades; the crushed mass may be extracted still further by solvents. In the case of edible oils, the first grade is used for food purposes; the lower grades are used for technical purposes, including the making of soap. In order to be edible an oil must be attractive; it must possess an agreeable flavor (olive oil) and must be free from disagreeable odor. It must be pale in color, usually yellow; it may be without attractive odor, yet be wholesome and well suited for food. The oils used as salad oils in the United States are olive oil, mainly imported, corn oil, peanut oil, and cottonseed oil. The chief use of linseed oil is in varnishes and paints; of rape oil in lubricants; and of coconut and palm oils in soap-making. Soybean oil, a comparative newcomer, is available in edible grade as well as technical grades suitable for use as paint vehicles, and for other purposes. Vegetable fats are mostly artificial, being made from the oils, such as cottonseed oil, by hydrogenation.

Animal oils and fats include: (1) whale oil and fish oil which are hydrogenated to fats used in part for soap stock; (2) lard and lard oil; (3) beef, mutton, and sheep tallow; fish-liver oils used for pharmaceutical purposes; and (4) sperm oil, a liquid wax used for lubrication. The method of extraction is essentially a warming so that the oil may run off or be pressed out.

It will be noted that nothing has been said about distillation; none of the oils and fats can be distilled under atmospheric pressure without at least partial decomposition. They are called fixed oils, as distinguished from the odoriferous oils which are frequently distilled. The oils obtained from petroleum may also be distilled, but they remain well characterized as one group because of their mineral origin. In discussing paints and varnishes, one adopts the point of view of the people in that industry and speaks of drying, semidrying, and nondrying oils. It is the state of unsaturation, indicated for certain fatty acids in Table 12.1, which permits the so-called drying because of oxidation and polymerization; it is the same unsaturation which is relieved in another fashion by hydrogenation.

To compare successive shipments of the same oil, and to detect adulteration, a number of tests are applied, some of which are very old. In the Maumené test, the heat caused by the addition of sulfuric acid is measured. The saponification test shows how much potassium hydroxide is consumed in forming the potassium salt of the fatty acid; an admixed mineral oil would not consume any caustic and would thereby be detected. The iodine value gives a measure of the unsaturation.

In addition to these time-honored methods, many modern analytical procedures are now used in the fat and oil field, particularly in connection with various research problems. For instance, intricate chromatographic methods have been worked out for the separation of lipids. Radioactive tracers have been used in connection with studies regarding fat metabolism, soil removal in detergency, and many other investigations. Also, instrumentation analysis has found wide application. X-ray diffraction methods are used for the phase study of fats and soaps, and the electron microscope has been

TABLE 12.2. DOMESTIC CONSUMPTION OF SOME IMPORTANT
FATS & OILS, 1957*

Primary Fats and Oils, by Principal Use	Millions of Lb
Edible	
Butter	1363
Lard	1813
Margarine	1452
Cottonseed oil	1313
Olive oil	55
Soybean oil	3052
Tallow	247
Drying Oil Products	
Castor oil dehydrated	19
Linseed oil	437
Oiticica oil	11
Tung oil	45
Tall oil	545
Other	
Coconut oil	614
Other lauric acid oils	48
Cod and fish liver oils	19
Fish and marine oils	134
Palm oil	43
Tallow, inedible and grease	1623

* *The Fats & Oils Situation*, Agricultural Marketing Service, United States Department of Agriculture, No. 188–193 (1958).

employed to investigate the structure of paint films, as well as in connection with many other problems. Ultraviolet spectrophotometry is used extensively to measure the presence of conjugated double bonds in fatty acids.

The extraction of linseed oil will be described in detail; the procedure for other seed-oils is similar.

LINSEED OIL

Linseed oil is made by pressing warmed flaxseed which has been previously crushed. The main product is the oil, but an important by-product is the press cake, which makes a valued cattle food.

The flaxseed is stored in elevators in much the same manner as grain. For the expression of the oil, the seed is elevated to the top of a five-story building so that in subsequent operations it may be fed by gravity. First it passes horizontal screens which remove all coarse admixed matter; then it is fed to a rotary bag blower with numerous small conical bags. These are connected periodically and automatically with compressed air, which blows out the chaff and small dirt. The clean seed is carried by a screw conveyor to one of a number of large storage bins; the crushing rolls are situated underneath on the next floor. Flaxseed is so slippery that if a man steps into a tall bin he will go through the seed to the bottom. The seed is small, about 3 mm long, 2 mm wide, and 1 mm thick, so that it will escape through the bottom of a farm wagon unless the boards are brought tightly together.

The crushing device consists of 5 heavy steel rolls placed in a vertical line; the two upper rolls are corrugated. Three rolls are driven, the first, third, and fifth; the second and fourth are idle. The speed is 175 rpm. The seed from the bin is fed by gravity to the top roll; by means of small troughs, the meal is collected from one roll and fed to the next, making four passages in all. A completely mashed product which has lost all trace of shape is the result.

The mashed meal passes by gravity to a two-stage steam-jacketed kettle of moderate size provided with slow agitation (30 rpm). The meal enters the kettle in the center of the first shelf and passes to the second shelf through circumferential openings. It is drawn from here onto the filter press plates (generally horizontal) of a hydraulic press, with hair mats above and below each plate charge. When the press is closed (30 shelves), the oil runs off into gutters to a main trough in the floor, and from there to collecting tanks. The press cake, resembling a stiff board and still retaining 5 to 6 per cent oil, is broken into small pieces by a rotating cylinder with projections, and then made into a powder in squirrel-cage disintegrators rotating at extremely high speeds.

The hydraulic press method has been partly superseded by the oil expeller, generally two-stage, in which rotating screw elements (worms) compress the cake against a grid of heavy steel bars, forming a cage through the spacings of which the oil escapes, while the worm moves the pressed cake to the discharge point. Unlike the hydraulic press, the operation of the oil expeller is continuous. Expellers are usually set up in batteries of 4, 8, 10, or more; the mashed meal from the crusher moves along in an overhead screw conveyor, with down spouts to the pressing machines. Each expeller consists of a horizontal cooker surmounting a short vertical worm and cage (the hopper feeder), which itself surmounts the main horizontal worm barrel (see Figure 12.2). In the steam-jacketed cooker, the meal is moved by a screw conveyor to the first vertical barrel in which the worm turns at perhaps 46 rpm, compressing the seed and delivering oil which runs off through the spaces in the grid. The partly pressed meal now enters the main horizontal barrel, wherein the pressing is continued with the worm turning at perhaps 21 rpm, the oil running off to the horizontal gutter. The cake is discharged at the far end and is made into pressed cake meal, having an oil content of not more than 3.7 per cent in a 10 per cent moisture cake. It is high in proteins and is a valuable livestock feed which has become so important that the fluctuations in its price are reflected in the price of linseed oil.

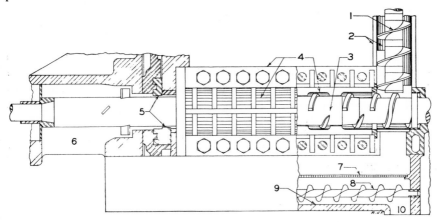

Figure 12.2. The working principle of the Anderson expeller: (1) vertical worm-shaft unit which receives the warm crushed seed from the cooker (not shown); (2) vertical barrel and spaced barrel bars; (3) horizontal integral main wormshaft (note interrupted flights); (4) horizontal barrel and spaced barrel bars; (5) upper and lower choke jaws; (6) discharge of exhausted cake in chip form; (7) screen for collection of settlings; (8) crude oil expeller screw; (9) bed for oil collection; (10) crude oil exit. (From sketches obtained from the V. D. Anderson Company, Cleveland, Ohio, with slight modifications)

The expeller method has the advantage of lower operation cost than the hydraulic press method.

Refining the Oil

The oil from the press, filtered through duck and flannel filter cloths in a plate-and-frame press, is the raw linseed oil of commerce; it is yellow-brown in color.

Large quantities are refined further by gentle heating for definite periods to remove moisture, and by the addition of fuller's earth followed by filtering through duck, flannel, and thick paper. The heating must be carefully regulated in order to avoid darkening the oil. The effect of the fuller's earth is partly to bleach the oil and partly to assist in the removal of finely suspended matter, called the "foots." For many purposes the oil must be "blown" to give it body, that is, to raise the viscosity. This may be done by heating with steam coils and blowing in air for certain periods. The blowing is usually followed by filtration.

Although linseed oil will "dry," that is, harden on exposure to air through oxidation and polymerization, such drying is too slow for practical purposes. The drying is greatly accelerated by adding small amounts of the oxides of lead, manganese, or cobalt, and then heating the oil under reduced pressure; the product is "boiled linseed oil," which dries in a few hours. The metals act as oxidation catalysts.

Linseed oil is used primarily as a vehicle in paints, varnishes, and enamels.

Not only flaxseed, but many other seeds are pressed for their oil in the hydraulic press or the expeller. About 25 per cent of the soybean oil in the U. S. A. is produced by pressing and the remainder is obtained from the beans by solvent extraction. One of the advantages of solvent extraction is that a more nearly exhausted residue is left; the extracted meal contains only about 1 per cent oil, compared with the press cake and press meal having 5 to 6 per cent. At times when the oil is in great demand, this advantage would weigh heavily.

OTHER VEGETABLE OILS

Olive Oil

Because of its flavor, olive oil is the most highly prized of the edible oils. The olive tree is cultivated in Italy, southern France (Provence), Spain, Algeria, Tunis, and southern California. In general, the fruit is picked just before it is ripe; its content of oil varies from 35 to 60 per cent. The pressing for the highest grade is done cold, sometimes with the stone, other times after the stone has been removed. One of the several methods used for the recovery of the oil proceeds as follows: The fruit is packed in muslin bags and placed in a cylindrical cage surrounded by a sheet-steel envelope to catch the squirting oil. A heavy cylinder is applied from above; the force is gradually increased by means of a hand-operated screw. The oil collects in the floor trough. The color is pale yellow.

The pulp is mixed with cold water and pressed again, best with hydraulic pressure, and a second quality of edible oil is obtained. Made up with hot water, still another quality of edible oil is secured. Finally the pulp is extracted with carbon disulfide, which gives a dark product suitable for soap making. There is a difference in composition in the various grades. The free fatty acids resulting from hydrolysis are less than 1 per cent in the highest grade, 5 per cent in the next grade, and as high as 20 per cent in the technical grade.

Olive oil contains mainly the glyceride of oleic acid, an unsaturated acid; it is a non-drying oil.

Peanut Oil

This oil is a very acceptable substitute for olive oil. It is obtained by pressing the peanut, or earth-nut; in Europe it is called arachis oil, from the name of the plant, *Arachis hypogoea*. The seeds or nuts contain 43–46 per cent oil. The shells and skins are removed and the nuts are ground in squirrel-cage disintegrators. The ground nuts are first cold-pressed; about 18 per cent of the oil is obtained by this operation. This product has a pleasant nutty flavor and is used for salad oil. Two additional expressions, performed at higher temperatures, provide technical grades of oil.

Corn Oil

When starch is made from corn (maize) the kernel is obtained as a by-product which, on pressing in the same way as flaxseed, yields an oil and a press cake which is a cattle food. The corn seed contains 50 per cent oil; when it is pressed cold, a pale yellow product is obtained which has a slight odor that is removed by refining. This oil finds a market as a salad oil. The lower grades are used for soap-making, and to a limited extent in paints and varnishes.

Palm Oil

The best grades of palm oil are edibile. The fresh fruit is pressed slightly warm, and a pale yellow, butter-like material is obtained; its consumption is limited to the natives of West Africa,* where the palm *Elaeis guineensis* grows. The greater part of the oil is obtained by allowing the fruit to ferment in holes in the ground, then either pressing the softened fruit, or boiling it in water and collecting the oil which rises. The oil so obtained is suitable only for technical purposes, largely soap-making. Several other varieties of palms are cultivated in South America and worked for oil.

The palm kernels, collected separately, yield a soft fat, the palm-kernel oil, of different composition from palm oil. The kernels are generally imported by Europe and the United States and utilized with modern working methods.

Cottonseed Oil

The second largest production of vegetable oil in the United States is that of cottonseed oil; only the production of soybean oil surpasses it.

The cottonseed contains 20 per cent oil. How much seed is available may be judged from the fact that two pounds of seed are available for each pound of cotton. The cottonseed shell is first freed from adhering short cotton fibers, the linters, an article of commerce of some importance. Next, the shell is cut by rotary knives and separated from the seed proper in a

---

* Except for a small quantity placed in some margarines for color.

wire-gauze basket which rotates, letting the seeds pass through and retaining the hulls. The decorticated seeds are crushed and pressed; crude cotton-seed oil, red or brown in color, is obtained. It is refined by warming with a solution of caustic soda, which removes much of the color and neutralizes the free fatty acids. The caustic solution forming the lower layer is run off, and the remaining oil is washed. On standing in the cold, solid glycerides separate and are removed by filtering under pressure. The oil may be bleached further by adding fuller's earth and filtering; edible grades are prepared in this way. It is used to some extent as an oil and to a constantly greater extent for hydrogenation, which gives cooking fats. It is also used in making butter substitutes. Formerly it was used primarily for making hard soap; to some extent soybean oil has displaced it. Cottonseed oil is a semi-drying oil.

In addition to seed-pressing mills, plants for the solvent extraction of cottonseed are increasing in number. The main piece of equipment in such a plant is the extractor, a vertical cylindrical column with shelves which have alternately central and peripheral openings to permit the descending solid matter to pass.* Arms and plows from a central shaft sweep the shelves at a very slow rate. The column is filled with solvent (here hexane), which enters near the base and leaves, loaded with oil, near the top. The cotton-seed mash is introduced near the top, travels downward, and is exhausted at the bottom. The treatment of the oil-rich solvent and of the exhausted mashed seed is not unlike the similar solution which has been discussed under linseed oil, or the description which follows under soybean oil.

Another solvent which has been used in seed oil extractions is isopropanol.[1]

Coconut Oil

The cocoa palm grows in South America, India, Cochin China, in the Philippine Islands, and other countries. The fruit is imported in the dried condition under the name of copra. The oil is expressed at 60° C, and is edible, either as such or mixed in margarines. The press cake is a cattle food.

Soybean Oil

The soybean has been the important crop in Manchuria for years. It was not raised in the United States to any extent until 1924, when its culture was recommended and vigorously promoted so successfully that in 1959, production stood at 538,000,000 bushels. It has increased still further since then. Over 30 states have soybean acreage; the four which head the list are Illinois, Missouri, Indiana, and Iowa.

The soybean pod contains from two to four beans, which vary in size and color with the plant. The Manchurian edible soybean is pale brown, and

* Allis-Chalmers Manufacturing Company.

about the size of a large pea. Other varieties include the U. S. No. 2 Yellow, the Virginia brown, the black soybean, and the domestic pale brown bean somewhat smaller than the best selected Manchurian edible. On an average, the bean contains 20 per cent oil. Modern methods of expressing the oil are by the two-stage Anderson expeller (already discussed under linseed oil), by the hydraulic press, and by solvent extraction. A method for such extraction, with specific reference to the soybean but applicable to other beans and seeds, after preliminary study, is as follows:

The beans are cleaned, cracked, heated, and then flaked on flaking rolls. Extraction of the oil from the flakes takes place in an extraction tower, essentially an upright vapor-tight steel box in which an endless belt carrying baskets with perforated bottoms and solid sides moves slowly up one side and down the other, like a bucket elevator. The solvent is hexane. As the baskets travel upward, a stream of fresh solvent fed in at the top of the casing reaches the top basket, wets its flakes and dissolves the last of the oil, then drains through the bottom to the basket below it, where the wetting and partial extraction are repeated. In this fashion the solvent with its oil travels downward, countercurrent to the flakes which travel upward. The nearly exhausted flakes receive the fresh, hence most active, solvent.

The oil-containing solvent collecting on the up side of the boot is pumped to the top basket on the descending side. The basket is freshly loaded with new, unextracted flakes, which are thus wetted and partly deprived of their oil. The liquid in the first basket drains through the perforation in the bottom to the second basket, and from there to the third, finally reaching the lowest one. The extraction here is on the concurrent principle. The oil-rich solvent is collected on the down side of the boot. In moving from the down side of the elevator to the up side, the baskets remain upright because they are free to swing in the chain and to retain the upright position. At the top of the up trip, the baskets dump their load of exhausted flakes to a conveyor for further treatment. A charge of fresh flakes is fed into the empty basket, which starts on its extraction trip once more.

The solvent-oil solution is screened, filtered, heated, and flashed twice, once at normal pressure, the second time at a reduced pressure; it then enters a combination evaporator-distilling column, with vertical evaporator tubes in the upper part and bubble-cap trays in the lower part, and with steam entering near the bottom. The solvent-free oil discharged from the bottom is cooled and forms the crude soybean oil, which is stored or shipped as such, or refined further. The vapors from the column and flash chambers are condensed, and the liquid solvent so recovered is used over again. The exhausted, solvent-bearing flakes travel to two steam-jacketed cookers, where the solvent is expelled, thence to two further cookers operated at higher temperatures, in which the flakes are "toasted" in multi-floor kettles provided with agitator sweeper arms. Finally, the flakes are cooled, ground and bagged for shipment, or mixed with other materials for special livestock feed.

The secret of the success of the process lies in the flaking, which exposes the bean material to the solvent while producing a fragment having enough strength to prevent it from disintegrating to a powder. The mass in the baskets remains permeable to the solvent.

Some of the crude soybean oil is made into boiled soybean oil; much of it is made into oils for lacquers, light paints, enamels, ink oil, oil for chocolate coatings, and for a long list of other specific uses, all in addition to the edible grade. The meal is made into pellets of various sizes (pea size, sheep size, and others), with or without additions, for livestock feed. Selected whole bean shipments are made into flour and other valuable products for human consumption.

One of the methods for refining a crude vegetable oil is the *Solexol* process, in which propane under pressure is the solvent. Its dissolving power varies with temperature; at its critical temperature (200° F) it dissolves the good oil only, leaving other materials undissolved. By varying (lowering) the temperature, a separation of materials is attained. Thus crude soybean oil will yield refined soybean oil, and separately, pigment-lecithin. Further fractionation of the refined oil yields edible oil, paint oil, and a sterol concentrate.

Castor Oil

Castor oil is obtained from the seed of the castor plant, *Ricinus communis,* which grows in the West Indies, India, and other tropical countries. The seed contains 45–50 per cent oil. The best grade, the cold-pressed oil, is widely used as a mild cathartic. Other grades, valuable as lubricants, are mixed with mineral lubricating oil. Castor oil is a non-drying oil; it is a plasticizer for Celluloid and for lacquers.

Soluble caster oil or Turkey Red oil is sulfonated castor oil. Concentrated sulfuric acid is mixed with castor oil at temperatures not exceeding 35° C; after some time, a small amount of water is added and the dilute acid formed, which separates as a lower layer, is drawn off. The sulfonated oil is washed with a sodium sulfate solution, and ammonia is added in amount insufficient to neutralize the remaining acid but sufficient so that the oil gives a clear solution with water. The more important uses of Turkey Red oil are as textile lubricants and assistants in the dyeing of textiles.

Dehydrated castor oil was developed and manufactured over the war years 1941–1946 as a substitute or "lengthener" for tung oil, the importation of which was stopped by the war with Japan. Castor oil consists mainly of the triglyceride of ricinoleic acid, which contains a hydroxyl group; the removal of a molecule of water leaves an unsaturation which, together with the unsaturation already present, gives the resulting oil excellent drying properties. Large amounts of castor oil are dehydrated by heating in a vacuum in the presence of a catalyst. Water vapors pass out in an amount equaling 5 per cent of the weight of the oil:

$$CH_3(CH_2)_4CH_2 \cdot \overset{12}{C}H(OH) \cdot \overset{11}{C}H_2 \cdot CH : \overset{9}{C}H \cdot (CH_2)_7COOH$$

Ricinoleic acid or 12-hydroxy-9-octadecanoic acid

The dehydrated product consists of the triglyceride of 9,12-octadecadienoic acid, with two double bonds, and the triglyceride of 9,11-octadecadienoic acid, also with two double bonds,

$$CH_3(CH_2)_4CH_2 \cdot CH : \overset{11}{C}H \cdot CH : \overset{9}{C}H \cdot (CH_2)_7COOH$$

which are conjugated. The catalysts employed are suspended granules of alumina, silica gel, or fuller's earth. Other processes employ sulfuric acid, phosphoric acid, or sodium bisulfate for the catalyst.[2]

Styrenated oil is an example of the efforts to copolymerize the monomers styrene, butadiene, and methyl methacrylate with linseed oil, for example, producing drying oils with superior hardening qualities and increased alkali resistance, which are attractively priced. *Maleated* oils are unsaturated oils, such as linolenic acid, which have been made to react with maleic anhydride (at 250° F), with the production of a tribasic acid (the Diels-Alder reaction). The new acid may be esterified with a tri-, tetra-, or penta-functional alcohol to give an ester which carries unreacted functional groups which permit further reactions in the molecule with desirable results. Polyfunctional alcohols used include pentaerythritol (tetra-functional), sorbitol (hexafunctional), and mannitol.[2]

Rape Oil

Rape oil, *Brassica campestris,* is cultivated in Europe; seeds are also imported from India, and oil from Japan. The seed has 40–45 per cent oil; the treatment is similar to that of flaxseed, and the press cake is a cattle food. Rape oil has non-gumming properties and is used extensively as a mixed lubricant with mineral oil.

Sesame Oil

Sesame oil is of some importance in Europe. The sesamum seed is imported from China and India. The best grades are edible, either as salad oil or in margarine; the lower qualities serve for soap-making.

Chinawood Oil (Tung Oil)

The seeds (*Aleurites cordata*), in a nut the size of a small orange, contain 53 per cent tung oil. When it is pressed by native methods, 40 per cent of the oil is expressed. In China, this oil is used by the river men to impregnate the wood of boats and rafts in order to make them waterproof, hence the name, "China wood oil." This oil has gained appreciable importance in varnish making; it dries in one-third the time required by linseed oil, and has other valuable properties, including excellent resistance to sunlight. Chinawood oil consists primarily of the glyceride of elaeostearic acid. Some years ago tung trees were cultivated in some of the southern states, and the United States production of tung oil in 1957 was about 25,000,000 pounds. The main source of supply is still China, however.

Tall Oil

Tall oil is obtained as a by-product in the production of paper from pine wood. In the course of preparing kraft pulp, the cellulosic and non-cellulosic constituents are separated by digestion or cooking of wood pulp with caustic soda and sodium sulfide. The fatty acids and rosin acids, present in pine wood, are converted into soap by this processing; the soap is separated and the acids are recovered from it. If distilled, they are known as refined tall oil. Commercial vacuum fractional distillation has recently been improved so that a fairly sharp separation of rosin acids from fatty acids can be obtained by this processing.

Tall oil recovery has reached an annual production of over half a billion pounds. It is used mainly in the paint industry, but also for soaps, detergents, flotation agents, and many other products.

ANIMAL OILS AND FATS

Whale Oil

Whale oil was formerly an important source of oil for burning; the advent of petroleum products has relegated it to an insignificant position. The seats of the whaling industry are Norway, Iceland, and the American Pacific Coast.

A large whale yields between 100 and 180 barrels of oil; the blubber or fat is rendered either on board the boat or in the home port. The fat is chopped fine and rendered by heating first alone, then with water; certain parts of the carcass may also be digested for oil. Whale oil is used for leather dressing, burning oil, soap, and, mixed with mineral oil, for a lubricant. Whale oil is also hydrogenated to a fat.

Fish Oil[5]

Fish oil is obtained by boiling either the whole fish or selected parts in water and collecting the oil which rises. The menhaden, herring, and certain salmon are used in large numbers for this purpose, and many other fish in smaller numbers. The residue in the rendering pots is dried and sold for fertilizer. The Solexol process, mentioned earlier in connection with the refining of crude vegetable oils, has been adapted to the fractionation of menhaden oils. In 1953 there were six such plants in service. Approximately 65 million pounds of menhaden oil are expressed annually, about equal to sardine and herring oil combined. The principal outlets for fish oils are in the paint and varnish industry, and in soaps and edible products. The animal foods industry uses large quantities. Fish oils used as drying oils must

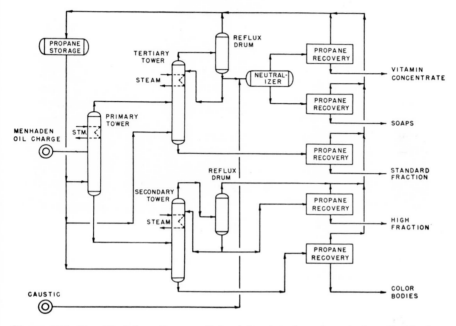

Figure 12.3. Simplified flow diagram, Solexol fractionation of menhaden oil. (*J. Am. Oil Chemists Soc.*)

be winterized and refined, while hydrogenation is required for soaps and edible products.[3]

A flow diagram of the Solexol fractionation of menhaden oil is shown in Figure 12.3. The same diagram applies in principle to the treatment of vegetable oils. A Solexol installation is illustrated in Figure 12.4.

Cod-liver Oil. The cods are brought alive to the home station in steam trawlers, opened, and the fresh livers heated in steam-jacketed kettles. The first oil is prized for its vitamin A and D content, and is used for medicinal purposes. On continued heating, a second grade of oil is obtained which is used in fine poultry raising. Livers which are brought in partly decomposed are rendered for an oil used in the dressing of leather.

Figure 12.4. A Solexol plant. (*Courtesy M. W. Kellogg Co.*)

The livers of many other fish, most important of which are halibut, tuna, and shark, are similarly treated.

Lard and Lard Oil

The bulk of the fat of the pig is rendered by heating it under pressure with water in closed cast-iron vessels provided with an outlet for the release of overpressure caused by the formation of gases. After digesting, the liquid is run off. Moderate cooling permits separation of the liquid lard oil from the solid lard.

In the circulating rendering process of Wurster and Sanger, Chicago, several desirable ends have been reached: (1) quick heating, which reduces the time factor and the objectionable yellow color; (2) low temperature, avoiding scorching; (3) larger capacity for a given time period.

The equipment for this process includes (1) a tubular heating element with vertical tubes through which the ground material passes, (2) flash chamber, (3) a circulating pump, (4) a separator, and (5) a vacuum pump. The tubes are heated by exhaust steam under 5 pounds pressure. The material is drawn from the base of the tubes by a centrifugal pump of the non-clogging type, and is returned at a point just above the tubes.

The heater is surmounted by a flash chamber in which the gases evolved are collected before they pass to a separator where the droplets of entrained fat are recovered, to be returned to the main drum. From the separator, the gases go to the steam ejector which maintains a low pressure on the system. After the material is completely melted it is discharged into a settling tank from which the clear fat is drawn off. The sediment, called cracklings, is run to a filter press.

With a heating surface of 1000 square feet, a charge of eight tons is rendered in two hours. Compared with the older type of jacketed melters using high pressure steam (50 pounds), the new rendering process equipment works four times as fast, and also produces a paler product.

Tallow

Tallow usually refers to beef tallow, which is rendered in the same way as lard. There is also mutton tallow, sheep tallow, and others, used mainly for soap-making.*

Butter and Oleomargarine

The cream in cow's milk isolated in a centrifugal separator is rich in small globules of fat which coalesce on churning; the lump so formed, after addition of salt (in the United States), is table butter; it is about 83 per cent butter fat; the rest is water and salt.

Oleomargarine† is a widely used composite food manufactured according to several recipes. It is made from pasteurized skim milk and vegetable oil, and fortified with vitamin A. Its composition is controlled to some degree by government specifications which require a minimum of 80 per cent fat, 2 to 3 per cent salt, 1 per cent nonfat milk solids, and approximately 16 per cent water. Colorants, flavoring, and preservatives may also be used in the blend, as well as lecithin (an antisticking agent), and monoglycerides or other emulsifying agents. In the United States, solidification conditioning of the margarine emulsion is now carried out almost exclusively in compact processing Votator units. Figure 12.5 is a 4500 pound per hour Votator unit which supplies three molding and packaging units. The margarine emulsion, comprising the appropriate refined and deodorized oils blended with the materials mentioned above, is pumped through a chilling unit where its temperature is reduced to about 50° F. From there it goes through an unagitated "B" unit—a tube about seven inches in diameter—where it slowly solidifies. Then it drops in noodle

---

* Lard, m.p. 36–40° C; tallow 40–45° C.

† "A Bread Spread Made Him Famous," brief story of the invention of the original margarine, by Mege-Mouries, Oilways, p. 21, April, 1948. "The Manufacture of Margarine," Andersen, A. J., *Trans. Inst. Chem. Eng. (London)*, **22**, 1 (1944); the same article in *Ind. Chemist (London)*, **20**, 82 (1944).

Figure 12.5. A single 4500-pound per hour Votator unit supplying three molding and packaging units. (*Courtesy Girdler Equipment Division, Chemstran Corp.*)

form into a screw hopper that pushes it into the molding head. The product is then immediately packed and sent out or stored.

WAXES

Sperm Oil

Sperm oil is obtained principally from the content of a cavity in the head of the cachalot or sperm-whale. When the oil is cooled it deposits a solid wax, the spermaceti, used in pharmacy and in candlemaking. Sperm oil is valued as a lubricant for light high-speed machinery; like rape oil, it has no gumming tendency. The chief ester in spermaceti is cetyl palmitate, $C_{16}H_{33}O \cdot OC \cdot C_{15}H_{31}$. Cetyl alcohol is a monohydric alcohol, $C_{16}H_{33}OH$. Sperm oil similarly contains alcohols combined with fatty acids different from glycerin.

Carnauba Wax

Carnauba wax is found on the leaves of a palm tree in Brazil, the *copernicia cerifera*. The leaves are gathered and rubbed to dislodge the coating. The wax is purified by melting, decanting from the deposit, and cooling. It has a high melting point, 105° C, and is used in the varnish industry, in furniture and shoe polishes, and in carbon-paper coating. It is the hardest wax known.

Beeswax

Beeswax is obtained from the honeycomb of the common bee; it is purified by washing and bleaching. Industrially, it is of small importance, though it is used in large quantities in the manufacture of church candles, many of which contain over 50 per cent beeswax.

Waxes are esters of monohydric alcohols—in a few instances, of dihydric alcohols—as contrasted with fats, which are esters of the trihydric alcohol glycerol (or glycerin). Any interest in waxes for the most part reflects an interest in their alcohol content. Wool wax has been studied, in part for its alcohol.

HYDROGENATION

The hydrogenation of oils with the aid of a catalyst is an important industry. The reaction is used mainly for hardening vegetable oils to edible fats; in the United States, cottonseed-oil hardening was developed first. Now, vegetable and fish oils are hardened to products, some edible and some suitable only for stock for soap manufacture and fatty acid preparation.

The general procedure is to suspend finely divided nickel in oil heated to 250–300° F (121–149° C), and to pump in hydrogen gas. The reactor is a tall cylindrical vessel almost filled with the oil mix, provided with a circulating pump which takes the oil at the bottom and returns it, for the main part, at the top. The part not returned is the product, which leaves as a side stream. The reactor or hydrogenator may have a turbine-type (or other) agitator with a vertical shaft entering from the top, or a propeller agitator entering at the side, below the liquid; or the agitation may be provided by a perforated pipe distributor at the base of the vessel. The returned liquid is generally sprayed in. The nickel is used in amounts 0.5–1 per cent of the oil; it may be introduced in the form of the oxide, which is soon reduced to the metal by the gas, or in the form of Raney nickel, obtained by treating a pulverized alloy of nickel and silicon (60 to 40, or 50 to 50) with caustic solution.[5] The finished product is filtered and stored warm, as a liquid; the recovered catalyst is mixed with fresh oil and used again. Palladium is a more effective catalyst than nickel; 1 part in 100,000 parts of oil is sufficient, and the reaction proceeds at a lower temperature and in less time. It is rarely used, however, because of its high cost. The catalyst may be supported on some inert medium, such as diatomaceous earth.

The hydrogenation reaction is exothermic for all oils, hence after the reaction is started, some of the oil circulated must be passed through an outside cooler. The product is removed after hydrogenation has proceeded to the desired point, which is conveniently determined by following its progress with a refractometer; it is cooled somewhat and, if desired, deodorized by passing carbon dioxide into the melted fat heated to 130° C (266° F) for an hour, or by some other method. On cooling, it is a soft solid, a semi-synthetic fat. It has been found advisable to hydrogenate until the desired melting point is reached and then to stop, rather than to hydrogenate to the limit and rely on mixing with fresh oil to attain the desired melting point. If completely hydrogenated, cottonseed oil would melt at 62° C (143° F). To be edible, a fat should melt below body temperature.

Among the oils, any glyceride which is unsaturated may be hydrogenated; for example, glycerotrioleate, a liquid, may be thus changed to glycerotristearate, a solid.

$$
\begin{array}{ll}
\mathrm{CH_2-O-OC \cdot H_{33}C_{17}} & \mathrm{CH_2-O-OC \cdot H_{35}C_{17}} \\
| & | \\
\mathrm{CH-O-OC \cdot H_{33}C_{17}} + 6H \rightarrow \mathrm{CH-O-OC \cdot H_{35}C_{17}} \\
| & | \\
\mathrm{CH_2-O-OC \cdot H_{33}C_{17}} & \mathrm{CH_2-O-OC \cdot H_{35}C_{17}} \\
\text{glycerotrioleate} & \text{glycerotristearate} \\
\text{(a liquid)} & \text{(a solid)}
\end{array}
$$

REFERENCES

1. *Chem. Eng.*, **54**, 8, 256 (1947).
2. *Chem. Industries*, **62**, 244 (1948).
3. Dickinson, N. L., and Meyers, J. M., *J. Am. Oil Chemists Association*, **XXIX**, 6, 235–39 (1952).
4. Lower, E. S., *Ind. Chemist (London)*, **20**, 319 (1944).
5. U. S. Pat. 1,563,587; 1,628,190; 1,915,473.

READING REFERENCES

1. Anderson, A. J. C., "Refining of Oils and Fats for Edible Purposes," New York, Academic Press, 1953.
2. Bailey, A. E., "Industrial Oil and Fat Products," New York, Second Edition, Interscience Publishers, Inc., 1951.
3. Deuel, H. J., Jr., "Lipids," New York, Interscience Publishers, Inc., 3 Vols., 1951.
4. Eckey, E. W., "Vegetable Fats and Oils," ACS Monograph #123, New York, Reinhold Book Publishing Corp., 1954.
5. Hilditch, T. P., "The Chemical Constitution of Natural Fats," New York. John Wiley & Sons, Inc., 3rd Edition, 1956.
6. Kirschenhauer, H. G., "Fats and Oils," Second Edition, Reinhold, 1960.
7. Markley, K. S., "Fatty Acids, Their Chemistry and Physical Properties," Interscience Publishers, Inc., 1947.
8. Mattiello, J. J., "Protective and Decorative Coatings," New York, John Wiley & Sons, 5 Vols., 1941–46.
9. Payne, H. F., "Organic Coating Technology," New York, John Wiley & Sons, Vol. I, 1954.
10. Sagarin, E., "Cosmetics; Science and Technology," New York, Interscience Publishers, Inc., 1957.

11. Waterman, H. I., "Hydrogenation of Fatty Oils," New York, Elsevier Publishing Co., 1951.
12. Adam, N. K., "Detergent Action and Its Relation to Wetting and Emulsification," *J. Soc. Dyers Colourists*, **53**, 121 (1937).
13. Adkins, H., "Hydrogenation: Role of the Catalyst," *Ind. Eng. Chem.*, **32**, 1189 (1940).
14. Markley, K. S., and Lynch, D. F., "The Technology of the Cottonseed-Crushing Industry," *Cotton Research Congr. Proc.*, **1**, 211 (1940).
15. Burr, G. O., and Miller, E. S., "Ultraviolet Absorption Spectra of Fatty Acids and Their Application to Chemical Problems," *Chem. Rev.*, **29**, 419 (1941).
16. Bailey, A. E., "Steam Deodorization of Edible Fats and Oils," *Ind. Eng. Chem.*, **33**, 404 (1941).
17. Robinson, W. M., "Fallen Animals, A Little Known Process Industry," *Chem. Met. Eng.*, **50**, 8, 112 (1943).
18. Piskur, M. M., "Review of Literature on Fats, Oils and Soap," *J. Am. Oil Chem. Soc.*, annually and in two parts.
19. Herrlinger, R., "Future of Tall Oil Industry as Refining Techniques Advance," *Southern Pulp Paper Mfr.*, **17**, 39–40 (October 1954).
20. "Full Scale Vegetable Oil Refining," *Chem. Eng. News*, **32**, 5106 (1954).
21. Henderson, B., "Chemicals From Castor Oil," *Can. Chem. Processing*, **39**, 94, 8 (October 1954).
22. Hilditch, T. P., "The Fats: A Story of Nature's Art," *J. Sci. Food Agr.*, **5**, 557–66 (December 1954).
23. Hutchins, R. P., "Some Improvements in Design in Solvent-Extraction Plants," *Am. Oil Chemists' Soc.*, **32**, 698–99 (December 1955).
24. Hawley, H. R., and Holman, G. W., "Directed Interesterification as a New Processing Tool for Lard," *J. Am. Oil Chemists' Soc.*, **33**, 29–35 (January 1956).
25. Mattson, H. F., "The Digestion and Absorption of Fat," *Food Research*, **21**, 34–41 (January–February 1956).
26. Wittka, F., "Hydrogenation of Fats," *Seifen-Ole-Fette-Wachse*, **82**, 353–54 (June 1956).
27. Eagle, Edward, and Robinson, H. E., "Fat, Cholesterol, and Atherosclerosis," *J. Am. Oil Chemists' Soc.*, **33**, 624–27 (December 1956).
28. Burner, A. H., "Recent Developments in Screw-Press Operations," *J. Am. Oil Chemists' Soc.*, **34**, 4–7 (January 1957).
29. Hartman, L., "Some Recently Discovered Constituents of Animal Fats," *J. Am. Oil Chemists' Soc.*, **34**, 129–31 (March 1957).
30. Schwitzer, M. K., "Continuous Processing of Fats," London, Leonard Hill Ltd., 1951.

13

SOAP AND SYNTHETIC DETERGENTS

In collaboration with J. C. Harris*

IT HAS BEEN SAID that the amount of soap consumed in a country is a reliable measure of its civilization. There was a time when soap was a luxury; now it is a necessity. The current manufacture of vast amounts of soap in every civilized country is possible only because new raw materials have become available through chemical science; the tallows and animal greases of the old days have been supplemented by coconut, palm, cotton-seed, and other oils. The "old days" are those when soap was practically the only detergent. Today syndets (synthetic detergents) account for greater than 70 per cent of all detergents used.

SOAP

Soap is the sodium or potassium salt of stearic and other fatty acids; it is soluble in water and the solution has excellent cleansing properties. Other metals such as calcium, aluminum, and lead also form compounds with fatty acids, but these compounds are insoluble and serve several purposes, e.g., lubricants in paints; they are always designated as "calcium soap," "lead soap," etc.

Soap is made by the action of a warm caustic solution on tallows, greases, and fatty oils, with the simultaneous formation of glycerin which at one time

* Monsanto Chemical Company.

was wasted or left in the soap, as it still is in certain cases; glycerin or glycerol is a valuable by-product. The reaction is as follows:

$$3NaOH + (C_{17}H_{35}COO)_3C_3H_5 \rightarrow 3C_{17}H_{35}COONa + C_3H_5(OH)_3$$

caustic   a typical fat   sodium stearate   glycerin
soda   glycero-stearate   (soap)
      or glyceryl stearate

Soap may also be made by the action of caustic soda on fatty acid without producing glycerin:

$$NaOH + C_{17}H_{35}COOH \rightarrow C_{17}H_{35}COONa + H_2O$$

caustic   stearic acid   soap
soda

The glyceride used is never a single one, but a mixture of several, hence the soap produced partakes of the properties of each. Sodium stearate dissolves too slowly, and the sodium soap made from coconut oil dissolves too fast; a mixture of the two has the right solubility. Mixtures of these fats affect and control other physical and use characteristics. The reaction may be performed in steel vats or kettles, in which a solution of caustic soda is mixed with the fat or oil, and heated; the soap is partially in solution in the water and must be separated by the addition of salt (NaCl). For high-grade soap, a steel tank with the upper part stainless steel, is used. The glycerin remains in the alkaline water and is drawn off at the bottom. The raw materials then are caustic soda or caustic potash (KOH), fats, greases and fatty oils, and salt.

Raw Materials

The caustic soda is usually received in drums of 700 pounds of solid caustic; this is made into a strong solution by inverting the opened drum over a steam jet with provision to collect the solution formed. The caustic may also be crushed and dissolved with occasional stirring. Caustic in flake form has advantages. Soap plants situated near an alkali factory receive the caustic in the form of a 50 or 24 per cent solution; for long distances this more convenient strength would mean a high freight bill. The caustic may also be made at the plant by causticizing soda ash with lime; this is rarely done. Caustic potash is usually received in drums as the solid. Bulk shipment of liquid caustic potash may be more economical.

Beef and mutton tallow of all grades are used, from the best No. 1 edible grade to the cheapest grade recovered from garbage; the grades chosen depend on the quality of the soap to be made. Tallow is not used without admixture with other fats or oils, for it gives a soap which is too hard and too insoluble; it is usually mixed with coconut oil.

Coconut oil is a solid (m.p. 20–25° C); it gives a soap which is fairly hard, but too soluble by itself. It is the basis of marine soaps, since it lathers even in salt water. According to the country of origin and to the manner of isolation, coconut oils differ in their content of free fatty acids: the lower the fatty acids, the better the quality of the oil; this applies to all fatty oils. Of the coconut oils, Cochin is the highest grade.

Palm oil is usually colored orange to brown, and has 6.0 per cent free fatty acids; it is an important raw material, and is used for toilet soaps. Palm oil may be bleached by warming it and blowing air through it. Palm kernel oil is an oil of light color. Castor oil is used for transparent soap.

Olive oil of the lower grades, no longer edible, is much favored by the soap maker; for fine toilet soaps, olive oil of the edible grade is used, but it is denatured by the addition of oil of rosemary, hence its import duty is low. Castile soap was originally a sodium-olive-oil soap, as was the Savon de Marseille.

In the refining of cottonseed oil, a treatment with a solution of caustic is the first step; the alkaline liquors contain the foots and are used in soap-making. Cottonseed oil itself is also used, usually combined with foots, or after being treated to form the free acids (Twitchell process).

The word "grease" to the buyer of soap stock means an animal fat, softer than tallow, obtained by rendering the carcasses of diseased animals, or from house and municipal garbage, from bones, and tankage. Rosin serves for laundry soaps.

Manufacture

Ordinary toilet soaps and laundry soaps may be made by the "boiled process," which is adapted to batches ranging from 1000 to 800,000 pounds; soap is also made by continuous saponification or neutralization of fatty acids. The "cold process" is used for special soaps.

Batch Kettle Soap. By the boiled process, a batch of 300,000 pounds of soap, for example, is made in a steel kettle 28 feet in diameter and 33 feet

TABLE 13.1. ESTIMATED WORLD CONSUMPTION OF INEDIBLE
TALLOW AND GREASE 1956*

Area	Total Consumption	1000 Pounds Toilet Soap	Laundry Soap
North America	1,871,121	425,377	653,872
Europe	1,424,161	317,635	670,991
South America	595,977	123,918	436,313
Asia	379,448	77,950	263,135
Africa-Oceania	324,599	65,850	256,250
Other	561,000	168,300	168,300

* Source—Preliminary, U. S. Dept. of Commerce.

deep, with a slightly conical bottom. A solution of caustic soda testing 18–20° Bé (12.6–14.4 per cent NaOH) is run into the kettle, and the melted fats, greases, or oils are then pumped (a Taber pump is suitable) in. The amount of caustic is regulated so that there is just enough to combine with all the fatty acids liberated. Heat is supplied by direct steam entering through a perforated coil laid on the bottom of the kettle. There is no stirrer, but agitation is provided by a direct steam jet entering at the base of a central pipe (Figure 13.1). The kettle is kept boiling until saponification is essentially complete; this requires about 4 hours. Salt (NaCl) is then shoveled in and allowed to dissolve, and the boiling is continued until the soap has separated, forming the upper layer. The lower layer contains glycerin (4 per cent) and salt, and is drawn off at the bottom of the kettle; its concentration is described under glycerin. The whole operation just described is termed

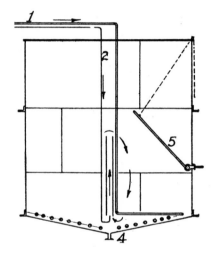

Figure 13.1. Kettle for soap by the boiled process: 1, steam inlet for the perforated steam coil; 2, steam for agitation; 4, run-off for lye liquors and glycerin liquors; the soap is pumped out through the swing pipe, 5.

the saponification change, and requires about 8 hours. The salt used is chiefly rock salt; most of it is recovered and used again.

On the second day, water and some caustic is run in and boiled with the soap; any glycerin caught in the soap is dissolved, and the solution, a lower layer again, is run off at the bottom and combined with the first glycerin water.

On the third day, a 10° Bé fresh lye (6.5 per cent NaOH) is run into the kettle and boiled with the soap. Any glyceride which escaped the first treatment is saponified; any uncombined free acid is neutralized. The soap, which is not soluble in the alkaline liquor, acquires a grainy structure. This is called the strengthening change. After settling, the lye is run off and used in a new batch.

On the fourth day, the soap is boiled with water, which is chiefly incorporated in the soap. (Some salt is added at this point.) By this treatment the melted soap acquires a smooth, glossy appearance. On settling, three layers are formed: the upper layer, the melted soap; the middle layer, or nigre,

TABLE 13.2. SOAP: FATS AND OILS USED, BY KIND, 1925–58*

Year, Average	Inedible Tallow and Greases, Million Pounds	Whale and Fish Oils, Million Pounds	Palm Oil, Million Pounds	Coconut Oil, Million Pounds	Palm Kernel Oil, Million Pounds	Other Hard Oils,[2] Million Pounds	Soft Oils,[3] Million Pounds	Secondary Fats and Oils,[4] Million Pounds	Rosin, Million Pounds	Tall Oil, Million Pounds	Total Saponifiable Materials, Million Pounds
1925–29	684	125	133	314	56	7	92	162	94	…	1,666
1930–34	695	107	175	332	17	4	64	171	106	…	1,670
1935–39	787	160	100	304	42	15	54	200	110	…	1,771
1940	1,043	108	85	397	[5]	43	47	170	80	…	1,972
1941	1,368	76	130	484	1	35	50	190	105	…	2,438
1942	1,528	72	56	140	1	20	53	190	99	…	2,160
1943	1,360	45	33	142	2	121	27	270	120	11	2,130
1944	1,530	51	20	132	4	243	28	303	193	29	2,534
1945	1,364	114	24	59	32	152	11	364	122	30	2,273
1946	1,210	40	7	185	19	46	16	335	75	25	1,957
1947	1,526	43	1	511	[5]	28	9	227	80	16	2,443
1948	1,451	35	1	417	3	25	9	181	53	18	2,193
1949[1]	1,346	10	1	282	[5]	27	10	156	40	14	1,887
1950	1,363	1	3	257	[5]	66	9	174	43	13	1,929
1951	1,195	…	3	197	…	41	9	149	38	22	1,654
1952	1,084	…	3	204	[5]	5	8	137	30	15	1,485
1953	1,026	[5]	4	175	23	[5]	6	135	20	14	1,403
1954	907	…	8	175	6	[5]	5	135	19	12	1,267
1955	864	…	12	173	5	5	6	116	18	14	1,213
1956	813	[5]	4	177	1	2	3	102	16	17	1,135
1957	789	…	2	173	…	1	1	98	9	12	1,086
1958[6]	727	…	1	161	…	…	1	86	7	12	995

[1] Prior to 1949, most of the fats and oils used in synthetic detergents were believed to have been reported as used in soap. Beginning 1949, this use of fats and oils was entirely included in "other inedible products" and thus is excluded from the figures shown in this table. [2] Includes beef fats, vegetable tallow, and babassu. [3] Includes the following oils: soybean, cottonseed, corn, castor, peanut, olive inedible and foots, edible olive, neatsfoot, linseed, perilla, sesame, tung, and other vegetable oils. [4] Includes inedible animal stearine, grease (lard) oil, tallow oil, foots and other soap stock, red oil, stearic acid, and other fatty acids. [5] Less than 500,000 pounds. [6] Preliminary.

* "Fats and Oils Situation," *Agricultural Marketing Service*, U. S. Dept. of Agriculture (March 1959).

432

dark in color, consisting of a mechanical mixture of soap in a soap solution and impurities; and a very small lower layer containing some alkali. The melted soap is pumped away by means of a swing pipe without removing the nigre; the latter may remain in the tank and be worked into the next batch; the small lower layer is wasted. This operation is the finishing change, and lasts several days because the settling must be very thorough. Approximately one week is customary for the entire cycle of operations.

The melted "neat" soap is pumped to dryers, crutchers, or storing frames; it contains 30–35 per cent water. One pound of fat or grease makes about 1.4 pounds of kettle soap; the factor varies with different raw materials.

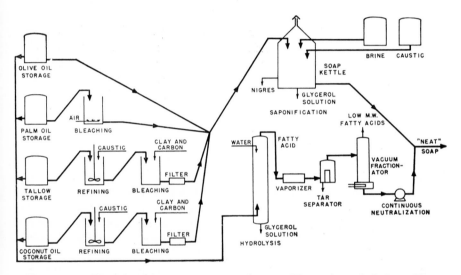

Figure 13.2. Flow sheet for neat soap manufacture. [*Taken from Ind. Eng. Chem.,* **49**, *No. 3, 338 (March 1957); copyright 1957 by the American Chemical Society and used by permission of the copyright owner.*]

Continuous Processing. Figure 13.2 shows an up-to-date pilot plant for "neat" soap manufacture, either by the conventional kettle method or as a continuous neutralization of hydrolytic fatty acids. Processing the fats prior to kettle boiling is indicated, the kettle charge being adjustable as desired. Similar adjustments may be made in the stock delivered to the continuous fat splitter where the fatty acids are separated from the glycerin. The fatty acid is passed through the vaporizer where tars and decomposition products are removed; the water-white fatty acids pass either directly to the continuous Stratco contactor for continuous neutralization, or they may be vacuum fractioned to remove low molecular weight or special acids, thence to the continuous neutralizer.

While fatty acid soap manufacture may be either batch or continuous, several continuous processes for manufacture from the fats have been developed.[5] The Monsavon process involves almost instantaneous saponification at 100° C of a previously colloid-milled emulsion of the fat in caustic solution. The soap flows across a column to a tank which acts as a buffer reservoir between saponification and washing, in which saponification is completed. Countercurrent washing takes place in six chambers. Constant 85° C temperature is maintained by a jacket in which water is circulated and thermostatically controlled. The arrangement also allows for recovery of heat of reaction to minimize heat input. The number of compartments may be increased for improved glycerin recovery.

A Sharples unit comprises each of the four steps of lye neutralization, completion of saponification, soap washing and glycerin recovery, and fitting to neat soap. Each of these sections consists of a pump-fed mixing unit and a supercentrifuge. The tank feeding the pump contains soap mass (called "reagent") from the preceding processing step; the mass is composed of the lyes returned from the following processing step to which have been added, if required, either caustic soda, saline solution, or water. The mass is conveyed by pump from the mixing unit to a supercentrifuge. The mixing vessel in the first section, slightly larger than the remaining ones permitting slightly longer contact time, is held at 100° C or slightly higher and under slight pressure. In this section are charged the fats and oils, fresh caustic soda, and the lyes from the second section. Neutral lyes result from the first section since saponification is incomplete, completion being obtained in the second step. Settling is usually completed on lye and not nigre, though it is indicated that nigre can be separated. Neat soap is separated by two parallel centrifuges. Proportioning pumps and flow control systems are integral parts of the unit.

The DeLaval "Centripure" soap process[35] consists of two stages, *viz.*, saponification and washing. In the process the fatty oils are fed into soap already present, improving the degree of mixing, the soap acting as a "catalyst" in the saponification. A centrifugal pump provides intense mixing, saponification reaching 99.8 per cent in two minutes passage time through one portion of the saponification column.

Correct soap phases are obtained by a definite excess of alkali to ensure complete saponification, and adequate control is provided in the system. Electrolyte content is carefully controlled to provide maximum mobility, and the mass is washed counter-currently with a carefully adjusted aqueous brine solution to provide a non-grainy or nigre soap form; the washing occurs in three stages, the neat soap and spent lye being separated in a Hermetic centrifugal separator. The lye is then available for glycerin separation. The washing, concentration of brine, and viscosity of the soap mass may be fully automated. Following the washing operations, deleterious substances, such as fat-soluble impurities comprising hydroxy and low molecular weight fatty acids, are still retained, and the fitting operation is designed to remove these and improve the milling properties of the soap. Investigation of the viscosity relationships as functions of percentage soap and sodium chloride provides data by which viscosity relationships with phase change may be determined. For a "hard" fitting, i.e., nigre with low soap-high electrolyte (1.2–1.4 per cent NaCl) content, viscosity measurements are used. After reaching the phase equilibrium for fitting, in the two columns, the fitted neat soap is separated by means of a Hermetic centrifuge. In the complete plant, the fitted soap then proceeds to an additive tower for mixing with builder or the like.

TABLE 13.3. CHARACTERISTICS OF GLYCERIN LYES OBTAINED BY DIFFERENT PROCESSES[2]

Percentages	Monsavon	Sharples	DeLaval	Kettle
Total alkali as N₂O	0.77	0.12	0.15–0.30	very variable
Glycerol	11	17 to 19	13 in two stages 18 in four stages	8–15
Fatty acids	0.2 plus oxidized acids			

Table 13.3 gives a comparison of the glycerin lyes obtained by several different continuous processes.

Batch-milled Toilet Soap. Neat soap is pumped from one of the kettles or from a soap storage tank to a paddle mixer or crutcher (Figure 13.3). Two of these mixers (mounted on scales) are provided for alternate use. In

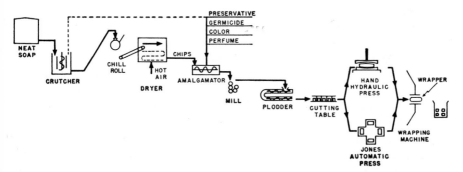

Figure 13.3. Flow diagram for toilet soap manufacture. [*Taken from Ind. Eng. Chem., 49, No. 3, 338 (March 1957); copyright 1957 by the American Chemical Society and used by permission of the copyright owner.*]

these, soap is mixed with preservatives or special additives and then pumped to a chilling roll located just ahead of the chip dryer. The chips leaving the chilling roll pass into a dryer where they make three passes through the hot air zone on a wire mesh belt before being discharged.

Chips from the dryer are collected in large four-wheeled carts having canvas walls and a cover, each holding about 1500 pounds of chips. These carts permit the chips to cool and reach a uniform humidity without any chance of sweating. The chips are dropped through the floor into a scale hopper and then discharged into a sigma-blade mixer called an amalgamator. Color, perfume, germicide, and other ingredients are added to the chips at this point and thoroughly mixed. The soap is made completely uniform by being put through a five-roll mill and a double-barreled vacuum plodder.

The extruded plodder bar is cut and pressed in dies. The bars are then automatically wrapped.

Continuous-milled Toilet Soap. In addition to the continuous process of toilet soap manufacture described under fatty acid utilization, a European process has been used extensively. The Mazzoni process,[30] instead of using the continuous belt dryer, utilizes a vacuum chamber into which the neat soap is sprayed, reducing the water content from 30 to 21 per cent. A scraper arm removes the soap from the sides of the chamber and pushes it into a plodder which extrudes the mass through the bottom. A continuously operated amalgamator is followed by two additional plodders, the last forming the final bar fed to an automatic cutter. A vacuum system is used between plodders, reducing the moisture content at each pass, finally giving a desired 12–15 per cent water content. The cut bar soap passes through a skin drying tunnel and then a cooling tunnel to the wrapper.

Laundry Soap. Though bar laundry soap is a rapidly disappearing sales item, it is still manufactured. The procedure for the boiled process is the same as that just described, but the raw materials are, for example, 4 parts tallow and greases, and 2–3 parts rosin. The latter is added, after the greases have been saponified, in the form of sodium resinate which is made in a separate kettle by the action of soda ash (which costs less than caustic) on the rosin. Saponification does not take place with rosin, which consists chiefly of abietic acid rather than glycerides; the formation of the sodium resinate is a neutralization.

The kettle soap for laundry is pumped from the kettle to a crutcher, which is a smaller tank (Figure 13.4) fitted with a special agitator and with a steam jacket; one of the following materials is added: silicate of soda, 41° Bé (with 40 per cent solids), up to 30 per cent; soda ash, 2 to 5 per cent, either alone or with borax, 1 per cent; or trisodium phosphate, up to 5 per cent. The mixture is crutched until homogeneous, and then run off at the bottom of the crutcher into a "frame," a box 4 feet high, 5 feet long, and 15 inches wide, with removable sides, two of metal and two of wood, and a base which is a small truck. The content of such a frame, of which there are hundreds, is 1000–1200 pounds of soap. A crutcher $4\frac{1}{2}$ feet high and $3\frac{1}{2}$ feet circular diameter has a capacity slightly greater than that of one frame. The content of the frame hardens in 3 days to a solid block; the sides of the box may then be removed. The block is dried somewhat and then cut into slabs which are, in turn cut into bars and pieces. The water content of the finished soap is 8–10 per cent.

Cold Process Soap. In order to make soap by the cold process, either a vertical crutcher like the one described in the discussion of laundry soap (capacity 1200 pounds), or a horizontal one of greater capacity may be used. The fat is run in and heated to 130° F (54° C) by the steam in the

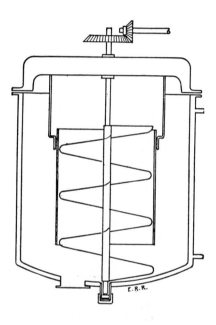

Figure 13.4. The soap crutcher.

jacket; then the lye is added and the mass agitated. The reaction is exothermic, so that the heat may be turned off at this point. After crutching for about an hour, the mixture stands for $3\frac{1}{2}$ hours; then it is agitated again, and again rested. The glycerin liberated remains in the soap, which is run off at the base of the crutcher into frames and milled as described in the section on milled toilet soap; alternatively, the perfume may be added in the crutcher and mixed with the mass there, at the end of the operation.

Sodium and potassium soaps mixed are always made by the cold process. Potassium soaps are soft soaps and cannot be salted out by NaCl since the sodium soap forms; neither can it be salted out by potassium chloride, KCl. The process is used for shaving soaps, toilet soaps, and special soaps; certain laundry soaps are also made by this method. Shaving soap is a potassium-sodium soap containing free stearic acid to give the lather a lasting property.

Granulated Soap. Granulated soap may be prepared as suggested in the flow sheet of Figure 13.5.

Miscellaneous Soaps. Transparent soap is made in a variety of ways. One method requires the best coconut oil, castor oil, and tallow, which are treated with caustic soda lye by the cold process; the glycerin remains, and cane sugar and alcohol are added.

A "soap powder" is a mixed soap and soda ash containing water in the form of crystal water, so that the powder is dry. The anhydrous soap content varies considerably (between 6 and 50 per cent) with appropriate

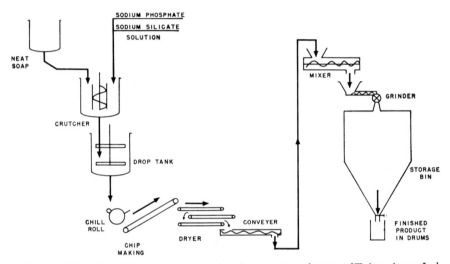

Figure 13.5. Flow diagram for granulated soap manufacture. [*Taken from Ind. Eng. Chem.,* **49,** *No. 3, 338 (March 1957); copyright 1957 by the American Chemical Society and used by permission of the copyright owner.*]

variations of soda ash and water. A typical soap powder contains 20 per cent soap, 40 per cent soda ash, and 40 per cent water (as crystal water).

Spray Drying

The boxed detergents offered to the consumer market are almost universally dried in spray towers, and have loose bulk densities of from 0.20 to 0.50 g/cc. The beads may be regular or irregular globules, the walls of which are either continuous or broken; the particle size varies from very small to relatively large, representing a distribution of sizes, and is free-flowing in character.

Spray drying is not a new art, apparently having been used successfully since the last quarter of the 19th century. The initial controlling patent in the detergent industry was that of Lamont,[27] and was the basis for several long and expensive infringement cases.

Several advantages of spray drying have been summarized:[29] control of product density within a range; control of particle shape and size; preservation of product quality. Heat-sensitive materials may be dried, high tonnages may be produced at costs comparable with other procedures, equipment corrosion or product contamination can be minimized, and spray

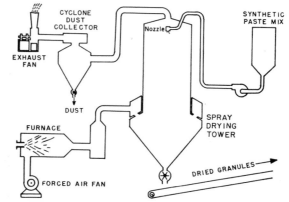

Figure 13.6. Simplified sketch for countercurrent flow in a spray-drying tower. [*Adapted from Chem. Eng. Progr., 53, No. 12, 593 (1957); copyright 1957 by the American Institute of Chemical Engineers and used by permission of the copyright owner.*]

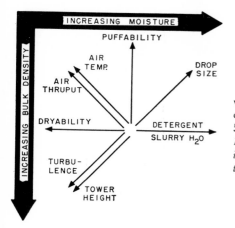

Figure 13.7. Independent variables which affect density, moisture, and tower capacity. [*Taken from Chem. Eng. Progr., 53, No. 12, 593 (1957); copyright 1957 by the American Institute of Chemical Engineers and used by permission of the copyright owner.*]

drying can simplify or eliminate other operations. Some disadvantages are relative inflexibility of bulk density and particle size variation, more fluid frequently having to be evaporated to enter the slurry in pumpable form, higher initial investment than for other dryers, and the existence of problems of product recovery, and dust collection and utilization.

Atomization may be accomplished by liquid flow from a rotating smooth or vaned disk and by pressure atomization from single or two-fluid nozzles.

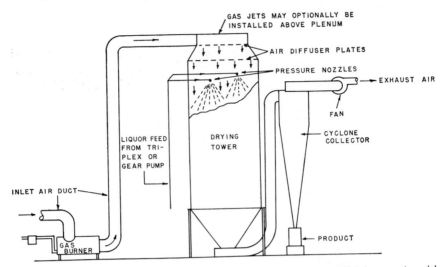

Figure 13.8. Vertical downward cocurrent spray dryer (Zizinia type) with straightline air flow. [*Taken from Chem. Eng. Progr.*, **46**, *No. 10, 501 (1950); copyright 1950 by the American Institute of Chemical Engineers and used by permission of copyright owner.*]

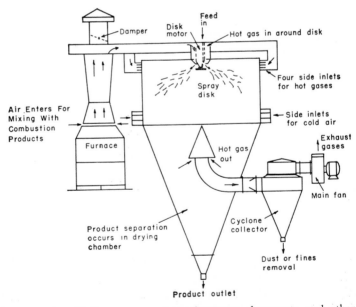

Figure 13.9. Bowen spray dryer for soaps, detergents, and other coarse particle products. [*Taken from Chem. Eng. Progr.*, **46**, *No. 10, 501 (1950); copyright 1950 by the American Institute of Chemical Engineers and used by permission of copyright owner.*]

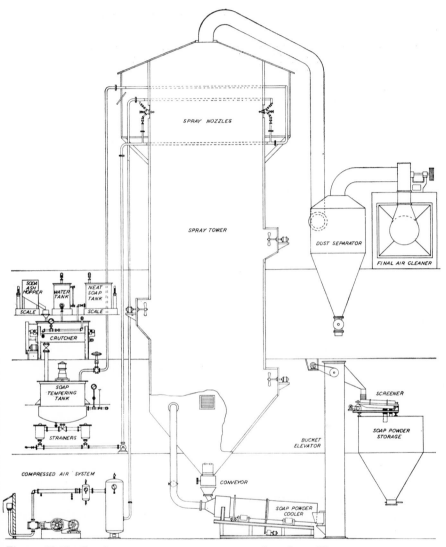

SPRAY NOZZLES

SPRAY TOWER

DUST SEPARATOR

FINAL AIR CLEANER

SODA
ASH
HOPPER

WATER
TANK

NEAT
SOAP
TANK

SCALE

SCALE

CRUTCHER

SOAP
TEMPERING
TANK

SCREENER

STRAINERS

SOAP POWDER
STORAGE

BUCKET
ELEVATOR

COMPRESSED AIR SYSTEM

CONVEYOR

SOAP POWDER
COOLER

Figure 13.10. Continuous spray process soap powder plant. The spray tower is 100 feet high. (*Courtesy Wurster and Sanger, Inc., Chicago, Ill.*)

The mathematics of atomization have been discussed rather extensively,[6,29] and factors such as tower design and operational procedures can be very important.

The application of chemical engineering principles to the spray-drying art can prove valuable.[8] A spray-drying tower is essentially a thermally balanced heat-exchange operation in which atomization produces a large surface for heat and mass transfer. Though Figure 13.6 is a simplified sketch of a countercurrent system, concurrent and mixed flow have also been used.

The independent variables in the spray-drying process may be visualized in the diagram of Figure 13.7, where feed moisture of the slurry affects the heat balance, dryability is the ease with which the slurry components lose water, and puffability is the character of the mix to steam-puff; the other terms are self-explanatory.

Some spray-drying units are shown in Figures 13.8, 13.9, and 13.10.

The investment cost of spray-drying units is one of the principal con-

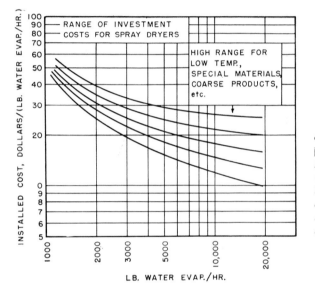

Figure 13.11. Spray dryer investment costs. [*Taken from Chem. Eng. Progr.,* **46**, *No. 10, 501* (*1950*); *copyright 1950 by the American Institute of Chemical Engineers and used by permission of copyright owner.*]

siderations, if an alternative drying process is available. Figure 13.11 shows a chart of installed cost against pounds of water evaporated per hour, indicating that low temperature, special materials, or coarse product costs remain high over the entire evaporation range. The second most important cost is that of operation, which includes fuel, labor, power, depreciation, and maintenance. Other costs may be involved if royalties are paid, and certainly overhead is an unavoidable item.

FATTY ACIDS

Manufacture from Glycerides

A glyceride may be hydrolyzed with the formation of glycerin and the free fatty acid; the latter may then be changed into a sodium soap, or it may be used as such for different purposes.

In the Twitchell process, the foots or greases are heated with 30 per cent sulfuric acid in the presence of a small amount of catalyst (0.5 to 1 per cent) in open lead-lined wooden tanks. The catalyst is made by sulfonating a mixture of oleic or other fatty acid and naphthalene.[46] The melted fatty acids produced are washed free of acid with water and used as such, or are refined by distillation at very low pressures, supplemented by crystallization from solvents. The acid waters are treated with lime and filter-pressed to remove the calcium sulfate; the clear filtrate is distilled for its glycerin.

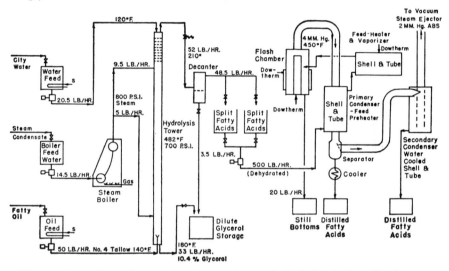

Figure 13.12. Flow diagram for the continuous hydrolysis of glycerides by water alone. [*Taken from Chem. Eng. Progr., 43, 459 (1947); copyright 1947 by the American Institute of Chemical Engineers and used by permission of copyright owner.*]

Hydrolysis. The hydrolysis of glycerides by means of water only, at higher temperatures and higher pressures, has been carried out in batch processes[49] with metallic oxides as catalysts; this is now a continuous process,[1] which does not require a catalyst. In the continuous process, the time involved is very short (two hours or less), compared with 6–10 hours for the batch process, and 30–40 hours for the Twitchell process. The temperature is held at about 485° F, and the pressure is maintained high enough to prevent the water from vaporizing (700 lb/sq in.), since the reaction is between liquid water and liquid glycerides.

The equipment is illustrated in Figure 13.12; its essential part is the hydrolysis tower, in which preheated water travels down, and the fatty acids formed by the hydrolysis rise. The tower in the pilot plant is 5 inches in diameter and 42 feet high, and is fitted with numerous trays. The trays

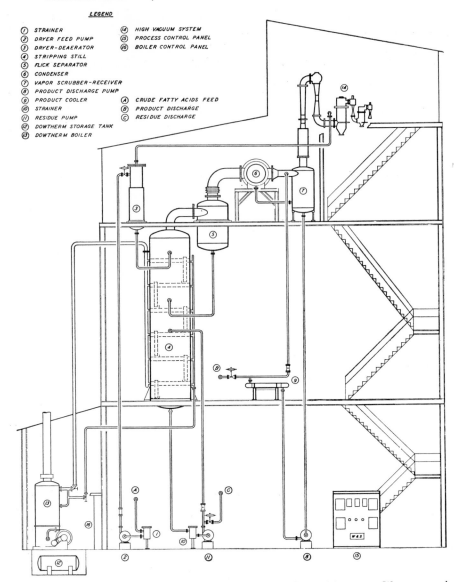

① STRAINER
② DRYER FEED PUMP
③ DRYER-DEAERATOR
④ STRIPPING STILL
⑤ FLICK SEPARATOR
⑥ CONDENSER
⑦ VAPOR SCRUBBER-RECEIVER
⑧ PRODUCT DISCHARGE PUMP
⑨ PRODUCT COOLER
⑩ STRAINER
⑪ RESIDUE PUMP
⑫ DOWTHERM STORAGE TANK
⑬ DOWTHERM BOILER

⑭ HIGH VACUUM SYSTEM
⑮ PROCESS CONTROL PANEL
⑯ BOILER CONTROL PANEL

Ⓐ CRUDE FATTY ACIDS FEED
Ⓑ PRODUCT DISCHARGE
Ⓒ RESIDUE DISCHARGE

Figure 13.13. A continuous fatty-acid distillation plant. (*Courtesy Wurster and Sanger, Inc., Chicago, Ill.*)

in the upper part have one riser and one downspout; those in the lower part are perforated, and carry one riser for the fatty phase. Good contacting of the two layers is thus assured. The oil-water ratio is usually 1.6 to 1. The glyceride is fed in near the bottom of the tower; the fatty acids leave at the top, comparatively cool. They may be purified by heating to 445° F, for example, and flash-distilled at a pressure of 4 mm Hg. A water solution of glycerin containing 10–24 per cent of the latter leaves at the bottom of the still, comparatively pure, so that its concentration offers no major difficulties. The over-all yield by this process is 96–99 per cent. The hydrolysis reaction may be represented as follows:

$$(C_{17}H_{35}COO)_3 \cdot C_3H_5 + 3H_2O \rightarrow 3C_{17}H_{35}COOH + C_3H_5(OH)_3$$
$$\text{a fat} \qquad\qquad\qquad \text{fatty acid} \qquad\quad \text{glycerin}$$

Another process for liberating the glycerin is the lime-soap process, used to some extent in Europe.

To the fatty acids from greases and glyceride oils there have been added, within the past several years, fatty acids obtained from tall oil, a by-product of the wood-pulp industry. This ill-smelling low-grade raw material is separated by fractional distillation at low pressure into a fatty acid fraction, a rosin acid fraction, and a light-colored pitch as residue. The first fraction may be used as such (88 per cent oleic-linoleic acids), or it may be redistilled to give a product with 94 per cent oleic-linoleic acid ("Neo-Fat D-142").

Purification by fractional distillation under vacuum and redistillation is supplemented by separation by means of solvents; this may involve a crystallization. In the Emersol process[21] the distilled fatty acid mixture is dissolved in methyl alcohol and the solution chilled in a multi-tubular crystallizer, causing the formation of stearic acid crystals, for example, leaving oleic acid in the solvent (again, for example). The crystals are separated on a rotary vacuum filter, washed with cold alcohol on the filter, and then melted and passed to a still where the solvent is driven off; the pure fatty acid is left as finished product. A similar treatment yields a finished oleic acid.

Stearic acid may be cast into cakes or fed to a flaker. Powdered stearic acid may be made by atomizing the molten acid at the top of a spray tower.

The fatty acid in any glyceride, animal or vegetable,* may be obtained in the free state by boiling with a caustic solution, forming the sodium soap, and treating the latter with sulfuric acid of medium strength; after good mixing, the warm fatty acid floats as an oil over the acidulated water and may be run off. The composition of the fatty acids varies as does their physical state,† their cost, and their applications. The latter have increased rapidly, as indicated in the following chart.

---

* It is interesting to note that all the naturally occurring fatty acids have an even number of carbon atoms which form a straight chain.

† After cooling, the free fatty acids in castor oil form a liquid, those in cocoa butter, a solid, those in tung oil, a soft solid, and those in coconut oil, a solid overlaid by a liquid.

Uses for fatty acids

↓	↓	↓	↓	↓	↓	↓
Soap	Long-chain alcohols (by reduction) for detergents	Blending agents for rendering certain synthetic resins oil-soluble (alkyds)	Emulsifiers in insecticides upon addition of alkali	Production of new chemicals	Cosmetic creams, brushless shaving creams	Surfactants

TABLE 13.4. UNITED STATES FATTY ACID PRODUCTION 1958*

	1000 Pounds
Unsaturated fatty acids	197,769
Saturated fatty acids	214,439
Total	412,208

* Source—Association of American Soap and Glycerine Producers, Inc.

Soap-Making with Fatty Acids

The fatty acids to be made into soap are neutralized with the proper equivalent of caustic in the form of a solution of definite water content. Salt is added (in small amount), and several batches are blended at 200° F. The soap then goes to crutchers, to equipment for milled soap or flake soap, or to a spray-drying tower. Additions of builders are made in the proper places. In the modern plant,[31] a floating toilet soap is made by heating the soap to 400° F under a pressure of 700 psi, then flashing, reducing the temperature to 220° F, at which point the soap is a viscous pasty mass, with 20 per cent water. It is cooled further in special machines (Votator) where air is introduced. The soap is fed to an extruder which delivers a strip moving at a rapid rate. The strip is cut into a 3-bar lengths and cooled further to eliminate stickiness; then it is cut to size, embossed, and wrapped. The time from fat to finished soap is reduced to one day, as contrasted to the two weeks required in the traditional kettle process. (Refer also to continuous processing of soap.)

Manufacture from Tall Oil

Sulfate paper pulp mills can accumulate, as a result of digestion, an upper black layer of skimmings (soda salts of the resins, etc.) which can be further converted to an oil, called crude tall oil. Tall oil was derived from the Swedish, "tall" being pine; since in the United States a pine oil of commerce already existed, the Swedish term was adopted.

Whole Tall Oil. Skimmings are made into crude or whole tall oil by treatment with sulfuric acid so that an upper dark-brown oily layer separates. No further processing for the whole tall oil is necessary, and since they vary considerably in their proportions of fatty and rosin acids, depending on the kind of pine wood from which they originate,[37] they are frequently sold under the brand names of the original producers.

A continuous process[54] for acidulation and crude tall oil recovery from sulfate soap skimmings has been developed. This utilizes, in a single stage, a continuous centrifuge to separate the crude tall oil from the spent acid. Sludge of lignin and some tall oil is recycled. High yields and good product quality are claimed.

Tall Oil Refining. *Solvent Refining.* Whole tall oil is thinned with mineral spirits and treated with sulfuric acid. The separated acid sludge containing

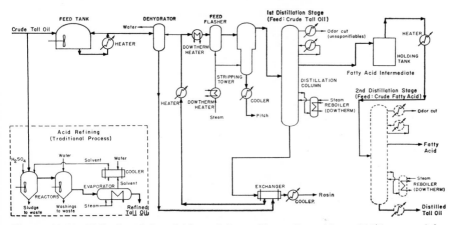

Figure 13.14. Tall-oil refining. [*Adapted from Chem. Eng. (June 1957); copyright 1957, McGraw-Hill Book Company, Inc.*]

much of the color bodies is discarded, and the mineral spirits are removed by distillation. The acid treatment also causes some of the rosin acids to dimerize, making them more soluble in the fatty acids, reducing their tendency to separate by crystallization, and causing marked increase in tall oil viscosity.

The tall oil so produced contains about 55 per cent fatty acids (oleic, linoleic, and palmitic), 35 per cent rosin acids (abietic, pyroabietic, and pimeric) and 10 per cent unsaponifiable matter (beta-sitosterol).

Distillation. Whole tall oil may be distilled into three or more fractions: nonvolatile residue of tall oil pitch; a volatile fraction rich in fatty acids and lean in rosin acids; a less volatile fraction rich in rosin acids and lean in fatty acids.

Figure 13.14 shows a flow sheet indicating the steps in both acid refining and refining by distillation.[16] It can be seen that tall oil fatty acids analyzing 99 per cent fatty acids and 0.5 per cent unsaponifiables may be produced, or that the rosin fraction may contain 95 per cent rosin and less than 3 per cent unsaponifiables.

In first-stage distillation, moisture is removed in the dehydrator (sodium sulfate). The crude is vaporized in a flash heater to feed a small stripping tower. The crude there cracks into pitch bottoms containing much of the colorant materials and heavy unsaponifiables, while the overhead cut consists of rosin, fatty acids, and light unsaponifiables. The rapidity of the stripping operation minimizes damage to heat-sensitive components. The overhead of the first distillation stage consists of (a) a high intermediate cut of crude fatty acids containing rosin (this must be re-run); (b) an overhead cut containing some undesired light unsaponifiables and some low molecular weight fatty acids; (c) the bottom cut of rosin stream for market.

In the second-stage distillation the collected intermediate fatty acid fraction is preheated and pumped to the main distillation column (may be a 125-foot high bubble-cap vacuum tower) where three fractions are separated: (a) fatty acid product, (b) bottom product of distilled tall oil, and (c) an overhead odor cut to remove unsaponifiables. Variation in operation can be made to control the compositions of these various cuts.

Tall Oil Soaps. About 12 million pounds of tall oil were used for soap production in 1958 (USDA 1959). These were frequently found in detergent compositions, or were used as liquid or paste products.

The ease of neutralization of tall oil or of tall oil fatty acids makes production of soaps from them a relatively simple process, requiring a minimum of stirring and heat. The products so formed are highly soluble, even in cold water, and their neutrality is easily adjustable. Table 13.5 gives the proportions of alkalies needed per unit of tall oil for a neutral soap, and reflects the wide variety which can be manufactured.

Tall Oil Statistics. It is probable that tall oil supplies exceeded one billion pounds in 1958. Many mills had as yet made no attempt at crude oil recovery in 1956.[10] Prices at that time were 2½–4¢ for crude and 5½–8¢ for the refined grade, while in 1959 distilled tall oil was quoted from 7–9¾¢ per pound.

GLYCERIN

Crude Glycerin

The spent lye drawn from the kettle in the boiled process contains the glycerin (5 per cent), the salt (10 per cent), some albuminous substances, free alkali, and soap in solution. The alkali content is normally 0.4 per cent or less; for purification, aluminum sulfate is added, and aluminum hydroxide and aluminum soaps, both insoluble, are formed. This precipitate settles well in the slightly acid solution; it is filter-pressed, and the filtrate is made slightly alkaline before concentration (Figure 13.15). The con-

TABLE 13.5. ALKALI PROPORTIONS FOR TALL OIL
SOAP MANUFACTURE*

Alkali Grades	Pounds per 1000 lb Tall Oil of Acid No. 175
Caustic Soda	
Pure, 100% NaOH	125
Commercial, 76% Na₂O	127
Solid, ground, flake or powdered	
Liquid, 50% NaOH	250
30%	417
20%	625
10%	1,250
Caustic Potash	
Pure, 100% KOH	175
Commercial, 90% KOH	194
Solid, ground, flake or powdered	
Liquid, 50% KOH	350
30%	583
20%	875
10%	1,750
Ammonia	
Anhydrous	53
Liquid, 26° Bé, 29.4% NH₃	181
Triethanolamine	443
Morpholine	278
Ethylamine, 70% solution	201

* Tall Oil Assn. Bull. No. 6 (1949).

TABLE 13.6. TALL OIL UTILIZATION
(Agricultural Marketing Service, U. S. Dept. of Agriculture, March 1959)*

Year	Millions of Pounds
1947	177
1950	287
1951	323
1952	270
1953	280
1954	331
1955	508
1956	599
1957	560
1958*	573

* Preliminary.

centration is performed in a closed, upright cylindrical steel vessel with a conical bottom and fitted with a steam chest. The steam in the coils is low-pressure, 5–25 pounds; this is sufficient because the pressure on the liquid is reduced by a vacuum-producing device, usually a steam jet ejector, to well below atmospheric. Water vapor passes out, and when the specific gravity of the liquid has reached 29° Bé, the salt, no longer able to be held in solution, separates and drops into the cone. The entire content of the evaporator is dropped into the salt box which has a false bottom covered with a filter screen; in this box, the salt settles on the screen. The clear liquor is sucked from below the screen into the still. Glycerin water from the soap kettle is run onto the salt, the suspension is settled again, and the liquor is also sucked into the still. The salt, now fairly free from glycerin, is blown with steam and then discharged by hand labor; it still retains approximately 0.5 per cent glycerin, but this is not lost since the salt is used over again in the kettle room.

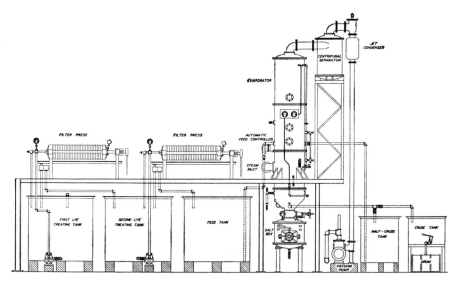

Figure 13.15. Spent-soap lye-glycerin treating and evaporating plant. (*Courtesy Wurster and Sanger, Inc., Chicago, Ill.*)

The liquid drawn back into the still from the salt box is much lower in specific gravity, since it has lost the salt; its glycerin content is about 49 per cent. The evaporation is continued to 80 per cent, and the red liquid then obtained is the "soap lye crude glycerin" of commerce. The test for this stage consists of heating a small sample in an open dish to a boiling point of 158–160° C.

When the drum is used, the salt is allowed to collect as it forms until the drum is filled with a sludge consisting of salt in the thickened glycerin. The sludge is then blown into a hopper from which it drops to centrifugals; the glycerin is returned to the evaporator, and the salt is washed with a little water and discharged. In this operation the salt drum functions as a blow case. A rotary drum suction filter may replace the centrifugal.

There is a second kind of crude glycerin called "saponification crude," produced by concentrating the glycerin waters from the catalytic, the batch pressure (the autoclave), or the continuous-pressure process for fat hydrolysis. Soap lye crude contains 80 per cent glycerin, saponification crude, 88 per cent.

Crude glycerin is the raw material of the glycerin distillers, a separate enterprise. Many large soapmakers, however, distill the glycerin in their own plants.

Purification. The crude glycerin with a red color is refined to a purer straw-colored glycerin by distilling it under reduced pressure in a current of steam. The earlier batch stills have been replaced by stills with continuous operation. By reducing the pressure to 6–12 mm Hg (absolute), the distillation takes place with the liquid at a temperature of 315–320° F (157–160° C); at this comparatively low temperature no decomposition takes place. About 0.25 pound of steam is injected per pound of glycerin distilled. The steam economy is important; in recently constructed units,[55] the over-all steam consumption for the heating coil, vacuum producers, glycerin discharge pump, and injected steam is held to 2½–3½ pounds per pound of glycerin distilled. The steam and glycerin vapors pass to three heat exchangers in series. The first two are held at temperatures high enough to permit the steam to pass, but cool enough to condense most of the glycerin. The vapors reach the third cooler, the condenser, where the remaining glycerin, with a little water is condensed to give a 90 per cent glycerin, which is concentrated further to dynamite glycerin. The rest of the steam is ejected. The condensates in the first two coolers enter a deodorizing unit; after leaving they are high enough in grade and strength to serve as commercial distilled glycerin without additional operation. The glycerin-salt slurry which forms in the crude still is filtered and its salt is re-used, while the filtrate is distilled for its glycerin in the foots still at low pressure. The total recovery in the refining operation is 97–98 per cent.

The traditional procedure applies primarily to glycerin obtained in the kettle (or boiled) process. The procedure is modified for the purer product obtained by the continuous-pressure process.

A considerable amount of distilled glycerin is made into dynamite glycerin by concentrating it again at reduced pressure, and pulling away the water vapors until the content of glycerin is 99.8–99.9 per cent and the specific gravity 1.262 at 15° C. Dynamite glycerin is straw-colored.

The distilled glycerin is made into the U.S.P. grade by treating it, while lukewarm, with bone char, filtering, and redistilling the filtrate in a separate still used for nothing else. The distillate is treated with bone char a second time, and filtered; then it is as white as distilled water, has a strength of about 98 per cent, and a specific gravity of 1.258 at 15° C.

The yield of glycerin as dynamite glycerin or U.S.P. glycerin is about 90 per cent of the glycerin contained in the solution from the soap kettle.

In the process of crude glycerin purification prior to distillation, it has been demonstrated[45] that by ion exchange substantially all the material fed to the process is obtained as C.P. product. In a straight distillation purification, approximately 70 per cent is C.P. grade, the rest, dynamite grade or glycerin foots. The ion-exchanged glycerin generally contains less color, ash, and fatty acids and esters than straight distilled product, and is more stable to sunlight.

Table 13.7 gives the domestic output and imports of glycerin since 1940. Estimates indicate that glycerin from propylene amounts to 100 million

TABLE 13.7. GLYCERIN SUPPLIES*

	Millions of Pounds	
	Domestic Output	Imports
1940	157.8	7.57
1945	172.5	7.68
1946	156.82	20.23
1947	207.77	3.06
1948	195.84	6.39
1949	193.85	18.52
1950	225.51	23.78
1951	211.35	14.61
1952	187.90	15.30
1953	215.00	35.38
1954	207.09	14.43
1955	228.00	25.00
1956	246.00	16.80
1957	238.[a]	25.[a]

[a] Estimated.
* *Chem. & Eng. News* (Feb. 4, 1957; Feb. 3, 1958).

pounds of the 1957 figure. Though glycerin from soap continues to lead the synthetic product by a few million pounds, the development of a wholly synthetic toilet bar (approximate production, 600 million pounds) could reduce glycerol production from soap lyes very significantly. Synthetic capacity approaches 260 million pounds (Table 13.8). The table also indicates that the initial producer of propylene glycerol is considering using an apparently more economic acrolein-hydrogen peroxide route; recent producers are utilizing the older procedure.

Synthetic Glycerin

Propylene and Chlorine. Since mid-1948, a large-scale plant has been producing synthetic glycerin, an achievement preceded by some 10 years of intense study and experimentation.[14] Since it is made from propylene, a petroleum hydrocarbon, synthetic glycerin must be given a place on the

TABLE 13.8. CURRENT SYNTHETIC GLYCERIN CAPACITY*

Company	Location	Capacity (Million Pounds)	Process (Starting Materials)	Status
Shell Chemical	Houston, Tex.	90–120	Propylene and chlorine	Now in operation: epichlorohydrin by-product
	Norco, La.	. . .	Propylene and chlorine	Now producing glycerin
	Norco, La.	35	Acrolein and hydrogen peroxide	Due onstream later this year
Dow Chemical	Freeport, Tex.	72	Propylene and chlorine	Now in operation: epichlorohydrin by-product
Olin Mathieson	Doe Run, Ky.	30–35	[a]	Due early '61

[a] Probably propylene and chlorine.
* *Chemical Week*, p. 76 (Aug. 15, 1959).

growing list of petrochemicals. The success of the synthesis was practically assured when it was discovered that allyl chloride could be produced by the hot chlorination (at 500° C) of propylene. One hydrogen of the methyl group may be substituted by the chlorine without affecting the double bond:

$$CH_2:CH \cdot CH_3 + Cl_2 \rightarrow CH_2:CH \cdot CH_2Cl + HCl$$

propylene   allyl chloride
(a gas)   (b.p. 44.9° C)

Allyl chloride may be reacted with chlorine at lower temperatures or with hypochlorous acid, and the product may be readily hydrolyzed to give glycerin.

$$CH_2:CH \cdot CH_2Cl + HOCl \rightarrow CH_2OH \cdot CHCl \cdot CH_2Cl$$

allyl chloride   chloroglycerolchlorhydrin

$$CH_2OH \cdot CHCl \cdot CH_2Cl + 2NaOH \rightarrow CH_2OH \cdot CHOH \cdot CH_2OH + 2NaCl$$

glycerin (a liquid)
(b.p. 290° C)

In practice, allyl chloride, purified of HCl and twice distilled, is reacted with chlorine, and caustic soda and water under controlled conditions to give a dilute solution of glycerin and salt. The solution is treated not unlike the similar solution of natural glycerin, already described. To produce the allyl chloride, chlorine and preheated propylene are fed to a reactor where the reaction heat added to the preheat produces a temperature of 500° C; at this temperature the substances react in seconds. Side reactions are few and limited. The vapors leaving the reactor are cooled and treated as follows: the hydrogen chloride is removed by water scrubbing; the allyl chloride and small amounts of other organic chlorides are absorbed in kerosene; the gas leaving the second absorber is unchanged propylene which is stored and recycled. The kerosene solution is fractionated, giving the allyl chloride fraction, among others.[41]

Glycerin may be obtained from the dilute isomers 1,2-dichloro-3-hydroxypropane and 1,3-dichloro-2-hydroxypropane (called DCH) by any one of several methods.[53] In one instance a DCH solution (containing one mole HCl per mole DCH) can be reacted with 20–50 weight per cent aqueous caustic solution to yield 95–96 per cent glycerin. However, these solutions are dilute and contain impurities difficult to remove. Another method involves the conversion of DCH to epichlorohydrin, this being diluted with water and hydrolyzed with caustic to glycerin. Impurities are minimized, but material loss in conversion is relatively high. A third process[50] combines the foregoing two methods. Important to economical recovery are the processing details indicated in these patents.

Competition for propylene glycerin is possible by a fermentation process, if blackstrap molasses prices remain sufficiently low. Glycerin in dynamite and explosives is being increasingly replaced by glycols and ammonium nitrate. More specialized polyols and modified alkyl formulations offer even greater competition in this large field. Some newer materials are also replacing glycerin in the toilet goods field. However, glycerin continues to find an expanding market as a humectant in cigarettes, and 30 million pounds were estimated to be used in cellophane in 1958. Increasing markets in cosmetic, tooth paste, shaving and hand cream manufacture continues. Six million pounds of glycerin were estimated to be consumed in the edible emulsifier (margarine) field, and growth continues.

The flow diagram of the Shell plant at Houston is shown in Figure 13.16 and the several possible routes from allyl chloride to glycerin in the diagram in Figure 13.17. The description of the commercial unit[11,14] follows:

"In the first step of the process the propylene feed is reacted with chlorine at elevated temperatures. Flow rates, temperature, and pressure are controlled to obtain optimum reaction conditions for the formation of allyl chloride. The reaction mixture is then purified through a series of distillation steps.

"The pure allyl chloride reacts with caustic soda, chlorine, and water in the synthesis unit to form crude glycerin. The conversion proceeds under controlled conditions of pH, flow rate, temperature, and time. The effluent stream from the glycerin unit consists of a dilute solution of glycerin and salt.

"The next steps consist of concentration, desalting, and purifying the crude glycerin. The raw solution is pumped to multiple effect evaporators which contain more than a quarter of an acre of heating surface. A concentrated salt-glycerin slurry is withdrawn from the last stage of the evaporators and pumped to a settling tank. From this vessel the glycerin

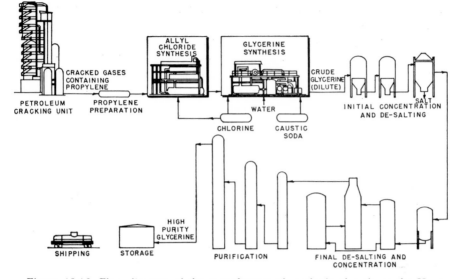

Figure 13.16. Flow diagram of the manufacture of synthetic glycerin at the Houston plant of the Shell Chemical Corp. [*Taken from Chem. Eng. Progr.*, **44**, *No. 10, 16 (1948); copyright 1948 by the American Institute of Chemical Engineers and used with permission of the copyright owner.*]

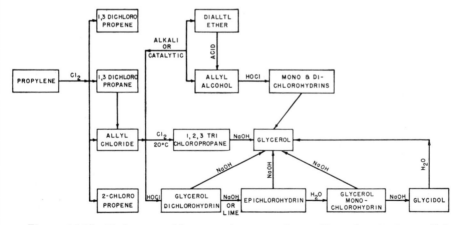

Figure 13.17. **Various** possible processing steps for making glycerin from allyl chloride. [*Taken from Chem. Eng. Progr.*, **44**, *No. 10, 16 (1948); copyright 1948 by the American Institute of Chemical Engineers and used with permission of the copyright owner.*]

solution is withdrawn and charged to another evaporator for further concentration.

"After the concentrating operations the glycerin is desalted and purified. Desalting is performed in a system of evaporators in which the glycerin is distilled under reduced pressure removing the last traces of salt. Following this the glycerin undergoes a series of purification treatments which result in a product of better than 99 per cent purity.

"The purified glycerin is sent to specially lined storage equipment until ready for shipment. In order to prevent contamination which might result if ordinary materials were used, the product is transported in a fleet of made-to-order aluminum tank cars."

Formic Acid. Using allyl alcohol, 95 per cent formic acid and methanol, glycerin of 99+ per cent purity is said to be produced[36] with yields of 94 per cent based on allyl chloride.

The reactions are hydroxylation, ester interchange and hydrolysis. Allyl alcohol is reacted with formic acid in the presence of hydrogen peroxide; the effective reactant is probably performic acid, and the reactions are:

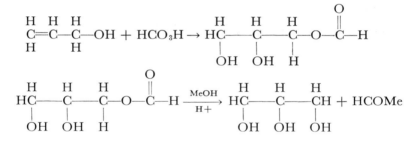

Acrolein and Hydrogen Peroxide. Figure 13.18 shows a flow sheet for this most recent process, based on a charge of propylene and oxygen co-producing glycerin and large amounts of acetone.[4]

"Propylene is first hydrated to isopropanol using a standard process. The isopropanol is oxidized in the liquid phase by bubbling pure oxygen through a liquid mixture of isopropanol and H_2O_2 at a pressure of about 2.5 atmospheres and at temperatures between 90 and 140° C. The reaction mixture is diluted with water, stabilized, and fractionated to yield hydrogen peroxide solution, acetone, and unreacted isopropanol, which can be recycled.

"A mixture of propylene with slightly more than an equal amount of steam is reacted with 25 per cent oxygen based on the weight of the propylene. The reaction is carried out over a fixed bed of catalyst based on cuprous oxide, supported on SiC or some other high thermal conductivity support. Close control of reaction temperature is necessary. The reaction pressure may be from 1 to 10 atmospheres and the temperature between 300 and 400° C. The reaction mixture is cooled and fractionated to give acrolein, unreacted propylene, and tarry byproducts. The yield of acrolein is near 86 per cent of the propylene consumed.

"The purified acrolein is mixed with pure isopropanol from the propylene hydration step and the mixture vaporized. The mixed vapors containing 2–3 moles of alcohol per mole of acrolein are passed through a catalyst bed containing both uncalcined magnesium oxide and zinc oxide, with the magnesia predominating. The reaction takes place at about 400° C and yields about 77 per cent allyl alcohol (based on acrolein charged) and an additional quantity of acetone which is added to that formed in the isopropanol oxidation step.

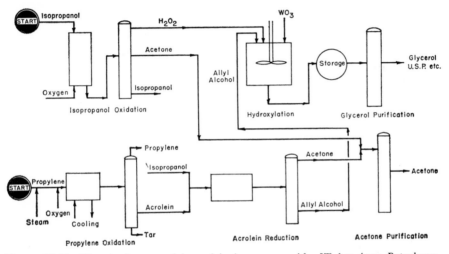

Figure 13.18. Glycerin from acrolein and hydrogen peroxide. [*Taken from Petroleum Refiner, 36, No. 11, 250 (1957); copyright 1957 by the Gulf Publishing Co.*]

"Purified allyl alcohol is agitated with a water solution of hydrogen peroxide containing a small amount of tungsten trioxide in solution. The effective catalyst is a 0.2 per cent pertungstic acid solution in 2 molar aqueous hydrogen peroxide. The reaction temperature is 60–70° C; reaction time is about two hours, producing glycerin in water solution.

"The reaction mixture is pumped to receivers and distilled to yield high-purity glycerin. The recovered catalyst solution is recycled. The yield of the final step is 80–90 per cent based on the allyl alcohol charged.

"The control of both the propylene oxidation step and the hydroxylation step must be exceptionally good for acceptable yields. The conditions quoted are approximate, and the practical operating limits are doubtless much less broad.

"The over-all yield of useful products (glycerin and acetone) is not known. The over-all glycerin yield on propylene charged to the oxidation is in the range of 50–60 per cent."

SYNTHETIC DETERGENTS

Synthetic detergents were initially developed as soap substitutes in an economy which was running short of edible fats and oils. These compounds were made resistant to deleterious and insoluble hard water salt formation, and were markedly improved in wetting, cleansing, and surfactancy in general. The term "synthetic detergents" has been shortened to "syndets" to describe the detergent compositions comprising the synthetic active ingredient along with other detergent additives. "Surface active agent" has been shortened to "surfactant" to describe the surface active principal or active ingredient (AI). The rise of syndets in commerce in the United States has been meteoric: In 1940 only $\frac{1}{100}$ as much syndet as soap was sold; in 1950 this had increased to $\frac{1}{2}$; in 1953 slightly more syndet was sold, while in 1957 this had risen to a ratio of about 3 syndet to 1 soap. A compilation by years is given in Table 13.9. An international survey for the years 1953–1954[3] indicated total production figures as follows:

	1000 Pounds
Soap	8,228,991
Syndet	4,015,329

In only three countries, Austria, West Germany, and the United States, did the syndet production exceed that of soap.

While soap production in the United States has been reduced, many uses for it still exist. Even though surfactants have entered the toilet soap field, soap is still an excellent medium for combined usage, and fatty anionics are increasingly being used with it. This represents a half billion-pound market, where soap will apparently retain a large proportion of the total. Other advantages of soap are: (1) it is among the least toxic of all surfactants; (2) it is biodegradable and does not cause steam pollution; (3) it makes antibacterial agents effective; (4) it does not require added soil suspending agents as do the syndets.

Recent sales figures are given in Table 13.10, with a breakdown into solid and liquid products. Increase in liquid syndets in the last five years has been a major change, and this trend continues. Currently, these liquid products are designed particularly for dishwashing and light-duty fabric cleansing or for medium-duty hard-surface cleaning. If the current trend continues, liquid heavy-duty products may supplant the dry laundry detergents. Fully automatic washers and washer-dryer combinations have triggered the demand for these easily dispensed products. As Table 13.11 indicates, almost half the total production of surfactants has applications in

TABLE 13.9. SOAP AND SYNTHETIC DETERGENTS: SUPPLY AND DISPOSITION, 1935–58*

	Supply							Disposition			
	Estimated Production[1]		Imports of Soap, Million Pounds	Total, Million Pounds	Exports and Shipments of Soap,[4] Million Pounds	Use of Soap in Synthetic Rubber,[5] Million Pounds	Military, Excluding Relief,[6] Million Pounds	Domestic Disappearance			
								Total, Million Pounds	Civilian per Capita		
Year	Soap,[2] Million Pounds	Synthetic Detergents,[3] Million Pounds							Total, Pounds	Soap, Pounds	Synthetic Detergents, Pounds
1935–39	3,105	10	7	3,122	66	...	...	3,057	24	24	7
1940	3,273	30	5	3,308	67	...	...	3,241	25	25	7
1941	3,886	40	11	3,937	84	1	50	3,802	29	29	7
1942	3,648	50	4	3,702	59	2	120	3,521	27	26	1
1943	3,524	75	8	3,607	59	22	350	3,176	26	25	1
1944	4,142	125	1	4,268	52	89	400	3,727	30	29	1
1945	3,888	150	3	4,041	129	94	400	3,418	27	25	2
1946	3,085	275	8	3,368	157	72	70	3,069	22	20	2
1947	3,650	408	1	4,059	138	47	40	3,834	27	24	3
1948	3,180	636	1	3,817	92	50	34	3,641	25	21	4
1949	2,985	864	1	3,850	80	46	40	3,684	25	19	6
1950	2,958	1,443	1	4,402	76	59	40	4,227	28	19	9
1951	2,510	1,565	1	4,076	69	104	85	3,818	25	16	9
1952	2,275	1,856	1	4,132	65	88	90	3,889	25	15	10
1953	1,986	2,118	1	4,105	63	94	95	3,853	25	14	11
1954	1,760	2,468	1	4,229	59	68	85	4,017	25	12	13
1955	1,625	2,704	1	4,330	55	105	80	4,090	25	10	15
1956	1,564	3,068	1	4,633	59	117	75	4,382	26	9	17
1957	1,432	3,507	2	4,941	66	122	84	4,662	28	8	20
1958[8]			1		39	115					

[1] Based on estimates of the Assn. of American Soap and Glycerine Producers, Inc. Excludes cleansers and liquid soaps. [2] Based on factory shipments of 53 companies as reported in the Assn. Sales Census who produced 70–83 per cent of the United States total in census years, adjusted to a U. S. total basis. [3] Includes only those with characteristics and end uses similar to soap. [4] Beginning 1947 includes shipments in CARE packages. [5] From Office of Rubber Reserve, R.F.C. through 1954. Estimated by AMS since then. [6] Estimates based in part on data given in Statistical Yearbook of the Quartermaster Corps for 1947. [7] Less than one-half pound. [8] Preliminary. Estimated production and domestic disappearance data not available as of March 25.

* "Fats and Oils Situation," Agricultural Marketing Service, U. S. Dept. of Agriculture (March 1959).

the household cleaning field, with smaller though appreciable tonnages used otherwise.

Surfactants may arbitrarily be subdivided into four categories, depending on ionic activity. 1958 production data are given in Table 13.12. Relative newcomers are the ampholytes and the nonionics; the latter have increased in importance markedly in the last several years.

TABLE 13.10. SOAP AND SYNDET SALES 1958*

| | in 1000 pounds | |
	1958	1957
Total Soap and Syndet Sales	4,089,500	4,104,675
Soaps, solid & liquid, total	1,138,148	1,188,909
Syndets, solid & liquid, total	2,951,352	2,915,766
Solid soaps	1,110,332	1,157,757
Solid syndets	2,520,608	2,552,286
	in 1000 dollars	
Total Soap and Syndet Sales	1,040,753	998,115
Soaps, solid & liquid, total	324,802	314,525
Syndets, solid & liquid, total	715,951	683,590

* Assn. of American Soap & Glycerine Producers, Inc.

TABLE 13.11. END-USE APPLICATIONS*

	Consumption Million Pounds†	Per Cent of Total
Household cleaning	548	51.5
Petroleum	182	17.0
Concrete	75	7.0
Formulated cleaners	46	4.0
Textiles	30	3.0
Food	25	2.0
Other aqueous cleaning	25	2.0
Metal cutting	21	2.0
Chemical intermediates	20	2.0
Cosmetics	18	2.0
Agriculture	16.5	1.5
Dry cleaning	10	1.0
Other	42.5	4.0
TOTAL	1,059	100.0

* Tariff Commission, Chemical Week, p. 90 (October 20, 1956).

† All figures are for 1955 on a 100 per cent active-agent basis; the total represents about 98 per cent of all United States production (1,071.5 million pounds in '55) as reported by the Tariff Commission.

In number alone, syndets are continuing to increase; McCutcheon[32] listed 125 in 1947, while his latest compilation cites over 2200 products.

Hydrophil-Hydrophobe Balance

Surface active agents are, as the term indicates, active at surfaces by preferential orientation of the molecule. This suggests that some built-in characteristic appears to contribute to, or control, molecular activity.

Because surfactants are effective in either aqueous or nonaqueous systems, depending on their solubility characteristics, the molecule may be tailored for either system. Starting out with alkylbenzene as an example, it is slightly surface active in nonaqueous media but insoluble in water, hence ineffective. By sulfonating alkylbenzene, for example dodecylbenzene (DDB), a single SO_3Na group provides high water solubility and excellent surfactant character in water, but the compound is then essentially insoluble in petroleum solvents. If DDB is di- or tri-sulfonated, the compound becomes more water soluble and, in effect, loses much of its surface activity, thereby approaching a simple electrolyte such as sodium sulfate or, by analogy, simple benzene sulfonate. In neither case is there sufficient hydrophobe influence to increase preferential orientation, the hydrophil balance having been exceeded. However, the DDB monosulfonate, highly water soluble and an excellent aqueous system surfactant, may be rendered hydrophobic and useful in nonaqueous

TABLE 13.12. UNITED STATES SURFACTANT PRODUCTION 1958*

| | | 1000 Pounds or Dollars | |
	Production	Sales Quantity	Sales Value
Anionic	976,620	899,491	148,351
Amphoteric	2,364	2,299	1,122
Cationic	26,807	25,699	14,497
Nonionic	328,755	272,479	70,922
Total 1958	1,334,546	1,199,968	234,892
Total 1957	1,206,000	1,123,000	217,000

All statistics are on the basis of 100 per cent active content.

* U. S. Tariff Commission, July 1959.

systems by neutralizing the SO_3H group with a long-chain amine to render the molecule water insoluble. It is also possible, in the case of a nonaqueous surfactant with a single SO_3Na group, to increase the C_{12} side chain to approach C_{18} or higher; the same effect can be obtained as that resulting from neutralization of the shorter alkylbenzene sulfonate with an amine.

For nonionic systems the same hydrophil-hydrophobe balance exists, except that in place of SO_3 or SO_4 water solubilizing groups to form ionized aqueous solutions, nonionics depend on a multiplicity of oxygen groups or linkages which can unite by means of hydrogen bonds, thus inducing water solubility. Nonionics of the ethylene oxide adduct type, therefore, introduce an extra dimension over ionics, since not only the hydrophobe may be varied but the hydrophil as well. This extra-dimensional feature may possibly account for some of the increasing usage of this class of compound.

In general, an optimum hydrophil-hydrophobe balance exists for specific applications and for a class of compounds for a given application. This optimum composition is generally arrived at by evaluation for the specific purpose, and in at least one instance (emulsions), physico-chemical measurements have been used to predict the most effective surfactant or combination for the particular purpose.

In studying the literature one might be led to believe that the various compounds mentioned, such as lauryl sulfate, sodium stearate, dodecylbenzene sulfonate, octylphenyl nonaethylene glycol ether, and the like, are the pure compounds. The compounds commercially used are mixtures, lauryl sulfate being a generic term for a mixture of sulfates whose largest content is the C_{12} alcohol; the remainder consists of higher and lower alcohols, the amount depending on the sharpness of the original alcohol distillation cut. The same is true for alkylbenzene derivatives and octylphenol compounds, while soaps are mixtures of the various fatty acids natural to fats and oils. A further example of the mixtures of a type compound is that of ethylene oxide adducts. The nonaethylene glycol ether designation suggests that this compound is the main constituent, but ethylene oxide adducts are manufactured on the basis of weight addition; the ethylene oxide adds to individual hydrophobe molecules in a manner which can give a normal (Poisson) distribution of adducts, the largest proportion representing an approximate 9 molar adduct. Both lower and higher adducts are also present. It might seem that a competitive edge could be gained by supplying a highly purified compound, but this is not necessarily true. Most surfactants are used for many different purposes having many and varied requirements; mixtures frequently permit usage where the pure compound might be less effective. Long experience with soaps has shown that except for very specific purposes, pure soaps are not competitive with properly chosen soap mixtures. This experience carries over to other surfactants.

Anionic Surfactants

Alkylaryl Sulfonates. The surfactant currently used in largest volume is represented by alkylbenzene sulfonates. The alkylbenzene portion is synthesized from petroleum tetrapropylene and benzene utilizing either an aluminum chloride or HF catalyst system. To the roughly 245 molecular weight of dodecylbenzene a further 103 for the SO_3Na grouping is added, the latter representing an appreciable portion of the molecular weight of the surfactant at relatively low cost.

Detergent Alkylate. Early manufacture of alkylbenzenes was routed through chlorination of a suitable kerosene cut of alkanes in the C_{10}–C_{15} range obtained from high paraffin crudes. These were then used to alkylate benzene using aluminum chloride in the Friedel-Crafts reaction to provide an optimum amount of the monoalkyl product. The product of purification by distillation then represented an optimum molecular weight distribution for the detergent operation.

More recently, detergent alkylate has been generally manufactured by means of tetrapropylene polymer in the C_{10}–C_{15} range. This is produced as a by-product of propylene polymerization for gasoline, using a phosphoric acid catalyst either in the vapor or liquid phase; or, to maximize the amount of desired product, the gasoline range may be recycled. The alkylation of benzene with the tetrapropylene polymer is made to occur either with hydrogen fluoride or aluminum chloride as catalyst. Purification again is by distillation, the final cut lying in the C_{11}–C_{13} range. A flow sheet[9] of this process is shown in Figure 13.19.

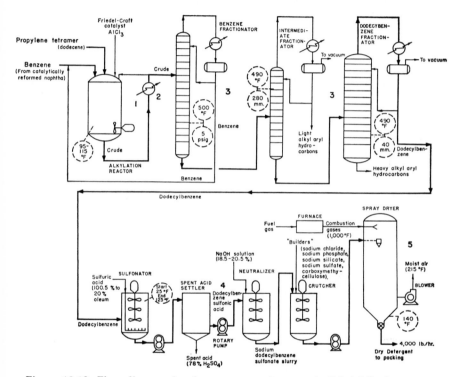

Figure 13.19. Flow diagram for detergent manufacture: 1, Friedel-Crafts reactors; 2, heat exchangers for temperature control of benzene alkylation; 3, fractionating towers; 4, settling tank and neutralizers; 5, spray-dryer equipment. [*Taken from Chem. Eng. (June 1954); copyright 1954 by McGraw-Hill Book Company, Inc.*]

Sulfonation. It is indicated[42] that with available alkylate the small processor can economically utilize a sulfonation unit on the basis of as little as 6,000 pounds per day of neutralized sulfonate. A cost of between $75–$85,000 is estimated for a 30,000 pound per 24-hour per day operation of a 60 per cent active material, a major portion of this cost representing drying equipment.

The usual means for sulfonation utilizes an excess of strong sulfuric acid or oleum to approximate 100 per cent sulfonation of the detergent alkylate.

The flow diagram[24] in Figure 13.20 shows the major forms of the sulfonated alkylate. Excess spent sulfuric acid is generally separated, since some recovery through sale of the still useful acid is frequently of value. The neutralization may provide a high concentration active product which may be dried (generally drum dried) or used as a slurry for combination with other ingredients for a variety of products.

Sulfonation of detergent alkylate using sulfur trioxide can be accomplished by passing the vaporized SO$_3$ (7 volume per cent) mixed with dry air (93

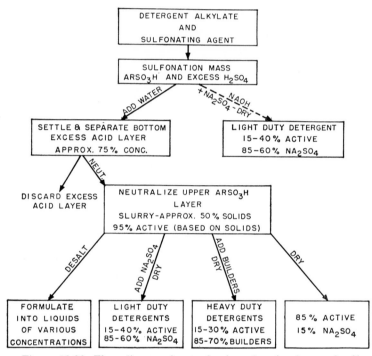

Figure 13.20. Flow diagram for production of major forms of sulfonated detergent alkylate. [*Taken from Ind. Eng. Chem.*, **46**, *1925* (*1954*); *copyright 1954 by the American Chemical Society and used by permission of the copyright owner.*]

volume per cent) into the alkylate, stirring, and cooling.[17] The advantage of this process is that as little as 2.2 per cent sodium sulfate, basis 100 per cent sulfonate, may be produced. The character of the alkylate will have considerable effect on the amount of unsulfonatable residue, the para alkylate isomer being more difficult to sulfonate.

A package sulfonation plant occupying an area 20 feet square has been developed which is capable of producing by continuous operation 20 million pounds of active ingredient per year, or 5 million pounds in an area 15 feet square. The flow diagram[43] is shown in Figure 13.21. Using oleum, the unit involves the three steps of sulfonation, dilution and separation of excess acid, and concentration of the sulfonic acid. Correct adjustment of the variables of reaction time and temperature, acid strength, and ratio of acid to alkylate can control the sulfonate quality to minimize odor, double sulfonation, and alteration of the alkyl side chain, and can assure good color and odor. One time-saving step is the rapid separation, following dilution of the sulfonation mass, giving a final sulfonic acid containing about 7.5 per cent sulfuric acid (0.2 per cent sulfonic acid in the separated spent acid). The separation step takes place in 30 minutes as compared with 6–8 hours in the batch process.

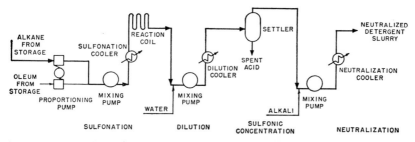

Figure 13.21. Schematic diagram of continuous detergent slurry plant. [*Taken from Soap Chemical Specialties,* **35,** *No. 4, 131 (1959); by permission.*]

It should be noted that this process is also useful for sulfating fatty alcohols, with either oleum or chlorosulfonic acid (for high active ingredient content) as the sulfation medium. By tandem arrangement, both sulfonated alkylate and sulfated fatty alcohol can be produced (blending either before or after sulfonation) for use as the mixed active ingredients in some syndets (see section on Fatty Alcohol Sulfates).

Anionic hydrophobes can also be sulfonated with sulfur trioxide.[7]

Following the manufacture of alkylaryl sulfonate detergent solution or slurry (Figure 13.22), this is pumped to a mixer or crutcher where other ingredients are added; the mix is strained, deaerated in the Versator, and then forced by high pressure pump to the spray tower. Subsequently, adequate means for dust control and collection are maintained, and the powder is cooled and perfumed, passing from a hold silo or bin to the automatic packaging line.

Fatty Alcohol Sulfates. *Fatty Alcohols.* Two general methods of producing fatty alcohols from natural fats and oils are currently in use: (1) hydrogenolysis[20] by reduction of fatty acids, anhydrides, or their esters, with hydrogen at high temperatures (50–350° C) and pressures (10–200 atmospheres) over a catalyst (copper chromite in the De Nora process):

$$C_{15}H_{31}COOR$$
$$C_{17}H_{35}COOR + 7H_2 \rightarrow C_{15}H_{31}CH_2OH + 2C_{17}H_{35}CH_2OH$$
$$C_{17}H_{33}COOR \qquad\qquad + 3ROH$$

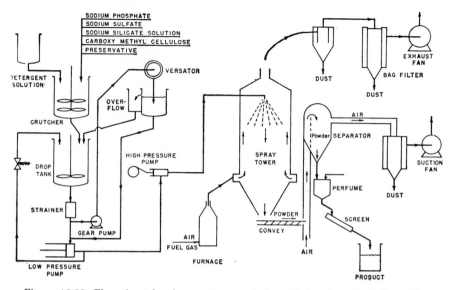

Figure 13.22. Flow sheet for detergent spray drying. [*Taken from Ind. Eng. Chem.*, **49**, *No. 3, 338 (1957); copyright 1957 by the American Chemical Society and used by permission of the copyright owner.*]

(2) the sodium reduction process,[19] at a slightly lower capital outlay, using fatty glyceride, lower alcohol (for esterification), and metallic sodium:

$$C_{15}H_{31}COO—CH_2$$
$$\begin{array}{l} C_{17}H_{35}COO—CH \; + \; 12ROH + 12Na \rightarrow \end{array}$$
$$C_{17}H_{33}COO—CH_2$$

$$C_{15}H_{31}CH_2OH$$
$$C_{17}H_{35}CH_2OH + glycerin$$
$$C_{17}H_{33}CH_2OH + 12RONa$$

Glycerin is recovered as a solution containing caustic. The usual impurities, such as soap and unreacted ester, are removed through fractional distillation.

The schemes of operation are shown in Figure 13.23. The advantages of hydrogenolysis are cheaper raw materials, and wide choice of feed stocks and suitable locations. The advantages of sodium reduction are production of both saturated and unsaturated alcohols, lower initial investment, simpler operation and maintenance, and superior quality products.

One large detergent manufacturer has converted from the sodium process to catalytic hydrogenation, using essentially the scheme[15] shown in Figure 13.23. It is claimed that the alcohols must be saturated for detergent use so that this process would be preferable to the sodium route. The alcohols are fractionated, C_8 and C_{10} products being sold to plasticizer manufacturers, the higher ones being retained for detergent manufacture.

The recent commercial production of oxo-process and Ziegler-process long-chain alcohols has resulted in the natural alcohols having to compete for both sulfation and use as alcohol-ethylene oxide adducts.

Sulfation. It was mentioned in the discussion of detergent alkylate sulfonation that a continuous process involving oleum or chlorosulfonic acid could be used to sulfate the fatty alcohols. The preferred process is the one which utilizes oleum, although chlorosulfonic acid is used for high active ingredient content. This latter process presents a corrosion problem; both the acid and the hydrogen chloride produced are difficult to handle and require corrosion-resistant equipment. Sulfamic acid and ammonium or

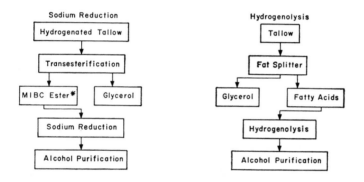

*MIBC — Methylisobutyl carbinol

Figure 13.23. Scheme of fatty-alcohol production. [*Taken from Ind. Eng. Chem., 46, 1917 (1954); copyright 1954 by the American Chemical Society and used by permission of the copyright owner.*]

amine sulfates are used where the end product is an ammonium or amine salt. Gaseous sulfur trioxide sulfation has also been employed successfully.

In sulfating a fatty alcohol the desired product is the monoalkyl sulfuric acid ester.[15] Since the reaction is rapid, oversulfation may be a problem, causing olefin, ether, or aldehyde formation, although other reactions can occur. An optimum set of conditions exists for sulfation. Excess time or temperature reduces the completeness of sulfation and causes the product to deteriorate. When conditions are below optimum, equilibrium is not reached. This equilibrium point is determined by the free water concentration in the reaction mix; the SO_3 in oleum helps to maintain the water concentration at a low level, oleum being superior to sulfuric acid in this respect.

Alkylbenzene is considerably simpler to sulfonate. The reaction, not reversible, follows a smooth time-temperature curve; longer contact time or higher temperature alters the degree of sulfonation to a negligible degree. However, a proper excess of acid, to maintain the strength above 95 per cent, is required to prevent the product from darkening as a result of color formation.

Figure 13.24 shows a flow sheet of simultaneous alkyl sulfate-alkylbenzene sulfonate production. However, this plant is multipurpose and can produce alkyl sulfates, alkylarylsulfonates, mixed alkyl sulfates and alkylarysulfonates, and layered alkylarylsulfonates. The reaction bath consists of a mixing pump and heat exchanger (only 8 inches in diameter and 5 feet long). The neutralization bath consists of a mixing pump, a heat exchanger (two units, each 2½ feet OD and 20 feet long), a neutralizer, and a surge tank. Since

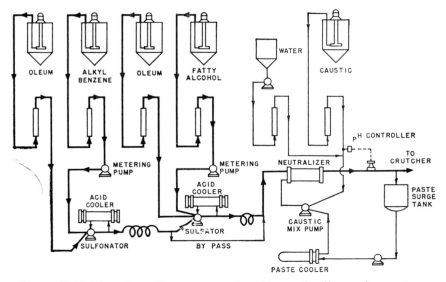

Figure 13.24. Flow sheet of process to make sulfate and sulfonate detergents continuously. [*Taken from Ind. Eng. Chem.,* **51,** *13 (1959); copyright 1959 by the American Chemical Society and used by permission of the copyright owner.*]

the excess acid is ordinarily neutralized to form sodium sulfate, and is left in the product, a higher active ingredient content product necessitates spent acid separation; this is accomplished by layering, or the separation of spent acid from the sulfonic acid. The process increases the active alkylarylsulfonate to sodium-sulfate ratio from 1:1 to 8:1.

Taurate Surfactants. In 1930 both H. T. Böhme, A.-G., and I. B. Farbenindustrie recognized that the weakness in soap was centered at the carboxyl linkage;[23] the former chose the alkyl sulfate route, the latter, esters of fatty acids. Subsequently, because the fatty esters were too unstable for many purposes, fatty amides which were taurine derivatives were developed. Igepon T (oleyl methyl taurate) was one of the first widely used surfactants which still has many applications.

The chemical reactions yielding Igepon T are:

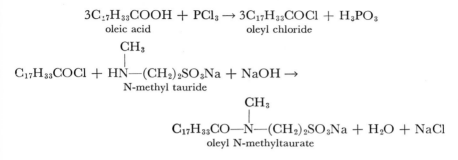

$$3C_{17}H_{33}COOH + PCl_3 \rightarrow 3C_{17}H_{33}COCl + H_3PO_3$$
oleic acid　　　　　　　　　　oleyl chloride

$$\overset{\displaystyle CH_3}{\underset{\displaystyle |}{}}$$
$$C_{17}H_{33}COCl + HN{-}(CH_2)_2SO_3Na + NaOH \rightarrow$$
N-methyl tauride

$$\overset{\displaystyle CH_3}{\underset{\displaystyle |}{}}$$
$$C_{17}H_{33}CO{-}N{-}(CH_2)_2SO_3Na + H_2O + NaCl$$
oleyl N-methyltaurate

It is of considerable interest that in the patent[47] covering these compounds of the type

$$\overset{\displaystyle O \quad R_2}{\underset{\displaystyle R_1{-}C{-}N{-}R_3}{\underset{\displaystyle \|\quad\; |}{}}}$$

in which R_1, R_2, and R_3 are branched or straight chain aliphatic, cycloaliphatic, or aromatic hydrocarbon groups, or heterocyclic rings, and in which R_3 may be a sulfonic or sulfuric ester (these groups may have many forms), that over 1,620,00 variations are possible. Obviously, only relatively few of this number have been synthesized, and of these, fewer still have been merchandized.

Nonionic Surfactants

As the name indicates, these products are not ionic in nature, and in contrast to sulfates, sulfonates, or phosphates, their solubility generally depends on hydrogen bonding through a multiplicity of oxygen groups in the molecule. The most widely manufactured products are ethylene oxide adducts, although mixed ethylene and propylene or butylene oxide compounds are, or can be, produced.

Ethylene Oxide Adducts. One main requirement of the nonionic hydrophobe for ethylene oxide addition is that it contain a reactive hydrogen; the most important hydrophobes are given in Table 13.13.[22] As discussed under hydrophil-hydrophobe balance, these adducts are not single compounds, but the products represent mixtures approximating Poisson distribution.

Production of ethylene oxide adducts is not difficult, but because of corrosion and explosion hazards the equipment is necessarily expensive, and handling and storing raw materials and products requires considerable capital. Operating costs are largely dependent on the volume produced; short-chain ethylene oxide adducts can be produced in much shorter cycles than the more generally used longer chain products.

Tall oil adducts have probably been the largest single hydrophobe-base nonionics, largely because of the relatively low cost of tall oil. It has been used primarily as the AI of a widely sold controlled sudsing detergent.

Polymeric Nonionics. Alkylene oxides such as ethylene, propylene, isobutylene or 1,2-epoxybutane can be polymerized alone to form homo-

TABLE 13.13. PREPARATION OF NONIONIC SURFACTANTS FROM ETHYLENE OXIDE*

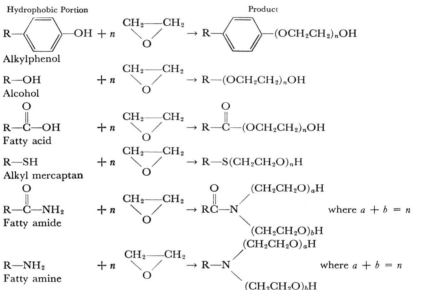

*Jelinek, C. F., Mayhew, R. L., *Ind. Eng. Chem.*, **46**, 1930 (1954); Copyright 1954 by American Chemical society and used by permission of the copyright owner.

polymers or, alternatively, they may be copolymerized as "block-type" products:[40]

$$A_n\text{---}A\text{---}B\text{---}B_m$$

"A" represents propylene oxide and "B" ethylene oxide, the polypropylene thus becoming the hydrophobe which is solubilized by addition of ethylene oxide.[51] Optimum polypropylene glycol molecular weights appear to lie between 800 and 2500. It is obvious that a large number of compounds varying markedly in characteristics can be produced; many of these have already been investigated.

If, instead of polypropylene glycol, the central portion of the molecule becomes ethylene diamine, block polymers having four hydrophilic tails can be made by reaction with ethylene oxide[44] (Figure 13.25). Where molecular weights of the polypropylene polyoxyethylene compounds can approximate

10,000, molecular weights of the ethylene diamine products can approach 27,000.

Alkylolamides. These are reaction products of alkanolamines with fatty acids and the 2:1 type[48] in which two moles of diethanolamine (DEA) are reacted with a single mole of coconut fatty acid which is said[26] to be responsible for the surface-active properties of the mixture:

$$RCOOH + 2HN(C_2H_4OH)_2 \rightarrow RCON(C_2H_4OH)_2$$

Excess DEA converts both amino ester and amido ester to the active 2:1 product N,N-bis(2-hydroxyethyl)lauramide.

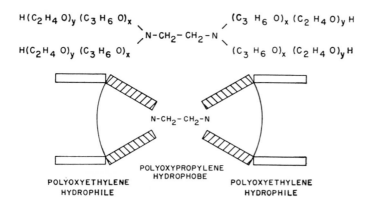

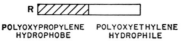

POLYOXYPROPYLENE   POLYOXYETHYLENE
HYDROPHOBE   HYDROPHILE

Figure 13.25. Typical block polymer surfactants. [*Taken from Soap Chemical Specialties*, **33**, *No. 6, 47 (1957); by permission.*]

New 1:1 types have recently been developed[25] having over 90 per cent crude amide content, achieved by an ester interchange of 1 mole DEA with 1 mole of fatty acid methyl ester under special synthesis conditions.

The importance of these compounds lies in their detergent and foaming ability, and the fact that they act as foam boosters and stabilizers for dodecylbenzene sulfonates, are compatible with both anionic and cationic surfactants, are emollients, affect viscosity of liquid detergents, and are corrosion inhibitors.

Sugar Surfactants. Sugar is a desirably priced raw material on which a process for surfactant has been based.[34] The product is the sucrose fatty acid monoester (the monostearate, for example), the eleven oxygen atoms of sucrose contributing about the same hydrophilic effect as a polyoxyethylene with the same number of oxygen atoms.

The process is typified by the following run:[13]

"Three moles of sucrose, one mole of methyl stearate, and 0.1 mole of potassium carbonate (catalyst) are dissolved in dimethylformamide (or dimethyl sulfoxide). Potassium carbonate is a preferred catalyst because, unlike a more alkaline catalyst (e.g., sodium methoxide), it will not take part in undesirable side reactions at high temperatures.

"The reaction mixture is agitated, heated at 90–95° C at 80–100 mm of mercury for 9–12 hours. The methyl stearate reacts with the sucrose to give the sucrose monostearate and methanol. The latter is stripped off.

"After the solvent is distilled off and the product dried, it contains about 45 per cent monostearate, 1–2 per cent potassium carbonate, and about 54 per cent unconverted sugar (because of the large excess used). The product can be used for many jobs, as is. More likely, however, the economics of the situation will dictate that the sugar be recovered by further purification of the product."

Conversions of over 90 per cent are claimed; the controlling factor appears to be the use of the fatty acid ester and a suitable solvent such as dimethylformamide (DMF). An excess of sucrose assures monoester production, the desired surfactant type, rather than the diester (useful as an emulsifier).

In the equipment shown in Figure 13.26, the reactants, the solvent, and the catalyst are placed in the reaction vessel (5) in which the conversion from non-sugar ester to sucrose monoester is carried out. The product alcohol and part of the solvent are stripped from the system in a turbulent-film evaporator (1). The product alcohol and solvent are fractionated in the packed reflux tower (2). The solvent is returned to the system through (4) while the alcohol is condensed in (3) and collected in vessels (7).

The recovery of the sucrose ester from the slurry containing unreacted sugar can be accomplished using xylene as the ester solvent, since filtration is unsuccessful due to the sugar particle size. The xylene is then recovered by steam distillation and the sugar ester remains. Important to economic operation is minimization of diester formation (by controlled water content during alcoholysis), recycling of unreacted sugar, and recovery of DMF and xylene. Several licenses have been granted for this process.

Sorbitol Compounds. Sorbitol may be produced by the hydrogenation of sugars such as glucose, and this hexahydric alcohol may be reacted with ethylene glycol and the reaction product esterified to varying degrees with lipophilic fatty acids; or sorbitol may be partially esterified with fatty acids and these inner-ester sorbitol anhydrides further reacted with ethylene glycol.

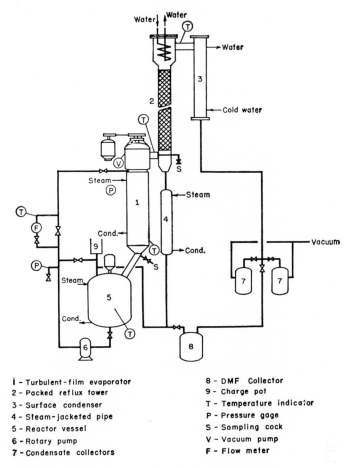

1 – Turbulent-film evaporator
2 – Packed reflux tower
3 – Surface condenser
4 – Steam-jacketed pipe
5 – Reactor vessel
6 – Rotary pump
7 – Condensate collectors

8 – DMF Collector
9 – Charge pot
T – Temperature indicator
P – Pressure gage
S – Sampling cock
V – Vacuum pump
F – Flow meter

Figure 13.26. Pilot-plant equipment for preparation of the sugar esters. [*Taken from* **J. Am. Oil Chem. Soc., 34, 185 (1957)**; *by permission.*]

Ampholytic Surfactants

These products are so named because they contain both cationic and anionic groupings. A typical example of preparation is the reaction of a fatty primary amine and methyl acrylate to give the N-fatty-β-aminopropionic ester which is saponified to the water soluble salt.[2]

$$RNH_2 + CH_2{=}CHCOOCH_3 \rightarrow RNHCH_2CH_2COOCH_3 \xrightarrow{\text{NaOH}}$$
$$RNHCH_2CH_2COONa$$

A specific use for sodium lauroylsarcosinate is in toothpaste compositions[52] in which these enzyme inhibitive surfactants are said to reduce dental caries.

The compounds are also used in shampoos, cosmetics, water emulsion paints, corrosion inhibitors, detergent-sanitizers, etc.

Cationic Surfactants

Because these compounds derive their surface activity from the positively charged long-chain portion of the molecule, they are also known as invert soaps:

$$R_1NH^+—Br^- \text{ (or } Cl^-) \qquad\qquad R_1COO^-—Na^+$$

cationic   anionic

These surfactants may be either nitriles, amines, amide-linked amines, or quaternary nitrogen bases such as

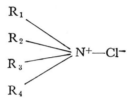

in which the R_1 is a long-chain group, the other R groups may be alkyl chains or hydrogen, and the negative group may be a halogen or sulfate. Other quarternaries are exemplified by sulfonium and phosphonium compounds.[51]

Perhaps cationic surfactants were first used as softeners for the textile industry. Because these chemicals are substantive to, and exhaust onto, cotton fiber, imparting lubricity and softness, they are used to a considerable extent for this purpose. More recently they have been used as fabric softeners which the housewife may apply to her towels and garments following the usual laundering operation. Because they are antistatic agents they are used as finishes on synthetic fabrics which exhibit an undesirable static charge, and because of their bactericidal character they are also used as antibacterial rinses and detergent-sanitizers.

Manufacture has never been on the scale of fatty alcohol sulfates or alkylbenzene sulfonates, and while considerable tonnages are produced, the manufacturing procedures appear to be much less standardized than those for the anionic or nonionic surfactants. A factor which tends to minimize standardization is the apparent necessity for specialty compositions in which raw materials of rather diverse character are used.

Most of the information on the manufacture of these compounds is to be found in the patent literature, and excellent reviews of these have appeared.[39]

Detergent Builders and Additives

The dried, and even many of the liquid detergent formulations contain electrolyte salts which at first glance might be considered diluents. Examination of the voluminous literature shows, however, that these products have a definite function, and in fact make detergent products as effective as they are. For example, dilution of sodium dodecylbenzene sulfonate to a 40 per cent active ingredient (AI) level with sodium sulfate will yield somewhat superior wetting and detergent values over an equivalent weight of 100 per cent active ingredient composition. Further, if the product containing 40 per cent AI and 60 per cent sodium sulfate is altered to substitute sodium tripolyphosphate for half the sodium sulfate, the detergent value of the composition is very markedly improved. Because of their effect, these inorganic salts are called detergent "builders" in the trade.

Sodium Sulfate. Any surfactant prepared by sulfation or sulfonation can carry with it greater or lesser amounts of sodium sulfate, sodium sulfite, and/or sodium chloride; the latter two originate from either SO_3 or chlorosulfonic acid sulfonation. Many surfactant applications require a minimum of electrolyte, and for this purpose an alcohol purification may be used. A sulfur trioxide sulfonation may leave as little as 2–3 per cent electrolyte, while the other sulfonation procedures may leave as much as 60 per cent sodium sulfate. Oleum sulfonation may leave as little as 15 per cent sodium sulfate in the product by proper spent acid layering and separation. A continuous sulfonation and neutralization procedure without spent acid separation may leave residual sodium sulfate of from 20 to 40 per cent in the product. Since spent acid disposal may be a problem, and since sodium sulfate addition can improve surface activity when used in proper amounts, it frequently proves most efficacious simply to adjust proportions to utilize all the sulfonation and neutralization products. In other instances it becomes desirable to add further quantities of sodium sulfate (salt cake), and in recent years the increased demand for this purpose has caused some scarcity and a price increase in this by-product raw material.

It is estimated[33] that the detergent industry uses about 7 per cent of the total United States sodium sulfate production, totaling about one million tons per year.

Sodium Silicate. Either light- or heavy-duty detergent formulations may require a corrosion inhibitor to prevent deleterious action on the metal or vitreous enamel surfaces of the washing machines in which the products are used. Sodium silicate proves to be a satisfactory answer to the problem, for in addition to effective inhibitor action, it also exerts functional effects in maintaining soil in suspension and in boosting detergency.

Sodium Phosphates. The introduction of tetrasodium pyrophosphate ($Na_4P_2O_7$) in the mid 30's and early 40's improved the soap products then generally used, and made it possible for surfactants to compete quality-wise in soil removal for heavy-duty cleaning. The more recent product now almost universally used in this country is sodium tripolyphosphate (STP; $Na_5P_3O_{10}$). The polyphosphates sequester the water-hardening Ca and Mg ions, soften water, help to adjust pH, and above all, sharply increase the soil removing and suspending characteristics of the surfactants with which they are used. In the spray-drying operation STP forms the hexahydrate, and this water of crystallization, because it cannot be reversibly removed, helps to stabilize the detergent moisture content. Spray-tower temperature-operating conditions are thereby imposed, however,[18] which demand that inversion to the ortho and pyrophosphates does not result.

It is estimated[28] that from 40 to 50 per cent of all phosphorus applications is accounted for by the sodium phosphates in detergents. A more precise estimate[38] states that the single largest use for phosphorus is in the production of STP (39.2 per cent) and tetrasodium pyrophosphate (6.6 per cent), totaling in excess of $1\frac{3}{4}$ billion pounds.

Soda Ash. Appreciable amounts of soda ash are used as a low-priced bulking diluent capable of maintaining pH of detergent solutions at a desired level. Since it exerts some builder action it may be used in certain heavy-duty products.

Other Additives. Sodium carboxymethyl cellulose is used extensively with syndets because of its ability to suspend and prevent redeposition of soil on the washed garment. Used in amounts from a fraction to about 2 per cent in the formulation, it helps syndets more than soap formulations, the latter appearing to have a built-in ability to reduce redeposition.

Another additive, the importance of which is completely out of proportion to the amounts used in the formulation, is the group of colorless dyes known as brighteners; their function is to adsorb on the washed garments and to reflect a visible blue color induced by the ultraviolet portion of the spectrum. Amounts may vary in a formulation from as little as a few hundredths of a per cent to 0.1 per cent. The visible improvement resulting from the use of these brighteners is so striking that all medium- to heavy-duty detergent products contain them.

Another less significant additive, important primarily in terms of consumer aesthetics, is perfume oil, used in amounts varying from 0.05 to 0.1 per cent on the formula basis.

REFERENCES

1. Allen, H. D., Kline, W. A., Lawrence, E. A., Arrowsmith, C. J., and Marsel, C., *Chem. Eng. Progr.*, **43**, 459 (1947).
2. Andersen, D. L., *J. Am. Oil Chemists' Soc.*, **34**, 188 (1957).
3. Association of American Soap and Glycerine Producers, Inc., May 1957.
4. Ballard, S. A., Finch, H. de V., and Peterson, E. A., British Patent 619,014, (March 2, 1949 to N. V. Bataafsche Petroleum Maatschappij).
5. Berglron, J., Revue Francaise des Corps Gras (1958).
6. Buckham, J. A., and Moulton, R. W., *Chem. Eng. Progr.*, **51**, No. 3, 126 (1955).
7. Carlson, E. J., Flint, G., and Gilbert, E. E., *Ind. Eng. Chem.*, **50**, 276 (1958).
8. Chaland, J. H., Martin, J. B., and Baker, J. S., *Eng. Progr.*, **53**, No. 12, 593 (1957).
9. *Chem. Eng.*, **61**, 372 (1954).
10. *Chem. Eng. News*, **34**, 5752 (1956).

11. *Chem. Eng. Progr.,* **44,** No. 10, 16 (1948).
12. *Chem. Industries,* 247 (1949).
13. *Chem. Week,* p. 90 (Oct. 8, 1955).
14. Fairbairn, A. W., Cheney, H. A., and Cherniavsky, A. J., *Chem. Eng. Progr.,* **43,** No. 6, 280 (1947).
15. Fedor, W. S., Strain, B., Theoharous, L., and Whyte, D. D., *Ind. Eng. Chem.,* **51,** 13 (1959).
16. Forbath, T. P., *Chem. Eng.,* **64,** 226 (1959).
17. Gilbert, E. E., and Veldhuis, B., *Ind. Eng. Chem.,* **50,** 997 (1958).
18. Hafford, B. C., *Ind. Eng. Chem.,* **46,** 1938 (1954).
19. Hatcher, D. B., *J. Am. Oil Chemists' Soc.,* **34,** 175 (1957).
20. Hill, E. F., Wilson, G. R., and Steinle, E. C., Jr., *Ind. Eng. Chem.,* **46,** 1917 (1954).
21. *Ind. Eng. Chem.,* **39,** 126 (1947).
22. Jelinek, C. F., and Mayhero, R. L., *Ind. Eng. Chem.,* **46,** 1930 (1954).
23. Kastens, M. L., and Ayo, J. J., Jr., *Ind. Eng. Chem.,* **42,** 1626 (1950).
24. Kircheo, J. E., Miller, E. L., and Geiser, P. E., *Ind. Eng. Chem.,* **46,** 1925 (1954).
25. Kritchevsky, J., *J. Am. Oil Chemists' Soc.,* **34,** 178 (1957).
26. Kroll, H., and Nadeau, H., *J. Am. Oil Chemists' Soc.,* **34,** 323 (1957).
27. Lamont, D. R., U. S. Patent 1,652,900, December 13, 1927.
28. Latourette, W. I., *Barron's* p. 11 (Sept. 8, 1958).
29. Marshall, W. B., Jr., and Seltzer, E., *Chem. Eng. Progr.,* **46,** No. 10, 501; No. 11, 575 (1950).
30. Mazzoni, G., S. p. A., Busto Arsizio, Italy, *Soap,* **34,** No. 3, 185 (1958).
31. McBride, G. W., *Chem. Eng.,* No. 8, 94 (April 1947).
32. McCutcheon, J. W., *Soap* (January–April 1958).
33. *Oil, Paint Drug Reptr.,* p. 3 (Oct. 5, 1959).
34. Osipow, L., Snell, F. D., and Finchler, A., *J. Am. Oil Chemists' Soc.,* **34,** 185 (1957).
35. Palmquist, F. T. E., and Sullivan, F. E., *J. Am. Oil Chemists' Soc.,* **36,** 173 (1959).
36. *Petroleum Refiner,* **36,** No. 11, 250–251 (1957).
37. Pollak, A., *Tappi,* **39,** No. 1, 60A (1956).
38. Riley, W. J., *Chem. Eng. News,* **34,** 5312 (Oct. 29, 1956).
39. Schwartz, A. M., and Perry, J. W., "Surface Active Agents," Vol. I, New York, Interscience Publishers, Inc., 1949.
40. Schwartz, A. M., Perry, J. W., and Berch, J., "Surface Active Agents and Detergents," Vol. II, New York, Interscience Publishers, Inc., 1958.
41. Sherwood, P. W., *Can. Chem. Process Inds.,* **32,** 1102 (1948).
42. Sittenfield, M., *Chem. Eng.,* **55,** 120 (1948).
43. *Soap,* **35,** No. 4, 131 (1959).
44. Stanton, W. B., *Soap,* **33,** No. 6, 47 (1957).
45. Stromquist, D. M., and Reents, A. C., *Ind. Eng. Chem.,* **43,** 1065 (1951).
46. U. S. Patent 601,603 (1897).
47. U. S. Patent 1,932,180.
48. U. S. Patent 2,089,212.
49. U. S. Patent 2,154,835.
50. U. S. Patent 2,605,293.
51. U. S. Patent 2,674,619; 2,677,700; British Patent 722,746.
52. U. S. Patent 2,689,170.
53. U. S. Patent 2,858,345.
54. Wetherhorn, D., *Tappi,* **40,** 879 (1957).
55. Wurster, O. C., "Glycerin Refining Plants," Chicago, Illinois, Wurster and Sanger, Inc.

14

PETROLEUM AND ITS PRODUCTS;
PETROCHEMICALS

In collaboration with A. F. Galli*

PETROLEUM AND ITS PRODUCTS

When first obtained from the ground, before refining in any way, petroleum (rock oil) is called "crude oil." It occasionally appears at the surface of the earth through seepage; it usually occurs at moderate depths; in some cases it must be sought by drill holes over a mile deep. When such a drill hole reaches an oil basin, the oil is frequently forced out under enormous pressures; gas, salty water, and sand usually accompany the oil. After a period which varies considerably, the flow becomes quieter; after some months it does not gush at all, and the oil must be pumped out; finally, no oil is obtained even by pumping—the well is dry. New wells are therefore constantly being sought. The oil prospector chooses lands possessing a subsoil which has characteristics indicating petroliferous strata; these characteristics vary in different fields, and in no case is it beyond doubt that a drill hole will reach oil. The search for oil is supplemented by accidental discoveries, in the course of drilling for water, for example. Where natural gas occurs, it is reasonable to prospect for oil;† it is by no means certain that oil will be

* College of Engineering, West Virginia University, Morgantown, W. Va.
† The Rodessa field, Caddo Parish, in Louisiana, was a gas field for many years; only in 1935 was it discovered to carry oil.

478

found, but since petroleum consists of a mixture of hydrocarbons, the lighter ones such as methane, CH_4, and ethane, C_2H_6, may have escaped, in part, leaving the main body of liquids and solids not very far away. The heaviest hydrocarbons, beginning for example, with eicosane, $C_{20}H_{42}$, which melts at blood temperature, are solid; the intermediate ones liquid.

Discovery of Petroleum

It was not the genius of man which discovered petroleum; the presence of petroleum was indicated by seepages which frequently coated small rivers, as in Pennsylvania; by contaminating brines, much to the disgust of the early (1806) salt refiners, like the brothers Ruffner along the Kanawha River in West Virginia; in the escaping gas, rich in vapors and known for centuries, as in the Baku Peninsula, where the "eternal" fire gave powerful support to religious cults (Zoroasters).[39] Only in more recent times, especially in the three decades past, has a more intensive search taken place, partly because the evident clues had been exhausted, and partly because petroleum has become a necessity to national as well as to civil life. To the study of the soil for indications of petroliferous strata, which has already been mentioned, scientific methods were added: the revival of the anticlinal theory, the measurement of temperature in adjacent wells in order to locate the anticlinal axis; gravitometry, including seismic or sonic apparatus; the electric log; and the magnetometer.[40]

The seismic method for underground exploration is an adaptation of the study of low-lying, deeply buried rock formations, by the echo characteristics of time and direction of an artificial vibration, such as the explosion of a charge of dynamite; it is called the seismic reflection method. A portable seismometer is set firmly on hard ground; it consists of a post bearing a long pointer rigidly fastened to it, and a heavy weight suspended from an arm. The post moves with the vibrations of the ground; the pointer magnifies them, and throws a point of light on the face of the weight which, by virtue of its inertia, does not respond to the vibrations. A moving-picture camera, set in rubber, records the path of the light; the rate of travel of the film gives the measure of time in thousands of seconds. A charge of dynamite, say 11 pounds, at a depth of 95 feet is set off, and the first vibration as well as the subsequent reflection from the low-lying rock formation are recorded. The time for the reflection to travel upward gives the depth; thus, in one case, two and 365/1000ths seconds indicated 18,000 feet. The slope of the strata is given by the shape of the curve. Many such records are made in order to plot an area.*

More recent still are a geochemical method, the "halo method," and an

---

* In part from a radio broadcast by Dr. John P. Buwalda, California Institute of Technology, in a series on Recent Developments in the Geologic Sciences, under the name, "Searchers of the Unknown," Jan. 4, 1936.

electrical method, such as the Eltran. In the geochemical method, soil surveys* are conducted by measuring hydrocarbon content and mineralization in subsoil samples which are gathered with an ordinary auger. Eight analyses per square mile are preferred. The hydrocarbons are ethane, measured in parts per billion of soil, or the more concentrated liquid or waxy hydrocarbons. The significant high values, determined by statistical means, are plotted. If they form a pattern such as an aureole or halo, the area is positive and the petroleum deposit is roughly outlined by the pattern. The mineralization figures are also plotted, and give in a number of published surveys a similar pattern for the same area.

Petroleum is found only in sedimentary rocks, and has its origin in the petrified remains of plants and animals,† which accumulated with clays and muds along the seashore. At a later geologic period, the droplets or gas migrated from the source muds into a "reservoir" rock, chiefly sandstone. The strata were lifted and warped, forming arches (anticlines) and troughs (synclines), from one mile to several miles in width. Oil is found in the anticlines, having risen above the water; it may also be found in synclines, if the upper space (to the neighboring anticlines) is filled with the still lighter gas, also formed from these deposits, and tapped as natural gas. An oil or gas pool is not a subterranean pond, but merely an accumulation of petroleum or gas in rock pores. The container rock is of a highly porous type‡ in which the interstices are such as to permit the oil, gas and water to move freely; the dense or non-porous retainer rock prevents the escape of the oil or gas from the container rock. The petroleum generally contains large amounts of gas in solution, under pressure.

It was in 1859, at Titusville, Pa., that Colonel Drake sank his now famous well; it was $59\frac{1}{2}$ feet deep. Since then, many wells have been driven, and the depth has steadily increased. In 1959, a total of 49,496 wells were drilled

---

* Geophysical Service, Inc., Dallas, Texas, publishes a bulletin called "Soil Surveys."

† There have been many theories for the formation of petroleum deposits in the ground. Among the earlier ones was that of Engler who referred the formation of petroleum to a store of fatty remains of all kinds of life, but especially animal life; his opinion was based on laboratory experiments with menhaden oil, from which he produced a petroleum-like substance. C. Engler, *Ber. Deutschen Gesellschaft,* **21,** 1816 (1888). Among more recent workers, Alfred Treibs assigned to plants the dominant role in forming petroleum, to animal remains a secondary role. His statement is based on the spectroscopic study of the light absorption of petroleums in which he thus identifies and estimates quantitatively porphyrins of chlorophyll origin in a high percentage, while he also finds porphyrins of hemoglobin origin, but in much smaller amounts, *Ann.,* 510, 42 (1934). A brief summary of the older theories will be found in "The examination of hydrocarbon oils and saponifiable waxes," D. Holde, tr. by Edward Mueller, New York, John Wiley and Sons, 1922.

‡ The porosity of a rock is defined as the property of containing interstices or openings, which may vary in size from caverns to subcapillary pores.

in the United States, of which 25,379 were oil wells, 3,761 were gas wells,* and 19,101 dry holes (Minerals Yearbook).

The producing oil wells in the United States on December 31, 1959, totaled 583,141, and the average production over the year per well per day was about 12.2 barrels. The cost of a 10,000-foot well is $250,000 or more. Depth drilling has been helped by the development of rotary drilling; several new chemical agents, the application of acids, and the use of special muds have contributed.

When first tapped, the well may be a gusher, with many thousands of barrels a day; this output begins to decrease at once, and gradually tapers off until a pump is needed to bring up the oil. A life of 20 years is a rough estimate for a newly tapped oil-bearing formation.

Petroleum Reserves

Taking petroleum from the ground means subtracting it from a finite store: less oil is left for the next generation. In past years the rate of discovery of new oil bearing formations has been larger than the rate of oil removal so that the petroleum reserves in the United States have increased. However, the margin has been narrowing and preliminary figures indicate that production of crude in 1960 may exceed new oil discoveries. Reserves are ample at present but small compared to the coal reserves. Thus there is concern over the diminishing rate of new discoveries; the proved reserves— that is, known reserves in well established formations—might diminish, while on the other hand, the amount of oil removed continues to increase year by year. Another consideration is that of exports and imports. In the past, the latter were less than exports of crude oil, but now they are greater. For example, in 1959, 354 million barrels of crude were imported, and only 2.5 million barrels exported. It might be noted also that finding oil and drilling wells now are far more costly than a decade ago. The military want to feel that there is a safe margin of oil supplies against a sudden emergency. The results are (1) the development and constant improvement of means for conserving oil, wasting none, and leaving the least possible unextracted in the formation, and (2) supplementing these means to conserve by developing other sources of motor fuel, such as the distillation of oil shales, and the manufacture of synthetic liquid fuel from natural gas and coal.

Means of conserving oil have commanded increased attention and study. One is to reduce or abolish waste caused by too-rapid removal of oil from

* In some cases, it is possible that an upper pool, which has been pumped out, is underlain by a lower pool. The Fox pool, Oklahoma, at the 2000-foot level, producing since 1916, was "on the pump" in 1935; in October of that year a new well, 8088 feet down, brought in a new producing pool, 6000 feet under the original one. It was gusher, with 8 to 10 thousand barrels a day. "The field that came back," C. E. Savage, *The Lamp*, February, 1936.

a formation which is accompanied by excessive lowering of the potential (pressure) of the well. Laws have been passed which regulate the rate of oil removal from wells and oil pools to conserve well pressure.

Another is the more complete extraction of oil from the oil sands. It should be explained that rarely is as much as 50 per cent of the total oil in a formation extracted; more often, it is 30 per cent or less. In order to recover the residual oil, the formation may be flooded with water, which drives the oil toward the well in which a pump may be working. For this

TABLE 14.1. CONSUMPTION, PRODUCTION AND IMPORT OF CRUDE OIL IN THE U. S., MILLIONS OF BARRELS PER YEAR*

(Year)	1955	1957	1959
Total consumption	2,763	2,974	2,933
Domestic production	2,479	2,606	2,578
Imports	284	369	354

* Minerals Yearbook, 1959.

TABLE 14.2. LEADING CRUDE OIL PRODUCING STATES, MILLIONS OF BARRELS PER YEAR*

(Year)	1955	1957	1959
Texas	1,053	1,074	984
California	355	340	307
Oklahoma	203	215	196
Louisiana	271	330	355
Kansas	122	124	120
New Mexico	83	95	106
Illinois	81	77	78

* Minerals Yearbook, 1959.

TABLE 14.3. PROVEN PETROLEUM RESERVES IN THE UNITED STATES*

(Year)	1952	1953	1955	1957	1959
Estimated Reserves, million barrels	27,961	28,945	30,012	30,300	31,719

* Minerals Yearbook, 1959.

method to be successful, the ground formations must be favorable. Much secondary oil is recovered also by pumping gas into the formation (repressuring). Flooding with water has given good results in some areas. Other methods are (a) fracturing oil bearing formations with explosives or hydraulic pressure, and (b) acid treatment to increase oil flow from wells (acidizing).

Another method of increasing the oil reserves is to utilize the oil bearing shales which occur in large amounts in Colorado, Utah, and Wyoming. High yield processes have been developed but are not presently competitive with petroleum from conventional sources.

Synthetic petroleum very much like the natural material can be produced from coal, natural gas, and other carbon containing materials. The cost of the synthetic product is considerably higher than for natural petroleum.

The United States continued to lead the world in production of crude oil in 1959 with a total of 2,574,590,000 barrels during that year. This represents about 36 per cent of the total world production. Table 14.4 shows the production of crude oil throughout the world.

TABLE 14.4. WORLD PRODUCTION OF CRUDE PETROLEUM, MILLIONS OF BARRELS*

Country	1955	1957	1959
North America	2,728	2,921	2,897
South America	885	1,132	1,163
Europe	669	897	1,140
Asia	1,324	1,464	1,883
Africa	14	18	42
Oceania	3	2	2
Total	5,626	6,436	7,127

* Minerals Yearbook, 1959.

Nature of Petroleum

As is generally the case with naturally occurring materials, petroleum is complex and variable in chemical composition. It varies in color from light greenish-brown to black and may be of low viscosity or so viscous as to be nearly immobile. The crude oil is usually dark-colored, of low viscosity, and contains gases and solids, either dissolved or dispersed. Much of the gas separates when the oil reaches the surface but may do so underground and be found as natural gas some distance from the oil.

The principal constituents of petroleum are the hydrocarbons; small amounts of combined sulfur, nitrogen and oxygen are present as impurities. It is estimated that several thousand compounds are present in petroleum but relatively few have been positively identified. They vary in composition from one to more than 200 carbon atoms; those containing up to four are usually gases, five to sixteen, liquids, and those containing seventeen or more are usually solids.

The classes of compounds occurring in petroleum are as follows:

(a) Paraffin hydrocarbons, general formula C_nH_{2n+2}. They are straight-chain (normal paraffins) or branched chain (isoparaffins). These compounds may be gaseous, liquid or solid (waxes), depending on their structure and molecular weight.

(b) Naphthene hydrocarbons, general formula C_nH_{2n}. These are saturated hydrocarbons possessing a ring structure usually containing five to seven carbon atoms in the ring.

(c) Aromatic hydrocarbons, formula C_nH_{2n-6}. The compounds are characterized by a six-carbon ring.

(d) Multi-ring cyclic hydrocarbons. These are naphthene and aromatic compounds containing more than one ring in their structure.

(e) Olefin hydrocarbons, formula C_nH_{2n} for mono-olefins (can add one molecule of hydrogen) and C_nH_{2n-2} for di-olefins (can add two molecules of hydrogen). Since these compounds are very reactive they are found only in trace amounts although large quantities may be formed during cracking.

(f) Sulfur compounds. Sulfur is generally found in petroleum in the combined form in amounts up to 6 per cent. Hydrogen sulfide and thiophenes are the most usual forms but it may also be present as mercaptans, sulfides, and other compounds.

(g) Oxygen compounds. Oxygen occurs in combined form in alcohols, phenols, resins and organic acids.

(h) Nitrogen compounds. These include pyridines, quinolines, indoles, pyrroles, and others.

(i) Inorganic compounds. These include the salts (from salt water), and the clay, sand, and similar compounds which associate with the oil during its passage from the oil-bearing strata.

Since most of the compounds are hydrocarbons having a fairly constant hydrogen to carbon ratio, the ultimate analysis of all crudes falls within a narrow range.

Carbon	83–87%	Nitrogen	0.1–1.5%
Hydrogen	11–15%	Oxygen	0.3–1.2%
Sulfur	0.1–6%		

Classification of Petroleum

An eminently satisfactory classification of crudes has been developed by the U. S. Bureau of Mines; the main features are given in Table 14.5. Class A comprises the paraffin-base crudes, which are wax-bearing; these contain mainly paraffinic hydrocarbons in all their fractions; their residue in the still becomes the much-sought after "cylinder stock." Straight-distilled gasolines from this crude would be paraffinic, and have "knocking" properties. Naphthene base oil, class G, contains mainly naphthenes, that is, cyclic compounds which are saturated, with side chains both naphthenic and paraffinic. Naphthene base and intermediate naphthene base, class E, may contain much black, brittle, almost infusible asphaltic material, although they often do not. The crudes differ also in the amounts of lower- and higher-boiling compounds. This is shown in Table 14.5.

The petroleum refiner classifies crudes according to their "base" as follows: (1) paraffin base crudes, high in wax and lube oil fractions, containing small amounts of naphthenes or asphalt and low in sulfur, nitrogen and oxygen compounds; (2) asphalt base crudes, which give high yields of pitch, asphalt, and heavy fuel oil; (3) mixed base crudes, which have characteristics about midway between those of paraffin- and asphalt-base crudes; and (4) aromatic-base crudes which contain large amounts of low

TABLE 14.5. CLASSIFICATION IN 7 CLASSES OF PETROLEUM CRUDES, ACCORDING TO THEIR "BASE," FROM THE DISTILLATION-ANALYSIS OF 800 SAMPLES FROM ALL OVER THE WORLD [R. I. 3279, U. S. BUREAU OF MINES, E. C. LANE AND E. L. GARTON (1935); CONDENSED].

	A Paraffin base oil (wax-bearing)	B Paraffin intermediate base oil (wax-bearing)	C Intermediate Paraffin base oil (wax-bearing)	D Intermediate base oil (wax-bearing)	E Intermediate Naphthene base oil (wax-bearing)	F Naphthene intermediate base oil (wax-bearing)	G Naphthene base oil (wax free)
A.P.I. gravity	49.7°	39.2°	29.5°	39.6°	15.3°	29.5°	24.0°
Specific gravity	.781	.829	.879	.827	.964	.879	.910
Pour point	below 5° F	below 5° F	40° F	below 5° F	40° F	below 5° F	below 5° F
Per cent sulfur	0.1	0.28	0.32	0.33	3.84	0.16	0.14
Saybolt Universal viscosity 100° F	34 seconds	41	120	39	4000	47	55
Color	green	greenish-black	greenish-black	green	brownish-black	greenish-black	green
Distillation 1st drop	93° F (34° C)	91° F (33° C)	176° F (80° C)	84° F (29° C)	280° F (138° C)	138° F (59° C)	315° F (157° C)
Distillates:							
Gasoline and naphtha	45.2%	32.0	5.8	38.6	2.9	21.3	1.1
Kerosene	17.7%	17.2	nil	4.9	4.5	nil	nil
Gas oil	8.3%	10.6	27.8	17.3	10.6	34.6	55.5
Nonviscous lubricating	9.8%	10.9	20.4	9.4	8.6	10.4	14.2
Medium lubricating	3.4%	5.2	9.2	6.3	6.7	7.0	4.7
Viscous lubricating	nil	nil	nil	nil	1.020	4.7	11.6
Residuum	14.7%	23.5	36.4	22.1	58.4	21.4	12.7
Distillation loss	.9%	.6	.4	1.4	1.9	0.6	0.2
Carbon residue of residuum	1.1%	6.2	6.9	7.3	18.2	8.7	4.5
Carbon residue of crude	0.2%	1.5	2.5	1.6	10.6	1.9	0.6

485

TABLE 14.5. CLASSIFICATION IN 7 CLASSES OF PETROLEUM CRUDES, ACCORDING TO THEIR "BASE," FROM THE DISTILLATION-ANALYSIS OF 800 SAMPLES FROM ALL OVER THE WORLD [R. I. 3279, U. S. BUREAU OF MINES, E. C. LANE AND E. L. GARTON (1935); CONDENSED] (*Continued*)

	A Paraffin base oil (wax-bearing)	B Paraffin intermediate base oil (wax-bearing)	C Intermediate Paraffin base oil (wax-bearing)	D Intermediate base oil (wax-bearing)	E Intermediate Naphthene base oil (wax-bearing)	F Naphthene intermediate base oil (wax-bearing)	G Naphthene base oil (wax free)
Key fraction No. 1. (250–575° C) 482–527° F, 750 mm pressure							
Per cent cut.......	6.8%	6.5	7.1	5.8	5.1	10.1	19.6
A.P.I. of cut.......	44.7°	40.6	36.4	37.0	37.0	30.2	27.9
Key fraction No. 2. (275–300° C) 527–572° F, 40 mm pressure							
Per cent cut.......	4.4	5.7	9.0	4.9	8.2	6.0	7.3
A.P.I. of cut........	34.4°	29.3	30.0	24.9	19.5	24.0	16.5
Viscosity at 100° F..	110 seconds	120	120	165	240	230	over 400
Cloud test, in °F....	90	90	90	80	70	90	below 5

If key fraction No. 1 reads 40.0° A.P.I. or lighter, the lower boiling fractions of the oil are paraffinic; if it reads 33.0° A.P.I. or heavier, they are naphthenic; if its gravity lies between 33.0° and 40.0° A.P.I., they are intermediate.

If the gravity of key fraction No. 2 is 30.0° A.P.I. or lighter, the higher-boiling fractions of the oil are paraffinic; if it is 20.0° A.P.I. or heavier, the fractions are naphthenic; while if the gravity lies between 20° and 30° A.P.I., the fractions are intermediate.

486

molecular weight aromatic compounds and naphthene, together with smaller amounts of asphalt and lube oils.

Petroleum is separated into fractions by distillation. The composition of each fraction is related to its boiling range and no pure compounds are obtained. The fractions may be classified as shown in Table 14.6. The fractions require further treatment, including removal of impurities, blending, addition of certain chemicals (additives) to improve certain characteristics,

TABLE 14.6. FRACTIONS FROM PETROLEUM DISTILLATION

Product	Approximate boiling range, °F
Natural gasoline	30–180
Light distillates	
Gasoline	80–380
Naphthas	200–450
Jet fuels	180–450
Kerosene	350–550
Light heating oils	400–600
Intermediate distillates	
Gas oils	480–750
Diesel oils	380–650
Heavy fuel oil	550–800
Heavy distillates	
Lubricating oils	600–1000
Waxes	Above 625
Residues	
Lubricating oils	Above 900
Asphalt	Above 900
Residium	Above 900
Petroleum coke	

and additional chemical processing (cracking, reforming) to increase the yield of desired products.

Transportation of Crude

Crude petroleum is transported in large part by pumping it through pipe lines; the oil is sent great distances in this way, avoiding the high freight bill which it otherwise would incur. The crude oil travels through especially constructed trunk pipe lines laid in the ground along a purchased right of way thirty feet wide, in sections 75 miles long or more. Each section has its own pumping station and storage tanks, and the right of way is patrolled for leaks. The capacity of an 8-inch line under a pressure of 400 pounds is 25,000 gallons a day. When a ridge is to be crossed, the line is so disposed that one leg is downhill, so that by its syphon effect it will help pull the oil up the hill. In this way crude oil from Oklahoma reaches Bayonne, N. J., and Marcus Hook, Pa., and Texas crude is carried to Chicago (Whiting, Ind.) and Buffalo, N. Y. A 12-inch pipe line 237 miles long, running from

South Portland, Me., to Montreal, operated by eight pumping stations, has a capacity of 60,000 barrels daily of light crude oil. No pipe line crosses the Rocky Mountains.

The other modes of transportation are by boat (oil tankers), by tank car, and tank truck. Shipments from the gulf coast to the east coast of the United States totaled 667.7 million barrels in 1959.

PETROLEUM REFINING

Crude oil usually requires more than one operation for the production of finished products. Thus, a refinery consists of a number of individual processing units carefully designed and operated to produce competitively the products for a market which may vary from week to week.

Crude oil contains a number of inorganic impurities which are detrimental to the operation of the refinery units. For example, chlorides may react with water to produce corrosive hydrochloric acid, while sand and other suspended matter will cause plugging of trays in distillation equipment. Water itself causes trouble during distillation and must be removed from the crude. Salt can cause fouling of heat exchangers while other impurities may poison the catalyst used in cracking or reforming operations.

Desalting

Chemical desalting of crude oil is accomplished by adding water in the amount of 6 to 15 per cent of the oil rate to the heated (200 to 300° F) oil under pressure sufficient to prevent vaporization. The mixture is emulsified, and the salt enters the water phase. Chemical additives may be used to break the emulsion, allowing the water phase to settle out. The water containing the salt is discharged from the system.

Electrical desalting[22] involves the addition of 4 to 10 per cent water under pressure at 160 to 300° F, emulsification in a mixture, and introduction of the emulsion into a high-potential electrostatic field. The field causes the impurities to associate with the water phase and at the same time causes the water phase to agglomerate so that it can be removed. The desalted crude continues to the distillation units.

Distillation

The various products obtained from distillation of the crude are given in Table 14.6. The number of fractions or cuts obtained depends on the crude base and operating conditions. Crude distillation systems can generally be classified into three types, viz., single stage, two-stage, and two-stage with a vacuum tower.

Single Stage. A single stage crude unit is shown in Figure 14.2. The crude feed is preheated by the outgoing streams and then enters a direct-

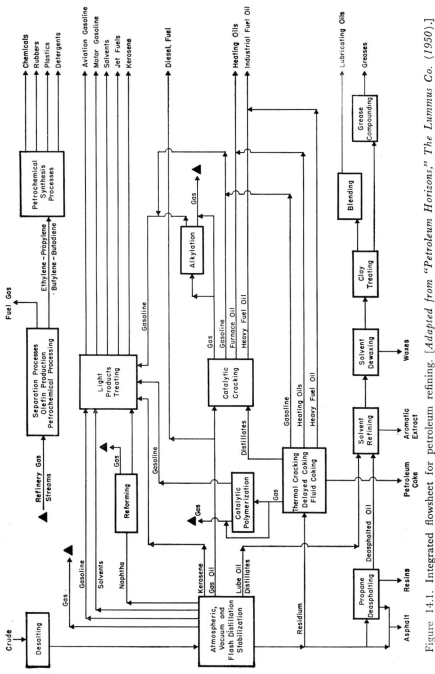

Figure 14.1. Integrated flowsheet for petroleum refining. [*Adapted from "Petroleum Horizons," The Lummus Co. (1950).*]

fired furnace type heater (pipe still). The materials separate in the distillation column according to their boiling points, the lowest boiling fraction leaving at the top of the column. Desired products may be withdrawn as side-streams at appropriate points on the column. The side-streams are further fractionated in small columns called strippers. Here, steam is used to free the cut from its more volatile components so that the desired initial boiling point of the product can be adjusted to its desired value.

Two-Stage Systems. The complexities of modern refinery operation frequently require the use of a two-stage system to provide sufficient cuts

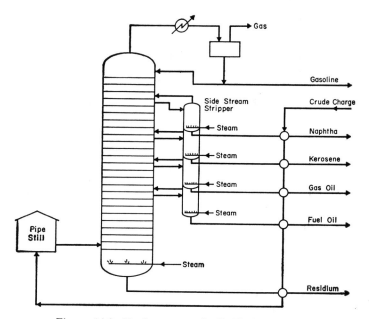

Figure 14.2. Single-stage crude-distillation process.

for the range of products desired. Such a system, shown in Figure 14.3, includes a primary tower which operates at about 50 psig, and a secondary tower which operates at atmospheric pressure, together with a stabilizing tower, and is used when the crude is to be separated into six to ten narrow cuts. Two or more side-streams may be withdrawn from the primary tower while the overhead becomes the feed to the stabilizer. The latter can be operated as a conventional stabilizer or as a debutanizer or depropanizer. The primary tower bottoms become the feed to the secondary tower. The latter uses a circulating reflux stream, the overhead product returns to the primary tower, and side-streams are withdrawn at appropriate points. All the side-streams are run through strippers to remove the light ends.

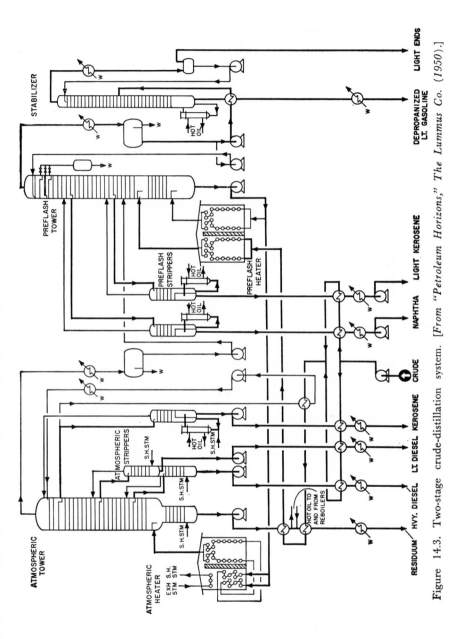

Figure 14.3. Two-stage crude-distillation system. [From "Petroleum Horizons," The Lummus Co. (1950).]

491

Two-Stage with Vacuum Tower. Coking in heater tubes or on trays and thermal degradation may result from high temperature operation. It is necessary therefore, in certain cases, to operate under vacuum so that the operating temperatures may be reduced.

The petroleum refiner uses vacuum distillation to obtain lubricating oil fractions, catalytic cracking charge stock, and asphalt. A vacuum tower is needed for the production of lube oil fractions and such a tower may be

Figure 14.4. A distillation system for crude oil. (*Courtesy Esso Standard Division, Humble Oil and Refining*)

added to a two-stage distillation unit (see Figure 14.5). The crude from the atmospheric tower is fed at about 800° F to the vacuum tower where the pressure is maintained at from 40 to 130 mm Hg absolute. The overhead gas oil fraction is removed and the side-streams are withdrawn through strippers. The bottom product is residium or asphalt.

A vacuum unit for producing catalytic cracking charge stock is depicted in Figure 14.6 Operating conditions are about the same as for lube oil production.

Cracking Processes

Crude oil contains at most about 18 per cent of gasoline. With the rapid growth of the automotive industry, it became necessary to devise methods

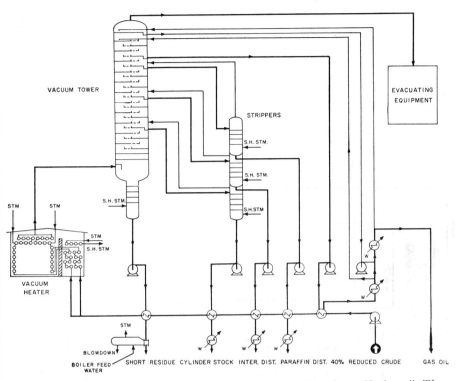

Figure 14.5. Vacuum distillation for lube oils. [*From "Petroleum Horizons," The Lummus Co. (1950).*]

whereby a larger portion of the petroleum could be utilized as gasoline. Thus, in 1959, the yield of gasoline from crude oil was 44.9 per cent. The difference is obtained by converting other fractions to gasoline. Motor gasoline may be obtained as shown below.

Motor gasoline including aviation gasoline are obtained by

Straight distilla-tion of crude oil	Cracking gas oil or fuel oil from petro-leum crude	Polymerization of C_3 and C_4 hydrocarbon gases	Natural gasoline from wet natural gas	Synthetic liquid fuels

On distilling crude oil, there is obtained a large percentage of middle oil, including gas oil, light fuel oil, and heavy fuel oil, for which, until the last few years, there was very little demand. By heating gas oil in an oil heater and allowing it to expand in a fractionating tower, it was found that a high percentage of lower-boiling components were formed, which were in fact gasoline. The decomposition of an oil during its distillation is a common and generally unwelcome occurrence of the organic laboratory. The large molecule is sensitive to heat; it breaks down into smaller fragments, some of which reunite, or unite in new ways. The cracking art makes skillful use of this defect, and guides the breakdown to produce a maximum of the desired gasoline. Cracking produces a variety of products: gases, low- and medium-boiling naphthas suitable for gasoline and kerosine, gas oil and

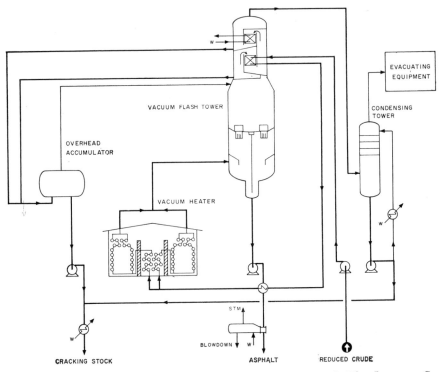

Figure 14.6. Vacuum flash unit. [*From "Petroleum Horizons," The Lummus Co.* (1950).]

fuel oil fractions, residual oil and carbon, depending partly on the kind of stock fed to the unit, and partly upon temperature, pressure and design of the equipment.

Thermal Cracking. In the early years of the cracking art, a flowing stream of gas oil, for example, was exposed for a period of time in steel tubes of high heat under a moderate pressure. It was then released to a large chamber at lower pressure, wherein gases, vapors and liquid could separate. The condensed vapors and the liquid were then separated by fractionation in the usual way. The oil could also be vaporized first, and then subjected to the heat of cracking. A large number of processes were developed and operated successfully; the most common was the so-called "tube and tank" process. Thermal cracking is still practiced, especially in smaller refineries; in most of the larger refineries, as well as in a number of the smaller ones, thermal cracking has been displaced by catalytic cracking, which is really thermal cracking in the presence of a catalyst.

Thermal cracking of petroleum begins at slightly under 700° F, but the rate is too low at this temperature to be useful. Industrial practice employs temperatures in the range of 850–1050° F for gasoline production (see Table 14.7). The reactions occurring during thermal cracking include cleavage of C-C bonds, dehydrogenation, polymerization, and cyclization. Cleavage and polymerization are the most important, the others occurring only to a limited extent.

TABLE 14.7. REACTION CONDITIONS FOR THERMAL CRACKING

Feed	Desired Product	Reaction Time, sec	Temp., °F	Press., psig
Methane	Acetylene	0.01–0.1	Above 2000	Vacuum
Ethane	Ethylene	0.1–2.0	1350–1550	5–30
Propane	Ethylene	1–3	1250–1450	5–30
Gas oil	Gasoline	40–300	850–1050	200–900
Reduced crude	Gasoline	. . .	850–1000	10–70

The operating conditions are fixed by the charge, the desired product, and undesirable reactions. It is usual to operate so as to obtain from 12 to 20 per cent conversion per pass and to employ recycle of the uncracked stock. Increasing the conversion per pass decreases the ultimate yield of gasoline, increases coking, and affects the properties of the gasoline. It results in shorter time on-stream between shutdown, due to the coking. The conditions chosen for a particular situation are, as usual, dictated by economic considerations.

It is necessary to maintain the charge in the liquid state during the cracking operation where gasoline is the desired product and this requires operation under pressure.

Variations in charge stock lead to different performance at a given set of cracking conditions. Also, large differences in yields occur as operating conditions are changed. The reaction rate of petroleum hydrocarbons increases as its molecular weight increases[12] so that lighter charge stock requires longer contact time to obtain a given conversion. Commercial practice is to raise the reaction temperature to increase the reaction rate rather than to use a longer contact time.

Prior to the introduction of catalytic processes, the two-coil Dubbs thermal cracking unit was the most widely used.[13] At present, however, coking processes predominate. These processes produce gas oil, gasoline

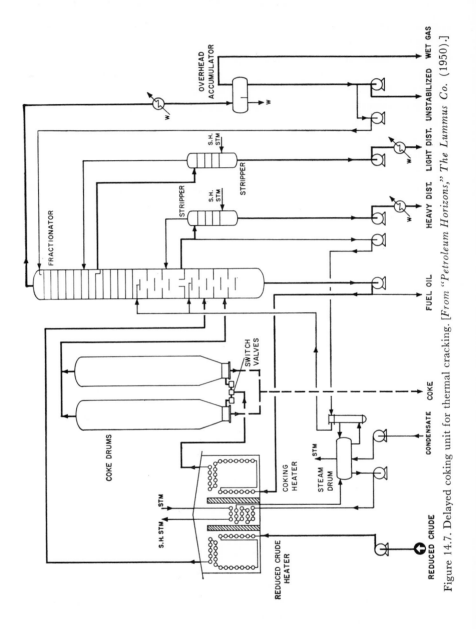

Figure 14.7. Delayed coking unit for thermal cracking. [*From "Petroleum Horizons," The Lummus Co.* (1950).]

and coke from a charge of reduced crude, cracked tars, heavy catalytic cycle oils and asphalts.[21] The feed is heated to about 900° F and charged into the reaction chamber (coking drum) where it remains until it is cracked to coke and volatile materials. The reaction chamber or drum is maintained at around 800–875° F. When the coke drum is filled it is taken out of service and steamed to remove volatile materials from the coke which is then sluiced out with water. The cleaned drum is returned to service. Two (or more) drums may be used in parallel and may be, typically, on-stream for 24 hours and out for cleaning for 24 hours.

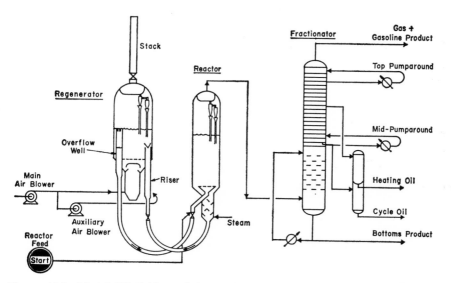

Figure 14.8. Model IV fluid catalytic cracking process. [*Pet. Ref.*, *39, No. 9, 187* (1960) *copyright 1960 by the Gulf Publishing Co.*]

In the fluid coking process[26] the charge is fed into the top of a fluidized bed of coke held at about 1000° F. The feed is cracked to lighter products and coke which deposits on the particles in the bed. A portion of the coke is continuously withdrawn from the reactor and sent to a coke burner where part of it is burned to provide heat for the reactor.

Catalytic Cracking. In the late thirties, the higher compression in gasoline motors demanded fuels with better antiknock properties, higher octane ratings, and higher lead susceptibility. It had been established that cracking in the presence of a catalyst produced a gasoline with higher octane number than thermal cracking of the same stock. The requirements of the armed forces in the war years for high-octane motor fuel, especially aviation gasoline, stimulated intense activity in the invention and construction of catalytic processes. The first catalytic process was the Houdry, with fixed catalyst beds, which dominated the scene for several years. The two general types of catalytic cracking units now in use are the *fluid bed* and *moving bed* units. Catalytic cracking at present accounts for some 70 per cent of total cracking capacity.

The reactions occurring during catalytic cracking include cleavage, isomerization, alkylation, dehydrogenation, and aromatization, among others.

Figure 14.9. Fluid catalytic cracking unit. (*Courtesy Standard Oil Co. of Ohio*)

Two types of catalysts are used, natural and synthetic. The natural product is composed of silica and alumina with small amounts of other materials. Synthetic catalysts, on the other hand, are manufactured from pure materials to rigid specifications. Catalyst pellets vary in size from 3 mm to 4 mm for moving bed units and from 2 microns to 400 microns for fluid bed units.

The Fluid Catalyst Cracking Process. In the fluid catalyst cracking process, the heated oil vapors pick up a fine powdered clay, or a synthetic catalyst in powder form and the two whirl about in intimate contact in the reactor, where the cracking of the oil molecules takes place. The catalyst is said to be *fluidized*, for the mixture of powder and vapors behaves in many respects as if it were a single fluid. The density of the fluid may be varied by altering the ratio of catalyst powder to vapor. The cracked vapor enters an internal cyclone where most of its dust is released and returned to the reactor, then to a fractionator which condenses, in rotation, heavy gas oil, light gas oil, and raw gasoline or naphtha; gases pass from a final cooler to a recovery system.

The catalyst becomes fouled, and must be reactivated. To this end, a portion of the fluidized catalyst is bled constantly from the reactor, separated from its accompanying vapors (which return to the reactor) in the "spent catalyst stripper," and travels downward to a stream of combustion air which carries it (upward) into the regenerator, where the carbon-rich deposit is burned off. The flue gases travel through an internal cyclone, depositing their dust, to a steam-producing heat exchanger, to an electrical precipitator, where the last of the powder is caught, and thence into the atmosphere. The recovered catalyst, now clean, reenters the regenerator, is joined there by make-up catalyst, and the two together, at a temperature of 1100° F, are ready to enter the reactor. On the way there, they meet the incoming preheated oil feed, or charge, which they flash-vaporize. The catalyst and vapors in the reactor feed line are forced along and up by the velocity of the entering vapors and by the head of fluid in the regenerator standpipe, and enter the reactor at its lowest point, rising through the bed of fluidized catalyst. The temperature in the reactor is maintained at 900–950° F; the cracking reaction consumes heat, but the catalyst powders bring in the necessary heat from the regenerator. In this function, the catalyst may be thought of as a heat-transfer agent.

The full-scale unit may have a capacity of 100,000 barrels a day or more. Smaller units are built to handle, for example, 3,300 barrels per day. In the full-sized unit, there are several hundred tons of catalyst in circulation. The cleaned catalyst from the regenerator is fed into the reactor at the rate of a box-car a minute, and let it be noted, without moving parts.

As already mentioned, the cracked vapors from the reactor enter the fractionator, in the bottom of which the slurry of heavier oils and residual catalyst is formed. If desired, the slurry oils may be recycled and returned to the reactor.

Operating conditions for the fluid process, and for the moving bed process described in the following section, are given in Table 14.8.

Airlift Thermofor Catalytic Cracking Process. The airlift process is depicted in Figure 14.10.[20] Catalyst from the separator enters the reactor where it contacts the preheated feed. Catalyst and oil flow downward through the reactor. The product vapors from the reactor are sent to

TABLE 14.8. OPERATING CONDITIONS FOR CATALYTIC
CRACKING UNITS

	Fluid Units	Moving Bed Units
Reactor temp. °F	870–1000	830–975
Reactor press. psig	10–21	5–18
Space velocity*	0.5–3	1–4
Catalyst-oil weight ratio	5–20	1.5–7
Carbon on regenerated catalyst, wt %	0.4–1.6	0.1–0.6
Carbon on spent catalyst, wt %	0.5–2.6	1.2–3.1
Max. regenerator temp. °F	1150	1350

* (wt oil feed per hr)/(wt catalyst in reactor).

fractionators and the catalyst flows through a purge zone, out of the reactor and into regenerators. The carbon deposit is oxidized by air flowing countercurrent to the catalyst; the latter is then sent to the cooling zone for temperature adjustment. From here it goes to the lift pot where a stream of low pressure air picks it up and lifts it to the top of the reactor for another cycle.

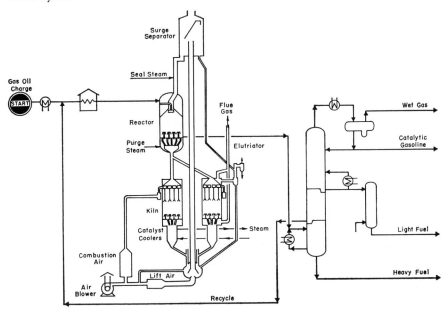

Figure 14.10. Air lift Thermofor catalytic cracking process. [*Pet. Ref.*, **37**, No. 9, 233 (1958); copyright 1958 by the Gulf Publishing Co.]

Catalytic Reforming. Catalytic cracking units can no longer economically meet the demand for high octane gasoline and it has become necessary to upgrade the octane rating of natural gasoline, naphtha and similar compounds. This is done by a process known as catalytic reforming, which has become the principal process for the upgrading of gasoline. It is a high temperature, catalytic process, and the action takes place in the presence of hydrogen; yet hydroforming is not hydrogenation; on the contrary it is dehydrogenation, and part of the hydrogen so produced is recirculated merely to control the rate and extent of the dehydrogenation. The catalyst is molybdena on alumina. The most important property of the catalyst is that which causes ring formation and permits ring preservation in molecules which have just undergone partial dehydrogenation (aromatization). The final product thus contains a high percentage of aromatic, and a small quantity of aliphatic hydrocarbons, compared with the feed. The product is unusually stable and may be blended directly with finished gasoline, after gas removal, in a separator followed by distillation in a stabilization tower.

It is well to have two catalytic reactors so that while one is functioning, the other may be freed of the small amount of coke deposited on the surface of the catalyst granules. The coke is burned off with caution, so as not to harm the catalyst; this is accomplished by adding controlled amounts of air to an inert flue gas. For any given octane level, coke deposition is a function of the amount of recycle gas and its hydrogen concentration. The removal of the coke restores to the catalyst its original activity.

Low-octane naphtha side-streams taken from the crude topping system are so enriched by the process of hydroforming that they contain 40 to 50 per cent of aromatic hydrocarbons, of which 15 to 20 per cent is toluene. The removal of the toluene from accompanying hydrocarbons in the same boiling range (200–240° F) is performed by azeotropic distillation. Methyl ethyl ketone-water, the best azeotrope-former for this purpose[11] is added to the naphtha, and the mixture introduced into a fractionating still. The azeotrope-former (MEK-water) passes out overhead, carrying with it the non-toulene hydrocarbons. The bottoms in the still consist of 99+ per cent toluene. The process is continuous. As would be expected, the number of reactions occurring during the process are numerous and complex. Several probable reactions[14] are given below:

1. Naphthene dehydrogenation

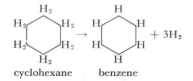

cyclohexane   benzene

2. Naphthene dehydroisomerization

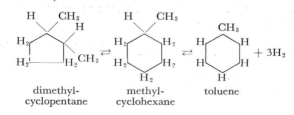

dimethyl-   methyl-   toluene
cyclopentane   cyclohexane

3. Paraffin dehydrocyclization

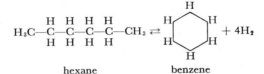

hexane   benzene

4. Paraffin isomerization

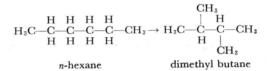

n-hexane   dimethyl butane

5. Paraffin hydrocracking

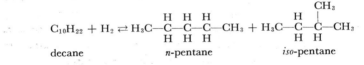

decane   *n*-pentane   *iso*-pentane

6. Hydrodesulfurization

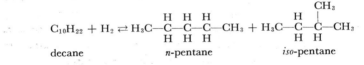

thiophene

Reactions 1, 2 and 4 predominate while others may become important at higher temperatures. Hydrocracking is particularly important since it can lead to excessive coke deposition and reduced yields of liquid products.

Catalytic reforming units may be of the regenerative or non-regenerative types. A *platformer* (a non-regenerative type reformer) is shown in Figure 14.11.[19] Naphtha feed is mixed with hydrogen and passed through the catalytic reactors containing a platinum catalyst. The charge is heated before entering each reactor to compensate for the endothermic reactions which occur. The final effluent is cooled, separated from the hydrogen which is recycled, and stabilized.

The *ultraforming* unit is of the regenerative type. Such a unit is shown in Figure 14.12.[28] Operation is similar to that for the platformer except that a spare or "swing" reactor is substituted when the catalyst activity of an on-stream reactor declines. This permits regeneration of the catalyst without interrupting operations. One swing reactor may service several units.

Typical operating conditions are:

	Temp., °F	Press., psig	Space Velocity, (lb oil/hr)/ (lb catalyst)	Hydrogen Rate, SCFH/bbl
Platformer	850–980	200–800	1–4	4,000–13,000
Ultraformer	900–950	200–350	1–5	3,500–8,000

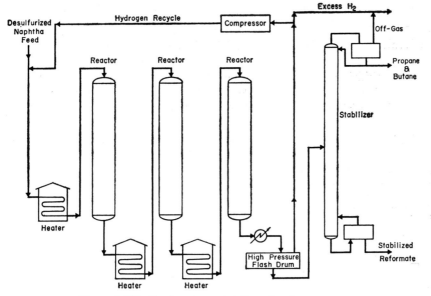

Figure 14.11. Platforming catalytic reforming process.

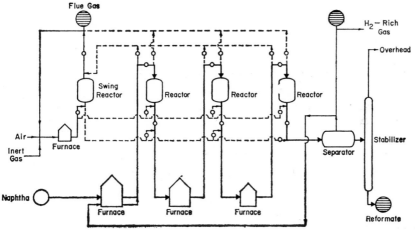

Figure 14.12. Regenerative platinum reforming process. [*Pet. Ref.*, **34**, *No. 9, 252 (1955); copyright 1955 by the Gulf Publishing Co.*]

It is estimated that at the beginning of 1961 catalytic reforming installed capacity was about 1,970,000 bpsd (barrels per stream day); this is expected to increase to 2,700,000 bpsd by 1965.[38]

Improving Gasolines by Additions and Reactions

Gasolines can be improved by the addition of foreign substances, by forming the hydrocarbon molecule in a definite manner, and by rearranging the molecular structure of the existing molecule, with or without simultaneous removal of hydrogen. The following processes alter the structure of the molecule, or add to its size, thus raising its octane rating:

stabilizing	alkylating	hydrogenating
reforming	hydrofining	polyforming
isomerizing	hydroforming	

Antiknock Compounds. In order to prevent the familiar knock in an internal combustion engine such as in automobiles, when hot and laboring, and the loss of power which occurs as a result, a number of substances may be added to the fuel with success. The effectiveness per unit weight of these substances varies greatly. The best known anitknock compound is tetraethyl lead, $Pb(C_2H_5)_4$, although tetramethyl lead is also used at present. The latter compound is more effective in highly aromatic fuels than is tetraethyl lead.

The antiknock compound also contains ethylene dichloride or ethylene dibromide to prevent the build-up of lead in engines. The lead oxide formed is changed to the volatile chloride or bromide which passes out with the exhaust gases.

Other Additives. Properties to be controlled in gasoline include boiling range, vapor pressure, octane rating, gum content, sulfur content, and others. The boiling range is adjusted by mixing straight-run gasoline, cracked gasoline, reformate, and others to provide the desired range and octane number before addition of lead compounds. Vapor pressure is controlled by butane and natural gasoline additions. The vapor pressure is made high in colder climates or during the winter months to help with easy starting, and low during the summer to prevent vapor lock. Antioxidants are added to minimize gum formation, dyes for identification and eye appeal, and antifreeze to prevent icing of the carburetor.

Properties of present-day gasolines are given in Table 14.9.

TABLE 14.9. TYPICAL PROPERTIES OF MOTOR GASOLINE

	Regular	Premium	Super-Premium
Distillation: 10%	116–147	116–147	116–147
50%	205–230	205–230	205–230
90%	325–370	315–360	315–360
E.P.	380–405	370–405	370–395
Reid vapor pressure	9.5–13.5	9.5–13.5	9.5–13.5
Gum, mg/100 cc max.	2.5	2.5	2.5
Octane number (research)	92.5–94	97.5–98.5	100.5–101.5(P.N.)
Sulfur, % max.	0.20	0.20	0.15

Natural Gasoline. Natural gasoline is the liquid which accompanies "wet" natural gas in many regions; it is removed by compression, or by absorption, mainly in straw oil, or by a combination of both processes. The gasoline values are mainly low-boiling, and correspond to hexanes and heptanes, with some octanes and pentanes. Intermediate hydrocarbons may also be separated, although less completely, in the form of liquefied petroleum gases (L.P.G.) such as propanes and butanes. The relative amounts are reflected by the figures for the daily production in a plant treating 30 million cubic feet of gas daily: propane 360 barrels; isobutane, 190; normal butane 210; isopentane 108, and debutanized gasoline 547 barrels. In this typical plant, the wet gas, compressed to 700 lbs/sq in. gauge, enters two 40-plate towers operated in parallel, where it meets the absorber oil which enters at the top and travels down, leaving the tower as saturated absorber oil. Unabsorbed gas leaves overhead; in part, it serves as fuel gas in the plant; the balance is compressed and returned to the field. The "fat" oil is first flashed to a pressure of 385 lb/sq in., to release most of the absorbed methane and ethane with some propane and higher components. By means of a reabsorber, such values in propane and higher hydrocarbons are in large part recovered. The flashed oil passes to a primary or high-pressure still, where again the lower hydrocarbons are driven out and saved for other purposes. The oil then passes to the low-pressure or main still where the gasoline components, all of which may be compressed to a liquid at practically atmospheric pressure, are removed and collected. The stripped lean oil is cooled and returned to the absorbers.

In 1959 there were 555 natural gasoline plants, of which 74 operated by compression, 434 by absorption, and 47 by cycling. To clarify the terms used: A natural gasoline plant may be defined as a light hydrocarbon processing plant which obtains its feed in vapor form. The feed vapor may be casinghead gas from oil-well separators, or it may be from gas wells, or from both. A "cycling plant" usually has a feed stock from high-pressure wells in the range of 1500 to 5000 lb/sq in. and higher. The gasoline values are extracted in high-pressure absorbers, working at 2000 lb/sq in., for example. The tail gas is recompressed to 4000 lb/sq in., and returned to the producing formation through an injection well. The average yield of natural gas liquids during 1959 was 1.47 gallons per 1000 cubic feet of gas treated.

The production of natural gasoline in 1959 was 4,222,226,000 gallons. Other products bring the total to 13,471,808,000 gallons for the natural gasoline industry.

Alkylation. The alkylation process for the production of high-octane gasoline is the result of the discovery that paraffin hydrocarbons in the presence of a catalyst unite with olefins. The "alkylate" produced from a properly selected stock, for example, the olefin-rich gas stream from cracking processes, can have an octane number of perhaps 95. The process may involve isobutane and olefins to produce high octane dimers or trimers. The reaction is carried out at 60° to 95° F in the presence of sulfuric or hydro-fluoric acid. The product is recovered from the acid in a settler and treated to remove propane, butane, etc.

Catalytic Polymerization. The polymerization of olefin-bearing refinery gases has as its objects the production of high-octane motor fuel and petro-chemicals. A process flow sheet for polymerization using solid phosphoric acid catalyst is shown in Figure 14.13. Preheated feed is passed over the catalyst in the reactor at 350 to 435° F and 400 to 1200 psi. The reactions are exothermic. The polymer gasoline thus produced is freed from butane

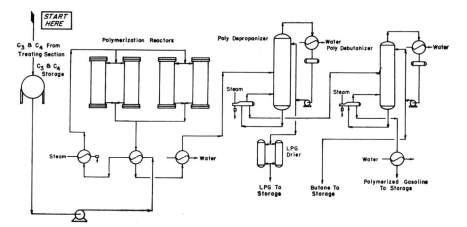

Figure 14.13. Solid phosphoric acid polymerization process. [*From a booklet prepared by the Ashland Oil and Refining Co. (1960)*.]

and propane to complete the process. Compounds such as propylene dimer, trimer, and higher homologs can be produced by this method.

Lubricating Oil Refining

Lubricating oils make up only about two per cent of the petroleum products sold in the United States.[6] They are, however, high profit items. Moreover, the incidental recovery of waxes, asphalt and other by-product materials obtained in the refining processes serves to further enhance their importance in the overall economics of petroleum refining.

The high boiling paraffin hydrocarbons comprise the materials having the properties necessary for lubricating oils. These properties include stability at high temperatures, fluidity at low temperatures, moderate change in viscosity over broad temperature range, and sufficient adhesiveness to keep it in place under high shear forces.

A general flow sheet for the manufacture of lubricating oils is shown in Figure 14.14. Since the desired fractions have high boiling points their separation into various boiling range cuts must be accomplished under reduced pressures. This is done in a vacuum distillation system (see Figure 14.5). The cuts thus obtained are further treated to remove naphthenes, aromatics, nitrogen and oxygen compounds, sulfur compounds, and other impurities. The asphalt is found only in the residium and therefore only this stream needs to be treated for asphalt removal.

Deasphalting. The residium from the vacuum still is contacted in a tower with liquid propane which dissolves all the constituents except the asphalt which passes out the bottom of the column. The column is operated under pressures up to about 500 psi to maintain the propane in the

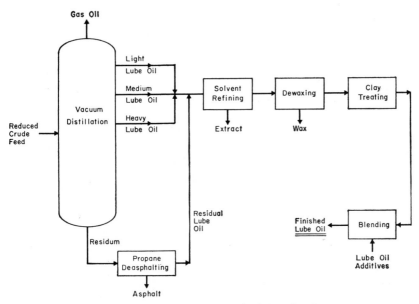

Figure 14.14. General flowsheet for lube oil refining.

liquid state at the operating temperatures. An interesting fact is that the column is kept about 50 degrees hotter near the top (140–200° F) than at the bottom. This reduces the solubility of the heavier hydrocarbons and helps to further narrow the boiling range of the fraction thus treated. Propane is recovered from the oil and asphalt and recycled. This process has become important in decarbonizing and deasphalting the charge stock for catalytic cracking.[9]

Subsequent treatment of the oil fraction is similar to that for the other fractions from the vacuum distillation. The steps are described in the following sections.

Solvent Extraction. The removal of non-paraffins by solvent extraction is usually the next step in lube oil refining. Two important solvents are furfural and phenol; other solvents may also be used.

The process using furfural is shown in Figure 14.16. The lubricating oil fraction enters at the center of the extraction column, the solvent near the top. The two streams flow countercurrent to each other, the solvent leaving at the bottom and the oil at the top. Contained in the furfural solvent are non-lubricating compounds including aromatics, naphthenes, sulfur compounds, and nitrogen compounds. The solvent is recovered by flashing and steam stripping.

Dewaxing. Waxes present in lubricating oils may crystallize out at low temperatures and impair operations. They are, however, good lubricants

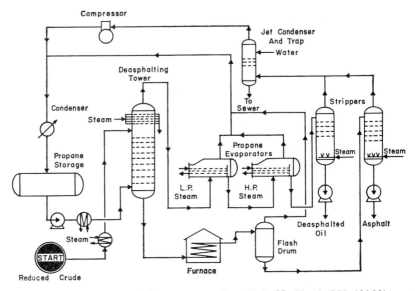

Figure 14.15. Propane deasphalting process. [*Pet. Ref.*, **39**, *No. 9, 239 (1960); copyright 1960 by the Gulf Publishing Co.*]

and the amount permitted to remain in the oil is determined by the operating conditions envisioned for the oil.

Conventional dewaxing processes, which can yield product with a pour point* as low as −15° F, involve contacting the oil fraction with a solvent, for example, methyl ethyl ketone, which will dissolve the oil and waxes. Chilling the solution causes the wax to crystallize and it may be removed by filtration. The wax may be fractioned to produce waxes of various melting ranges (from 90° F to above 200° F). Solvent recovery systems recover the solvent from the oil and wax. A flow diagram for dewaxing is shown in Figure 14.17.

Lubricating oils with pour points as low as −70° F can be obtained by a new process using urea.[36] Urea (three parts) and the oil (one part) are

* The pour point is the temperature at which the oil ceases to flow.

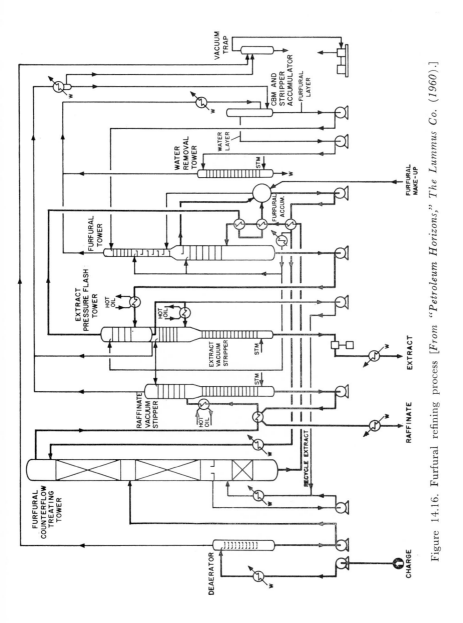

Figure 14.16. Furfural refining process [*From "Petroleum Horizons," The Lummus Co. (1960).*]

509

mixed and heated to about 100° F. There is formed a wax-urea complex which is insoluble in the oil and can be filtered off. The urea and wax are recovered by treating the complex with water at about 170° F.

Clay Treating. Oxygen, nitrogen and sulfur compounds remaining in the oil following the refining steps described above are removed by adsorption on Attapulgus Clay, Fullers Earth, or other suitable adsorbent. Two methods in use are the percolation method and the contact filtration process. In

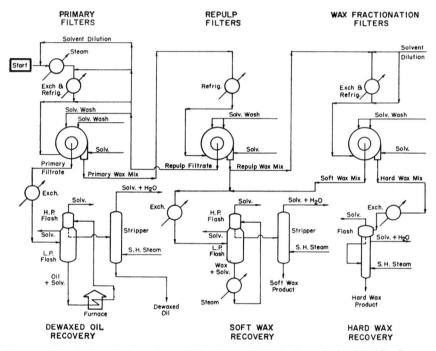

Figure 14.17. Lube oil dewaxing. ["*The Story Behind One of the World's Largest Paraffin Wax Plants,*" *Badger Manufacturing Co. (1959).*]

the former the oil is passed (percolated) through a bed of the adsorbing material. Depending on the adsorbent and the impurities to be removed, one ton of clay might treat well over a hundred barrels of oil before requiring regeneration. The latter operation consists of washing with naphtha and steaming, followed by heating at about 1000° F to remove the adsorbed impurities.

The contact filtration process[18] is continuous. The adsorbent is mixed with the oil and the resulting slurry, heated to 225 to 550° F, is passed through a contact tower where the residence time may be from $\frac{1}{2}$ to 1 hour. The effluent from the tower is cooled and filtered to remove adsorbent. The adsorbent may or may not be regenerated, depending on the economics involved.

Blending of Lube Oils. Lubricating oils having particular properties are obtained by blending the various refined fractions and by the addition of certain non-petroleum materials (additives). Modern lubricating oils contain a large number of additives including: oxidation inhibitors, to reduce susceptibility to oxidation, particularly at high temperatures; detergents to dissolve engine deposits; anti-foam agents; and pour point depressants, to name a few.

Greases. The semi-solid consistency of greases is obtained by adding thickening agents to the oil. These may be metallic soaps, modified silicas, certain organic materials and special clays; they comprise from about 3 to 30 volume per cent of the grease.

Auxiliary Processes

It becomes necessary in many cases to perform operations not mentioned in the preceding sections. Some feed stocks require special treatment to make them suitable for processing while some of the refined products require additional operations to make them suitable for particular applications.

Acid treating to remove olefins, asphaltic substances and others, and caustic washing to remove hydrogen sulfide and mercaptans from petroleum fractions are widely practiced. Hydrosulfurization is finding favor for the removal of sulfur compounds by using hydrogen to form easily removable H_2S gas. Hydrofining[25] uses hydrogen for removal of olefins to reduce the carbonization tendency of feed stock for catalytic crackers.

THE PETROCHEMICAL INDUSTRY

The petrochemical industry may be generally defined as comprising those areas of chemical manufacturing which use raw materials extracted wholly or largely from petroleum or natural gas. Dominating the petrochemicals are organic compounds manufactured from such basic compounds as methane, acetylene, ethane, ethylene, propane, propylene, butane, butylene, butadiene, and benzene and other aromatic compounds. Additionally, many inorganic chemicals, including ammonia, urea, nitric acid, sulfur and sulfuric acid, carbon black and others are being manufactured in ever-increasing amounts from petroleum sources.

"Already the fastest-growing segment of America's giant chemical industry, petrochemicals accounted for over 30 per cent of all chemicals produced in the United States in 1960, and about 60 per cent of the year's total chemical sales volume. Over the past ten years, the average annual petrochemical growth rate has been nearly 15 per cent, compared to an average of only four per cent for the American economy as a whole."[37] Figure 14.18 shows this growth and anticipated growth in the years ahead.

In the aliphatic segment of the chemical industry petrochemicals accounted for 73 per cent of the volume output in 1950 and 86 per cent of the volume in 1959; in the aromatic segment the figures for 1950 and 1959 were 28 per cent and 68 per cent, respectively.[16] Petroleum-derived inorganics (ammonia, carbon black and sulfur) increased from a volume of 3.4 billion pounds in 1950 to about 13 billion pounds in 1959.[16]

One may logically divide the petrochemical industry into two sections, one comprising production and separation of the basic raw materials mentioned earlier, the other dealing with conversion of these raw materials

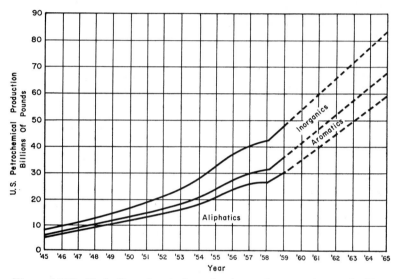

Figure 14.18. U. S. Petrochemical production and expected growth. [*Pet. Ref.*, **38**, *No. 11, 189 (1959), copyright 1959 by the Gulf Publishing Co.*]

into the numerous chemical compounds of commerce. The manufacture of several of these compounds are described in other chapters of this book; ammonia in Chapter 5, butadiene in Chapter 9, sulfur and sulfuric acid in Chapter 4, and many of the organics in Chapter 25. The remainder of this chapter will be devoted to discussion of the processes used to produce the basic raw materials from petroleum and natural gas.

The aliphatic materials are found in natural gas and refinery gas and are produced by the cracking of petroleum fractions. The aromatic compounds are produced by catalytic reforming and dealkylation processes; they are purified using extraction and distillation processes.

Hydrocarbons from Gases

Natural gas, as taken from the earth, contains a large number of compounds which usually include hydrogen, methane, ethane, propane, butane,

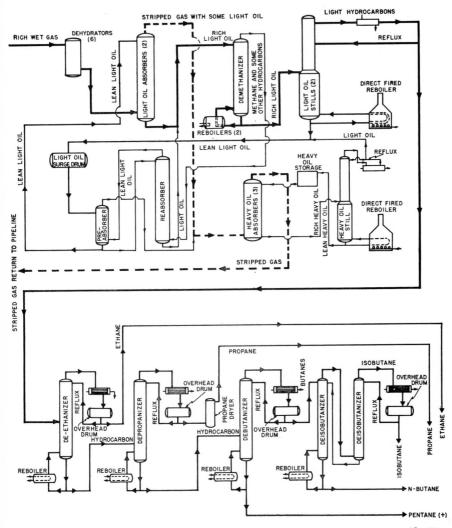

Figure 14.19. Natural gas separation for petrochemicals. [*Ind. Eng. Chem.*, **48**, *No. 2, 170 (1956); copyright 1956 by the American Chemical Society.*]

heavier hydrocarbons, and hydrogen sulfide. The methane may be recovered by an absorption process (the methane and hydrogen are not absorbed) and the remaining hydrocarbons fractionated to obtain pure components. Figure 14.19 shows a complete flow sheet for natural gas processing.[10] The natural gas as it leaves the well contains moisture and so must be dehydrated to prevent freezing and hydration in the absorption column which operates at —20° C under a pressure of about 500 psi. The absorbing oil is normally a hexane fraction. The gas leaving the absorber is mainly methane and hydrogen although some methane is dissolved in the oil. It is recovered by passing the gas laden absorption oil through a demethanizer; the methane leaving this apparatus contains some ethane and propane and these are removed in another absorber. The hydrocarbons dissolved in the oil from the two absorption columns are separated from the oil in a light oil still. (The methane stream is passed through a heavy oil absorber to recover the light oil it carries from the light oil absorbers.) The hydrocarbon mixture from the light oil still goes next to a distillation system where it is separated into its components; ethane, propane, n-butane, isobutane, and natural gasoline.

Refinery gases contain in addition to the materials present in natural gas, ethylene, propylene and butylenes. Therefore, if it is necessary to produce high purity ethane or propane, additional distillation equipment must be used to separate ethylene from the ethane and propylene from the propane. Extractive distillation with acetone as the entraining agent is commonly used to separate butylene from butane.

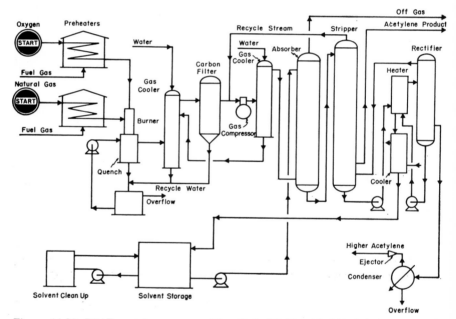

Figure 14.20. BSAF acetylene process. [*Pet. Ref.*, **38**, *No. 11, 202 (1959); copyright 1959 by the Gulf Publishing Co.*]

Acetylene Manufacture

In the past acetylene has been manufactured mainly from calcium carbide (Chapter 17). This picture has changed somewhat due to the development of economic petrochemical processes. One of these is shown in Figure 14.20. Oxygen (98% pure) and natural gas are preheated to 950°–1200° F and then mixed in the ratio 1.00 mole methane to 0.60 mole oxygen, less than enough to support combustion of all the methane. The reactor consists of three zones, viz., mixing, flame chamber and quenching. After being rapidly and thoroughly mixed in the first zone the mixture enters the flame chamber through the ports of a specially designed burner block and the methane is cracked according to the reaction:

$$2CH_4 \rightarrow C_2H_2 + 3H_2$$

Part of the methane is burned, the heat of combustion being used to raise the temperature of the reactants to reaction temperature and to supply the heat for the endothermic cracking reaction. About one third of the methane is cracked, most of the remainder being burned. The flame temperature is about 2700° F.

The gases from the flame chamber enter the quenching zone where they are cooled to prevent further reactions, then cooled in a spray chamber to around 100° F. The cooled gas is filtered to remove carbon, compressed and purified by absorption in selective solvents, for example, dimethyl-formamide[31] and ammonia.[30]

Several compounds other than methane can be used to produce acetylene including heavy gas oil,[7] naphtha[30] and others. In some cases steam[3] may be used instead of oxygen and in others[7] the hydrocarbons may be used alone.

Ethylene Manufacture

Based on volume produced and number of derivatives, ethylene is one of the most important members of the petrochemicals family. Production in 1959 amounted to 4,954,000,000 pounds, of which 30.4 per cent was used for ethylene oxide, 27.2 per cent for polyethylene, 20.7 per cent for ethyl alcohol, 10 per cent for styrene and 6.9 per cent for ethylene dichloride.[16] It was reported[29] that 47 per cent of the ethylene produced in 1956 was manufactured from propane, 38 per cent from ethane, 10 per cent from refinery gases, and 5 per cent from the cracking of heavy hydrocarbons. Propane is also a good source of propylene, which appears as a by-product in the preparation of ethylene. Other raw materials for the production of ethylene include n-butane, which yields propylene and butylene as by-products, and certain crude oil fractions. The latter may be used to pro-duce some aromatic compounds simultaneously with the production of ethylene. Figure 14.21 is a photograph of an ethylene purification unit.

In the production[23] of ethylene and propylene from ethane (see Figure 14.22) and propane, the feed streams are first mixed with steam to pro-mote higher yields of olefins and then cracked in separate furnaces at tem-peratures ranging from 1150° to 1500° F. The combined effluents are water scrubbed and cooled to 100° F to condense polymers and aromatics. The gas streams are then compressed and, should an acetylene-free product be required, sent to a unit where the acetylene is hydrogenated. The gases are then chilled, dehydrated and cooled before entering the separation process.

Ethylene and lighter hydrocarbons are removed in the deethanizer, leaving in the overhead product stream. The bottom stream contains propylene and higher hydrocarbons. Recovery of ethylene is accomplished by chilling the overhead stream to about −195° F and treating the condensed liquid

Figure 14.21. Ethylene purification unit. (*Courtesy Esso Standard Division, Humble Oil and Refining*)

in a demethanizer. The bottom product from the latter apparatus next enters an ethylene fractionator for purification. Recovery of propylene involves treatment of the bottoms from the deethanizer in a depropanizer and a propane splitter.

In addition to the low-temperature distillation process described above, ethylene may be purified in an absorption system operating at near 0° F.

Propylene and Higher Olefins

Recovery of propylene in 1959 amounted to 2.15 billion pounds. Of this amount 48 per cent was used to produce isopropanol, 27 per cent for

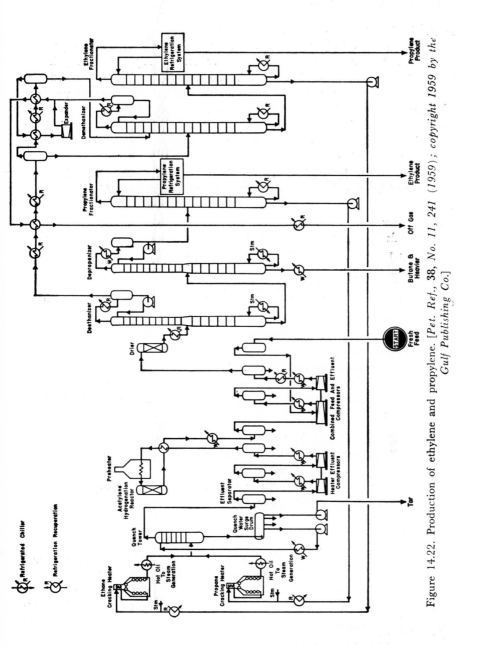

Figure 14.22. Production of ethylene and propylene. [*Pet. Ref.*, 38, *No. 11, 241 (1959); copyright 1959 by the Gulf Publishing Co.*]

517

propylene trimer and tetramer to be used in detergent manufacture, 12 per cent for propylene oxide, and about 8 per cent for cumene and glycerin production.[16] Polypropylene plastics manufacture, begun in 1957, is expected to promote a rapid increase in the rate of propylene production.[34] Refinery off-gas contains large amounts of propylene and about 95 per cent of present production comes from this source; the balance is manufactured as a by-product of cracking operations for ethylene production. About three fourths of the estimated 20 billion pounds[35] of propylene produced is converted to gasoline.

Certain of the by-product streams in refinery operations contain large amounts of butane, iso-butane, n-butenes and isobutylene. About 181 million pounds of isobutylene were used during 1959 for the manufacture of butyl rubber, 43 million pounds for polybutene production,[51] and 86 million pounds in other applications. 1-Butene is mainly produced for use in butadiene production while sec-butanol, polybutene and other compounds consume relatively small amounts.

The C-4 olefins can be produced by catalytic dehydrogenation of butane or butene in conjunction with selective solvent purification processes,[24] by recovery from certain refinery gases, and by cracking of naphthas and other stock. The manufacture of butadiene is described in Chapter 9. With proper selection of operating conditions, the same processes can be made to yield butylenes as the main product.

The demand for olefins containing more than four carbon atoms is comparatively small at present. Some of these, together with method of manufacture, are:

> C_5 olefins, from dehydrogenation of pentanes;
> C_6 olefins, from dimerization of propane;
> C_8 olefins, from dimerization of butane;
> C_9 and C_{12}, from trimerization and tetramerization, respectively, of propylene.

Aromatic Chemicals

Benzene, Toluene, Xylene. During 1958 the chemical industry consumed 811 million gallons of benzene, toluene and xylene; 525 million gallons of this amount was supplied by the petroleum industry which had a production capacity in reforming units of about 5 billion gallons.[33] Most of this capacity is used to make aromatics for raising the octane rating of gasoline as described in an earlier section.

The consumption of benzene in 1959 was 410 million gallons,[15] most of which was produced from petroleum. Of this amount 45 per cent was used for styrene, 22 per cent for phenol, 7 per cent for decylbenzene and 7 per cent for synthetic fibers.[15] Most of the toluene produced is used in gasoline manufacture but a substantial volume, 32 million gallons in 1958, is used by the chemical industry. Para-xylene finds use in the manufacture of polyester fibers and film while ortho-xylene is used to produce phthalic anhydride and other compounds.

Naphthalene. The production of naphthalene was for many years derived entirely from the coking of coal and tar distillation. In 1959 all of the 485 million pounds consumed in the United States was produced from these sources. In 1960, however, three plants to produce naphthalene (see section on dealkylation of aromatics) from petroleum were commissioned. These new plants have a combined capacity of some 330 million pounds per year, and additional plants are under construction. With a plentiful supply

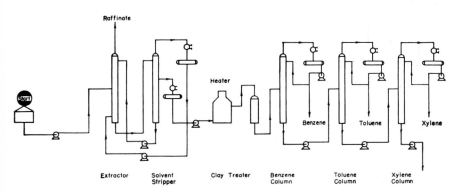

Figure 14.23. Udex extraction process for purification of aromatics. [*Pet. Ref.*, **36**, *No. 11, 304 (1957); copyright 1957 by the Gulf Publishing Co.*]

of naphthalene assured we may expect the development of many new products and processes which will utilize this material.

Purification of Aromatics. Aromatic chemicals are found in the effluent streams from catalytic reformers and catalytic crackers, in amounts ranging from 10 per cent to 65 per cent, together with paraffin and naphthene hydrocarbons. Thus, purification of the aromatics consists of (1) separating them from the non-aromatics, and (2) separating them into the pure compounds. Several methods are available for carrying out the first step. These are: (1) liquid-liquid extraction; (2) extractive or azeotropic distillation; and (3) adsorption.

Extraction. The Udex[17,27] process (Figure 14.23) is widely used for separation of aromatics from the non-aromatic compounds previously mentioned. The solvent used in this process is aqueous diethylene glycol, which exhibits a selectivity directly proportional to the C/H ratio of the feed components and inversely proportional to their boiling points. The solubility of the hydrocarbons is dependent on the water content of the glycol.

Reformate from catalytic reformers is contacted with the glycol-water solvent in an extraction tower where the aromatic components dissolve in the solvent and leave the bottom of the column. The aromatics are recovered from the extract by stripping and then sent to the purification section for recovery of the pure components. The stripped solvent is recycled to the extraction tower.

Recovery of the individual aromatics is accomplished by heating and clay treating the aromatic mixture from solvent extraction and then distilling it in a three-column distillation train. There are obtained relatively pure fractions of benzene and toulene, and a xylene fraction which is a mixture of the

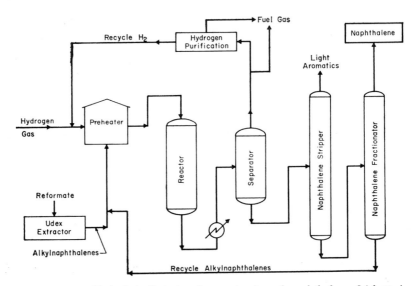

Figure 14.24. Hydeal dealkylation for production of naphthalene. [*Adapted from Chem. Week,* **88**, *No. 11, March 18 (1961)*.]

ortho, meta and para isomers (20, 40, 20 per cent, in the same order), together with some 20 per cent of ethylbenzene. Some C_8 compounds are present and must be removed. The process for separation and purification of the xylenes and ethylbenzene combines distillation with fractional crystallization.[8] Separation of o- from p-xylene is by distillation, p-xylene from ethylbenzene by fractionation (350 plates), and m- from p-xylene by fractional crystallization.

Dealkylation of Aromatics. Dealkylation processes for producing benzene,[2,5] naphthalene, and phenol[32] were introduced during 1960. The raw material for the process can be either toluene or a C_8 fraction for benzene, alkylnaphthalenes for naphthalene and cresols for phenol. The process is typified by the production of naphthalene (Figure 14.24).

Alkylnaphthalene fractions from naphthenic crude oils, cycle oils (from catalytic cracking units), or other sources is combined with hydrogen and heated to about 1000 to 1200° F.[4] The heated mixture enters the reactor where dealkylation occurs:

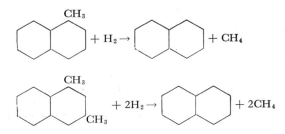

It is thought that the reactor contains an alkalized chromia-alumina catalyst and operates at about 800 psig.[4] The effluent from the reactor is cooled and hydrogen is separated from the liquid product which is stripped to remove light hydrocarbons and fractionated to remove the unreacted heavy materials. The product is naphthalene.

A production unit using a similar process, the Houdry Detol Process,[2] to produce benzene is reportedly under construction.

REFERENCES

1. Benedict, Q. E., *Pet. Ref.*, **31**, No. 9, 103 (1952).
2. *Chem. Eng.*, **68**, No. 5, 76 (1961).
3. *Chem. Eng. Prog.*, **54**, No. 1, 41 (1958).
4. *Chem. Week*, **88**, No. 9, 47 (1961).
5. *Chem. Week*, **88**, No. 11, 32 (1961).
6. Guthrie, V. B., *Pet. Engr.*, **30**, No. 1, C-7 (1958).
7. *Ind. Eng. Chem.*, **45**, No. 11, 2596 (1953).
8. *Ind. Eng. Chem.*, **47**, 250 and 1096 (1955).
9. *Ind. Eng. Chem.*, **47**, No. 8, 1578 (1955).
10. *Ind. Eng. Chem.*, **48**, No. 5, 168 (1956).
11. Lake, G. R., *Trans. Am. Inst. Chem. Engr.*, **41**, 327 (1945).
12. Nelson, W. L., "Petroleum Refinery Engineering," 4 ed., p. 651, McGraw-Hill Book Co., Inc., New York (1958).
13. Ibid, pp. 682–686.
14. Ibid, p. 810.
15. *Pet. Engr. for Manag.*, **33**, No. 1, C-11 (1961).
16. Ibid, p. C-8.
17. *Pet. Proc.*, **10**, No. 8, 1199 (1955).
18. *Pet. Proc.*, **12**, No. 5, 97 (1957).
19. *Pet. Ref.*, **31**, No. 5, 97 (1952).
20. *Pet. Ref.*, **31**, No. 8, 71 (1952).
21. *Pet. Ref.*, **32**, No. 7, 102 (1953).
22. *Pet. Ref.*, **32**, No. 9, 125 (1953).
23. *Pet. Ref.*, **33**, No. 7, 135 (1954).
24. *Pet. Ref.*, **33**, No. 12, 173 (1954).
25. *Pet. Ref.*, **36**, No. 6, 179 (1957).

26. *Pet. Ref.*, **36**, No. 9, 211 (1957).
27. *Pet. Ref.*, **36**, No. 11 (1957).
28. *Pet. Ref.*, **37**, No. 9, 223 (1958).
29. *Pet. Ref.*, **37**, No. 11, 215 (1958).
30. Ibid, p. 180.
31. *Pet. Ref.*, **38**, No. 11, 204 (1959).
32. Ibid, p. 258.
33. Ibid, p. 196.
34. *Pet. Ref.*, **39**, No. 11, 169 (1960).
35. Ibid, p. 170.
36. Rogers, T. L., *Pet. Ref.*, **36**, No. 7, 141 (1957).
37. The Texaco Star, **XLVII**, No. 4, Texaco, Inc. (1960).
38. Venema, M. P., *Pet. Engr. for Manag.*, **33**, No. 1, C-8 (1961).
39. White, David, *Bull. Am. Assoc. Petroleum Geologists*, **19**, 469–502 (1935).
40. Ibid, 501.

SUPPLEMENTARY REFERENCES

1. Sittig, M., "Catalytic Cracking Techniques in Review," Petroleum Refiner, Vol. 31, No. 9, pp. 263–316 (Sept. 1952).
2. Sittig, M., "How to Get Those Top Octanes," Petroleum Refiner, Vol. 34, No. 9, pp. 230–280 (Sept. 1955).
3. Kay, H., "What Hydrogen Treating Can Do," Vol. 35, No. 9, pp. 303–318 (Sept. 1956).
4. Process Handbook Issue, Petroleum Refiner, Vol. 37, No. 9 (Sept. 1958).
5. Process Handbook Issue, Petroleum Refiner, Vol. 39, No. 9 (Sept. 1960).
6. Petroleum Horizons, Published by The Lummus Company, New York (1950).
7. Hengstbeck, R. J., Petroleum Processing, McGraw-Hill Book Co., New York (1959).
8. Nelson, W. L., Petroleum Refinery Engineering, 4th ed., McGraw-Hill Book Co., New York (1948).
9. Purdy, G. A., Petroleum-Prehistoric to Petrochemicals, McGraw-Hill Book Co., New York (1958).
10. Bell, H. S., American Petroleum Refining, 4th ed., D. Van Nostrand Co., Inc., Princeton, New Jersey (1959).
11. Kalichevsky, V. A. and Kobe, K. A., Petroleum Refining with Chemicals, D. Van Nostrand Co., Inc., Princeton, New Jersey (1956).
12. Petrochemical Handbook Issue, Petroleum Refiner, Vol. 36, No. 11 (Sept. 1957).
13. Petrochemical Issue, Petroleum Refiner, Vol. 37, No. 11 (Nov. 1958).
14. Petrochemical Handbook Issue, Petroleum Refiner, Vol. 38, No. 11 (Nov. 1959).
15. Petrochemical Development Issue, Petroleum Refiner, Vol. 39, No. 11 (Nov. 1960).
16. Petroleum Processing, Vol. 10, No. 8, pp. 1157–1204 (Aug. 1955).
17. Astle, J. A., The Chemistry of Petrochemicals, Reinhold Publishing Corp., New York (1956).
18. Goldstein, R. F., The Petroleum Chemicals Industry, John Wiley & Sons, Inc., New York (1958).

15

INDUSTRIAL CHEMISTRY OF WOOD

In collaboration with Edwin C. Jahn* and Frank W. Lorey*

Wood was first used by man in his distant prehistoric antiquity. Certainly, the use of wood goes back to his most primitive culture. Wood has been employed by man for hundreds of millenia in two general ways, viz., (1) as found in nature and reshaped for specific uses, and (2) as a raw material to make something else, such as heat. Today, this ever-renewable resource from the forest provides the raw material for these same two basic classes of use, though on a greatly expanded level.

Present demands for wood are enormous and are continuously growing. Wood is almost as basic as food and is about as plentiful. Wood remains today the world's most widely used industrial raw material. It is the source not only of lumber and wood products but also of most of the world's packaging materials. Most of the world's rayon, cellophane, and cellulose lacquers and plastics are now made from chemical wood pulp.

Despite this huge and growing demand for wood, the nation's forests have been brought back in less than 25 years by professional foresters in government service and industry from a traditional annual deficit growth to an excess of growth over timber removal. This gain is all the more impressive when considered in the face of the war demands, the exploding population growth, and rising living standards, as well as the ever-present depredations caused by diseases and pests, fire, and human wastefulness and carelessness.

* State University College of Forestry at Syracuse University.

The growing consumption of paper is an index of the changed timber situation. People now use 50 per cent more paper than they did 15–20 years ago and there are 20 million more people. Yet, our forests supply the increased demand and stay ahead of the total timber cut.

However, the manufacture of forest products utilizes only a portion of the available wood. There are great losses in terms of unsuitable or neglected species, in logging residues, in manufacturing residues, such as bark, slabs, edgings, trimmings, shavings, and sawdust left during the manufacture of wood products, and in the lignin and other organic materials dissolved in the pulping liquors. It is estimated that the combined wood residue not utilized is nearly 40 per cent of the forest drain.

Chemical utilization of wood has always been attractive to the chemist and the conservationist as a means of getting greater value from a given quantity of timber. Progress has been made in this direction through integrated forest operations and the use of wood residues from sawmilling for pulp.

Wood is not only one of our greatest resources, but, like agriculture, it is continually renewable. By most measures, forest products rank fifth in importance among industries in the United States. In terms of value of products produced, the pulp and paper industry by itself ranks fifth. Though the pulp and paper industry is a major industry, the other wood chemical industries are small by comparison. Some have gone into decline, such as wood distillation, due to competition by synthetic processes, and others are comparatively new, such as chemically modified wood. The chemical wood industries also differ in other ways. Some, such as charcoal burning, which is centuries old, are still primitive in many areas. Others, such as paper, are modern and aggressive. The products which are treated in this chapter include pulp and paper, fiber boards, paper-base laminates, products by pyrolysis and by chemical degradation, wood sugars and alcohol, tree exudates, extractives, modified wood, plastics and composite boards.

CHEMICAL NATURE OF WOOD

Wood is a supporting and conducting tissue for the tree. To serve these functions, about 90 per cent of wood tissue is composed of strong, relatively thick-walled long cells. These, when separated from each other, are fine fibers very suitable for paper making.

Chemically, the cell wall tissue of wood is a complex mixture of polymers. These polymers fall into two groups, the polysaccharides and lignin. The polysaccharides of wood are collectively known as *holocellulose*, meaning total cellulosic carbohydrates. The holocellulose accounts for about 70 to 80 per cent of the extractive-free woody tissue, with lignin making up the remainder.

The holocellulose is composed of cellulose and a mixture of other polysaccharides, collectively termed *hemicellulose*. Cellulose is a high molecular weight linear polymer composed of glucose anhydride units. Hemicellulose is a mixture of shorter-chain polymers of the anhydrides of xylose, arabinose, glucose, mannose and galactose, with xylan as the most prevalent species. Cellulose makes up the main frame-work of the cell walls of the wood fibers. It is highly resistant chemically, whereas the hemicelluloses have relatively low resistance to acids and alkalis.

Lignin serves as the adhesive material of wood, cementing the fibers and other cells together to form the firm anatomical structure of wood. Lignin is a complex polymer of condensed substituted phenols. It is susceptible to degradation and dissolution by strong alkalis at elevated temperatures, by acid sulphite solutions at elevated temperatures and by oxidizing agents. Thus, lignin can be removed from the wood, leaving the separated cellulosic fibers in the form of a pulp.

In addition to the cell-wall substance, wood also contains extraneous materials present in the cavities of the cells. In some woods these are present in considerable amounts and are commercially important. The volatile oils and resins of the southern pines are an example. The extraneous materials are numerous and cover a wide range of chemically different materials. Most of these may be separated from the wood by steam distillation and solvent extraction as indicated below.

Steam distillation: terpene hydrocarbons, esters, acids, alcohols, aldehydes, aliphatic hydrocarbons

Ether extraction: fats, fatty acids, resins, resin acids, phytosterols, waxes, non-volatile hydrocarbons, and the above volatile compounds if not previously removed by steam distillation

Alcohol-benzene extraction: most of the ether soluble materials plus phlobaphenes, coloring matter and some tannin

Alcohol extraction: tannin and most of the above organic material, except some resins

Water extraction: sugars, cyclitols, starch, gums, mucilages, pectins, galactans, and some inorganic salts, tannins and pigments.

The chemical composition of wood varies between species. The hardwoods and softwoods of the temperate zone show consistent differences. The hardwoods have less lignin and more hemicellulose than the softwoods. The chemical composition of a few North American woods is shown in Table 15.1.

MANUFACTURE OF PULP AND PAPER

The importance of the pulp and paper industry to the American economy is exemplified by the growth rate in the use of paper and paper products. New uses are continuously being found for paper, and these developments together with the rising standard of living have resulted in a constant increase in the per capita consumption of paper. As shown in Table 15.2, the paper industry in the 19th century, dependent on rags as the source of fiber, was stagnant until the middle part of the century when processes were invented for the utilization of wood fiber, and since that time the industry has shown a constant growth. Table 2 also shows the breakdown of paper con-

TABLE 15.1. CHEMICAL ANALYSIS OF SOME NORTH AMERICAN WOODS

	Hardwoods				Softwoods			
	Aspen	White Birch	Beech	Basswood	White Spruce	Balsam Fir	Jack Pine	Eastern Hemlock
Lignin	18.1	18.5	21.0	20.0	27.0	27.7	27.4	29.6
Holocellulose	80.3	79.3	75.7	76.7	72.0	70.0	68.0	71.4
Hemicellulose	21.2	27.3	. . .	. . .	16.4	15.4	16.2	12.5
Alpha cellulose*	49.4	44.2	51.2	48.2	50.2	49.4	47.5	53.0
Pentosans	17.2	22.0	20.2	16.6	8.0	7.0	10.1	5.1
Acetyl groups	3.4	4.9	6.6	. . .	1.1	1.5	1.1	1.3
Solubility in:								
Hot water	2.8	2.7	1.5	2.4	2.2	3.6	3.7	3.4
Ethyl ether	1.9	2.4	0.7	2.1	2.1	1.8	4.3	0.7

* Cellulose resistant to 17.5% NaOH solution at R. T.

TABLE 15.2. PAPER CONSUMPTION IN THE UNITED STATES

Paper Consumption by Year		Paper Consumption for 1956 by Grades	
Year	Consumption (lb/Capita)	Grade	Consumption (lb/Capita)
1810	1	Newsprint	83.7
1819	2	Book paper	51.4
1869	20	Wrapping	46.5
1899	58	Tissue and sanitary	21.8
1919	119	Fine papers	18.2
1929	220	Building paper	16.8
1939	224	Other paper	8.0
1948	356	Paperboard	167.4
1956	434	Building board	20.3

sumption into various grades, of which newsprint is the only grade heavily imported (73% comes from Canada). The 493 companies operating 330 pulp mills and 804 paper mills in the United States in 1956 produced 22,000,000 tons of wood pulp and 31,000,000 tons of paper and paper products. The wood pulp production represents a consumption of 36,000,000 cords of wood. Wisconsin was the leading paper producing state with 2,100,000 tons, with New York, Louisiana, Georgia, Florida, Maine, Michigan, Pennsylvania, Ohio and Washington following closely in that order (see Table 15.3). In the production of wood pulp, Washington was the leading state with 3,000,000 tons, followed by Georgia, Florida, Maine, and Louisiana in that order (see Table 15.4). Thus the timber-rich state of Washington produces far more pulp than paper, and much of this pulp is sold to paper mills near the population centers of the east and midwest.

TABLE 15.3. U. S. PAPER AND PAPERBOARD PRODUCTION BY STATES (1956)

State	Quantity in Short Tons
Wisconsin	2,100,000
New York	2,000,000
Louisiana	1,900,000
Georgia	1,800,000
Florida	1,800,000
Maine	1,800,000
Michigan	1,700,000
Pennsylvania	1,700,000
Ohio	1,600,000
Washington	1,600,000
New Jersey	1,200,000
Virginia	1,200,000
South Carolina	1,000,000
California	1,000,000
Illinois	900,000
Minnesota	800,000
North Carolina	800,000
Massachusetts	800,000
Mississippi	700,000
Alabama	700,000
Texas	600,000
Tennessee	600,000
Maryland	300,000
New Hampshire	300,000
Indiana	300,000
Connecticut	300,000
Vermont, Rhode Island	200,000
Delaware, West Virginia	100,000
Missouri	100,000
Total (these and other states)	31,900,000

Market pulp is also made in appreciable quantities in Oregon and in many of the southern states, although southern mills for the most part are integrated mills, using the abundant southern pine for the manufacture of bag, wrapping, paperboard, and, more recently, newsprint papers.

The different kinds or classes of paper and paperboard produced in the United States are shown in Table 15.5. Similarly the different kinds or types of pulp produced are shown in Table 15.6.

TABLE 15.4. U. S. WOOD PULP PRODUCTION BY STATES
(1956)

State	Quantity in Short Tons
Washington	2,800,000
Georgia	2,200,000
Florida	2,100,000
Maine	1,700,000
Louisiana	1,600,000
Alabama, Tennessee*	1,200,000
Wisconsin	1,200,000
South Carolina, Maryland*	1,100,000
Mississippi	1,100,000
North Carolina	1,100,000
Virginia	1,000,000
Oregon	900,000
New York	600,000
Minnesota, Iowa, Missouri*	600,000
Texas	500,000
Arkansas, Oklahoma	400,000
Pennsylvania	400,000
N. H., Vt., Mass., R. I., Conn.	400,000
Michigan	300,000
Ohio, Illinois*	200,000
New Jersey	100,000
Total (for all states)	21,500,000

* Combined in order not to disclose production of a single company.

TABLE 15.5. U. S. PAPER AND PAPERBOARD PRODUCTION BY KINDS
(1956)

Kind	Quantity in Short Tons
Newsprint	2,000,000
Groundwood and book papers	4,000,000
Fine paper	2,000,000
Coarse wrapping, converting, and bag papers	4,000,000
Tissue paper	200,000
Sanitary paper	1,600,000
Building paper	1,400,000
Other paper	700,000
Paperboard	14,000,000
Building board	1,600,000
Total of paper and board	31,500,000

Raw materials for the pulp and paper industry can be classified as fibrous and non-fibrous. Wood accounts for over 90 per cent of the fibrous raw material used for paper in the United States. Cotton and linen rags, cotton linters, cereal straws, esparto, hemp, jute, flax, bagasse, and bamboo are used to lesser extent. Waste papers are also reprocessed, especially for making multi-ply paperboards, where waste paper is used in the inner plys.

Wood is converted into pulp by mechanical, chemical, or semichemical processes. Sulphite, sulphate (kraft), and soda are the common chemical processes while neutral sulphite is the principal semichemical process, although cold soda and chemigroundwood are semichemical processes that have recently come into commercial operation. Coniferous wood species

TABLE 15.6. U. S. WOOD PULP PRODUCTION BY KINDS
(1956)

Kind	Quantity in Short Tons
Dissolving and special alpha grades	900,000
Sulphite paper grades	2,700,000
Kraft paper grades	12,100,000
Soda	500,000
Groundwood and other non-chemical grades	4,200,000
Semichemical grades	1,500,000
Screenings	100,000
All Grades	22,000,000

(softwoods) are most desirable for the mechanical, sulphite, and sulphate processes, while broad-leaf trees are more commonly used for the soda and semichemical process.

Dissolving pulps, also termed "alpha" pulps, which are used for producing rayon, film and cellulose derivative products, are generally made by the sulphite process, although new methods have opened this field to the sulphate process as well. Sulphite pulp is otherwise used for most grades of paper with the exception of wrapping. Mechanical (groundwood) pulps have poor strength but good printability characteristics, and are used extensively for newsprint and book grades and in board grades where a relatively inexpensive pulp is desirable. Kraft pulp is the strongest of all grades and is used for bag, wrapping, and boxboard, and more recently in the bleached form in place of sulphite pulp. Semichemical pulps are used as groundwood and sulphite substitutes.

Non-fibrous raw materials include the chemicals used for the preparation of pulping liquors and bleaching solutions and the various additions to the fiber during the papermaking process. For pulping and bleaching, these raw materials include sulphur, lime, limestone, caustic soda, soda ash, salt cake, sodium and hydrogen peroxide, and chlorine; for papermaking they include rosin, starch, clay, titanium dioxide, dyestuffs, alum, and numerous other materials.

Wood Preparation

Wood bark contains relatively little fiber, which is weak, and much strongly colored non-fibrous matter. Its appearance is that of dirt in the finished paper. Therefore, for all but low-grade pulps, bark is removed for the most part, and, for groundwood and sulphite pulps, it must be thoroughly removed if the finished white-paper grades are to appear clean.

Figure 15.1. Wood being barked by two 12 ft by 45 ft barking drums. (*Courtesy Chicago Bridge and Iron Co.*)

Debarking is generally done with a friction-type machine called a drum barker, where bark is removed by the rubbing action of wet logs against one another in a large rotating drum (see Fig. 15.1). Hydraulic, chain, and knife barkers are also common. Hydraulic barkers, which use high pressure water jets for removing bark, are excellent for big timber and are, therefore, in extensive use on the West coast for logs above forty inches in diameter. Chain and knife barkers have a common disadvantage in that they remove some useful wood, along with the bark. They are used in some small operations and as secondary units in wood rooms where complete bark removal is necessary. A reserve supply of several months of debarked pulpwood is normally stored in the mill yard (see Fig. 15.2).

Regardless of the means for removing bark, the ease of debarking is dependent on the time of year and condition of the wood. Wood cut in the spring of the year, when the sap runs, peels very readily, and, if this wood is not hand peeled at the logging site, it is very readily debarked by mechanical means. Wet wood is more easily debarked than dry wood, and for this reason many mills thoroughly soak logs in ponds prior to debarking.

Recent years have seen the initiation of chemical debarking, a method in which living trees are girdled about the base during May, June and July

Figure 15.2. Pulpwood storage in mill yard by high stacker. (*Courtesy of St. Regis Paper Co., Deferiet, N. Y.*)

and sodium arsenite solution applied to the freshly exposed cambial areas. When the dead trees are cut some 6 to 24 months later, they are either bark free or peel very readily.

The standard log length used in the Northeast is four feet while five feet three inches is more common in the South. Wood is generally measured by log volume, with a rack four feet high and eight feet wide being used. The large timber on the West Coast is generally measured in board feet solid volume. The measurement and purchase of wood on a weight basis is now gaining ground and has several advantages, since it is more directly related to fiber content.

Debarked wood used for mechanical (groundwood) pulping and for the chemigroundwood process requires no further preparation, but wood used for other chemical processes must first be chipped. Chipping is necessary to increase the surface area of wood which in turn permits faster and more uniform penetration of chemical.

Chipping is accomplished with a machine of one basic design, consisting of a rotating disc with knives mounted radially (or almost so) in slots on the face of the disc. Early chippers had as few as four knives, while modern units have as many as ten or twelve knives (see Fig. 15.3). The logs are fed through the spout of the chipper at a 45° angle against the disc, which is rotating at high speeds. Each knife cuts a layer of wood having a thickness equal to the distance of protrusion of the knife from the disc. Small chip size (⅜″) is used for processes and wood species where liquor penetration is difficult, while large chip size (1″) is used where penetration is rapid. In chipping, it is necessary to cut the wood across the grain only, since the layers of wood cut on the chipper immediately break up along the grain due to the vibration from the stress and shock of the action of the machine. The reason for feeding the chipper at an angle is to increase the chip surface across the grain, which is the surface of greatest liquor penetration, since liquor moves more readily along the lumen or "pores" of the wood fibers. A typical chipper in the Northeast would have a disc about seven feet in diameter, rotating at 600 rpm, and handling 15 cords of wood per hour. Chip size is by no means uniform and screens are necessary to separate the oversize chips and sawdust from the acceptable chips.

Mechanical Pulping

Mechanical pulping, as the term implies, is not a chemical process. However, it cannot be omitted from this discussion, since it is one of the important methods of making pulp for certain grades of paper, especially newsprint.

Mechanical or groundwood pulp is made by forcing logs against the face of a cylindrical abrasive stone, rotating at high speeds. The position of the logs is such that their axes are parallel to the axis of the rotating stone. Sufficient water must be added to the stone to serve as a coolant and as a vehicle for carrying the pulp away.

Grindstones at one time were made of natural sandstone, but presently artificial stones are used almost exclusively, and characteristics can be built into the stone so pulps can be "tailor-made" to fit their desired end use. Groundwood pulps for roofing or flooring felts must be extremely coarse and free draining and require a stone with large abrasive particles, whereas pulps for newsprint are very fine and are made with a stone having small abrasive particles. Artificial abrasives in common use are silicon carbide and aluminum oxide, with vitrified clay used as the abrasive binder.

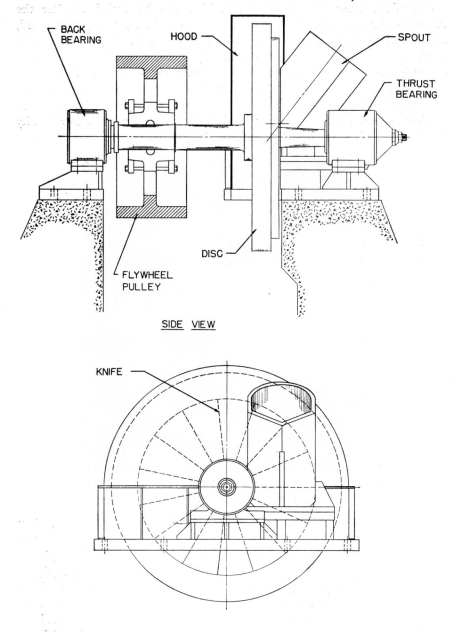

SIDE VIEW

END VIEW

Figure 15.3. Sketch of modern wood chipper. (*Courtesy Carthage Machine Co.*)

Conditions other than stone composition can be varied to alter the characteristics of the pulp. These include stone surface pattern, stone speed, pressure of the logs against the stone, and temperature of the ground pulp slurry. Generally, a coarser and more freely draining pulp is obtained with a coarse surface pattern and high speed, pressure, and temperature. Type and condition of the wood are also factors, but groundwood pulps are usually made from the coniferous or long-fibered species, since the deciduous or short-fibered species give very weak pulps. However, some low density hardwoods, such as aspen and poplar, are also ground.

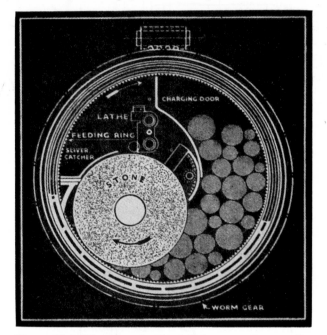

Figure 15.4. Elevation sketch of Roberts continuous ring grinder. (*Courtesy Appleton Machine Co.*)

The types of machines used for grinding wood are many and of various designs. They can be classified, however, as pocket or magazine, continuous or intermittent. The grinder in early use was the Great Northern grinder, which was a pocket, intermittent type. This machine was generally equipped with three or four pockets located radially along the upper half of the machine, and logs were placed into these pockets and forced against the rotating stone by pistons. When the wood in a pocket was consumed the piston was retracted and more wood inserted. The cycles of the different pockets were staggered to balance the power loading on the machine.

Modern grinders are mostly pocket, continuous types, of which the ring or Roberts grinder is most common in the United States (see Fig. 15.4). This machine contains the grinding stone inside a large, slowly rotating iron ring which moves eccentric to the stone and in the same direction, coming almost in contact at the 7 o'clock position of the clockwise rotation. This leaves a large crescent-shaped area into which the logs can be continuously loaded, and the ring serves to force the logs against the stone. A Roberts grinder with the stone rotating at 240 rpm by a 2000 hp motor produces 25 tons per day of newsprint groundwood. Ring rotation is 3 to 5 rpm depending on the pressure desired.

Groundwood or mechanical pulp is low in strength compared to the chemical pulps. It is composed of a mixture of individual fibers, broken fibers, fines, and coarser groups or bundles of fibers. Papers made from groundwood also lose strength and turn yellow with time. Thus, groundwood pulps are used only in relatively impermanent papers, such as newsprint, catalogue, magazine, and paperboard. Groundwood papers have excellent printing qualities because of high bulk, smoothness, resiliency, and good ink absorption. Newsprint contains about 85% groundwood and printing papers may have 30 to 70% groundwood, the remainder being a chemical pulp, usually sulphite.

Chemical Pulping

The principal chemical pulping processes are the sulphite, sulphate (kraft), and soda processes. The common purpose in each of these processes is to dissolve the lignin sufficiently so the wood will be completely reduced to fibers. Lignin is the adhesive substance of wood which binds the cellulosic fibers together. It accounts for 20–30 per cent of the weight of the wood.

All these processes use aqueous systems under heat and pressure, but the chemicals in each differ. The cooking liquor for the sulphite process consists of sulphurous acid and a salt of this acid. Usually the calcium salt is used and as such would be referred to as calcium base, but calcium-base liquor cannot be recovered, and newer mills are using recoverable bases such as magnesium, sodium, and ammonium.

The kraft and soda processes are commonly known as the alkaline processes. Both have chemical recovery systems and both use sodium hydroxide as the principal pulping reagent. The kraft cooking liquor also contains sodium sulphide which greatly accelerates the rate of pulping and has less degradative action on the pulp. The presence of sulphur, however, results in the formation of mercaptan, sulphide, and disulphide gases which, when liberated at the end of the cooking, create severe odor and public relations problems. Thus, alkaline pulp mills near population centers usually use the soda process with hardwood for producing printing papers. The southern states and the Northwest are centers for the kraft industry. The kraft process is now the most important in the United States in terms of production.

Chemical pulps are composed of separate unbroken individual fibers. By any of the commercial processes a variety of grades may be produced from unbleached to bleachable grades and from strong hard pulps for bags and wrapping papers to soft grades for tissues and book papers. Processing subsequent to pulping, such as bleaching and refining, can greatly alter the characteristics of a pulp and bring about a wide variety of paper properties. Some of the common paper grades are indicated in Tables 15.2 and 15.5.

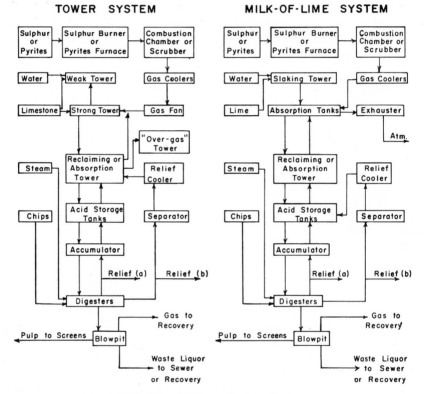

Figure 15.5. Flow diagram of acid sulphite process.

Sulphite Process. Calcium-base sulphite cooking liquor is prepared by burning molten sulphur (less commonly, pyrites) to form sulphur dioxide gas, and passing the gas either through a milk-of lime slurry or counter-current to water (or weak liquor) in a limestone-packed tower (see Fig. 15.5). The air supply to the sulphur burner must be carefully controlled, since too much air will enhance the formation of sulphur trioxide and too little air will result in sublimed sulphur passing along with the gas and fouling equipment after the gas is cooled. The gas leaving the combustion chamber is at a temperature close to 1000° C. It is necessary to cool the gas to 25–30° C because the solubility of sulphur dioxide increases with decrease in temperature. Cooling is a very critical operation, and the gas must be very rapidly cooled through the range of 1000° down to 400° C, since in this range the rate of formation of sulphur trioxide is greatest and is catalyzed by the presence of iron from the equipment. Modern spray coolers are much more efficient than the old pond coolers for rapidly cooling sulphur dioxide gas.

Both the milk-of-lime and limestone systems for gas absorption utilize two towers which are known as the strong and weak towers. The gas passes into the bottom of the strong tower, out the top, and then into the bottom of the weak tower. The milk-of-lime or water, depending on the system, flows countercurrently, and thus flows down through the weak tower and then

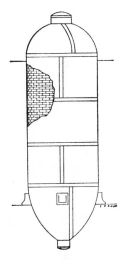

Figure 15.6. Digester for sulphite pulping.

down through the strong tower. In the limestone system, the strong tower generally has wooden checkerwork at the bottom to build up the sulphurous acid content. The absorption in the milk-of-lime system is aided by Raschig rings and bubble caps.

Recoverable base sulphite liquors (magnesium, sodium, ammonium) are generally prepared by reacting sulphur dioxide gas with the appropriate hydroxide solution in absorption towers.

The liquor from the absorption towers is known as "weak acid" and is strengthened in recovery towers with sulphur dioxide recovered from the digesters, before being pumped to the accumulator. The accumulator is a pressure vessel held at 40 psi which is used for storing hot liquor, thereby eliminating the need for cooling gas and liquor recovered from the digester and the need for completely reheating liquor pumped to the digester. Liquor stored in the accumulator is known as "strong acid."

Wood digestion by the sulphite process is generally done in vertical stationary digesters which must be lined with acid resistant brick due to the corrosive nature of the strong acid (see Fig. 15.6). Also all lines and pumps handling the strong acid must be made of stainless steel. The digesters, having capacities up to fifteen tons of pulp per charge, are heated either by direct admission of steam or with steam-heated heat exchangers. Wood chips flow into the digesters through chutes from chip storage bins (see Fig. 15.7).

Since sulphite liquor penetrates wood slowly and since the rate of reaction is slow, a digestion takes from 7 to 10 hours. Maximum cooking temperature of 140° C and pressure of 80 psig is reached in 3 to 4 hours, at which time the chips are penetrated and then one-third of the liquor is removed from the digester for recovery purposes. Pressure in the digester is due to a combination of steam pressure and sulphur dioxide gas pressure. At the end of

Figure 15.7. Digester operating floor of consolidated pulp mill at Covington, Va. (*Courtesy West Virginia Pulp and Paper Co.*)

the digestion period the digester is relieved to 40 psi to recover sulphur dioxide and is then blown, i.e., a large valve is opened at the bottom and contents of the digester are expelled to a blow pit by the force of the remaining pressure. The blow pit has a perforated bottom for initial washing of the pulp. Yield in sulphite pulping is 40–45 per cent depending upon wood species and cooking conditions. Sulphite pulps made for bleaching grades are cooked to the lower yields.

Since calcium base sulphite mills cannot reuse the chemicals, severe problems are encountered in disposing of the waste cooking liquors, since many states are imposing strict stream pollution regulations. Various uses for the waste liquor have been evaluated and presently small amounts are used in the production of alcohol, yeast, and vanillin, and as road binders, adhesives and paper additives. Mills which use a recoverable base do not encounter these problems since the organic matter is burned in the recovery process.

Alkaline Processes. Pulp mill and liquor recovery equipment is identical for the kraft and soda processes, the only difference being in chemical makeup. All alkaline pulp mills have recovery systems, where the waste liquor, known as "black liquor," is concentrated in multiple effect, steam-heated evaporators to 50 per cent solids and then further concentrated in direct contact evaporators to 65 per cent solids, using furnace gases as the heat source (see Fig. 15.8). Makeup chemical (Na_2SO_4 for kraft and Na_2CO_3 for soda) is then added and the concentrated black liquor burned in a furnace with the dissolved wood matter serving as fuel. The flue gases from the furnace first go to the direct contact evaporators and then to

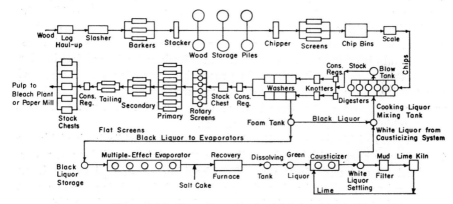

Figure 15.8. Flow diagram of sulphate process.

electrostatic precipitators for recovery of "fly ash," while the molten chemical or smelt flows from the bottom of the furnace into dissolving tanks. The dissolved smelt or "green liquor" is then causticized by mixing with slaked lime, the reaction being as follows:

$$Na_2CO_3 + Ca(OH)_2 \rightarrow 2NaOH + CaCO_3$$

The calcium carbonate is then clarified from the now "white liquor" and kilned, with the resulting lime being reslaked.

The only difference between the kraft and soda recovery systems is that the kraft makeup is sodium sulphate and the soda makeup is sodium carbonate. The sodium sulphate is reduced in the furnace to sodium sulphide by carbon in the black liquor according to the following reaction:

$$Na_2SO_4 + 2C \rightarrow Na_2S + 2CO_2$$

The temperature in the reducing zone is maintained at 930 to 980° C. The reaction is endothermic, requiring about 3000 Btu per pound of sodium sulphate. The reduction should be as high as possible (90 per cent or more) since sodium sulphate has no pulping action. The sodium sulphide remains unchanged during the causticizing of the sodium carbonate.

Digestion by the kraft and soda processes is done in vertical steel digesters, requiring no lining, and heated by steam either directly or indirectly. The cooking period for kraft is 2–3 hours and for soda 5–7 hours, since the rate of reaction with kraft is much faster due to the presence of sodium sulphide. With both processes, maximum cooking temperature of about 170° C is reached as quickly as possible, and there is no liquor or gas relief as with sulphite, and all the waste cooking liquor is recovered. Digester pressure during cooking is due only to steam pressure, and the digester is blown to cyclone tanks at this pressure, which is about 100 psig.

Washing is generally not done in the blow tank but with a series of three vacuum washers, where washing is done countercurrently, i.e., the unwashed pulp is added to the first washer and fresh water is used for dilution in the third washer, with the pulp proceeding successively to the second and third washers and the effluent countercurrently to the second and first washers. In this way, washing is done with a minimum amount of fresh water, which benefits evaporation economy.

Soda pulp yields are generally about 45 per cent, while kraft yields are 45 to 50 per cent or higher depending on the pulping conditions as predetermined by end use. Kraft pulps for bleaching are cooked to the lower yields, and practically all soda pulps are bleached since their main use is for the manufacture of white printing papers. It is only since about 1940 that methods for bleaching kraft pulps were developed. Presently kraft pulps are used for dissolving and white paper grades as well as for brown grades such as wrapping and board. Kraft mills for producing dissolving pulps incorporate a prehydrolysis stage, the chips being first steamed to hydrolyze short-chain carbohydrate material (hemicellulose) which is then more completely removed during cooking.

Hardwoods pulp well by the soda process and are the main species used, since their short fibers are well-suited for book and white printing papers. The kraft process produces excellent strong pulps from softwoods, and unlike the sulphite process can utilize the resinous pines. From the resin-rich pines the sulphate process yields by-products in the form of sulphate turpentine and tall oil, a material containing mainly fatty and resin acids. Tall oil is used in making soap and as a chemical raw material for various products.

Semichemical Pulping

Semichemical pulping processes are those where wood is given a mild chemical treatment, but not to the extent of sufficient lignin removal to bring about fiber separation. Partial delignification and softening are brought about so that mechanical means may be used to complete the fiber separation. Three important semichemical processes in commercial use are the neutral sulphite, cold soda, and chemigroundwood processes. Also, some mills produce semichemical kraft, soda, or sulphite pulps by reducing the cooking time or chemical concentration so that only partial delignification occurs. With all of these processes, high yields are obtained, thus giving more pulp per given weight of wood than with the chemical processes.

Space-saving continuous digesters, instead of the large batch digesters used in chemical pulping, are finding wide use for neutral sulphite semichemical pulping, and as impregnating vessels in the cold soda process. Only limited use for continuous digesters has been found for the full chemical processes, due to the necessity for short cooking times in the continuous operation.

The neutral sulphite semichemical process is one in which wood chips, usually from hardwoods, are cooked with sodium sulphite liquor, buffered with sodium bicarbonate. Continuous, rotary and stationary digesters are used. The wood is cooked at 170° C or higher to yields of 75 per cent for unbleached grades and 65 per cent for bleachable grades and is then fiberized by disc refiners. Unbleached neutral sulphite pulp is extensively used for corrugating medium, while bleached neutral sulphite pulp is used as a sulphite substitute in printing and fine papers. A flow diagram of the neutral sulphite process is shown in Figure 15.9.

The cold soda process is one which is coming into wide use as a means of obtaining a satisfactory grade of groundwood pulp from hardwoods. In this process, hardwood chips are treated with cold sodium hydroxide solution either under room temperature and pressure or with hydrostatic pressure, and then fiberized by disc refiners. Yields of cold soda pulps are generally in the range of 85 to 90 per cent, with the pulps being used unbleached for corrugating medium and bleached for printing grades.

The chemigroundwood process is one in which whole hardwood bolts, usually 4 feet long, are cooked in stationary digesters for 4 to 6 hours with neutral sulphite liquor at 160 to 170° C, using a hydrostatic pressure of 150 psig. The penetrated logs are then ground by conventional wood grinders as used in the mechanical pulping process. Like the cold soda process, chemigroundwood is a means of obtaining a good grade of groundwood pulp from the short fibered hardwoods. Yields from this process are in the range of 85 per cent and the pulps are used for printing grades of paper.

Screening and Cleaning of Wood Pulp

Screening of wood pulp is commonly divided into two operations, coarse screening and fine screening. With groundwood pulp a third type of screen, known as a bull screen, is used for removing very large slivers up to eight inches in length. Bull screens generally consist of one-inch mesh wire through which the ground pulp slurries pass, with doctors being used to scrape off the slivers caught by the screen.

Coarse screens are generally referred to as knotters, which are either of rotary or flat vibratory design. In either case, the screen perforations are generally round, ranging in size from $\frac{1}{4}''$ to $\frac{3}{8}''$, and the pulp is fed to the screens at consistencies of 0.6 per cent or less. The function of the knotter

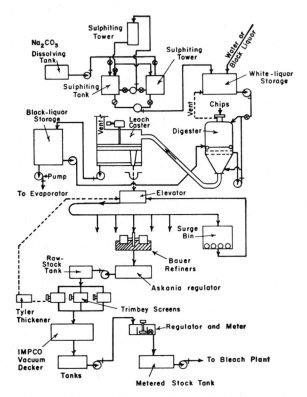

Figure 15.9. Flow diagram of neutral sulphite semi-chemical process.

is to remove knots and uncooked chips from chemical pulps, and coarse, stringy matter from groundwood pulps.

Fine screens are also of either rotary or flat design, but in either case the perforations are slot-like and range from 0.008″ to 0.020″ in width. Flat screens are diaphragm-type screens which depend on the sucking action of the diaphragm for the passage of accepted pulp through the perforations; centrifugal force or vibration is utilized in the operation of rotary screens. Fine screens are operated at low consistencies (0.6 per cent or less) and are usually installed in primary-secondary arrangements, in which the primary rejects go to secondary units, from which the accepts go back to the primary units and the rejects go to refiners or to the sewer.

In recent years centrifugal cleaners have come into wide use in the paper industry for removal of specks and heavy fine materials from pulp. The functioning of this equipment depends upon the difference in specific gravity of the dirt particles and the fiber. These devices are either conical or cylindrical in shape and are positioned vertically (see Fig. 15.10). The

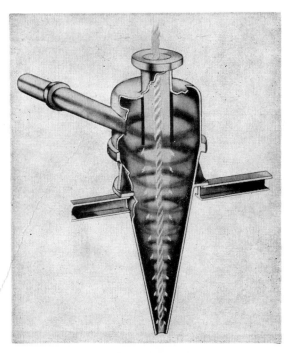

Figure 15.10. Centrifugal cleaner for removal of dirt.
(*Courtesy Bauer Brothers Co.*)

pulp slurry at low consistencies (less than 1 per cent) is pumped into the device through a tangential inlet at the top, which in conical units is the wide end of the cone. The main outlet for the slurry is also at the top but symmetrical with the body of the unit. The slurry enters the unit continuously and swirls downward in a helical motion, with the heavy and speck material being thrown to the outside. The accepted material then changes direction and moves up the center and out the top while the rejected material passes out through a restricted opening at the bottom. Centrifugal cleaners are generally operated in a primary-secondary-tertiary arrangement, with the rejects being passed from the primary to the secondary to the tertiary units, while the accepts from the secondary and tertiary units are fed back to the primary units. In such an arrangement, the cleaned pulp would be the accepts from the primary units, and the dirt removed from the system would be that rejected by the tertiary unit(s).

Bleaching of Wood Pulp

The objective of pulp bleaching is the production of brighter pulps, as measured by light reflectance. For groundwood, cold soda, neutral sulphite, and chemigroundwood pulps, extremely high brightnesses (85 to 90) are commercially unfeasible due to high lignin content of the pulps, and brightness increments are obtained solely through the removal of color bodies with oxidizing agents (peroxides) and reducing agents (hydrosulphites). For sulphite, kraft, soda, and neutral sulphite pulps, however, the bleaching process generally includes further delignification of the pulps by chorination, followed by a caustic treatment for the removal of alkaline-soluble chorolignins, and then by one or more bleaching stages with oxidizing agents, such as sodium or calcium hypochlorite or chlorine dioxide. Washing is necessary after each stage in multi-stage bleaching processes.

Bleaching of groundwood and high yield semichemical pulps with peroxide or hydrosulphite is generally done in one stage. With both of these methods, the rate of bleaching is increased with increased consistencies, and the emphasis is on equipment design for handling high consistencies (up to 25 per cent). Brightness increments up to 12–15 points can be obtained with each type of bleaching chemical, and thus a groundwood pulp of 60 brightness could readily be bleached to 72 brightness with little reduction in yield. Cold soda pulps are being bleached in two-stage peroxide-hydrosulphite processes with resulting brightness increments of 20 points or better.

Chlorination of chemical pulps is a very rapid reaction and must be done at low consistencies and low temperatures. Since chlorination is a continuation of delignification initiated in the digester, loss in pulp yield results. However, for production of high brightness pulps, removal of as much lignin as possible prior to oxidative bleaching is desirable. Caustic treatment following chlorination is necessary for kraft and neutral sulphite pulps, but is quite often omitted with sulphite pulps.

Oxidative bleaching with calcium and sodium hypochlorites, prepared by chlorinating milk-of-lime or caustic soda solutions, has been done for many years. In early bleach plants, sulphite and soda pulps were bleached with one or two stage calcium hypochlorite processes, and only in later years with the introduction of chlorination and caustic extraction has the bleaching of kraft pulps been feasible at all. Presently sulphite and soda bleaching consists of one hypochlorite stage following chlorination and caustic extraction, whereas kraft bleaching will contain two or three hypochlorite stages. Increases in temperature and consistency accelerate the rate of reaction in hypochlorite bleaching, but also bring about a greater degradative effect on pulp strength, so a balance must be reached between equipment capacity and the strength of the finished product.

In recent years, chlorine dioxide has been used extensively for oxidative bleaching of chemical pulps, usually as the last stage of a chlorination-caustic extraction-hypochlorite process. Chlorine dioxide facilitates the production of very high brightness pulps with no decrease in pulp strength as is experienced with hypochlorite. The engineering of systems for efficient, safe generation of chlorine dioxide has greatly enhanced the recent growth of this process.

Pulping Other Fibrous Materials

Fibrous materials for papermaking other than wood are waste paper, cotton and linen rags, waste rope, cotton linters, and grasses, such as bamboo,

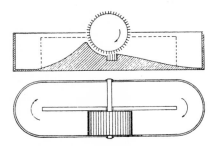

Figure 15.11. Beater; side elevation in upper drawing and top view in lower drawing.

esparto, bagasse, straw, flax, jute and hemp. However, wood remains and will continue to remain the world's chief papermaking fiber. In the United States over 90 per cent of papermaking fiber is wood fiber.

Most grades of paper can be reused. The cheaper grades, such as newsprint, are used in board grades and to some extent for cheap toweling, while better grades such as book and magazine paper are deinked and reused for book, magazine and other white grades. In addition, all mills except those making wet strength grades reuse their "broke," which is that paper wasted in threading the paper machine, changing reels, and trimming rolls.

Rag and rope mills generally have the same process, the first step being the boiling of waste rags or rope under pressure with caustic soda, lime, and/or soda ash. The purposes of boiling are to remove natural waxes and resins, remove oils, and grease, strip dyes, and to facilitate the subsequent beating operation. The boiled matter is drained and allowed to mellow for twelve hours, after which it is placed in a beater, where the fiber is separated (drawn out), washed, and bleached. The beater is basically a refiner, and consists of a horizontally placed roll having lateral bars on its surface, and a stationary bedplate arrangement with similar bars on which the roll rotates (Fig. 15.11). The roll and bedplate are placed in an oblong tub in such a manner that pulp passing under the roll circulates around the midfeather of the tub and then again under the roll (Fig. 15.12). Washing is accomplished in the beater by continuously adding fresh water and continuously removing effluent with a wire cylinder. Following the beater operation the bleached, drawn-out fiber or "half-stuff" is dumped into a drainer and allowed to age for 5–7 days, after which it is ready for further refining and, then, the papermaking operation.

Rag pulps of good cotton and linen fibers are generally used for fine paper grades, such as expensive bond and writing paper. Low grade rags,

Figure 15.12. The beater separates the fiber "bundles," reduces them to proper length and slightly frays the ends and sides so that they will mat together properly on the papermaking machine. During the beating, the necessary dye stuffs, pigments and sizing are introduced. (*Courtesy West Virginia Pulp and Paper Co.*)

having no chemical treatment, find wide use in flooring and roofing felts. Rope pulps, which are mainly hemp fibers, have very long fiber length and are used in twisting and other grades requiring high tear resistance.

Several methods are used for pulping straw, bagasse, and flax. Straw and bagasse are commonly cooked with caustic soda at atmospheric pressure, although digestions by the soda or kraft processes or with lime at low pressures are also common. Pulps from these grasses are used for corrugating and building boards in the United States, although in countries lacking ample wood supplies they find wide use for bleached paper grades. Most cigarette paper is made from flax, cooked by the kraft process and then bleached.

Bamboo is one of the chief fibrous raw materials in the Orient. The alkaline processes are best suited to bamboo. All grades of paper, including high-grade bleachable pulps, are made from bamboo.

Stock Preparation

Stock preparation in a paper mill includes all intermediate operations between preparation of the pulp and fabrication of the paper, and can be subdivided into (1) preparation of the "furnish" and (2) beating and refining. *Furnish* is the term for the water slurry of fiber and chemicals which ultimately goes to the paper machine for fabrication into paper. It is so prepared, either in beaters or mixing chests, to give desired characteristics to the finished paper. The furnish may contain rosin or other sizing agents to give the paper water and ink resistance, inorganic filler matter such as clay or titanium dioxide for opacity and smoothness, organic dyes for color, or organic resins for wet strength properties. Refining of the pulp is necessary for strength development, and is done either before or after the furnish is prepared, using beaters, jordans, or disc mills.

The furnish of a paper machine system varies widely depending on the grade being made. Newsprint is generally a mixture of 15–20 parts of unbleached sulphite pulp and 80–85 parts of groundwood pulp with no chemical additives. However, rotogravure papers have 2 to 3 per cent filler to improve printing characteristics. Bag paper generally is 100 per cent unbleached kraft pulp together with 4 per cent size on the weight of the pulp for water resistance and 3 per cent alum to set the size. Linerboard is made of 100 per cent unbleached kraft with no beater additives, but starch is applied to the surface of the dried paper to improve sizing and surface characteristics. Bond paper may be 100 per cent sulphite, 100 per cent rag, or a combination of sulphite and rag, and usually contains 5–10 per cent filler and a starch surface sizing application. Papers for bread-wrap are highly refined for increased density and are heavily loaded with a filler having high opacifying power. Thus the grade of paper being made determines the makeup and treatment of the furnish. Although good paper machine operation is necessary for obtaining desired paper characteristics, proper furnish preparation is most important in determining the properties of the finished product.

The type and extent of refining is dictated by the desired properties of the finished product. Beaters, the nature of which has been previously described, find extensive use for refining only in rag, rope, and fine paper mills. Most mills use the jordan or conical refiner, which has a conical plug rotating inside of a stationary inverted conical shell (Figs. 15.13 and 15.14). Both the plug and shell are equipped with bar tackle on their surfaces, and the pulp slurry passing through this machine is refined by the bar-to-bar action of the plug and shell, with the extent of refining determined by the rotational speed of the plug and the pressure, as determined by distance, of the plug against the shell. Disc mills which were previously used only for fiberization of semi-chemical pulps are finding wide use in paper mills, particularly for wrapping, linerboard, bag, and other kraft grades. These machines consist of two parallel discs, again having bar surfaces, with either one or both of the discs rotating. The stock passes out through the bar-to-bar action of the discs (Fig. 15.15). For preparation of strong, highly refined pulps for such grades as glassine, tracing, and bread-wrap, beaters,

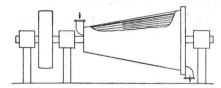

Figure 15.13. The Jordan or conical refiner.

conical refiners, and disc mills can all be equipped with stone tackle, which effects less cutting and more brushing of the fibers.

Refining brings about fundamental changes in pulp fibers and increases the degree of interfiber bonding in the paper sheet. Therefore, refining is a very important step in the production of paper and greatly influences the properties of the final sheet. Refining, as carried out commercially, not only brings about a more complete fiber separation and a smoother pulp, but increases most paper strength properties, except tear resistance. Beating also tends to increase smoothness and hardness of the paper sheet, but decreases opacity and lowers the bulk and dimensional stability of the paper. Thus, the proper refining conditions must be selected to bring out the desired properties without detracting too much from other properties.

Many paper mills are not integrated with pulp mills, and it is necessary for these mills to use dried, baled pulp made at other locations. Such pulp is dispersed either in beaters or by machines known as pulpers, which utilize vigorous agitation at consistencies of 6 to 8 per cent to break up effectively the dried pulp sheets into fibers.

Papermaking Process

Batches of prepared furnish from the beaters or mixing chests are dumped into stock chests from where it is fed continuously at 3 per cent consistency through finishing jordans into the paper machine system. These jordans are so placed that they can be used for direct control of pulp drainage on the paper machine. The stock is then diluted with "white water"—the effluent drainage from the paper machine—to about 0.5 per cent consistency, is given a final screening with rotary or flat fine screens to remove as much dirt and undesirable solids as possible and to help obtain a maximum separation of the fibers before the stock is delivered to the paper machine.

Figure 15.14. Refiners at Covington, Va., plant separate fibers, reduce them to proper length and fray their edges for matting. (*Courtesy West Virginia Pulp and Paper Co.*)

Figure 15.15. Single rotating disc refiner. (*Courtesy Sprout, Waldron & Co.*)

The screening of the stock is accomplished in either diaphragm or flat (similar to the screen of the same designation used for screening pulp), or rotary machines. There are two types of rotary screen; the inward flow and the outward flow. In the inward flow screen (Fig. 15.16), accepted stock passes inwardly from a vat through slots of a screen-plate cylinder positioned within it. The cylinder is open at one end, and this end serves as the discharge for the accepted stock. Rejects, in turn, are removed from the bottom of the vat. Conversely, in the outward flow screen, stock to be screened enters the screen-plate cylinder. The accepted stock passes through the openings in its plates into a vat beneath it; the rejects, in turn, are removed from within the cylinder by the use of a discharge pan located within it.

Dirt too small in size to be rejected by the screens may be separated by centrifugal cleaners of the type also used in cleaning pulp (see Fig.

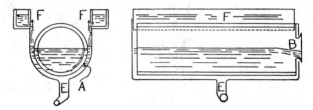

Figure 15.16. Inward flow screen for paper stock. *A*, slotted screen which rotates; *B*, open discharge for cleaned stock; the vat itself is shaking in horizontal plane; *E*, waste pipe for tailing removal; *F*, flow boxes.

15.10) The screened and cleaned stock now flows to the wet end of the paper machine.

The wet end of the paper machine is that part of the machine where the paper is formed. There are two types of units used for this purpose, namely the fourdrinier and the cylinder wet ends. The fourdrinier machine is characterized by a headbox, from which the dilute stock slurry flows through a narow opening called the "slice" onto a flat moving wire, which is actually an endless belt that returns on the underside of the machine (Fig. 15.17). Water and some solids drain rapidly through the wire, while the remainder of the stock felts into a wet mat on the surface of the wire. Low headbox consistency is necessary for good sheet formation and a vigorous sidewise shaking of the wire also aids in formation, but once the sheet is formed the principal objective is water removal without disturbing the sheet formation. This is accomplished first by the action of numerous table rolls which support the wire in the forming area immediately following the headbox, and by suction boxes which also support the wire and which have flat perforated tops for the removal of water by applied vacuum. The sheet consistency is about 2 per cent at the end of the table rolls and 15 to 20 per cent after the suction boxes. From the suction boxes the wire and sheet move to the couch roll from where the wire returns in the direction of the headbox, while the sheet, usually unsupported, jumps a short gap to the press section. For grades where the wet sheet is too weak to support itself, felt pickup arrangements are used for carrying the sheet through the press section. A diagram of a fourdrinier machine in shown in Figure 15.18. The largest fourdrinier machines are used for newsprint and range in width up to 345 in. and in operating speeds up to 2500

Figure 15-17. 264-inch high-speed Kraft paper machine. (*Courtesy Beloit Iron Works*)

ft/min. A typical fourdriner for bond paper, however, may be 180 in. wide and operate at 800 ft/min.

The cylinder wet end consists of one or more cylinder vats, on each of which is formed a separate wet web of fibers (see Fig. 15.19). Each vat consists of a wire cylinder rotating in dilute stock slurry. The liquid head on the outside of the cylinder is greater than on the inside, resulting in water and some solids passing through the wire and a mat of pulp forming on the cylinder surface. The felted stock is removed from the cylinder by an endless woolen felt, which moves in contact with the cylinder through the aid of a rubber roll riding on top. With machines having more than one cylinder, the same felt moves from one cylinder to the next, and the felted wet sheets are laminated to one another on the bottom side of the felt. By this means, very heavy sheets or, more commonly, boards can be fabricated with machines having up to ten vats. White furnish can be supplied to the end vats to give white surfaces to the board, while the

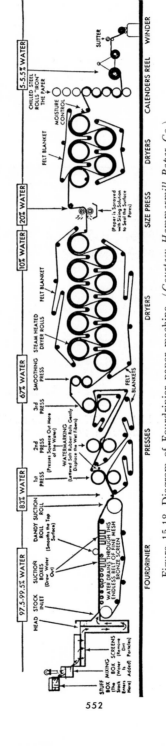

Figure 15.18. Diagram of Fourdrinier paper machine. (*Courtesy Hammermill Paper Co.*)

middle or filler vats can run on waste newsprint or some other cheap grade of waste paper. One-vat cylinder machines are used in the production of tissue. Cylinder machines, by their nature, are limited in speed, and the fastest machines with large diameter cylinders generally do not exceed speeds of 800 ft/min. Few cylinder machines have widths in excess of 200 inches.

From the wet end of the paper machine, the wet sheet is conveyed by woolen felts through a series of roll-type presses for further water removal, increasing the consistency to about 35 per cent. The sheet is then

Figure 15.19. Wet end of eight-cylinder papermaking machine; view from suction return drum toward press section. (*Courtesy Black-Clawson Co.*)

threaded through the drier section, consisting of a long series of steam-heated cast iron cylinders, for drying down to 5 per cent moisture content. Another type of drier used is a Yankee drier, consisting of one large highly polished steam-heated cylinder, ranging from 9 to 15 feet in diameter. Yankee driers are used to impart a high finish to one side of the sheet or for lightweight papers requiring continuous support through the drying operation.

After the drying operation, the sheet surface is smoothed by passing through a calendar stack consisting of a vertical row of highly polished cast iron rolls. Power is supplied to the bottom roll and the other rolls turn by frictional contact. It is this same friction which applies finish to the paper as it passes through the roll nips. The paper is then wound into large rolls at the reel, from which point it is rewound and slit into finished rolls, or else sheeted and trimmed into desired size. The dry end of a large fourdrinier machine is illustrated in Figure 15.20.

A summary schematic chart of the materials and equipment used in the manufacture of paper is shown in Figure 15.21. The chart illustrates a composite picture of the major steps in papermaking, but does not represent a layout of any typical mill.

Figure 15.20. Dry end of large Fourdrinier machine. (*Courtesy St. Regis Paper Co.*)

Paper is converted into its end product by many different means. Some papers are sheeted, shaped, or fastened into final forms, while others require more elaborate processing. Corrugated boxboard, for instance, is made by gluing sheets of linerboard to each side of a fluted sheet of corrugating medium. Probably the most extensive converting operation is coating which is done by machines that both apply and smooth the coating formula. Many coatings are for specialty papers, such as polyethylene for ice cream and other food cartons. However, the largest amounts of coated papers are for printing purposes, where mineral coatings are applied to smooth and brighten the paper surface.

BOARD AND STRUCTURAL MATERIALS

Board, sheets, panels and other structural materials are manufactured from wood fibers and various other vegetable fibers, from wood particles

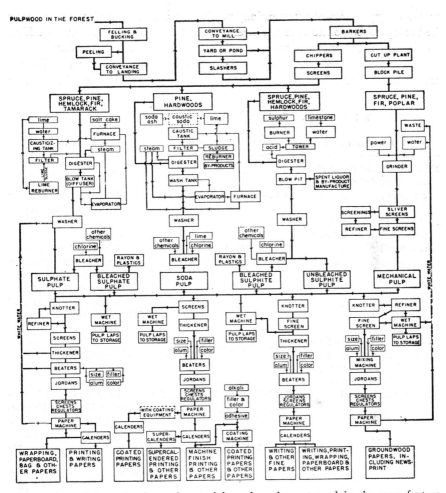

Figure 15.21. Schematic chart of materials and equipment used in the manufacture of paper. (*Courtesy American Paper and Pulp Association*)

and from paper. The industries making these products are not generally classified as chemical industries; nevertheless, they are closely related to chemical industry. Fiberboard manufacture is similar to papermaking; particle boards and paper laminates involve the use of synthetic resins and, therefore, chemical technology.

Fiberboard

Fiberboard is the term for rigid or semi-rigid sheet materials of widely varying densities and thicknesses manufactured from wood or other vegetable fibers. The board is formed by the felting of the fibers from a water slurry or an air suspension, producing a mat. Bonding agents may be incorporated to increase the strength, and other materials may be added to give special properties, such as resistance to moisture, fire or decay.

Fiberboards are manufactured primarily for panels, insulation and cover materials in buildings and other structures where flat sheets of moderate

TABLE 15.7. CLASSIFICATION AND USES OF FIBERBOARDS*

Fiberboards	Density Classification		Major Uses
	g/cm³	lb/cu ft	
Non-compressed (insulation board) semi-rigid insulation	0.02–0.15	1.25– 9.5	Heat insulation as blankets and batts; industrial cushioning
Rigid insulation board (includes wallboard and softboard)	0.15–0.40	9.5 –25.0	Heat and sound insulation as sheathing, interior panelling, base for plaster or siding, thick laminated sheets for structural decking, cores for doors and partitions, acoustical ceilings
Compressed			
Intermediate or medium density fiberboard (includes laminated paper-boards and homo-geneous boards)	0.40–0.80	25–50	Structural use and heat insulation as sheathing base for plaster and siding, interior panelling, containers, underflooring
Hardboard	0.80–1.20	50–75	Panelling, counter tops, components in doors, cabinets, cupboards, furniture, containers, and millwork, concrete forms, flooring
Densified hardboard (superhardboard)	1.20–1.45	75–90	Electrical instrument panels, templets, jigs, die stock

*From information in "Fibreboard and Particle Board," Food and Agriculture Organization of the United Nations, Rome, 1958.

strength and/or insulating capacity are required. They are also used as components in doors, cupboards, cabinets, furniture and millwork.

Classification of fiberboards is best done on the basis of density, since there is a great deal of overlap when classifying by use only. Table 15.7 shows the density classification of fiberboards as well as some of their major uses.

The production of fiberboards goes back to 1898 when the first plant was built in Great Britain. However, large-scale production, mainly of insulation board, developed in the United States between the two world wars. Though the United States is still the largest producing country, it now accounts for less than half of the world output. Fiberboard production figures on a world basis over a number of more recent years are shown in Table 15.8. There has been a much more rapid increase in the production of compressed fiberboards (hardboards) than noncompressed fiberboards (insulation board) during recent years.

TABLE 15.8. FIBERBOARD PRODUCTION BY REGIONS FOR SOME
RECENT YEARS*

Figures in 1000 Tons

Region	1938	1946	1948	1951	1954	1956
U. S. A.	600	867	1153	1152	1367	1516
Canada	34	80	125	169	167	213
Norway, Sweden, Finland	119	274	347	532	590	678
Rest of Europe	49	74	167	350	467	630
U.S.S.R.	3	2	8	24	54	68
Australia and Oceania	18	13	38	58	102	115
Asia	. . .	12	13	20	34	50
Africa	. . .	. . .	. . .	15	55	75
Latin America	. . .	. . .	. . .	17	26	45
World Total	823	1322	1851	2337	2862	3390

* From "Fibreboard and Particle Board," Food and Agriculture Organization of the United Nations, Rome, 1958.

Wood is the principal raw material for the manufacture of fiberboards. The species used are numerous, including both softwoods (coniferous) and hardwoods (broad-leaved) and vary from region to region. The wood may be from the harvesting of commercial timber and pulp species, as well as from species not commonly used for lumber or pulp, from cull timber, from logging and forest management residues and from industrial wood residues. Other fiber raw materials for fiberboard manufacture are bagasse (sugar cane residue after sugar extraction) and waste paper. Only minor amounts of other plant fibers are used.

Wood handling and preparation for fiberboard manufacture is much the same as described for pulp and paper. Wood is debarked and chipped with the same type of equipment. If the chips are to be first extracted for resins or tannin, then cylinder or drum-type chippers may be used instead of disc chippers.

Fibers for fiberboard are coarser and less refined chemically than for paper. Processes are used which bring about fiber separation with minimum loss in chemical components and in maximum yield. The pulping processes used are generally the following: (1) mechanical, (2) thermal-mechanical, (3) semichemical and (4) explosion methods.

Mechanical Pulping. The mechanical pulping process is the same as that described for making paper pulp. Stones of coarse grit are used to give a somewhat coarser fiber of higher freeness than the usual groundwood for papermaking. Freeness is a measure of the ease of drainage of water from the pulp. A fast drainage rate is required since a thick mat is produced in forming the wet sheet and this must drain rapidly to maintain an economical rate of production.

A very coarse shredded wood fiber is made by a shredder, consisting of two cylinders to which are attached numerous small pointed hammers, which swing freely as the cylinders are rotated. These hammers "comb" or shred wet green wood, such as aspen, into stiff coarse bundles of fibers, producing a bulky pulp. This type of equipment is not widely used, and most mechanical pulp is made on conventional stone grinders.

Untreated green or water-soaked wood chips may also be directly ground in disc mills of either the single-rotary or double-rotary type (similar to those used for refining pulp; see Fig. 15.15), giving a coarse pulp acceptable for insulation board.

Thermal-Mechanical Pulping. Generally, chips are given a steaming or other heat-treatment prior to or during defibering in a disc mill. Steaming or heating in hot water softens the wood so that, upon grinding, a pulp is produced with fewer broken fibers and with less coarse fiber bundles. Steaming is generally preferred and is carried out in a digester under a variety of conditions of time and temperature. A typical steaming period is about 30 min at 75 psi. If iron digesters are used, a small amount of alkali may be added to the chips to prevent corrosion by the organic acids produced by the hydrolytic action on the wood.

The steamed chips are defibered in a disc-type attrition mill having two discs made of special alloys, one or both rotating. Various disc patterns are available and the choice and spacing depend upon the species of wood, type of pretreatment, and the properties of the pulp desired.

The pulp may or may not be screened, as necessary. It is usually given some further refining to give maximum strength. Sizing and other additives are introduced and the pulp suspension is delivered to the wet sheet-forming machine.

A special continuous thermal-mechanical process has been developed whereby the wood chips are steamed and ground while at elevated temperatures and pressures. The feature of the process is the combination of steaming and defibering in one unit in a continuous operation. The entire operation is carried out under pressure and no cooling takes place prior to defibering. Wood chips are continuously introduced by a plunger feed mechanism into a preheater where they are heated to 170–190° C by steam at 100–165 psi. Passage through the preheater takes 20–60 seconds, after which the hot chips are fed by a screw directly to the single rotating disc refiner, where they are ground while at the above temperature and pressure conditions. At these conditions the lignin, which is concentrated in the intercellular regions (middle lamella) of the wood, becomes some-what thermoplastic, permitting easier separation of the fibers. Due to the very short steaming time, it is claimed that little hydrolysis takes place so that there is little loss in wood substance, the yields being 90–93 per cent. Additional refining is necessary for the preparation of insulation board stock, and slight refining may be desirable for hardboard stock, especially to break down slivers.

Semichemical Pulping. In some cases wood or other fibrous raw mate-rial may be given a mild chemical pretreatment prior to mechanical de-fibering. The processes are similar to those described for making paper pulps by semichemical methods. Generally, the conditions of treatment are somewhat milder than for paper pulp in order to get maximum yields. The chemical treatments usually involve cooking with neutral sulphite, caustic soda or lime solutions. Yields from wood chips generally are in the range of 70–85 per cent.

Explosion Process. A unique process for defibering wood was developed by W. H. Mason. Wood chips, about ¾″ long, prepared in conventional chippers and screened, are subjected to high pressure, in a cylinder, com-monly called a gun, about 2 feet by 6 feet in size, and ejected through a quick opening valve. The elevated temperature softens the chips and, upon ejection, they explode into a fluffy mass of fibers and fiber bundles. The process involves thermal plasticization of the lignin, partial hydrolysis and a disintegration by the sudden expansion of the steam within the chip.

About 260 lb of wood chips are fed into the cylinder and steamed to 600 psi for 30–60 seconds. Then the pressure is quickly raised to 1000 psi (about 285° C) and held only about 5 seconds before suddenly releasing the charge into a cyclone. The time of treatment at this high pressure and temperature is critical and depends upon the species of wood, chip size, moisture content and the quality of product desired. The steam is con-densed in the cyclone and the exploded fiber falls into a stock chest where it is mixed with water and pumped through washers, refiners and screens.

The high temperature to which the chips have been subjected causes ap-preciable hydrolysis of the hemicelluloses, resulting in a somewhat lower yield of pulp than obtained by mechanical or thermal-mechanical pulping. The hydrolysis results in a final board product with an enriched lignin con-tent; about 38 per cent compared to about 26 per cent in the original softwood. The lignin content of the pulp can be varied by controlling the steaming process.

Board Forming. Pulp prepared by any of the above processes may be used for making insulation board. Mechanical or groundwood pulp was the first type of pulp used in large-scale production of insulation boards, and is still being used in many plants. Pulps from other sources, such as disc mills, may be admixed with it. Groundwood pulp is not considered satisfactory for hardboard, and most hardboard is made from pulp prepared by the explosion process or by defibering with disc refiners.

Board making is basically similar to papermaking and involves refining, screening, mixing of additives, sheet forming, and drying operations. Pressing is also required for hardboards. The pulp is refined and screened prior to sheet formation.

Sizing agents in amounts up to one per cent of the fiber are added to the pulp in mixing chests. Paraffin wax emulsion is commonly used for all types of board. For insulation boards rosin, cumarone resin and asphalt are also used. Often a mixture of rosin and paraffin emulsion is used, with 10–25 per cent rosin in the mixture. For hardboards, paraffin wax is the most common sizing agent, though tall oil derivatives and phenol-formaldehyde resins are also used. The sizing agent is precipitated on the fibers by alum, with careful control of pH; the latter may be between 4.0 and 6.5, according to the conditions.

The strength properties of a fiberboard depend mainly upon the felting characteristics of the individual fibers and to a lesser degree upon their interfiber bonding. The felting or forming process is usually done from a water suspension of the fiber at a consistency of around one per cent. This is the *wet-felting* process. A relatively new *air-felting* or dry-forming process has been developed and is being used in a few American plants for hardboard manufacture.

The wet-felting process is generally carried out in a manner similar to papermaking, i.e., in a continuous operation on a fourdrinier machine or on a cylinder machine. The machines move more slowly than in the case of papermaking 5–45 ft/min on the fourdrinier) and a coarser mesh wire is employed. In the cylinder machine method, a single large vacuum cylinder, 8–14 ft in diameter, is most commonly used. Further water removal is effected by suction boxes and press rolls. The wet sheet is conveyed from the press sections to the drier on roller conveyers and is trimmed to desired width and cut into lengths suitable for final trimming after drying.

A third type of wet-felting is a discontinuous method, known as the *deckle-box* method. The deckle box consists of a bottomless frame which can be raised or lowered onto a screen. A measured quantity of stock sufficient to form one sheet is pumped into the deckle box and vacuum applied to the lower side of the screen. After most of the water has drained off, pressure is applied from the top to express more water and compact the sheet, reducing its thickness. The deckle-frame is then raised and the sheet conveyed to the driers.

For the recent air-felting process, defibering is usually done in disc mills with control of the moisture content to give the minimum amount possible, consistent with good defibering conditions. Additional moisture may be removed by pre-heating the air that conveys the fiber from the refiners to a cyclone. The fiber may be further dried in a tunnel or other type of drier. Fines are removed either by air classification or screens after the drier. Wax for sizing is introduced either with the chips or added as a spray before or after passing the disc mills (about 2.5 per cent of the weight of the fiber). Sometimes 0.5–5 per cent of phenolic-resin is added, depending upon the quality of board desired. The fiber blend is fed to a moving screen by a metering unit through a combined air and mechanical action. The fibers felt as they fall on the screen and the fiber mat thus formed is precompressed between belts and/or rollers. If the board is to be wet pressed, water is added by spraying.

After the felting or sheet-forming operation, the subsequent operations differ for insulation board and hardboard (see Fig. 15.22). For insulation board, the sheets are dried without further compression and, for hardboard, the sheets are either pressed and dried simultaneously (wet-pressing) or are first dried and then pressed (dry-pressing). Air-felted sheets are pressed directly after forming.

Drying and Pressing. The wet-felted sheets for insulation board or for dry-pressed hardboard, containing 50–80 per cent water, may be dried by any of three methods, namely (1) tunnel kilns using racks or carts to support the sheets, (2) steam-platen dryers and (3) continuous roller driers of single or multi-deck arrangement. Most widely used is the continuous roller-type multi-deck drier, which has an average length of 150 to 300 ft but may be more than 600 ft long. An average drier will have 8 decks and be 12 ft wide.

The pressing conditions greatly affect the board properties. The conditions of time, temperature, pressure, and moisture content will depend upon the fiber in the board and the product desired. In wet pressing, a typical cycle has 3 phases and lasts from 6–15 minutes. First is a short high pressure stage (up to 710 psi) to remove most of the free water and bring the board to the desired thickness; the second step serves to remove water vapor and requires most of the time; and the third stage is a final short period at high pressure to effect a final "cure" or bonding by plastic flow of the lignin. To secure this fiber-to-fiber bond a temperature of 185° C must be attained and temperatures up to 210° C may be used to increase production rate. In the dry pressing process the cycles are shorter (1½–3½ min) and the temperatures and pressures usually higher.

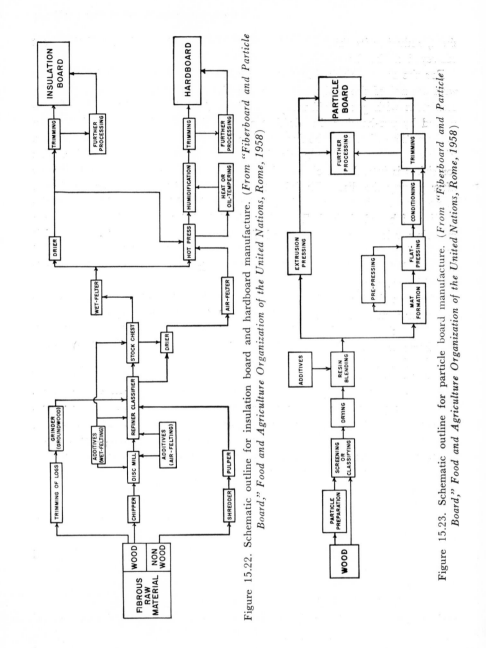

Figure 15.22. Schematic outline for insulation board and hardboard manufacture. (*From "Fiberboard and Particle Board," Food and Agriculture Organization of the United Nations, Rome, 1958*)

Figure 15.23. Schematic outline for particle board manufacture. (*From "Fiberboard and Particle Board," Food and Agriculture Organization of the United Nations, Rome, 1958*)

Conditioning. After hardboard has been hot-pressed or has been heat-treated or oil-tempered, its moisture content is well below what it will reach in equilibrium with the atmosphere in normal use. Such very dry boards will change dimensions upon picking up moisture and may warp. It is important, therefore, to humidify the boards under controlled conditions before packaging. The desired equilibrium moisture content (E.M.C.) reached will vary from 5 to 12 per cent depending upon the nature of the board and the general humidity conditions in the region of use.

Most humidifying is done in chambers or tunnels, kept at 80–85 per cent R. H. and 38–50° C. A lesser-used system of conditioning is by water spraying and dipping followed by standing to allow uniform absorption.

Special Treatments. Hardboards are often given a special treatment to improve strength and resistance to moisture. *Heat treatment* is a method which has come into wide use. The boards, which are kept apart to permit hot air circulation, are heated in chambers by either batch, continuous or progressive systems. Typical conditions are 5 hr at 155–160° C. The strength is increased (except impact), sometimes as much as 25 per cent, and the water resistance improved. This operation may replace sizing wholly or in part. Some exothermic reaction takes place in the board and the heat developed must be removed by the hot circulating air to prevent burning. Probably some chemical condensations occur in the wood fiber, producing an internal resin system, and there is the possibility of some cross-linking of large molecules.

Some hardboard is *oil-tempered*. A drying oil, such as linseed, tung, perilla, soya or tall oil or alkyd resins, is impregnated into the board, by passing the hot-pressed board through a hot oil bath. About 4–8 per cent of oil is absorbed. The board is then heated in a kiln with circulating air at 160–170° C for 6–9 hr. This treatment hardens the oil as well as brings about chemical reactions in the fiber and results in greater strength and moisture resistance.

Various additives may be incorporated into insulation boards and hardboards, or they may be surface treated to bring about resistance to decay, insects and fire. Pentachlorophenol, copper pentachlorophenate and several arsenicals are commonly used for preservative treatments. The sodium salt of pentachlorophenol is added before sizing and is precipitated on the fiber along with the size by the alum. Arsenic trioxide is usually added at the headbox of the board-forming machine. Special fire-retarding paint coatings are sometimes used to give resistance to the spread of flame.

Particle Board

Particle boards are composed of discrete particles of wood bonded together by a synthetic resin adhesive, most commonly urea-formaldehyde or phenolformaldehyde. The material is consolidated and the resin cured under heat and pressure. The strength of the product depends mainly upon the adhesive and not upon fiber felting as in the case of fiberboards, although the size and shape of the particles influence strength properties. They may be fine slivers, coarse slivers, planer shavings, shreds or flakes. They are divided into two main groups, namely (1) hammer-mill produced particles (slivers and splinters from solid wood residues, feather-like wisps to block-shaped pieces from planer shavings) and (2) cutter-type particles, sometimes called "engineered" particles (flakes and shreds). The various steps in particle-board manufacture are illustrated in Figure 15.23.

Hammer-milled particles usually vary appreciably in size. Dry raw material produces greater amounts of fines than green wood. Cutting machines (either cylinder-type or rotating-disc-type) give more uniform particles, with the length dimension in the direction of the grain of the wood. The thickness, size and shape of particles influence the strength of the board. Boards made from sawdust have the lowest strength properties, hammer-milled particles give boards of intermediate strengths and solid wood cut to flakes gives boards of highest strengths.

Particle boards may be made in a wide range of densities. Low density or insulating types are a comparatively recent development in Central Europe, whereas the high density hardboard types are an American development. Most particle-board production is in the middle density range.

Particle boards are most commonly used as core stock for veneer in furniture and in doors, as interior panels for walls and ceilings, in sub-flooring and as components in interior millwork. The hardboard types are used in the same way as fiberboard hardboard, as described in the previous section.

Paper-Base Laminates

Paper-base laminates are panels or other laminated assemblies composed of many plies of resin-treated paper molded together under high temperatures and pressure to produce rigid structures which no longer have the characteristics of paper. These products are widely used in the electrical and machine industries for insulators, gears, pulleys and a multitude of machine parts. They possess high impact strength and toughness, good electrical insulation, high dimensional stability, and are not subject to corrosion and have a dampening effect on sound, eliminating rattle and drumming in steel cars and machinery. Furthermore, they can easily be manipulated into complex shapes and can be drilled, turned and sawed. These properties make these products of great industrial value. They are also used in making trays, light flooring panels, table and counter tops and many other products employing panels.

Paper-base laminates fall into four major classes, namely (1) mechanical or structural, (2) electrical, (3) punching and (4) decorative. Phenolic resins are especially suitable and mostly used where mechanical strength and resistance to heat, water and electricity are required. For punching grade laminates, phenolic resins are especially modified with plasticizers or drying oils to yield laminates having good plasticity and elasticity. For electrical grades the phenolics are generally catalyzed with ammonia, amines or less conductive catalysts in place of the stronger alkaline catalysts otherwise used.

For decorative laminates, urea and melamine resins are the principal resins used. The melamines are used where translucent, light-colored products with good heat and water resistance are required. Polyesters are used for low pressure laminating, enabling the continuous production of counter and table tops by passing the assembly through a set of rolls and then through a heating chamber.

There are two broad general methods for introducing resins into papers for making paper-base laminates; namely (1) by the beater addition process and (2) by impregnation of the paper sheet. In the beater addition process the resin is added to the pulp in the beater and then precipitated on the fiber by alum or an acid. The resin adheres to the pulp fibers, which are then formed into a sheet. This type of paper-plastic combination is commonly termed *resin-filled paper*. These resin-filled papers may be made into flat or shaped preforms. The former are flat sheets, the latter are vacuum-felted to a shape closely conforming to that of the final molded product. Shaped preforms are used for deep forms requiring high strength contours. Little flow is required on molding, hence the paper sheet does not break and greater strength is thereby obtained.

The more common method of application of the resin is by impregnation of the wet or dry paper sheet (web) with a solution of resin. Such papers are termed *resin-impregnated papers.*

Water-soluble and alcohol-soluble types of phenolic resins are both used for paper-base laminates. The former tend to give more brittle but more dimensionally stable products than the latter. Phenolic resins are mostly applied by impregnation of the wet or dry paper sheet producing *resin-impregnated papers,* although some progress has been made in the slush stock addition procedures to produce phenolic *resin-filled papers.*

In the wet-web process for impregnating paper for laminates, the wet sheet of paper on the paper machine is carried through a resin bath while the sheet is supported by a wire. The sheet contains up to 65 per cent water and the amount of resin taken up depends upon the moisture content of the paper, solids content of the resin solution, viscosity of the resin solution, temperature of the bath, machine speed and pressure of the squeeze-rolls. Only water soluble or water dispersible resins can be used in the wet-web process.

Generally, however, phenolic impregnations of paper for laminates, and other purposes demanding a high resin content are done with dry paper on off-machine equipment. The dry paper sheet is continuously passed through a resin solution, generally an alcoholic solution, and then moves under and between two metering rolls, after which the paper is dried to remove solvent and to complete the condensation of the thermosetting phenolic resin.

The addition of phenolic resins in the form of emulsions to the slush stock by the beater addition process has received considerable study in recent years. Papers containing 45 to 55 per cent resin and even as high as 65 per cent have been prepared. The resin is precipitated by adding alum to the beater. Papers prepared in this way are highly plastic and are suitable for low pressure molding. The phenolic resins can also be used in combination with elastomers, such as GR-S types, neoprene, hycar and vinyl polymers, to produce laminates of high impact strength and greater elongation under tension.

Lignin is also commercially used as a resin for paper laminates. Its cheapness and availability as a by-product in pulp manufacture make it attractive. One of the most successful products is made with lignin recovered from the spent liquor of the soda pulping process. The lignin may be added to the pulp suspension in solution and precipitated directly among the fibers or added in a pre-precipitated form.

Properties of paper-base laminates depend both upon the resin and the paper. In general, the final product has the characteristics of the resin used, provided over 30 per cent of resin is present. The paper acts as a structural reinforcer, greatly enhancing toughness, and tensile, flexural and impact strength.

Electrical properties of the laminate depend both upon the paper and the resin, though the amount of resin absorbed is the most important factor affecting electrical insulating properties. Papers of low power factor, good dielectric strength and high dielectric constant are necessary for electrical grades of laminates. Other desired paper properties for good paper-base laminates are uniformity, cleanliness (freedom from slime, dirt and fiber bundles), low finish, neutral pH, freedom from chemicals (bleach residues, etc.), low and uniform moisture content (under 4 per cent) and uniform absorbency. High absorbency is desired when high electrical resistance and minimum water absorption are required, since greater amounts of resin are taken up by high absorbency papers. For high impact strength punching grades of laminates, a low absorbency paper is necessary to reduce the amount of resin absorbed.

Polymer Modified Papers, Overlays for Lumber, Honeycomb Cores. In addition to paper-base laminates, polymers are combined in many ways with paper to develop new properties or to modify or enhance certain properties. Paper is commonly combined with polymers, such as synthetic resins, elastomers, and plastics in general, to produce products which may be classified as follows: (1) wet strength papers, (2) special purpose papers containing large amounts of resins or elastomers (chemical resistant papers, sandpaper backings, gaskets, imitation leather, shoe parts, wood overlay and honeycomb core papers, air and oil filters, battery separators, etc.), (3) plastic coated papers and (4) paper-base laminates. The use of plastics in combination with paper has grown enormously during the past decade. For example, 23 million pounds of urea and melamine resins and 10 million pounds of polyvinyl chloride were used to treat paper in 1958. Also in the same year 42 million pounds of polyethylene were used in coatings, much of it for paper coating. Polymer modified papers are thus very important in our present-day economy.

The paper-base laminates have already been discussed. Two other polymer treated papers used in construction and industrial materials will be briefly mentioned here, namely, overlay papers for lumber and plywood, and paper honeycomb cores. For the many other applications of polymer modified papers the reader is referred elsewhere.

Overlaid lumber is a composite of lumber and phenolic resin-treated kraft paper. Paper honeycomb cores are also made from phenolic resin-treated kraft paper, which is formed into a honeycomb of different geometrical designs, such as figure eight or hexagonal, in special machines. Simpler types are made from resin impregnated corrugated sheets which can be assembled in several ways. This material permits construction of sandwich panels of light weight and high strength. Kraft papers for lumber overlays or for honeycomb cores are treated with phenolic resin in the same ways as described above for paper-base laminates.

A typical overlay paper contains 20 per cent of phenolic resin. It is bonded to lumber with an acid catalyst in a cold press operation to prevent the natural resins in the wood and around knots from being driven through the overlay sheet. The overlay sheet swells and shrinks much less than wood and thus exerts a resistance to the dimensional changes of the wood and may reduce lateral swelling by as much as 40 per cent. Overlay papers also upgrade the appearance of low grade lumber, increase strength properties, improve finishability and increase resistance to weathering.

For honeycomb cores, either water or alcohol soluble phenolic resins may be used. Many types of facings may be glued to the honeycomb cores, viz.: veneers, plywood, hardboards, asbestos board, aluminum, stainless steel, paper-plastic laminates, etc. Thin sheet material may be used due to the almost continuous support of the core.

The honeycomb sandwich possesses great strength in relation to its weight. It may carry loads as much as 25 tons per sq ft. Strength and weight vary with weight of the paper, quantity of resin impregnated and honeycomb design.

Honeycomb sandwich construction has many uses, such as in airplanes, cargo containers, truck and trailer bodies, railway passenger cars, cabins, barns, airplane hangars, house floors, walls, roofs, doors, and in a variety of other products. Besides combining strength with lightness, honeycomb sandwich material has high rigidity, good insulation properties, resistance to fungus and pests, and durability to temperature extremes.

Wood-Resin Combinations and Polymer Modified Wood

As in the case of paper, the use of synthetic resins in the wood industry has advanced with the developments in polymer chemistry. Resins permit greater and better use of wood raw material, including waste and low-grade wood. They also improve strength and appearance, and decrease dimensional change, thereby improving the competitive position of wood in relation to other materials.

Conversely, large amounts of wood flour, estimated at 80,000 tons annually in the United States, are used as fillers in compositions for plastic molding with phenol-formaldehyde and urea-formaldehyde resins and also in flooring, roofing and linoleum compositions. Recent experiments indicate that wood flour may be successfully incorporated in rigid and flexible foams to give improved products for acoustical and thermal insulation, packaging, sandwich structures and other engineering products. Such foams may be made by reacting a diisocyanate with a polyester containing an excess of acid groups, with or without the presence of wood flour.

The combinations of polymer resins with wood in the manufacture of particle board, as well as the application of polymer treated papers as overlays for lumber and plywood and as honeycomb cores for sandwich construction have been discussed above. Brief consideration will be given to the "modified" woods.

Modified wood refers to wood that has been subjected to chemical or heat treatment, with or without pressure, to bring about changes in its properties. Much research has been done, especially by the U. S. Forest Products Laboratory, on the modification of wood to overcome its dimensional instability and to impart other properties. Impregnation with water-soluble phenol-formaldehyde resins gives good results. Thin veneers are treated with resin solutions usually under pressure. They are then cured slowly in a kiln to set the resin. This material, termed *impreg*, contains resin bonded to the internal capillary surfaces of the wood and, due to the volume of the resin, this keeps the wood in a partly swollen condition. Therefore, the wood retains a volume nearly corresponding to its water-swollen dimensions and goes through a much smaller volume change than untreated wood when immersed in water.

Wood impregnated with phenol-formaldehyde resin and dried, but not cured, has greater plasticity than untreated wood and, therefore, can be compressed at considerably lower pressures than untreated wood. For example, impregnated spruce, aspen and cottonwood dried to 6 per cent moisture can be compressed at 149° C to one-half their original thickness at a pressure of 17.6 kg/cm.² In contrast untreated woods of the same species and pressed under the same conditions will compress only 5–10 per cent.

There are two types of compressed resin treated wood. (*compreg*) being produced. One is a high resin content (25–30 per cent) product of very high dimensional stability and suitable for electrical insulators in high tension lines, knife handles, and most important of all, for tooling jigs and forming dies. Compreg dies are lower in cost, easier to repair and are harder to scratch than metal dies.

The other type of compreg contains 5–10 per cent resin and has higher shock resistance and greater toughness than the high resin content material.

Reduction in hygroscopicity and improved dimensional stability of wood have been experimentally developed by the acetylation of wood and by heat stabilization. Heat stabilization is brought about by heating wood, preferably under the surface of molten metal or a fused salt to exclude oxygen; this procedure gives good temperature control and a minimum of loss in strength. Temperatures varying from 150° to 320° C have been used, with the time necessary to give a certain dimensional stability being reduced by half for each 10° C increase in temperature. Wood treated in this way has been termed *staybwood*.

When wood is heated, it exhibits a certain degree of thermoplasticity, as has been described in the discussion of fiberboards. Therefore, if heated wood is compressed (165–175° C at 100–140 kg/cm²), the internal stresses due to compression are relieved by the plastic flow of the wood. Such a compressed wood, termed *staypak*, has improved resistance to moisture and to shrinking and swelling and improved strength properties. The mechanism of the stabilization of hot compressed wood is probably due to the plastic flow of the lignin component of the wood.

PRESERVATIVE AND FIRE-RETARDANT TREATMENT OF WOOD

Wood Preservation

Wood, a natural plant tissue, is subject to attack by fungi, insects and marine borers. Some species of wood are more resistant to decay than others, as, for example, the heartwood of cedars, cypress and redwood, due to the presence of natural toxic substances among the extractable components. Most woods, however, are rapidly attacked when used in contact with soil or water, or when exposed to high relative humidities without adequate air circulation. Wood for such service conditions requires chemical treatment with toxic chemicals, collectively termed *wood preservatives*. The length of service life of wood may be increased from 5 to 15-fold, depending upon the conditions of preservative treatment and the nature of the service.

The preservative treatment of wood is the second largest chemical wood-processing industry; pulp and paper manufacture is the most important. Since 1940, the average annual volume of wood treated has been 260 to 270 million cu ft (see Table 15.9). The more important types of wood products treated are also shown in Table 15.9.

TABLE 15.9. WOOD PRODUCTS TREATED WITH PRESERVATIVES:
1940–1957 *

(in thousands of cubic feet)

Product	1940	1950	1957
Crossties and switch ties	136,859	127,465	106,069
Poles	74,129	77,622	78,624
Lumber and construction timbers	32,007	32,821	37,402
Piling	15,660	12,523	15,746
Fence posts	1,494	12,269	12,706
Wood blocks	2,730	1,826	1,599
Cross arms	675	2,493	4,209
All other	1,919	2,966	3,194
Total	265,473	269,985	259,549

* From Statistical Abstract of the United States 1958, U. S. Dept. of Commerce, Bureau of the Census.

Preservative Chemicals. Toxic chemicals used for the preservation of wood may be classified as follows:

1. organic liquids of low volatility and limited water solubility
   coal-tar creosote
   creosote-coal tar solutions
   creosote-petroleum solutions
   other creosotes (water-gas-tar, wood-tar, and oil-tar creosotes)
   anthracene oils (carbolineums)
2. chemicals dissolved in organic solvents, usually petroleum oils
   chlorinated phenols (principally pentachlorophenol)
   copper naphthenate
3. water soluble inorganic salts
   zinc chloride
   chromated zinc chloride (zinc chloride and sodium dichromate, approximately 4:1)
   zinc meta arsenite

Wolman salts (mixture of sodium fluoride, disodium hydrogen
arsenate, sodium chromate and dinitrophenol)
other proprietary compositions containing two or more salts, usually
of zinc chloride, chromates, fluorides, copper salts and arsenic
compounds

Creosote from coal tar is the most widely used wood preservative because
(1) it is highly toxic to wood-destroying organisms, (2) it has a high degree
of permanence due to its relative insolubility in water and its low volatility,
(3) it is easy to apply and to obtain deep penetration and (4) it is relatively
cheap and widely available.

For general outdoor service in structural timbers, poles, posts, piling, mine
props and for marine uses, coal-tar creosote is the best and most important
preservative. Because of its odor, dark color and the fact that creosote-treated
wood usually cannot be painted, creosote is unsuitable for finished lumber
and for interior use.

Coal-tar creosote (see Chapter 8) is a mixture of aromatic hydrocarbons
containing appreciable amounts of tar acids and bases (up to about 5 per
cent of each) and has a boiling range between 200 and 325° C. The
important hydrocarbons present include fluorene, anthracene, phenanthrene
and some naphthalene. The tar acids are mainly phenols, cresols, xylenols
and naphthols; the tar bases consist of pyridines, quinolines and acridines.

Often coal tar or petroleum oil is mixed with coal-tar creosote, in amounts
up to 50 per cent, as a means of lowering preservative costs. Since coal tar
and petroleum have low toxicity, their mixtures with creosote are less toxic
than creosote alone.

A number of phenols, especially chlorinated phenols, and certain metal-
organic compounds, such as copper naphthenate and phenyl mercury oleate,
are effective preservatives. Pentachlorophenol and copper naphthenate are
most commonly used, and they are carried into the wood in 1 to 5 per cent
solutions in petroleum oil. Pentachlorophenol is colorless, and can be applied
in clear volatile mineral oils to millwork and window-sash which require a
clean, non-swelling and paintable treatment.

Zinc chloride was the most extensively used water-borne preservative up
to 1938, but since then mixtures of zinc chloride with other salts, especially
sodium dichromate, have been used in larger quantities. Sodium fluoride
has preservative properties about equal to zinc chloride, but, since it usually
costs more and is more toxic to man, is not so widely used and only in combination with other salts, such as in Wolman salts. Inorganic salts are
employed in preservative treatment where the wood will not be in contact
with the ground or water, such as for indoor use or where the treated wood
requires painting. They are also satisfactory for outdoor use in relatively
dry regions.

Preservation Processes. The methods for applying preservatives to wood are classified as follows:

1. Non-pressure processes
   Surface (superficial) applications by brushing, spraying, or dipping
   Soaking, steeping and diffusion processes
   Hot- and cold-bath treatments
   Vacuum processes
   Miscellaneous processes
2. Pressure processes
   Full-cell process (Bethell)
   Empty-cell processes (Rueping and Lowry)

Brush and spray treatments usually give only limited protection because the penetration or depth of capillary absorption is slight. Dip treatments give slightly better protection. Organic chemicals dissolved in clear petroleum solvents are often applied to window sash and similar products by a dip treatment of 1 to 3 minutes.

Cold soaking of seasoned wood in low viscosity preservative oils for several hours or days and the steeping of green or seasoned wood in water-borne preservatives, such as zinc chloride, for several days, are methods sometimes employed for posts, lumber and timbers on a limited basis. The diffusion process employs water-borne preservatives that will diffuse out of the treating solution into the water in green or wet wood.

The most effective of the nonpressure processes is the hot- and cold-bath method of applying coal-tar creosote or other oil soluble preservatives, such as pentachlorophenol solution. Sometimes aqueous solutions of zinc chloride are applied by this method. The wood is heated in the preservative liquid in an open tank for several hours, after which it is quickly submerged in cold preservative in which it is allowed to remain several hours. This is accomplished either by transferring the wood at the proper time from the hot tank to the cold tank, or by draining the hot preservative and quickly refilling the tank with cooler preservative. During the hot treatment the air in the wood expands and some is expelled. Heating also lowers the viscosity of the preservative so that there is better penetration. When the cooling takes place, the remaining air in the wood contracts, creating a partial vacuum which draws the preservative into the wood. For coal-tar creosote the hot bath is at 210–235° F and the cold bath at about 100° F. This temperature is required to keep the preservative fluid.

The hot- and cold-bath process is widely used for treating poles and, to a lesser extent, for fence posts, lumber and timbers. The results obtained by this process are the most effective of the common non-pressure processes and most nearly approach those obtained by the pressure processes.

The vacuum processes involve subjecting the wood to a vacuum to draw out part of the air. The wood may be either subjected to a vacuum alone or to steaming and a vacuum before submerging in a cold preservative. These methods are used to a limited extent in the treatment of lumber, timber and millwork.

Commercial treatment of wood is most commonly done by one of the pressure processes, since they give deeper penetrations and more positive results than any of the non-pressure methods. The wood on steel cars is run into a long horizontal cylinder, which is closed and filled with preservative. Pressure is applied, forcing the preservative into the wood.

There are two types of pressure treatment, the full-cell and the empty-cell. The full-cell process seeks to fill the cells (capillary structure) of the wood with the preservative liquid giving a retention of a maximum quantity of preservative. The empty-cell process seeks deep penetration with a relatively low net retention of preservative, by forcing out the bulk liquid in the wood cells, leaving the internal capillary structure coated with preservative.

In the full-cell process the wood in the cylinder is first subjected to a vacuum of not less than 22 inches of mercury for 15–60 minutes, to remove as much air as possible from the wood. The cylinder is then filled with hot treating liquid (usually 190–200° F) without admitting air. The liquid is then placed under a pressure of 125–200 psi and the temperature and pressure maintained for the desired length of time, usually several hours. After drawing the liquid from the cylinder, a short vacuum is applied to free the charge of surface dripping preservative.

In the empty-cell process the preservative liquid is forced under pressure into the wood containing either its normal air content (Lowry process), or an excess of air, by subjecting the wood first to air pressure before applying the preservative under pressure (Rueping process). In the former case the preservative is put in the cylinder containing wood at atmospheric pressure and, in the latter case, under air pressure of 25–100 psi. After the wood has been subjected to the hot preservative (about 190–200° F) under pressure (100–200 psi in Lowry process and 150–200 psi in the Rueping process) and the pressure released, the back pressure of the compressed air in the wood forces out the free liquid from the wood. As much as 20–60 per cent of the injected preservative may be recovered, yet good depth of penetration of preservative is achieved.

Preservative Retention. Retentions of preservative are generally specified in terms of the weight of preservative per cubic foot of wood, based on the total weight of preservative retained and the total volume of wood treated in a charge. Some specifications require determination of retention by chemical analysis of borings from treated wood. Penetrations and retentions vary widely between different species of wood, as well as with woods of the same species grown in different areas. In most species heartwood is much more difficult to penetrate than sapwood. The minimum retentions of some common preservatives for various products according to Federal specifications are shown in Table 15.10.

Fire-Retardant Treatments

Protection of wood against fire may be accomplished by application of certain chemicals. Because of the cost, commercial treatments are limited to materials used in localities where fire building codes require fire-retardation

TABLE 15.10. RECOMMENDED MINIMUM NET RETENTIONS OF SOME COMMON WOOD PRESERVATIVES*

Product and Service Condition	Coal-tar Creosote lb/cu ft	Pentachlorophenol, 5% in Petroleum Oil lb/cu ft	Copper Naphthenate, 0.75% Copper Metal in Petroleum Oil lb/cu ft	Chromated Zinc Chloride lb/cu ft	Wolman Salts lb/cu ft
Lumber and structural timber					
For use in contact with ground or in fresh water and for *all* important structural members	10				
For use in contact with ground		10	10		
For use under moderate leaching conditions				1.15	0.55
For use not in contact with ground or water	6	6	6	0.75	0.35
Piles					
For marine use					
Douglas fir (coast type)	14				
Southern yellow pine	20				
For land or fresh water use	12				
Poles	8	8	8		
Posts	6	6	6	1.15	0.55
Ties, railway	8				

* From Wood Handbook, U. S. Forest Products Laboratory, Forest Service, U. S. Dept. of Agriculture, 1955.

treatment. Fire-retardant chemicals are water soluble, which limits the use of treated wood to places where it is not subjected to leaching.

Two types of treatment are used for improving the fire resistance of wood; namely (1) impregnation of the wood with fire-retardant chemicals and (2) coating the surface of the wood with an oxygen-excluding envelope. Among the most commonly used chemicals for impregnation treatments are mono- and di-ammonium phosphates, ammonium sulphate, borax, boric acid and zinc chloride. These compounds have different characteristics with respect to fire resistance. The ammonium phosphates, for example, are effective in checking both flaming and glowing; borax is good in the checking of flaming but is not a satisfactory glow retardant. Boric acid is excellent in stopping glow but not so effective in retarding flaming. Because of these different characteristics, mixtures of chemicals are usually employed in treating formulations.

The methods for impregnation are similar to those employed for preservative treatment of wood by the pressure processes. For most uses, the wood must be kiln dried after treatment to a moisture content of 6 to 9 per cent. Larger amounts of chemical must be deposited in the wood for effective fire protection than is necessary with toxic chemicals for decay prevention. Whereas retentions of up to about 1 pound of a preservative salt per cu ft of wood are effective against decay and insects, as much as 5 to 6 pounds are required for a high degree of effectiveness against fire. Smaller amounts of some chemicals will give a good degree of protection; for example, a mixture of 80 per cent chromated zinc chloride (zinc chloride and sodium dichromate dihydrate, approx. 4:1), 10 per cent boric acid, and 10 per cent ammonium sulphate when impregnated in amounts of 1½ to 3 lb per cu ft of wood provides combined protection against fire, decay and insects.

There are various explanations for the fire-retardant effect of the chemicals impregnated into wood for this purpose. There is probably no single mechanism but rather a combination of mechanisms which are operative, including (1) the fusing of the chemical within the wood at high temperatures to form thin noncombustible films which exclude oxygen, (2) the evolution of noncombustible gases in some cases and (3) the catalytic promotion of charcoal formation, instead of volatile combustible gases, with the added benefit of increased thermal insulation.

Surface coatings for fire-retardation are less effective than impregnation of chemicals into the wood. Formulations are used containing either ammonium phosphate, borax, or sodium silicate, together with other constituents to provide good bonding to the wood. Paints containing substantial amounts (30 to 50 per cent) of these fire-resistant chemicals provide moderate protection against fire.

WOOD HYDROLYSIS

The availability of enormous quantities of wood residues from logging, sawmilling and woodworking operations, estimated at 60 million tons annually, has stimulated much attention to the production of sugars and ethyl alcohol from this cheap raw material. Problems were encountered in developing commercial acid hydrolysis processes due to the serious corrosive action of the acid and the difficulties in removing the sugars from the scene of the reaction before they are subjected to too much degradation.

Cellulose, the major component of wood, gives almost quantitative yields of pure glucose under laboratory conditions of hydrolysis, according to the following equation:

$$(C_6H_{10}O_5)_n + nH_2O \xrightarrow{\text{acid}} nC_6H_{12}O_6$$

where n is in the range of 2000–3000. The hemicellulose fraction gives a mixture of sugars, mainly xylose, together with arabinose, mannose, galactose and glucose. Glucose, galactose and mannose are yeast fermentable sugars, whereas the pentoses (xylose and arabinose) are nonfermentable. The potential total reducing sugar yield from wood averages 65–70 per cent, whereas the fermentable sugar yield is about 50 per cent for the hardwoods and 58 per cent for the softwoods. The lower quantity of fermentable sugar from the hardwoods is due to their higher content of pentosans, compared to the coniferous woods.

Hemicellulose hydrolyzes much more easily and rapidly than cellulose. Temperatures and acid concentrations that hydrolyze the cellulose to glucose

TABLE 15.11.* DECOMPOSITION OF WOOD SUGARS IN 0.8 PER CENT
SULPHURIC ACID AT 180° C

Sugar	First-order Reaction Constant K (min^{-1})	Half-life (min)
Glucose	0.0242	28.6
Galactose	0.0263	26.4
Mannose	0.0358	19.4
Arabinose	0.0421	16.4
Xylose	0.0721	9.6

*From J. F. Saeman, *Ind. Eng. Chem.*, **37**, 43 (1945).

in a matter of a few hours readily convert much of the hemicellulose into simple sugars in minutes or even seconds. Under industrial conditions of hydrolysis the sugars formed undergo decomposition, the pentoses decomposing more rapidly than the hexoses. Thus, the conditions of hydrolysis cause variations in the ratio and yields of the various sugars due to (a) their different rates of formation by hydrolysis and (b) their different rates of decomposition. Table 15.11 shows the relative rates of decomposition of the sugars obtained by the hydrolysis of wood.

The polysaccharides of wood (holocellulose) may be hydrolyzed by two general methods; (1) by strong acids, such as 70–72 per cent sulphuric acid or 40–45 per cent hydrochloric acid, or (2) by dilute acids, such as 0.5–2.0 per cent sulphuric acid. The hydrolysis by strong acids is constant, proceeds as a first-order reaction and is independent of the degree of polymerization. The reactions may be represented as follows:

$$\text{Holocellulose} \xrightarrow[\text{acid}]{\text{strong}} \left. \begin{array}{l} \text{Swollen Cellulose} \\ \text{and Soluble Pentosans} \end{array} \right\} \rightarrow \text{Soluble Polysaccharides} \downarrow \begin{array}{l} \text{dilute} \\ \text{acid} \end{array}$$

$$\text{Simple Sugars}$$

In dilute acid hydrolysis the reactions are heterogeneous and more complex because no swelling and solubilizing of the cellulose occurs. Cleavage of the insoluble cellulose takes place directly to low molecular weight oligosaccharides (intermediate products), which are rapidly converted to simple sugars, as indicated below:

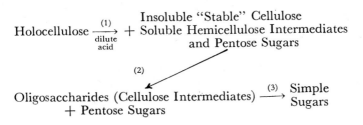

Reaction (1) is rapid and occurs under mild conditions, hydrolyzing mainly the hemicelluloses. Reaction (2) is slow, proceeds as a first-order reaction and is the limiting reaction in this process. Reaction (3) is rapid.

Based on the above two methods, two industrial methods have been developed, namely: the Bergius-Rheinau method, based on the use of concentrated hydrochloric acid at ordinary temperatures, and the Scholler-Tornesch method, in which very dilute sulfuric acid is used at temperatures of 170 to 180° C (338 to 356° F). The latter method in an improved form is known as the Madison process, thanks to work done at the United States Forest Products Laboratory in Madison, Wis.

Bergius-Rheinau Process

Hydrochloric acid of about 40–45 per cent (by weight) is produced by reinforcing recovered, weaker acid with hydrogen chloride from salt-sulfuric acid retorts, or by burning chlorine with illuminating gas.

Wood chips are air dried, then charged into a tile-lined reactor and extracted countercurrently by the acid. The fresh strong acid enters that part of the battery of diffusers or reactors which contains the most nearly exhausted wood and is pumped through the next following containers until it is nearly saturated with the carbohydrates dissolved from the wood. Part of this solution is mixed, under slight cooling, with fresh wood and the mixture charged into the head-container of the battery. After filling this, and allowing a few hours for reaction time, an amount of solution is drawn from this container, through the pressure of the incoming acid, which corresponds to the yield from one charge.

The solution drawn off contains hydrochloric acid and carbohydrates in about equal parts, and at a concentration of about 25 per cent (by weight) each. It is concentrated in stoneware tubes under vacuum. The distillate, containing about 80 per cent of the hydrochloric acid, with minor proportions of acetic acid and furfural is reused after fortification. The concentrated sugar solution is dried to a powder in a spray-drier, where it also loses most of the remaining acid.

The dry, somewhat acid, powder contains the carbohydrates in the form of intermediate polymers (oligosaccharides). They are water-soluble and must be given further hydrolysis to obtain simple sugars, either for fermentation or crystallization.

This is done by dissolving, diluting to approximately 20 per cent sugar concentration, and heating for 2 hr, in the presence of 2 per cent acid, at 125° C. Part of the glucose can be crystallized from the neutralized and

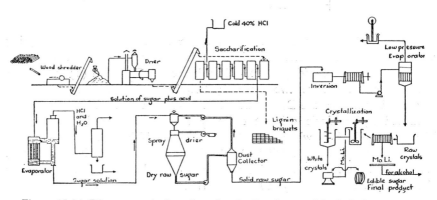

Figure 15.24. Diagrammatic flow sheet for the Bergius wood hydrolysis process.

reconcentrated solution, while the mother liquors are fermented to alcohol or used for growing yeast. A diagrammatic flow chart for the Bergius process is shown in Figure 15.24.

When hardwoods are to be used it is necessary to remove a part of the hemicellulose first by prehydrolysis. This has been carried out on a large scale with straw, a substance chemically similar to hardwood, by heating it in a 8 to 1 liquid to solid ratio, with 0.5 per cent sulfuric acid for 2 to 3 hr at 130° C (266° F). Without prehydrolysis, hardwoods and straws form slimy materials, probably because of their high hemicellulose content, which prevent the flow of the hydrolyzing acid.

Madison Process with Continuous Percolation

In the Madison process, dilute sulfuric acid with an average concentration of 0.5 per cent is pressed through wood in the form of sawdust and shavings. Regular flow of the acid and of the resulting sugar solution is one of the two principal requirements; the other is a lignin residue which can be discharged from the pressure vessels without manual labor. Both depend upon careful charging of the wood, which should not contain too many very fine particles, and upon maintaining a pressure differential of not more than 5 to 6 lb sq in. between top and bottom of the digester.

The digesters or percolators are pressure hydrolyzing vessels, commonly employing a pressure of 150 lb/sq in., and having a capacity of 2000 cu ft each. In the original Scholler plants in Germany, the digesters are lined with lead and acid-proof brick; in the Madison process a lining of "Everdur" metal was found to give sufficient protection.

The wood, about 15 tons, is pressed down with steam, and then heated by direct steam, after which the acid is introduced. The practice in Germany was to bring the dilute acid into the digester in several batches, with rest periods of about 30 min, heating the wood to temperatures of 130° C (266° F) at first, then to 180° C (356° F), and keeping the temperature of the entering acid 10 to 20° C lower. A total of about 14 hr was required to exhaust the wood, yeilding about 50 lb of carbohydrates for 100 lb of dry wood substance. In the Madison process, continuous flow of the acid, and correspondingly, of the sugar solution, is provided—in other words, continuous percolation. The cycle is thereby reduced to 6 hr, and the yields are increased somewhat.

The lignin is blown out of the digester by opening the specially constructed bottom valves while the vessel is still under pressure.

The sugar solutions usually contain about 5 per cent of carbohydrates and 0.5 per cent of sulfuric acid. The solutions, still under pressure (150 lb/sq in.), are flash-evaporated to 35 lb/sq in., neutralized with lime at that pressure, and filtered. Calcium sulfate is much less soluble at the elevated temperature corresponding to the pressure than it is at 100° C. This is a fortunate circumstance, for it must be removed to a sufficient extent so that it will not cause difficulties by forming incrustations in the subsequent alcohol distillation. The filtered solution is cooled by further flash evaporation and heat exchange with water to fermentation temperature. A materials relationship for a dilute acid process is shown in Figure 15.25.

Sugar yields from coniferous woods (softwoods) are about 50 per cent at an average concentration of 5 per cent. When fermented, the average ethyl alcohol yields per ton of dry wood are 50–60 gal and sometimes higher.

Comparison of the Processes

In the Bergius-Rheinau process the concentrated hydrochloric acid employed requires dried wood, and recovery of the acid is essential. The process gives high yields of sugars (60 to 65 per cent) at high concentrations. The intermediate sugars first obtained, however, call for an extra processing step to reduce them to monomers, before fermentation or crystallization.

The dilute sulfuric acid employed in the Madison process gives lower yields (49 to 55 per cent) of sugars, and only very dilute solutions are obtained directly. The difference in yield is not too important with a low-cost material such as wood waste. Recovery of heat is easier in this process and the acid need not be recovered. In general, the dilute acid process of the Madison type appears to offer greater economy than the concentrated acid process.

However, neither process offers sufficient economy in the United States to compete with agricultural sources of sugars and ethanol and petroleum

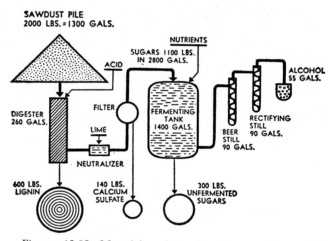

Figure 15.25 Materials relationship for a dilute acid hydrolysis process. (*From E. Farber, Chemurgic Digest, March 31, 1945*)

sources of ethanol. In Europe, however, wood hydrolysis plants are operative and several are in production in both Western Europe and in the Soviet Union. Furthermore, the Russians maintain a Wood Hydrolysis Research Institute and are active[6] in research in this field.

Prehydrolysis of Wood for Pulp Production

When wood is pulped by the sulphate process a large part of the hemi-cellulose is converted to sugars and organic degradation products, using up pulping chemicals. The spent sulphate liquor is burned to recover pulping chemicals, and the sugars and their decomposition products contribute to the calorific value of the total liquor, though only to the extent of 18 per cent.

A process has been developed whereby the easily hydrolyzable sugars are removed from the wood by prehydrolysis and subsequently used for the production of fodder yeast or as a source of sugar for fermentation products.

Hydrolysis of pine, fir or spruce for 15 min at 165–175° C by 0.3 per cent sulphuric acid removes about 16 per cent of the wood. The sugars contain about 50 per cent hexoses (mainly glucose) and 50 per cent pentoses, and have been found to have a yeast yield of about 5 per cent of the weight of the wood.

The residual wood is pulped by the sulphate process and gives about 40 per cent yield of high alpha content pulp for dissolving purposes (rayon, film, plastics, etc.).

Fermentation of Sulphite Waste Liquor

The sulphurous acid used in the sulphite pulping liquor causes hydrolysis of the more easily hydrolyzable components of wood, especially the pentosans in the hemicellulose. About 35 per cent of the potentially fermentable sugars in the wood are hydrolyzed. However, most of these are decomposed during the long pulping procedure, so that only one-fourth to one-third, including much of the more resistant hexoses, remains in the waste sulphite liquor. If these are fermented by yeast about 12.5 gal of 95 per cent alcohol per ton of wood may be produced.

A large number of plants in Europe and a few in North America have been constructed to utilize the sugar hydrolyzate in sulphite waste liquors. In Sweden alone there were 33 such plants by 1940.

The procedure as carried out in one American operation is as follows. The liquor is recovered from the digester by discharging in a manner to remove as much sugar as possible with a minimum of dilution by washing. Free sulphur dioxide is removed and recovered by blowing steam through the solution, which decreases the acidity from a pH of 2.2 to about 3.9. The liquors are cooled by a vacuum flash and neutralized by lime to a pH of about 4.2. A small amount of inorganic nitrogen is added for yeast growth and about 1 per cent by volume of yeast added continuously. Fermentation is carried out in a series of tanks, the solution flowing from one to the other with agitation to keep the yeast in suspension. The yeast is recovered by centrifuging and mixed with the new sugar solution entering the fermenter. About 30 hr is required for fermentation. The alcohol content of the fermented liquor is about 1 per cent by volume. The ethyl alcohol is recovered in stainless steel stills. Methanol and other alcohols are obtained in small amounts as by-products.

Vanillin

Vanillin is not a product of hydrolysis or of fermentation; in fact, it does not originate from the holocellulose, but rather from the lignin portion of the wood. The major organic material in sulphite waste liquor (spent liquor after pulping wood by the sulphite process) is the lignin dissolved from the wood as lignosulphonic acid. Alkaline degradation of this lignin product produces vanillin, the same substance which occurs naturally in the vanilla

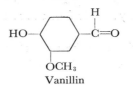

Vanillin

bean. By the Howard process[3] 5–10 per cent of vanillin is produced, based on the lignin in the waste sulphite liquor. Some vanillin is produced from sulphite waste liquor in both the United States and Canada.

WOOD CARBONIZATION AND DISTILLATION

Wood has been carbonized from the beginning of recorded history to produce charcoal, which was valued as a light-weight and smoke-free fuel. Much later, the development of the iron smelting industry greatly increased the demand for charcoal. The charcoal was produced in simple earth kilns, often called "pit-kilns" which involved the slow burning of properly piled wood with a flue opening in the center and with the pile covered with turf and earth to reduce air circulation. Even today charcoal is still widely produced by this ancient method.

The yield of charcoal represents only about one-third of the weight of the wood, the remainder being accounted for as gases and vapors. The first commercial recovery of by-products from the gases and vapors was undertaken by James Ward at North Adams, Massachusetts, in 1830.[1] The gases and vapors were cooled and the condensible portions converted to liquors. From the aqueous portion, known as pyroligneous acid, acetic acid and its salts were recovered. This was the beginning of the hardwood distillation industry. Later, methanol was also recovered from the pyroligneous acid, and the tars were separated and used for fuel, or were fractionated into creosote oil, soluble tars and pitch.

In time, improvements in equipment and chemical engineering technology resulted in better control, reduction in heat losses, and continuous operation, and led to increased yields, better quality products, and the separation and purification of additional products from the condensed aqueous and tar liquors. The non-condensible gases were in part recycled to bring fresh retorts to desired temperature; the greater part was utilized by burning under the boilers to generate heat and power.

With the development of low-cost continuous processes for the synthetic production of methanol, acetic acid and acetone, the hardwood distillation industry went into a decline after World War II. However, the demand for charcoal has held firm and even increased. As a result, improved methods for charcoal production have been developed and the recent trend is toward continuous carbonization. Thus, the carbonization of wood has gone through full cycle, from the production of charcoal only to the production of industrial organic chemicals, with charcoal playing a secondary role, and now back to the production mainly of charcoal. The annual production of charcoal today approaches 500,000 tons.

The carbonization of wood is a process of thermal decomposition. When wood is subjected to temperatures above 100° C, thermal decomposition occurs, i.e., chemical decomposition brought about solely by elevating the temperature. The more active decompositions occur above 250° C and industrial carbonizations employ temperatures up to 500° C. Beginning at about 270° C exothermic reactions set in, which bring about complete carbonization without the further application of external heat. A number of terms are used interchangeably for the thermal decomposition of wood, namely: carbonization, pyrolysis, wood distillation, destructive distillation and dry distillation.

Thermal decompositions result in drastic changes in the wood. The large, complex polymeric molecules of the wood tissue are broken down to carbon and a wide variety of relatively simple molecules, producing a molecular debris. These products separate naturally into four groups; charcoal, pyroligneous acid liquor, tar, and non-condensible gases.

The products obtained by the distillation of hardwoods differ from those of the softwoods. This is due to the fact that only resinous softwoods are profitably distilled, the resin giving rise to turpentine, pine oil and rosin oil; products which are equally if not more important than the charcoal. Softwoods, however, yield only about one-half as much methanol and one-quarter as much acetic acid in the pyroligneous acid fraction as do the hardwoods. Generally, it has not been profitable to isolate these chemicals from the pyroligneous acid of softwoods. The ratio of hardwoods to softwoods used for carbonization and distillation in the United States is approximately 4:1.

Hardwood Distillation

Products. Charcoal is the major industrial product of hardwood distillation. It remains as a residue after most of the volatile decomposition products have been driven off. Charcoal consists mainly of carbon, together with incompletely decomposed organic material and adsorbed chemicals. The amount of these secondary materials (containing hydrogen and oxygen) associated with the carbon decreases rapidly with increase in the distillation temperature as shown in Table 15.12. Commercial charcoal corresponds to about the 400° C (or somewhat higher) product and has a volatile content (organic residues) of 15–25 per cent.

Commercial charcoal is sold in the form of lumps, screenings, powder and briquettes. For special uses it is also classified according to specific gravity and volatile content. The average industrial yield of charcoal is 37–40 per cent.

Charcoal has a wide range of uses, which may be classified as fuel, metallurgical, chemical and miscellaneous uses. Large tonnage outlets for fuel are for tobacco curing, restaurants, railway dining cars and picnic fuels. The use of charcoal in metallurgy has largely given way to coke. Charcoal is an important material for the chemical industry, such as for the manufacture of calcium carbide, sodium and potassium cyanides, carbon disulphide, magnesium chloride, hydrochloric acid, carbon monoxide, electrodes, fireworks, black powder, catalysts, pharmaceuticals, glass, resin molding, rubber,

TABLE 15.12. COMPOSITION AND AMOUNT OF CHARCOAL PRODUCED AT DIFFERENT MAXIMUM TEMPERATURES

Distillation Temperature	Composition of Charcoal			Charcoal Yield on Dry Wt. of Wood
	Carbon	Hydrogen	Oxygen	
°C	%	%	%	%
250	70.6	5.2	24.2	65.2
300	73.2	4.9	21.9	51.4
400	77.7	4.5	18.1	40.6
500	89.2	3.1	6.7	31.0
600	92.2	2.6	5.2	29.1
1000	96.6	0.5	2.9	26.8

brake linings, gas cylinder absorbent, paint pigment, and, in the form of activated carbon, as an adsorptive agent for the purification of gases and liquids. Miscellaneous uses include nursery mulch, crayons, and poultry and stock feeds.

The pyroligneous acid is the dilute aqueous condensate obtained by cooling the vapors from the retort or oven. It contains acetic acid, methanol, acetone and minor quantities of numerous other organic compounds, of which more than 30 have been identified. Formerly hardwood distillation was the exclusive source of acetic acid, methanol and acetone, and these were considered the primary products of the process. These important industrial chemicals are now produced by other cheaper methods and their annual production from wood has diminished so that they are now considered only secondary products to charcoal. The average yields based on the dry weight of the wood are: acetic acid, 4–4.5 per cent; methanol, 1–2 per cent; acetone, 0.5 per cent.

The wood tars are largely used for fuel at the plant. There is a small demand for some of the tar components, however. The wood tars are of two types, namely (1) the soluble tars and (2) the settled tars. The soluble tars are dissolved in the pyroligneous acid and are separated as tars in the refining process. The settled tars are insoluble in, and heavier than, the aqueous pyroligneous acid and are mechanically separated from it.

The settled tars can be fractionated into (a) light oils with boiling points up to 200° C, specific gravities less than 1.0, and containing aldehydes, ketones, acids and esters, (b) heavy oils that boil over 200° C, have specific gravities greater than 1.0 and contain many phenolic components, and (c) pitch. Maple, beech and birch give total tar yields of 10–12 per cent and oaks give 5–9 per cent tar.

The heavy oil fraction contains phenols, especially cresols, and is known as *wood-tar creosote*. It is used as a preservative for timbers, as a disinfectant and for staining. Another important product is medicinal beechwood creosote, used as a disinfectant. The light oil fractions are used as solvents, and the pitch for waterproofing and insulating agents.

The noncondensible gases produced during the distillation of hardwoods vary widely in amount and composition with the distilling conditions. The average range of composition of the gas is: 50–60 per cent carbon dioxide; 28–33 per cent carbon monoxide; 3.5–18 per cent methane; 1–3 per cent higher hydrocarbons; and 1–3 per cent hydrogen. The hydrogen content of the gas increases with increasing temperature of distillation. The gas mixture has a heating value of about 300 Btu per cu ft. The gas is normally used as a fuel in the distillation plant and as a heat-conveyor in the internal gas-heated processes.

The Externally Heated Oven Process. An outgrowth of the kiln method for producing charcoal was the hand-loaded iron retort developed in 1850. However, the large-scale development of the chemical wood industry did not begin until 1875, when the large car-loaded ovens were employed. The use of retorts is now limited to only a few of the pinewood plants in the southeastern United States.

The externally heated ovens (*retorts*) use steel cars or buggies. About 2.5 cords of wood in 4-foot lengths are piled on each car. The common 10-cord oven holds 4 cars. The oven is made of steel and is enclosed in a brick chamber, which leaves a space around the sides and top of the oven in which the fire gases circulate. The doors are closed, and heat applied by burning natural gas, oil or coal. Two openings in the rear wall allow the volatile products to pass out.

The cycle is 24 hours. During the first few hours, the heating is rapid in order to reach the distillation temperature. Water comes over first. An exothermic reaction takes place next, after which the outside heat must be decreased. The vapors pass out to the condenser where they form the liquid condensate, the pyroligneous acid. The uncondensed gas is piped to the boiler house. After about 10 hours, the flames in the burners are raised again, but not so high as at first. After 22 hours the distillation is over; all burners are turned off, and the retort is allowed to cool for 2 hours.

The buggies are placed in air-tight cooling chambers for two to three days, usually with a quenching spray of water after the first day. The charge shrinks considerably during the distillation, but the charcoal is obtained in the form of rather large pieces, with very little dust.

Some hardwood oven plants have discontinued chemical by-product recovery and are now producing only charcoal. The vapors, instead of being condensed are led with the noncondensible gases to an outside burner, or under the ovens as an additional fuel supply. There are a few exceptions, however, where the process has been modernized, and such plants are producing both chemicals and charcoal.

One such plant[4] employs 22 horizontal ovens, each of 10-cord capacity. One thousand buggies, each holding 2.5 cords of wood, circulate continuously on standard-gauge railroad tracks from the sawmill, where they are loaded with wood in 12-inch blocks, or pieces, through predriers, retorts, coolers, charcoal-handling facilities and back to the sawmill. In addition there is a vertical retort of a capacity of 30 cords per day. The wood consists of about 50 per cent maple, 30 per cent birch, 15 per cent beech and 5 per cent other hardwoods. It is a mixture of cull logs, split cordwood, veneer cores, slabs and edgings cut to 12-inch lengths. The buggies of wood first go to tunnel-type pre-driers heated by flue gas and remain there for three times the length of the carbonizing cycle, which reduces the moisture content of the green wood from about 43 per cent to about 23 per cent. After the hot charcoal is removed from the retorts it is cooled and conditioned for 72 hours. A chart of the products obtained by this process is shown in Figure 15.26.

The Internally Heated Retort Process. Several processes have been developed whereby the retort is heated internally by hot circulating gases. A vertical retort is employed and is filled with wood blocks or chunks. Oxygen-free gases, resulting from carbonization of wood in neighboring retorts, is freed from condensible gases in condensers and scrubbers and part of it is used to heat the remaining gas in a furnace, usually to 500–600° C. These hot gases are then circulated through the wood charge. As carbonization occurs, the vapors are passed to condensers and the charcoal is dropped to a cooling chamber at the base of the retort.

Several variations of this process have been developed, some of which are continuous instead of batch systems. In the continuous system, exothermic reaction is first initiated by hot gases and then this reaction continues near the center of the retort as the wood in small sizes passes downward. The rising hot gases heat the incoming wood, and the charcoal is dropped to a cooling chamber at the bottom (such as in Badger-Stafford, Lambiotte and Pieters processes).

Chemical Recovery. The gases and vapors passing out of the oven or retort are cooled, the condensed pyroligneous acid is stored, and the gas is

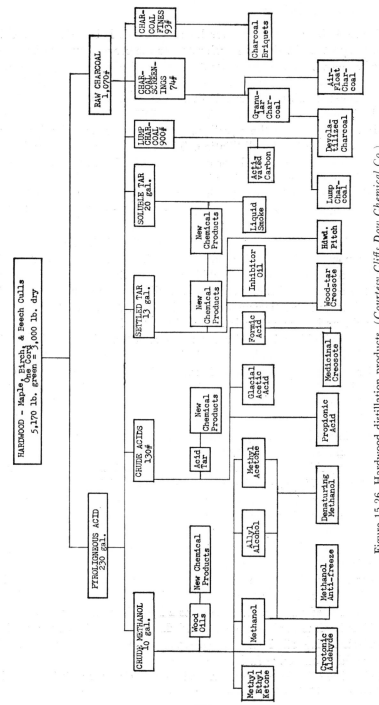

Figure 15.26. Hardwood distillation products. (*Courtesy Cliffs Dow Chemical Co.*)

scrubbed and blown to the power house where it is burned under boilers, except the part used to bring a fresh retort to the proper temperature.

The pyroligneous acid is separated mechanically from the settled tar. Modern plants use a continuous refining process to fractionate the pyroligneous acid into water, tar, wood oils and pure chemicals.

Several processes have been invented and perfected by which the acetic acid is extracted from the pyroligneous acid by means of solvents, with subsequent separation by distillation. The Brewster process uses isopropyl ether as the solvent; the Suida process uses a high-boiling wood-oil fraction, produced from the wood in the plant, and used over and over again for a reasonable number of cycles. In the latter process the extraction is carried out in the superheated vapor phase. The settled pyroligneous acid is run to the primary still which sends out vapors of acetic acid, alcohol, and water, retaining the dissolved tar, which is run off periodically.

The vapors of acetic acid, crude methanol, and water enter at the base of a plate column, called the scrubbing column. Solvent oil enters near the top of the column and flows downward, while the vapors pass upward. The solvent oil takes up acetic acid vapors and some water. Solvent oil containing acetic acid and some water is drawn from the base of the tower; crude methyl alcohol, aldehydes, and water pass out of the column at the top. This overhead distillate is condensed and, for the most part, run to the weak alcohol storage; a small amount is returned to the still as reflux. The oil with acetic acid passes down the dehydrating tower, and from there to the second boiler, which delivers the heated liquid to the stripping tower, operated under vacuum. Here the acetic acid vapor is flashed off and enters the rectifying column, carrying with it a small amount of oil and all the water present. The lower part of the stripping column serves to exhaust the oil of acetic acid. In the rectifying column, the oil is retained on the first few plates, and 92 per cent acetic acid is drawn off from the twelfth plate from the bottom. The upper 18 plates receive most of the water which entered the rectifying tower; they carry an acetic acid solution which becomes gradually weaker. From the top of the column a 15 per cent acetic acid passes out which is condensed and returned, mainly to the pyroligneous storage.

The solvent oil leaves the stripping tower free from acid; it is cooled and returned to the scrubbing tower. It is obtained in the first place as follows: the tar is distilled and the distillate gives a light oil, and a heavy oil fraction. The latter is placed in the tar still, and distilled again into light oil, heavy oil, and scrubbing oil. It is the last fraction which serves as solvent. The excess is sold or burned as fuel.

The methanol need not be removed in a preliminary distillation of the pyroligneous acid. Distilling the alcohol simultaneously with the removal of acetic acid by the solvent reduces by half the amount of esters formed; to that extent the alcohol as such is preserved, and also the acid.

Other distillation processes have also been devised, such as adding butyl alcohol or ethylene chloride to form an azeotropic mixture for distilling off the acetic acid. The mixture separates into layers on cooling.

The crude alcohol fraction is refined in continuous distillation towers, which separate it into a number of substances. The main products are methanol, methyl acetate and acetone.

An example of the chemicals produced today by hardwood distillation is illustrated in Figure 15.26. Other special chemicals that may be produced include National Formulary creosote, guaiacol, maltol, cyclotene, and others.

Destructive Distillation of Softwoods

Softwoods have less acetyl content than hardwoods and, therefore, yield less acetic acid upon distillation. The methanol yield is also much lower than from hardwoods. Recovery of these and their related chemicals is not practical in softwood distillation. Only resinous softwoods, especially longleaf and slash pine, are distilled because of the value of the products obtained from their resin content. Old stumpwood from logged-off areas and pitchy portions of fallen trees are the preferred material. This is because the sapwood, which is low in resin content has decayed away, leaving primarily the resin-rich heartwood. Some timber and sawmill wastes are also used, but generally only material is used which contains 20 per cent or more of resin.

Both the older small, hand-filled retorts of 1- to 2-cord-capacity and the larger car-loaded ovens up to 10-cord-capacity, similar to those used in hardwood distillation, are used for the destructive distillation of resinous softwoods. Also some retorts are made of concrete and are internally heated by flues of large iron pipe. In general the distillation procedure is similar to that for hardwoods, and, in the case of the larger retorts, the cars (buggies) containing charcoal are withdrawn to cooling chambers.

The vapors pass through a condenser and the liquids are collected for subsequent fractionation. The non-condensible gases are piped for fuel use or are vented to the atmosphere. In some cases, the early heating is carefully controlled prior to the destructive or carbonization stage, to allow most of the wood turpentine and light pine oil to distill off first. This crude light oil fraction is then redistilled.

The combined oil-tar distillate, contrary to the hardwood tars, is lighter than the pyroligneous acid. It is mechanically separated and fractionated by different methods.

Whether the crude oils are collected from the retort or oven as a whole, or in fractions, they must be re-distilled for separation into primary products. Copper stills, known as pine-tar stills, are commonly used, and are provided with both steam coils and steam jets for steam distillation. There is no standard procedure for preparation of the end products from the crude oil distillates, since special products (different fractions of different boiling ranges) may be produced at different plants and at different times to fit specific use and market requirements. The products from the pine-tar still are usually light and heavy pine oils and pitch, and a composite of several light solvent oils. Further fractional distillation of the solvent oils yields turpentine, dipentene, pine oil, and small amounts of other hydrocarbons. The yields vary greatly according to the resin content of the wood and the operating conditions. On the average, the yields per ton of southern pine stumpwood and "lightwood,"* are:

Total oils	35– 40 gal
Wood turpentine	4– 6 gal
Tar	20– 30 gal
Charcoal	350–400 lb

The wood turpentine obtained by destructive distillation differs chemically from gum turpentine, i.e., turpentine from the gum obtained by tapping of living trees. Wood turpentine contains a large amount of alpha-pinene and also a large amount of dipentene, differing in these respects from gum turpentine. The general properties of the two turpentines and their uses, however, are similar. Likewise the properties and uses of destructively distilled dipentene and pine oil are similar to those of the steam distilled products.

Some of the common uses of the less important products of the destructive distillation of resinous pines are:

Tar and tar oils:	Cordage, rubber, oakum, fish nets, tarpaulins, paper, soaps, insecticides, roofing cements, paints
Pyroligneous acid:	Limited use in meat smoking, leather tanning and as weed killer
Charcoal:	Similar to those for hardwood charcoal

Continuous Carbonization for Charcoal Production

The demand for charcoal remains high, especially the recreational consumer demand. This has brought about need for additional charcoal production facilities and the trend is toward continuous conversion of wood. The continuous process utilizing only the exothermic heat of the reaction for carbonization of small wood pieces (scrap and waste) in vertical retorts was described earlier.

* Resinous portions of wood, mainly heartwood, after decay of the sapwood; also termed "fatwood."

Other, more recent, developments in continuous carbonization have taken place, primarily for the production of charcoal. One example involves the heating to about 700° F of a continuously travelling 3-inch layer of fine wood chips over electrically heated platens. The carbon fines are briquetted.

Another example[2] of the trend toward continuous carbonization involves the use of horizontal tubes which pass through a brick and concrete heating chamber (for diagram see Fig. 15.27). A single metal tube with a screw conveyor carries the sawdust or finely divided wood to a hopper for equal distribution to 13 parallel horizontal tubes. Screw-conveyors move the wood

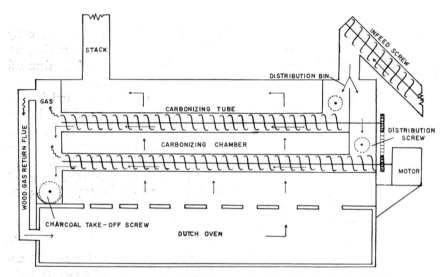

Figure 15.27. Continuous wood residue carbonizer. [*From Ervin E. Dargan and Walton R. Smith, Forest Products J., 9, 395 (1959) and Courtesy Forest Products Research Society.*]

particles through the tubes, which are heated to 800–900° F by the combustion chamber. Passage through the tubes takes 1 to 2 hours. From the tubes the charcoal particles are discharged to a single exit tube where they are sprayed with steam to reduce the temperature and bring about some activation. From the exit tube the charcoal may be mixed with starch binder and is transported to storage chambers or directly to the briquetting machine.

The combustion chamber is heated by a dutch oven under the chamber, with the heat passing through ducts to the combustion chamber above, where the carbonizing tubes are located. In operation, the dutch oven is fired for an initial period of several hours until a temperature of 800–900° F has been reached in the combustion chamber. Then after carbonization is underway, the wood gases are diverted from the carbonizing tubes to the dutch oven and the process then becomes automatic without further supplemental heat.

Considerable research continues on the development of efficient carbonization units, as well as on the chemistry and technology of thermal degradation. Increased yields of charcoal, as much as 15 to 30 per cent above normal, by the addition of ammonium chloride during the carbonization have been reported.[5] Perhaps the most significant trends in the industry are towards continuous carbonization, the use of finer wood particles (wood wastes and residues) and the consumer preference for briquettes.

NAVAL STORES

The naval stores industry in the United States began in the very early Colonial days, when wooden vessels used tar and pitch from the crude gum or oleoresin collected from the wounds of living pine trees. The demand for tar and pitch from crude gum is now of minor importance.

The industry is centered in the southeastern United States and is confined to the longleaf and slash pine areas. There is also a small, but locally important, naval stores producing area in the Londes region of southwestern France, based on the maritime pine. Turpentine and rosin are the two important products obtained from the oleoresin gum of living pine trees.

The Federal Naval Stores Act, passed in 1923, recognizes four types of turpentine, according to methods of production. They are (1) *gum spirits of turpentine* made from the gum or oleoresin collected from living trees, (2) *steam-distilled (S.D.) wood turpentine* obtained from the resin within the wood (scrapwood, knots, stumps or other wood residues commonly called "lightwood") by steam distillation of the wood or of a solvent extract of the wood, (3) *destructively distilled (D.D.) wood turpentine* obtained by fractional distillation of the oily condensate recovered from the vapors formed during the thermal degradation of resinous pine wood, and (4) *sulphate turpentine,* recovered as a by-product during the sulphate pulping of resinous woods. Over half the world's supply of turpentine comes from the United States.

Turpentines differ in odor and composition according to method of production. Gum turpentine is considered the highest quality and has a pleasant odor. Steam-distilled turpentine is but slightly inferior in odor and quality to the gum spirits. The destructively distilled turpentine has a pungent odor due to contamination with thermally decomposed substances. The gum turpentine differs chemically from the wood turpentines, though their properties are not greatly different. Gum turpentine is distinctive for its large beta-pinene fraction, which is virtually absent from the wood turpentines.

Turpentine is a volatile oil consisting primarily of terpene hydrocarbons, having the empirical formula $C_{10}H_{16}$. These 26 atoms can have many different arrangements. Only six are present in appreciable amounts in commercial turpentines, namely: alpha-pinene (b.p. 156° C), beta-pinene (b.p. 164° C), camphene (b.p. 159° C), Δ^3-carene (b.p. 170° C), dipentene (b.p. 176° C), and terpinoline (b.p. 188° C). The molecular configurations of most of these are shown in Figure 15.28.

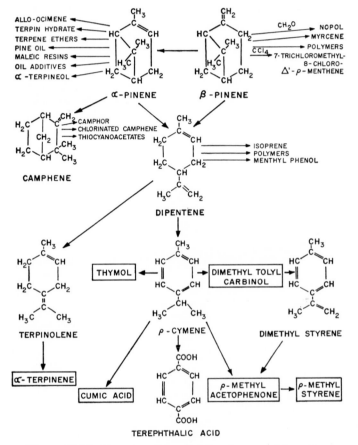

Figure 15.28. Some reactions of alpha-pinene and beta-pinene. (*L. A. Goldblatt, Yearbook of Agriculture, U. S. Dept. of Agriculture, 1950–51*)

Rosin, the other major naval stores product, is a brittle solid which softens at 80° C. Chemically it is composed of about 90 per cent resin acids, and 10 per cent neutral matter. The resin acids are mainly *l*-abietic acid and its isomers, $C_{20}H_{30}O_2$.

Rosin is graded and sold on the basis of color, the color grades ranging from pale yellow to dark red (almost black). The color is due almost entirely to iron contamination and oxidation products. Fresh oleoresin, as it exudes from the tree, will yield a rosin that is nearly colorless. Color bodies are removed by selective solvents and selective adsorption from a 10–15 per cent gasoline solution passed through beds of diatomaceous earth. About 70 per cent of the world's rosin is produced in the United States.

Gum Turpentine and Rosin Production

The crude gum or oleoresin is caused to flow from healthy trees by incising the sapwood. The lower part of the tree is faced, i.e., a section of bark is removed, giving a flat wood surface for the gutters which are inserted into a slanting cut made by a special axe. The gutters conduct the gum to a container which can hold 1–2 qt of gum. At the top of the exposed face, a V-shaped gash or streak is cut about $\frac{1}{2}''$ deep and $\frac{1}{2}''$–$\frac{3}{4}''$ wide. This wound opens the resin ducts in the wood and causes the oleoresin to flow. Each week a new streak is cut above the last one. Application of 40–60 per cent sulphuric acid spray stimulates the rate and duration of oleoresin flow.

The operations of inserting gutters, hanging cups and cutting the first streak is preferably done in December or January, since early facing stimulates early season gum flow. The gum continues to flow until November, with the height of the season being from March to September. The average composition of crude gum is 68 per cent rosin, 20 per cent turpentine, and 12 per cent water.

The collected gum is distilled from a copper still; turpentine and water pass over, and the rosin is left in the still. The remaining molten rosin, plus impurities, is passed through a series of strainers and cotton batting to remove dirt particles. The liquid rosin is then run into tank cars, drums or multi-wall paper bags for shipment. Annual production figures for gum turpentine and rosin are shown in Table 15.13.

Extraction and Steam-Distillation Process. This process is applied to resinous wood chips from pine stumps and "lightwood." The products removed remain essentially unchanged, whereas in the destructive distillation process previously described, new products are formed by thermal decomposition, which contaminate the turpentine and pine oil.

In the older practice, a two-stage process was followed; first steam distillation to remove the turpentine, followed by solvent extraction of the wood chips to remove the rosin and pine oil. In modern practice the steam distillation step is eliminated, and all the resin products are removed by solvent extraction. The solvent retained by the extracted wood chips is recovered by steaming. Extraction is carried out with naphtha (b.p. 90–115° C fraction) or benzene. Multiple extraction is carried out in a series of vertical extractors in a counter-current manner, whereby fresh solvent is used for the final extraction of a charge.

The solution from the extractors is vacuum distilled and the solvent recovered. The remaining terpene oils are fractionally redistilled under vacuum and recovered as turpentine, dipentene and pine oil. The nonvolatile rosin is of dark color and is upgraded by clarification methods, such as by selective absorption treatment of its solution (bed-filtering). Annual production figures of the products are shown in Table 15.13.

TABLE 15.13. NAVAL STORES PRODUCTION*

Annual Production—For Periods April 1—March 31

Product	1958–59	1957–58	1954–55	1950–51	1948–49
Turpentine			*Barrels of 50 gal*		
Gum	120,300	129,080	175,940	271,880	324,330
Steam Dist.	172,600	185,980	207,700	237,080	207,160
Destr. Dist.	. . . .	840	2,410	5,410	2,780
Sulphate	315,340	311,760	231,750	194,180	124,870
TOTAL	608,240	627,660	617,800	708,550	659,140
Rosin			*Drums of 520 lb net*		
Gum	369,350	399,910	527,700	797,620	921,220
Steam Dist.	1,182,620	1,195,990	1,342,370	1,339,410	1,154,890
Tall oil	305,060	269,270	. . . .	. . . .	. . . .
TOTAL	1,857,030	1,865,170	1,870,070	2,137,030	2,076,110
Miscellaneous			*Barrels of 50 gal*		
Dipentene	21,400	24,950	32,010	44,630	26,170
Pine oil	194,260	185,420	189,310	173,170	148,670
Other monocyclic					
hydrocarbons	108,770	95,910	76,210	50,530	39,470
Rosin oil	22,760	40,750	20,000	30,910	18,620
Pine tar	. . . .	. . . .	90,530	119,020	107,250

* From Naval Stores Annual Report, U. S. Dept. Agr. (1959, 1958, 1955, 1951, 1950).

Sulphate Turpentine and Tall Oil

Sulphate turpentine is obtained as a by-product during the kraft pulping of pine woods. Vapors are periodically released from the top of the digesters; these are condensed and the oily turpentine layer separated and purified by fractional distillation and treatment with chemicals to remove traces of sulphur compounds.

The spent black liquor from the sulphate pulping of pine woods contains the less volatile products of the wood resin in the form of sodium salts or soaps. When these salts are acidified by sulphuric or sulphurous acid, the organic acids collect on the surface of the aqueous phase and are separated mechanically as tall oil (tall is the Scandinavian word for pine). Tall oil contains 45–55 per cent fatty acids, 40–45 per cent resin acids and 6–10 per cent unsaponifiables. The yield of tall oil varies from about 100 lb per ton of pulp from northern pines to 250 lb per ton of pulp from the southern pines. It is used in the manufacture of soaps and grease, and as an emulsifying agent. For production figures for sulphate turpentine and tall oil see Table 15.13.

Uses of Naval Stores Products

The naval stores products have a wide range of usefulness from ordinary household commodities to complex industrial uses, as outlined below.

Turpentine is widely used as a household solvent and paint thinner and in industry for many purposes. The chemistry of the terpenes offers many possibilities for conversion to other substances, as illustrated by the chart in Fig. 15.28. The more common uses of turpentine are: paints, varnishes, enamels, waxes (shoe, floor and furniture), polishes, disinfectants, soaps, pharmaceuticals, sealing wax, inks, wood stains, insecticides, crayons, synthetic camphor, and general solvent use.

Dipentene is present in large amounts in the higher boiling fractions of wood turpentine (not in gum turpentine). It is used in paints and varnishes and as a penetrating and softening solvent in rubber reclamation.

Pine oil has a wide range of industrial uses. A synthetic pine oil is also made from turpentine to meet the demands for the natural product. The more common uses of pine oil are: soaps, disinfectants, polishes, insecticides, deodorants, protective coatings, solvent and wetting agent in rubber and dye industries, and as a flotation agent in metallurgical operations.

Gum and wood rosins can be produced in similar grades and have the same uses. About three-fourths of the production is used in varnishes, lacquers, protective coatings, and in linoleum and roofing cements. Its sodium salt is used in sizing paper and in soaps. Derivatives of rosin, such as rosin esters, rosin-phenol-formaldehyde resins, limed rosins, zinc resinates, etc., are commonly prepared for varnishes. Rosin may also be hydrogenated, dehydrogenated, disproportionated or polymerized to obtain special properties for use in varnishes. Rosin and its derivatives perform many functions in varnishes and lacquers, such as improving the resin film, retarding gelation, improving viscosity characteristics, serving as driers and catalysts, etc.

Rosin and its derivatives are used in formulations for pressure-sensitive adhesives. Rosin also is frequently used as a bonding agent for sand cores of molds for preparing steel castings.

Rosin oil is a viscous liquid prepared by the destructive distillation of rosin. It is used in lubricating greases.

TANNIN AND OTHER EXTRACTIVES

The tissues of wood, bark and leaves of trees contain a great variety of chemical substances of considerable scientific interest and some of practical value. Turpentine, pine oil and rosin from the resins of pines are the most important commercial extractives from American woods.

Tannin is a commercially important substance that can be extracted from the wood, bark or leaves of certain trees and other plants. Tannins are complex dark-colored polyhydroxy phenolic compounds, related to catechol or pyrogallol, and which vary in composition from species to species. They have the important property of combining with the proteins of skins to produce leather.

For many years most of the leather in the United States was tanned with domestic tannins from hemlock and oak bark and from chestnut wood. Today only a small amount of tannin comes from these and other domestic sources. The most important source of vegetable tannin today is the wood of the quebracho tree which grows mainly in Paraguay and Argentina. The tannin content of this tree and a few other sources of vegetable tannin are shown in Table 15.14.

TABLE 15.14. TANNIN CONTENT OF SOME PLANT MATERIALS

Plant Material	Per Cent Tannin
Domestic Sources	
Chestnut wood	4–15
Eastern hemlock bark	9–13
Western hemlock bark	10–20
Tanbark oak	15–16
Chestnut oak	10–14
Black oak	8–12
Sumac leaves	25–32
Foreign Sources	
Quebracho heartwood	20–30
Mangrove bark	15–42
Wattle (*acacia* bark)	15–50
Myrobalan nuts	30–40
Sicilian sumac leaves	25–30

The wood or bark for tannin production is reduced to chips and shreds by passing the material through hoggers or hammer mills. It is then extracted with warm water in diffusion batteries. The dilute solutions are evaporated to the desired concentration. Loss of solubility of the tannin can be counteracted by treatment of the concentrate with sodium sulphite.

Essential Oils

Various essential oils are obtained by steam distillation of wood chips, barks or leaves of trees. Chemically they are related to turpentine, being mainly terpene hydrocarbons. In the United States the following oils are produced; cedar-wood oil from the wood of red cedar, conifer-leaf oils from the needles and twigs of spruce, hemlock, cedar and pine, sassafras oil from roots, wood and bark of the sassafras tree, and sweet-birch oil from the bark and twigs of birch (*Betula lenta*).

Medicinals

The bark of the cascara tree of the northwestern region of the United States yields cascara, a laxative used in medicine. Several hundred tons of bark are harvested annually.

The red gum tree of the southern United States exudes a yellowish balsamic liquid or gum from wounds. This is known as storax. It is produced by removing a section of bark and incising the wood much in the same manner as for the production of naval stores gum as described above.

Storax is used in medicinal and pharmaceutical preparations, such as adhesives and salves. It is also used as an incense, in perfuming powders and soaps, and for flavoring tobacco.

REFERENCES

1. Brown, Nelson C., "Forest Products," 197, John Wiley & Sons, Inc., New York (1950).
2. Dargin, Ervin E., and Walton R. Smith, *Forest Products J.*, **9**, 395 (1959).
3. Howard, Guy C., U. S. Patents 1,848,292 (1932) and 2,057,117 (1936).
4. Jenner, R. W., *Northeastern Logger*, **6**, No. 8, 28 (1958).
5. Kishimoto, S., *et al.*, Bull. 115, Forest Experiment Station, Meguro, Tokyo, Japan (1959).
6. Pearl, Irwin A., and John W. Rowe, "Review of Chemical Utilization," *Forest Products J.*, **X**, 91–112 (1960).

READING REFERENCES

"Wood Chemistry," Vols. I and II, L. E. Wise and E. C. Jahn, New York, Reinhold Publishing Corp., 1952.

"Chemistry of Wood," Erik Hägglund, New York, Academic Press, 1951.

"Chemical Processing of Wood," Alfred J. Stamm and Elwin E. Harris, New York, Chemical Publishing Co., Inc., 1953.

"Forest Products," Nelson C. Brown, New York, John Wiley & Sons, Inc., 1950.

"Papermaking through Eighteen Centuries," Dard Hunter, New York, Wm. Edwin Rudge, 1930.

"Pulp and Paper; Chemistry and Technology," 3 vols., James P. Casey, New York, Interscience Publishers, Inc., 1960 and 1961.

"Chemistry of Pulp and Paper Making," 3rd Ed., Edwin Sutermeister, New York, John Wiley & Sons, 1941.

"Modern Pulp and Paper Making," 3rd Ed., G. S. Witham, Sr., revised and edited by John B. Calkin, New York, Reinhold Publishing Corp., 1957.

"Pulp and Paper Manufacture," Vols. I, II, III, and IV, J. Newell Stephenson, Ed., New York, McGraw-Hill Book Co., Inc., 1955.

"The College Textbook of Pulp and Paper Manufacture," Vol. I and II, P. S. Bolton and C. E. Libby, Eds., New York, TAPPI, 1958.

"Pulp and paper," R. B. Hobbs and W. T. Jones, *Ind. Eng. Chem.*, **48**, 1, 32A–34A (Jan., 1956).

"The paper industry today and tomorrow," George Olmstead, Jr., *Chem. Eng. Progr.*, **53**, 4, 163–65 (April, 1957).

"Revolutionary trends in pulp and paper technology," *Chem. Eng. Progr.*, **53**, 2, 110 (Feb., 1957).

"Problems in materials separation on a Fourdrinier paper machine," C. A. Sankey and B. Cowan, *Chem. Eng. Progr.*, **44**, 745 (1948).

"Fibreboard and Particle Board," Report of an International Consultation on Insulation Board, Hardboard and Particle Board, Geneva, 1957, Rome, Food and Agriculture Organization of the United Nations, 1958.

"Fibreboard and Particle Board," Vol. I, II, III, IV, V and VI, Technical Papers submitted to the International Consultation on Insulation Board, Hardboard and Particle Board, Geneva, 1957, Rome, Food and Agriculture Organization of the United Nations, 1958.

"Polymer Modified Papers," Edwin C. Jahn and V. Stannett, Chapter in "Modern Materials," Vol. 2, edited by Henry H. Hausner, New York, Academic Press, 1960.

"Expanding Wood Utilization through the Use of Resins," Edwin C. Jahn, Chapter in "Problems in Wood Chemistry," Jerusalem, the Weizmann Science Press of Israel, 1957.

"Report of Dimensional Stabilization Seminar," Madison, Wis., U. S. Forest Products Laboratory Report No. 2145, 1959.

"Wood Preservation," George M. Hunt and George A. Garratt, New York, McGraw-Hill Book Company, Inc., 1953.

"Wood Handbook," Agriculture Handbook No. 72, The Forest Products Laboratory, Forest Service, U. S. Department of Agriculture, Washington, Superintendent of Documents, 1955.

"Conversion of wood to carbohydrates," F. Bergius, *Ind. Eng. Chem.*, **29**, 247 (1937.)

"The development of wood saccharification by the Rheinau process," Erik Hägglund, *The Organization* (Food and Agriculture Organization of the United Nations), 1954:8–12.

"Madison wood sugar process," Elwin E. Harris and Edward Beglinger, *Ind. Eng. Chem.*, **38**, 890 (1946).

"Molasses and Yeast from Wood," Elwin E. Harris, Chapter in "Crops in Peace and War," The Yearbook of Agriculture, U. S. Department of Agriculture, Washington, Superintendent of Documents, 1950–51.

"New Products from wood carbonization," A. W. Goos and A. A. Reiter, *Ind. Eng. Chem.*, **38**, 132 (1946).

"Cliffs Dow Chemical Company," R. W. Jenner, *Northeastern Logger*, **6**, 8, 28 (Feb., 1958).

"Distillation of Resinous Wood," Madison, Wis., U. S. Forest Products Laboratory Report No. 496 (Revised), May, 1958.

"Production and Uses of Charcoal," Edward Beglinger, Chapter in "Crops in Peace and War," The Yearbook of Agriculture, U. S. Department of Agriculture, Washington, Superintendent of Documents, 1950–51.

"Charcoal Production and Uses," New Haven, Conn., Northeastern Wood Utilization Council, Inc., Bul. 37, Jan., 1952.

"Continuous Carbonization and Briquetting of Wood Residue," Ervin E. Dargin and Walton R. Smith, *Forest Prod. J.*, **IX**, 395 (1959).

"Modern Turpentining Practices," Washington, U. S. Department of Agriculture, Farmers' Bul. No. 1984, Feb., 1947.

"Chemicals We Get from Turpentine," Leo A. Goldblatt, Chapter in "Crops in Peace and War," The Yearbook of Agriculture, U. S. Department of Agriculture, Washington, Superintendent of Documents, 1950–51.

"The Industrial Utilization of Rosin," Ray V. Lawrence, Chapter in "Crops in Peace and War," The Yearbook of Agriculture, U. S. Department of Agriculture, Washington, Superintendent of Documents, 1950–51.

"The Chemistry and Utilization of Bark," New Haven, Conn., Northeastern Wood Utilization Council, Inc., Bul. 25, Jan., 1949.

"Native Sources of Tanning Materials," Jerome S. Rogers, Chapter in "Crops in Peace and War," The Yearbook of Agriculture, U. S. Department of Agriculture, Washington, Superintendent of Documents, 1950–51.

"Tannin from Waste Bark," New Haven, Conn., Northeastern Wood Utilization Council, Inc., Bul. 39, Sept., 1952.

"Review of Chemical Utilization," Irwin A. Pearl and John W. Rowe, *Forest Prod. J.*, X, 91 (1960).

16

SUGAR AND STARCH

In collaboration with Dr. Sidney M. Cantor*

THREE FOOD ELEMENTS essential to the well-being of man are proteins, fats, and carbohydrates. A particularly palatable form of the latter, sucrose, is found in nature and needs only to be extracted from plant sources, namely, sugar cane and sugar beets. Another important carbohydrate is starch, found in many plants and consumed primarily in the form of refined cereal. Starch may be isolated for both food and non-food applications, and hydrolyzed to produce another sugar, dextrose (D-glucose).

Sources

Because of the universal popularity of sugar both as a food and a source of energy, and because of its relatively low cost, its extraction from plant sources and the refining of crude or raw sugar made directly from this extract are important world-wide industries. In the United States, for example, the annual per capita distribution of refined sugar is nearly 100 pounds. There are two major sources of sugar (chemically identified as

* DCA Food Industries, Inc., New York, N. Y.

sucrose, a disaccharide) : sugar cane* in tropical and semi-tropical regions; sugar beet† in temperate regions.

The sugar cane industry is concerned with cultivation of the cane, extraction of the sugar, production of raw or crude sugar from the extract, and refining of the raw sugar into crystalline and liquid (syrup) products. The last operation is generally executed near the point of distribution, in or near large population centers in temperate regions and at a sea or river port, so that the raw sugar may be transported economically from its source. Aside from tradition, the refining process developed independently because of seasonal variations in the demand for refined sugar, maintenance (for practical reasons) of limited refined stocks, and relatively few refineries compared to the number of raw sugar factories.

Some direct-consumption centrifugal sugars, e.g., "Yellow Crystal," "Plantation White," are produced for local use in tropical countries at sugar factory sites. The quality of this sugar has improved steadily in response to demand and with the advent of low cost decolorizing carbons. Although its cane flavor is often preferred locally as compared to the otherwise unflavored sweetness of completely refined sugar, some direct-consumption sugar is also exported.

Refined beet sugar, the chemical equivalent in all respects to cane sugar, is not produced in a raw state but in refined form directly from beet juice recovered from the beet by a diffusion process. In the 1959–1960 crop year, beet sugar accounted for over 40 per cent of the world's sugar pro-

---

* Although sugar cane is thought to have originated in India, recent research has traced its path westward from New Guinea to the Islands of Indonesia, the Philippines, the Malay peninsula, Indochina, and the arc around the Bay of Bengal which earlier evidence had indicated to be the point of origin. Sugar cane was known to the Greeks and later to the Romans. It was transported from India to China, Arabia, Tunis, Morocco, Madeira, the Azores, Cape Verde Islands, and finally to the Canaries; from there Columbus carried it to San Domingo on his second voyage in 1493. It spread rapidly to the West Indies, Central America, and the Northern part of South America, and by 1600 the production of raw sugar from cane grown in tropical America was the largest industry in the world.

† The beet sugar industry began in 1747 when Andreas Marggraf, a German chemist, discovered that sugar crystals identical to sugar cane crystals could be obtained from beet roots. The first beet factory was built in 1803 in Silesia by Frederick Wilhelm III, King of Prussia, but it was Napoleon who gave impetus to the industry. Because the British blockade cut France off from the West Indies, he was forced to look for another source of cane. In 1812, one year after his interest was aroused, there were 40 factories in France producing 3 million pounds of sugar annually. After Waterloo the industry collapsed, but as the beet source and processing were improved the industry rallied; receiving new encouragement from a changed economic situation when West Indian slaves were emancipated, it continued to develop to its present high level. In the broadest sense, the beet sugar industry is recognized as being a product of scientific research.

duction compared to about one-third in the crop year of 1946–47. In the United States beet sugar presently accounts for 25 per cent of the sugar distributed to consumers.

Economics

Recent data on world sugar production (centrifugal sugar) is given in Table 16.1. The sugar, whether cane or beet, is indicated regionally, and important sugar-producing countries are identified. Sugar characterized as non-centrifugal, that is, not separated as a crystalline entity, is not included. Such sugar produced in a preferred form for local consumption (gur, muscovado, rapadura, etc.) amounted to an estimated 9 million short tons in the 1958–1959 crop year.

In general, sugar production expanded rapidly when the shipping restrictions imposed by World War II were lifted. During the crop years 1957–1958 and 1958–1959 world sugar production jumped about one tenth each year, and 1959–1960 production is estimated to be almost three times that of 1913–1914. The efforts of most countries are directed toward controlling production somewhere near domestic consumption and export requirements to keep the world market price reasonable. The exception, of course, is in those countries which maintain a relationship, for political or other reasons, with sugar-producing areas. For example, since the United Kingdom is committed to provide a market for those countries associated with the British Commonwealth, the market for home-grown beets is restricted.

The United States also restricts its domestic production of sugar by means of a quota system, imposed by several amended Sugar Acts, which favors certain sugar-producing countries while allowing for increasing demand.* In addition to the quota system, the domestic industry in the United States is protected by a sugar tariff which, since its inception in 1903 when Cuba became the most important source of United States sugar, has given a 20 per cent lower tariff to Cuban imports. The actual rate has changed under various tariff policies, but since 1948 the tariff on Cuban sugar has amounted to 0.5 of a cent a pound while the "full-duty" rate since 1951 has been 0.625 of a cent a pound.

The Sugar Acts and their amendments have contributed in large measure to the remarkable stability, in relation to other commodities, of the price

* For example, according to the amendment (enacted in 1956 and extending through 1960) to the 1948 Sugar Act, as of March 1960, based on an estimated U. S. consumption of 9,400 (units of 1,000 short tons, raw value) for 1960, quotas were as follows: Domestic beet, 2,043; Mainland cane, 629; Hawaii, 1,140; Puerto Rico, 1,192; Virgin Islands, 16; Republic of the Philippines, 980; Cuba, 3,120; Others, 279. Recent political developments have led to reapportionment of the Cuban quota among other producers. This has caused no great trouble in supplying U. S. sugar needs.

TABLE 16.1. CENTRIFUGAL SUGAR (RAW VALUE):[a] PRODUCTION IN SPECIFIED COUNTRIES

Continent and Country	Average 1950–51 through 1954–55 1,000 Short Tons	1958–59 1,000 Short Tons	1959–60 1,000 Short Tons
North America (cane and beet):			
North			
Canada (beet)	142	184	170
Mexico	900	1,477	1,670
United States			
Continental (beet)	1,785	2,225	2,350
Continental (cane)	566	578	710
Hawaii	1,066	975	1,065
Puerto Rico	1,228	1,087	1,250
Virgin Islands of the United States	11	12	12
Central	167	289	311
Caribbean			
Cuba	6,078	6,577	6,000
Dominican Republic	657	1,020	1,040
Jamaica	364	423	430
Other Caribbean	639	734	756
Other North America	52	82	89
Total North America	13,655	15,663	15,853
South America (cane):			
Argentina	773	1,184	1,050
Brazil	2,110	3,770	3,562
British Guiana	266	360	325
Peru	628	825	850
Other South America	446	730	779
Total South America	4,223	6,869	6,566
Europe (beet):			
West			
Austria	176	327	385
Belgium-Luxembourg	395	510	245
Denmark	351	440	370
Finland	30	43	45
France	1,551	1,764	1,225
Germany, West	1,255	2,098	1,650
Ireland	113	127	125
Italy	828	1,255	1,300
Netherlands	457	643	600
Spain	392	524	570
Sweden	331	309	372
Switzerland	34	40	45
United Kingdom	764	899	975
Total West Europe	6,677	8,979	7,907

604

Continent and Country	Average 1950–51 through 1954–55 1,000 Short Tons	1958–59 1,000 Short Tons	1959–60 1,000 Short Tons
East			
Bulgaria	83	145	180
Czechoslovakia	803	1,050	950
Germany, East	855	1,030	799
Hungary	284	330	425
Poland	1,047	1,335	1,215
Rumania	148	230	330
Yugoslavia	158	206	320
Total East Europe	3,378	4,326	4,219
Total Europe	10,055	13,305	12,126
U.S.S.R., Europe and Asia (beet)	3,010	6,900	6,500
Africa (cane):			
North			
Egypt	264	363	375
Other	11	52	53
Central			
Mauritius	535	580	640
Mozambique	102	174	185
Reunion	163	185	225
Other	189	335	338
South			
Union of South Africa	689	1,135	1,070
Total Africa	1,953	2,824	2,886
Asia (cane and beet)			
South-West			
Iran (beet)	80	131	140
Turkey, Europe and Asia (beet)	205	428	437
East Central			
China, Mainland	293	1,200	1,400
South and East			
Burma	19	47	48
China, Taiwan	724	1,066	950
India	1,690	2,642	2,900
Indonesia	578	854	885
Japan (beet)	38	143	165
Pakistan	85	203	210
Philippines	1,190	1,522	1,557
Thailand	40	75	90
Other Asia	10	36	50
Total Asia	4,952	8,347	8,832

TABLE 16.1. CENTRIFUGAL SUGAR (RAW VALUE):[a] PRODUCTION IN
SPECIFIED COUNTRIES (*Continued*)

Continent and Country	Average 1950–51 through 1954–55 1,000 Short Tons	1958–59 1,000 Short Tons	1959–60 1,000 Short Tons
Oceania (cane):			
Australia	1,125	1,525	1,390
Fiji	165	216	260
Total Oceania	1,290	1,741	1,650
World total (cane)	23,728	31,869	31,960
World total (beet)	15,410	23,780	22,453
World total (cane and beet)	39,138	55,649	54,413

Source: Foreign Agricultural Service.

[a] Raw sugar value is expressed in terms of a normal solution of pure sugar, 26.0 grams in 100 milliliters, read in a 2-decimeter saccharimeter tube. The saccharimeter scale is a linear scale calibrated to read directly in per cent of sugar ($1° = 1$ per cent), it is assumed that impure sugar solutions read similarly. Thus 96° raw sugar (a general figure for a raw sugar) is approximately 96 per cent sucrose.

of consumer sugar in the United States.* In 1958 the index of wholesale prices for all foods was 255 (1940 = 100), for sugar, 209. In general, the system of controls and quotas has also influenced profitably domestic production operations so that the United States sugar industry is in a much healthier condition than it was in 1934 before controls were instituted.

Evaluation of Sugar

The property of optical activity is utilized in evaluating sugar. Sucrose dissolved in water rotates the plane of polarized light to the right, while invert sugar, an equimolar mixture of dextrose (D-glucose) and levulose (D-fructose) formed by hydrolysis of sucrose, rotates the plane of polarized light to the left. Impurities have little effect on the polarized beam. In a pure sucrose solution the rotation of the light beam to the right is a measure of the sucrose content. It is arbitrarily assumed that the same holds true for a solution of raw sugar.

The instruments used are the polarimeter,† which reads in circular degrees,

* Sugar prices have shown little fluctuation over the past few years: the 1954–1958 average monthly price of raw sugar in New York was 6.13 cents a pound (duty paid), while the world price was 3.73 cents (f.a.s. Cuba). The average prices for the last 12 months in October 1959 were New York, 6.25 cents; the world, 3.06 cents. Similarly, the wholesale prices for refined cane and beet sugars were New York, 9.31 cents; the world, 8.70 cents.

† The polarimeter in the form of the polariscope, a half-shadow instrument, was an invention of Antoine Laurent. Now there are many forms and variations of the instrument.

or the saccharimeter, which permits readings on a horizontal scale running from 0 to 100, 0 representing pure water and 100 a solution of pure sucrose in a definite concentration (26.0 grams in 100 milliliters, read in a 2-decimeter tube). The readings are called degrees, and raw sugar usually reads 96° and a fraction on this instrument.

The reaction for sugar inversion, with the degrees of rotation for the pure substance in each case, and the direction of rotation (+ for right or dextro; — for left or levo) is:

$$C_{12}H_{22}O_{11} + H_2O \rightarrow$$
sucrose
+66.56°

$$\underset{\underset{+52.8°}{D(+)\text{-glucose}}}{C_6H_{12}O_6} + \underset{\underset{-92.8°}{D(-)\text{-fructose, hence}}}{C_6H_{12}O_6} \frac{+52.8 - 92.8}{2} = -20.0°$$

The sum of the rotation of the two monosaccharides, on the right of the equal sign, is a negative rotation; hence there is an inversion of the sign.* Glucose and fructose are sometimes called reducing sugars because they reduce Fehling's or Benedict's solution, whereas sucrose does not. The reducing value expressed as glucose is often used to evaluate mixtures of sugars, for example, the complex mixture arising from the hydrolysis of starch. There are also specific reducing methods by which it is possible to measure glucose or fructose alone.

Starch. Cereal and root starches are another important source of carbohydrates. In the western hemisphere, corn starch (maize) is the most significant of the starches used for sweeteners, that is, sugars, syrups, and other products derived from starch. In Europe the white potato is a more important source of starch and its derivatives, although corn is becoming a rival as production, particularly in the Soviet Union, increases.

Distribution by the corn refining industry of refinery products (sugars and syrups) on a per capita basis in 1959 in the United States was over 16 pounds. Syrups produced by the acid- or enzyme-catalyzed partial hydrolysis of corn starch† are either used directly in food processing or mixed with syrups to provide many products of varying sweetness and viscosity which also may be used in food processing or marketed directly to the consumer. The more complete hydrolysis of starch provides pure dextrose (D-glucose, a monosaccharide) in both hydrate and anhydrous forms as well as various crude forms.

* The name "invert sugar" is derived from the change in the sign of rotation, as are the names of the constituent sugars of sucrose (dextrose and levulose).

† The acid-catalyzed hydrolysis of starch was discovered in 1811 by the German chemist, G. S. C. Kirchoff, who was working in St. Petersberg at the time. Just as interest in sugar beets had been aroused, so was interest in this discovery quick to develop: both suggested a new source of sugar.

Other corn fractions may also be separated to produce corn oil (from the germ), feedstuffs (from the hull and the gluten), modified starches and dextrines for sizes and adhesives, a number of protein derivatives and modifications, and zein and monosodium glutamate (from the gluten). Table 16.2 gives shipments for the United States corn refining industry over the last decade.

TABLE 16.2. SHIPMENTS OF UNITED STATES CORN REFINING INDUSTRY:*
TOTAL DOMESTIC AND EXPORT PRODUCTION (1000 POUNDS)

	1948	1958
Corn Ground	6,153,164	8,068,363
Corn Starch	1,388,719	1,994,306
Corn Syrup, Unmixed	1,333,378	1,798,797
Corn Sugar, Crude and Refined	711,764	834,430
Dextrine	157,598	159,568
Corn Oil		
Crude	27,281	48,693
Refined	151,218	216,983
Feeds		
(1000 Short Tons)	840	1,031

* Source: Price Waterhouse and Co., New York, N. Y.

CANE SUGAR

The sugar cane is a large perennial grass which attains a length of 10 to 24 feet at maturity. There are a number of species and numerous varieties. Sugar cane is propagated by cuttings, each cutting consisting of portions of the cane plant having two or more buds. The buds develop into cane plants on which several other shoots arise from below the soil level to form a clump of stalks (stool). From 12 to 20 months are required for plant crops (new plants) and about 12 months for ratoons, that is, cane stalks arising from stools which have been previously reaped. Fields are replanted after 2 to 5 reapings have been obtained from the original cuttings. The cane stalk is round, 1 to 3 inches in diameter, and is covered with a hard rind which is light brown, or green, yellowish green, or purple in color, depending on variety. The stalk consists of a series of joints or internodes separated by nodes (not unlike bamboo). The rind and the nodes are of a woody nature, while the internode is soft pith. The internode contains the greater part of the juice. In harvesting, the canes are cut at ground level, and the leaves and tops of the stalks are removed. The sucrose content of the ripened cane varies between 10 and 15 per cent of the total weight; 13 per cent is about average.

Juice Extraction, Mill House. The cane is first cut into short lengths by rapidly revolving knives and then passed to a milling train (Fig. 16.1) which may consist, for example, of a two-roll crusher followed by four three-roll mills, 14 rollers in all where the juice is squeezed out by pressure (Figure 16.2). The rolls in the three-roll mills are under a pressure of 75 to 80 tons per foot of roll length, and the length ranges from 2½ to 7 feet; the crushing varies with the length of the roll, from 500 tons for the small length

Figure 16.1. A modern cane mill in Peru. (*Courtesy The Squier Corp., Buffalo, N. Y.*)

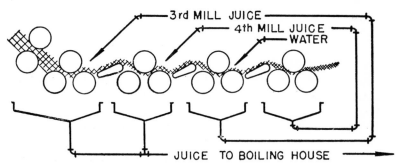

Figure 16.2. A milling train consisting of a crusher and four three-roll mills, grinding with the application of water; compound imbibition.

to 5000 tons per 24 hours for the larger mills. In the process of milling, water is applied to the crushed cane and the lean (dilute) juices are returned to the mills. In a 14-roller milling train, water is applied to the cane at the third mill, and its juice is fed to the first mill; the juice from the fourth mill is fed to the second mill. The method is known as compound imbibition. The approximate percentage of the sucrose in the cane extracted by each unit of the milling train is about as follows:

Crusher	1st Mill	2nd Mill	3rd Mill	4th Mill	Total
70.0	12.5	7.0	4.5	2.0	96.0

Extraction of cane juice by passing water counter-current to sliced cane is currently being investigated as a means of improving sugar recovery.

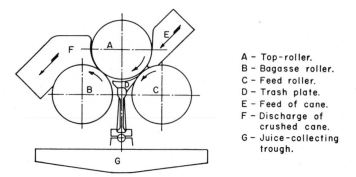

A – Top-roller.
B – Bagasse roller.
C – Feed roller.
D – Trash plate.
E – Feed of cane.
F – Discharge of crushed cane.
G – Juice-collecting trough.

Figure 16.3. A cane mill with its three crushing rolls and with a typical turn-plate arrangement. An hydraulic piston maintains pressure on A, while B and C are fixed; the rolls are under pressure of 75–80 tons per foot of roll width.

The composition of the juice varies with soil and climatic conditions, cane variety, and degree of maturity, within the limits indicated below:

Water	Sucrose	Reducing Sugars	Other Organic Compounds	Ash	pH
78–86%	10–20%	0.5–2.5%	0.5–1.0%	0.3–0.7%	5.1–5.7

As shown by the pH value, the juice is acid; it is strained through a per-forated metal sheet and sent to the boiling house where it is clarified and concentrated by boiling. The bagasse from the last mill of a train contains from 52 to 58 per cent of solid matter, mainly cane fiber; the remainder is water. It is used primarily as a fuel for raising the steam required by the factory.

Clarification of the Juice; Defecation. The juice from the strainer is clouded by small amounts of suspended and colloidal matter, and hence must be clarified. For the manufacture of raw cane sugar which is to be refined elsewhere later, simple lime defecation is practiced. Milk of lime is added to the juice in amounts sufficient to raise the pH to 7.6 or 7.8. The limed juice is pumped through high-velocity juice heaters (heat exchangers, steam versus juice); insoluble calcium phosphates, sulfates, and other salts absorb and entrain in their precipitation a large proportion of colloidal impurities (waxes, pectins, and pentosans), the flocculation of which is also promoted by the alkaline reaction. In addition, insoluble proteinates are formed, and the elimination of proteins is fairly complete. Should the juice contain less than 0.03 of a gram of P_2O_5 per 100 milliliters, enough phosphoric acid or superphosphate is added to bring the amount up to that figure. Precipitation may take place in settling tanks or in continuous shelf clarifiers such as the Graver* or the Dorr.† The juice emerges from these in crystal clear condition and is pumped to the evaporators. The sediment from the settlers is filtered and the filtrate returned to the subsiders; the solids are sent to the fields as fertilizer.

First Evaporation to Syrup. The clear juice from the settlers passes to a triple- or quadruple-effect evaporator where it is concentrated to a clear, brilliant, pale-yellow syrup (about 30° Bé). The operation is continuous.

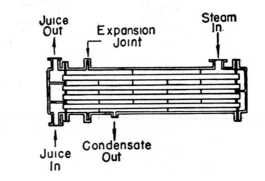

Figure 16.4. A juice heater.

The evaporator functions under a vacuum which differs from effect to effect.‡ Examination of the diagrammatic flow sheet (Fig. 16.5) will reveal that part of the "vapor" raised in the pre-evaporator is drawn off to the juice heaters, while another part may be used to operate a vacuum pan (see later). The remaining "vapor" enters the calandria of the second effect evaporator. About 70 to 75 per cent of the water present in the clarified juice is removed in the evaporators, the resulting syrup having a content of from 55 to 64 per cent soluble solids. The syrup is pumped to storage tanks situated on the pan floor.

Crystallization of Sucrose. The syrup is concentrated further in a single-effect vacuum pan (the strike pan) in which vacuum and steam may be regulated as the operator deems necessary. In the triple- or quadruple-effect evaporator used for the first evaporation, exhaust steam (5 to 12 pounds per

* Described and illustrated in "Chemical Process Machinery," by Emil R. Riegel, New York, Reinhold Publishing Corporation, 1953.

† *Ibid.*, p. 256.

‡ See Chapter 15, on Evaporators, in "Chemical Machinery," by Emil R. Riegel, New York, Reinhold Publishing Corp., 1944.

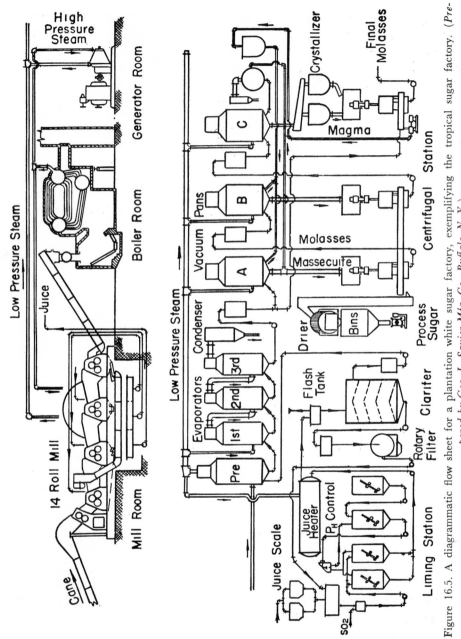

Figure 16.5. A diagrammatic flow sheet for a plantation white sugar factory, exemplifying the tropical sugar factory. (*Prepared by Geo. L. Squier Mfg. Co, Buffalo, N. Y.*)

square inch) is employed; in the vacuum pans equipped with large copper heating coils, boiler steam is used; in the vacuum pans with calandrias, low-pressure steam may also be used. All vacuum pans require batch operation. By suitably arranging the heating surface and the shape of the pan, constant circulation of the mass within the pan is assured; a mechanical circulator is provided in the more recent vacuum pans.

The syrup is evaporated until a sample on a glass plate glistens when examined under light. This means that numerous small crystals or nuclei have been formed, and that the graining point has been reached. More

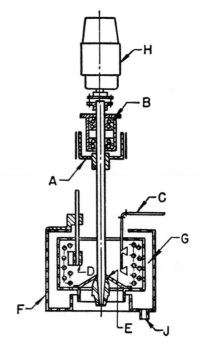

Figure 16.6. A centrifugal for the separation of sucrose crystals from the mother liquor. A, brake drum; B, ball bearings; C, wash water; D, plow for discharging the dry crystals; E, discharge gate; F, curb or casing or monitor; G, perforated basket. Not shown, the fine-screen lining on inside of basket.

syrup is then added, in small portions, and sugar, forced out of solution by evaporation, deposits on these nuclei, causing them to grow. This is continued until the desired growth has been attained and until the pan is full; the semi-solid mass in the pan is called "massecuite" and contains a total of about 82 per cent sucrose in the case of massecuites produced from syrup ("A" massecuites). The "A" massecuites will yield about 54 per cent of their weight as crystals; the others ("B" and "C" massecuites) less. The control of the number of nuclei is very important; if they are too few there will be more sugar ready to deposit than surface to receive it, resulting usually in a new crop of nuclei which will grow poorly (false grain). If too many nuclei are present the crystals will be too small, and the separation in the centrifuge will be slow and imperfect; when this happens only part of the pan is dumped, and more syrup is introduced on the rest as a "footing." Thus with the proper number of nuclei the regular crop of crystals is developed.

When a vacuum pan that has been working on syrup from the evaporators is full and ready, it discharges its massecuite, while hot, into receivers. From there the latter is fed to centrifugal baskets. The centrifugal machine has a vertical shaft, and its perforated cylindrical basket is lined with a closely woven metal screen through which the molasses can pass but the crystals cannot. When the basket is set in motion the centrifugal force drives the massecuite against the wall of the centrifugal, and the molasses goes through the crystals and the screen into the outer casing. After the molasses has drained away, the centrifugal is stopped and the sugar is discharged through a valve at the base of the centrifugal basket into a conveyor placed beneath it.

The crystals so obtained are coated by a film of molasses which gives them a grayish brown color. Water in the form of a spray added to the surface of the sugar in the centrifugal while revolving at high speed dilutes and washes off this layer of molasses and yields a whiter sugar.

A single crystallization does not permit all the recoverable sucrose from cane syrups to crystallize; accordingly, after obtaining a crop of crystals from the syrup massecuites, it is necessary to reboil the molasses to obtain a further yield of sucrose crystals. Usually two or three reboilings of molasses are necessary to recover the maximum of crystallizable sucrose. Sugar from the "C" massecuite is not ordinarily one of the products of a cane-sugar factory, since this grade of sugar is used as nuclei for "A" and "B" massecuites which are converted into a product of higher grade and value; "C" sugar also serves to reduce the amount of "graining" which would otherwise be necessary. The crystals obtained from the "A" and "B" massecuites are mixed and bagged together as raw sugar, the principal product of a cane-sugar factory.

The massecuites yielding exhausted molasses contain considerably higher proportions of non-sucrose components relative to sucrose than the original cane syrups. Consequently, these low-grade massecuites are extremely viscous. Since the mother liquor obtained from them will finally become molasses, it is necessary to ensure that as high a yield of sucrose as possible is obtained from them. When discharged from the pan, massecuites have a temperature of from 145 to 155° F (63 to 68° C), and since the solubility of sucrose decreases with temperature, sucrose may be further crystallized by allowing these massecuites to cool to room tempertaure. Cooling takes place at a slow rate in U-shaped or cylindrical vessels having hollow, water-cooled stirring arms which maintain a gentle movement in the massecuite. This movement causes the sucrose to come out of solution and deposit on crystals already present rather than form "false grain." The process is called crystallization-in-motion, and the vessels termed "crystallizers."

Molasses obtained from the "C" massecuite is the final or exhausted molasses and is also known as blackstrap.

Approximate data for syrups and molasses massecuites and the molasses obtained therefrom vary considerably; the figures given below are indicative only of general practice. "Apparent Purity" expresses the sucrose determined by simple polarization as a percentage of total solids indicated by specific gravity.

TABLE 16.3

Type of Massecuite	Solids Per Cent	Massecuite Polarization Per Cent	Apparent Purity	Yield of Sugar Per Cent	Molasses Apparent Purity
"A" (syrup).................	93.0	76.26	82.0	52–54	62.0
"B" (magma footing + syrup + "A" molasses)......	94.0	65.80	70.0	40–42	48.0
"C" (syrup + "B" molasses).....	96.0	53.76	56.0	35–38	28–30

The various products of the tropical cane-sugar factory are therefore the 96° crystal sugar (raw sugar), direct-consumption sugars, occasionally the "C" sugar (molasses sugar) of lower grade, blackstrap molasses, bagasse, and filter cake (used as a fertilizer).

Direct-Consumption Sugars. The manufacture of direct-consumption sugars is similar to that of raw sugar except that special care is taken in the clarification process, and reducing agents may be added to the syrup or massecuites. Clarification is improved by adding sulfur dioxide or carbon dioxide at the liming stage. The precipitated calcium sulfite and calcium carbonate remove greater quantities of non-sugars than simple lime defecation.

Cane Sugar Refining

Raw cane sugar purchased by the refinery in the temperate zones contains, as a rule, 96 to 97½ per cent sucrose. The task of the refiner is basically recrystallization, preceded by a treatment to remove color. Analysis of a typical raw cane sugar is approximately as follows:

Sucrose	Reducing Sugars	Other Organic Compounds	Ash	Water
97.50%	0.86%	0.46%	0.43%	0.75%

At the refinery, raw sugar is mixed with a mother liquor from a previous batch, to remove a large part of the color, but leave the crystals for the most part undissolved (affination). The mass is centrifuged; the crystals are washed while in the basket, then removed and dissolved in hot water to form a syrup. A small amount of lime is added and steam blown in, after which the syrup is passed through bone char held in tall cylindrical tanks of varying size. The function of the bone char is to adsorb the remaining color and to act as a filter. The liquor then goes to the "strike pan" where it is concentrated to massecuite (described under raw sugar). The massecuite is centrifuged, and the crystals are dried in a rotary drier to produce granulated sugar. The white massecuite may be solidified to a loaf which may, in turn, be cut into regular cubes or flat pieces. Numerous modifications provide many other special forms.

In recent years the importance of liquid sugars (sugar syrups) has increased markedly. In 1929 less than 9,000 short tons of liquid sugar was produced in the United States, while in 1959 the figure reached 540,200 tons. Although a considerable portion of these syrups is redissolved solid sugar, some is also the first or highest quality flow from the decolorizing systems (bone char), some is washed raw sugar refined with vegetable carbons, and some is raw sugar refined by a method using ion exchange resins in separate or mixed bed operation. The marketing of sugar in liquid form offers many advantages to the manufacturing consumer: savings in storage space and handling costs, greater cleanliness, lower process losses, increased uniformity, elimination of dissolving equipment, and ease of metering liquids.

The bone char in the filters is used until it no longer decolorizes, its pores having become clogged with impurities. To reclaim it, water is turned into the cylinders to remove most of the adhering sugar; the char is dumped and revivified by heating in the absence of air. It may then be reused. After a number of such treatments it disintegrates, and is relegated to the fertilizer and feed trade. Continuous char processes have recently been developed.

Under favorable circumstances a raw sugar may be refined to produce a nearly white product simply by mixing with a mother syrup, centrifuging, and washing the crystals first with a sugar solution, then with steam.

New methods have been introduced, some of them especially adapted to refining in the tropics. The activated carbon process has been most successful. Raw sugar is washed in the centrifugal to give a sugar polarizing 98.5 to 99°. It is then made into a syrup to which calcium phosphate, slaked lime, and kieselguhr are added. The mixture is heated and filtered. The filtrate, with pH 6.0 to 6.4, is mixed with a small percentage of vegetable carbon ("Suchar," "Norit," "Darco") and filtered again on precoated filters. The resulting syrup, clear and colorless, is crystallized in the usual manner and dried or distributed as liquid sugar. The vegetable char is used once, or at most a few times, and then discarded.

Another successful and quite different method employs "Sucroblanc." The raw sugar is first "washed" by washing it with green liquor or some other sugar liquor and purging it in centrifuges. The resulting "raffinated sugar" is dissolved in hot water to 60 or 65° Brix,* and 0.1 to 0.3 per cent of the reagent "Sucroblanc"[2,5] is stirred in at room temperature or slightly higher. The reagent contains high-test calcium hypochlorite, calcium superphosphate, lime, and filteraid. A slight evolution of gas (oxygen) causes the colloidal impurities to rise to the top of the solution; the clear, decolorized sugar solution may be drawn off from the bottom. Thus two steps in the older process (defecation and bleaching) are combined. The clear sugar solution goes to the evaporator and strike pan to make crystal sugar.

Among the more recent developments in sugar processing are methods using ion exchange resins.[1] Although natural materials with ion exchange properties are known (zeolites), the development of synthetic resins having greater capacities for ash constituents has led to improvements in the production of refined sugars directly from cane juice and in the refining of raw sugars. Cation resins, those which will exchange cations for hydrogen, are usually sulfonated or carboxylated high molecular weight polymers (sulfonated polystyrene, for example), while anion resins, which will exchange anions for hydroxyl, are aminated polymers (polystyrene containing quaternary ammonium residues, for example). Used successively in multiple columns or in mixed beds, these demineralize sugar solutions, yielding extremely low ash syrups which may be concentrated and crystallized in the usual fashion or marketed as liquid sugars after appropriate decolorization.

Resins have also been developed which serve as decolorizing agents, many of the color bodies in sugar solutions being weak acids. Demineralizing resins are used repeatedly with intermittent regeneration by dilute solution of acid (sulfuric) or base (caustic soda or ammonia) followed by rinsing with water.

In general, the cost of ion exchange treatment is higher than conventional processing; use of resins for sugar refining, aside from liquid sugars, is negligible. Ion exchange resins may also be used in the form of membranes for partially de-ashing raw sugar where the driving force is provided by an electric current passing through a stack of alternating cation and anion membranes with the sugar solution running countercurrent to a dilute solution of the ash.

BEET SUGAR

In the United States, twenty-two states grow sugar beets, with California, Colorado, Idaho, Michigan, Montana, Nebraska, and Utah leading in production. The average yield per acre is about 12.5 tons; the average sugar content is 15.5 per cent.

---

* The Brix scale is a density scale for sugar (sucrose) solutions. The degrees Brix are numerically equal to the percentage of sucrose in the solution. The term "Brix solids" refers to the solid content as determined by the Brix hydrometer.

At harvest time the beet root, free from the leaves, is carted to the sugar house, washed, and cut into V-shaped slices about one-quarter inch thick. These are called "cosettes." They are fed to a number of diffusion vessels so arranged that the cosettes may be delivered to any of the 20 or more from one overhead spout. Extraction is by hot water, in contact with the slices, on the countercurrent principle. Hot water enters the diffuser in which the charge is nearly exhausted; sugar diffuses from the cells of the beet into the water; the solution travels to the next diffuser where the slices are richer. The solution leaving the last diffuser, in contact with a fresh charge, is strengthened until it contains about 12 per cent sucrose; a dark solution is formed. The exhausted slices are washed out of the tank to a receiver where they are dried and converted to cattle feed.

The warm diffusion juice is agitated with 2 to 3 per cent lime for 2 hours, after which carbon dioxide is passed in to saturation. The precipitate carries down nearly all impurities. The juice is filter-pressed and, in some plants, treated with lime and carbon dioxide 2 or even 3 times. The filtrate is pale yellow, though most of this color is removed by sulfur dioxide. The latter also decomposes some organic salts of calcium, precipitating calcium sulfite. Ordinarily the sulfur dioxide treatment follows the first lime treatment. The filtered solution ready for the evaporators is purer than the corresponding solution from the sugar cane. Concentration to a clear syrup (as for cane juice) is effected in double- or triple-effect evaporators, and is followed by graining in the vacuum pan. The crystals are separated by centrifuging and washed in the basket; after drying they are ready for the market. The mother syrup is concentrated again, giving crystals which are re-worked and a mother liquor, the molasses. The maximum amount of sugar is crystallized from the molasses; the remainder is recovered by a chemical process to yield, for the most part, crystal sugar. In some factories the molasses is sold as a feed constituent.

The sugar in beet molasses may be recovered by precipitating it after appropriate dilution as a metal saccharate (calcium, strontium, or barium). Lime is the most widely used precipitating agent, and the lime process is known as the Steffen process after its inventor, Carl Steffen. Under favorable conditions about 90 per cent of the sugar in the molasses is recovered; the calcium saccharate dispersed in water is added to the regular process liquors where it is carbonated to liberate the sugar.

The Steffen filtrate is concentrated and used as raw material for the production of monosodium glutamate. Ion exchange techniques have been applied more extensively in beet sugar technology than in cane. The removal of one pound of impurities from beet molasses releases 1.5 pounds of sugar for crystallization, hence ion exchange treatment of preclarified juice makes available almost 32 pounds of additional sugar per ton of beets. However, it is only in times of sugar shortage that ion exchange systems are profitable to employ, and since ion exchange also interferes with by-product recovery its use is considered marginal.

By-Products. A great deal of attention has been paid to by-product recovery in the cane sugar industry. The most plentiful by-product from the manufacture of raw sugar, blackstrap molasses, was at one time used almost exclusively for fermentation to alcohol and other solvents. The advent of petrochemicals, however, has cut this market significantly, and most blackstrap is used as an adjunct in mixing animal feeds.

Aconitic acid,[4] a tribasic acid, is found in molasses and may be recovered by lime precipitation as its calcium-magnesium salt, or by ion exchange.

Bagasse, the cane residue left after expression of the juice, consists essentially of fiber (cellulose) and pith (pentosan). Aside from its primary use as a fuel in raw sugar factories, bagasse is used in the manufacture of wallboard for sheathing and insulation, and in the manufacture of paper for newsprint, particularly in tropical countries; it has also been considered as a base for animal feed after first being pre-treated by alkali cooking and by mixing with nitrogen-containing adjuncts. In one particular operation in the Dominican Republic the pith is separated and the pentosan converted to furfural by acid dehydration. Furfural is an important industrial chemical used in the manufacture of nylon intermediates.

Major by-products of the beet sugar industry are beet pulp and beet molasses. The pulp is used almost exclusively for animal feed as are extensive amounts of molasses. Because of its high nitrogen content (higher than cane molasses), some beet molasses is used in specific fermentation processes, for example, citric acid production.

Steffenized beet molasses is an important raw material for the manufacture of monosodium glutamate,[3] an amino acid salt used as a flavor enhancer. Glutamic acid, occurring naturally in beet juice in a cyclic modification, accounts for well over half the approximate 20-million pound annual United States consumption of monosodium glutamate.

STARCH, DEXTROSE AND RELATED PRODUCTS

Although starch, like sugar, occurs in the plant, its removal is quite different from sugar and depends on the type of starch concerned. Root starches (potato) are prepared commercially by grinding or rasping the washed roots and separating the starch which sediments out from the rasped pulp residue. Separation is carried out in solid bowl centrifugal machines (Uhland protein-water separation); the starch is further purified by causing it to settle on long narrow tables and sieving it through 200-mesh silk screens. Bacteriological purity is maintained by addition of sulfur dioxide. The starch is dried in rotary, cascade, or tunnel driers; pulverized, screened, and packed.

Corn starch (maize), the most important commercial starch in the United States, is prepared somewhat differently. The field-dried corn (13 to 15 per cent moisture), grown primarily for animal feed, not for its starch content (about 65 per cent), is steeped in dilute sulfur dioxide solution (0.08 to 0.20 per cent SO_2) countercurrently for 40 to 48 hours at approximately 125° F. This serves to hydrate the corn and loosen the starch in its protein matrix. The corn then goes to Foos or coarse mills where it is cracked enough to loosen the germ which is removed by flotation. The germ is expressed or extracted for its oil content (corn oil). The residual hull and endosperm are carried to fine grinding mills (Buhr mills); the finely ground mass is put, successively, through copper reels and cloth (nylon) screens until the starch and protein (mill starch) fraction is separated from the fiber. The mill starch is separated into a high-starch low-protein fraction, and the starch is washed and dried as previously described. The gluten fraction may be extracted by isopropyl alcohol for the alcohol soluble prolamine, zein.

The dried starch may be sold as ordinary powdered or pearl starch, or it may be converted into partially hydrolyzed or thin-boiling starches, dextrines (pyrolyzed or slightly hydrolyzed starches), or oxidized (hypochlorite or peroxide) starches. Starches are also derivatized (ethers, esters) or cross-linked chemically to produce characteristically different properties within reasonable limits for a multitude of uses.

Starch which is to be hydrolyzed is not dried but passed to the refinery where it is hydrolyzed either in a batch operation in bronze pressure vessels called converters, or continuously as illustrated in Figure 16.7.

Hydrolysis to corn syrup is distinguished from hydrolysis to dextrose by the catalyst (hydrochloric or sulfuric acid) concentration, the holding time, and the starch concentration. Starch is a polysaccharide consisting essentially of anhydroglucose units ($C_6H_{19}O_5$) arranged in α-1,4 and α-1,6 linkages.*

In acid-catalyzed hydrolysis the starch chain is attacked randomly to give glucose, the ultimate monosaccharide; maltose, the disaccharide; and oligosaccharides of increasing size ranging from the higher sugars to the only slightly depolymerized starch generally referred to as dextrine. Since glucose also condenses in the presence of acid to form higher sugars, the hydrolysis process to glucose is limited by substrate concentration.

Corn syrup is partially hydrolyzed starch in which the D-glucose or dextrose content is about 25 per cent, the remainder being maltose, higher sugars, and dextrines. The total reducing value or D.E. is calculated as

---

* Most starches consist of a linear polymer, amylose (about 25 per cent) and a branched polymer, amylopectin (about 75 per cent). Exceptions are the genetic waxy starch varieties which contain only amylopectin. Geneticists have recently been able to produce corn varieties in which the amylose polymer is increased to nearly 90 per cent.

dextrose and is approximately 42. Corn syrup (CSU) is marketed as a viscous (43° Bé) product—a clarified, decolorized, concentrated hydrolyzate —and is either used in food manufacture or mixed with sugar syrups. Higher D.E. corn syrups are made by acid hydrolysis to a D.E. of 50 to 55; and by a combination of acid- and enzyme-catalyzed hydrolysis to a D.E. of 60 to 65.

In the manufacture of dextrose (D-glucose), starch is hydrolyzed at low concentration (10 to 12° Bé) in the presence of about 0.003 N hydrochloric or sulfuric acid. Hydrolysis time is about 30 minutes at 45 psig, and correspondingly less in the continuous converter. The hydrolyzate is clarified,

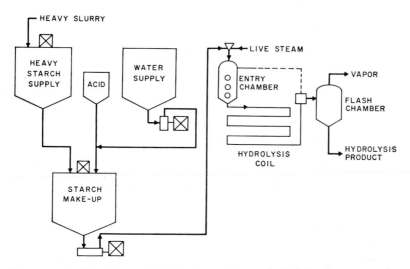

Figure 16.7. Flow of materials in the continuous hydrolysis of corn starch. [Reproduced from *Chem. Eng. Progr.*, **44**, 399 (1948).]

after neutralization with soda ash, by skimming and filtering; then it is partly concentrated (light liquor), passed through a thermally regenerable carbon for decolorization, concentrated again (heavy liquor), decolorized and evaporated to crystallizing gravity, cooled, and added to about 25 per cent seed (foots) contained in a slowly rotating, horizontal, water-cooled cylinder called a crystallizer. Crystallization as α-D-glucose or dextrose hydrate takes from 90 to 110 hours if the temperature is dropped to approximately 70° F. The crystals are removed, as in cane sugar manufacture, washed, dried, and packed. The process is usually a two-stage one in which the mother liquor from the first crystallization (greens) is reconverted, reprocessed as first liquor, and crystallized to give a second sugar; the mother liquor from that is called hydrol after concentration. Second sugar is remelted and mixed with first liquor for crystallization.

Recent modifications in processing involve enzyme hydrolysis of starch to dextrose. This promises to increase yield and minimize or eliminate hydrol.

Anhydrous dextrose in either the alpha (regular) or beta (quick solution) form is prepared from the hydrate by a crystallization process which, except for temperature control and rate of crystallization, is very much like sucrose crystallization.

Ion exchange refining has also been applied to dextrose processing and has been found to improve both the yield and quality of this sugar. Crude corn sugar, an important article of commerce, is made by allowing the concentrated sugar liquor to crystallize in slabs which are then mechanically chipped (chip sugar).

REFERENCES

1. Cantor, S. M., and Spitz, A. W., "Sugar Refining and By-Product Recovery," Chapter 18 in "Ion Exchange Technology," Nachod, F. C., and Schubert, Jack, Ed., New York, Academic Press, Inc., 1956.
2. *Chem. Met. Eng.*, **47**, 119 (1942).
3. Manning, D. D. V., Shafor, R. W., and Catterson, F. H., *Chem. Eng. Progr.*, **44**, 491 (1948).
4. Miller, R. E., and Cantor, S. M., *Advances in Carbohydrate Chem.*, **6**, 231 (1951).
5. U. S. Patents 1,989,156 and 2,091,690.

GENERAL REFERENCES

Prinsen Geerligs. H. C., "Cane Sugar and its Manufacture," London, Norman Rodger, 1924.

Spencer, G. L., and Meade, G. P., "Cane Sugar Handbook," New York, John Wiley & Sons, Inc., 1945.

Lyle, Oliver, "Technology for Sugar Refinery Workers," London, Chapman and Hall, Ltd., 1941.

"Polarimetry, Saccharimetry and the Sugars," Circular C 440, U. S. Dept. of Commerce, National Bureau of Standards, 1942.

Deerr, Noel, "Cane Sugar," London, Norman Rodger.

Honig, P., ed., "Principles of Sugar Technology," New York, Elsevier, 1953.

McGinnis, R. A., ed., "Beet Sugar Technology," New York, Reinhold Publishing Corp., 1951.

Hockett, R. E., "Sugar the Unknown," New York, Sugar Research Foundation, 1944.

Kerr, Ralph W., ed., "Chemistry and Industry of Starch," New York, Academic Press, Inc., 1953.

17

INDUSTRIAL GASES

In collaboration with R. M. Neary*

THE INDUSTRIAL GASES fall into two groups; hydrogen, helium, oxygen, nitrogen, argon and carbon monoxide, the less easily liquefiable gases; and chlorine, sulfur dioxide, ammonia, nitrous oxide, carbon dioxide, and ethyl chloride, the more easily compressible gases. At ordinary temperatures, the former do not liquefy in spite of considerable pressure whereas the latter at ordinary temperatures form liquids under rather moderate pressures; hence the content by weight of a standard cylinder for the gases in the first group will be small, for those in the second group, considerable. It follows that gases in the first group are generally used as free gases as soon as they are generated, or will be shipped short distances, from many plants, each serving a small territory; gases in the latter group may economically be shipped long distances, from a few central plants.

The distinction between the two groups is less sharp today, however. By 1939, oxygen in the liquid form was transported in tank cars and tank trucks. Nitrogen and argon similarly are transported over great distances in the liquid state. Liquid methane has been transported by boat from the United States to England. All of the above gases are now being transported in the liquid state. For miscellaneous industrial uses the familiar steel cylinder with its charge of compressed gas remains standard.

The producing and using of the ultra-low temperatures associated with

* Linde Company, New York.

TABLE 17.1. PROPERTIES OF INDUSTRIAL GASES*

Property	Oxygen	Nitrogen	Argon	Helium	Acetylene	Hydrogen	Neon	Krypton	Xenon	Carbon Dioxide
Molecular Weight	32.00	28.016	39.944	4.003	26.036	2.016	20.183	83.70	131.3	44.010
Boiling Point, 1 atm, °F	−297.3	−320.4	−302.5	−452.0	(S) −118.5†	−423.0	−410.9	−243.8	−162.5	(S) −109.17†
Latent Heat, Btu/lb	91.62	85.67	70.02	10.26	356‡	194.22	37.44	46.40	41.4	246.6‡
Critical Pressure, Atm.	49.7	33.5	47.99	2.26	62	12.8	26.86	54.18	58.20	72.92
Sp. Heat, Cp, at 70° F	0.219	0.248	0.125	1.251	0.400	3.418	0.25	0.06	0.04	0.2016
Cp/Cv, at 70° F	1.400	1.400	1.67	1.66	1.233	1.41	1.642	1.689	1.666	1.307

* Compiled from data in Catalog 300, Air Reduction Co., Inc. (1959).
† Sublimation temperature.
‡ Latent heat of sublimation.

liquid helium ($-269°$ C) and liquefied hydrogen ($-253°$ C) have opened up an entirely new scientific field commonly referred to as Cryogenics.

Acetylene, C_2H_2, lies midway between the two groups; it is in a class by itself, partly because its explosive nature requires that special precautions be taken in handling it.

In addition to a variety of technical uses, several members of the second group serve as ordinary refrigerants—ammonia, carbon dioxide, sulfur dioxide, and ethyl chloride; to these must be added the newer refrigerant, dichlorofluoromethane. Members of the first group are used as extraordinary refrigerants; for example, nitrogen in liquefaction of the carbon monoxide impurities in hydrogen.

HYDROGEN

During recent years hydrogen has become industrially important in the direct synthesis of ammonia, in the synthesis of hydrogen chloride, in the hydrogenation of fatty oils, of petroleum oil fractions, of coal, of hydrocarbons, of metallic hydrides, and single organic substances; its other uses are for balloons, and for hydrogen-air, hydrogen-oxygen, and atomic hydrogen flames. Liquefied hydrogen is used as a rocket fuel by the explorers of outer space.

It is obtained from water gas, producer gas, or coke-oven gas, by the removal of the non-hydrogen constituents; it is made by the catalytic action of steam on oil refinery gases and natural gas, by the thermal decomposition of natural gas, by steam on heated iron, by the electrolysis of water, and by miscellaneous processes. It is a by-product in the electrolytic cell for caustic,* in several fermentation processes, and in other types of processes. The choice of a process will be decided by the resources at hand, and by the degree of purity required. Rapid generation with a minimum of apparatus in an isolated place may be demanded; in such a case the steam-methanol process or the ferrosilicon process would serve.

The Water Gas and Steam Process (Continuous Catalytic Process). Water gas with steam in excess is passed over an iron oxide catalyst, just as is done in the Bosch process, except that since no producer gas is added, the amount of nitrogen is small. The converter has several trays, on which the catalyst rests. The reaction

$$CO + H_2O \rightarrow CO_2 + H_2$$

is exothermic; as the temperature must be maintained at $450°$ C ($842°$ F), the converters are insulated and the incoming gases heated in exchangers. Once the reaction has begun, no outside fuel is required. Three volumes of steam to one of gas are used; the great excess of steam drives the reaction

---

* Hydrogen from mercury cells for caustic has a slight contamination of mercury, which for certain uses, must be removed.

to the right. After passing the exchangers the reacted gas is freed from its steam by water-cooling. The carbon dioxide formed, as well as the small amount which entered with the water gas (4 per cent), is removed by scrubbing with cold water while under pressures of 25 to 30 atmospheres, in tall steel towers; under such pressures carbon dioxide is freely soluble in water. The gas leaving the last scrubber has the composition:

	Per Cent
Hydrogen	92–94
Nitrogen	1–4
Methane	0.5
Carbon monoxide	2–4
Carbon dioxide	small
Moisture	small

The crude hydrogen may be further purified from carbon monoxide by scrubbing in ammoniacal cuprous chloride solution. The nitrogen impurity may be lowered by careful operation of the water-gas plant. The methane is not wanted, and may be almost avoided by using well-burned coke.

A similar process in which the catalytic agent is lime at the temperature of 450° C (842° F) instead of iron oxide has been proposed; its great advantage is that the carbon dioxide is simultaneously removed. Unfortunately this absorption is accompanied by a powdering of the lime granules, as the carbonate forms, and the powder tends to clog the lime towers.

Water Gas Process with Liquefaction of the Carbon Monoxide. There are two processes in which the carbon monoxide in water gas is liquefied by cold and pressure and removed in that state, leaving the hydrogen gas comparatively pure. The Linde-Fränkl-Caro process uses liquid air boiling under a few millimeters of pressure for the final cooling of the water gas already precooled by three steps, first by an ammonia refrigerating system (−35° C or −31° F), then in an exchanger wherein the uncondensed hydrogen takes up heat, third by the liquid carbon monoxide separated in the final cooling. The carbon monoxide at the same time boils, and is used as a gaseous fuel. The other process is Claude's, which uses no liquid air, but obtains the necessary final cooling by the expansion of hydrogen from a pressure of 20 atmospheres to a lower pressure while doing work against a piston. The hydrogen is pre-cooled in exchangers by outgoing gases, and by the evaporation of the carbon monoxide which has been previously liquefied.

The hydrogen in coke-oven gas,[3] and in the gas from petroleum-cracking stills may be recovered by liquefaction of the non-hydrogen components.

Steam on Heated Iron. The interaction of steam and iron takes place at an elevated temperature, such as 650° C (1202° F) in a multiplicity of relatively small, upright steel cylindrical retorts. The iron packing is selected so as to have a porous structure and little tendency to disintegrate; a calcined iron carbonate (spathic ore) has been found suitable. A plant for the production of 3500 cubic feet (about 100 cubic meters) per hour would consist of three sets of 12 retorts each, each retort being 9 inches in diameter and 12 feet high. The action is intermittent. The steaming period (hydrogen production) lasts 10 minutes (upward travel of steam).

$$3Fe + 4H_2O \rightarrow Fe_3O_4 + 4H_2$$

The iron oxide formed is reduced by water gas, for example, and the water gas period lasts 20 minutes (downward travel), because the reduction of the oxide is slower than the oxidation of the iron. A brief purging with steam sends the first hydrogen to the water gas holder. By the stepwise operation of such a plant a continuous flow of hydrogen is obtained. The spent water gas is cooled and burned (for it still contains combustible gases) around the retorts to maintain the reaction temperature. The steam reaction is exothermic; the over-all reduction by the water gas is endothermic.

The hydrogen passes out with the great excess of steam which is employed to drive the reaction to the right; it is cooled to remove the steam, and freed from carbon dioxide and hydrogen sulfide by lime purifiers. The gas obtained is 98.5 to 99 per cent pure; by careful purging, using closed condensers instead of scrubbing towers, and other modifications, the purity may be raised to 99.94 per cent. The steam-iron process is used chiefly in connection with the hydrogenation of fatty oils. The iron mass lasts six months, the retorts one year.

For the production of 1 volume of hydrogen, the continuous catalytic process requires 1.25 volumes of water gas, the liquefaction process (CO liquefied) 2.5 volumes, and the steam-on-heated-iron process, also 2.5 volumes.

Electrolysis of Water. In commercial cells, the direct current is passed between iron electrodes, which may be nickel-plated, suspended in a bath consisting of a 10 to 25 per cent caustic soda or potassium hydroxide solution. Only distilled water is added to the cells, for the electrolyte is not consumed. Cells differ in the method of gathering the hydrogen (at cathode) and the oxygen (at anode), in size, and in details of construction. The efficiency is close to 7.5 cubic feet of hydrogen per kilowatt hour, and 3.8 cubic feet of oxygen.

The decomposition voltage for the reaction $H_2O \rightarrow H_2 + \frac{1}{2}O_2$ is 1.48; the operating voltage about 2. The amperage varies with the size and intensity of operation; with maximum load, it may be as much as 1000 amperes for electrodes 40 inches wide and 60 inches high, with a number of electrodes in each cell. The electrodes are separated by an asbestos diaphragm, and suspended in cast-iron containers.

Other Processes and By-Product Hydrogen. Hydrogen gas is also prepared by the thermal decomposition of natural gas. The operation is a cracking of the gas, and is performed in apparatus similar to those used for making water gas. A five-minute cycle is used: the gas is burned to heat up the checkerwork in the generator (2 min.); then the gas, without air, is passed in. Elemental hydrogen gas with suspended carbon particles forms; the carbon is filtered out in bag filters. After 2 minutes, the generator is too cool, and the cycle is repeated.

In the oil industry, hydrogen may be prepared from hydrocarbons in the refinery gases, or in available natural gas, by treating with steam, with or without a catalyst. The reaction is

$$CH_4 + 2H_2O \rightarrow 4H_2 + CO_2$$

For the reaction

$$CH_4 + H_2O \rightarrow CO + 3H_2$$

the catalyst nickel-magnesia, and the temperature 800° C are suitable.

In the ferrosilicon process, powdered ferrosilicon containing as much silicon as possible (90 per cent is frequent) is added to a 20 per cent solution of caustic soda at a temperature of 80° to 90° C; very pure hydrogen is produced. Aluminum in the form of shavings also gives hydrogen with a solution of caustic soda. An alloy of sodium and lead reacts with water to give hydrogen, again of high purity (hydrone). These three processes serve for military purposes and as supplementary plants for emergency or rapid operations. In addition to these, portable hydrogen manufacturing plants carried on trucks were built for Army use in the recent war, in which methanol and steam react catalytically to produce hydrogen and carbon dioxide. The reaction is exothermic, and outside heat is furnished by flue gases which pass through the converter, heating the outside of the catalyst-containing tubes. The temperature in the converter is 500° F (260° C). The carbon dioxide produced

$$CH_3OH + H_2O \rightarrow 3H_2 + CO_2$$

is scrubbed out in a monoethanolamine solution.

Liquefied hydrogen is assuming increased importance as a fuel for rocket engines and is being produced in tonnage quantity for this purpose. It boils at minus 252.9° C and is transparent, odorless and one-fourteenth as heavy as water; it weighs 0.59 pound per gallon.

Liquefied hydrogen is produced by liquefaction of very pure hydrogen gas, using liquid nitrogen, expansion engines and other ultra-low temperature techniques. The hydrogen gas is produced from natural gas or other sources and it is purified by low temperature techniques.

Recent improvements in insulation has made it possible to transport liquefied hydrogen in vacuum insulated tank cars, tank trucks and cylinders (similar to Fig. 17.5) without liquid nitrogen shields.

OXYGEN

Oxygen is vitally important to industry, medicine, and explorers of outer space because it is one of the primary tools of their trade. It is well established as a basic industrial chemical with a production of 3,275,000 tons in 1959. Some 57% of this was exceptionally high purity (99.5%) and the remainder had a purity well above that of most industrial chemicals, being 95 to 99%. The latter is often referred to as low purity, "tonnage" or "combustion" oxygen.

The primary use of oxygen stems from its ability to support combustion and to sustain animal life. Materials that burn in air burn faster in oxygen. Thus, the use of oxygen or oxygen enriched air in place of ordinary air in many metallurgical and chemical processes increases the intensity and speed of reaction, resulting in shorter cycle time, greater yield per volume of equipment and lower costs.

Over one million tons of oxygen are used in the production of ingot steel—in open hearth, blast furnaces, and the basic process. Another 340 thousand tons are used in the processing and fabrication of steel mostly in conjunction with the oxygen-acetylene flame. Oxygen is used for the "cracking" of methane or natural gas by partial oxidation to produce acetylene, an important basic chemical. It serves as a raw material for synthesizing oxygen compounds (ethylene oxide, sodium peroxide).

The missile industry consumes large volumes of liquid oxygen in the testing and firing of rocket motors. Oxygen, stored as a liquid and converted to gas as used, provides a dry supply for aviator's breathing apparatus at high altitudes. Medicinal and breathing oxygen is piped from a central supply to rooms in most hospitals where it is administered to patients by tent, mask and catheter. Most high purity oxygen sold for industrial purposes is sufficiently pure to meet the requirements of United States Pharmacopoeia for breathing purposes.

Production

The oxygen industry is unique in that its raw material is available in abundance everywhere for over 99% of it is obtained from atmospheric air, the remainder from the electrolysis of water. Generally, oxygen is produced by liquefying air and then separating it into its components, (oxygen, nitrogen, and argon), by fractional distillation.

There are three fundamental steps in the production of oxygen: purification, refrigeration, rectification. Purification is the removal of dust, water vapor, carbon dioxide and hydrocarbon contaminants. Refrigeration in an oxygen plant means cooling the compressed air until it becomes a liquid at about $-190°$ C. Rectification is the separation of liquid air into its components, oxygen and nitrogen, by repeated distillation. In actual practice, these three steps overlap or are performed at the same time.

Purification

The atmosphere holds dirt, water vapor, and carbon dioxide which must be removed from the compressed air stream as these would "plug up" the rectification column. Purification can be accomplished in three ways: chemical method, mechanical method, or a combination of both. Mechanical filters are usually employed ahead of the compressor to remove atmospheric dirt. An example of chemical purification is the removal of carbon dioxide by passing air up through towers filled with coke, down which a solution of caustic soda or caustic potash travels; also a sodium hydroxide solution will remove carbon dioxide from the air.

Removal of impurities from a large volume of air by chemical methods is expensive. Thus, mechanical methods are employed in modern plants. Water vapor is removed in traps. Ice and solid carbon dioxide are removed in cold heat exchangers, reversing heat exchangers and various types of filters.

Refrigeration

All plants cool the incoming compressed air by transferring heat to the cooler outgoing plant's waste and product in counter-current heat exchangers. Also, in liquid producing plants, the incoming air is cooled by a conventional refrigerant, such as ammonia. After purification and preliminary cooling, the air is refrigerated by expansion which may partially liquefy the air.

Figure 17.1 illustrates the fundamental refrigeration cycles used in all air separation plants today. The left side of Figure 17.1 shows the expansion of air through a throttle valve or nozzle which produces a drop in pressure with a corresponding drop in temperature. This is a constant enthalpy process called a Joule-Thompson expansion. As it passes through the expansion valve some of the air is liquefied. The liquid air is then transferred to a separator or distillation column. This simple liquefaction process was utilized in Dr. Karl Linde's first cycle for the commercial separation of air.

A second method of producing refrigeration in air is to expand it in an engine, doing useful work, for the temperature is reduced because of the removal of energy. The temperature reduction is greater than for a Joule-Thompson effect, making the system more efficient and better adapted to large-scale plants.

This cycle, known as the Claude principle, does not produce liquid air, as liquid would damage the machine.

The cycles used in many production plants today employ both of the above refrigerating techniques. About 40% of the air is expanded in a turbo or

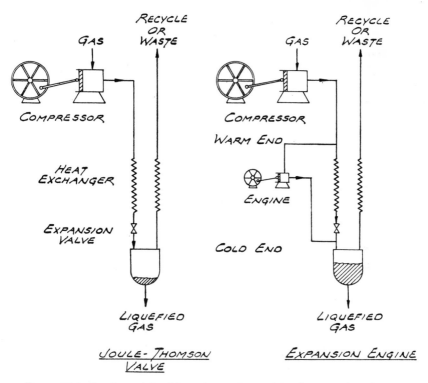

Figure 17.1. Fundamental refrigeration cycles used in air separation plants.

reciprocating expander. Since some of the air is expanded in the engine a smaller portion is left to be cooled in the counter-current heat exchanger. Consequently, the incoming air can be cooled to a lower temperature, with the net result that a much greater fraction of the air is liquefied by the expansion valve.

Rectification

For practical purposes air may be considered a binary mixture of oxygen and nitrogen. As illustrated in Table 17.2, nitrogen boils at $-195.8°$ C and oxygen at $-183°$ C, so the difference in boiling points is almost $13°$ C. It is upon this fact that fractionation is based.

If a body of liquid air is warmed, the initial gas released is 93% nitrogen and 7% oxygen, leaving a liquid that becomes richer in oxygen. The last liquid to be evaporated would be about 45% oxygen. Also when air is condensed, the first droplets in equilibrium with the air are about 45% oxygen.

The distillation column consists essentially of a cylindrical shell that contains trays spaced at regular intervals. These trays are perforated metal, permitting the liquid to pass transversely over the trays while the gas rises through the perforations and bubbles through the liquid. This brings the liquid and gas into intimate contact. The lower boiling constituents, particularly nitrogen, are boiled off at each tray so the gas going up the column becomes richer in nitrogen. At the same time the higher boiling constituents, particularly oxygen, are condensed at each tray so that the liquid becomes richer in oxygen. With a single column, 99.5% oxygen accumulates at the bottom, but the waste gas at the top is 93% nitrogen and 7% oxygen, representing an efficiency of only 66%.

All commercial plants employ a double rectification column separated by a boiler-condenser. The lower or high pressure column operates at 75 to 90 psi, while the upper column operates at 10 to 12 psi. The physical principle

TABLE 17.2. COMPOSITION OF AIR

Atmospheric air contains:

	Per Cent by Volume	Boiling Point °C
Nitrogen	78.14	−195.8
Oxygen	20.93	−183.0
Argon	0.93	−186.0
Carbon dioxide	0.03	− 73.3 (Solidifies)
Water vapor (not included)	amounts variable	0° (Solidifies)

for operation of the double column is that increased pressure on a liquid increases its boiling point. The temperature of the 10 psi liquid oxygen on the outside of the tubes in the condenser is lower than the boiling (or condensing) point of nitrogen at 75 psi. Thus the oxygen boils producing vapor for the upper column while the nitrogen gas in the high pressure column that reaches the reboiler is condensed. It flows down over the trays in the lower column becoming increasingly rich in oxygen. The distillation in the lower column produces high purity nitrogen at the condenser and oxygen-enriched liquid at the bottom. Each of these liquids is transferred to the upper column after being refrigerated through an expansion valve.

The high purity nitrogen liquid is introduced at the top of the low pressure column where it acts as a reflux to strip out oxygen. As a result, relatively high purity nitrogen gas is vented from the top of the upper column so that the oxygen recovery efficiency for a double rectification column is about 90 per cent.

Liquid Oxygen

About 25 companies operate about 60 plants that produce liquid oxygen—all high purity. When the oxygen is produced as a liquid, a large quantity of refrigeration is removed from the cycle with the product and therefore, is not available to cool the incoming air. Thus, cycles for liquid oxygen must develop large amounts of refrigeration. This is accomplished by the Heylandt

Cycle which includes compression of the air to a very high pressure and use of external refrigeration.

It will be noted that the Heylandt Cycle makes use of both the Linde principle of cooling by expansion from a high to a low pressure through a valve (Joule-Thompson effect), and the Claude principle of the conversion of energy (heat) into work by the expansion of a gas in an engine (or turbine). Figure 17.2 gives details of the cycle as used in most liquid plants today.

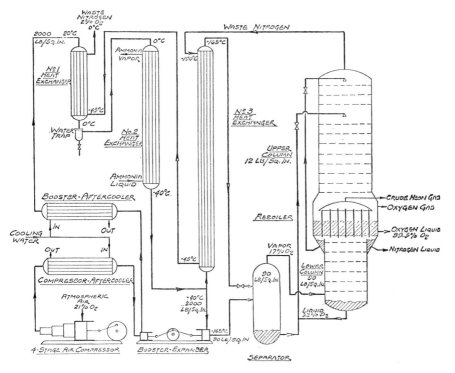

Figure 17.2. Air separation plant for liquid oxygen production. (*Courtesy The Linde Co.*)

The air is compressed to about 1500 psig in a 4-stage compressor and cooled in conventional water-cooled intercoolers and aftercoolers. The cooled air is compressed to 2000 psi in a fifth stage in a booster-expander, which will be explained later. The air is cooled to room temperature in an aftercooler and delivered to the heat exchanger section, consisting of three units.

In No. 1, the air is not permitted to cool below the freezing point of water. This permits most of the water to be condensed out and drained off through the water trap at the bottom of the unit. The cooling agent here is waste nitrogen. It enters the heat exchanger at about —45° C and leaves at about zero. This heat exchanger operates with a relatively large temperature difference.

The high pressure air then enters the No. 2 heat exchanger, often called a forecooler, and is cooled by the evaporation of liquid ammonia or other refrigerant that is processed in an ordinary refrigeration system. This cools the air to about —40° C. and freezes out any remaining water. Eventually this heat exchanger becomes plugged with ice and must be thawed out. Consequently, the No. 2 heat exchanger is provided in duplicate.

The air stream leaving the No. 2 heat exchanger is divided, 60 per cent passing through the No. 3 heat exchanger where it is cooled to an extremely low temperature, about —165° C. The air does not liquefy under these conditions because it is at a pressure of 2,000 psig, well in excess of the critical pressure of air (530 psig). This extremely cold air fluid is expanded through a valve to about 90 psig, which liquefies a sizable fraction of the air.

The 40 per cent portion of air that does not go through the No. 3 heat exchanger is expanded in an engine to about the same temperature and pressure it would have reached in the heat exchanger. The air expanded in the engine is still gaseous. The work done by the engine is absorbed by direct coupling with the compression cylinder of the booster compressor mentioned before. This expanded air stream enters the separator along with the throttled stream from the heat exchanger and the two are mixed together.

The vapor which leaves this separator is only about 17 per cent oxygen. Since the liquid formed is in equilibrium with the vapor in contact with it, it is about 32 per cent oxygen, much richer in oxygen than the entering air.

The liquid and vapor products of the separation are dealt with individually. The vapor stream enters at the bottom of the lower rectifying column at 90 psi. The liquid stream is combined with a similar liquid stream leaving the lower column, and the two are throttled to the pressure of the upper column (about 12 psig). The liquid stream then enters the middle of the upper column. The double rectification column previously described is used to separate the gases. The liquid oxygen accumulates in the main condenser and is piped through filters to an insulated storage tank.

Since liquid oxygen is continuously fed from the main condenser, the traces of hydrocarbon contaminants such as acetylene are drained off with the oxygen. Thus, elaborate hydrocarbon removal systems are not needed in liquid producing plants.

Gaseous Oxygen

Recent developments have made it possible to produce low-cost gaseous oxygen in large quantities. This has made is economically feasible to use oxygen extensively in many steel-making and chemical processes. Oxygen-enriched air can be made economically by mixing the low cost oxygen with appropriate volumes of air.

Gaseous oxygen is expensive to transport so these plants are built adjacent to the consuming plant, and are commonly referred to as "On Site" plants. In the late 1950's, the oxygen producing facilities of the nation were more than doubled, and most of the expansion was by "On Site" plants. These plants are equipped with modern instruments to improve their operating efficiency. Many facilities are completely automatic and operate unattended. In such cases, signal lights that indicate any operating difficulty are installed in the customers plant where they are continuously observed.

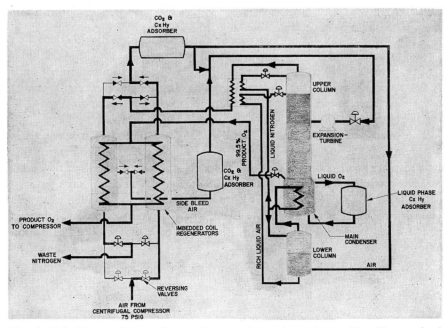

Figure 17.3. Process diagram for an air separation unit producing 80 million cu ft of oxygen per month. (*Courtesy The Linde Co.*)

These new large scale oxygen plants are being designed to produce a number of products to meet customer demands. These include high purity oxygen, 99.5%; low purity oxygen, 95%, high purity nitrogen, 99.85% for ammonia synthesis, and argon. Figure 17.3 illustrates the fundamental cycle used in many modern plants. Air is compressed to about 75 psig in a centrifugal compressor, cooled in an aftercooler and freed of liquid water. It then enters a regenerator (installed in pairs) where it is cooled to the saturation temperature. The air is then processed to remove small amounts of contaminating solids as well as the vapor phase carbon dioxide and some hydrocarbons. The air then enters the lower column without any expansion.

To maintain self-cleaning conditions in the regenerators and to provide a preheat stream to the turbine, some air is withdrawn at the −100 to

—120° C level. This air is cleaned of carbon dioxide and its temperature adjusted so that the turbine discharge temperature remains just above the liquid region. The turbine discharge goes to the middle of the low pressure column. It should be noted that the refrigeration for this cycle employs primarily the Claude principle of conversion of energy (heat) into work by the expansion of gas in a turbine.

The conventional double column with condenser-reboiler is used to separate the gases. The rich liquid air and the liquid nitrogen from the lower column are subcooled by waste nitrogen prior to transfer to the upper column. From this heat exchanger the waste nitrogen goes through the regenerators where it picks up heat, water vapor and carbon dioxide deposited by the incoming air.

The gaseous oxygen product in high purity plants passes through coils or heat exchangers heated by the incoming air. In low purity plants, the oxygen passes through a pair of reversing regenerators similar to those used for nitrogen.

The temperature of the waste nitrogen and product oxygen leaving the regenerators is a few degrees below that of the incoming air so that in this type of plant most of the refrigeration is recovered. However, since no liquid oxygen is withdrawn from the reboiler, hydrocarbon contaminants tend to concentrate in the liquid oxygen. Thus, it is necessary to remove all traces of hydrocarbons from the reboiler liquid. This is often done by continuous recirculation of liquid through an adsorption trap, using silica gel as the adsorbent.

In the Linde-Frankl system, the unbalance is secured in another way. Part of the incoming air is compressed to 200 atmospheres, precooled with ammonia, cooled with a special stream of cold nitrogen, and cooled further by expansion in a valve, after which it is introduced into the upper column. In this way, the unbalance is provided by supplying a larger volume of nitrogen to cool a smaller volume of air than the normal one. There are still other methods.

Regenerators are cylindrical shells packed with channels, rings, or aluminum, and set up in pairs. In the pair marked "2" in Figure 17.4, nitrogen travels up the right hand regenerator, cooling it while air travels down the left hand regenerator, "picking up cold." In the right-hand vessel of the pair marked "3," oxygen travels upward, while air travels down in the vessel at the left, "picking up cold." The unbalance is produced as explained previously; the amount of revert gases traversing the accumulator is greater in mass than the entering air.

Distribution

Most people are familiar with the steel cylinders in industry and hospitals where the oxygen is contained at very high pressure (1800–2200 psi). The

large cylinders which have a water volume of about 1.5 cubic feet hold
244 cubic feet of oxygen measured at atmospheric temperature and pressure.
These cylinders weigh about 125 pounds and contain about 15 pounds of
product. Thus, the ratio of the weight of lading to weight of container is
about 1 to 8, an uneconomical ratio. Oxygen is also transported at these
high pressures in clusters of high pressure cylinders and long tubes permanently mounted on semi-trailers. Although the production costs of gaseous

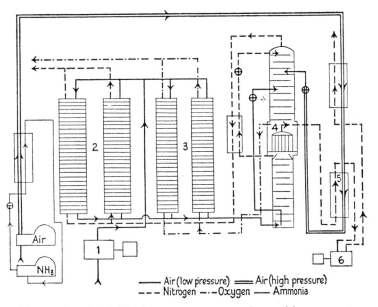

Figure 17.4. Linde-Fränkl tonnage oxygen plant, with recuperators,
working in pairs. The air for unbalance is the double line, leading
finally to the upper column of the rectifier. The main body of air is
compressed at 1. (*From Ruhemann, "The Separation of Gases"*)[3a]

oxygen are considerably less than for liquid oxygen, the transportation costs
are usually higher because of the heavy containers employed.

The lowest cost oxygen available today is produced in large volume gaseous oxygen plants. As mentioned in the previous section, most of these are
installed at the consumer's plant. However, recently, pipelines similar to
natural gas pipelines have been employed to transport gaseous oxygen at
moderate pressure (200 psi) from a central large-capacity plant to several
nearby industrial users. This type of installation incorporates low-cost
production plus low-cost distribution.

Oxygen, nitrogen and argon are transported commercially as pressurized
liquids in ICC 4L cylinders. The cylinders have a built-in or attached vaporizer that automatically converts liquid to gas as the products are withdrawn.

One cubic foot of liquid oxygen when evaporated or warmed to atmospheric temperature and pressure will produce 862 cubic feet of gaseous oxygen. Thus the Linde LC-3, shown in Figure 17.5, weighs about 250 pounds and contains about 250 pounds of lading. It has a weight-of-lading to weight-of-container ratio of 1 to 1 as compared to 1 to 8 for the high pressure cylinder. This vessel contains the equivalent of 12 high pressure

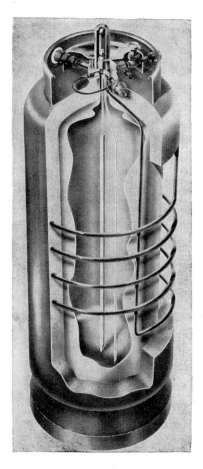

Figure 17.5. LC-3 cutaway view. (*Courtesy The Linde Co.*)

cylinders while occupying about ⅓ of the floor area, and weighing ¼ as much (a weight saving of about ½ ton). It is about the same size and weight as a 55-gallon drum and can be moved with the same ease.

The vessel will stand several days with no withdrawal and no release of oxygen because of the unusually good properties of the fiber-glass-aluminum laminate insulation, the conductivity of which is about 5×10^{-4} Btu/hr/ sq ft/° F. This is about ¼ the value for 6 inches of powder-vacuum insulation or about 150 times better than 4 inches of cork.

Actually, liquid oxygen is pumped and handled in much the same manner as water except that the pumps and containers are well insulated (see Figure 17.6). This liquid is normally transferred from the transport equipment to the storage tank by connecting a single pipe or hose to the liquid phase of the transport container. Pumps are used to transfer the liquid if the pressure in the receiving container is much above atmospheric pressure. If the storage tank operates at essentially atmospheric pressure, the transfer of liquid is often made by building a small amount of pressure in the transport vessel.

Figure 17.6. Containers for liquid oxygen. (*Courtesy The Linde Co.*)

Actually liquid oxygen has been transported by tank truck since 1932 and by tank car since 1939. It is estimated that in 1960 there were about 500 tank trucks and an equal number of tank cars in liquid oxygen service.

Customer storage tanks range in capacity from 25,000 cubic feet (220 gallons) to 10 million cubic feet (86,700 gallons). (The capacity of a tank is usually expressed as equivalent cubic feet of gaseous product at 70° F and one atmosphere.)

NITROGEN

The economical way to utilize liquefied air is to make use of both the oxygen and the nitrogen. This is not always possible. In general, oxygen plants liquefy air, save the oxygen and waste the nitrogen while the manufacturer of cyanamide, for example, uses the nitrogen and is willing to waste the oxygen. There are increasing demands for nitrogen, however, as well as for oxygen. Nitrogen for the direct ammonia synthesis is frequently made from liquid air. Liquid nitrogen which boils at $-195.8°$ C at atmospheric pressure is used as such for shrink-fitting of parts, storage of biologicals such as whole blood and bull semen, and the refrigeration of frozen foods. Liquid nitrogen is transported in its own special containers, similar in construction to the liquid oxygen containers.

HELIUM

Most of the helium produced for commercial use is obtained from certain natural gases. About 95 per cent of the known helium-bearing natural gases in the United States are contained in four helium-bearing gas fields: the Hugoton field of Kansas, Oklahoma, and Texas; the Panhandle field of Texas; the Greenwood field of Kansas; and the Keyes field of Oklahoma.

The rapidly increasing use of helium heavily taxed the production facilities which are operated exclusively by the U. S. Bureau of Mines. However, in 1959, operations were resumed at the Bureau's plant in Shiprock, New Mexico, when supplies of suitable natural gas became available. In addition, a new plant went on stream at Keyes, Oklahoma, with a capacity of 290-million-cu ft/yr. It is expected that this plant and the other facilities will keep production ahead of demand until about 1963. Total production of helium at Bureau of Mines plants amounted to 477 million cubic feet in 1959, an increase of 43 per cent over 1958.

Production

The Keyes plant takes gas from a natural gas pipeline (the gas contains about 2 per cent of helium), recovers the helium and returns the stripped gas to the line. In general, the process involves two phases; (a) production of crude helium; (b) purification.

A recent article[1] describes the process which includes the following: (1) scrubbing the natural gas to remove water and condensed hydrocarbons; (2) dust removal; (3) CO_2 removal in a scrubbing tower; (4) drying; (5) chilling to liquefy and remove the natural gas; (6) rectification of the gaseous materials from (5) to produce the crude (75% He, 25% N_2, 0.1% each of H_2 and CH_4) helium.

The pure helium is obtained from the crude by: (1) oxidizing the hydrogen with air; (2) removing the water formed by the oxidation; and (3) removing the last traces of hydrogen and nitrogen with activated charcoal. The final product is 99.99 plus per cent pure.

Liquid helium boils at 4.26° K. and this ultra-low temperature can liquefy any other gas. It is being used increasingly in laboratory work for investigating the properties of matter at ultra-low temperatures. These include the study of super-conductivity, cryogenic chemistry, and as a moderator of high energy beams.

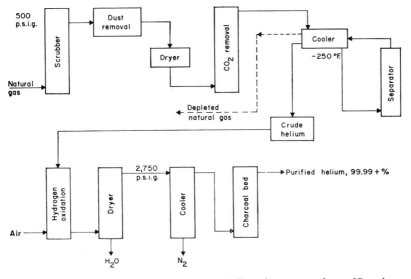

Figure 17.7. Flow diagram for recovery of helium from natural gas. [*Based on a drawing in Chem. Eng., 67, No. 15, 96–97 (1960).*]

Helium may be liquefied by the low temperature techniques used for hydrogen. Liquid helium also is transported in vacuum insulated tank trucks and cylinders, with and without liquid nitrogen shielding.

ARGON

Mass markets for argon are a recent development resulting chiefly from the development of gas-shielded arc-welding processes. These are used to join hard-to-weld metals such as aluminum, bronze, copper, Monel and stainless steels. Once considered a "rare" gas, argon is available in tonnage quantities. The metals titanium and zirconium, which are finding wide application in our nuclear-space technology, depend heavily on argon or helium for their production. An inert gas envelops the manufacturing process for these metals from start to finish. These metals must also be welded under an inert atmosphere.

Argon is also used in incandescent lamp bulbs, in fluorescent luminous tubes, and in the manufacture, of various semi-conductor devices.

Production

Argon is relatively scarce; it represents only 1.4 per cent by weight of the earth's atmosphere. However, the advanced technology developed to produce other atmospheric gases in quantity permits the recovery of this "rare" gas in tonnage quantities. The boiling point of argon, under conditions used in the fractional distillation of liquid air, lies between the boiling points of oxygen and nitrogen. The first argon fraction contains both oxygen and nitrogen. The former is removed by catalytic combination with hydrogen and the residual nitrogen is removed by liquefaction. Welding grade argon is produced at a purity of about 99.995 per cent.

RARE GASES

The rare or "noble" gases include krypton, xenon, neon, helium, and argon. The availability of helium (other than atmospheric) and argon in large quantities makes the designation "rare" a misnomer insofar as these two are concerned. However, atmospheric helium is rare, as is argon specially purified for particular applications; the terminology for argon and helium appears to be a matter of philosophy. All these gases are characterized by extreme chemical inertness and some of them, primarily neon, krypton, and xenon, ionize or become electrically conducting at a substantially lower voltage than other gases. While passing current they also emit a brilliant colored light used to advantage in the tubular display signs so prominent in what has been termed the "neon jungle."

Present commercial applications for the rare gases rely principally on their inertness. They are used singly or in mixtures by the electronics industry in gas-filled electronic tubes. The lamp industry uses all the rare gases, including atmospheric helium and specially purified argon as fill gas in specialty lamps, neon and argon glow lamps, high output lamps, and others. The gases are also used as fill gas for ionization chambers, bubble chambers, and related devices.

Production

Partial separation of the rare gases is accomplished by the same liquefaction-fractional distillation process used to produce most other industrial gases. Final purification requires the use of special processes and equipment.

ACETYLENE

Acetylene is an important industrial gas. The oxygen-acetylene flame produces the highest temperature of any combustible gas, hence its great value in welding and cutting of steel and other metals. A large volume of acetylene is being used at present as a basic raw material in the chemical industry for the production of synthetic rubber-like materials, flexible vinyl plastics, rigid plastics, paints and textile finishes, to name a few. Acetylene is generally made by the action of water on calcium carbide, a product of the electric furnace:

$$CaC_2 + 2H_2O \rightarrow C_2H_2 + Ca(OH)_2$$

Acetylene,   Hydrated lime,
a gas   a by-product

One method of distribution is by means of portable steel tanks, containing a porous solid filler saturated with acetone, in which the acetylene is dissolved by pressure. Acetylene alone is not compressed to pressures higher than 2 atmospheres because of its tendency to decompose explosively; dissolved in acetone it may be under pressures of 10 to 15 atmospheres with safety. In order to fill the cylinders, the acetylene gas is dried over calcium chloride and compressed in a slow compressor (60 rpm). Several cylinders are connected at one time to the compressor and occasionally shut off to allow time for the solution in acetone.

In cases where the rate of consumption is high, it is sometimes feasible for the user to install and operate his own acetylene generator. This equipment reacts calcium carbide with water to produce acetylene gas. Calcium carbide is normally available in 100-pound drums, and in larger containers holding 250, 300, 500, and 600 pounds and 2½ and 5 tons.

In the low-pressure generator, the pressure is below 6 pounds; in the "high-pressure" generators, it must not exceed 15 lbs per sq in. Carbide is fed a little at a time to a body of water. The volume of gas generated may be as low as 1 cubic foot an hour.

Large industrial establishments employ "dry generation" of the gas, in which a small continuous stream of water is added to the carbide; a mechanical agitator stirs the residual carbide and the dry lime formed, to prevent "hot spots." The ratio is about 1 pound of water to 1 pound of carbide, with the production of 0.31 pound of acetylene.

There are two kinds of welding torches, high pressure and low pressure, and they differ in important details. Cutting torches differ from welding torches in the following way: in addition to the oxygen and acetylene conduits, which both torches have, the cutting torch receives a stream of oxygen around the flame; it is this oxygen which cuts the steel, by oxidizing it and forcing away the particles of oxide formed; the flame serves merely to attain the oxidizing temperature. The flame in each has an inner brilliant part, whose temperature is estimated at 3000° C.; in the welding torch this is surrounded by a larger envelope into which the air penetrates. The inner portion, which does the welding, is sometimes called the neutral part. The use of acetylene is not without danger; the directions and cautions of the manufacturer must be observed.

The oxyacetylene torch has many uses besides the welding and cutting of steel. It serves for metal cladding, in certain special circumstances; for steel conditioning, pressure welding, flame spinning, and flame hardening. In the shaping of synthetic sapphire and ruby (hexagonal crystals of alumina) the torch is in constant application. The synthetic ruby, for example, is obtainable in the form of slim rods and boules (balls); the rods when heated in the torch may be bent, in the form of a thread guide, let us say, which is a complete loop. At the same time, the material acquires a flame finish of extreme smoothness. Ruby in rod form is made into precision gauges. It is made into extrusion dies, phonograph needles, and knife edges on balances.

Economic petrochemical processes have been developed for the manufacture of acetylene and now account for an important percentage of the total acetylene production. (See Chapters 14, 25.)

Acetylene undergoes a number of reactions which are the bases of several large industries. Acetylene as a chemical substance is presented in Chapter 25.

CARBON DIOXIDE

Sources

Carbon dioxide is used commercially as a gas (soda ash manufacture), compressed as a liquid in steel cylinders (soda fountains, for refrigeration, and as convenient source of the gas), and as the solid. It is obtained from (1) the combustion of coke; (2) the calcination of limestone; (3) as a by-product in syntheses involving carbon monoxide; (4) as a by-product in fermentations; (5) by the action of sulfuric acid on dolomite; (6) from wells. Gas from any one of these sources may be made into the gaseous, liquid, or solid form of carbon dioxide.

The utilization of the carbon dioxide in the combustion gases of coke involves the alternate formation and decomposition of alkali bicarbonates in solution. Hard coke is burned under boilers and the fuel gases are so regulated that a maximum content of carbon dioxide, 16 to 17 per cent, is obtained. The gases enter a scrubber (tower) packed with limestone to remove sulfur compounds and fed with water to cool the gas and arrest the dust. The cold gases enter the absorber, a tower packed with coke down which a solution of potassium carbonate passes; carbon dioxide is absorbed, and the saturated solution is run to a boiler where the absorbed gas is liberated by heat. It is under this boiler that the coke is burned. The operation is continuous; charged solution flows in constantly, while the spent liquor is run off constantly. By means of an interchanger, the outgoing liquor heats the incoming liquor to some extent. The outgoing liquor, cold, returns to the absorber. The gas from the boiler is very pure. It is dried in a calcium chloride tower, and compressed to 100 atmospheres, at which pressure it liquefies at ordinary temperatures. (See Figure 17.8.)

In addition to the uses which have been mentioned, carbon dioxide serves as a chemical in the manufacture of salicylic acid, white lead, and other products, as well as in fire fighting devices of various kinds. Fire extinguishers of the wall type, also called the soda-acid type, contain $2\frac{1}{2}$ gallons of saturated sodium bicarbonate solution and 4 ounces of concentrated sulfuric acid in a small bottle. On inversion, the acid reaches the solution and liberates carbon dioxide; the pressure developed expels the liquid through a nozzle to a distance of 30 to 40 feet. The main extinguishing agent is the

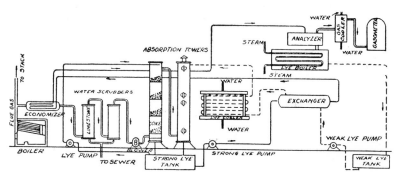

Figure 17.8. Diagrammatic flow sheet for the absorption of carbon dioxide in the fire gases from burning coke. The gas dissolves in a strong lye solution, from which it is driven out by heat, giving 100% CO_2 gas. (*Courtesy Frick Co., Waynesboro, Pa.*)

water. Liquid carbon dioxide under pressure in steel cylinders may be released so that a carbon dioxide snow forms which may be directed into the gaseous blanket over the fire. The "firefoam" extinguisher system relies upon the smothering action of a foam blanket produced by the interaction of a sodium bicarbonate solution with an alum solution, in the presence of a foam stabilizer.

Solid carbon dioxide is obtainable in commercial quantities. It is supplied in block form resembling the familiar artificial ice cake. Its uses are similar to the uses of ice, but it functions without melting, and without producing drips; it vaporizes, and leaves only a gas, which may be easily vented, so that it has received the rather apt name of "Dry Ice." Its manufacture will be described for the case of a particular plant.

Pure, liquid carbon dioxide under a pressure of 1000 pounds and at a temperature of 70° F (21° C), is delivered to the plant by a pipe system. It is sent to the "evaporator" (Figure 17.9), where its pressure is reduced to 500 pounds, with a simultaneous drop in temperature to 32° F (0° C).

With the pressure set at 500 pounds, the liquid maintains itself at that temperature; as this is lower by several degrees than the room temperature, heat flows in and causes the liquid to simmer quietly. About 25% of it boils away. The vaporized portion is sent to a special compressor which delivers it as gas to the main compressor gas line, at a pressure of 1000 lbs.

The 32° F liquid from the evaporator is admitted to the press chambers; these have movable tops and bottoms, worked by hydraulic pressure. The chamber is 20 by 20 inches, and 24 to 30 inches deep. The liquid enters through an ordinary nozzle; part of it expands to gas, and draws its heat largely from the incoming liquid, which is thus solidified to a fluffy snow. The gas formed is drawn off constantly by the suction line of the main compressors and recompressed. By operating the top and bottom walls, the snow is compacted to a solid block 20 by 20 by 10 inches. Each press makes

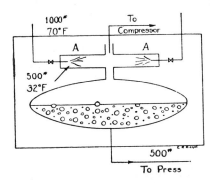

Figure 17.9. The "evaporator," in which liquid carbon dioxide is formed and stored.

6 to 8 cakes per hour. The density of the resulting cake is controlled by the amount of snow pressed into the 10-inch space. After discharge to a conveyor, the block reaches band saws, which cut it into four smaller blocks, each a 10-inch cube, weighing about 20 pounds. This is wrapped in brown paper and stacked in a specially insulated railway car for transportation to distant points, or into trucks for local delivery.

Of the liquid delivered to the press, 20 to 45 per cent is solidified; the rest turns to gas and must be reliquefied. The colder the temperature of the liquid CO_2 and the colder the press chest, the higher the percentage frozen. Based on heat content, it is found that it takes 3.75 pounds of liquid to produce 1 pound of solid. The expansion in the chest is due to atmospheric pressure.

The critical temperature of carbon dioxide is 88° F (31.1° C), the critical pressure 1073 pounds. At 70° F (21° C), it is considerably below the critical temperature, so that a pressure of 1000 to 1100 pounds suffices to keep it in the liquid state.

It will be clear that much of the expense in the plant will be that for recirculating the carbon dioxide gasified at the presses. The compressors are four-stage machines: 0 to 5 lb, 65 to 70 lb, 300 to 325 lb, and 1000 to 1100 lb. From the last stage the gas enters oil-removing filters, then a condenser cooled with tap water, which reduces its temperature to about 70° F (21° C). In the condenser, the carbon dioxide liquefies, and enters the "evaporator" with the new liquid, at the same temperature and pressure. Carbon dioxide from any source may be made into the solid form.

The uses of carbon dioxide are as a refrigerant for the frozen food, dairy product and meat packing industries; grinding of dyes and pigments; and in the manufacture of certain pharmaceuticals and chemicals.

SULFUR DIOXIDE

Of the more compressible gases, chlorine and ammonia are discussed elsewhere. Sulfur dioxide, SO_2 anhydrous, liquefied under a moderate pressure (2 to 3 atmospheres) at room temperature, is shipped in steel cylinders of 50 or 100 pounds capacity, in 1-ton containers, and in single-unit 15-ton car tanks. It is used from such cylinders and tanks in preparing hydroxylamine sulfate, which in turn serves in making dimethylglyoxime, the nickel reagent; for refrigeration, for bleaching, and, increasingly, in petroleum refining. The boiling point is $-10°$ C.

The burner gas from sulfur (or pyrite), freed from dust, and cooled, is dissolved in water in two towers used in series; the solution from the second tower is elevated to the top of the first tower, where it meets the rich gas. Burner gas with 8 to 12 per cent sulfur dioxide yields a 1 per cent solution. In a third tower this solution is sprayed, at the top, and flows down, while steam is injected at the base of the tower; previously the 1 per cent liquor was heated in a closed coil laid in the spent liquor from the base of the still. The packing in all the towers may be coke, or special earthenware cylinders. The gas issuing from the third tower is cooled to remove most of its moisture, and is passed up a fourth tower down which concentrated sulfuric acid flows. The dried gas is compressed in a bronze pump to $2\frac{1}{2}$ atmospheres, which suffices to liquefy it.

NITROUS OXIDE

Nitrous oxide, N_2O, is made by heating ammonium nitrate to 200° C, in small lots (50 pounds) in aluminum retorts. The gas is cooled in a condenser, washed in a solution of sodium dichromate to remove nitric oxide, in caustic to absorb nitric acid, and in water. Under a pressure of 100 atmospheres it liquefies, in small shipping cylinders, for instance; or it may be stored in a gas holder. The reaction is

$$NH_4NO_3 \rightarrow N_2O + 2H_2O.$$

Nitrous oxide is used as general anesthetic, usually mixed with oxygen, and sometimes with ether vapor.

REFERENCES

1. *Chem. Eng.,* **67,** No. 15, 96–99 (1960).
2. *Chem. Met. Eng.,* **39,** 381 (1932).
3. *Ind. Eng. Chem.,* **14,** 1118 (1922).
3a. Ruhemann, M., "The Separation of Gases," International Series of Monographs of Physics, Oxford, Great Britain, University Press (1945).
4. *Trans. Am. Inst. Chem. Eng.,* **41,** 453 (1954).
5. *Trans. Am. Inst. Chem. Eng.,* **42,** 396 (1946).

READING REFERENCES

"Production of Industrial Gases from the Air," R. L. Shaner, Linde Co.

"Extremely Low Temperature," O. A. Hansen, *Chemical Engineering,* 2/23/59.

"Handling Cryogenic Fluids," R. M. Neary, N.F.P.A. Quarterly, July 1960.

"Trends in the U. S. Oxygen Industry," Business and Defense Services Administration, U. S. Department of Commerce, Chemical and Rubber, June, 1960.

"Safety in Air and Ammonia Plants," Symposium, *Chemical Engineering Progress,* **56,** No. 6, 73 (1960).

"Superinsulations," R. F. Barron, *News in Engineering,* Ohio St. U., Feb. 1961.

"Metals Industry Bolsters Chemical Growth," *Chem. & Engr. News,* Nov. 21, 1960.

"How to Design a Hazard-Free System to Handle Acetylene," H. B. Sargent, *Chemical Engineering,* **64,** No. 2, 250 (1957).

18

PHOSPHATES, PHOSPHORUS; FERTILIZERS, POTASSIUM SALTS, NATURAL ORGANIC FERTILIZERS, UREA

In collaboration with Vincent Sauchelli*

INTRODUCTION TO PHOSPHORUS

ASIDE FROM MINOR QUANTITIES of calcium phosphate from bones and guano, all the commercial phosphorus containing compounds are derived from phosphate rock (phosphorite). In the United States phosphate rock is found in commercial quantities in Florida, Tennessee, and many of the Western States.

The production of phosphate rock ore in the United States in 1956 was more than 52 million long tons. This was a 32 per cent increase over the previous year, and 15 per cent above 1954, the previous second year. As indicated in the table below, the State of Florida is by far the largest producer of phosphorite, followed by the Western States.

Approximately 70 per cent of the phosphate rock mined in the United States goes into agricultural uses. The remaining 30 per cent is used

---

* National Plant Food Institute, Washington, D. C.

TABLE 18.1. PHOSPHATE ROCK PRODUCTION*

(Millions of long tons)

	1956	Value/Ton	1959	Value/Ton
Florida	10.53	$6.23	11.76	$6.20
Western States	1.92	5.64	2.53	5.35
Tennessee	1.66	7.69	1.78	7.47
United States	14.11		16.07	

* "Mineral Yearbook."

in cleaners and detergent building (Chapter 13), water softening, dentifrices, foods, feed, metal treatment, petroleum additives and insecticides. Triple superphosphate, a principal fertilizer (and a relatively expensive one), sells at 13 cents per pound whereas the usual phosphate detergent builder sells at about 8 cents per pound. The phosphates used in dentifrices and

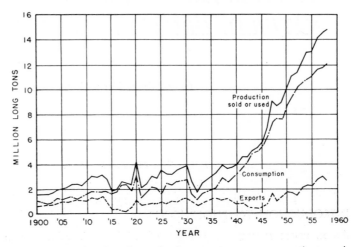

Figure 18.1. Marketed production, apparent consumption, and exports of phosphate rock, 1900–1958. (*Minerals Yearbook, 1958*)

food are about 10 cents per pound. Considerably more money is spent on making phosphates for detergent building and water softening than on all phosphatic fertilizer ingredients.

It appears that more than one billion tons of phosphate rock will be mined in the United States in the next fifty years. The production curve for the last half-century is shown in Figure 18.1.

PHOSPHATE ROCK DEPOSITS

Florida Deposits. The Bone Valley formation in Florida is the source of much phosphate rock. Covering an area of 2600 square miles, this formation is geologically complex. A representative description would be:

	Thickness, feet
Overburden	18
Leached Zone	6
Matrix	16
Clay Bed	200

The overburden is principally quartz sand. Clay, quartz sand, and calcium-aluminum phosphates make up the leached zone. The matrix is the source of commercial phosphate rock. It consists of the phosphate pebble-ore, siliceous

Figure 18.2. Open-pit mining in Florida pebble phosphate fields. (*Courtesy International Minerals and Chemicals Corp., Skokie, Ill.*)

sand, and slimes. The slimes are composed of sand and phosphate fines with clay. The average size range of the phosphate pebble is from 1 to 150 mesh. A phosphate-containing clay bed exists below the matrix but is not mined.

The factor determining whether a given area is mined for matrix is the ratio of the thickness of the overburden plus leached zone to the matrix bed.

Tennessee Rock. Of four types of phosphate rock occurring in Tennessee [nodular, blue, brown, and white] principally the brown rock is mined. The brown rock formations consist of phosphate rock, clay, and phosphatic sand. This brown rock matrix bed may be from 3 to 50 feet thick, and is covered by a negligible to 50 foot layer of overburden, with an average thickness of 7 feet.

Western Fields. The Western States field is one of the largest in the world. It covers an area of over 100,000 square miles in portions of Idaho, Montana, Wyoming, Utah, and Nevada. The deposits occur as two main formations. These are the Park City (Utah) and the Phosphoria (Idaho, Wyoming, Montana]. The latter occurs as a shale having an oily appearance and a high organic content.

Mining Operations. In the Florida fields, electric cranes (draglines) are used to remove the overburden and leached zone from the matrix (Figure 18.2). The draglines then remove the matrix, placing it in open pits. Hydraulic guns serve to disintegrate the matrix and sluice it to large centrifugal sand pumps which transfer the slurry to the washer plant in 10 to 16 inch pipe lines or hoses. The slurry may contain from 20 to 30 per cent solids.

The mining operations employed for Tennessee brown rock are similar to those just described. However, the brown rock occurs as fillings (cutters) between limestone "horses" so that narrow strips rather than entire areas are mined for improved economy of operation. The brown rock is truck transported to the washer plant.

In the Western States field most deposits are mined only by underground methods, although there are a few high-grade deposits in Idaho and Wyoming which are being strip-mined.

BENEFICIATION FOR FERTILIZER USAGE

A flow sheet of a typical phosphate flotation process is shown in Figure 18.3. The process is described below.

Washing and Screening. The phosphate rock matrix slurry from the mines of the Florida fields is received at a washer plant by a surge bin. A washing and screening operation is then conducted. Mud balls and pebble which constitute a $+\frac{1}{2}''$ oversize from the screens is transferred to a hammer mill for crushing and is returned to the screens. Log washers in this section free mud, clay, and other foreign matter adhering to the phosphate pebble. A washer rock $-\frac{1}{2}''$ $+14$ mesh is removed as product. The -14 mesh material is passed to a large hydroclassifier (thickener) which discards the -150 mesh silica, colloidal clay, and phosphate with the excess water. This stream is pumped to a large settling area where the 2–3 per cent of suspended slimes is allowed to settle and water obtained for reuse. After two years of settling the slimes still contain 70–75 per cent water.

Classification. A spiral or rake classifier receives the -14, $+150$ mesh material from the hydroclassifier where a partial classification is effected, the overflow going to a second, smaller hydroclassifier and the bottoms to a hydraulic classifier. From the hydraulic classifier is obtained a +20 mesh pebble phosphate product, a —20, +35 mesh stream which is conducted to the agglomeration plant, and a —35 mesh fraction. This —35 mesh phosphate and sand along with a —35 mesh stream from the secondary hydroclassifier make up the feed to the flotation plant.

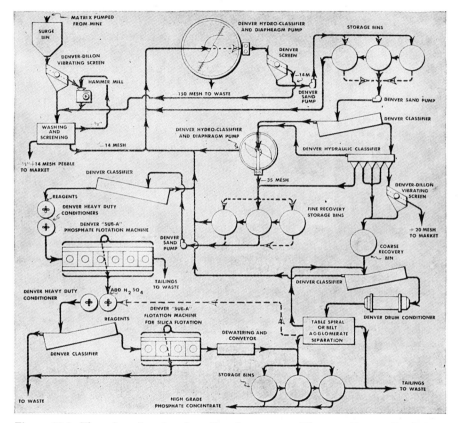

Figure 18.3. Flow sheet for phosphate flotation process. (*Courtesy Denver Equipment Co., Denver, Colo.*)

Agglomeration. The concentration of the —20 +35 mesh fraction is known as an agglomeration operation. Sodium hydroxide, fuel oil, and fatty acids are added to the particles in a conditioner. The phosphate particles are selectively coated and tend to agglomerate or cluster. The separation of the sand from agglomerates may then be made by tabling, spiraling, agglomerate screening, or belt agglomerate treatment. These operations take advantage of one or more of three properties of the agglomerates, namely, their larger size, light texture, and surface oil film. A high-grade phosphate concentrate is thus obtained.

Flotation. To the flotation feed (−35 mesh) are added sodium hydroxide, fuel oil, and fatty acids in a conditioner where the phosphate particles are filmed. The slurry is fed to flotation cells where rising air bubbles attach themselves to the filmed particles and form a froth on the surface of the slurry. The froth is removed as overflow by froth paddles, while sand settles and is removed as waste. This operation produces a phosphate which is 68 to 72 per cent BPL (Bone Phosphate of Lime or Calcium Phosphate). Sulfuric acid is used to remove the flotation reagents from the phosphate in neoprene lined conditioners.

A second or silica flotation increases the concentration to 72–78 per cent BPL. In this operation the sand is activated and floated to waste with the phosphate becoming the bottoms product. A cationic surfactant and a frothing agent are added to the feed to effect the desired separation. The surfactant is usually an amine of a higher fatty acid or a quaternary ammonium compound. Pine oil and branched-chain alcohols are employed as frothers.

In some plants the product from the agglomeration section is subjected to the silica flotation along with the −35 mesh material. A product of 76–78 per cent BPL may be obtained in this manner.

In the Tennessee fields low-grade matrix is processed in a washer plant which recovers approximately one-half of the matrix as concentrated product. The high-grade rock is usually utilized without beneficiation.

In the Western fields beneficiation is not practiced. Mine run, lump, crushed, and pulverized rock are produced.

Regardless of its source, product phosphate rock is used principally (1) as acidulation rock for superphosphate manufacture, (2) as electric furnace feed for elemental phosphorus production, and (3) for direct application to the soil.

PRODUCTION OF ELEMENTAL PHOSPHORUS AND PHOSPHORIC ACID

Phosphate rock is converted into usable chemicals by two major methods; the wet acid process which produces an impure phosphoric acid which is generally used in fertilizers; and by burning elemental phosphorus to give a very pure phosphoric acid which is then converted to phosphates.

Electric Furnace Process for Phosphorus. The electric furnace process, Figure 18.4, involves the preparation of a phosphate rock furnace charge, a proportioned charging operation, the furnace reaction, electrical precipitation of dust, and condensation of phosphorus vapors.

Phosphate Rock Preparation. The electric furnace charge usually contains phosphate rock particles at least $\frac{1}{4}$ inch in diameter. Particles much smaller than this prevent proper descent of the charge in the furnace and block the escape of the product gases from the reaction zone.

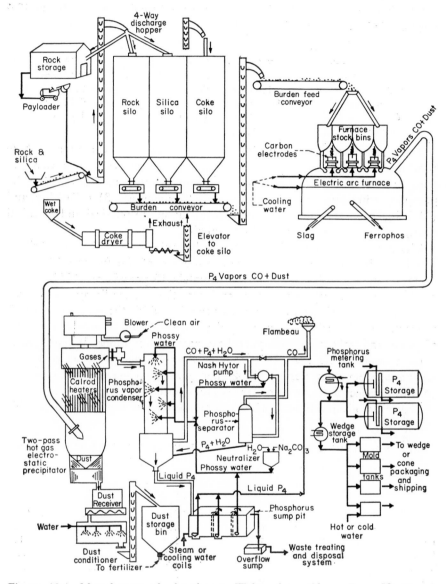

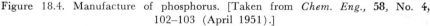

Figure 18.4. Manufacture of phosphorus. [Taken from *Chem. Eng.*, **58**, No. **4**, 102–103 (April 1951).]

Callaham[2] gives the following figures for the flow diagram of Figure 18.4 per ton of phosphorus product:

In		Out	
Phosphate rock	7.25 tons	Ferrophosphorus	0.09 ton
Silica pebbles	2.66 tons	Silicate slag	7.1 tons
Coke	1.43 tons	Gases	3.3 tons
Electricity	11,850 kwh	Dust	0.04 ton
Water	3,000 gal	Phosphorus	1.0 ton
Electrodes	30 lb		

Except for some Florida pebble and hard rock sources, most phosphate rock must be subjected to particle size enlargement (agglomeration) to ensure proper furnace bed porosity. Four agglomerating methods used in the phosphorus industry are: (1) nodulizing, (2) sintering, (3) pelletizing, and (4) briquetting. The method used depends upon the physical and chemical characteristics of the phosphate fines available.

Charging the Furnace. The furnace is charged with phosphate rock, silica, and coke through feed chutes entering the top of the furnace. The consumption of electrodes, usually approximately 15 pounds per 1000 pounds of phosphorus, as well as the consumption of the furnace lining and of electrical energy are affected by the accuracy with which the furnace charge is proportioned. A variety of weighing devices are in use to control the ratio of silica and coke for given phosphate rock compositions. Whereas acid-grade phosphate rock has a P_2O_5 content of approximately 32 per cent, rock having a higher silica content (20–25 per cent P_2O_5) may be used economically in the electric furnace since the contained silica is a required reactant.

Bixler[1] has given a typical analysis of the furnace charge materials (Table 18.2).

TABLE 18.2. TYPICAL BURDEN ANALYSIS FOR THE ELECTRIC FURNACE*

Analysis	Per Cent			
	Raw Shale	Nodules	Coke	Silica
P_2O_5	24.0	25.5	...	...
CaO	36.6	38.8	...	1.0
SiO_2	23.3	25.1	...	92.2
Al_2O_3	6.5	6.8	...	4.5
Fe_2O_3	1.8	1.8	...	1.3
F_2	2.0	1.8	...	...
V_2O_5	0.28	0.25	...	...
Cr_2O_3	0.23	0.20	...	...
MnO_2	0.12	0.13	...	...
U_3O_8	0.0008	0.0008	...	...
C	3.0	0.2	86.5	...
Volatile carbonaceous matter	...	...	1.8	...
H_2O	...	...	1.1	...
Ash	...	...	11.8	...

* Reprinted from *Ind. Eng. Chem.*, Vol. 48, p. 4, Jan. 1956, Copyright 1956 by the American Chemical Society and reprinted by permission of the copyright owner.

The Furnace. Modern electric furnaces are three-phase units using three electrodes connected in "Y" or in delta. The hearth and lower walls are of monolithic carbon construction, while the upper walls and roof are cement. The furnace is enclosed by a steel shell which is water cooled. Cylindrical graphite electrodes 35 to 45 inches in diameter enter the top of the furnace through water-cooled stuffing boxes. These electrodes are automatically moved vertically so as to maintain constant electrical energy consumption during furnace operation. The larger furnaces are operated at around 42,000 KVA.

The furnace reaction may be represented as:

$$12Ca_5F(PO_4)_3 + 43SiO_2 + 90C \rightarrow 90CO$$
$$+ 20(3CaO \cdot 2SiO_2) + 3SiF_4 + 9P_4$$

although many such reactions take place due to the variable nature of the phosphate rock. Between 2300 and 2700° F, phosphorus pentoxide is liberated by the acidic silica, which is reactive at these temperatures. Incandescent coke reduces the pentoxide to elemental phosphorus forming carbon monoxide. These vapors rise through the bed preheating the upper regions, while slag and ferrophosphorus collect on the furnace hearth. The ferrophosphorus, formed from the ferric oxide present in the phosphate rock charge, is more dense, collecting below the slag. Both are tapped periodically.

Precipitation. The furnace off-gases, which exit between 550 to 750° F, are given a two pass treatment in a Cottrell electrostatic precipitator which removes dust. The dust after treatment contains some phosphorus pentoxide, and is sold as a fertilizer ingredient.

The size of the precipitation equipment required may be an important factor in determining the capacity of an electric furnace installation.

Condensation. The gases (approximately 85 per cent CO) are passed to a condenser where water sprays lower their temperature below the phosphorus dew point of approximately 550° F. The liquid phosphorus and water flow to a sump pit from which the settled phosphorus is pumped to storage.

Phosphoric Acid from Phosphorus. Phosphoric acid manufacture from elemental phosphorus involves burning the phosphorus, hydrating the phosphorus pentoxide thus produced, and collection of the mists.

Phosphorus is fed from a storage tank by displacing it with hot water and passes under pressure to the burning nozzle in a phosphorus burner where it is atomized with air. Additional air for the combustion is supplied to the burner. The combustion gases are cooled and sprayed with water in a unit called the hydrator, an acid-proof vessel about 9 feet in diameter by 35 feet high. Phosphoric acid is drawn off from the bottom of the hydrator. The gas from the hydrator is passed through an electrostatic precipitator where acid which left the hydrator as a mist is recovered. The product is 75–85 per cent H_3PO_4. Higher concentrations of acid may be obtained, for example, by absorbing P_2O_5 in phosphoric acid.

Wet Acid Process For Phosphoric Acid. The wet-acid process is the oldest method for making crude phosphoric acid. Phosphate rock is treated with sulfuric acid, giving phosphoric acid and a precipitate of calcium sulfate. The phosphoric acid thus produced is suitable for fertilizer use but is partially purified for other applications, with additional purification often being used in reaction of the acid. Such partial purification is obtained by concentrating by evaporation, then blowing steam into the concentrated acid to drive off fluorine. Iron and vanadium are removed by addition of potassium ferrocyanide. When sodium phosphates are manufactured, the necessary additional purification is realized in several steps during neutralization by soda ash. The nature and extent of the overall purification depends on the composition of the phosphate rock and the intended use of the final product.

PHOSPHORUS COMPOUNDS NOT USED AS FERTILIZERS

Manufacture

Sodium Phosphates. Mono- and disodium orthophosphates are generally made by reacting electric furnace phosphoric acid with soda ash. The trisodium compound is prepared by adding sodium hydroxide to a slurry of the disodium phosphate.

Tetrasodium pyrophosphate is made by calcining anhydrous disodium orthophosphate at from 300 to 900° C. Heating monosodium orthophosphate at 250° C under controlled conditions produces sodium acid pyrophosphate, $Na_2H_2P_2O_7$. Sodium tripolyphosphate is prepared by calcining a mixture equivalent to one mole of mono- to two moles of disodium orthophosphate.

Calcium Phosphates. Monocalcium phosphate is prepared by reacting phosphoric acid with hydrated lime. The reaction mass has a pasty consistency and requires good mixing to produce a suitable product. A Stedman mixer is often used for this purpose. When reaction is complete the thick reaction mass is vacuum dried and the product, the monohydrate of monocalcium phosphate, is ground and packed. The dihydrate and anhydrous forms of the phosphate are also prepared, the former by using a dilute lime slurry and dilute phosphoric acid, the latter from phosphoric acid and quicklime. The anhydrous product is kept in that form by treating the particles with aluminum phosphate or potassium and sodium phosphates.

Other Phosphates. Miscellaneous phosphates can be made by reacting phosphoric acid with a metal oxide or acid salt.

Other Phosphorus Compounds. Phosphorus trichloride, PCl_3, is made by blowing chlorine into a reactor containing liquid white phosphorus. The oxychloride, $POCl_3$, can be prepared by oxidizing the trichloride with oxygen or by combining the proper proportions of PCl_3 and P_4O_{10}. Commercial phosphorus pentoxide, P_4O_{10}, is manufactured by burning liquid white phosphorus in dry air, and phosphorus pentasulfide, P_4S_{10}, is made by combining the elements. All of these compounds are used primarily in the manufacture of organic phosphorus compounds. Esters are generally produced by heating the appropriate alcohol with phosphorus pentoxide. The thiophosphate esters and the sulfur-containing organic phosphorus insecticides are prepared from P_4S_{10}, which is also used in the manufacture of oil additives.

Uses

The phosphate salts of commerce consist of cations and chain anions. The latter may contain from one to one million phosphorus atoms per anion. Most of the industrial uses of the chain phosphates depend on their ability to deflocculate colloidal particles and to form soluble complexes with cations. An example of deflocculating action is the ability of a fraction of a per cent of sodium tripolyphosphate to liquify a firm plastic clay-water mass.

Calcium and magnesium in hard water can be solubilized by the addition of stoichiometric amounts of chain phosphates. The formation of soluble calcium and magnesium phosphates (an example of sequestering) effectively softens the water. Another use of chain phosphates is in prevention of the formation of scale from hard water. Only trace amounts are required, the phosphate being sorbed on the scale as it begins to form and inhibiting further deposition of the scale-forming salts (see Chapter 2).

The major detergent builder (see Chapter 13) is sodium tripolyphosphate. This phosphate comprises 30–50 per cent by weight of detergent formulations for washing clothes. The results are softened water and dispersion of inorganic soil, which lead to more effective cleaning.

Monocalcium phosphate and sodium acid pyrophosphate, $Na_2H_2P_2O_7$ are leavening agents in cake mixes, baking powder, self-rising flour, and similar applications. Dicalcium phosphate is the commonly used polishing agent in toothpaste. Calcium phosphates are also employed as mineral supplements in animal feeds.

Phosphatizing metal surfaces, which covers the surface with a thin corrosion resistant layer of orthophosphate salts, utilizes orthophosphoric acid in mixtures with other compounds. The treatment also provides an excellent base for paint. Esters of orthophosphoric acid find use as plasticizers, and as additives for improving the characteristics of oil and gasoline. Other organic phosphorus compounds are used as insecticides.

INTRODUCTION TO FERTILIZERS

History

The greater part of the food supply of the human race comes from the soil in the form of vegetables and grains, or meat from domestic animals fed on the products of the cultivated soil. Plants need the following substances for their growth: water, nitrogen, phosphorus, potassium, magnesium, calcium, and sulfur in large quantities; iron, manganese, boron, copper, molybdenum, zinc, and sometimes chlorine and sodium in trace amounts. This explains why the former group is called major elements and the latter minor or trace elements. The observation that soils become exhausted by successive crops was made many centuries ago; in order to prevent this exhaustion the ancients allowed a field to "lie fallow" every third season. During that period the particles of rock in the soil weathered, and with the help of microbial and chemical agencies in the soil many insoluble sources of plant nutrients were converted to available forms. Potassium from the feldspars and, to a lesser extent, phosphates from the phosphate rocks, were thus accumulated in the soil. The same process goes on today.

The ancients also knew the use of manure and the fact that to plant certain grasses and plow them into the soil enriched it. Manure is still used, and crops of clover are grown and plowed under in order to enrich the soil with nitrogen compounds. Wood ashes were used and supplied, as is now known, potassium carbonate. Thus the merit of modern fertilizing science is not that it has discovered the process, but rather that it has explained it. The particular elements furnished by manure, wood ashes, and clover are known; the essential plant foods are now supplied by mines and factories in almost limitless quantities.

Nitrogen Sources

In stable manure, the nitrogen compounds are chiefly urea, $NH_2 \cdot CO \cdot NH_2$, and ammonium salts; manure supplies organic materials which form the "humus" of every fertile soil. Manure is a by-product of the farm and need not be purchased. It is supplemented by nitrogenous compounds from various sources: ammonium phosphate or sulfate from ammonia recovered during the distillation of coal or from synthetic ammonia: synthetic urea; sodium nitrate from Chile or synthetic sodium nitrate; calcium and other nitrates made with nitric acid resulting from the oxidation of synthetic ammonia; calcium cyanamide. The manufacture or method of extraction of these substances is discussed under the appropriate headings. Other important sources of nitrogen as well as phosphorus for fertilizer use are dried blood, tankage (from garbage), sewage disposal sludge, bone meal, dried albumen, dried fish scraps, oil meal such as pressed cottonseed meal which for one reason or another cannot be used as cattle food, and a number of other materials of animal origin.

Phosphorus Sources

Phosphorus is applied in various forms. Finely ground phosphate rock is applied directly and in some states, such as Illinois and Missouri, this practice is quite general. In 1957 and 1958 Illinois consumed 517,500 tons and Missouri 200,733 tons out of a total of 836,183 tons for the United States. However, raw phosphate rock is relatively insoluble in water (although it weathers rapidly) and is not recommended as a source of phosphorus for cash raw crops. Superphosphates, both normal 18 to 20 per cent P_2O_5 and triple 44 to 46 per cent P_2O_5, comprise the principal sources of phosphorus in commercial fertilizer use. Superphosphate with 16 to 18 per cent P_2O_5 is used to a far greater extent; its phosphate is soluble and therefore of immediate service to the plant. Triple superphosphate with 45 per cent P_2O_5 is rapidly coming into use.

Bessemer slag contains a calcium phosphate which is insoluble in water but which weathers more readily than phosphate rock; it is applied directly to the soil after powdering.

Potassium Sources

Potassium salts, chiefly the chloride, are obtained from deposits in the earth, brine ponds in arid regions, and other sources fully discussed in this chapter; they are sold in various grades or strengths reported on the basis of potassium oxide K_2O.

Mixed Fertilizers

Mixed fertilizers contain nitrogen as nitrates, urea, ammonium salts, or other nitrogen-containing compounds; phosphorus as superphosphate, and potassium salts, chloride, or (for tobacco) sulfate. The order given above is the one generally used, so that a 5-10-10 fertilizer would contain 5 per cent nitrogen, 10 per cent phosphorus pentoxide (P_2O_5), and 10 per cent potash (as K_2O). Formulas or grades differ for different crops and soil conditions, and each state agricultural experiment station recommends a list of grades suitable to local requirements. This method of evaluation in terms of nitrogen, phosphoric acid, and potassium oxide is merely for convenience; the compounds actually present are those given above. Sodium nitrate may be mixed with superphosphate or applied by itself. Some grades of fertilizer contain filler or inert make-weight materials comprising dolomitic limestone or some other cheap material. Modern high analysis grades have no space for filler.

"Complete" fertilizers are mixed in a revolving mixer not unlike a cement mixer, or in any other suitable type of mixer. The several ingredients are introduced into a hopper and a bucket elevator feeds the mixer. The batches are of several tons each. Batch mixing is rapidly being replaced by continuous operation in all modern plants.

The "complete" fertilizers refer to nitrogen, phosphoric acid (as P_2O_5), and potassium oxide, but although these three elements are the most important to be added, calcium, sulfur and magnesium are needed in appreciable amounts as are a host of "trace elements" including iron, boron, zinc, managanese and molybdenum.

Fertilizing values may be concentrated by manufacturing ammonium phosphate, for example, which would contain both nitrogen and phosphoric acid, or potassium nitrate containing potassium and nitrogen. For long shipment high concentrations are desirable since the freight on inert matter is saved. The wider use of concentrated fertilizers has been an important development of the past decade.

AMMONIATED SUPERPHOSPHATES

There has come into prominence of late the method of spraying a very strong ammonia, as for example a hydrous ammonia with 40 to 80 per cent NH_3, onto a charge of superphosphate contained in a revolving mixer so that new surfaces are continually exposed. The relation may be 5 parts of NH_3 to each 100 parts of superphosphate (18 per cent P_2O_5). The ammoniated superphosphate has an increased value; also any residual sulfuric acid is neutralized and the "rotting" of the bags from that cause is avoided. A mixed fertilizer may also be ammoniated by means of very concentrated hydrous ammonia delivered from a steel pressure tank similar to the anhydrous ammonia containers. For example, superphosphate 900 pounds, sulfate of ammonia 52 pounds, manure salts 267 pounds, filler (sand) 673 pounds (total 1892 pounds) may be treated with 108 pounds of NH_3 in the form of 40 to 80 per cent hydrous ammonia. The anhydrous material is rarely used, for a certain quantity of water seems necessary to produce the essential grain structure and to avoid the undesirable powder structure which anhydrous ammonia produces.[14] This development is a result of the decreased price of ammonia made from synthetic sources.

As a logical extension of this practice a urea-containing ammonia liquor, on the market since 1932, has found increasing favor; it contains 15.1 per cent nitrogen as urea and 30.4 per cent as ammonia (NH_3), with a total of 45.5 per cent nitrogen. Rivaling this is the sodium nitrate-containing ammonia liquor with a total nitrogen content of 44.4 per cent, and ammonium nitrate in ammonia liquor with a total of 37.5 per cent.* About 180 pounds of the urea-ammonia liquor and 400 pounds of the ammonium nitrate-ammonia liquor may be added to a ton of superphosphate without causing reversion.

The ammoniation of superphosphates in this way has been a distinct advance in the science of fertilizer manufacture.

Ammonium nitrate for fertilizer purposes is shipped over both short and long distances in the solid state; under certain conditions of heat and con-

* Compare p. 57, report 114, U. S. Tariff Commission, Washington, 1937; also booklets "Urea-ammonia Liquor-A" and "UAL-B," Du Pont Company, Ammonia Department, Wilmington, Del. and similar literature from all the nitrogen producers.

finement, and probably in the presence of organic impurities, it may explode. The disaster at Texas City early in 1947 is reported to have started with the explosion of ammonium nitrate on board a ship in the harbor.

A safe way to transport ammonium nitrate is in the form of Nitraprills—small shapes produced by dropping the hot concentrated solution down a tower swept by an upward flow of air.[9] The product, conditioned with diatomaceous earth, is shipped all over the world.

SODIUM NITRATE SOLID PELLETS

It has been found advisable to alter the condition of Chilean nitrate intended for fertilizer mixing by forming it into round pellets to remove its hygroscopic property. The method[13] consists of melting the nitrate at a temperature not over 350° C (662° F), forcing it through a filtering screen, and

TABLE 18.3. U. S. CONSUMPTION OF FERTILIZER NITROGEN MATERIALS, YEAR ENDING JUNE 30, 1957*

Used for Direct Application	Short Tons
Anhydrous ammonia	452,702
Ammonium nitrate	1,105,196
Ammonium nitrate-limestone mixture	300,586
Ammonium sulfate	516,183
Calcium cyanamide	46,978
Nitrogen solutions and aqua ammonia	627,310
Sodium nitrate	493,159
Urea	108,916
Other chemical nitrogen	55,398
Organic, natural	479,671

Primary plant nutrient *nitrogen*, consumed in mixtures and materials combined, year 1956–57 (short tons)†

1956–57	2,135,287
1955–56	1,933,342
1954–55	1,960,536

* U. S. Department of Agriculture.
† U. S. Department of Agriculture.

spraying it into a cooling chamber; the result is small balls with a hard outer surface and solid throughout. Another method[15] provides for the incorporation of 5 per cent potassium nitrate, magnesium nitrate, or ammonium sulfate, giving a non-hygroscopic, solid, hard pellet, well suited to the agricultural drill which applies the mixed fertilizer to the soil. This improvement has been carried over into synthetic nitrate manufacture. Furthermore, ammonium nitrate in pellet form is available.[16]

POTASSIUM SALTS

The most extensive mineral deposits of soluble potassium salts are those at Stassfurt in Germany; until 1914 they supplied nearly all the world's requirements. Since the end of World War I, deposits in upper Alsace near

Mulhouse have been developed until they yield about one-third the Stassfurt tonnage; they are similar in nature to the German deposits. A third deposit of similar character lies in Poland, near Kalusz in the southeastern part; in 1931 it yielded 261,310 tons of potassium salts of all grades. The German production for that year was about one and a half million tons. A fourth deposit is the one in Carlsbad, New Mexico; it began shipments in 1931 and in 1958 produced 3,650,000 short tons of merchantable salts or 2,157,000 short tons equivalent K_2O.

The Stassfurt area lies in the central part of Germany between Magdeburg and Halle. The deposits of the potash beds are at a depth of about 1000 feet and overlie a bed of salt ($NaCl$) 3000 feet thick. Over the potash beds a layer of clay separates them from another deposit of salt ($NaCl$) of more recent geological origin. Three potash layers are distinguished; the upper, 300 feet thick and extending over many square miles, consists of carnallite, $MgCl_2 \cdot KCl \cdot 6H_2O$ (40 per cent), mixed with salt (20 per cent) and other impurities. Polyhalite, $2CaSO_4 \cdot MgSO_4 \cdot K_2SO_4 \cdot 2H_2O$, lies below the carnallite, and below that, kainite, $MgSO_4 \cdot KCl \cdot 3H_2O$. According to the geological history of these deposits, salt from sea water left a mother liquor which gradually gained in potassium salt content; a change in the topography caused the isolation of the bay, and the lake so formed dried completely. It was during this dry period that the potassium salts deposited. A similar relation of solubilities is exhibited by present-day sea water which is evaporated for salt in the south of France. After the salt has deposited, the more soluble magnesium salts with some potassium remain in the mother liquor and are run off because the magnesium is bitter.

Mining is done at Stassfurt by shafts and tunnels. The mineral, dislodged by blasting with black powder, is loaded in mine cars and hauled to the refining plant at the mouth of the shaft.

The German potash salts for fertilizer purposes are produced in four grades. Their value is based largely on the calculated potassium oxide equivalent: kainite, with 12 per cent K_2O; manure salts, with 20 per cent; potassium chloride, with 50 per cent; potassium sulfate with 50 per cent.

The crude carnallite is refined to potassium chloride by treating the crushed material with a hot solution of 20 per cent magnesium chloride from a previous operation. In this solution the salt ($NaCl$) is insoluble and is left behind with calcium sulfate and other impurities; potassium chloride deposits on cooling. The mother liquor is concentrated and when cooled gives a lower grade of potassium chloride utilized as manure salts. The first crop of potassium chloride may be refined further by washing with cold water; this treatment is applied only to limited quantity.*

* Potassium salts are also found to the north and northwest of the Stassfurt basin, in Hannover, Braunschweig, and Mecklenburg; these deposits are smaller and consist chiefly of sylvine or sylvinite, $KCl \cdot NaCl$, more or less pure.

The Alsatian deposits[17] consist of two strata. The upper one is about 3 feet thick and contains 35 to 40 per cent potassium chloride; the depth is 1500 feet below the surface in one section but more in others. The lower layer is 7.5 to 16 feet in thickness and lies about 50 feet lower; it contains 24 to 32 per cent potassium chloride. Both layers are essentially sylvinite, $KCl \cdot NaCl$, containing sodium chloride as impurity, and clay; the purification is by crystallization and yields potassium chloride 98 per cent pure (or with 61 per cent K_2O content). Lower grades are obtained from mother liquors; a part of the mine product is shipped after mere crushing. The grades marketed are: sylvinite, 12 to 16 per cent K_2O; sylvinite rich, 20 to 22 per cent or 30 to 32 per cent; potassium salt (*sel de potasse*), 40 to 42 per cent; and potassium chloride (*chlorure de potasse*), 62 per cent K_2O. The first two are crushed mineral; the last two have been concentrated by solution and crystallization.

The American deposits lie in the southeastern part of New Mexico, in Eddy and Lea counties, and in the neighboring counties in Texas, Loving, Winkler, Ector, Crane, Upton, Reagan, and Crocket. The deposits are of the Permian geologic age. The area covers underground deposits of rich potassium salts, chiefly chloride; in Eddy County there are ten beds at depths between 800 and 1762 feet below the surface, varying in thickness from 14 to 54 inches and having an arithmetical total of 36 feet. The potassium minerals are sylvinite (the richest), kainite, and some polyhalite. At a depth of 1267 feet the bed is 3 feet 6 inches sylvinite; at 1311 feet another deposit of 3 feet consists of sylvinite and polyhalite, while at 1365 feet a 2-foot thick bed of sylvinite occurs. A shaft sunk near Carlsbad, New Mexico, serves a mine operating since 1931; in that year a large tonnage was produced with a content of 25.6 per cent K_2O. The mineral was higher in potash than the test cores had indicated.

In addition, there are numerous beds of polyhalite, an impure potassium sulfate averaging close to 10 per cent K_2O, at depths of 1100 to 2752 feet. The thickest bed is in Eddy County: 15 feet 6 inches at a depth of 1459 feet with 8.8 per cent K_2O; the deepest is in Winkler County, Texas: 9 feet 8 inches at a depth of 2267 feet with 7.23 per cent K_2O, and just over that, at 2257 feet, a layer 6 feet thick with 10.63 per cent K_2O. The richer mineral tapped by the Carlsbad shaft has not been found in the Texas counties.

A refinery has been erected at Carlsbad (Potash Company of America) in which a flotation method is used for the separation of potassium chloride from its valueless companion in sylvinite, sodium chloride. The production is near 100,000 tons of KCl, with 60 per cent K_2O.

The New Mexico and Texas deposits were probed during and since World War I by private citizens and government agencies. The Mulhouse deposits are the sole result of private enterprise; they were discovered before 1914 during a search for petroleum.

Potassium Salts from Brines. Besides the important deposits of Stassfurt, Alsace, southestern Poland, and New Mexico and Texas, brines from certain lakes in dry areas constitute a source of potassium salts. Of the several enterprises begun in the United States during World War I to relieve the shortage resulting from the blockade of the German seaports, only one has survived: the American Trona Company* at Searles Lake in the desert between California and Nevada. This "lake" is really a deposit of solid salts permeated by a brine.† The salts are stiff enough to carry a dirt road. From a depth of 70 feet below the surface of the lake, the brine is pumped to a large modern plant, situated on the shore four miles away, where it is mixed with end liquors from various plant operations and concentrated in triple-effect evaporators. The flow of steam through the evaporators is counter to the flow of brine, so that the strongest brine is at the highest temperature; thus potassium chloride and borax are retained in solution even as their concentration rises because they are more soluble at the higher temperature. During the evaporation much of the salt (NaCl), mixed with sodium carbonate and sodium sulfate, separates out and is continuously removed from the evaporators. The concentrated liquor, essentially saturated with potassium chloride, is cooled to 100° F in vacuum crystallizers in three stages; the potassium chloride deposits in these and, after discharge from the crystallizing vessel, is collected and removed by treatment in continuous thickeners. After centrifuging and drying, this salt is ready for shipment. The mother liquor is cooled to about 80° F, at which point the crude borax separates out and is dissolved in hot water, filtered, and crystallized in pure form by controlled cooling in vacuum crystallizers.

The main products are potassium chloride and borax, about twice as much of the former as of the latter. For example, in 1946, 212,000 tons of potash salts, and 102,148 tons of borax were produced.

The sodium chloride deposit formed during the evaporation contains

---

* Now the American Potash and Chemical Corporation, Trona, California.
† Composition of Searles Lake Brine:

NaCl	16.35 per cent by weight
Na_2SO_4	6.96
KCl	4.75
Na_2CO_3	4.74
*$Na_2B_4O_7$	1.51
†Na_3PO_4	0.155
NaBr	0.109
Miscellaneous	0.076
Total solids	34.65
Water by difference	65.35

* Equivalent to 2.86 per cent $Na_2B_4O_7 \cdot 10H_2O$.
† Equivalent to 0.067 per cent P_2O_5.

sodium carbonate and sodium sulfate which are removed from the evaporation cycle by filtration, and processed to produce natural soda ash and natural salt cake. The 1960 United States capacity for natural soda ash amounted to about 930,000 tons.[4]

Figure 18.5. A large triple-effect evaporator in the Trona plant of the American Potash and Chemical Corp., Trona, California. (*By permission*)

Lithium phosphate is recovered in the soda ash and salt cake process; it is separated from burkeite (sodium carbonate-sodium sulfate double salt) by pneumatic flotation as lithium sodium phosphate, with ordinary stove oil as the flotation agent.[6]

Other products from the Searles Lake brine include "Pyrobor," dehydrated borax, potassium sulfate, boric acid, and bromine. The total 1946 production for all Trona chemical products was 541,327 tons.

Before the developments at Searles Lake, most of the world's borax was produced from colemanite, $Ca_2B_6O_{11} \cdot 5H_2O$, which was decomposed with a boiling sodium carbonate solution, filtered, and crystallized. The production at Searles Lake of not only borax but muriate of potash and many by-products, made it possible to obtain borax more cheaply. Since then, however, extensive deposits of rasorite, $Na_2B_4O_7 \cdot 4H_2O$, have been discovered near Kramer, California, and are now mined. The ore is shipped to Los Angeles harbor, dissolved in water under heat and pressure, strained, filtered, and crystallized as pure borax, $Na_2B_4O_7 \cdot 10H_2O$.[3]

Figure 18.6. View of the Trona plant of the American Potash and Chemical Corp., Trona, California. (*By permission*)

Boric acid, HBO_3, a white solid, is made by treating borax with sulfuric acid. A technical grade and a U.S.P. grade are made; the latter is available in the form of flat crystals or as a powder.

In 1960 United States consumption of boron minerals and compounds was about 340,000 tons. Borax of technical grade in bulk (carload lots) was quoted at $83.00 a ton in 1960.

A brine from a drying salt lake near Zarsis in Tunis has become the origin of a growing industry. Active exploitation of the brine in the Dead Sea* is continuing: Dead Sea Works, Ltd., made plans to increase annual production of potash salts at Sodom, Israel, to 660,000 tons.

* "The Dead Sea: a storehouse of chemicals," M. A. Novomeysky, *Trans. Inst. Chem. Eng.* (*London*), **14**, 60 (1936).

Other mineral sources of potassium are alunite, $K_2Al_6(OH)_{12}(SO_4)_4$, mined for three years during World War I and worked for potassium sulfate in Sulphur, Nevada, and Marysvale, Utah; and leucite, $(KNa)AlSi_2O_6$, successfully worked for potassium in Italy by means of hydrochloric acid. Greensand in New Jersey (Odessa, Del.), shales in Wyoming and other states, and feldspar also contain potassium as do the nitrate deposits of Chile; and now a 25 per cent KNO_3 material is recoverable by means of the Guggenheim process. If necessary, this method could be applied to all the Chilean nitrate produced, and with normal production, approximately 300,000 tons a year of potassium nitrate could be obtained. Other deposits occur in Spain, Abyssinia, Canada, Russia (Solikamsk), Saskatchewan (Canada), Great Britain and Italy.

Until World War I the United States had imported all or nearly all its potash salts. Beginning with the 1914 to 1918 period, domestic sources were actively sought and vigorously developed. In 1935, 76.4 per cent of the world production of potassium salts from minerals or brines was the Stassfurt-Mulhouse one, and of that production the United States imported 13.9 per cent. During World War II nearly all the potash needed for agriculture and industry was supplied from domestic sources; since 1940 exports have exceeded imports of fertilizer potash. In 1958 the United States exported 254,000 short tons of potash salts, basis K_2O.

Aside from minerals and brines, potassium salts are obtained by collecting the flue dust which passes out of cement kilns[7] by means of a Cottrell precipitator; it is estimated that 2 to 5 pounds of K_2O may be recovered for each barrel of cement made. For iron blast furnaces similar installations indicate that 17 pounds of K_2O may be conserved for each ton of pig iron manufactured. The ashes from fermented molasses residues, ashes from the spent pulp of the sugar beet (7000 tons yearly), wool washings, and kelp[7] are commercial sources of potassium compounds.

Potassium nitrate may be used for fertilizing; it has the advantage of combining two of the essential elements. Formerly the extraction of potassium nitrate from the upper layer of the soil near stables was of some importance (India); the constant re-formation of nitrate is due to the growth of bacteria. Potassium nitrate may be made by double decomposition of potassium chloride with sodium nitrate:

$$KCl + NaNO_3 \rightarrow KNO_3 + NaCl$$

Solid potassium chloride is added to a strong hot solution of sodium nitrate; sodium chloride first separates; then, on cooling, potassium nitrate crystallizes. Another method is to pass nitrogen peroxide into a potassium chloride solution.[8]

In Spain, a new potash company was formed to exploit some recently discovered rich deposits. Initial production is expected to be 50,000 tons (K_2O equivalent) per year, reaching 200,000 tons by 1970.

Potassium salts are also in demand in the chemical industries because they crystallize well, as a rule, whereas sodium salts do not. As a result it is easier to separate potassium compounds from other reaction products than to separate the corresponding sodium compounds. Purification by crystallization is also easier for potassium compounds than for sodium com-

TABLE 18.4. WORLD PRODUCTION OF POTASH MINERALS, SHORT TONS, IN EQUIVALENT K_2O BY COUNTRIES

	1954	1956	1957	1958
North America: USA	1,948,721	2,171,584	2,266,481	2,147,670
South America: Chile	550	12,000	11,000	11,000 *
Europe:				
France	1,192,083	1,463,006	1,545,267	1,613,000 *
Germany				
East	1,488,000	1,598,000	1,653,000	1,700,000
West	1,783,394	1,823,000	1,862,000	1,892,000
Spain	243,166	263,468	251,460	236,000 *
U.S.S.R. *	593,700	983,600	1,040,000	1,100,000
Asia				
Israel	12,000 *	31,000 *	50,000 *	80,000 *
Japan	454	474	1,650 *	1,900 *
World Total	7,300,000	8,300,000	8,700,000	8,800,000

Source: Minerals Yearbook, 1958.
* Estimates.

pounds. Examples of potassium salts manufactured on an industrial scale in preference to the sodium salts because the former crystallize with ease, are potassium permanganate, dichromate, chlorate, and ferricyanide. In some cases the potassium compound is preferred because the corresponding sodium compound is hygroscopic; in other cases it is preferred because of its specific action, which differs from that of sodium.

World reserves are indicated by the following figures: Stassfurt, 8 billion tons K_2O; Mulhouse basin, 350 million; Dead Sea, 2 billion; U.S.S.R., of the order of the Stassfurt deposits; Searles Lake, 20 million; total United States reserves, 73 million short tons.[5]

NATURAL ORGANIC FERTILIZERS

By-products of the packing industry which are of value as fertilizers are dried blood, bone meal, and tankage. The fish industry contributes fish scrap. In a number of other industries there are by-products which serve primarily as cattle feed, but if, for any reason, they are unacceptable for that purpose they may be of value as fertilizing agents.

In the slaughter house the blood is pumped to a coagulating tank with a conical bottom. It is cooked until coagulated and of the consistency of liver. Separation takes place after a few hours; water settles out at the bottom and is drawn off. The coagulum is pressed, dried, and powdered to form a dark reddish meal. It is either sold as such or mixed with potash salts and phosphates to make a rich fertilizer.

Bones are cooked in open tanks or steamed under pressure; in either case grease is removed and the degreased bones are crushed and powdered.

Tankage is used primarily for feeds; it is a brown meal containing 9.5 to 11 per cent nitrogen as NH_3 and 12 to 20 per cent bone phosphate of lime. Applied to the soil, tankage decomposes more slowly than dried blood. Fertilizer tankage is produced from meat scraps, intestines, bones, and carcasses of dead or condemned animals by cooking under a steam pressure of 40 pounds for 4 to 12 hours. Grease and tallow float to the surface and are removed; the solids are separated from the tank water and ground. The tankage still contains 10 to 20 per cent grease which is generally removed by naphtha before it is sent out as a fertilizer.

Guano is a mixture of birds' excrements, fish bones and other fish refuse found on certain islands off the Peruvian coast where the rainfall is slight. The deposits, surface ones, are still in the process of formation, but their importance as to tonnage has decreased as has their quality since the materials rich in urea and ammonium oxalates are practically exhausted. Guano is found and mined in other localities.

A nitrogenous material called "Milorganite" is produced from activated sludge in sewage disposal plants.

SYNTHETIC UREA

A nitrogenous material of synthetic origin is synthetic urea, $(NH_2)_2CO$; in solution its formula is probably $HN{:}C{\big\langle}{\begin{smallmatrix} NH_2 \\ | \\ O \end{smallmatrix}}$. Its nitrogen content is remarkably high, 46.6 per cent for the pure substance. Before the outbreak of World War II it was manufactured in Germany on a large scale. Its production in the United States has grown steadily; consumption in the 1956–1957 crop year was 108,916 short tons. The suitability of synthetic urea as a plant food is equal to that of the natural urea in manures.

The process of Carl Bosch and Wilhelm Meiser[11] consists in passing mixed ammonia and carbon dioxide gases, with some moisture, into an autoclave held at 130 to 140° C (266 to 284° F); ammonium carbamate, $NH_2 \cdot CO \cdot ONH_4$, forms first and is transformed into urea:

$$2NH_3 + CO_2 \rightleftarrows NH_2 \cdot CO \cdot ONH_4$$
ammonium
carbamate

$$NH_2 \cdot CO \cdot ONH_4 \rightleftarrows NH_2 \cdot CO \cdot NH_2 + H_2O$$
urea

The conversion is about 40 per cent, and a melt is discharged from the autoclave, continuously if desired, which is introduced directly into a plate still. Steam enters at the base and drives out the uncombined ammonia and carbon dioxide, while a solution of urea, concentrated and crystallized, is discharged at the bottom of the still.

The make-up gas may be conveniently introduced by running a solution of ammonium carbamate into the upper part of the column; the gas driven out is compressed in warmed compressors and conveyed by warmed lines (to prevent the deposition of ammonium salts) to the autoclave.

The Krase process[10] provides for the introduction of liquid ammonia and liquid carbon dioxide into an autoclave. Modifications[12] provide for neutralizing unchanged ammonia with phosphoric acid, producing a concentrated fertilizer containing two of the essential elements.

Developments in the nitrogen industries are part of a study of the general field of fertilizers; these developments have been presented in Chapter 5, and many statements and figures of primary interest to those in the fertilizer field are included there.

REFERENCES

1. Bixler, G. H., *et al., Ind. Eng. Chem.,* **48,** 1–16 (1956).
2. Callaham, J. R., *Chem. Eng.,* **58,** No. 4, 102 (1951).
3. Bowman, F. C., *Chem. Met. Eng.,* **42,** 430 (Aug. 1935).
4. *Chem. Week,* p. 92, July 16, 1962.
5. Dolbear, S. H., "Potash Reserves of the United States," a report to the American Potash Institute, Washington, D. C., 1946.
6. Gale, W. A., *Chem. Ind.,* **57,** No. 3, 442 (1945).
7. *Ind. Eng. Chem.,* **10,** 834 (1918).
8. *Ind. Eng. Chem.,* **23,** 1410 (1931).
9. Kirkpatrick, S., *Chem. Eng.,* **55,** 99 (Apr. 1948).
10. Krase, H. J., *et al., Ind. Eng. Chem.,* **22,** 289 (1930).
11. U. S. Patent 1,429,483.
12. U. S. Patents 1,797,095 and 1,782,723.
13. U. S. Patent 1,937,757.
14. U. S. Patent 2,060,310.
15. U. S. Patent 2,021,927.
16. U. S. Patent 2,402,192.
17. Vigneron, H., *Chem. Met. Eng.,* **24,** 655 (1921).

READING REFERENCES

"Chemistry and Technology of Fertilizers," V. Sauchelli, Reinhold, 1960.

"Commercial Fertilizers," 4th ed., G. H. Collings, McGraw-Hill Book Co., Inc., N. Y.

"Fertilizer Technology and Resources in the United States," Vol. III, American Society of Agronomy Monographs, Academic Press, Inc., New York, N. Y.

"Manual on Fertilizer Manufacture," V. Sauchelli, The Davison Chemical Co., Baltimore, Md., 2nd ed., 1956.

"Fertilizers," T. Lyttleton Lyons, Encyclopedia Americana (8 pages).

"Potash in North America," J. W. Turrentine, Reinhold Publishing Corp., 1943.

"Soilless Growth of Plants," C. Ellis and W. W. Suaney, Second Edition revised by T. Eastwood, Reinhold Publishing Corp., 1947.

"Fertilizer materials," Oswald Schreiner, Albert R. Merz, and B. E. Brown, in the Yearbook 1959, U. S. Department of Agriculture.

"Bonneville potash," *Mining World,* **7,** No. 9 (August, 1945), pp. 27–32, quoted through "Minerals Yearbook."

"Utah desert yields potassium chloride for Western agriculture," H. R. Smith, *Chem. Met. Eng.*, **51,** 94 (Dec., 1944).

Yearbook 1957, U. S. Department of Agriculture, Soil.

"Fundamentals of Soil Science," C. E. Millar, L. M. Turk, H. D. Foth, John Wiley & Sons, 1958, 3rd Ed.

"Soil Conditions and Plant Growth," E. J. Russell, 8th ed., Longmans.

"Soil Fertility and Fertilizers," S. L. Tisdale & W. L. Nelson, 1956, The Macmillan Co., N. Y.

"Phosphorus and Its Compounds," Vol. I, John R. Van Wazer, 1958, Interscience Publishers.

"Phosphorus and Its Compounds," Vol. II, John R. Van Wazer, 1961, Interscience Publishers.

19

CHEMICAL EXPLOSIVES—MISSILE PROPELLANTS

In collaboration with Dr. Melvin A. Cook* and Dr. George F. Huff†

CHEMICAL EXPLOSIVES

EXPLOSIVES SERVE TWO MAIN PURPOSES. First, they are utilized in industry to save billions of man-hours of work each year, e,g,. in mining coal, and metallic and nonmetallic ores; in quarrying, clearing land, ditching, loosening formations in oil and gas wells, and in road building; for sporting ammunition, and for such important specialized applications as blind rivets and starter cartridges for aircraft and diesel engines, high-speed machining and metal forming, and in perforating oil-well casings. Second, they are of major importance in the field of rockets, missiles, space vehicles, and military and civilian weapons. The manufacture of commercial explosives is a growing industry; production has risen steadily in America from about 200 million pounds in 1920 to approximately 815 million pounds in 1956. Bebie[1] lists some 135 chemicals and formulations which are useful as explosives; of these, 75 are used in the industry alone, 45 are primarily military explosives, and 15 are used for both purposes.

An explosive is a substance or mixture of substances which, when raised to a sufficiently high temperature, whether by direct heating, friction, im-

* University of Utah.
† Callery Chemical Company.

pact, shock, spark, flame, or sympathetic reaction from a primary or donor explosive, suddenly undergoes a very rapid chemical transformation with the evolution of large quantities of heat and gas, thereby exerting high pressures on surrounding media. With some explosives the rate of this transformation (or burning rate) is so great that the explosive exerts a very great shattering action (or *brisance*), while with others the reaction may take place at a much slower, controlled, but still explosive rate to give pressure-time characteristics which make them suitable for use as propellants in guns, rockets, etc., where much lower rates of pressure development and peak pressures are required. Another characteristic property of explosives is *sensitivity*, or ease of initiating the explosion, whether of the fast (shattering) type or the much slower, propellant type. *Strength*, or the maximum explosive energy available for useful work, is another important factor. It depends much less on the rate of reaction than does the brisance, peak pressure, or pressure-time curve of the explosive. The uses of explosives depend on all three of these characteristics (pressure or pressure-time curve, sensitivity, and strength) ; these are the bases for the grouping used in Table 19.1 and the classifications presented in the next paragraph.

The usual classification of explosives is into two general groups, *high* or *detonating* explosives, and *low* or *deflagrating*, sometimes also called *propellant* explosives. The latter have a low burning rate which permits them to have a relatively slowly-rising pressure-time curve; the peak pressure seldom rises above 50,000 psi. The rate of burning of the low explosive directly into the grain never exceeds a few centimeters per second, whereas in detonation the reaction rates are hundreds of times faster. The low explosives exert a powerful "heaving action" or push and while they are used today primarily as propellants, they have a very desirable blasting action for lump coal. However, the most prominent of this type, from the historical viewpoint, namely black powder, has been used extensively in the past in borehole blasting. Today "Hydrox," "Chemecol," and "Cardox," which are compounds designed to have the "heaving action" of black powder without its hazards, continue to be used in coal mining. In high explosives the reaction takes place to a large extent in a peculiar type of shock wave known as the detonation wave which propagates in accord with well-known principles of hydrodynamics at velocities ranging from one to seven miles per second, depending on the density, heat of explosion, in some cases the particle size and shape, and in gelatins the air bubble content and distribution. An important, recently discovered characteristic of detonation in condensed explosives is that the reaction zone comprises an ionized gas or plasma existing with high cohesion in a quasi-lattice structure, pictured to resemble the metallic state.[5,6] This plasma causes the pressure rise in the detonation front to be much less steep than was at first thought. That is, instead of being infinitely steep, the detonation rises to its characteristic pressure of

TABLE 19.1. CHARACTERISTICS AND USES

PRIMARY EXPLOSIVES

Name	Composition or Chemical Formula	Density (g/cc)	Detonation Velocity* (km/sec)	Detonation Pressure* (kilobars)	Detonation Temperature* (°K)
Mercury Fulminate	$Hg(ONC)_2$	3.6	4.7	220	6900
Lead Azide	PbN_6	4.0	5.1	250	5600
Lead Styphnate	$C_6H(NO_2)_3O_2Pb$	2.5	4.8	150	...
Nitromannite (Mannital Hexanitrate)	$C_6H_8(ONO_2)_6$	1.73	8.3	300	6000
Dinitrodiazophenol (DDNP)	$C_6H_2N_4O_5$	1.5	6.6	160	...

SECONDARY HIGH EXPLOSIVES

Name	Composition or Chemical Formula	Density (g/cc)	Detonation Velocity (km/sec)	Available Energy (kcal/g)
Ammonia Gelatin Dynamites	30–90% grades same as straight gelatins except for some NG and NaNO₃ replacement by NH₄NO₃	1.2–1.5 *	4–6.5 *	0.75–1.15 *
Semi-Gelatin Dynamite	15–20% NG, 1–2% DNT oil, AN-SN dope	1.2	3.5–5 (depends on diameter)	0.9
Prilled AN-Fuel Oil	94/6 NH₄NO₃/oil	0.8	2.5–4	0.84
Slurry Explosives	Basically 30–65% NH₄NO₃, 20–45% coarse TNT, 12–18% water	1.4–1.55	5–6.5 (depends on diameter)	0.8–0.9
"Nitramons"	High NH₄NO₃ explosives; non-explosive fuel	1.15–1.35	3–5 (depends on diameter and density)	0.9

* Most important properties of detonators.

Sensitivity	Major Characteristics	Uses
Very high	Best primary explosive for single-component (fuse) detonators; easily detonated by flame, spark, heat, friction; easily dead-pressed.	In fuse caps (mixed with $KClO_3$); propellant primer; in fuses for shells; small arms cartridge caps.
Very high (higher than NG; less than mercury fulminate)	Powerful detonator but requires strong igniters, e.g., lead styphnate.	Primary explosive in composition (EB) caps; military fuses.
Exceedingly high	Extremely sensitive to sparks, static electricity; explodes rapidly on ignition; good thermal stability.	Igniter in composition caps, military fuses; not a satisfactory detonator explosive.
Very high (greater than NG; less than lead azide)	Stronger and more brisant than NG, RDX, PETN.	In composition caps and fuses.
Very high (less than lead azide)	Does not dead-press. About $\frac{3}{4}$ as strong as TNT.	In composition caps and fuses.

Sensitivity	Major Characteristics	Uses
High	More economical; only slightly less brisant than straight gelatin; exhibits low-order detonation with threshold priming and high pressures.	General small and large diameter blasting in hard rock and under water.
High	Stringy, plastic; easily loaded in "uppers"; economical; high strength; moderate brisance.	Popular small diameter metal mining explosive.
Very low (requires large booster)	Cheapest source of explosive energy available today; flammable and will explode when ignited under strong confinement; no water resistance; adaptable to do-it-yourself operations.	Open pit blasting in diameters above 3 inches where dry conditions prevail; most adaptable to soft, easy shooting.
Very low (requires large booster)	Thick pea-soup consistency; high pressure; economical—believed comparable to prilled AN-fuel oil on do-it-yourself basis in very hard rock, dry hole blasting. Most economical source of explosive energy for blasting under water.	Open pit blasting in wet or dry holes; adaptable to very hard rock; ideal for submarine, oil well, wet and water-filled borehole blasting.
Very low (requires booster)	Water-proofed by container; most economical (until prilled AN-fuel oil and slurry explosives came along).	Quarrying; seismic prospecting.

TABLE 19.1. CHARACTERISTICS AND USES

SECONDARY HIGH EXPLOSIVES *(Continued)*

Name	Composition or Chemical Formula	Density (g/cc)	Detonation Velocity (km/sec)	Available Energy (kcal/g)
Nitrostarch Powders	Nitrostarch in place of NG	1.2	4–5	0.8–1.0
Composition B	40/59/1 RDX/TNT/wax	1.7	7.8	1.1
Halite or EDNA	$(CH_2NHNO_2)_2$	1.6 (pressed)	7.9	1.2
Ammonium Picrate (Explosive D)	$(ONH_4)C_6H_2(NO_2)_3$	1.56 (pressed)	6.6	0.7
Nitrostarch	Mixtures of various esters of starch	1.4 (pressed)	6.4	0.95
Tetryl	$(NO_2)_3C_6H_2NCH_2NO_2$	1.45 (pressed)	7.0	0.95
PETN (penta-erythritol tetra-nitrate)	$C(CH_2ONO_2)_4$	1.6 (pressed)	7.92	1.31
Pentolite	50/50 TNT/PETN	1.63 (cast)	7.7	1.1
Trinitrotoluene (TNT)	$CH_3C_6H_2(NO_2)_3$	1.59 (cast) 1.45 (pressed) 1.03 ("Pelletol") 0.8 (grained)	6.9 6.3 5.1 4.2	0.9 . . . . . . 0.8
Amatols	50/50 AN/TNT	1.55 (cast)	5–6.5 (depending on diameter)	0.95
	80/20 AN/TNT	1.0 (loose)	4 (large diameter)	0.93
		1.45 (pressed)	5.6 (large diameter)	
Dinitrotoluene (DNT)	$CH_3C_6H_3(NO_2)_2$	1.28 (liquid) 0.8 (granular solid)	5 2–3.5 (depending on diameter)	0.7

Sensitivity	Major Characteristics	Uses
Moderately high but less than dynamites	Good "fumes"; fair water resistance; powerful; economical.	Small diameter blasting.
Average	Very high brisance.	Bursting charge and special weapons.
High	High brisance; less sensitive than RDX and PETN.	In Ednatols for bursting charges.
Very low	Insensitive to shock and friction; melts with decomposition; shells filled with high-pressure pressing.	Armor-piercing shells.
High	Highly inflammable, white powder.	Demolition blocks and Trojan blasting explosives.
High	Very sensitive; rapidly reacting; easily pressed with 1–2% graphite; high brisance.	Booster; base charge in caps; in tetrytols for bursting charges.
High	Very powerful and sensitive (more sensitive than RDX, less than NG).	In primacord fuse; base charge in caps.
Moderate	High pressure or brisance; primacord-sensitive.	Booster and special weapons; commercial booster for prilled AN-fuel oil and slurry explosives.
Low	Easily melted and cast; suitable liquid for slurrying with other explosives; easily pressed into blocks; completely waterproof.	Military; "Nitropel" TNT used in slurry explosives and in filling annulus between charge and borehole in water-filled holes; in amatols.
Low Low	Insensitive; hygroscopic; not waterproof; less brisant but stronger than TNT; 50/50 can be cast; 80/20 either pressed or granulated.	Military; oil well shooting; quarrying; dry hole booster for very low sensitive types.
Very low	Reddish-brown liquid or yellow solid, depending on isomers; desensitizer for NG; sensitizer for AN.	Sensitizer in "Nitramons"; 60/40 NG/DNT in oil well shooting; up to 20% in TNT bursting charges; in FNH (flashless) propellant; 6% in small-arms ammunition (with guncotton).

TABLE 19.1. CHARACTERISTICS AND USES

SECONDARY HIGH EXPLOSIVES (*Continued*)

Name	Composition or Chemical Formula	Density (g/cc)	Detonation Velocity (km/sec)	Available Energy (kcal/g)
Cyclonite (RDX)	$C_3H_6N_6O_6$	1.2 (loose) 1.6 (pressed)	6.8 8.0	1.32
HBX	Mixtures of RDX, TNT, aluminum and wax	1.78	7.5	1.5
Plastic Explosives (Compositions A, C, C-2, C-3, C-4)	Waxed RDX	1.45–1.6	8.0	1.1–1.3
Nitroglycerin (NG)	$C_3H_5(ONO_2)_3$	1.59	7.8	1.41
Ethylene Glycol Dinitrate (EGDN)	$C_2H_4(ONO_2)_2$	1.48	7.4	1.43
Straight Dynamites †	20–60% NG, in balanced SN dope 20% grade ≡ 20% NG, etc.	1.3	4–6	0.55–0.85 †
Ammonia Dynamites (and permissibles)	As above except NH_4NO_3 replaces part of NG and $NaNO_3$	0.8–1.2 †	1.5–5.5 depends on AN particle size, NG content	0.7–0.9 †
Blasting Gelatin	92/8 NG/nitrocotton ("Solidified" NG contains some wood pulp to minimize low-order detonation)	1.55 (1.45)	7.5 (7.2)	1.45 (1.4)
Straight Gelatin Dynamite	20–90% grades	1.3–1.6 †	4–7 †	0.75–1.15 †

PROPELLANTS

Name	Composition or Chemical Formula	Sensitivity
Colloidal Nitro-Cellulose (N.C.) Powders	Pyrocotton: cellulose nitrate with 12.6% N	Low

† Depends on grade.

Sensitivity	Major Characteristics	Uses
High	High thermal stability in solid state; excessively sensitive in pure state; 1.65 times as strong as low density TNT; 1.45 times as strong as cast TNT.	Major ingredient in plastic explosives; one of most brisant explosives in cast TNT (composition B); base charge in caps.
Average	Very powerful.	Underwater explosive.
Moderate	Plastic, easily molded or pressed.	Specialized military demolition.
Very high (almost a primary explosive)	Oily, toxic liquid; volatile above 50° C; gelatinized by nitrocotton; exhibits low-order detonation with threshold priming.	Shooting oil wells; main explosive in dynamites; used in double-base powders.
Very high	Closely resembles NG; more volatile, toxic, slightly stronger but less brisant (owing to lower density).	Used in solution with NG as freezing point depressant.
High	Cheesy, plastic substance; packed in paper cartridges; may be slit and tamped in borehole for greatest blasting effect; fired by detonator, as are all dynamites; heat, friction, shock, flame sensitive.	Ditching, stumping, other uses where high propagation-by-influence "sensitiveness" is required.
High	Cheaper than comparable grade straight dynamites; must be waterproofed by special additives.	General small and large dynamite blasting; permissible (some grades).
High	Strongest, most brisant dynamite; completely waterproof; exhibits low-order detonation with threshold priming and under high pressures.	Oil well and submarine blasting, tunnel drilling, demolition.
High	Jelly-like substance; powerful, waterproof; exhibits low-order detonation under threshold primering and high pressures.	In hard rock; mudcapping; demolition; submarine blasting.

Major Characteristics	Important Uses
Burning rate controlled by graining; hygroscopic; smokeless flame, with intense flash; gelatinized with alcohol-ether.	Combined with stabilizers and modifiers to make smokeless powders for artillery, small-arms, and sporting ammunition.

TABLE 19.1. CHARACTERISTICS AND USES

PROPELLANTS *(Continued)*

Name	Composition or Chemical Formula	Sensitivity
	Guncotton: cellulose nitrate with 13.2% N	
Double-Base Powders	60–80% nitrocellulose 20–40% nitroglycerin	Moderate
Cordite	65% N.C., 30% NG, 5% vaseline	Low
FNH (Flashless Non-Hygroscopic Powders)	Either straight N.C. or double-base powders with additions of coolants, etc., to prevent muzzle flash, and decrease water absorption	Low
Albanite; DINA Powder	Di-(2 nitro-oxyethyl)-nitramine	Low
Rocket Powder (Solventless Powder)	Nitrocellulose plasticized with about 50% NG, plus stabilizers and potassium salts	Low
Chemical Propellants ‡	Hydrogen peroxide, 80–90% H_2O_2, plus Ca, Na, or K permanganate (solid or aqueous solution)	
	Hydrazine hydrate plus methyl alcohol	
	Fuming nitric acid—aniline	
	Mixed acid—monoethylaniline	
	Liquid oxygen—kerosene	
Black Powder	75% KNO_3 (or $NaNO_3$), 15% charcoal, 10% sulfur (example)	High

‡ Many new rocket propellants have been described; the best ones are under security classifications.

500,000–4,000,000 psi in a period ranging from a few tenths of a microsecond to several microseconds, depending on the explosive. Subclasses of high explosives are the primary explosives (used as detonators) and the secondary explosives. The former are characterized by the fact that even in very small quantities they develop (via the essential plasma formation) detonation waves in extremely short periods of time following simple ignition, e.g., by flames, sparks, hot wires, friction, etc. The secondary explosives, however, usually require detonators and sometimes also boosters to bring them to detonation, at least in practical applications. A booster may

Major Characteristics	Important Uses
Pyrocotton and guncotton are usually blended to secure an average of 13.15% N.	Dry guncotton in fiber form is used in primers fired by an electric current.
Very rapid burning rate, controllable by surface area; more powerful and more readily ignitable than straight N.C. powders; causes erosion of gun bores; can be detonated and is subject to DDT.§	Propellant for mortars and sporting ammunition; not used by U. S. armed forces as cannon powder because of bore erosion.
Gelatinized with acetone.	Propellant for large caliber naval guns (English).
Like other smokeless powders, but can be rolled into sheets; flash reduced by DNT, potassium salts, etc.	Propellant for small armor-piercing rockets such as the "Bazooka" (NG base); for naval ammunition (NG base).
Better flashless powder than FNH powders.	Naval ammunition.
Very rapid, uniform burning rate; can be made with thick section since no solvent need be removed.	For rockets up to 4.5 inches.
Catalytic decomposition into water and O_2 releases about 1000 Btu per pound. Supplies oxygen to burn petroleum fuel.	For driving turbines on submarines: V-2 rocket-fuel pumps; jet motors; launching device for ram-jets.
Rapid combustion; fuel and oxidizer are both liquid.	For torpedo turbine drives.
Rapid rate of reaction. Generates heat and gases.	For launching device for ram-jets; jet motors.
As above.	As above.
	Rocket motors.
Cheap; excellent "heaving action"; persistent smoky flame; very sensitive to friction, spark, heat; hygroscopic.	Time (delay) fuses for blasting and shell; in igniter and primer assemblies for propellants. Pyrotechnics. $NaNO_3$ powder, in commercial black powder and for practice bombs and saluting charges. As blasting charge it is being discontinued.

§ T = deflagration to detonation transition.

be one of the more sensitive secondary explosives, such as pressed tetryl, TNT, RDX, waxed RDX, or cast pentolites (TNT-PETN). The commercial detonators are the ordinary (or fuse) and electric (or EB—sometimes also called composition) caps which contain either mercury fulminate alone (fuse caps) or separate elements consisting of (1) an ignition element (e.g., lead styphnate), (2) a primary explosive (e.g., lead azide), and (3) a base charge comprising a secondary explosive (e.g., pressed tetryl, PETN, or RDX). These are the EB or composition caps. The commercial dynamites are all secondary explosives which may be detonated directly by commercial detonators or primacord. The latter is a detonating fuse usually containing about 50 grams of PETN per foot in a special wax-impregnated cloth or plastic sheath which may or may not be reinforced by a binding wire. The least sensitive secondary explosives, of which the 94/6 prilled "guhr"-coated ammonium nitrate-fuel oil mixture is currently the most popular, require a relatively large booster. Another series of explosives of this type, recently announced by Cook and Farnam,[5] comprise ammonium nitrate-coarse TNT-water slurries for use under water and in dry, hard rock shooting. The smallest effective boosters for these relatively insensitive explosives are 150 grams or more of cast 50/50 pentolite, waxed pressed RDX, pressed tetryl, or several pounds of fine-grained TNT, amatol, and

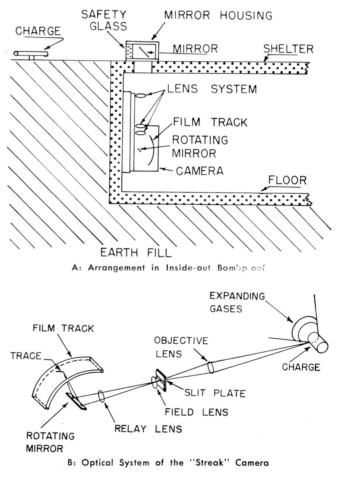

A: Arrangement in Inside-out Bomb proof

B: Optical System of the "Streak" Camera

Figure 19.1. Measurement of detonation velocity by means of the streak camera.

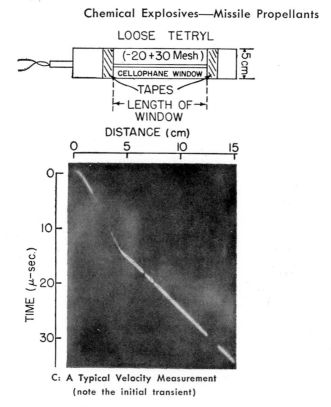

LOOSE TETRYL

C: A Typical Velocity Measurement
(note the initial transient)

Figure 19.1. (*Cont.*)

the higher grade dynamites. Most military explosives also require boosters; a 10 gram tetryl or pentolite charge usually satisfies the booster requirements of the secondary military explosives, illustrating the level of sensitivity of the explosives used by the armed forces. Artillery rounds may contain igniters, primary explosives, boosters, and secondary explosives, all assembled so that each element serves a definite function.*

Detonation wave velocities are currently measured by high-speed photography methods involving framing cameras capable of taking millions of frames per second, streak cameras with writing speeds of several miles per second, elaborate electronic timers called "pin-oscillographs," and centimeter wave systems[5] using wave guide and doppler principles. Figure 19.1

* The design of ammunition is an interesting subject. A description of the function and requirements for cartridge primers and fuse primers (which are frequently different formulations) for propellant igniters and bursting charge detonators, etc., is available in a War Department publication, T19-4-205, "Coast Artillery Ammunition." This pamphlet also provides a description of mechanical base and nose fuses of various types, and explains how they work.

Strictly speaking, a "round of ammunition" includes "everything necessary to fire the gun once."

illustrates how the detonation velocity is measured by means of the streak camera. Since World War II, the above methods have largely replaced the older "Dautriche" and "Metegang" methods.[7]

Some Principles of Explosives Technology

The most fundamental requirement of an explosive is that its characteristic chemical reaction be highly exothermic. The most prominent explosives exhibiting exothermic reactions are the ones which undergo oxidation-reduction reactions. These are of two general types: first, the *internal redox* compounds in which the oxidation-reduction involves oxidant and reducer radicals both *within* the same molecule; second, *redox mixtures,* i.e., simple mixtures in which the oxidant and reducer are separate and distinct molecules. Examples of the internal redox compounds are NG (nitroglycerin), EGDN (ethylene glycol dinitrate), PETN, RDX, TNT, tetryl, and Halite (or EDNA). These internal redox compounds generally have $C_x H_y$ radical or trunk units as the reducer part of the compound and nitrate ($-ONO_2$), nitro ($-NO_2$), nitramine ($-NHNO_2$), or other similar oxygen-bearing radicals as the oxidant. For example, NG has as the internal reducer the

$-CH_2\overset{|}{C}HCH_2-$ unit and as the oxidant three nitrate groups; EGDN has $-CH_2CH_2-$ as the reducer unit and two nitrate groups as the oxidant. PETN has as the internal reducer $C(CH_2-)_4$ and as the oxidant four nitrate groups; RDX has as the internal reducer three $-CH_2-$ units and as the internal oxidant three $=N-NO_2$ units; TNT has as the internal

reducer the unit
and as the internal oxidant three nitro groups;

Halite, or EDNA, has as the internal reducer the ethylene radical $-CH_2CH_2-$ and as the internal oxidants two nitramine groups; and finally, tetryl has two internal reducer units, the phenyl and the $-CH_2-$ radical, and two types of internal oxidant units, the nitro and the nitramine radicals. The practical internal redox compounds are necessarily stable compounds, otherwise they would be unduly hazardous. While nitrate, nitro, nitramine, chlorate, perchlorate, and similar groups are sometimes referred to as "explosophore" groups, this is a misnomer since they are actually entirely stable groups. For instance, there are many compounds containing nitrate and nitro groups that are non-explosive, including many inorganic nitrates and nitro compounds. HNO_3 and HNO_2 are not explosive because their reducer unit (one H atom) can use up only a very small part of the oxygen of the oxidant radical. Also, ordinary metal nitrates and nitrites are non-explosive. Ammonium nitrate is a very insensitive explosive even though its fuel radical $NH_4—$ reacts in a redox-type reaction with only two of the three oxygen atoms of the $—ONO_2$ radical. As evidence that the internal redox explosives are stable chemically, note that the heats of formation ΔH_f (positive for heat evolved and negative for heat absorbed, relative to the constituents in their standard states) are 83, 56, 123, and 13 kcal/mol for NG, EGDN, PETN, and TNT, respectively. Of the seven examples at the beginning of this discussion, only RDX and tetryl have negative heats of formation (-18.3 and -9.3 kcal/mol, respectively). The heats of explosion of RDX and tetryl are about 290 and 190 kcal/mol, respectively, showing that the "explosophore" character of the $—NHNO_2$ and $=N—NO_2$ groups is far less important than the internal redox character of these compounds.

Explosives of the redox mixture type are exemplified by the currently very popular 94/6 prilled ammonium nitrate-fuel oil, black powder, dithekites (i.e., mixtures of nitric acid and nitrobenzene), the Thiokol propellants based on ammonium perchlorate, and many others.

Many internal redox explosive compounds may be made more powerful by combining their internal redox with the redox mixture principle. For example, TNT has appreciably more reduction than oxidation potential, i.e., it is highly oxygen-deficient. Therefore its explosion potential is enhanced by mixing with an oxidant. Likewise, an explosive compound that has internal redox character but is rich in oxygen may be made more powerful by mixing it with almost any fuel or combustible substance. Ammonium nitrate and ammonium perchlorate are the outstanding examples of explosives of this character. An example of an oxygen-balanced mechanical mixture of both an oxygen-rich and an oxygen-deficient explosive substance is 80/20 amatol (AN/TNT). It is nearly always advantageous to oxygen-balance an explosive by mixing it with a suitable fuel or oxidant, although the highest strength frequently occurs in mixtures, especially the high temperature ones, having a somewhat negative oxygen-balance. Aluminized and some other metallized explosives are exceptional, the maximum strength occurring at much more negative oxygen-balance. For example, 80/20 tritonal (TNT/Al), although much more oxygen-deficient, is appreciably more powerful than pure TNT.

Explosives based strictly on "explosophores," i.e., single groups or radicals the rearrangement or decomposition of which generates large quantities of heat, are common among the primary explosives. For example, lead azide,

(PbN_6), contains only an "explosophore" group ($—N=N=N$ or $—N{<}^{N}_{N}{\parallel}$).

All the heat of explosion, Q, of lead azide is therefore attributed to the rearrangement of this group to yield nitrogen, and in this case the heat of explosion is entirely the negative of the heat of formation ΔH_f. Another "explosophoric" group is the acetylide ($—C{\equiv}C—$) group in which $Q = -\Delta H_f$ at low pressure. Under very high pressures the products of detonation of acetylene consist of CH_4 and carbon instead of H_2 and carbon; then Q is somewhat greater than $-\Delta H_f$, i.e., about 73 instead of 55 kcal/ mol. The fulminate group ($-ONC$) is another "explosophore" group, however $Q \doteq -2\Delta H_f$ because of the formation of CO and CO_2 in the products of detonation at high pressures.

The heat of explosion and the nT product, i.e., maximum temperature times the expanded volume of the gaseous products, are each roughly proportional to the total available energy. But the detonation pressure, p_2, is determined by the density and velocity, approximately by the relation $p_2 = \frac{1}{4}\rho_1 D^2$, where ρ_1 is the density and D is the detonation velocity. Furthermore, D usually increases almost linearly with ρ_1; the pressure therefore involves terms in the cube of the density. Hence in order to obtain high densities, casting a molten material into a shell is preferred to loading loose grains and tamping. However, if the melting point of the explosive is excessively high, the charge may undergo decomposition or even explode upon melting. TNT, with a melting point of 80.3° C, is easily and safely cast, whereas the casting of picric acid (m.p. 123° C) is hazardous; casting substances of still higher melting points is impossible. For example, PETN and tetryl (m.p. 139 and 130° C, respectively) are extremely hazardous and may even explode on melting. It is therefore common practice, in obtaining high density explosives, to make a slurry of a high-melting more powerful explosive in TNT, or in some cases to make eutectic solution of two explosives, e.g., tetryl and TNT, to permit casting at lower temperatures. High densities are also obtained by pressing the charges.

On the other hand, the burning rate of the low explosive decreases with increasing denisty; this is the basis for time-delay pellets used in fuses. The rate of burning of a propellant may be controlled by designing the grain so that the surface area available for burning increases as the weight of the grain decreases. This is called progressive burning and is typified by smokeless powders which are fluted on the outside and provided with one or more longitudinal perforations to control the burning rate. In the case of spherical propellant powders where the surface decreases with decreasing weight (regressive burning), the surface is coated with a chemical called a deterrent. This decreases the rate of burning while it is present, to match the slower rate prevailing when the diameter of the sphere is less. The control of the area of surface burning of the single-grained rocket propellants is tremendously important in rockets; it is accomplished by carefully shaped longitudinal perforations, each patterned to give a particular predetermined pressure-time curve.

Heat-absorbing compounds, such as mineral salts, powdered metals, dinitrotoluene, etc., may be added to smokeless powders to make them flashless. A graphite coating applied to grained propellants not only acts as a deterrent, but also decreases the hazard of handling by removing static charges, acts as a lubricant to facilitate pressing to a higher density, and increases the ignitability of the powder. Flame retardants and coolants are also used to some extent to cut down flame and increase safety in the detonating explosives ("permissibles") used in coal mining.*

The availability of raw materials frequently governs the choice of explosives in wartime. For example, during World War II the Italian forces used PETN rather than tetryl as a booster because the former is made from synthetic methanol while the latter requires benzene, which was in short supply in Italy.

Many other factors are considered in evaluating an explosive. These include the toxicity of the raw materials or intermediates that must be handled in its manufacture, the toxicity of the gases produced on explosion,† hygroscopicity or water-resistance, stability in storage, cost of manufacture, and others.

The high explosives used for peacetime applications (industrial explosives) are chiefly the dynamites and the ammonium nitrate mixtures. Coal mining utilized 41.2 per cent of all commercial explosives in 1950, metal mining 17.8, quarrying and non-metal mining 19.6, railway and other construction 19.4, and all other uses 2.0 per cent. Currently, prilled "guhr"-coated ammonium nitrate-fuel oil mixtures are being used extensively on a do-it-yourself basis, thus effecting considerable savings in explosive costs in open-pit blasting. It is estimated that this explosive comprises more than 30 per cent of all explosives currently used in the American industry, although exact figures regarding the use of the 94/6 ammonium nitrate-fuel oil are difficult to obtain since the substance may be mixed on the spot and used immediately as needed. Slurry explosives are also gaining rapidly in commercial blasting, not only in open pit but also in underground mining.

Nitroglycerin

Nitroglycerin (glyceryl trinitrate) is a colorless (when pure) oily liquid which freezes at 13° C and is very sensitive to shock, especially when it contains air bubbles or when conditions are such that air may be trapped in the shocked liquid. It is made commercially in a steel nitrator which has steel cooling coils and a mechanical agitator. In the interests of safety and stability a very pure glycerin, above 99.9 per cent pure, is required. A typical

---

* For use in gaseous or dusty mines, explosives must pass tests conducted by the U. S. Bureau of Mines. If approved, they are placed on a "permissible list." Permissibles are usually ammonium nitrate explosives compounded to suit specific conditions. For a list of available U. S. brands, see Bebie, *op. cit.*, page 118.

† Toxic gases produced in detonation are called *fumes.*

process is as follows. About 6800 pounds of mixed acid having the composition 50 per cent HNO_3 and 52 per cent H_2SO_4 (oleum)* is charged into the nitrator with agitation and is cooled by the circulation of $CaCl_2$ brine at $-20°$ C through the coils. A total of about 1300 pounds of glycerin is then added slowly in a steady stream. The temperature of nitration is 2–3° C,† and if there is any tendency for the temperature to rise, the flow of glycerin is stopped. The addition step takes about 50–60 minutes; agitation is continued a few minutes and then the spent acid is allowed to separate from the oily nitrated glycerin. The spent acid carries away in solution about 5 per cent of the total yield. The acid is given an additional settling, then is denitrated for recovery of the HNO_3 and H_2SO_4. The glycerin trinitrate is washed with warm water, then with a 2–3 per cent Na_2CO_3 solution, and finally with a concentrated solution of NaCl which breaks down any emulsion and partly dehydrates the nitroglycerin. The product, which contains about 0.5 per cent water, is stored in lead-lined tanks. A process was recently developed in Italy for continuous nitration of glycerin, and is rapidly being adopted throughout the world.

The Dynamites

The high sensitivity of nitroglycerin to shock was a deterrent to its use until the chance discovery by Nobel in 1862 that large quantities of the liquid explosive could be absorbed in kieselguhr (diatomaceous earth), forming a plastic cheesy substance which could then be transported and used with appreciably less hazard. This original formulation (kieselguhr dynamite) is now rarely used, however, since the presence of 25 per cent of the inert "guhr" diminishes the blasting effect by absorbing energy. The absorbent used today is generally a mixture of wood pulps, meals, sawdust, flour, starch, cereal products, or the like, to which is added appropriate oxidizers, e.g., ammonium nitrate and/or sodium nitrate, and a small amount of antacid ($CaCO_3$, ZnO). The explosively active absorbents are called "balanced dope" because they are always carefully oxygen-balanced for maximum strength and minimum fumes. Various amounts of nitroglycerin

---

* A mixture of nitric and sulfuric acid is commonly used for organic nitration reactions because the sulfuric acid is capable of forming a hydrated molecule, thereby effectively removing one of the products of any nitration reaction, i.e., water. This shifts the equilibrium to the right, allowing more of the nitrated product to form and resulting in a higher yield than would otherwise be possible. The sulfuric acid does not otherwise take part in the reaction and normally is completely recovered for reuse, except for minor wastage.

† This is below the freezing point of nitroglycerin, but in acid solutions the oil will not freeze to the coils if there is sufficient agitation. Adapted from "Explosives Manual," Lefax, Inc., Philadelphia, Chap. XI, part 2.

may be used in the formula, depending on the strength desired. The commercial *straight dynamites* contain from 20 to 60 per cent, the grade being the same as the percentage of nitroglycerin in the straight dynamites.* Ethylene glycol dinitrate ($O_2NO \cdot CH_2 \cdot CH_2 \cdot ONO_2$) or other explosive oils† are now added to all domestic dynamites to make them low-freezing. Nitroglycerin may be gelatinized with 7–8 per cent collodion cotton to make *blasting gelatin*. Gelatin dynamites are mixtures of gelatin and balanced dope ranging from 20 to 90 per cent grades, depending on the ratio of gelatin to balanced dope used. Gelatin dynamites comprise two types: the "straight" gelatins and the "ammonia" gelatins. The straight gelatins are based on sodium nitrate dopes and the ammonia gelatins use NH_4NO_3 or mixtures of NH_4NO_3 and $NaNO_3$ dopes.

Straight dynamites have been replaced for many uses by the *ammonia dynamites*, which provide the same blasting strength but contain much less nitroglycerin for a given grade. Some of the high ammonium-nitrate dynamites are really ammonium nitrate-fuel or combustible explosives in which a small percentage of nitroglycerin is used to sensitize the NH_4NO_3 to detonation. Other ammonia dynamites (the highest grades) still contain appreciable nitroglycerin. Gelatin dynamites (ammonia and straight) have the greatest shattering action or brisance;‡ the straight dynamites are intermediate, and the ammonia dynamites have the least brisance for a given grade of dynamite, although there is some overlapping from one series to the other if grade is not also taken into consideration. The explosives with highest brisance are preferred for "mudcapping," hole "springing," and very hard rock shooting, although brisance must also be balanced against cost. Finally, mention is made of the *semi-gelatin dynamites* which contain sufficient gelation agent (nitrocellulose) to thicken the liquid NG appreciably, but not enough to make a stiff gel.

To make any of the above compositions, the carbonaceous material and

---

* A "40% straight dynamite" contains, for example, 40% nitroglycerin, 44% $NaNO_3$, 14% carbonaceous material, 1% antacid, 1% moisture. A "40% ammonia dynamite," with the same strength, may contain about 15% nitroglycerin, 32% NH_4NO_3, 38% $NaNO_3$, 4% sulfur, 9% carbonaceous material, 1% antacid, 1% moisture.

† Dinitromonochlorhydrin and tetranitrodiglycerin are also used.

‡ A test for comparing the brisance of explosives is the sand bomb test: 80 grams of standard Ottawa sand, sized to minus 20 plus 30 mesh, is placed in a thick-walled cylinder. A cap containing 0.400 grams of the explosive is then inserted and the remainder of the cavity filled with 120 grams of sand. The explosive is suitably detonated. The weight of sand which then passes the 30 mesh screen is a measure of the brisance of the explosive. For further details see Olsen and Greene, "Laboratory Manual of Explosive Chemistry," New York, John Wiley and Sons, Inc., page 80, 1943.

the other "dope" ingredients are dried together in a steam-heated pan dryer, then mixed with ammonium nitrate and/or sodium nitrate in a spiral-blade mixer. For dynamite, the "balance dope" is placed in an edge runner (muller) and nitroglycerin is added carefully. For gelatin dynamite, the dope and nitrocellulose are blended with the nitroglycerin in a sigma-blade mixer. All equipment must be of non-sparking construction, and liquid nitroglycerin is handled in small lots in rubber-tired buggies and rubber pails. The blended products are packed in paper cartridges by automatic machinery and the cartridges are then paraffin-coated and boxed in sawdust.

TNT (2,4,6-trinitrotoluene)

One of the most important military explosives, TNT, is made by stepwise nitration of toluene. Mixtures of nitric and sulfuric acids are used and the reactions are carried on in well-agitated steel nitrators equipped with steel cooling (or heating) coils. In 1941, the accepted daily production of a TNT "line" was about 36,000 pounds. By the middle of 1945, however, the output of the same line, with but few modifications of equipment, was nearly 120,000 pounds per day. This increase was brought about by many factors, including adoption of the principle for all three nitrations of adding the organic material to the mixed acid (indirect nitration). Previously, for mono- and trinitrations, the oil was first added to a large volume of cycle acid or oleum to "cushion" the reaction, and this was followed by slow addition of the nitrating acids. Since, in the newer method, only a small amount of nitratable material is present in the acid at any time, the hazards of the operation are appreciably reduced. Also, much less time is required for the reaction cycle.[14]

Temperature control and agitator speed are important. The acid charge is first preheated to near reaction temperature by passing hot water through the coils; then as the toluene, or mono- or dinitrotoluene is added, cooling water is turned on the coils to maintain the proper temperature. In mononitration, 1,600 pounds of toluene are run into some 11,000 pounds of mixed acid, and the temperature is allowed to rise to 140° C. The batch is held at this temperature for a cooking period of about 25 minutes, or until the proper specific gravity is reached. In dinitration, the cooking is done for 5 minutes at 180° C. The temperature in trinitration is allowed to rise to 180° C, but after the oil addition is complete the temperature is raised at a predetermined rate to 230° C, where it is held for 30 minutes. A strong upward circulation is maintained during the addition of the oil, but the agitator speed is changed during the cooking period. When nitration is complete the charge is cooled somewhat, allowed to settle, and separated into waste acid and nitrated oil by visually examining the flow as the nitrator is emptied and switching valves as the low-gravity oil appears in the sightbox following the acid. Di- and trinitrations are carried on in the same nitrator; the mono-nitrator is located some distance away in another building. Nitrated oil is handled by pumps, while waste acid is moved by air pressure. The spent acids* are fortified in steel tanks similar in construction to the nitrators.

The trinitrotoluene is washed, while still in the liquid state, by agitation with a dilute ammoniated solution of sodium sulfite. The ammonia neutral-izes the residual acid while the sulfite removes as soluble complexes any 3,5-dinitrotoluene and other undesirable by-products of nitration. The TNT is then crystallized by rapid addition of cold water, filtered on a Nutsch filter, melted with steam, dried by passing warm air through the melt, and then resolidified on a flaker drum. The flakes are packed in paper-lined boxes. Properly prepared product will have a setting point of 80.2° C, mini-mum. Two other types of TNT are also available, namely the "shot tower" product sold by duPont under the trade name "Nitropel," and a very fine-meshed fluffy graining-kettle product. The latter was the form of solid TNT common prior to World War II.

Cyclonite (RDX)

Cyclonite (RDX) (symmetrical trimethylene-trinitramine) is over 50 per cent more powerful than low-density granular TNT and has good stability. Its excellent thermal stability makes it highly adaptable, especially at high temperatures. Its sensitivity and high melting point (about 200° C) were deterrents to its use until the discovery that it could be desensitized with beeswax for press-loading into shells, slurried with TNT for casting, and mixed with a special oil to make "plastic explosives" for demolition work.†
The problem of its high cost was resolved first by a reduction in the cost of the raw material, hexamethylenetetramine, as it became more available, and second by the development of an ingenious method which combines two chemical reactions, one of which does not require hexamethylenetra-tramine:

* The strongest acid mix (concentrated HNO_3 plus oleum; no water) is required to introduce the third nitro group (trinitration). The diluted spent acid from the trinitration step is fortified with 60% HNO_3, and water is added to adjust the strength for dinitration. The waste acid from this operation is again fortified and diluted for use in the mononitration. The monowaste acid is denitrated with steam in a packed tower, the nitric oxides are recovered by absorption in water, and the 75% sulfuric acid is concentrated to 66° Bé and remade into oleum. While some 220 pounds of 109% oleum is required for each 100 pounds of TNT made, all but 2.5 pounds of this is recovered and recycled.

† From a paper by Ralph Conner, formerly Chief, Division 8, NDRC, presented Sept. 9, 1946 at the Chicago meeting of the American Chemical Society. See also "Chemistry, Science in World War II," edited by W. A. Noyes, Jr., Chapters 2 to 11 by G. B. Kistiakowsky and Ralph Connor, Boston, Little, Brown and Co., 1948.

Reaction 1 (nitrolysis)

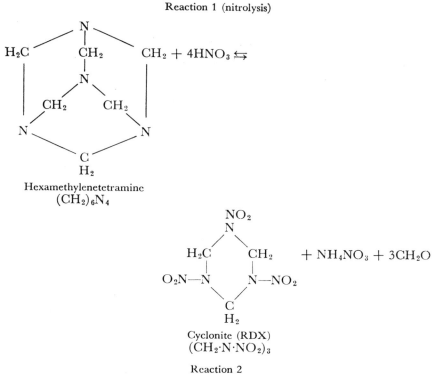

Hexamethylenetetramine
$(CH_2)_6N_4$

Cyclonite (RDX)
$(CH_2 \cdot N \cdot NO_2)_3$

Reaction 2

$$3CH_2O + 3NH_4NO_3 + 6(CH_3CO)_2O \rightleftarrows (CH_2 \cdot N \cdot NO_2)_3 + 12CH_3COOH$$

| Formal-
dehyde | Ammonium
Nitrate | Acetic An-
hydride | Cyclonite | Acetic Acid |

Combined Reaction

$$(CH_2)_6N_4 + 4HNO_3 + 2NH_4NO_3 + 6(CH_3CO)_2O \rightleftarrows$$
$$2(CH_2 \cdot N \cdot NO_2)_3 + 12CH_3COOH$$

The formaldehyde and part of the ammonium nitrate required by Reaction 2 are supplied as products of Reaction 1. Two moles of cyclonite are thereby theoretically produced from each mole of hexamine. The actual yield is about 1.25 moles per mole, due to the formation of some fifty undesired compounds, but this yield is better than the total obtained if the two reactons were carried on separately. The capacity reached at one point, during World War II, was over a million pounds per day of RDX-TNT and waxed RDX mixtures.*

---

* RDX was used in World War II in mixtures: British and U. S. Composition "A": 91% RDX, 9% wax; Composition "B": 60% RDX, 40% TNT, 1% wax; Composition C: 87% RDX, 13% wax mixture; Compositions C-2, etc.; Russian:

EDNA

EDNA or Haleite* (ethylenedinitramine), while not quite as powerful nor as stable as cyclonite, is somewhat less sensitive, and is appreciably more powerful than TNT. Although several reactions have been developed for its production, the most economical appears to be the synthesis of ethylene urea, starting with formaldehyde and hydrogen cyanide, and followed by nitration of the amine groups:

$$CH_2O + HCN \rightarrow HO \cdot CH_2 \cdot CN \xrightarrow{\text{NH}_3} H_2N \cdot CH_2 \cdot CN \xrightarrow{\text{H}_2} H_2N \cdot CH_2 \cdot CH_2 \cdot NH_2$$

Formaldehyde   Ethylene urea
cyanohydrin

$$H_2N \cdot CH_2 \cdot CH_2 \cdot NH_2 + 2HNO_3 \rightarrow O_2N \cdot NH \cdot CH_2 \cdot CH_2 \cdot NH \cdot NO_2 \quad \text{(Haleite)}$$

Tetryl

Tetryl (2,4,6-trinitrophenyl-methylnitramine), the standard booster used by the United States armed forces, may be made from dimethylaniline or from 2,4-dinitrochlorobenzene, both of which are made from benzene. Nitration of dimethylaniline is carried on by first dissolving the oil in 96 per cent sulfuric acid and adding the solution slowly to a mixed acid consisting of approximately 67 per cent HNO_3 and 16 per cent H_2SO_4. The temperature is controlled at about 70° C by cooling coils and agitation. In the nitrator, several reactions occur in sequence: (1) orthopara nitration of the benzene ring, (2) oxidation of one of the N-methyl groups to carboxyl, (3) loss of CO_2, leaving an amine, (4) introduction of the third nitro group of the benzene ring, and finally (5) nitration of the amine to nitramine. The result is tetryl, $(NO_2)_3C_6H_2 \cdot N(CH_3)NO_2$. The solid product is purified by boiling with water, followed by filtration. It may be recrystallized from benzene. In the alternate method the raw material is treated with methylamine to make monomethyldinitraniline, which is then nitrated with mixed acids to make tetryl directly. The yields are higher and the product does not require as many water washings. Also, the nitration is easier to control. On the other hand, the extreme toxicity of dinitrochlorobenzene is an unfavorable factor. Besides being used as a booster, where a small amount of graphite is added to facilitate pressing, tetryl is slurried with molten TNT and cast for use as a bursting charge (Tetrytol).

71.9% RDX, 16.3% TNT, 11.8% tetryl. German compositions were similar to U. S. "A" and "B"; the Italians used an RDX-ammonium nitrate-wax mixture. Only the Japanese used RDX without a desensitizer, hence the shell loading had to be pressed to an extremely high density to avoid premature explosion.

* Named for Dr. G. C. Hale of Picatinny Arsenal.

PETN

PETN (pentaerythritol tetranitrate) is made by nitration of the four hydroxy groups of pentaerythritol $[C(CH_2OH)_4]$ by reaction with 94 per cent HNO_3 at about 50° C. Pentaerythritol may be made by the reduction of a mixture of formaldehyde and acetaldehyde, both of which are obtained from the corresponding alcohols. The pentolites made by casting slurries of PETN with TNT are used as boosters and in many specialized uses where relatively high detonator and primacord sensitivity is required. Recently, cast 50/50 pentolite was introduced by the M. A. Cook, H. E. Farnam and Canadian Industries Limited as a booster for slurry blasting agents and prilled ammonium nitrate-fuel oil mixtures.[8] It is currently being used extensively for that purpose in the United States, Canada, and South America, not only in pentolite but also as the core charge along with composition B as the main charge in the currently popular protected core or "Procore" boosters introduced in 1958.

Picric Acid

Picric acid (trinitrophenol) may be prepared* from benzene directly by simultaneous oxidation and nitration with nitric acid in the presence of mercuric nitrate (Russian), from monochlorobenzene, or from phenol. *Ammonium picrate*[9] is made rather easily by adding picric acid filter cake and aqua ammonia simultaneously and in small increments to a large amount of water in such a way that the batch is at all times slightly alkaline. These two explosives are much less important today than they were during World War I.

Initiators, Primers and Igniters

The common primary explosives used in detonators and fuses (military detonators) are mercury fulminate, lead azide, lead styphnate, nitromannite, and diazodinitrophenol. These are highly sensitive to shock, heat or flame, spark, etc. Igniter compositions do not always include one of the highly sensitive initiators, but may be flame or friction-sensitive mixtures of such compounds as potassium chlorate, antimony sulfide, and an abrasive. A black-powder charge is usually used in propellant and fuse primers. In the first instance it transmits the explosion to the igniter charge which may be black powder or a mixture of barium peroxide or nitrate with magnesium powder. In the second case it provides a delay action before detonating the booster charge.

Mercury fulminate $[Hg(ONO_2)_2]$ is made in small batches. One pound of mercury is added gradually to about 8 pounds of concentrated HNO_3 to

* See the Lefax "Explosives Manual" previously mentioned, or refer to the 4th Edition, page 601.

make mercuric nitrate. This solution, which contains an excess of HNO_3, is refluxed with 10 pounds of 95 per cent ethyl alcohol. The reaction is vigorous, and is moderated in the later stages by addition of dilute alcohol. The solid fulminate crystallizes out as gray crystals which are screened, washed with cold water, drained, and stored in cloth bags under water. It is commonly used with other substances, such as potassium perchlorate, in a mixture which gives a larger flash. Powdered glass, TNT, $Pb(CNS)_2$, and Sb_2S_3 may also be added.

Lead azide, used extensively in composition caps, is made by adding a 2 per cent aqueous solution of sodium azide* to a 5 per cent aqueous solution of lead acetate containing a small amount of dextrin which makes the product safer to handle. When lead azide is used in a percussion primer, it must be mixed with a suitable sensitizing explosive such as lead styphnate (lead trinitroresorcinate). While lead azide is the most common primary explosive or detonator element in blasting caps and fuses (a fuse is a military detonator), it is sometimes replaced by diazodinitrophenol, nitromannite, or other primary explosives.

Lead styphnate is a common igniter for lead azide in the composition cap and is used in direct contact with the bridgewire to obtain fast ignition of the primary explosive. It is a primary explosive but serves better as the igniter because of its extremely high heat sensitivity and the great rapidity with which it ignites the detonator. It is used, for example, in bead form on the bridgewire as the igniter in the duPont seismograph cap, which is one of the fastest of the EB caps when fired by small-current blasting machines. It is extremely sensitive to spark, static electricity, and flame, and therefore requires highly specialized equipment in processing and assembling in caps.

Black Powder

The many uses of this explosive are listed in Table 19.1. Since the 16th century, the formula for the standard fast-burning powder has been approximately 75 per cent potassium nitrate, 15 per cent charcoal, and 10 per cent sulfur. A slow-burning powder contains 59 per cent KNO_3, and powders suitable for time fuses are obtained by blending the two types. For blasting, a weaker powder, e.g., 40 per cent nitrate, 30 per cent charcoal, and 15 per cent sulfur, may be used. Its manufacture consists of a series of batch operations. The finely-ground components are moistened and kneaded together in a sigma-blade mixer, then milled in an edge-runner to make a more homogeneous mixture. The mass is pressed into dense cakes which are then granulated, dried, and screened to various sizes. The dust is used in

---

* Sodium azide, NaN_3, is made by heating a mixture of sodamide ($NaNH_2$) and lime or other water absorber in a stream of nitrous oxide, N_2O.

pyrotechnics and to make fuses; the oversize is recrushed. The sized grains are "polished" and provided with a coating of graphite by tumbling in rotating cylinders or coating pans. The blasting cartridge (coal mining) is a single cylindrical piece with one perforation in the long axis, formed by extruding a paste made of the proper sized grains. All the operations from granulation to screening are hazardous and are performed with remotely controlled machinery located in barricaded buildings. Black powder is rapidly becoming obsolete as a blasting agent but remains the best fuse and igniter composition yet developed.

MISSILE PROPELLANTS

An extremely important application of explosives is in the field of missiles. Rocket propulsion depends on the rapid formation of heat and gas in a chemical reaction, and a rocket engine, by conducting the hot gases at high velocity in a single direction, converts the chemical energy of the explosive or propellant to the kinetic energy of the rocket vehicles in flight. The chemical rocket is a high-thrust device which can deliver much higher levels of power for its weight, even if for short times, than any other known engine. Thus only the rocket can achieve the high velocities required in space applications.

The idea of rockets is not new; it goes back to about the 13th century when a crude form of powder rocket was used by the Tartars against the Mongols. Since that time rockets have appeared occasionally as substitutes for artillery. For example, the British employed rockets against United States forces during the War of 1812 with some measure of success. The concept of the modern rocket, capable of transporting large payloads over intercontinental distances, or of escaping from the earth into interplanetary space, did not begin until the end of the 19th century. K. E. Tsiolkovskii in Russia, R. H. Goddard in the United States, and H. Oberth in Germany were the pioneers. Goddard's work during the 1920's and '30's established both theoretically and experimentally the practicability of the liquid propellant rocket.[10]

The Principle of the Rocket Engine

Figure 19.2 is a simplified illustration of how a rocket engine works. Figure 19.2.a represents a completely closed chamber in which gases are released from a point source to the extent that a pressure, P, is achieved. Assuming that this pressure is not great enough to rupture the chamber, P will be exerted equally in all directions and there will be no motion imparted to the chamber. Figure 19.2.b represents the same chamber with a nozzle opening at one end. If gases are now generated at a rate sufficient to maintain the pressure in the chamber at P while gas is escaping from the nozzle, simple considerations indicate that the force generated by the pressure on the end of the chamber opposite the nozzle will not be balanced by an equal force on the nozzle end. Therefore there will be a resultant motion of the chamber in the direction of the arrow. It will also be evident that the propelling force or thrust will be roughly equal to $A(P-p)$, where A is the area of the nozzle throat and p is the external pressure of the medium in which the rocket is operating.*

The *thrust* of a rocket may then be defined as the reaction force produced by expelling particles at high velocity through a nozzle. These particles, which may be molecules of gas or even solid or liquid particles, are generally referred to as the *working fluid*. Without the expulsion of working fluid there will be no production of thrust, no matter how much energy is

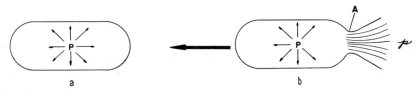

Figure 19.2. Principle of rocket propulsion.

available. In chemical rockets the working fluid is produced at high temperatures and pressures by rapid chemical rearrangements of the *propellant.*

The prime criterion of rocket propellant performance is *specific impulse,* which is a measure of the kinetic energy-producing ability of the propellant. The fundamental equation for specific impulse, or *Isp,* is:

$$Isp = 1/g \sqrt{\left(\frac{2\gamma}{\gamma - 1}\right)\left(\frac{gRT_c}{M}\right)\left[1 - \left(\frac{P_e}{P_c}\right)^{\frac{\gamma - 1}{\gamma}}\right]}$$

where γ = ratio of specific heat at constant pressure to specific heat at constant volume

R = gas constant

T_c = combustion chamber temperature

M = average molecular weight of exhaust products

P_e = external pressure

P_c = chamber pressure

The value of the specific impulse of a propellant is the number of pounds of thrust produced per pound of propellant consumed per second. Examination of the above equation shows that the conditions favoring high specific impulse are high chamber temperature and pressure, low molecular weight of exhaust products, and low external pressure. The higher the temperature

* For a rigorous treatment of the thermodynamics and fluid mechanics of rocket propulsion, see Dow, R. B., "Fundamentals of Advanced Missiles," New York, John Wiley and Sons, Inc., 1958.

and pressure achieved in the chamber, the higher the kinetic energy of the gases escaping through the nozzle. The combination of temperature and pressure is, however, limited by the structural materials of the chamber. The desirability of low molecular weight arises simply because a unit weight of propellant will produce a larger volume of gas if the molecular weight of the gas is low rather than high. The propellant chemicals must therefore be selected carefully so that the average molecular weight of the product gases is as low as possible. One strives, for example, to have as much free hydrogen in the exhaust as is consistent with high chamber temperatures. The desirability of low external pressure simply shows that a rocket will perform better in outer space than it will at sea level. It also demonstrates clearly the invalidity of the notion that the rocket derives its thrust from a push against the air, since the presence of air actually diminishes the forward thrust.

The calculation of specific impulse from known thermodynamic data is a difficult and tedious task since not only must all possible molecular species be taken into account, but also shifts in the chemical equilibria which occur upon expansion of the gases through the nozzle.* Most of this calculation is done today with the aid of high-speed electronic computers. The results of these computations are only as good as the thermodynamic data available, and experimentally determined Isp's are almost always required before a new propellant can be confidently compared with known ones. These experimental measurements are made with actual rocket motors in static firings on elaborately instrumented thrust stands.

Types of Rocket Propellants

Chemical rocket propellants are usually classified into three categories: *solid propellants, liquid bipropellants,* and *liquid monopropellants.* Each category has its own characteristic advantages and disadvantages which will be discussed below. The propellant chemicals are of two types, *fuel* and *oxidizer*. The fuel and the oxidizer are so selected and proportioned that upon reaction they will produce the maximum volume of gas at high temperatures and pressures.

Solid Propellants. In the solid-propellant rocket the fuel and oxidizer are intimately mixed and cast into a single solid *grain* in the combustion chamber which also serves as the fuel tank (Figure 19.3). The grain is bonded firmly to the case and is provided with an axial hole called a *perforation*. The propellant grain is ignited by means of a pyrotechnic device over the entire surface of the perforation, and the burning proceeds from inside to outside. Careful case-bonding prevents hot gases from getting between the grain and the case, causing ignition on the outside of the grain.

---

* There are a number of standard works on the subject of performance calculations. One such text is Penner, S. S., "Chemistry Problems in Jet Propulsion," New York, Pergamon Press, 1957.

This is an important consideration in the modern solid rocket since by constraining the grain to burn from the inside to the outside, the case is insulated against the high combustion temperatures by the unburned portion of the grain. This fact allows the use of relatively light-gauge metal or even plastics for case construction. The perforation, in cross section, may take the form of a star, a cross, or some other shape. The design of this shape affects the rate of burning by varying the total surface area exposed to combutsion which, in turn, affects the rate of production of gas and therefore the thrust.

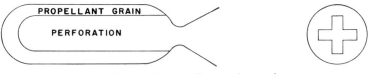

Figure 19.3. Solid propellant rocket engine.

Propellant grains must be completely homogeneous and without bubbles or other inclusions if reliable, reproducible performance is to be attained. They must also possess certain mechanical strength characteristics so that they will not develop cracks during handling, storage, or under the severe thermal shock of ignition. A crack which develops in the grain will give rise to irregular burning or even an explosion.

Solid propellant grains are of two types: *double-base* and *composite*. The double-base propellant resembles smokeless gunpowder and is composed principally of nitrocellulose and nitroglycerine. The composite propellant, which is now more widely used, consists of a solid inorganic oxidizer, such as ammonium perchlorate, which is intimately mixed with a polymeric material serving at once as a *binder* and a fuel. Common binders are synthetic rubbers, or plastics such as polyurethane.

In Table 19.2 are indicated the specific impulses of a number of common solid-propellant combinations. These impulses vary between 175 and 250

TABLE 19.2. SPECIFIC IMPULSES OF SOME COMMON SOLID
PROPELLANT COMBINATIONS

Propellant Type	Composition (weight per cent)	*Isp* (sec)
Composite	Asphalt (22–30)	180–195
	KClO$_4$ (78–70)	
Composite	Rubber or plastic (50–20)	
	NH$_4$ClO$_4$ (50–80)	175–240
Extruded double base	Nitrocellulose (50–60)	
	Nitroglycerine (30–45)	
	Miscellaneous (1–10)	205–230
Cast double base	Nitrocellulose (45–55)	
	Nitroglycerine (25–40)	
	Plasticizer (12–22)	
	Miscellaneous (1–2)	160–220

seconds, with the higher values belonging to the composite type. Solid propellants have the advantage of reliability—there are no moving parts to malfunction—and instant readiness. Care must be taken in storage and handling, however, to assure that cracks do not develop in the grain.

Liquid Bipropellant. The liquid-bipropellant system is used today for the largest rockets. In this system the liquid fuel and the liquid oxidizer

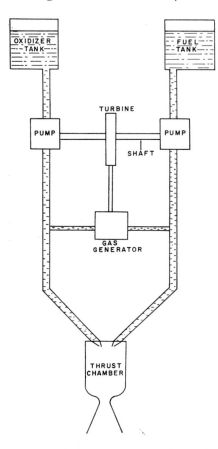

Figure 19.4. Liquid bipropellant rocket engine.

are stored in separate tanks and are fed separately to the combustion chamber. The propellants are fed either by means of pumps or by pressurization with an inert gas. In the case of the pump-fed rocket, the pumps are driven by gas turbines. The gas for these turbines is supplied by a generator which is actually a small rocket motor operating off a side stream of the main rocket propellants (Figure 19.4) or, in some cases, a separate propellant system. In the largest rockets, thousands of pounds per second of propellants must be pumped to the engine, and the pump drives must develop thousands of horsepower.

In liquid engines, the designer has the opportunity to provide a cooling system which will protect the chamber and nozzle from the effects of the high temperature gases but will not decrease the efficiency of the engine by wasting energy. This is accompanied by providing cavities in the walls of the chamber and the nozzle through which the propellant is circulated before being introduced to the chamber where it is burned. This technique is known as *regenerative cooling*.

Some typical liquid fuels are kerosene, alcohol, hydrazine, and liquid hydrogen. Typical oxidizers are nitric acid, nitrogen tetroxide, liquid oxygen,

TABLE 19.3. PROPERTIES OF SEVERAL COMMON LIQUID
BIPROPELLANT SYSTEMS

Oxidizer	Fuel	Specific Gravity	Boiling Point (°F)	Isp (sec)*
Red fuming nitric acid		1.56	142	
	Ammonia	0.68	−28	232
	JP-4	0.80	470	232
	Hydrazine	1.00	236	246
Hydrogen peroxide		1.39	288	
	JP-4	0.80	470	235
	Hydrazine	1.00	236	243
Nitrogen tetroxide		1.49	70	
	Analine	1.02	364	221
	Hydrazine	1.00	236	256
Liquid oxygen		1.14	−297	
	Ethyl alcohol	0.79	174	242
	JP-4	0.80	470	263
	Hydrazine	1.00	236	263
	Liquid hydrogen	0.07	−422	347
Liquid Fluorine		1.51	−306	
	Ammonia	0.68	−28	311
	Hydrazine	1.00	236	315
	Liquid hydrogen	0.07	−422	364

* 300 psi chamber pressure, exhausting to 1 atmosphere.

and liquid fluorine. Liquid-propellant systems are usually classified as either *storable* or *cryogenic*. The cryogenic systems generally exhibit higher performance,* but because of the handling difficulties presented by the low boiling point material involved, reliability is lower than in other systems, and instant readiness is a practical impossibility. The reliabilty and readiness characteristics are improved in the case of storable systems, but at the expense of performance.

Table 19.3 gives the specific impulses of several common liquid-bipropellant systems. Also indicated are the boiling points and densities of the

* The system liquid hydrogen-liquid fluorine approaches the limit in specific impulse obtainable with chemical propellants. Recent advances in the technology of handling these substances have made such a system practical from an engineering point of view and a hydrogen-fluorine engine is currently being developed. See Sloop, J. L., *Astronautics*, p. 28 (Sept. 1958).

propellants involved. In comparison with solid propellants, liquid bipropellants exhibit higher performance but lower reliability, although storable liquids may approach solids with respect to the latter characteristic. Liquid engines possess an on-off capability not possible in solid engines, and there is a practical engineering limit to the size a single solid grain can be successfully manufactured. Thus the largest engines have up to now been liquid engines, although recent advances in the technology of solid propellants have indicated that very large solid engines are feasible.[11]

Liquid Monopropellants. In a monopropellant rocket, the propellant is an "unstable" liquid chemical which, in the presence of a catalyst or a small amount of initiating energy, will decompose to give heat and large volumes of gas. Examples of such materials are hydrogen peroxide:

$$H_2O_2 \rightarrow \tfrac{1}{2}O_2(g) + H_2O(g)$$

and hydrazine:

$$N_2H_4 \rightarrow N_2(g) + 2H_2(g)$$

In general, monopropellants exhibit low performance (at 300 pounds chamber pressure, exhausting to 1 atmosphere, hydrogen peroxide has a specific impulse of 133 seconds; hydrazine, 174 seconds); materials containing enough energy to give a high theoretical specific impulse are usually too shock-sensitive to be useful in rocket work. The discovery of a high performance monopropellant which is stable enough to be handled and used safely would lead to a rocket engine with all the advantages of a liquid bipropellant engine and a reliability approaching that of a solid propellant engine.[4,13]

Propellant Manufacture

The development and manufacture of missile propellants represents a significant market for the chemical industry. The United States government budget for fiscal 1958 for this type of activity was $130,000,000, and for 1959, $270,000,000.[3] Some of the factors involved in the manufacture of solid propellants, and several selected liquid propellants are described below.

Double-Base Solid Propellants. The manufacture of double-base propellants depends on the conversion of nitrocellulose from its raw fibrous form to a dense plastic form. The process for accomplishing this is called *colloiding*. In the solvent process for colloiding, nitrocellulose, nitroglycerine, and other ingredients are mixed with suitable solvents, such as ether or alcohol, to the consistency of a dough. The dough is extruded to the desired shape and the excess solvent removed by evaporation. The solvent process is unsuitable, however, for the manufacture of the large grains required for rockets because of the long drying times required for the release of the processing solvent. A solventless method has accordingly been developed where colloiding is accomplished by hot working the ingredients on rolls before forming the desired shape by hot extrusion. A more recent development, allowing the fabrication of much larger grains than can be formed by extrusion, is the casting method, wherein the ingredients are introduced into a mold having the shape and dimensions desired in the finished grain.

Composite Solid Propellant. The composite propellant, which is now dominant in the solid field, uses a solid oxidant with an organic resin or rubber which serves as both fuel and binder. In the manufacture of a solid grain, the oxidant, such as ammonium nitrate or ammonium perchlorate, is first subjected to a series of grinding operations to maintain strict control over particle size. The particle size of the oxidizer has a definite effect on the burning rate and therefore on the ballistic properties of the finished propellant. The oxidizer is then mixed with the polymer to form a semifluid slurry. This mixing process is often carried out in a mixer of the Baker-Perkins type. The propellant mixture is poured or "cast" into the rocket motor case itself, where it is cured by heating for several hours under carefully controlled conditions. After curing, the slurry becomes a tough elastic solid which is bonded strongly to the walls of the motor. The motor case is initially fitted with a metal mandrel which will provide the perforation in the finished grain; after curing the mandrel is removed and the fabrication of the rocket motor is complete, except for the installation of the nozzle assembly and the igniter.

Cryogenic Liquid Propellants. The ability to design and fabricate the large, high performance rockets needed for ballistic missile and space applications depends in large measure on the advances in the engineering technology of the handling of such intractable materials as liquid oxygen (b.p., $-297°$ F), liquid fluorine (b.p., $-305°$ F), and liquid hydrogen (b.p., $-423°$ F).

The principal factor responsible for the ability to put these low-boiling liquids to practical use is the development of highly efficient insulating systems. One such system consists of alternating layers of aluminum foil and glass fiber mats in a jacket evacuated to one micron or less. A 40 gallon liquid-hydrogen cylinder, surrounded with only a one inch thickness of this insulator, has only two per cent per day evaporation loss. Large tank trailers for up to 8000 gallons of liquid hydrogen are now in service. This equipment allows the overland hauling of liquid hydrogen for long distances with evaporation losses of less than one per cent.[2]

Molecular hydrogen exists in two forms: orthohydrogen, where the nuclei of the two atoms are spinning in the same direction, and parahydrogen, where the nuclei spin in opposite directions. These two forms are in equilibrium with each other, and at room temperature the equilibrium mixture contains 75 per cent of the ortho form and 25 per cent of the para form.

When cooled to the boiling point ($-423°$ F), this mixture is unstable, since the equilibrium concentration of parahydrogen at this temperature is 99.8 per cent; the orthohydrogen will convert very slowly to the para form. The conversion from 25 per cent para to 90 per cent takes about one month. This conversion is accompanied by the evolution of heat which is sufficient to cause severe evaporation losses of the liquid. In order to overcome this difficulty, a hydrous ferric oxide catalyst is used in connection with the liquefaction process to speed up the conversion so that a stable product may be obtained. Modern liquefiers can produce liquid hydrogen which is more than 95 per cent parahydrogen.[12] It has been estimated that it may be possible to produce liquid hydrogen for as little as 40 cents per pound.

Liquid fluorine is difficult to handle and use, not only because of its low boiling point, but also because of its extremely reactive nature. Fluorine will violently attack nearly all oxidizable substances, including metals. Fortunately the action of fluorine on most structural metals causes a solid fluoride film to form which protects the metal from further attack. Nickel alloys which possess suitable strength characteristics at low temperature and are resistant to fluorine attack are used as the materials of construction of liquid fluorine containers. Fluorine is produced by the electrolysis of hydrogen fluoride in fused potassium fluoride.

Storable Liquid Propellants. Typical examples of storable propellants are nitrogen tetroxide (N_2O_4) and hydrazine (N_2H_4). Both materials are now produced in fairly large quantities. It is significant that both of these materials are of commercial importance independent of their use in missiles. However, if it had not been for the propellant application, neither would have been developed as quickly. A brief discussion of the production processes for these chemicals is given below.

Hydrazine* is produced by the controlled oxidation of ammonia in the well-known Raschig synthesis. Sodium hypochlorite, formed by the chlorination of caustic soda, reacts with excess ammonia in a two-step process to form, successively, chloramine and aqueous hydrazine:

$$NH_3 + NaOCl \rightarrow NH_2Cl + NaOH$$
$$NH_2Cl + NaOH + NH_3 \rightarrow N_2H_4 + NaCl + H_2O$$

Hydrazine and water form an azeotrope which boils at $120.1°$ C. Anhydrous hydrazine is obtained by dehydration of the azeotrope with caustic, followed by a vacuum distillation. By another method, the azeotrope is broken by the addition of aniline as a third component, followed by a distillation in which the water-aniline azeotrope is taken overhead and

---

* For a discussion of the factors involved in the safe handling and use of hydrazine, see *Liquid Propellant Safety Manual* (Oct. 1958), published by the Liquid Propellant Information Agency.

anhydrous hydrazine is obtained as a bottoms product. By this latter method hydrazine may be produced at 98+ per cent purity.

Although many methods for preparing N_2O_4 have been described, only four methods have been considered practical for large-scale production. The catalytic oxidation of ammonia is the most important commercial method. A mixture containing about 9 per cent ammonia in air is oxidized at pressures between 25 and 100 psig. This step is identical with the oxidation process used for the production of nitric acid. The gaseous products containing nitric oxide (NO) and water are cooled and dried by scrubbing with cold nitric acid. The dry nitric oxide containing unreacted nitrogen from the air is further oxidized by the addition of air to form NO_2. Nitrogen dioxide forms an equilibrium mixture with its dimerized form of dinitrogen tetroxide, N_2O_4, so that on cooling, the equilibrium shifts to favor the formation of N_2O_4. The sequence of reactions is illustrated by the following equations:

$$4NH_3 + 5O_2 \rightarrow 4NO + 6H_2O$$
$$2NO + O_2 \rightarrow 2NO_2$$
$$2NO_2 \rightarrow N_2O_4$$

The direct fixation of atmospheric nitrogen may be economically feasible where a cheap electric power source is available. The fixation is accomplished by passing air through an electric arc of 4000–5000° F to yield nitric oxide. The hot nitric oxide is quenched by introducing cold air which results in the oxidation of nitric oxide to nitrogen dioxide.

More detailed descriptions of the manufacture of these compounds may be found in Chapter 5.

REFERENCES

1. Bebie, J., "Manual of Explosives, Military Pyrotechnics and Chemical Warfare Agents," New York, The Macmillan Co., 1943.
2. *Chem. Eng.*, **66**, No. 19, 69 (1959).
3. *Chem. & Eng. News*, **36**, No. 1, 79 (1958).
4. Clark, J. D., *Astronautics*, **4**, No. 9, 34 (1958).
5. Cook, M. A., "The Science of High Explosives," New York, Reinhold Publishing Corp., 1958.
6. Cook, M. A., and McEwan, W. S., *J. App. Phys.*, **29**, 1612 (1958).
7. Davis, T. L., "The Chemistry of Powders and Explosives," New York, John Wiley and Sons, Inc., 1941.
8. Farnam, H. E., Jr., Paper presented at Eighth Annual Drillers' and Blasters' Symposium, U. of Minn., Oct. 2, 3, 4, 1958. Cook, M. A., *Science*, **132**, 1105 (1960).
9. Gerber, T. C., *Chem. Met. Eng.*, **51**, 100 (1944).
10. Goddard, R. H., "Rocket Development," New York, Prentice-Hall, 1948.
11. Haite, W. F., *Astronautics*, **3**, No. 9, 38 (1958).
12. *Missiles and Rockets*, **5**, No. 33, 21 (1959).
13. Pursglove, S. D., *Missiles and Rockets*, **5**, No. 30, 28 (1959).
14. Raifsnider, P. J., *Chem. Ind.* **57**, No. 7, 1054 (1945).

20

PHARMACEUTICAL INDUSTRIES

In collaboration with John J. Miskel and John E. Carlson*

COMPANIES THAT MANUFACTURE CHEMICALS or medicinals for use in the treatment or prevention of disease, for relief of pain, or for the promotion of general health, for either humans or animals, may be said to be in the "pharmaceutical" industry. The field is large, and it is therefore possible for a company, depending on management philosophy, to be engaged in producing only one product, perhaps even a by-product of some other line of business, or to be devoted to the manufacture of several major types of pharmaceuticals such as antibiotics, hormones, vitamins, nitrofurans, tranquilizers, or vaccines.

History

Most of the large established manufacturers trace their origin to the latter half of the 1800's. Their growth up to the time of World War I may be described as the simple expansion of a small prescription laboratory to a large prescription laboratory, the major differences being in the size of the batch. Production volume was primarily biological—prophylactic and therapeutic organic medicinal preparations derived from animal and plant tissues or cells. Products were extracted from various herbs, leaves, roots, barks, and animal glands at atmospheric pressure using wooden vats, cop-

* Chas. Pfizer and Company, Inc., Brooklyn, N. Y.

per, and iron equipment. It is interesting to note that chemical engineering was first recognized as a field in the early 1900's, and that each advance in unit operations and processing equipment was directly applicable to the pharmaceutical industry where trace elements, temperatures, and other extremely critical factors can nullify or destroy the desired chemical reaction. World War I forced companies in the United States, heretofore dependent on Germany as a source of supply, to establish their own production programs. Emphasis was still not on primary research for the cure of specific

TABLE 20.1. TOTAL U. S. DRUG SALES AT MANUFACTURERS' LEVEL
(Millions of Dollars)

Ethical Sales	1939	1949	1950	1951	1952	1953
Antibiotics:						
Penicillin	...	124	130	250	110	120
Streptomycin	...	35	33	60	45	48
Broad Spectrums	...	...	125	145	150	137
Others	...	1	2	5	9	23
(Antibiotics total)		160	290	460	314	328
Vitamins and Hematinics	17	136	140	180	190	195
Endocrines:						
Cortisone and ACTH	...	...	13	35	36	43
Others	16	70	62	65	67	67
(Endocrines total)	16	70	75	100	103	110
Sulfonamides	5	31	39	53	48	48
Antihistamines	...	14	28	46	48	48
Barbiturates	9	30	32	36	40	44
Biologicals	9	29	31	37	44	46
Acetylsalicylic Acid	5	12	14	15	19	20
Others	88	232	208	173	139	140
Total Ethical Sales	149	714	857	1,100	945	979
Proprietary Sales	152	451	480	500	518	530
Total Drug Sales	301	1,165	1,337	1,600	1,463	1,509

ills; the aim was merely to replace materials no longer available through normal trade channels to supply the domestic market. Surprisingly, it was not until 1943 that a major breakthrough was made in medicine. Sulfa drugs had proved ineffective against microbial infections among the armed forces in Guadalcanal and New Guinea. Given no chance for recovery and with nothing to lose, these men were treated with penicillin. That the treatment was successful is evidenced by the current widespread use of this drug.

Pharmaceutical companies have since taken specialists from every field of scientific endeavor—biologists, botanists, chemists, chemical engineers, microbiologists, pharmacologists, pharmacists, clinicians, physicians, and many others—and coordinated their efforts in an integrated scientific search for drugs to cure specific diseases. The benefits of their research is apparent in the continuing introduction of new products serving mankind.

Growth of Industry

Some indication of the rapid growth of the pharmaceutical industry is given in Table 20.1. In 1939 drug sales in the United States at the manu-

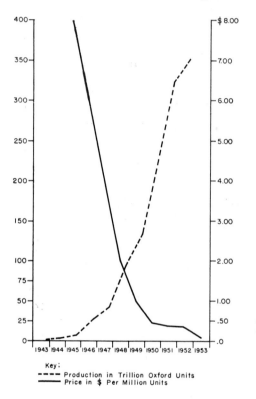

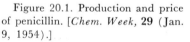

Figure 20.1. Production and price of penicillin. [*Chem. Week,* **29** (Jan. 9, 1954).]

facturers' level were $301 million; this figure had increased to $1,509 million by 1953. More significant is the nature of the product mix with antibiotics, cortisone, and antihistamines, all nonexistent in 1939, accounting for a majority of the sales in 1953. Rapid obsolescence of products and steep price declines are characeritsic of the industry; Figures 20.1 and 20.2 show the latter trend for penicillin, streptomycin, and dihydrostreptomycin. The apparent high profit margin for penicillin in 1943 attracted several new companies into the field, but they could not compete economically and by 1952 had ceased operating. Table 20.2 lists the volume and price of some of the synthetic medicinals produced in 1957.

Research

There is no stability in the sales market; a high profit item may become obsolete overnight with the introduction of a competitor's discoveries. A company is therefore forced to invest in research to maintain its economic existence. In 1957 total research expenditures of the pharmaceutical industry

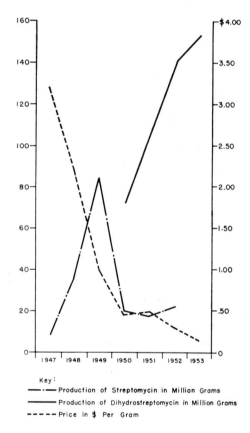

Figure 20.2. Production and price of streptomycin and dihydrostreptomycin. [*Chem. Week,* **29** (*Jan. 9, 1954*).]

Key:
— · — Production of Streptomycin in Million Grams
———— Production of Dihydrostreptomycin in Million Grams
– – – – Price in $ Per Gram

were $127 million, or 7.5 per cent of sales, as compared with a general industry average of 0.5 to 1.0 per cent.

The following table indicates how pharmaceutical products have contributed to a longer life expectancy and the curbing of epidemics:

Period in History	Life Expectancy (years)
Ancient Times	20 plus
1840	41
1935	60 minus
1950	68 men
	73 women

TABLE 20.2. PRODUCTION OF SYNTHETIC MEDICINALS IN THE
UNITED STATES (1957)*

(Items selected for their interest)

	Pounds	Unit Value
Acetylsalicylic acid (aspirin)	18,054,000	$ .52
Procaine hydrochloride	588,000	2.75
Salicylic acid	7,611,000	.38
Sodium salicylate	612,000	.70
Antibiotics for human or veterinary use, total	2,373,000	162.91
Antibiotics for animal feed supplements, food preservation, and crop spraying	870,000	39.38
Antihistamines	232,000	32.45
Barbituric acid and derivatives, total	755,000	5.18
5-Ethyl-5-(1-methyl-n-butyl) barbituric acid (Pentobarbital) and sodium salt	140,000	6.06
5-Ethyl-5-phenylbarbituric acid (Phenobarbital) (Luminal)	294,000	3.27
All other	238,000	8.17
Caffeine, natural and synthetic	1,636,000	2.69
Hormones (steroid), total	52,000	2,573.60
Piperazine	987,000	1.92
Tranquilizers	205,000	335.20
B1 (Thiamine derivatives)	294,000	17.45
B2 (Riboflavin for human consumption) (100%)	140,000	18.07
B2 (Riboflavin for animal and poultry consumption) (100%)	265,000	17.22
Niacin (Nicotinic acid)	2,204,000	2.42
Niacinamide	825,000	3.68
All other	330,000	12.18

* U. S. Tariff Commission.

Regulation

Superimposed on other aspects of the industry is the positive impetus afforded by a strong government position in regard to regulation, based on provisions of the Federal Food, Drug, and Cosmetic Act of 1938. In no other industry does similar regulation exist.

The elixir sulfanilamide tragedy, in which a drug used in many preparations was dissolved in diethylene glycol causing 108 deaths, occurred as recently as 1937. Simple animal testing for toxicity would have prevented this incident which greatly influenced passage of the Act in 1938. This Act prohibits the use of deleterious substances, demands proof of the safety of new drugs, imposes definite labeling requirements, and provides for the actual inspection of manufacturing plants as well as the final product.

On July 6, 1945 Congress amended the Act so that every batch of penicillin must be certified before it can be marketed. Antibiotics are also similarly controlled.

Because their reputation in the field is of utmost importance to them, many manufacturers go far beyond what is demanded by the government, but the latter establishes a minimum control, thereby ensuring the public's trust and contributing to the industries' growth.

Development of a Product

Concentrated effort and a coordinated organization of many specialists are prime requisites for developing and marketing a product in the pharmaceutical industry. The following is an outline of the necessary procedure; each step represents a stumbling block that may, if not hurdled, render all previous work valueless:

(1) Thorough market studies aimed at evaluating sales potentials, competition, and distribution of products.

(2) Laboratory research conducted to formulate a practical means of attaining desired product characteristics and of establishing the product's therapeutic value.

(3) Medical Department supervision, in cooperation with physicians and hospitals, of their clinical study to evaluate the efficacy of the drug and to determine dosage forms.

(4) Pilot plant trial runs, determination of stability data, and submission of all records to the Food and Drug Administration for approval to place the drug on the market.

(5) Large scale production aimed at meeting estimated sales forecasts in various dosage forms recommended by the Medical Department.

(6) Full scale marketing launched with detailing of physicians and druggists, combined with a comprehensive advertising program for ethical products; advertising directed to the public through popular media for proprietary products.

Pharmaceutical Preparations

Dosage Forms. In the manufacture of a finished salable drug product, the "drug"—the constituent having the therapeutic value—is only one component. Its production may be by synthesis, fermentation, or extraction, whichever is economically feasible; any one or all methods may be practical. The drug is then compounded with other ingredients in a formulation and packaged as a powder, liquid, capsule, tablet, sugar-coated tablet, ointment, or aerosol. The drug prepared as a liquid or powder may be sterile or nonsterile. A sterile product is one that is completely free of microorganisms.

Sterilization may be achieved in many ways: by the use of dry heat at 170° C for two hours, steam (15 psig) at 121° C for twenty minutes, or gas (formaldehyde and ethylene oxide); by filtration using porcelain, asbestos filter pads, diatomaceous earth, and sintered glass; by freeze-drying; or by ultraviolet radiation. The method employed depends on the physical and chemical properties of the material.

Sterile Filling. The personnel and areas involved in sterile filling operations are governed by strict procedures common to the industry. Before entering the sterile working area, employees must first go to a dressing room in which there is a low long bench dividing the room. All items to be worn in the sterile area are previously sterilized. A worker puts on a shoe cover on one side of the bench and then places his foot on the other side, repeating the procedure with the other foot. He then dons gown, hat, eye shields, and rubber gloves (see Figure 20.3).

The working areas and the dressing room are under positive sterile filtered air pressure so that atmospheric air may not enter; ultraviolet lights

Figure 20.3. Sterile area dress includes hood, visor, mask, gown, rubber gloves, and shoe covers. (*Courtesy Chas. Pfizer and Co., Inc.*)

are arranged to keep the microorganism count low, and the areas and equipment are frequently wiped with disinfecting solutions.

All materials, preparations to be filled, bottles, caps, and equipment are sterilized before being brought into the filling area. Washed bottles are sterilized by dry heat in electric ovens. Sealed sterile bottles of powder and equipment are wiped with a disinfecting solution and passed through an air lock equipped with high-intensity ultraviolet lights and highly reflective porcelain tile walls. Open tanks and similar equipment are steam sterilized.

Packaging. The pharmaceutical industry is a leader in the field of packaging because it is concerned not only with the aesthetic appeal of the wrapping, but also with the stability requirements of the drug as well as the fact that the drug must reach the consumer without tampering and, if necessary, in a sterile condition.

The problem of compatibility arises in that components of a glass vial or rubber stopper may affect the contained liquid, or if air causes oxidation of a product the vial may have to be filled with an inert gas such as nitrogen. Plastic bottles provide a necessary vapor barrier but an ingredient such as flavor may be lost. Each product and form of packaging has unique characteristics which must be completely investigated.

Figure 20.4. Steam sterilizer for processing equipment. (*Courtesy Chas. Pfizer and Co., Inc.*)

To utilize the features of new packaging materials special packaging machines are required. A pharmaceutical manufacturer stated recently that in 1947 90 per cent of his packaging was done by hand, while in 1959 90 per cent was done by high speed machines. This trend is typical; machines are rated by capacities of 100 to over 300 packages per minute, with continued emphasis on more speed for reduced costs.

Products

The products of the pharmaceutical industry are quite varied, ranging from tincture of iodine and ether to drugs in multiple dosage forms.

Ordinary sugar may be converted into a pharmaceutical product by simple processing. A sterile sucrose solution used for intravenous injection to reduce intracranial pressure is prepared by boiling sucrose in pyrogen-free water for ten minutes and cooling it, adjusting the concentration with additional sterile pyrogen-free water, then filtering it and filling appropriate vials.

Natural pharmaceuticals are always being supplemented and replaced by synthetic products; at the same time the search for materials of vegetable or animal origin is often successful: reserpine, a tranquilizer for mental patients, comes from a plant. Insulin, from the pancreas of the steer, is being supplanted by oral chlorpropamide (*Diabinese*) and tolbutamide (*Orinase*). Arsphenamine ("Salvarsan"), the specific for syphilis, is strictly synthetic; its modern form, "Neosalvarsan," is more stable in air. Quinine sulfate, from the bark of the cinchona tree (Peru and Bolivia), is an antipyretic; it is supplemented by the synthetics acetanilide (used for headache powders) and acetylsalicylic acid (aspirin). Quinine, the antimalarial, scarce during

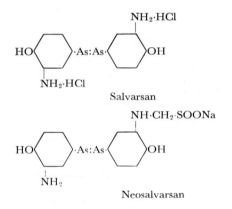

Salvarsan

Neosalvarsan

the war, was supplemented first by "Atabrine" (also known as mepacrine and quinacrine), then by chloroquine and "Paludrine." "Atabrine" is a suppressive drug which generally turns the skin yellow. "Plasmochin" (8-amino quinoline) is a curative drug and is toxic. "Paludrine" is a suppressant. Some of the synthetics must be taken simultaneously with quinine. The narcotic morphine sulfate, the local anesthetic cocaine hydrochloride, and the mydriatic (pupil-dilating) atropine sulfate are natural products. Cocaine is now supplemented by synthetic substances such as procaine hydrochloride ("Novocaine") and several other similar products used in dental surgery. Laxatives are still essentially vegetable in origin, for example, cascara sagrada bark extract and castor oil; of the synthetic laxatives, phenolphthalein is successfully prescribed. The important anesthetic liquids, chloroform and ether, which have revolutionized surgery, robbing operations of their terrors and removing the resistance of the conscious patient, are synthetics of comparatively simple manufacture. Both are made from ethyl alcohol and might be called semi-synthetic, since alcohol is a fermentation product. Alcohol may, however, be made from acetylene, in which case it would be strictly synthetic. The hypnotic paraldehyde is polymerized acetaldehyde from the distillation of wood, hence it may be called a semi-synthetic. "Veronal" (a sleeping powder) and saccharin (a sweet nonsugar) are true synthetics. Phenol, formaldehyde, hydrogen peroxide, and iodoform are described in other chapters.

That many compounds may possibly be of some therapeutic value, thus making them products of the pharmaceutical industry, is not difficult to imagine. The products discussed in the following pages are only a small sampling from the industry, but their processing is typical.

Ethyl Ether

There are several methods of producing ethyl ether which has an R-O-R structure. The Williamson synthesis reacts an alkyl halide and sodium alkoxide:

$$C_2H_5ONa + C_2H_5I \rightarrow C_2H_5OC_2H_5 + NaI$$

The sulfuric acid method, a commercial one, produces ether by the dehydration of ethyl alcohol in a continuous process. The sulfuric acid mixed with the required amount of alcohol is heated to 140° C in a lead-lined steel boiler by means of steam in a closed lead coil; alcohol is vaporized in a separate vessel and the vapor is sent through the acid-alcohol mixture in the still.* A mixture of ether, alcohol, and water is emitted from the still in vapor form. This vapor is passed through a dilute caustic solution for removal of sulfur compounds, thence to a column still. The water flows out at the bottom and the alcohol, containing some ether and water (5 per cent), is removed in vapor form half way up the column, condensed, and reused in the vaporizer. At the top of the rectifier ether vapors are emitted and condensed in a separate condenser; this ether contains a small amount of water and alcohol. The efficiency of the process is high, about 94 per cent. The reactions are:

$$C_2H_5OH + H_2SO_4 \rightarrow C_2H_5 \cdot HSO_4 + H_2O$$
Ethylsulfuric acid

$$C_2H_5OH + C_2H_5 \cdot HSO_4 \rightarrow C_2H_5 \cdot O \cdot C_2H_5 + H_2SO_4$$
Ether

The sulfuric acid is regenerated; benzenesulfonic acid has been proposed in lieu of sulfuric acid. A temperature of 128° C is preferred in a British plant.[1]

---

* Or an intermediate tower with quartz packing may be used in which the regenerated acid mixes with the alcohol and the mixture overflows in the still proper; U. S. Patent 1,328,258.

Much commercial production in the United States employs ethylene as a starting material. This is reacted with sulfuric acid to form ethylsulfuric acid; the rest of the process is the same as above.

Ether is a volatile inflammable liquid, colorless, slightly soluble in water, lighter than water. It boils at 34.6° C and contains 96 to 98 per cent $C_4H_{10}O$, the remainder consisting of alcohol and water. Ether U.S.P. (Pharmacopeia of the United States recognized as government standard for purity)* for anesthetic use must be preserved in tight containers of not more than 3 kilograms capacity and must not be used for anesthesia if it has been removed from the original container for 24 hours. It is still the principal anesthetic in use.

Chloroform is more rapid than ether in its anesthetic action, but it is more depressing to the heart. Both are being supplemented with nitrous oxide mixed with oxygen, even in major operations. The anesthesia may, for instance, be begun with ether and continued with nitrous oxide, applied at whatever intervals are necessary to keep the patient unconscious.

Cocaine

Cocaine is extracted from coca leaves of the *erythroxylon coca* and related plants found in Ceylon, Java, Peru, Brazil, and Bolivia. Commercially the leaves come from South America and contain 0.5 to 2 per cent of the cocaine base. The ground leaves are moistened with a sodium carbonate solution and percolated with a solvent such as benzene. The liquid is mixed with dilute sulfuric acid, and the acid solution is then treated with an excess of sodium carbonate. The precipitated alkaloids are removed with ether, dried with sodium carbonate, and filtered; the ether is distilled off. The residue is dissolved in methyl alcohol, heated with alcoholic hydrogen chloride, and diluted with water; the organic acids formed are removed with chloroform. The aqueous solution is concentrated, neutralized, cooled with ice, and benzolated by heating with benzoyl chloride at 150° C; the cocaine is precipitated by adding water and sodium hydroxide, extracted with ether, and crystallized out. This material is purified by recrystallization. The hydrochloride is made by adding cocaine to an alcoholic solution of hydrochloric acid and then crystallizing the solution.

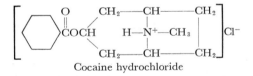
Cocaine hydrochloride

---

* These standards are listed in the U. S. Pharmacopeia, XVth edition (1955), obtainable from the Mack Printing Company, Easton, Pa. The newer remedies are listed separately, in "New and Non-official Remedies," published yearly by the American Medical Association, 535 N. Dearborn Street, Chicago, Ill.

Sterilization difficulties and the habit forming tendencies of this compound led to a search for more desirable local anesthetics. Procaine is made from *para*-aminobenzoic acid by forming the diethylaminoethyl ester; the resulting base is insoluble in water but its hydrochloride is freely soluble. It is used chiefly in the latter form. The successful introduction of procaine hydrochloride, also called "Novocaine," as a local anesthetic replacing cocaine has resulted in the preparation of many similar esters and also of substances with different structures, such as lidocaine (xylocaine), ethyl aminobenzoate (anesthesin), pontocaine hydrochloride, and tetracaine hydrochloride. For example, lidocaine is prepared commercially by the chloroacetylation of 2,6-xylidine to give chloroacetoxylidide which in turn is condensed with diethylamine.

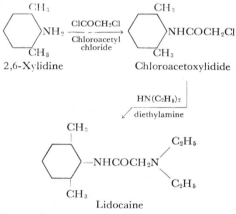

Acetylsalicylic Acid

Acetylsalicylic acid, sold in part under the name of aspirin, is made by dissolving salicylic acid in glacial acetic acid and adding an excess of acetyl chloride. The vessel or still, usually lined with stoneware or glass, is jacketed, and the charge is heated by steam which passes through the jacket until the reaction starts. The steam may then be turned off, since the reaction is exothermic. Hydrogen chloride exits through a worm, which condenses the acetyl chloride carried out, and goes to a small tower where it is absorbed in water. At the end of the process, steam is sent through the jacket and the remaining acetyl chloride is distilled. The crude acetylsalicylic acid is left in the still to be purified by solution in alcohol and precipitation by water.

A more recent (1953) commercial process[3] engineered for good yields, high purity, and low cost is shown in Figure 20.5. Salicylic acid powder, acetic anhydride, and mother liquor are reacted in a 500-gallon glass-lined reactor for 2 to 3 hours. The mass is then pumped through a stainless steel filter to a crystallizing kettle which may be a 500-gallon glass-lined

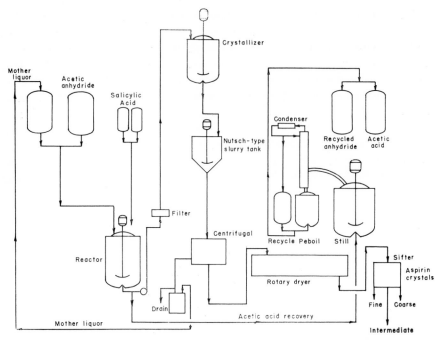

Figure 20.5. Flow diagram for production of bulk aspirin. [*Chem. Eng.*, **60**, *No. 6,* *116–120* (*1953*).]

reactor. The temperature is reduced to 3° C, and after crystallization a portion of the mother liquor is drawn off for the next batch (step 1) in a modified nutsch-type slurry tank. The remaining slurry is centrifuged, and the crystals are dried in a rotary dryer to yield salable bulk aspirin. Excess mother liquor is stored and then distilled to acetic acid.

Sulfanilamide and Sulfathiazole

Among the new drugs, sulfanilamide and sulfathiazole, both white solids, have rapidly attained commercial importance.

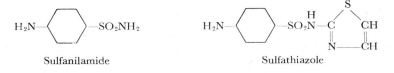

Sulfanilamide   Sulfathiazole

Ascorbic Acid (Vitamin C)

This vitamin is necessary for the prevention and cure of scurvy and is produced commercially by synthesis. Sorbitol, made by hydrogenating dextrose, is the raw material. It is converted by the action of the organism *Acetobacter suboxydans* to L-sorbose, which is condensed with acetone by means of sulfuric acid to diacetone sorbose, oxidized by potassium permanganate and then hydrolyzed forming 2-keto-1-gluconic acid. This acid is esterified with methanol, and an intermediate sodio compound is formed with sodium methoxide. The methyl group and sodium are removed with aqueous hydrochloric acid by hydrolysis, and lactonization yields ascorbic acid. The formulas for the commercial process are:

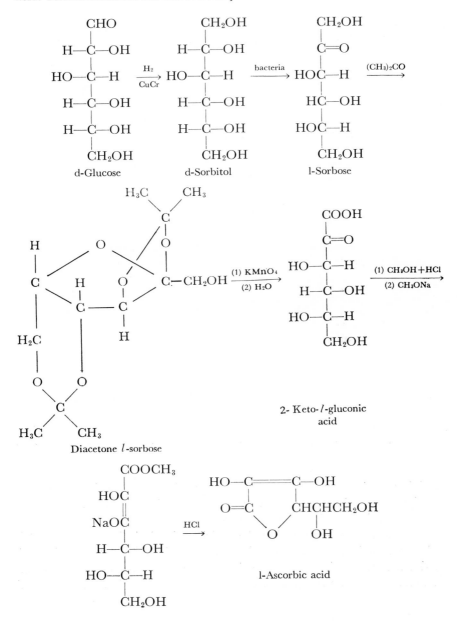

2- Keto-*l*-gluconic acid

l-Ascorbic acid

Reserpine

Reserpine is a tranquilizer; it is obtained by liquid extraction from the African root *Rauwolfin vomitoria* now that India has cut off the supply of *Rauwolfia serpentina*. A flow diagram[2] for the production of reserpine is shown in Figure 20.6. The root is cut to sawdust fineness, charged into

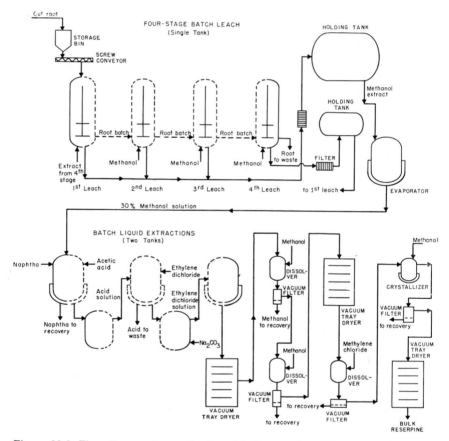

Figure 20.6. Flow diagram for production of bulk reserpine. [*Chem. Eng.*, **64**, *No. 4, 231–33 (1957).*]

stainless steel extractors, and leached four times with boiling (154° F) methanol. The first leach is 1½ hours, the second 1 hour, and the last two, ½ hour each. The first three extractions are kept in one holding tank, the fourth in another, to be used as the initial leach solution for the next batch. The methanol extract from the first three leachings flows to a continuously fed evaporator and is concentrated to a 30 per cent solution, then goes to an extractor where it is acidified with 15 per cent acetic acid after which petroleum naphtha is added. The lower layer, an acid solution of reserpine, is pumped to a second extractor. Returned to the first extractor, the acid solution is extracted with ethylene dichloride, the solvent layer going back to the second tank where it is neutralized with dilute sodium carbonate solution, evaporated to drive off the ethylene dichloride, and dried to leave crude reserpine crystals. These are recrystallized from methanol and dried. The crystals are dissolved in methylene chloride which is then evaporated while methanol is simultaneously introduced to wash the crystals. The pure crystalline reserpine is finally dried and made available for bulk sale.

Saccharin

Saccharin is an intense sweetening agent, five times as sweet as sucrose in dilute solution. Because it does not enter bodily metabolism it is used by diabetics and others who cannot take sugar. Production is from toluene by reaction with chlorosulfonic acid to yield orthotoluenesulfonyl chloride; this is reacted with ammonia to yield the sulfonamide. Oxidation of the aliphatic side chain with dichromate gives orthosulfamylbenzoic acid which on heating yields saccharin.

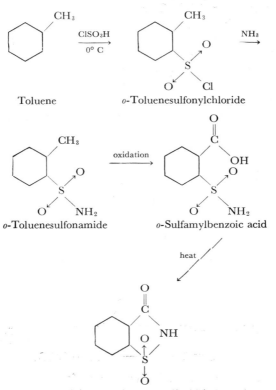

Saccharin (*o*-benzosulfimide)

Antibiotics

Antibiotics, as the term is generally used today, are metabolic products of microbial origin that inhibit the growth of, or destroy, other microorganisms. The first antibiotic to be prepared on a large scale was *pyocyanase*. This material was isolated from the microbe *Pseudomonas aeruginosa* in 1901 by Rudolph Emmerich and Oscar Low of the University of Munich and was successfully used in the treatment of several hundred patients. Because of inadequate biological and chemical controls in the manufacturing process, and poor methods of standardization resulting in variable lot-to-lot clinical results, its use was discontinued.

Penicillin was discovered by Alexander Fleming, a bacteriologist, at St. Mary's Hospital in London; he summarized his findings in a paper published in 1929 in the "British Journal of Experimental Pathology." Great potential lay dormant until Ernest Chain, a biochemist working with Professor Howard Florey at Oxford University, came across the papers and made further investigations in 1938. The first clinical trial, made on January 12, 1941, showed great promise, and commercial production in the United States began in 1943. Other antibiotics introduced since that time are streptomycin, dihydrostreptomycin, terramycin, bacitracin, chloromycetin, aureomycin, neomycin, polymyxin, erythromycin and viomycin; many others are being investigated.

Fermentation is discussed in detail in Chapter 7; however, detailed descriptions of the processes used to produce two typical antibiotics, penicillin and tetracycline, will be given here.

Penicillin. The typical production of an antibiotic is exemplified by the manufacture of penicillin. The mold used industrially is from the *Penicillum chrysogenum* group and is particularly effective against staphylococcus, streptococcus and pneumococcus, mostly gram positive microorganisms; generally it has little effect on gram negative microorganisms.

The penicillin produced commercially is designated as penicillin G (Benzyl penicillin) although there are several types produced by the mold. These compounds are strong acids and very unstable, thus the marketable products are the salts of sodium, calcium, aluminum, potassium, or procaine. The formula for Penicillin G is shown below. Other forms of penicillin contain different groups in the bracketed portion.

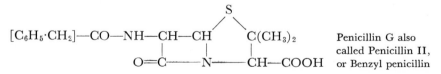

In 1943 the means of production was the surface process; the mold grows on the surface of a shallow layer of media in trays or bottles. With the development of the commercial method of submerged fermentation in 1944, reduction in space and labor requirements resulted in a tremendous reduction in cost.

Penicillin by Submerged Fermentation. The inoculum or "seed" for the large fermentation tanks with a 5,000 to 30,000-gallon capacity is prepared by growing a master stock culture of the mold from lyophylized spores on a nutrient agar substratum with incubation. Several gallons of culture medium, generally constituting 5 to 10 per cent of the charge, are prepared in a series of seed tanks to "seed" a large tank.

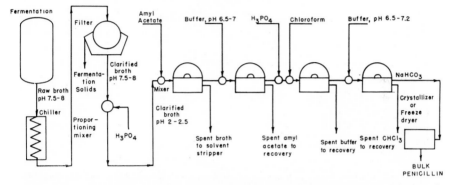

Figure 20.7. Flow diagram for manufacture of penicillin. [*Chem. Eng., 64, No. 5, 247 (1957).*]

The four main stages in the manufacture of bulk penicillin are:

(1) Fermentation.
(2) Removal of mycelium from the fermented broth and extraction of penicillin by solvents.
(3) Solvent purification and formation of the penicillin sodium salts.
(4) Testing, storage, and shipping.

The fermentation broth is made from corn steep liquor, to which 2 to 3 per cent lactose has been added, and such inorganic materials as hydrogen, oxygen, phosphorus, sulfur, potassium, magnesium, nitrogen, and traces of iron, copper, and zinc. The addition of some compounds desirable for mold growth must be omitted since they can be neither tolerated in the end use of the product nor economically removed. After adjusting the pH to 4.5 to 5.0 the culture medium is fed into the fermenter which is equipped with a vertical agitator, a means of introducing air sterilized by filtration, and coils for controlling temperature. The mold is introduced through sterile pipe lines by air pressure. During its growth the medium is sterilized with high pressure steam, and the temperature is maintained at 23 to 25° C. Sterile air permits growth of the aerobic mold; agitation distributes it uniformly in the batch. One volume of air per minute is required for each volume of medium. Assays are made every 3 to 6 hours; after 50 to 90 hours, when the potency stops increasing, the mold is harvested. The batch is cooled to 5° C because of the instability of penicillin at room temperatures, and the mycelium are removed by filtration on a rotary drum filter.

In the old process, penicillin was recovered from the filtrate by charcoal adsorption. It was eluted with amyl acetate, the eluate being concentrated, cooled to 0° C, and acidified with organic acid to pH 2.0. In the solvent

Figure 20.8. Antibiotic recovery plant for penicillin manufacture. (*Courtesy Chas. Pfizer and Co., Inc.*)

extraction process the activated carbon step is omitted and the filtered liquor ("beer") is adjusted to a pH of 2.5 with phosphoric acid in the line. Continuous countercurrent extraction is carried out with amyl acetate and then chloroform, with successive concentration in Podbielniak centrifugal extractors; the final liquor is treated with buffered phosphate and sodium bicarbonate to form the sodium salt. This material is made sterile by filtration and is freed asceptically of water and other solvents by crystallization; crystalline penicillin is thereby formed which, when dried, may be packed in bulk in polyethylene bags, or glass or stainless steel containers.

Section 507 of the 1938 Food, Drug and Cosmetic Act requires that all forms of penicillin be tested prior to sale. Specifically, potency, toxicity, pyrogens, sterility, and moisture (since this affects stability) are extremely important. Potency is the unitage *available,* compared to a standard, *to assure* consistent clinical results; toxicity refers to a test made with mice that determines the toxic effect of the drug on humans when taken internally; pyrogens testing determines the presence of fever-inducing substances which may be undesirable in treatment; sterility, defined earlier, refers to the absence of microorganisms.

A numerical lot number and code system is maintained for each lot from bulk to finished product so that in case of necessity (e.g., lapse of the "expiration" period) the material may be withdrawn from trade channels.

Penicillin is now produced in the United States, Canada, Mexico, Australia, Japan, Italy, England, and many other countries. Initial United States production was 250 billion units a year; in 1946 production was 25,000 billion units; in 1957, 525,738 billion units. The quality has improved with improvements in technology; the present product is practically pure, crystalline, and white.

In the treatment of septicemia although the sulfa drugs seemed to offer promise, penicillin succeeded where sulfanilamide and other sulfa drugs failed. Open flesh wounds and wounds in the head, if treated with penicillin parenterally and by local application, heal in three weeks instead of the previous eight or so. After a serious surgical operation treatment by penicillin injection generally inhibits fever. In parenteral application (organs other than the alimentary) the drug is in water solution as the sodium salt; as procaine penicillin, for slower action, prepared in suitable oils; or as a microcrystalline suspension in water. When taken orally the dose is 5- to 7-fold since absorption by this method is less effective. Penicillin is also administered in spray form for infections of the nose and throat. It is now the main therapeutic agent in the treatment of gonorrhea and syphilis.

Various units have been employed for evaluating the drug; at the present time the accepted one is the International Unit. This is defined as that amount of penicillin having the activity of 0.6 of a microgram of pure sodium penicillin G against a certain strain of *Staphylococcus aureus* to which, by agreement between the United States and Britain, a potency of 1667 units per milligram has been assigned.

Tetracycline. Newer antibiotics, effective against more organisms than penicillin, are termed "broad spectrum" antibiotics. The manufacture of one of these, tetracycline, is illustrated in Figure 20.9 and described below.[4]

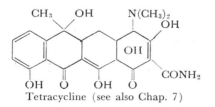

Tetracycline (see also Chap. 7)

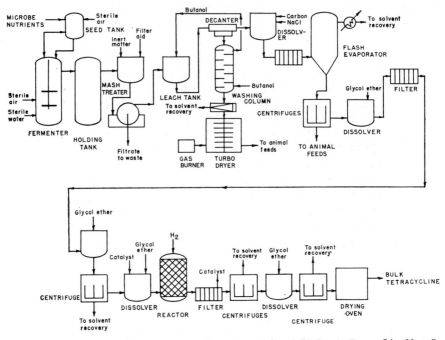

Figure 20.9. Flow sheet for tetracycline manufacture. [*Chem. Eng.*, **64**, *No. 3*, 229–31 (1957).]

The mold *Streptomyces aureofacien* is used in 20,000 gallon fermentation tanks which are run by a batch process. Several such tanks are used so that with proper scheduling the rest of the process may be continuous. The filtered fermentation mash is slurried in butanol and separated in a decanter into an antibiotic-rich layer and a solid mycelia layer. The solids drop through a baffled column countercurrent to a solvent stream for washing. This solvent stream flows back to slurry the filtered fermentation mash; the solids, which contain some activity, are dried and marketed as animal feed supplements.

The liquid layer goes to a vacuum concentrator where crude crystals are precipitated. These are redissolved and recrystallized to purify the chlorotetracyline. These crystals are slurried in glycol ether with catalyst pellets of palladium-on-carbon and are introduced into a reactor. After dechlorination and hydrogenation the pure tetracycline is crystallized, dried, and packaged for bulk sale.

Immunizing Biologicals

Another broad field deals with the bacterial vaccines, toxoids, and vital vaccines. Immunity to disease is obtained by stimulating the production of

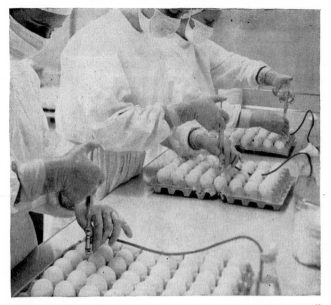

Figure 20.10. The good eggs are punctured with a small drill and then seeded with influenza viruses. The eggs are then sealed with collodion gelatin. (*Courtesy Chas. Pfizer and Co., Inc.*)

Figure 20.11. The next step involves separating the egg fluid from the live virus which is grown in the eggs. The fluid is spun at 50,000 rpm, and the heavier virus particles separate and become caked in the centrifuge cartridge. The virus is collected, reconstituted in a saline solution, and inactivated with formalin at 4° C for 24 hours, after which another series of tests is made for inactivation and sterility. (*Courtesy Chas. Pfizer and Co., Inc.*)

specific antibodies or by transmitting antibodies which have been formed. Vaccines for typhoid, plague, diptheria, tetanus, influenza virus, mumps, poliomyelitis, rabies, smallpox, and typhus are included in this group. The influenza virus vaccine is typical. It is a mixture of two or more strains, each of which is produced and tested separately from cultures supplied by the National Institutes of Health. The virus is in an ampoule which is processed and ultimately diluted 100,000 times before being innoculated into eggs.

Figure 20.12. Polio vaccine coming off the production line. (*Courtesy Chas. Pfizer and Co., Inc.*)

The actual production cycle starts with fertile eggs which are first candled, then disinfected by a coating of an iodine solution, and finally punctured with a small drill (Figure 20.10). The virus is introduced through this hole which is then sealed with collochon gelatin and incubated at 99° F for 48 hours. A circular top section of the egg is removed and the allantoic egg fluid extracted in the harvesting operation. The live virus is separated from the egg fluid by centrifuging (Figure 20.11); the heavier virus particles separate and cake out on the centrifuge cartridge. The virus is collected and reconstituted in a saline solution. The live virus is inactivated with formalin at 40° C for 24 hours.

It is estimated that the use of the influenza virus vaccine has reduced the incidence of that infection by 70 per cent during epidemic periods.

REFERENCES

1. Barrowcliff, Marmaduke and Carr, Francis H., "Organic Medicinal Chemicals," 128, New York, D. Van Nostrand Co. (1920).
2. *Chem. Eng.,* **64,** No. 4, 230–33 (1957).
3. *Chem. Eng.,* **60,** No. 5, 116–20 (1953).
4. *Chem. Eng.,* **64,** No. 3, 228–31 (1957).

21

INSECTICIDES, FUNGICIDES, HERBICIDES, AND RELATED PRODUCTS

In collaboration with Dr. E. R. de Ong*

INTRODUCTION

THE APPLICATION OF CHEMICALS to plants as a protection against insects is a practice almost as old as agriculture. However, only within the last 50 years have there been concerted efforts to protect orchards from both insects and plant diseases. The latter include attacks by fungi, viruses, and bacteria, and physical disturbances such as malnutrition. Now the field for the use of protective chemicals includes growing and stored crops, livestock insects and mites, forest insects and diseases, wood protectants, weeds, and household insects.

The need for an elaborate campaign of protection is self-evident when it is learned that despite all efforts toward protection, billions of dollars worth of growing crops are lost annually. Rodents, insects, and molds cause annual losses throughout the world of 33 million tons of stored grain and rice, according to estimates of the United Nations Food and Agriculture Organization. This is a year's supply of food for 150 million people. Losses of stored grain in the United States alone are estimated at 18 million tons. To hunger resulting from food losses must be added the illnesses and deaths

* Albany, California.

732

caused by disease-carrying insects. This group, including a number of flies, mosquitoes, and lice, is being controlled in the United States, with the result that malaria, dysentery, and typhus fever are declining. In other parts of the world, however, the fight is only beginning.

The term "insecticide" was commonly applied at first to all control agents. The Federal Insecticide Act of 1910 includes both insecticides and fungicides. The Federal Insecticide, Fungicide and Rodenticide Act (1947) uses "economic posion" for all these groups, and in addition includes herbicides. The term "pesticide" is now used officially to include all toxic chemicals, whether used against insects, fungi, weeds, or rodents and other specified animals. Agricultural disinfectants are in many instances also included under the term "pesticides."

The first State laws on insecticides were enacted in 1900 to establish standards of purity for the arsenical, Paris green. Gradually these laws were extended to cover a wide list of inorganic compounds and plant extracts, many of which are violent poisons. Included in this group are such compounds as arsenic combined with copper, lead and calcium; phosphorous pastes for ants and roaches; strychnine in rodent baits; thallium in ant and rodent baits; and selenium for plant-feeding mites. Mercury, both as corrosive sublimate and calomel, was used as an insect repellent and later as a seed disinfectant. Sodium fluoride was the common ant poison, and sodium and calcium cyanide the universal fumigants. Concentrated nicotine was used generally in the garden and on the farm. These compounds, although the most toxic of any known at that time, were marketed widely without supervision under any of the early State laws. There was no provision for public health, either in regulating the amounts applied or the possible danger of minute amounts (residues) remaining on the marketed produce. This lack of care in protecting the operator and the public against the dangerous qualities of the insecticide is the chief difference between the early laws and the present ones. Under the current Federal and State regulations, pesticides are among the most carefully supervised of any line of chemicals or drugs.

The trend toward safer use of pesticides, begun in 1919, was started as a result of reports in England of poisoning from eating apples grown in the United States. To meet this difficulty, the Federal Food and Drug Administration ruled in 1927 that fruit in interstate shipment should not show more than 0.025 grain of arsenic trioxide per pound of fruit (3.57 ppm). Food exceeding established tolerances would be subject to seizure. To meet this requirement, the growers were compelled to use chemical washes in cleaning their fruit. This practice has become general and also adds to the attractiveness of the market fruit.

Another progressive step in the safety campaign was the development of two plant extracts which are effective insecticides but only slightly toxic to man. Both materials are safe to apply to growing crops up to within a few days of harvest, since they quickly break down into harmless compounds. The first, marketed as "pyrethrins I and II," is derived from pyrethrum, a chrysanthemum-like flower. The extracts have been standardized[9,10,14] and are now used in many forms of commercial extracts, including both fly sprays and other sprays for garden use. The second material, known as *rotenone* is derived from tropical plants such as *Derris, Lonchocarpus, Tephrosia,* and others.[13] Both the unextracted ground root and standard extractives are used for garden applications and for the cattle grub, *Hypoderma.*

Despite the increased efficiency of the new synthetic organic insecticides, there has been a striking reduction in the hazards of chemical pest control, as shown by the records of accidental deaths in the reports of the United States Health Service of the Department of Health, Education and Public Welfare. This is due in part to the cooperative efforts of Federal and State officials and the manufacturers in developing greater care in the handling and use of dangerous compounds, and to the concern over spray residues on treated produce. Stricter regulations in the Federal Insecticide, Fungicide and Rodenticide Act of 1947 and the substitution of organic for toxic mineral compounds have also contributed strikingly.

As a further aid toward safeguarding the user of pesticides, plans are developing for a central laboratory, approved by the American Medical Association, which would give advice regarding first-aid treatment and follow-up treatment to the medical profession throughout the United States on a 24-hour day basis. All physicians and hospitals would be able to call at any time for advice on the treatment of accidental exposure.[6]

Safety Regulations

All pesticides proposed for sale in interstate commerce must be registered with the United States Department of Agriculture at Washington, D. C. with a fully warranted statement of active and inert ingredients. Materials that have a record of years of safe and effective usage are registered without question. New materials must furnish satisfactory evidence of effectiveness for the purpose sold, and if there is any question about safety, confirmatory data are required. Such tests include both short- and long-term exposures to varying amounts of residues. The label must give directions for use, with safety warnings if necessary, and highly dangerous pesticides must be appropriately marked and the antidote given. Toxic white powders must be colored so that they may be readily recognized.

The insecticide DDT, related compounds, and other chlorinated hydrocarbons have been largely restricted in their use on dairy animals and cattle being fed for the market. Milk showing detectable signs of these chemicals is not allowed to be marketed. These measures are purely precautionary, however, for to date no injury is known to have occurred to any persons consuming such milk or the meat from animals showing DDT or similar compounds absorbed in the body fat. In a recent world review of the "Toxic Hazards of Certain Pesticides to Man," Barnes[1] states that "There is a possible risk to health from the ingestion of small quantities of pesticides in food, but there is no evidence that anyone has suffered illness from this cause." There are, however, instances of illness arising in persons working in recently treated crops.

In 1954 the Federal Food, Drugs and Cosmetic Act was amended (Miller bill) to provide methods for controlling the amount of residues of pesticides

Figure 21.1. A B-17 spraying for grasshoppeer control in Montana.
(*Courtesy United-Heckathorn*)

in raw agricultural products, such tolerance to be established within 90 days after the Secretary of Agriculture has filed a certificate of usefulness for the product. There would thus be a dual system of regulating chemicals used for pest control of food or growing food crops. The United States Department of Agriculture is to be responsible for maintaining warranted standards of purity, requiring demonstrable proof of the value for purposes claimed, and harmlessness both to the operator and the plants when used as directed. The Food and Drug Administration must then pass on the safety to human beings of any residual chemicals in food products and must establish tolerances for safe amounts, if any. The establishment of such dual control over the development and use of pesticidal chemicals can do much to further present supervision. Such regulation, wisely administered, will minimize the expense of research in the development of needed chemical products.

Classification of Insecticides

Insecticides are commonly grouped as stomach poisons and contact poisons, and to these should be added fumigants and repellents. These are not accurate distinctions, for many may function in two or even more groups. Nicotine acts both as a contact poison and as a fumigant. It may also be formulated in a less volatile form and become an active stomach poison. Chlordane is a contact poison and also has a slight fumigating action. Lindane acts as a contact poison but is also used as a room fumigant with the aid of artificial heat.

Two new compounds differing radically from the accepted form of insecticides are a chemically inert toxicant and a microbial pesticide. The former compound is an inert silicate that kills insects by desiccation rather than by toxic action. The latter compound is described under "Microbial Insecticides."

The classification of stomach and contact insecticides is based on the feeding habits of the insect. Stomach poisons are applied on the leaf surface to be consumed as the chewing insect feeds on the leaf. Persistent poisons, for example, lead arsenate and the organic compound DDT, may be present for several days before being ingested with food.

The contact insecticide is used principally against the sucking type of insect such as aphids and scale insects. The toxicant is absorbed through the body wall or the breathing tubes. Examples are nicotine and the organics parathion and toxaphene.

Fumigants are simple types of organic compounds of rather high order of volatility. Methyl bromide is used principally as a stored product fumigant but is used also in the soil. Dibromo-3-chloropropane is primarily a soil fumigant used against nematodes.

Repellents have been developed mainly by the military as protection against mites, ticks, mosquitoes, and biting flies. Materials commonly used include dimethyl phthalate; ethyl hexanediol, 2-ethyl-1,3-hexanediol; 2-ethyl-3-propyl-1,3-propanediol; and Indalone, butyl mesityl oxide, n-butyl-3,4-dihydro-2,2-dimethyl-4-oxo-1,2-H-pyran-6-carboxylate. These compounds used individually and as mixtures (known as 6-2-2), have been the standard repellents for years. Later studies have added N,N-diethyl-m-toluamide as a mosquito repellent.

The production of pesticides and estimates of domestic requirements are given in Table 21.1.

Classification of Fungicides

Eradication is the principle of treating sick plants. Protection is the treatment of a plant or its environment so that the pathogen is destroyed before

TABLE 21.1. PESTICIDAL CHEMICALS: PRODUCTION IN 1955–56, AND
ESTIMATES OF DOMESTIC REQUIREMENTS FOR 1956–57*

Material	1955–56 Production (1,000 lb)	Minimum (1,000 lb)	1956-57 Requirements[a] Probable Maximum (1,000 lb)
Benzene hexachloride (gamma basis)	13,535[b]	7,000	9,000
Calcium arsenate	24,000 (est)	15,000	25,000
Copper sulfate	146,056	30,000	45,000[c]
2,4-D acid	29,000 (est)	27,000	30,000
DDT	137,747	50,000	70,000
Lead arsenate	14,000 (est)	10,000	12,000
Pyrethrum (flower equivalent)[d]	6,960	6,500	7,500
Rotenone (roots)[d]	6,350	6,000	6,500
2,4-T acid	4,501	3,000	4,000
Aldrin, chlordane, dieldrin, endrin heptachlor, toxaphene	80,418	40,000	50,000

* H. H. Shepard, *J. Agr. Food Chem.*, **5**, 182 (1957).
[a] Preliminary estimates.
[b] Not including lindane grade BHC; estimated requirements include lindane.
[c] Includes all agricultural uses.
[d] Imports; 135,566 pounds pyrethrum extract included in terms of flowers.

the plant becomes sick. Chemical treatments may blend into one another, as is the case in the classification of insecticides.

The first eradicant treatment was probably that of chemical applications to wheat seed to kill the spores of bunt. Eradicants are seldom applied to living plants since they are often phytoxic. An example is spraying the fallen leaves of apple trees to kill the spores of the fungus causing apple scab. The fungicide commonly used for this purpose is dinitro-*o*-cresylate.

Protection, rather than eradication, is the usual method of chemically guarding plants against diseases. The application of elemental sulfur in the control of apple scab is a well-known example of this method. The coverage must be uniform and sufficiently adhesive to withstand weathering. Spores blown onto the sulfur coating will be killed before infection occurs. The application of bordeaux mixture (copper sulfate, lime, and water) on dormant orchard trees is common practice. A chemical reaction occurs between the copper sulfate and the lime, resulting in a complex copper compound which is very tenacious and which thus holds the toxicant on the fruit twig through the winter and early spring.[8]

Insect Parasites and Predators

Plant-feeding insects are under continuous attack by some form of parasite or predator. This may be true in every stage of the host insect, or it may be confined to any one stage of the immature or the adult form. The value of such natural control has become increasingly evident with many forms of pest insect. It is now possible, by careful use of the less dangerous insecticides, and then only when necessary, to protect the beneficial insects (including pollinating insects).[2]

INORGANIC COMPOUNDS

Insecticides

The insecticides used prior to the advent of DDT were almost exclusively inorganic materials, the exceptions being largely plant derivatives, petroleum oil, creosote, and limited amounts of thiocyanates. Refinements in dosage and application were the principal subjects of investigation. Since the materials used—compounds of arsenic, fluorine, copper, mercury, sulfur, thallium, and partly refined petroleum oil—are in varying degrees inherently dangerous to plants, the margin of safety between pest control and plant tolerance is small.

Antimonyl Potassium Tartrate. Potassium antimony tartrate is the only antimony compound attaining commercial importance. Tartar emetic, as it is also known, is used in ant syrups and for the control of thrips on citrus trees and gladiolus.

Arsenical Compounds. White arsenic (As_2O_3) is obtained primarily as a product of smelting operations. It is the source of an unstable acid solution, H_3AsO_3. This acid combined with an alkali forms arsenites. Arsenious trioxide is oxidized with hot nitric acid to form arsenic pentoxide, As_2O_5. Arsenic acid combined with a base forms arsenates. When currently used as an insecticide, white arsenic is combined with a base to form compounds of varying solubility, such as sodium arsenite, Paris green, calcium arsenate, and arsenite and lead arsenate. Paris green has been supplanted by calcium, lead, and other forms of arsenates. Monocalcium arsenite, $CaHAsO_3$, has limited use as a dormant application for the control of brown-rot blossom blight on apricot. The dosage used is 3 pounds per 100 gallons of water. Copper sprays must be substituted for the calcium arsenite in foilage applications because of the danger from the latter.

Calcium Arsenate. The arsenical content (20–28 per cent) of this compound is higher than that of lead arsenate (19–21 per cent), making it more economical. Calcium, as an ingredient of the residue, has certain advantages over lead which is a cumulative poison. However, calcium arsenate is usually of variable composition and unstable under acid conditions; it frequently contains more water-soluble arsenic than lead arsenate, and is therefore limited in its use to the more resistant plants.

The commercial form of calcium arsenate is usually a mixture of dicalcium arsenate, $CaHAsO_4$; pentacalcium arsenate, $Ca_5H_2(AsO_4)_4$; tricalcium arsenate, $Ca_3(AsO_4)_2$; and the basic calcium arsenate $[Ca_3(AsO_4)_2]_3 \cdot Ca(OH)_2$.

Small amounts of calcium hydroxide and calcium carbonate are also present. The excess calcium hydroxide combines with any free arsenic, thus reducing plant injury.

An early method of making calcium arsenate involves the direct addition of arsenic acid to calcium arsenate. The product was variable in particle size and was unstable. Pearce and Evans[15] developed a process for producing a calcium arsenate of about 90 per cent basic arsenate and 10 per cent free or uncombined calcium hydroxide. The total arsenic content amounted to about 46 per cent arsenic pentoxide, As_2O_5, and about 0.40 per cent water-soluble arsenic. Zinc may be combined in the formula to reduce the hazard to the plant.

Calcium arsenate is now used essentially against the boll weevil, the cotton leaf worm, and bollworms.

Lead Arsenate. This compound was developed in 1892 by Moulton for combating the gypsy moth. Its stability, lower solubility, adhesiveness, and plant tolerance have led to general use. It is marketed as a light, fluffy, pink powder with a particle size of from a fraction of a micron to 20–40 microns in diameter. The density ranges from 5.70 to 5.90. There are two forms of commercial lead arsenates—the acid or standard, and the basic. The latter is more stable and safer for use with sensitive plants.

Standard lead arsenate ($PbHAsO_4$) is also known as "dilead," "acid," or simply as lead arsenate. Its molar ratio of PbO/As_2O_5 ranges from 2.02 to 2.14. Commercial standard lead arsenate usually contains about 30 per cent arsenic pentoxide.

Basic lead arsenate includes 4,1,3,1-lead hydroxy arsenate [$Pb_4(PbOH)(AsO_4)_3 \cdot H_2O$], and 5,2,4-lead hydroxy arsenate [$Pb_5(PbOH)_2(AsO_4)_4$]. Commercial basic lead arsenate contains about 22 per cent arsenic pentoxide.

For many years standard lead arsenate was used extensively in apple and pear orchards for controlling the codling moth and a number of defoliators. The organic insecticide, DDT, has partially supplanted it for this purpose, but in many districts it is included in the spray program for apples. Ferric oxide may be included in the spray tank formula to reduce plant hazard, but zinc sulfate and manganese sulfate are now more generally used for this purpose.

Residual deposits of lead arsenate in the spray programs are frequently above the legal tolerance; this has led to various procedures for washing and wiping the fruit. A satisfactory formula for use in the washing machine for apples is a 1 per cent hydrochloric acid solution. Exposure time of the fruit in the washing machine is 2–3 minutes. Wetting agents may also be used for fruit which is difficult to clean. Alkaline materials should not be used because of their solvent action on the waxy covering of the fruit.[4]

Fluorine Compounds. The fluorides, fluosilicates, and fluoaluminates are salts of hydrofluoric acids having wide commercial use. They are usually marketed as fine crystalline compounds which vary greatly in their solubility. Because of their solubility, the fluorine compounds used as insecticides are somewhat dangerous to foilage. An exception is cryolite, which is used rather frequently.

Sodium Fluoride. This compound has been much used to control roaches in homes and wherever foods are stored. The powders are made with concentrations of 10–95 per cent. Pyrethrins, in amounts ranging from 0.03 to 0.15 per cent, may be added to increase efficiency.

Another use of sodium fluoride is in the control of body lice on poultry.

Sodium Fluosilicate. Under semi-arid conditions this material has been used commonly on cotton, tobacco, and tomatoes. It has been used for years as the standard toxic material in grasshopper baits. The formula requires 4 pounds of sodium fluosilicate, 100 pounds of wheat bran or a substitute, and 10–15 gallons of water. This formula is also used against cutworms and for mothproofing woolens and upholstered furniture.

Cryolite (Na_3AlF_6), or sodium fluoaluminate, occurs both as a natural mineral and as a manufactured product. It is very insoluble in water but decomposes in alkali solutions. Cryolite is less toxic to mammals than sodium silicate, but care should be taken to prevent contact with food.

The insecticidal value of cryolite as a codling moth control was demonstrated in the Pacific Northwest, but it has been displaced by organic compounds. However, in parts of Canada, cryolite is recommended for use in apple orchards since it is less lethal to beneficial insects. It is also used on cotton and other crops for the control of defoliators.

Sulfur is the only pesticide in general use both in the elemental form and in various compounds. It is used both as an insecticide and as a fungicide. Of the total amount of pesticides used in the United States during 1950–51 (681,868,000 pounds), more than one half consisted of ground sulfur and dithiocarbamates.[12]

There are two principal sources of sulfur in the United States: pyrites (sulfide ore), and the subterranean deposits in Texas and Louisiana. The latter is mined in almost pure elemental form. In addition to these two sources, increasingly large amounts of sulfur are recovered in the purification of utility (illuminating) gas and in the refining of oil. The sulfur which is present as sulfur dioxide and as hydrogen sulfide is washed out and precipitated as a light spongy mass floating on the surface of the recovery liquid.

Sulfur occurs in both crystalline and amorphous forms. The common form is rhombic crystals, readily soluble in carbon disulfide. There are also two amorphous forms of sulfur, one of which is soluble in carbon disulfide.

The use of sulfur as an insecticide and fungicide in agricultural practice requires very uniform distribution through the foliage and sufficient adhesion to prevent weathering off or mechanical shattering. Such adhesion may be obtained by application as a spray, especially with an adhesive substance, or as a dusting sulfur with particles sufficiently fine to aid adhesion.

There are four common types of commercial sulfur, *viz.*, sublimed, ground, micronized, and flotation sulfur. The sublimed form is made by the rapid cooling of sulfur fumes generated by heating crude sulfur. The particles are large, ranging from 10 to about 200 microns in diameter. It is used for burning in the bleaching of fruits. Ground sulfur is prepared by grinding crude sulfur in a hammer mill or Raymond mill. The particle size usually ranges from 5 to 25 microns, 7 to 10 microns being the preferred size. Ninety to 95 per cent of the sulfur should pass through a 325-mesh screen. Ground sulfurs are commonly used in the pure form, except for small amounts of conditioners which are added to improve the physical qualities. Micronized sulfur is a finely divided form produced by the Micronizer Reduction Mill. The particles are quite uniform in size, ranging from 3.5 to 5 microns. Flotation sulfur is a chemically produced product used for dusting and spraying purposes, and is characterized by extremely fine particle size and a grayish color varying in intensity with the amount of carbon and other impurities present.

The use of elemental sulfur as an insecticide has decreased with the development of synthetic organic insecticides, but it is used as a carrier for chlorinated hydrocarbons such as DDT and related compounds. Such combinations are common in recommendations for insect control of cotton.

Fungicides

Sulfur is one of the most important substances used in the control of plant diseases, particularly in the treatment of mildews. It is effective both in the elemental form and in combinations such as lime-sulfur solution. The elemental form is effective only at temperatures of about 70° F and above, with exposures of 4 or 5 hours or more. Susceptible plants are sometimes injured with sulfur applications at 90° F and above.

Sulfur has been used quite frequently to control apple scab, especially in the northeastern area of the country, but it has been partly displaced by organic compounds. However, reduction in the consumption of sulfur led to increased mildew and hence an increase in sulfur combination sprays.

Brown rot on stone fruits, especially the peach, is controlled almost entirely by sulfur dusts or sprays. Not only are a number of sulfur applications made in the orchard, but sulfur is also used on the packed fruit to reduce loss in transit. It is in the control of powdery mildew on table, raisin, and wine grapes in California, however, that immense amounts of dusting sulfur are used. It is common practice to apply sulfur dusts from 2 to 5 times during the growing season. The application varies between

5 and 10 pounds per acre. Sulfur is also used on some of the vegetable crops, e.g., to control powdery mildew on beans and cabbage, leaf blight on celery and carrot, and downy mildew on onion.

Copper sulfate has been recognized as a control agent for wheat bunt and smut for more than 100 years. Recently, copper compounds have increased in value until they have become a principal means of protecting plants against disease. Although a number of organic fungicides have been developed, their use is confined primarily to foliage; bordeaux mixture (copper sulfate, lime, and water) is still the main protection for dormant trees. Bordeaux applications sometimes cause foliage injury or fruit russetting which has led to a study of substitutes that would be less corrosive. The fixed (insoluble) coppers were found to qualify, and a number have been developed. These include basic copper sulfate, copper oxychlorides, copper silicate, cuprous oxide, and mixtures of these compounds. The fixed coppers are available in ready-to-use form and have a high copper content. The fixed coppers lack the tenacity of bordeaux, and an additive is usually required to increase adhesion.

The most important copper compound from the agricultural standpoint is copper sulfate. Although this material is too dangerous to use alone on plants, the danger can be essentially eliminated by combining it in water with about an equal amount of lime and applying as a liquid. This mixture, or bordeaux as it is known, may be varied in composition from 8 pounds of copper sulfate, 8 pounds of lime, and 50 gallons of water for winter use, to 0.5:0.5:100 for foliage application in the control of pear blight.

Monohydrated copper sulfate, $CuSO_4 \cdot H_2O$, is produced by heating the sulfate crystals to a temperature of about 105° C. The dehydrated powder absorbs moisture readily and hence must be packed in tight steel drums. It is commonly mixed with hydrated lime, usually 20 parts of powder to 80 parts of lime, and applied as a dust. The copper sulfate absorbs moisture, after application, tending to form bordeaux on the leaf. Applications of 20–30 pounds of dust per acre are made in the control of pear blight.

The fixed coppers are usually marketed at 50–53 per cent copper, but some forms vary from this range. They are usually formulated with the same copper content as bordeaux. Small particle size is important, both for adhesion and fungicidal value. The fixed coppers are used primarily for treating vegetables, but are included in certain orchard spray programs. They may also be alternated with organic fungicides.

Copper carbonate, a product of hot copper sulfate solution combined with a carbonate such as soda ash, was one of the first copper compounds commonly used as a seed disinfectant. It may be used at the rate of 2 ounces or more per bushel of seed for the control of bunt on wheat seed.

Copper oxides, both the cuprous and cupric forms, are also used as seed disinfectants. The smallest particle size of the red cuprous oxide is the most toxic. The oxides are used to protect various vegetable seeds from attacks by fungi during the seedling stage.

Copper naphthenate in oil solution is used in treating nursery flats and benches to prevent "damping-off" of seedlings. It is also used as a wood and cloth preservative.

Herbicides

Solutions of sodium arsenite are commonly marketed as "weedkillers." The product may be purchased as a dry powder or as stock solutions ready for dilution. The dosage varies, depending on the type of soil and the amount of rainfall. It should be applied at the rate of 4 pounds arsenic trioxide per square rod and repeated as often as necessary to maintain a sterile condition. The toxicity is greatest in light sandy soils and least in clay soils. Permanent sterilization of the soil is best attained with arsenic trioxide, which can be handled with less danger and which is not attractive to livestock as is sodium arsenite on foliage. Its low solubility gives long persistence, it may remain in the soil for years. For quick results it should be combined with chlorates which sterilize during the first year.[3]

Borates in a form available to plants and in sufficient quantity will sterilize any soil. Since they are soluble they are not as permanent as arsenic trioxide, and repeated applications may be required. The dosage ranges from 10 to 40 pounds per square rod. They are most toxic in sandy soil and least toxic in clays. The borates are not toxic to animals and humans, hence may be used with considerable safety.

Sodium chlorate is used in 2 per cent concentration to kill both broad-leaved and grassy weeds. For killing perennial weeds it is used at the rate of 1 pound per gallon of water. Fertile soils and sandy soils require heavy dosages. Dosages range from 1 to 6 pounds per square rod. An average dosage is 3 pounds per square rod applied in 3 gallons of water. Sodium chlorate should be stored in metal containers, for when mixed with organic matter it is highly inflammable. Proprietary mixtures with other chemicals reduce the danger of fire.

Ammonium sulfamate ($H_6N_2O_3S$) is used for killing trees, woody shrubs, poison oak, poison ivy, and deep-rooted herbaceous weeds. Best results are obtained from application to expanded growing foliage in summer or early fall. It may be applied in the dry crystal form or as a solution (2–4 pounds of crystals per gallon) to frills in the bark made by overlapping ax strokes all around the tree. For foliage treatment of brush, a solution of $\frac{3}{4}$–1 pound of the chemical to 1 gallon of water is used.

Rodenticides

White arsenic has limited use as a rodenticide. Three to five per cent solutions are added to rodent baits and to drinking water.

Thallous sulfate, Tl_2SO_4, and thallous acetate, $TlCOOCH_3$, are both used as rodent baits. Thallium rodent baits are made of 1 pound thallium sulfate to 99 pounds of grain.

Zinc phosphide is used in the control of rats, mice, and ground squirrels. One part of the chemical is combined with 96–100 parts by weight of dry cereals or other bait materials.

ORGANIC COMPOUNDS

Petroleum Oil Products

The use of petroleum (mineral oil) in agricultural practice has, within the last 50 years, passed from a hazardous application of "stove oil" or even crude oil on dormant deciduous trees to the application of highly refined fractions and a number of complex derivatives. The latter include herbicides, solvents, carriers for insecticides, such as pyrethrins and DDT, and adhesives in the formulation of dusts and sprays. Petroleum fractions are valued for their insecticidal properties and for certain physical properties, coupled with availability and low cost. Research at the California Agricultural Experiment Station showed the value of removing the aromatic and other unsaturated ingredients by refining processes. This resulted in the development of the so-called "white oils" or foliage oils.[4]

Unsulfonated Residue. Petroleum is refined by means of concentrated sulfuric acid combined with the unsaturated compounds to form sulfonated products. The saturated compounds (naphthenes and paraffins) which remain are known as the *unsulfonated residue;* this term is used generally as the basis for plant tolerance. This method has been standardized as ASTM Spec. D483-40, 1949, and has become the basis for tremendous development in the use of refined petroleum oil as an insecticide for use on plants.[7]

Distillation Range. The fractional distillation of an oil between stated temperatures determines the quantity and density of the fractions distilling within the indicated range. A standardized method (ASTM Spec. D447-41, 1949) has been developed as a guide for the preparation of spray oils. This range is based on the percentage distilled at 636° F.[11]

Oxidation. The oil in diluted sprays for foliage may develop acidity to an extent injurious to the plants. This reaction is an oxidation process and depends on the character of the oil, the amount and type of unsaturates present, temperature, intensity of light, and the presence of oxygen. This reaction is not, however, the principal cause of foliage injury. Rather, the incomplete removal of injurious unsaturates naturally present in the oil is responsible.[5]

Petroleum oils with an unsulfonated residue (u.r.) of 70–85 per cent are used extensively in the control of scale insects on dormant deciduous trees. On citrus trees under conditions similar to those existing in California, the use of oils with a u.r. of about 92 per cent, viscosity 50–75 seconds Saybolt, and a distillation range of 45–50 per cent at 636° F is very common. Light, refined petroleum fractions are in general use as carriers for pyrethrins in fly and mosquito applications, and also for rotenone and nicotine.

Plant Derivatives

A number of extracts derived from plants are in great demand as pesticides. These extracts, or "botanicals" as they are sometimes known, break down into harmless compounds soon after application and, with the exception of nicotine and strychnine, may be handled with moderate care. Red squill and strychnine are rodenticides; the others are insecticides. The latter are used principally against flies, mosquitoes, and other household insects, and against aphids, thrips, and the younger stages of caterpillars attacking plants. The more important toxicants are alkaloids, but include pyrethrins, rotenone, and certain related compounds. All are of a complex structure, and although much effort has been made to develop certain of them by synthesis, there has been but slight success, with the exception of the recently developed allethrin and related compounds as substitutes for pyrethrins.

Nicotine is the main alkaloid found in all parts of the tobacco plant of commerce, *Nicotiana tabacum*. It is the most important member of the nitrogen heterocyclic compounds. The alkaloid nicotine is basic in its reaction, levorotatory, volatile, and much more toxic in this form than when combined with acids (dextrorotatory) to form nonvolatile or fixed compounds. Nicotine is one of the most rapid and deadly poisons known. It is toxic orally, by inhalation of concentrated vapor, and by absorption through the skin. It is unstable as a vapor and in alkaline dusts, probably because of oxidation.

Nicotine is produced commercially by steam distillation of waste tobacco in the presence of alkali. The alkaloid is commonly marketed as a nicotine sulfate containing 40 per cent actual nicotine. The sulfate form is nonvolatile and hence will not lose nicotine on exposure; also, it is less toxic than the alkaloid itself and therefore somewhat safer to handle. Free or uncombined nicotine is also marketed in 40 and 80 per cent concentrations, the latter being sold only to manufacturers.

Since nicotine sulfate is less toxic than free nicotine, it is necessary to neutralize all or the greater part of the combining sulfuric acid by the addition of alkali. This may be accomplished in part by using alkaline water as a carrier for the nicotine, and also by the use of an alkaline soap or other form of spreading or wetting agent. Waters which are only slightly alkaline should be supplemented by the addition of one or more table-spoonsful of hydrated lime to 100 gallons of spray.

Nicotine is also prepared for use as a dust in the orchard and garden. Such dusts are made with the nicotine content varying from 2 to 4 per cent concentration, depending on the type of insect against which it is to be used. Either nicotine sulfate or free nicotine may be used in such combinations. Where the former is used the dust base is usually hydrated lime. When sulfur is desired in the combination, free nicotine may be preferred. Nonvolatile dusts are also manufactured using clays or other absorbent types of carriers where nicotine is to be used as a stomach poison.

Ground tobacco stems are sometimes marketed as insecticides, but since the nicotine content varies it is doubtful if dependable results are obtained.

Nicotine sprays at concentrations of 0.03–0.05 per cent nicotine are used against aphids, thrips, psyllids, and moth larvae.

Pyrethrum is the active ingredient of many "insect powders." The group *Pyrethrum* is a section of the genus *Chrysanthemum* which belongs to the Compositae. Commercial production is predominantly that of the species *P. cinerariaefolium*. The Kenya district of British East Africa is the principal source of supply, although large amounts are also produced in parts of South America. The toxic ingredients of the plant are two closely related esters, pyrethrin I and pyrethrin II. A kerosene type of solvent with a flash point of 125° F is commonly used to avoid the hazard of a low flash point since the extract is frequently used as a household spray in the form of an aerosol bomb.

Ground pyrethrum powder is combined with a base such as talc or bentonite for household use and for garden application. It is used for the control of moths, ants, roaches, and bedbugs.

The pyrethrins are usually combined with a synergist, such as piperonyl butoxide, for use against household insects and stored-product insects. For the latter purpose the formula used is 0.08 per cent pyrethrins and 1.1 per cent piperonyl butoxide.

Rotenone and Rotenoids. These compounds are extracts principally of the tropical plants *Derris elliptica* and *D. malaccensis.* The main sources of supply are the Philippines, Polynesia, and Brazil. The genus *Loncho-carpus,* from South and Central America, is another source. The dried rotenone-bearing roots and chopped and powdered roots are imported to this country where they are ground into powders with standardized rotenone content, or extracted and marketed in various grades. The extractives of derris and related plants include, in addition to rotenone, varying amounts of resin from which other toxic substances have been isolated. The rotenone compounds are used against garden insects, cattle lice, and the cattle grub.

Ryania is the ground stems of the plant, *Ryania speciosa*. The alkaloid ryanodine is extracted by means of water and methanol. The ground dust of 40 per cent concentration is effective in the control of the European corn borer, but it is being displaced by the organic insecticide, DDT. Demonstrations are now being made of the value of ryania as a control for codling moth on the apple. Its value as a control agent is comparable to that of DDT and other organic insecticides, but it has the advantage of being less injurious to beneficial insects.

Fumigants

Chemicals that are effective fumigants must be highly volatile, stable, and capable of penetration. Extreme volatility, like that of hydrocyanic acid, makes confinement for an effective period difficult. Concentrations required for insecticidal effect may be explosive; this difficulty may be overcome, however, by blending with less explosive gases. High solubility in either water or fats limits the field of usefulness. The physical attributes of a fumigant are more frequently recognized as being of importance than is its molecular structure. Numerous instances have been shown, however, of the value of introducing elements or radicals into the molecule, such as Cl, Br, SO_2, and NH_3.[4]

Hydrocyanic acid (hydrogen cyanide, HCN) was for many years in many parts of the world the standard fumigant for citrus trees and for building fumigation. It has been replaced in large measure in the former application by refined petroleum oil, and in the latter by methyl bromide. Despite these encroachments, HCN is still much used as a fumigant, especially since the liquified form in cylinders has displaced the pot generator.

Tree fumigation is possible by confining the generated gas inside a heavy duck tent spread over the tree. The volume enclosed by the tent is determined and a corresponding dosage discharged from the fumigating machine which is placed beside the tree. This method of fumigation is standard procedure for controlling infesting scale insects on citrus trees and in the greenhouse.

Carbon disulfide (carbon bisulfide, CS_2) is a commonly used fumigant for killing grain infesting insects, ground squirrels, and deep-rooted weeds. The explosive limits in air (2–50 per cent) retards its general use, but this difficulty may be overcome by blending it with carbon tetrachloride in amounts ranging from 20 to 80 per cent. The dosage per 1000 bushels of wheat, in concrete or steel bins, is 2 gallons of the carbon disulfide-carbon tetrachloride mixture (20–80 blend). It is used at 80° F or above.

The vapor tension and penetrating qualities of carbon disulfide makes it a very efficient soil fumigant. Because it is only slightly soluble in water, it does not penetrate moist soil readily, nor should it be used in extremely dry soil.

Sulfur dioxide is used extensively as a fungicidal gas to prevent mold during storage and transit of table grapes. It is also an effective insecticide, but its low boiling point requires that it be handled in cylinders, an inconvenience which limits its use.

Methyl bromide vapor is stable under varying conditions of moisture, temperature, and pressure; it is very penetrating, slightly soluble in water, and effective at rather low temperatures. It is widely used in the fumigation of grain, dried fruit, nuts, and other foods and nursery plants. The customary dosage is 2 pounds per 1000 cubic feet.

Miscellaneous Fumigants. Ethylene dichloride and ethylene oxide are grain fumigants. The latter, together with propylene oxide and ethyl formate, is added to sealed packages of dried fruit to retard the growth of yeasts and molds.

Soil fumigants include ethylene dibromide, chlorobromopropene, chloropicrin, and "D-D" (chlorinated propane-propylene mixture). Their principal value is in controlling nematodes and soil inhabiting insects.

SYNTHETIC ORGANIC INSECTICIDES AND FUNGICIDES

Aldrin (hexachlorohexahydro-endo,exo-dimethanonaphthalene; HHDN)[16] is insoluble in water but soluble in a number of organic solvents. It is moderately toxic and can be absorbed through the skin, by ingestion, and by inhalation. The official tolerance ranges from zero to 0.75 ppm. It is formulated as a seed dressing (75 per cent), as wettable powders (20–40 per cent), and as emulsifiable concentrates (2 and 4 lb per gallon).

This product is used against soil insects, grasshoppers, and as a general insecticide.

Antibiotics. Following the sucessful use of antibiotics against animal diseases, the same type of materials have been used against plant-attacking fungi, bacteria, and viruses. A compound known as Acti-dione is used as a fungicide on certain orchard trees and for turf diseases. Dosages used on cherry trees range from 1 to 2 ppm.

Aramite [2(*p-tert*-butylphenoxy) isopropyl-2-chloroethyl sulfite] is used principally on cotton and on decoratives for control of plant-feeding mites. There is no tolerance for it on food crops.

Benzene hexachloride (1,2,3,4,5,6-hexachlorocyclohexane; BHC). This product is a mixture of five isomers and related compounds: alpha, 60–70 per cent; beta, 6–8 per cent; gamma, 12–15 per cent; delta, 2–5 per cent; epsilon, 3–7 per cent; related compounds, 2–3 per cent. The oral toxicity to mammals varies with the isomer, the gamma form being the most toxic. It imparts an undesirable flavor to fruits and vegetables. BHC is used as a soil insecticide when not followed by potatoes, and on cotton and tree trunks.

Lindane,[17] a product containing not less than 99 per cent gamma isomer of BHC, is used more extensively, but may impart objectionable odors to sensitive crops. It is one of the few compounds recommended as a residual application in dairy barns. Lindane is also used as a room fumigant.

Captan (N-trichloromethylmercapto-4-cyclohexene-1,2-dicarboximide) is a fungicide used generally on vegetables and fruits. It may not be applied to vegetables or fruits within 15 days of harvest.[18]

Ceresan (2 per cent ethyl mercuric chloride) is one of the earlier developed organic mercurial seed fungicides. It is used on cereal seeds at the rate of 2 ounces per bushel. The toxic volatile fumes from the compound penetrate the hulls of oats, barley, and sorghum, thereby increasing its effectiveness.

Chlordane (1,2,4,5,6,7,8,8-octachloro-2,3,3a,4,7,7a,-hexahydro-4,7,methanoindene) is a persistent type of general insecticide, especially when used in the soil. It is effective against wireworms, grasshoppers, ants, and termites. Official tolerance: 0.1 ppm on certain fruits and vegetables; 0.3 ppm on or in sweet potatoes.[19]

DDT [1,1,1-trichloro-2,2-bis-(p-chlorophenyl)ethane]. The commercial standard has a chlorine content of 48–50.1 per cent. The official tolerance is 7 ppm on fruits and vegetables and in or on the fat of meat from cattle, sheep, and hogs. It is used as a general insecticide to control a wide variety of insects, both in the field and the home.

Dinitro Compounds. The nitro-phenols are used as contact and stomach insecticides. They are used in the orchard chiefly during the dormant stage. Dinitro-o-cresol is one of the more toxic of the dinitro group. The official tolerance is zero. It is used as an ovicide on dormant trees and as a weed-killer. The dinitros have limited use as fungicides.

Dithiocarbamates.[20] This group of fungicides, derived from dithiocarbamic acid, is very important (1) in the control of vegetable diseases, and (2) as seed disinfectants, orchard sprays, insect repellents, and textile fungicides. The following are the more important:

Ferbam (ferric dimethyldithiocarbamate) is used largely as an orchard spray, having been displaced as a vegetable spray by ziram.

Maneb (manganous ethylenebisdithiocarbamate; Manzate) is a commonly used vegetable application.

Zineb (zinc ethylenebisdithiocarbamate; Parzate) is used extensively on vegetables and flowers. It is becoming a common orchard spray.

Ziram (zinc dimethyldithiocarbamate; Zerlate) is used in the control of early blight of tomatoes and potatoes, other vegetable diseases, and in orchard control work.

The official tolerance for the dithiocarbamate is 7 ppm as Zineb.

Glyodin (2-heptadecyl-2-imidazoline acetate) is a potent orchard fungicide; it acts both as an eradicant and a protectant. It also has value in the control of orchard-attacking mites. Glyodin has a low order of toxicity. The official tolerance is 5 ppm on fruits and vegetables.

Lethane 384 (β-butoxy-β'-thiocyano-diethyl ether) is a contact insecticide used against flies. It is frequently combined with pyrethrins.

Methoxychlor [1,1,1-trichloro-2,2-bis(p-methoxyphenyl)-ethane][21] came into prominence as a livestock applicant when it was discovered that DDT sprays on dairy cattle resulted in the secretion of small amounts of DDT (0.06 ppm) in the milk. Methoxychlor is not stored in the fat of treated animals and is used on dairy cattle at a concentration of 0.5–1 per cent, a dosage of 2 quarts per medium-sized animal. The material may also be used as a residual application in dairy barns to control flies, and on the walls of grain-storage bins as a protection against stored-product insects. Official tolerance is 100 ppm on forage plants, grain, and currants.

Phosphate Compounds

Bayer 21/199 (3-chloro-4-methylumbelliferone, 0,0-diethyl thiophosphate) is a systemic insecticide used against the cattle grub. It is applied as a wash, scrubbed into the back at the rate of 1 pint per animal. Dosages used range from 1.0 to 0.1 per cent. Another systemic phosphate compound, Dow ET-57, has given favorable results when administered orally by mixing with the animal feeds.

Diazinon [0,0-diethyl 0-(2-isopropyl-6-methyl-4-pyrimidinyl) thiophosphate] has been used as a systemic insecticide against the cattle grub. The principal use, however, has been as baits for houseflies. The concentration of the insecticide ranges from 1.0 to 0.1 per cent in a molasses-corn meal bait.

Malathion (0,0-dimethyl dithiophosphate of diethyl mercaptosuccinate) has a very low oral and dermal toxicity to mammals. This insecticide is used in gardens and orchards and in baits for houseflies.

Parathion (0,0-diethyl-0-p-nitrophenyl thiophosphate) has high toxicity from dermal absorption and inhalation. It is used in the control of aphids, mites, caterpillars, beetles, thrips, and leafhoppers on fruits, vegetables, and forage crops.[22] The official tolerance is 1 ppm on fruits and vegetables.

Schradan [bis(dimethylamino) phosphoric anhydride] is a systemic insecticide for many sucking insects and mites. It may be applied via the soil; however, a dosage much higher than the 1 pound per acre required for foliage application must be given.

Toxaphene (chlorinated camphene having a chlorine content of 67–100 per cent)[23] is used in the control of insects on field and forage crops and certain vegetable crops. Official tolerance is 7 ppm on food crops.

MICROBIAL INSECTICIDES

Recent reports[1a] describe a major new development in the control of crop pests. This involves use of a microbial insecticide composed of spores of *B. thuringiensis Berliner,* a microorganism which, although nontoxic to animals and plants, induces disease in certain insects. The product has been used successfully in controlling certain pests on cabbage, lettuce, and cauliflower, and shows promise as an insecticide for other vegetables and fruits, for trees and lawns, and for other applications.

A flow diagram of the manufacturing process is shown in Figure 21.2.

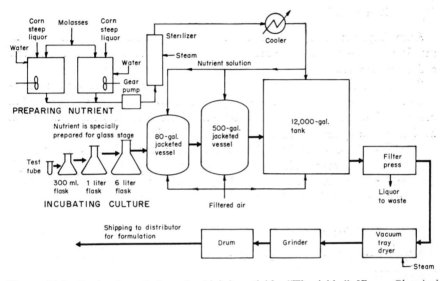

Figure 21.2. Production of the microbial insecticide "Thuricide." [*From Chemical Engineering, 67, No. 60, 43 (Oct. 3, 1960).*]

SYNTHETIC ORGANIC HERBICIDES AND RODENTICIDES

Cloro IPC [isopropyl N-(3-chlorophenyl) carbamate] is a selective pre-emergence herbicide which controls grassy weeds in broad-leaved crops. It is used on cotton, strawberries, onions, and lettuce.

Diuron [3-(3,4-dichlorophenyl)-1,1-dimethylurea]; Karmex, Telvar, is a selective herbicide for certain crops, and applied at the rate of 1–6 pounds per acre. It is also used at much higher dosages for temporary sterilization of the soil.

Dalapon (sodium 2,2-dichloropropionate; Dowpon) is a herbicide used in the control of annual and perennial grasses. It inhibits seed germination for several days.

2,4-D (2,4-dichlorophenoxyacetic acid) is a herbicide used against broad-leaved weeds and sensitive brushy plants, and for clearing grain fields and pastures of weeds. There are many legal restrictions to prevent its drifting to susceptible crops. Official tolerance is 5 ppm on fruits and vegetables.

2,4,5-T (2,4,5-trichlorophenoxyacetic acid) is a systemic herbicide similar to 2,4-D but used largely in the control of shrubs, brambles, and trees.

Dinitro compounds, such as dinitro-*o*-cresol, dinitro-*o*-sec-amyl phenol, dinitro-*o*-sec-butyl phenol, are all used as general contact herbicides effective on both grasses and broad-leaved plants. They may be used alone at 3–4 pounds per 100 gallons of low grade oil or combined with the so-called "weed oils," which are high in unsaturated compounds.

Rodenticides

Antu (alpha-naphthyl thiourea). Two mg is a lethal dose to the Norway rat. It is dangerous to all mammals, and may be used both as a bait and a dust on runways.

Sodium fluoroacetate is extremely toxic and is colored black for identification. It is used against ground squirrels as well as house rodents. The use of sodium fluoroacetate has supplanted fumigation with hydrocyanic acid in the de-ratting of ships at the Port of London.

Warfarin [3(-acetonylbenzyl)-4-hydroxycoumarin]. This compound is lethal in that it retards blood clotting. It is only slightly toxic after a single dose and requires a number of feedings to be fatal. It is packaged in baits of coarse cereals such as rolled oats.

Wood Protectants

Wood exposed in moist situations is subject to decay, fungi, and the subterranean termite. The dry-wood termite also attacks wood products of low moisture content.

Creosote coal tar (creosote oil) both alone and combined with low-grade petroleum oil is the most frequently used material for protecting railroad ties, mine timbers, and utility poles. Lumber is usually treated by immersion, preferably under pressure, in large tanks. Brush application of creosote is not usually considered satisfactory.

Pentachlorophenol is formulated as a 5 per cent solution as a wood preservative. It may be applied by brush or cold soaking. This offers protection not only against decay organisms but also against termites and insect borers.

Other chemicals used as wood protectants include copper sulfate, sodium fluoride, zinc chloride, and zinc meta-arsenite.

Disinfectants

Alrosept MM (1-tridecyl-2-methyl-2-hydroxyethylimidazolinium chloride) is a germicide and deodorant. It is used for slime control in water-cooling systems.

Emulsept E 607 Special (N-lauroyl ester of colamino formyl methyl pyridinium chloride). This product is a sanitizer-detergent, germicide, antiseptic, and deodorant; it is used for hand washing and as a germicidal rinse for previously cleaned surfaces.

Hyamine 2389 (Methyl dodecyl benzyl ammonium chloride) is used as a disinfectant and an algaecide, and as a disinfectant in food-processing plants and dairies.

REFERENCES

1. Barnes, J. M., World Health Organization, "Toxic Hazards of Certain Pesticides to Man," Monograph Series 16 (1953).
1a. *Chemical Engineering*, **67**, No. 60, 43 (1960).
2. Clausen, C. P., "Biological Control," *U. S. Dept. Agr. Tech. Bull.,* 1139 (1956).
3. Crafts, A. S., and Harvey, W. A., *Calif. Agr. Exp. Sta. Cir.,* 446 (1955).
4. de Ong, E. R., "Chemistry and Uses of Pesticides," 2nd ed., New York, Reinhold Publishing Corp., 1956.
5. de Ong, E. R., *Ind. Eng. Chem.,* **20**, 826 (1928).
6. Gardner, Leo R., *Agr. Chemicals,* **9**, No. 6, 48 (1954).
7. Gray, G. P., and de Ong, E. R., *Ind. Eng. Chem.,* **18**, 175 (1926).
8. Horsfall, J. G., "Fungicides and Their Action," Waltham, Mass., Chronica Botanica Co., 1945.
9. Laforge, F. B., *et al., J. Org. Chem.,* **9**, 242 (1944).
10. Levy, L. W., *et al., J. Agr. Food Chem.,* **2**, 269 (1954).
11. Marshall, W. G., *Calif. Dept. Agr. Spec. Pub.,* 116 (1932).
12. McAlister, L. C., and Shepard, H. H., *J. Econ. Entom.,* **46**, 370 (1953).
13. Roark, R. C., *Ind. Eng. Chem.,* **25**, 639 (1933).
14. Staudinger, H., and Ruzika, L., *Helv. Chim. Acta,* **7**, 177 (1924).
15. U. S. Patent 2,344,895.
16. U. S. Patent 2,635,979.
17. U. S. Patent 2,502,258.
18. U. S. Patent 2,553,770.
19. British Patent 618,432.
20. U. S. Patent 1,972,961.
21. U. S. Patent 2,420,928.
22. U. S. Patent 2,482,063.
23. U. S. Patents 2,565,471 and 2,657,164.

ADDITIONAL PATENTS

Copper-ammonium silicate, U. S. Patent 2,051,910.
Water soluble defoliants, U. S. Patent 2,368,274.
Refined petroleum oil, U. S. Patent 1,707,468.
Oxidizing pine oils, U. S. Patent 1,996,100.
Petroleum oil as herbicide, U. S. Patent 1,917,754.
Particle dimension measurement, U. S. Patent 2,295,529.
Particle dimension measurement, U. S. Patent 2,261,802.
DDT, U. S. Patent 2,329,074.
2,4-D as growth stimulant, U. S. Patents 2,322,760 and 2,322,761.
2,4-D as herbicide, U. S. Patent 2,390,941.
Semicarbazones as insecticides, U. S. Patents 2,361,735; 2,374,479; 2,408,307 and 2,292,756.

ADDITIONAL READING REFERENCES

Atwood, W. G., and Johnson, A. A., "Marine Structures-Deterioration and Preservation," Nat. Research Council, 1924.

Kofoid, C. A., *et al.* "Termites and Termite Control," Univ. Calif. Press, 1934.

Metcalf, R. L., "Advances in Pest Control Research," New York, Interscience Pub., 1958.

Martin, Hubert, "Scientific Principles of Crop Protection," New York, St. Martin's Press, 1959.

de Ong, E. R., "Chemical and Natural Control of Pests," New York, Reinhold Publishing Corporation, 1960.

Gunther, F. A., and Blinn, R. C., "Analysis of Insecticides and Acaricides, New York-London, Interscience Publishers, 1955.

22

PIGMENTS, PAINTS, VARNISHES, LACQUERS, PRINTING INKS

In collaboration with Dr. Robert F. Toomey*

THAT THE PREPARATION of protective coatings for lumber and metals is an important industrial activity is apparent when it is considered that the interior and exterior of buildings, railway and motor cars, the bottoms as well as the superstructure of ships, and the cables, girders, and arches of bridges are treated with such coatings. Since World War I the manufacture of protective organic coatings has evolved from an art to a complex science. A significant percentage of industrial chemists and chemical engineers is employed in developing improved resins and new paint systems of which resins are an integral part.

PIGMENTS

The pigment industry is usually thought of as associated with paints; actually it is a separate industry and should be considered as such. Although a considerable tonnage of pigments is mined or manufactured for use in paints and enamels, almost as much is used in rubber goods, linoleums, oilcloth and artificial leather, plastics, ceramics, and other articles.

* John Carroll University, Department of Chemistry.

White Pigments

Among the white pigments titanium dioxide is undisputedly foremost; its production surpasses the combined production of leaded and unleaded zinc oxide which, in turn, exceeds that of white lead, first in line only a few years ago. The tonnages of lithopone and zinc sulfide blends are also significant. Carbon black is the principal black pigment. The oxides of iron, both natural and synthetic, are produced in large quantities. Prussian blue and phthalocyanine blue are the prominent blues, with ultramarine used in smaller amounts. Lead chromate (yellow), chrome oxide (green), and other chrome greens are used extensively; however, several of the older natural pigments are also in demand. Use of metallic salts of organic dyes, among them other phthalocyanines, is increasing. Metallic oxides are employed for ceramics; metal powders, particularly of aluminum and copper, are used to provide metallic finishes. Brilliant luminescent pigments are now available in several hues.

TABLE 22.1. COMPARISON OF ANATASE AND RUTILE
TITANIUM DIOXIDES*

	Anatase	Rutile
Refractive index	2.55	2.72
Specific gravity	3.88	4.20
Relative hiding power	100%	133%
Bulking value (lb/gal)	32.3	35.0

*"Paint and Varnish Technology," Von Fischer, New York, Reinhold Publishing Corporation, 1948.

Titanium Dioxide. The "hiding power" of a pigment in a given system depends on particle size and differences in refractive indexes between pigment and binder. Both commercial forms of titanium dioxide, rutile and anatase, have higher refractive index values than other white pigments and therefore give excellent covering power per pound of pigment.

Titanium ores are very widespread, the chief ores being ilmenite ($FeTiO_3$) and rutile (TiO_2). Although much is imported, important deposits occur along the eastern seaboard of the United States. Preparation of a high quality white pigment requires that the removal of impurities be carefully controlled; in the case of titanium dioxide this is a fairly expensive process necessitating many separate operations.

The pigment is prepared from the concentrated ore by mixing with sulfuric acid; the reaction which takes place is exothermic and violent. After digestion and solution, the iron is reduced to the ferrous state and much of it removed by crystallization as ferrous sulfate. The liquor is filtered, concentrated in vacuum evaporators, and boiled with sulfuric acid to precipitate the titanium dioxide pigment which is washed, dried, and calcined at a temperature of about 900° C. The calcining operation converts the titanium dioxide from the amorphous to the crystalline state, thereby raising the refractive index. Controlled grinding and bagging follow.

After the purification steps the process varies depending on the grade and type of product desired. Each manufacturer makes several grades, so it is essential to use the proper one to obtain the best results for a particular purpose. A type developed for a chalking house paint would hardly be suitable for an automotive finish.

"Extended" titanium pigments are prepared either by mixing or coprecipitating TiO_2 with cheaper pigments of low hiding power. Titanium calcium may be prepared by two methods: (1) by precipitating hydrated TiO_2 in the presence of $CaSO_4$, the coprecipitate being filtered and washed, and calcining and dry grinding; (2) TiO_2 and $CaSO_4$ may be mixed as

TABLE 22.2. RELATIVE TINTING STRENGTH OF THE MORE COMMON WHITE PIGMENTS*

Titanium dioxide, rutile crystal form	1600
Titanium dioxide, anatase crystal form	1275
Zinc sulfide	850
Titanium calcium, 30% TiO_2, rutile form	600
Titanium calcium, 30% TiO_2, anatase form	460
Lithopone, regular	280
Zinc oxide	170
White lead, regular	140

* "Physical and Chemical Examination of Paints, Varnishes, Lacquers and Colors," 8th ed., p. 92, Institute of Paint and Varnish Research, Washington, 1937.

a wet slurry, filtered, dried, calcined, and dry-ground. The composite pigment contains 30 per cent TiO_2 and 70 per cent $CaSO_4$, and has much better hiding power than would be obtained from a simple dry mix of the two components in the same proportion. Titanium-barium and titanium-magnesium pigments, each containing 30 per cent TiO_2, are also available.

Titanium dioxide in the pure state or as a composite pigment is used extensively in the paint, paper, rubber, ceramic, floor covering, and cosmetic industries. Its chief value stems from its bright white color and opacity. The tinting strength and opacity of titanium dioxide surpass that of any other white pigment.

Titanium dioxide paints with controlled chalking are extensively used for house paints; they stay white longer because of the gradual erosion of the soiled surface. A large proportion of anatase, sometimes combined with a small amount of an oxide of antimony or aluminum, is used for this purpose.

White lead, used as a pigment before the time of Christ, is still the only one which, when used as the sole pigment in an oil-based paint, will give an exterior finish that has good adhesion and is tough, elastic, and durable. It is a basic carbonate of the general formula $4PbCO_3Pb(OH)_2PbO$. Several methods have been used for its manufacture, different processes requiring from one day to several months for completion.

The Dutch Process. Lead, in the form of cast buckles, is corroded by the vapors of acetic acid and water in the presence of carbon dioxide emanating from fermenting tanbark. Lead acetate, the first compound formed, is transformed by carbon dioxide and moisture partly into lead carbonate and partly into lead hydroxide. The buckles are placed in small earthenware crocks, 8 inches in diameter and 10 inches high, into which a pint of 28 per cent acetic acid has been poured. The buckles lie over the acid, resting on a small shoulder in the inner wall of the crock. A layer of these crocks is placed in a thick bed of spent tanbark, then covered by boards over which more tanbark is shoveled, then by another tier of crocks. This is repeated until 10 or more tiers have been made. Some ventilation to the center is provided by a stack-like opening in the middle. The room is then closed. Fermentation of the tanbark proceeds and the temperature rises to about 70° C. The pots remain undisturbed for three months; after that they are unpacked, and the buckles, now white, are lifted out, crushed free from any uncorroded center, and ground dry or wet.

Other Processes. The Dutch process is slow and requires much hand labor. Extremely pure lead is required, otherwise the corrosion does not proceed far enough. Although the high quality of the product obtained by this process justifies its continued use, several other processes are employed, all of which require less time and turn out an even better product. The Carter process, which uses powdered lead, acetic acid, and carbon dioxide, requires one week. The French process, starting with litharge (PbO) instead of lead, yields a product in two days. Rowley uses atomized lead in water to form a hydroxide suspension through which carbon dioxide is passed. The Sperry process uses a lead anode and iron cathode, with sodium acetate and sodium carbonate as electrolytes, in an electrolytic cell in which the electrode compartments are separated by a membrane.

White lead is often wet ground since the poisonous nature of dry dust constitutes a health hazard. After wet grinding, the suspended solid is thickened by settling, giving "pulp lead." If it is intended for paint purposes, linseed oil may be mixed with the pulp. The oil displaces the water and the resulting paste is ground on roller mills and sold as *lead-in-oil*. The pulp may also be dried and disintegrated, and sold as dry powder.

Zinc Oxide. Zinc oxide is made in several ways. The original method, still in use, is the French or indirect process; zinc metal (spelter) is heated in stoneware retorts, vaporized, and burned in a combustion chamber placed at the mouth of the retort. An exhauster draws the white dust first to an air chamber where the heavier, less desirable particles are deposited, then to a filter chamber where the fine dust is collected.

In order to obtain the whitest pigment a very pure spelter must be used; if it contains lead, for instance, a frequent impurity in zinc, the lead burns to litharge and gives a yellowish tinge—a serious fault. To render the lead harmless, a modified indirect method has been developed where the burning is done in air mixed with carbon dioxide. The lead is changed to white lead, thus the yellow tinge is avoided; the zinc oxide is unaffected. This modification has been extremely successful and has made possible the use of spelters containing appreciable quantities of lead.

Another modification involves the use of a retort which is open at both ends; carbon monoxide, sent in at one end, passes over the heated metal and assists in its vaporization. The gas and vapor issue from the other end of the retort into a combustion chamber where they burn together with an intense yellow-white flame. An exhauster pulls the fumes through a cooling chamber and forces them through bag filters.

A direct process, that is, one producing the oxide directly from the ore, was developed by Weatherill about 80 years ago for the New Jersey Zinc Company. In the Weatherill furnace, franklinite, an oxide of zinc containing iron and manganese (Zn 18 per cent), is mixed with coal and burned on a grate. The natural oxide is first reduced and then re-formed by the air and carbon dioxide from the fire. Provision is made to admit more air over the fire if unburned zinc vapors should rise. The grate is a casting with tapering holes rather than the usual bars. The residue on the hearth is made into spiegeleisen, a manganese-iron mixture which also contains carbon.

Approximately 15 per cent of the zinc oxide pigment used in 1958 was "leaded" zinc oxide. This pigment is essentially a mechanical mixture of zinc oxide with 5 to 50 per cent of either lead sulfate or basic lead sulfate. The lead content of the pigment results in better through-dry and toughness in the film. This pigment is commonly used in exterior house paints.

Lithopone. Lithopone is formed when a solution of zinc sulfate is mixed with one of barium sulfide. Barium sulfate and zinc sulfide are formed, both of which are white. This precipitate is not suitable for a pigment,

$$ZnSO_4 + BaS \rightarrow BaSO_4 + ZnS$$

however, until it has been dried, heated to a high temperature in a muffle furnace, and plunged when still hot into cold water. Lithopone is 30 per cent zinc sulfide and 70 per cent barium sulfate, with slight variations. It has fair covering power, is brilliant white, and cheap. It is used extensively in interior wall coatings.

"High strength lithopones" are made by blending lithopone with titanium dioxide or, more commonly, zinc sulfide, giving improved pigments known as "titanated lithopones" and "zinc sulfide-barium," respectively.

All the pigments discussed thus far are white: white lead, sublimed white lead, zinc oxide, leaded zinc oxide, titanium dioxide, and lithopone. They are similar not only in color but also in quality of opaqueness and hiding power in oleoresinous vehicles. They are the basis of most exterior house paints and many interior paints and enamels. *Blanc fixe* ($BaSO_4$), also white in color, has no hiding power in oleoresinous vehicles and is used as an extender. Other extenders are magnesium silicate, whiting (finely divided calcium carbonate), finely divided silica, etc. It should be noted that such inerts in oleoresinous vehicles (blanc fixe, calcium sulfate, calcium carbonate, aluminum silicate, magnesium silicate, silica, and others) do have hiding power where their refractive index differs from that of the vehicle in which they are dispersed, e.g., calcimine paints and whitewash. A few of the more common colored pigments are discussed below.

Colored Pigments

Litharge. Litharge (lead oxide) may be prepared in several ways. The oldest method, still practiced, is to heat metallic lead in a low-arched reverberatory furnace with the usual bridge wall dividing the fireplace from the hearth. The atmosphere is kept oxidizing by allowing a large quantity of air to enter; the temperature is just above the melting point of lead oxide (PbO). As the oxide forms it floats on the surface and is pushed to one side by iron hoes. When enough oxide has collected it is drawn off by means of the hoes, cooled, ground, and levigated. The color is buff. A continuous furnace has been used successfully in which air jets impinge on the surface of the lead, sweeping the molten oxide to the front end of the oval furnace; fresh lead is added in a stream so regulated that the amount of lead in the furnace remains constant. The molten oxide overflows into a conical receiver and is cooled, broken up, ground, and air-floated to remove unoxidized lead particles.

Litharge is also made as a by-product in the manufacture of sodium nitrite which is melted in a large iron pot at a constant 340° C. Lead is added in the form of thin plates. After they have disappeared the temperature is maintained for twenty minutes. The brown mass which has formed is then cooled and extracted with water and the sodium nitrite is crystallized from the decanted solution. The residue is litharge; it is washed and used "as is" for red lead.

Red Lead. Red lead is made by calcining litharge in a muffle furnace. A current of air is admitted into the muffle; the temperature must be maintained within narrow limits, near 340° C, and the period is usually 48 hours. Whereas the use of white lead has been steadily decreasing, the use of red lead in priming paints is increasing, and the production of red lead now surpasses that of white lead.

Carbon Black. There are several kinds of carbon black: *thermal black,* produced by the thermal decomposition of natural gas; *channel black,* produced by the impingement of numerous small regulated flames against a relatively cold steel surface which is constantly scraped free of the deposit; *furnace black,* produced by the partial combustion of the gas in a furnace, with recovery of the carbon product in cyclones and electrical precipitators; *lampblack,* used mainly as a tinctorial pigment; and *oil black.* Thermal black is used as a filler and an extender in rubber. Until recently, channel black has been the important black in rubber compounding. Following the introduction of the synthetic GR-S, and more recently of "cold rubber," it has been found that certain furnace blacks with particle size larger than that of the standard channel black (such as 45 to 100 millimicrons) give superior reinforcement. The great advantage of furnace black is that its yield is higher (as high as 8 pounds per 1000 cubic feet of gas) than that of channel black (1 to 2 pounds per 1000 cubic feet of gas).

TABLE 22.3. U. S. PRODUCTION OF MAJOR PIGMENTS IN 1958*

	Tons
Titanium dioxide	420,000
White lead	15,000
Red lead	22,000
Zinc oxide (lead free)	145,000
Zinc oxide (leaded)	25,000
Chrome colors	33,000
Carbon black	850,000
Powdered aluminum	14,000

* Estimated from monthly production figures.

Carbon black may be pelleted, by either a dry or a wet process, for greater convenience and success in handling. Thus carbon blacks which have been treated with zinc naphthenates, and the "beaded" blacks, from which entrapped air has been removed, can be wetted much more quickly and effectively by the vehicle.

Lampblack is an older pigment; it has been made for thousands of years by the Chinese, Egyptians, and other ancient races for the manufacture of ink. It consists of the free soot or smoke collected in chambers from burning oils of hydrocarbon gases. In many of its earlier uses it has been replaced by carbon black.

Iron Oxide. Iron oxide (Fe_2O_3) is made on a large scale by roasting ferrous sulfate obtained from the vats used for pickling steel. Water and sulfur oxides are driven off and led through a stack to the atmosphere. The shade can be varied by altering the firing time, the temperature, and the atmosphere. It is a relatively cheap pigment and is usually used in red barn paint and metal prime. The use of selected grades for polishing glass and lenses is determined by their resistance to grit and the hardness of the glass; such grades of iron oxide are called *rouges.*

Prussian Blue. Prussian blue or iron blue is manufactured by reacting sodium ferrocyanide, ferrous sulfate, and ammonium sulfate. The precipitate is then oxidized with sodium chlorate or sodium dichromate.

Phthalocyanine Blue. The phthalocyanine pigments are greens and blues of extremely high tinting strength. Structurally they are quite similar to chlorophyll, but copper is the chelating metal rather than magnesium. Although expensive, they are such effective tinters that they are now used extensively in both oil- and water-based paints.

Ultramarine Blue. A bright blue inorganic pigment of complex structure, ultramarine is made by heating a mixture of soda ash, clay, and sulfur with charcoal or pitch. Although used for tinting and for outside paints, its primary use is in colored granules for asphalt shingles.

Chrome Yellows. To prepare chrome yellows, soluble lead salts are precipitated from solution by adding sodium or potassium dichromate. The colors are clean and bright, and have a high tinting strength. The shades may be varied by adjusting the pH of the precipitating solution.

Chrome Greens. Chrome greens are manufactured by coprecipitating Prussian blue and chrome yellow. The color is dependent on the proportions of the two pigments used.

Natural Pigments. Among the natural pigments still in use are umber (brown), ochre (a poor yellow), and Sienna (a deeper yellow).

Metallic Pigments

Although gold, zinc, and copper bronze powders are used as pigments, powdered aluminum is the most important. In addition to its principal use in organic coatings it is also currently used in solid rocket propellants and as a filler for thermosetting resin systems. As a leafing pigment it reflects sunlight, thus preventing degradation of the organic film and affording insulation. As a non-leafing pigment it is used extensively in automotive finishes to provide a metallic sparkle.

Aluminum powder is prepared in a stamping mill. Thin aluminum sheets, usually mixed with a small amount of lubricant (e.g., stearic acid), are pounded into a powder which is then screened and polished. Much of the powder is converted to a paste by grinding it in a ball mill with oil or mineral spirits.

Luminescent Pigments

Luminescent paints are used in advertising displays and on aircraft because of their daylight brilliance. The most efficient luminescent pigments are organic dyes of the rhodamine, auramine, and thioflavin types. The dyes are effective in low concentration, hence the commercial pigments are prepared by combining an organic solution of the dye with a resin solution.

The pigment is precipitated in the body of the resin as the resin is condensed; the solid resin is coarse-ground and handled as a pigment.

PAINTS

In 1958 approximately 650,000 gallons of nitrocellulose lacquer was used in the United States for painting wooden pencils. Indeed, the manufacture of organic protective coatings has become one of the major chemical industries. Paint manufacture has been transformed from an art to a science within the past forty years. Water-based paints, of little importance before World War II, have now captured over 20 per cent of the do-it-yourself market. This represents a fifteenfold increase in ten years. There is a strong probability that within the next decade water-based systems will become of major importance for exterior finishes, not only for houses but for automobiles as well.

A paint consists essentially of a pigment suspended in a suitable liquid called a vehicle. The vehicle may be a drying oil, a varnish, or a solution or suspension of natural or synthetic resins in an organic solvent or water. When spread in a thin film (generally 0.5 to 2.0 mils), the volatile components evaporate, leaving a mixture of pigment and binder in the form of a solid, continuous, adherent, thin coating which is both decorative and protective.

Modern paints are "tailor-made" coatings, usually designed by skilled scientists for specific purposes. Exterior paints generally lack the esthetic qualities demanded by decorators and architects for the interior of homes and institutions. On the other hand, interior paints would not be sufficiently resistant to the damaging action of rain, frost, sunlight, or industrial fumes—a resistance expected of an exterior paint.

The usual components of ready-mixed oil-based exterior house paints are pigments, "semi-drying" and "drying" vegetable oils, driers, and a solvent. Certain paints also contain resins, usually long-oil alkyds. One function of the oil is to give elasticity to the paint so that the coating can withstand the expansion and contraction induced by temperature changes without cracking and chipping.

Oil paints "dry" by oxidation and polymerization of the vehicle; these processes are hastened by the incorporation of driers, catalysts which consist usually of the naphthenates, oleates, resinates, or oxides of cobalt, lead, manganese, iron, calcium, zinc, or zirconium.

Solvents such as mineral spirits or turpentine are added in various amounts to decrease the viscosity of the paint, making it possible to apply it in thin uniform layers, to spray it onto a surface, or to use it as a dip. The pigment gives the paint opacity, color, and added durability, the latter, in part at least, by protecting the oil and resin film from ultraviolet light and, in the case of zinc oxide, by the protection its fungicidal properties afford.

Pigments frequently used for their protective and opaque characteristics are white lead, zinc oxide, titanium dioxide, lithopone, red lead, and iron oxide. Small amounts of tinting colors are often added to these pigments for decorative purposes. The relation between the refractive index and hiding power has been illustrated earlier in the chapter. Invariably a white paint formula will list at least three different white pigments. Included will be an inert—magnesium silicate for example—with several valuable functions, one of which is to prevent too rapid settling of the other pigments, another to aid in protecting the paint from weathering.

TABLE 22.4. FORMULA FOR AN EXTERIOR HOUSE PAINT*

Component	Total formula	Pigment 61%	Vehicle 39%
Basic sulfate-white lead	11.1%	18.2%	...
Zinc oxide	20.7	34.0	...
Titanium dioxide	10.5	17.2	...
Magnesium silicate	13.5	22.2	...
Silica	5.1	8.4	...
Linseed oil	29.7	...	76
Driers	.7	...	1.8
Mineral spirits	8.7	...	22.2
	100%	100%	100%

* From Pratt and Lambert, Inc., label, March 1949; subject to change at any time.

There are several methods for preparing paints, but all strive for a homogeneous dispersion of the pigment in the vehicle.

One of the most efficient factory layouts consists of a four-story building which makes possible gravity flow of the raw materials and finished products through the plant. The pigments and grinding liquids are stored on the top floor whence they can be fed, by means of chutes, to mills located on the floor below. After the grinding or dispersing action is completed, the paint is discharged from the mills through chutes or pipe lines to storage tanks on the floor below. The "floor tanks" have agitators to keep the mix from settling. For certain formulas additional vehicle is added in these tanks. The batch is held until quality control tests are completed. Then it is strained and placed in shipping containers and sent to the ground floor where shipping and warehousing activities are centered.

Proper dispersion of pigments is essential. Various types of equipment may be used for this purpose, all of them subjecting the agglomerated pigment particles to very great shearing stress in the vehicle medium. The shearing action reduces pigment aggregates to primary particles and simultaneously promotes wetting of these particulates by the vehicle. Wetting agents and dispersants are often added to promote stabilization and prevent reagglomeration.

The most important grinding methods are the following:

(1) *Roller mill grinding.* In the United States three- and five-roll mills are used. These consist of a series of water-cooled, hardened steel rollers, each turning at different speeds and in the opposite direction to the ones adjacent to it. There is very small clearance between the rolls. A scraper blade on the last roll removes the well-mixed paste, into which additional vehicle is incorporated (Figure 22.1).

Figure 22.1. A three-roll mill. (*Courtesy The Glidden Co.*)

(2) *Pebble mill grinding.* The pigment and vehicle are placed in a porcelain-lined water-cooled pebble mill which is about half full of pebbles the size of golf balls. The mill is then rotated until the desired fineness of dispersion is obtained. The time for this operation may vary from 4 to 48 hours, 16 to 20 hours being the most common. The pebbles impinge against the walls of the mill and against each other, thus reducing the size of the agglomerates in the pigment and vehicle mix. The capacity of the pebble mills for this purpose may vary from 5 to 500 gallons, 300 gallons being the average.

When blacks or colored paints are ground, the grinding time may be shortened by replacing the pebbles with steel balls. The pebble or ball mill is the most economical grinding method. Occasionally a buhrstone or steel lining is used in the mill in place of porcelain. The steel lining increases the speed of production but discolors the whites to some extent (Figure 22.2).

(3) *Moorehouse mill* (Hy-R-Speed Mill). This is essentially a commercial adaptation of a laboratory colloid mill. Relatively small in size, it is a high speed continuous mill used primarily for house paints, flats, and water emulsion finishes. A mixture of pigment and vehicle is fed into the mill,

Figure 22.2. Ball mill for grinding pigment. (*Courtesy The Glidden Co.*)

passing between a rotor and stator. It is a high capacity machine and is generally used where fine grind standards are not required (Figure 22.3).

(4) *Stone mill*. Mixing by grinding between stones has been done for ages. Some stone mills are still in use where a fine grind is desired and capacity is not important.

(5) *Sand process*. The most recent commercial development for pigment dispersion consists basically of a bucket of sand (of controlled particle size) which is rapidly agitated by hardened steel discs. A pigment-vehicle mix of low viscosity introduced into the top of the bucket passes through the churning sand where the shear rate is extremely high. Such units may be used in tandem (Figures 22.4 and 22.5).

Latex and Emulsion Paints

A latex consists of a dispersion of a resinous solid in water, whereas in an emulsion the dispersed phase is a liquid. In general, latex systems yield films which are more water resistant than those formed from emulsions. An electron micrograph of a latex shows the resin particles to be perfect

Figure 22.3. A Moorehouse mill for fine grinding. (*Courtesy The Glidden Co.*)

spheres. After spreading a thin layer of latex paint the water evaporates from the surface, leaving the resinous particles which coalesce and form a continuous film.

The common constituents of a latex paint are the following: (1) a latex of 40 to 55 per cent solids content; (2) a water-soluble binder which acts as a protective colloid; (3) a thickening agent which may improve brushing and adhesion; (4) pigments low in salt content; (5) a preservative to prevent mold or bacterial action; (6) wetting agents for easier dispersion of pigments; (7) a plasticizer for external plasticization, if necessary; (8) a freeze-thaw stabilizer, often a glycol, to improve package stability. Ordinary mixing equipment is used for combining the many ingredients.

Production of latex paints has increased from approximately 2,000,000 gallons in 1948 to 62,000,000 gallons in 1957, and it should be noted that this production is at present limited almost entirely to interior finishes. Intensive research is being directed toward improving the suitability of

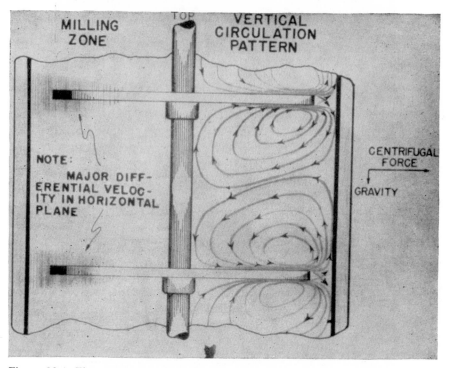

Figure 22.4. Flow patterns in a Du Pont sand grinder. (*Courtesy E. I. du Pont de Nemours and Co., Inc.*)

latices for use in maintenance paints and exterior wood and metal finishes; baking primers and topcoats for appliance and automotive finishes are now being road-tested, and exterior house paints have been found satisfactory for use in mild climates. Difficulties encountered include poor adhesion over chalky surfaces, low gloss, poor freeze-thaw stability, and high permeability to moisture.

The principle resins used in latex systems are the vinyl acetates, acrylics, and butadiene-styrene types, all available to formulators as 40 to 50 per cent solids dispersed in water. Polyvinyl acetates and alkyds are the leading systems in emulsion paint developments.

Epoxy Paints

Epoxy coatings may be either 100 per cent solids epoxy finishes or formulations containing epoxy esters which can be formulated for either air-drying or baking and which dry by oxidation as do conventional drying

Figure 22.5. A Du Pont sand grinder. (*Courtesy E. I. du Pont de Nemours and Co., Inc.*)

oils. The presence of an epoxy improves the adhesion and toughness of a coating. Where the ultimate is required in abrasion and chemical resistance, a 100 per cent epoxy is the usual choice.

Epoxies are used in floor coatings, marine varnishes, highway toppings, and as interior coatings in concrete sewage pipe. The use of flexibilizing agents result in epoxy systems with considerable stretch.

Fluorescent Paints

A fluorescent paint is one with a pigment which will absorb electromagnetic radiation and emit part of this energy as visible light. In 1958, 13,000 airplanes were striped with fluorescent paints so that they could be seen from great distances. Vehicles for luminescent coatings must be transparent to the exciting and emitted radiation; alkyd resins are usually used. Pigments are only rough-ground to prevent loss of brilliance. When used outdoors a transparent overcoat is applied to reduce the deactivating effect of ultraviolet radiation. When properly applied and topped by the clear protective film, fluorescent paints are effective for about two years.

Radioisotopes may be used in paints, the emitted radiation causing the production of visible radiation from certain pigments. Such paints could be effective indefinitely, depending on the half life of the isotope, but would require a protective coating transparent to light and opaque to harmful radiation.

VARNISHES AND ENAMELS

Varnishes

The term "varnishes" includes many and varied coating systems which differ essentially from enamels in that they contain no pigment and produce clear transparent coatings. Most are oleoresinous materials made by cooking drying oils and resins and then adding drying oils and thinners. The most characteristic drying oil used is tung oil, while the resin is ester gum or a special synthetic resin. Linseed oil, dehydrated castor oil, and other modified oils are often used in place of tung oil which has a tendency to yellow quite rapidly. The latter, heated for 5 minutes at 550° F, cools to a solid gel, whereas linseed oil, heated for several hours at the same temperature, cools to a viscous liquid. *Oiticica* oil, from Brazil, is rapidly gaining in popularity; it dries faster to a harder film than linseed, but not as fast nor as hard as tung oil. (See Chapter 12 for more information on drying oils.) Soybean oil, a semi-drying oil, dries too slowly for general use but is used extensively in baking enamels and in the preparation of alkyd resins. The composition of fatty acids in soybean oil is:

	%
Saturated	
Palmitic acid	6.5
Stearic acid	4.5
Arachidic acid	0.7
Unsaturated	
Oleic acid	33.5
Linoleic acid	52.5
Linolenic acid	2.3

The first four acids are desirable for edible use, while the two remaining ones are paint oils. It is the low linolenic content of soybean oil which keeps paints from yellowing.

The principal varnish resins in addition to those already mentioned are *Congo copal* (a natural resin), rosin, and rosinates. Congo copal is a fossil resin dug out of swampy ground in the Belgian Congo. Similar resins of lesser importance are *Manilla copal* from East India and *Kauri* from New Zealand. Suitable synthetic resins are all oil-soluble and include modified and unmodified phenolics, maleic, alkyd coumarone, petroleum, and terpene resins. The oil imparts elasticity, toughness, and weather resistance, while the resin contributes hardness and gloss.

The modified phenolics of special interest are phenolformaldehyde resins in which the "phenol" is *para-tertiary* butyl phenol, *para-tertiary* amyl phenol, *para*-phenyl phenol, or bisphenol.

Rosin is used extensively in the varnish industry but usually in a modified form. It has a relatively low melting point, is easily softened by pressure as well as by heat, and becomes tacky. It can be hardened either by reacting with zinc or lime to form the metallic resinate, or by esterifying with glycerin or pentaerythritol to form ester gum.

The quick-drying or four-hour varnishes resulted from the combining of synthetic resins with tung oil. Generally speaking, synthetic resins hasten the drying and improve resistance to water and chemicals. It is possible, furthermore, to incorporate into a varnish a larger percentage of synthetic resin than of fossil resins. The former absorbs ultraviolet light without alteration, protecting the more sensitive components by its screening effect.

The ratio of resin to oil varies with the different types of varnish; in general, the higher the percentage of resin the more brittle and faster-drying the varnish will be. The following classification illustrates the various types and their usage.

"Short"—12–15 gal oil/100 lb resin . . . . for furniture to be rubbed
"Moderately short"—15–25 gal oil/100 lb resin . . . . for many household enamels
"Medium length"—25–35 gal oil/100 lb resin . . . . for spar and floor varnish
"Long oil"—35–50 gal oil/100 lb resin . . . . for durable exterior varnishes

In making a typical varnish the gum resin and the oil are placed in a kettle and heated over the flame of an oil burner set below the floor. The temperature is raised rapidly to 500–600° F, depending on the product, and is maintained until the correct body is obtained or until the mixture becomes homogeneous. If driers in powder form are used they are added during the cooking process. The kettle is pulled from the fire and the charge is cooled and thinned. Liquid driers such as the metallic naphthenates are usually added after thinning. After cooling, dirt and foreign material are

removed by pumping the varnish through a filter press or centrifuge.* The varnish is then pumped into storage tanks. Numerous laboratory tests are conducted to determine specific gravity, viscosity, color, clarity, drying time, water resistance, chemical resistance, baking, and elasticity.

Baking japans are varnishes made with asphaltum instead of resin; the baking is done, for metal surfaces, at 400° F (204° C) and lasts 3 to 4 hours. This temperature melts the asphaltum easily and distributes it evenly. During the baking the oxidation of the oil is rapid, so that on removal of the article the coat is dry. A very beautiful black luster is obtained. Varnishes containing the usual resins may be used if baking is done at lower temperatures. Such coatings are highly chemical resistant.

Enamels

Enamels are varnishes that contain pigments. Their constitution varies greatly depending on the final application and whether or not the finish is to be baked. Most enamels are of the alkyd type and often include a urea or melamine resin for greater whiteness or hardness. The use of tung oil in a baking enamel will cause the film to shrink while being heated, giving an attractive wrinkled finish frequently seen on metal cases.

TABLE 22.5. A CLASSIFICATION OF CLEAR AND PIGMENTED COATINGS
(EXTERIOR HOUSE PAINTS NOT INCLUDED)
(After O. J. Schultes)

I	II	III	IV
Oleoresinous	Alkyd	Cellulose	Resin
varnishes	varnishes	clear lacquer	lacquers
and	and	and	and
enamels	enamels	lacquer enamel	enamels

I. The oil-resin varnishes and enamels have been fully discussed.

II. The alkyd resins are esters of polyhydric alcohols and polybasic acids. Glyceryl phthalate, its most prominent representative, is modified with fatty acids from drying oils to render it soluble in organic solvents. Most alkyd varnishes are pigmented and serve as enamels.

III. The typical clear lacquer consists of cellulose nitrate, resin (synthetic), plasticizer, solvent, and diluent. Here again the pigmented lacquers, called lacquer enamels, comprise most of the production.

IV. Dispersions or solutions of resins in organic solvents, often plasticized with oil or chemical plasticizers, are the resin lacquers and, when pigmented, the resin enamels. Several of the new synthetic resins are being used in resin lacquers: "Vinylite" dissolved in ketones; "Pliolite," in turpentine; "Parlon," a chlorinated rubber hydrocarbon, in toluene and xylene. Spirit varnish belongs in this group as, for example, shellac varnish.

Most baking enamel production lines now include a "baking tunnel" lined with infrared lamps and reflectors. The workpieces are mounted on

---

* The filter press is the more searching device; all clear varnishes are filter-pressed. The centrifuge is more rapid and is used for varnishes which are to be pigmented into enamels.

a conveyor system which carries them through the spray room, where they are coated either manually or automatically, and then into and through the baking tunnel at a predetermined rate of speed.

Automotive finish-coats are alkyd systems which contain either 20 to 30 per cent melamine resin or 20 to 30 per cent nitrocellulose or acrylic resin. Because solvent requirements and other characteristics are quite different in the two systems, the former is an enamel system whereas the latter is classified as a lacquer.

LACQUERS

A lacquer is a protective coating which dries by evaporation of volatile components and the film-forming constituent is usually a cellulose ester (nitrate, acetate, acetate-butyrate) combined with a resin. Plasticizers are incorporated to add flexibility to the film. Now acrylics and other thermoplastic polymers are being employed more and more in lacquer systems.

Nitrocellulose, which continues to be the dominant film-former, will be considered in detail.

In addition to nitrated cotton, a nitrocellulose lacquer contains for example, (1) a solvent mixture which usually includes a ketone, an alcohol, a volatile ester, and frequently an ether-alcohol of the "Cellosolve" or "Dowanol" type; (2) a resin such as an alkyd, a phenolic, or an ester gum; (3) a plasticizer for flexibilizing the film; (4) inexpensive volatile diluents; and (5) a dye or pigment, omitted if a "clear" lacquer is desired. Table 22.6 shows the ultimate particle size of various pigments used in paints, enamels, and lacquers.

A lacquer coating dries rapidly by the evaporation of the solvents, whereas the standard varnish dries slowly, partly by evaporation, partly by oxidation and polymerization.

Nitrocellulose, also called pyroxylin, is made by nitrating cotton linters with mixed acid. Nitration is not allowed to proceed as far as it is when making nitrocellulose for explosives since the highly nitrated cellulose (12.5 per cent N and over) is not soluble in the selected solvents. For that reason a "cotton" containing only 11 to 12.4 per cent N is prepared. The linters are purified from oils by boiling with caustic, washed, and if colorless lacquer is sought, bleached. Nitration is carried out by placing 32 pounds of cotton in 1500 pounds of mixed acid, the large excess of acid being used to ensure negligible change in concentration (during nitration) due to consumption of nitric acid and production of water.

$$C_{24}H_{40}O_{20} + 8HNO_3 \rightarrow C_{24}H_{32}O_{12}(NO_3)_8 + 8H_2O$$

Cellulose   Nitrated cellulose
                                     or nitrocellulose

The reaction given here is an ideal one and is meant to indicate the change taking place. Actually a series of nitrocelluloses are formed having various numbers of nitrate groups in the molecules. The total nitrogen content is the guide.

After 15 minutes in the acid the cotton is dropped to a centrifuge for removal of adhering acid. Then it is beaten in pulping machines (8 hours) and boiled in poaching tubs (12 hours) with several changes of weak alkaline waters. Finally the 25 per cent adsorbed moisture is displaced by denatured alcohol forced in under a pressure of 300 psi. At this stage the

TABLE 22.6. ULTIMATE PARTICLE SIZE OF VARIOUS
STANDARD PIGMENTS

Material	Maximum residue on No. 325 screen (opening 44 microns) (per cent)	Average ultimate particle size (microns)
Carbon black	1.0	0.1
Fine-particle zinc oxide ("Kadox")	. . .	0.12 to 0.18
Zinc oxide (Florence French process "Green Seal")	1.0	0.21 to 0.26
Lithopone	1.0	0.25 to 0.35
Titanium barium pigment	1.5	. . . . . .
Zinc sulfide	. . .	. . . . . .
High-strength lithopone	. . .	. . . . . .
American process zinc oxide	1.0	0.28 to 0.35
Lamp black	1.0	0.4
High-leaded zinc oxide	1.0	0.35 to 0.45
Iron oxide (Spanish)	3.0	0.4 to 0.6
Low-leaded oxide (5% leaded)	1.0	0.50 to 0.65
Sublimed white lead	1.0	0.65 to 0.67
Basic carbonate white lead (Old Dutch process)	1.0	0.75 to 1.21
Chrome green	2.5	. . . . . .
Ultramarine blue	. . .	5.0

nitrocellulose, moist with alcohol, resembles cotton waste in appearance. It is made in a few plants and bought by the lacquer maker who dissolves and blends it to suit his requirements.

Originally the nitrocellulose so made was dissolved in amyl acetate, for example, and articles dipped in the solution. On evaporation of the solvent a film remained. It was soon observed that only 6 ounces of nitrocellulose could be dissolved in one gallon of the solvent—more than this amount gave a solution too viscous to flow. In fact, with 6 ounces the resulting solution was quite thick. Nitrocellulose which gives rise to such solutions is called *high-viscosity nitrocellulose*. It became desirable to modify the nitrocellulose so that a greater quantity could be placed in solution and the solution thinned enough to be applicable with a spray gun. Such a modified material is *low-viscosity nitrocellulose*, the manufacture of which

is described below. It is now possible to place 24 ounces of nitrocellulose together with 16 ounces of additional gums in one gallon of solvent for a total of 40 ounces of the film-forming material, instead of only 6. The important product now is low-viscosity nitrocellulose. Suitable gum additions are dammar, shellac, kauri, rosin, ester, etc. High-viscosity "cotton" is still made, however, for use in bronzing liquid and in many lacquer formulas because the film made from low-viscosity cotton is slightly weaker.

Low-viscosity cotton is produced by heating the first product of nitration with water, under pressure. The earlier batch process, in which 4000 pounds of cotton were heated with 60,000 pounds of water, established that during heating there is a decrease in the nitrogen content from 12.25 to 12.05 per cent nitrogen, and that gas is formed. In the continuous process nitrated cotton (1 part) suspended in water (20 parts) is pumped continuously through a 4-inch tube 1000 feet long ending in a 200-foot standpipe. Rate of flow and temperature are controlled, with a resultant reduction in viscosity. The residence period is generally 25 minutes. The mixture overflows to tubs and then passes to centrifugals; the product may be kept moist until called for, or its water may be displaced by alcohol in a dehydrating press, leaving the cotton alcohol-moist. It may be shipped in barrels in that condition. Low-viscosity nitrocellulose may also be produced by heating the product of nitration with benzene or ethyl alcohol.

The lacquer is made by first dissolving the selected resin in the diluent and adding it to the cotton-solvent solution; then solvent or diluent is introduced, and finally the pigment is added as a suspension in nitrocellulose solution or in the plasticizer. A tank with an agitator is used for these operations.

Plasticizers

When used alone, the film of nitrocellulose contracts after the solvents evaporate, wrinkling and buckling away from the surface being coated. This serious defect may be counteracted successfully by the use of a substance in the formula which will not volatilize when the film dries and hence will remain in the film and render it plastic. Such substances are castor oil, camphor, diethylphthalate, dibutylphthalate, diamylphthalate, tricresyl phosphate, tributyl phosphate, butyl stearate, and many others. Castor oil is used if pigments are to be incorporated in the lacquer. By adding certain substances such as the chlorinated diphenyls (*Aroclors*), flammability of the film may be decreased and plasticization increased.

Use of Lacquer

The main outlets for lacquer are automobile finishes, woodwork and furniture, and artificial leather which is made by coating a cotton fabric

TABLE 22.7. PRODUCTION FIGURES FOR CERTAIN VARNISH AND
LACQUER RESINS FOR 1957*

Resin Type (includes modified resins)	Production (thousands of lb, dry basis)
Phenolics	29,950
Urea and melamine resins	36,442
Styrene resins	83,927
Vinyl and vinyl copolymers	31,500
Alkyd resins	
phthalic anhydride types	332,493
polybasic acid types (except phthalic)	14,813
Rosin modifications	
esterified with glycerin and other alcohols	23,739
modified with phenolics	23,350
modified with maleic and fumaric acids only	31,191
all other rosin modifications and all other uses	43,611
Miscellaneous resin materials, for protective coatings only †	13,217

* Compiled from data in United States Tariff Commission's monthly reports on production and sales of plastics and resin materials.
† Includes data for epichlorohydrin, acrylic, silicone, and other protective coating resins.

with a pyroxylin solution and then embossing it to simulate the grain of leather. In the latter market embossed vinyls are offering considerable competition.

PAINT PRODUCTION IN FOREIGN COUNTRIES IN 1957
(TONS ESTIMATED)*

France	300,000
West Germany	364,000
Japan	187,000
Sweden	90,000
Netherlands	20,865
Mexico	4,500
India	43,000

* This compares with United States production of 18,000,000 tons in trade sales alone.

Figures 22.6, 22.7 and 22.8 give a general picture of the relative quantities of major constituents required for the production of organic coatings. Figure 22.9 shows how rapidly the use of synthetic resins has increased since 1930.

COMMERCIAL APPLICATION OF COATINGS

Progress in the methods of coating wood and metal articles has kept pace with improvements in the physical properties of the coatings used. Large scale applications involve either dipping, flow coating, or spraying operations. The Volkswagen and American Motors Companies make widespread use of huge dipping tanks for immersing an entire auto body in finish-coat material.

Air-spray is the most common finishing method, but increasing attention is being given to the use of airless spray. Whereas an air gun will deliver over 500 volumes of air per one volume of paint, an airless gun delivers

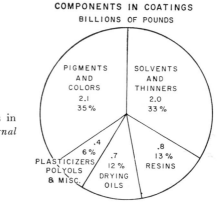

COMPONENTS IN COATINGS
BILLIONS OF POUNDS

Figure 22.6. Use of various components in coatings manufacture. [*American Paint Journal (April 21, 1958)*.]

DISTRIBUTION OF RESINS
IN COATINGS – TOTAL 830
MILLIONS OF POUNDS

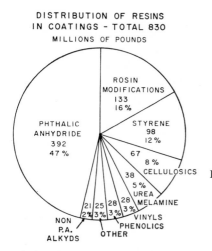

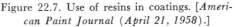

Figure 22.7. Use of resins in coatings. [*American Paint Journal (April 21, 1958)*.]

only paint; thus, overspray is almost eliminated, the paint is used more efficiently, and there is less air contamination and more uniform coating of inside corners.

Electrostatic spraying, done either automatically or by hand, involves the use of an electrostatic field surrounding the workpiece to be coated. The atomized coating is propelled through the electrical field where the particles are charged and then forcibly attracted to the grounded workpiece. Advantages of electrostatic spraying include efficient use of coating material, more rapid application, and the use of automatic conveyorized systems for painting complex shapes which would otherwise require hand methods.

In the field of coating formulation, development has lagged regarding water- and oil-based products which will maintain their integrity over a wide range of temperatures. Wood and metal finishers are increasingly making use of "hot spray" techniques where the coating material is heated to as high as 400° F before spraying, the usual spray temperature being

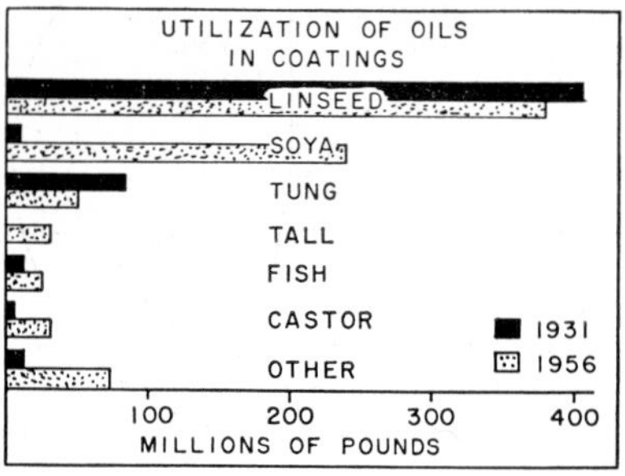

Figure 22.8. Use of oils in coatings. [*American Paint Journal* (*April 21, 1958*).]

Figure 22.9. Use of synthetic resins in surface coatings. [*American Paint Journal* (*April 21, 1958*).]

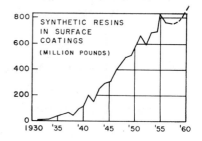

in the range of 120 to 180° F. Materials with higher solids content may be used at elevated temperatures, allowing the application of thicker films and thereby reducing the number of finish coats required. Other advantages of hot spray are increased gloss, better flowout, and smoother finish.

A portable commercial system which combines the advantages of hot spray and airless spray is shown in Figure 22.10.

PRINTING INKS OR NEWS INKS

Printing inks should not be compared to ordinary writing inks since they are actually paints. They must dry as fast as applied, mainly through penetration into the paper. They are made by mixing carbon black or lamp black with linseed and rosin oils, rosin varnish, and a drier.

Rosin oil is included because it is cheaper than linseed oil. It is made by distilling rosin in simple stills fired by the staves from the rosin barrels. The distillate comprises water, acetic acid, an impure "pinoline," then rosin oil; the residue is pitch which is run off hot. The rosin oil is refined by a second distillation. Rosin varnish is made by heating rosin until water, acetic acid, and pinoline have passed over, then by running all the residual liquid into a mixer containing warm linseed oil which has been previously

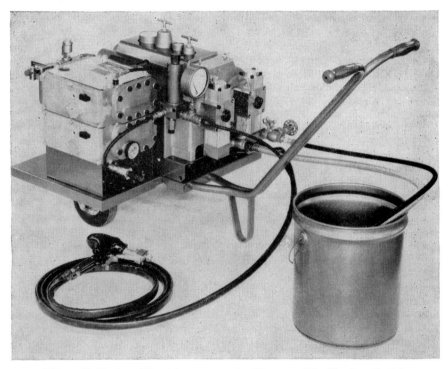

Figure 22.10. A mobile airless spray unit. (*Courtesy The Nordson Corp.*)

hardened by the following treatment: it is heated in a kettle over an oil burner, flashed (i.e.) ignited when hot enough, and allowed to burn in this way for four hours; then the flame is extinguished by placing a cover over the kettle. Only 5 per cent of the oil is consumed during the burning.

The proper proportions of rosin oil, rosin varnish, and lamp black are mixed together. This mixture is then fed to a number of rather small mills consisting of two horizontal steel disks; the upper disk rotates on a hollow shaft and drags the lower one, which is larger, with it. The lower disk rotates more slowly than the upper one and a shearing action results. The mixture is fed into the mill through the hollow shaft and discharged at the edge by a scraper.

Colored printing inks are similarly made, using metallic compounds of organic dyes as well as inorganic pigments such as Prussian blue and chrome yellow. Some of the organic pigments are *Lithol Red, Lake Bordeaux,* and *Helio Fast Red.*

The importance of news ink is emphasized by the fact that the New York Herald-Tribune alone consumes over 4,000,000 pounds of such ink in one year.

REFERENCES

"Organic Protective Coatings," W. von Fischer and E. G. Bobalek, New York, Reinhold Publishing Corporation, 1953.

"Manufacture and Use of Lacquers," lecture, Dr. L. A. Pratt, *Am. Paint J.,* **17,** No. 3, p. 52 (Oct. 31, 1932).

"Compatibility Relationships of Aroclors in Nitrocellulose," R. L. Jenkins and R. H. Foster, *Ind. Eng. Chem.,* **23,** 1362 (1931).

"Shellac," A. F. Suters, *Paint Varnish Production Mgr.,* **14,** No. 5, 22 (1937).

"Paint Pigments," Dr. H. Samuels, *Paint Varnish Production Mgr.,* **14,** No. 5, 10 (1937).

"Printing Inks," Carleton Ellis, New York, Reinhold Publishing Corporation, 1940.

"Protective and Decorative Coatings," Vol. I, "Raw Materials for Varnishes and Vehicles," edited by Joseph Mattiello, New York, John Wiley and Sons, Inc., 1941; Volume II, "Pigments," 1942.

"Titanium Pigment Industry," W. J. O'Brien, *Chem. Eng. Progr.,* **44,** 809 (1948).

"Silicone-Containing Finishes to Have Wide Application," *Paint, Oil Chem. Rev.,* **110,** No. 12, 16 (1947).

"Titanium Pigments," *Paint, Oil Chem. Rev.,* **110,** No. 3, 18 (1947).

"Fractionation of Vegetable Oils," Dr. Henry Farr, *Oil and Color Trades J.* (Sept. 24, 1948).

"Carbon Black Shifts to Furnace Process," C. A. Stokes and R. E. Dobbin, *Chem. Ind.,* **64,** 40 (1949).

"Paint and Varnish Technology," ed. by William von Fischer, New York, Reinhold Publishing Corporation, 1948.

"Recent Developments in Colloidal Carbon," W. B. Wiegand, *Can. Chem. Process Ind.,* **28,** 151 (1944).

"Developments and Status of Carbon Black," Isaac Drogin, United Carbon Company, Charleston, W. Va., 1945.

"Today's Furnace Blacks," Isaac Drogin and Hester R. Bishop, United States Carbon Company, Charleston, W. Va., 1948.

"Minerals for Chemical and Allied Industries," Part XXVI, "Titanium," Sidney J. Johnstone, *Ind. Chemist,* **24,** 750 (1948).

"Printing Inks," L. M. Larsen, N. Y., Reinhold Pub. Corp., 1962.

"Organic Coating Technology," Vol. I, L. F. Payne, 2d Edition, N. Y., John Wiley & Sons, Inc. (1961).

"Organic Coating Technology," Vol. II, L. F. Payne, N. Y., John Wiley & Sons, Inc. (1961).

23

DYE APPLICATION, MANUFACTURE OF DYE INTERMEDIATES AND DYES

In collaboration with Dr. R. A. Brooks*

DYES ARE COLORED SUBSTANCES that can be used to produce a significant degree of coloration when dispersed in or reacted with other materials. Modern dyes are products of synthetic organic chemistry. To be of commercial interest, they must be strongly colored and produce dyeings of some permanence. The degree of permanence required varies with the end use of the dyed material.

The primary use for dyes is textile coloration, although substantial quantities are consumed for coloring such diverse materials as leather, paper, plastics, petroleum products, and food.

The manufacture and use of dyes is an important part of modern technology. Because of the variety of materials that must be dyed in a complete spectrum of hues, manufacturers now offer many hundreds of distinctly different dyes. An understanding of the chemistry of these dyes requires that they be classified in some way. From the viewpoint of the dyer, they are best classified according to application method. The dye manufacturer, on the other hand, prefers to classify dyes according to chemical type.

* Jackson Laboratory, E. I. du Pont de Nemours & Company.

Both the dyer and the dye manufacturer must consider the properties of dyes with relation to the properties of the materials to be dyed. In general, dyes must be selected and applied so that, color excepted, a minimum of change is produced in the properties of the substrate. It is necessary, therefore, to consider the chemistry of textile fibers as background for an understanding of the chemistry of dyes.

TEXTILE FIBERS

Cotton and Rayon

Cotton and rayon (regenerated cellulose) fibers are composed of cellulose in quite pure form. Cellulose lacks significant acidic or basic properties but has a large number of alcoholic hydroxyl groups. It is hydrolyzed by hot acid and swollen by concentrated alkali. When cotton is swollen by concentrated alkali under tension, so that the fibers cannot shrink lengthwise, it develops a silk-like luster. This process is called mercerization. The affinity of mercerized cotton for dyes is greater than that of untreated cotton.

Cotton and rayon fibers are easily wetted by water and afford ready access to dye molecules. Dyeing may take place by adsorption, occlusion, or reaction with the hydroxyl groups. It is also possible to make cotton and rayon receptive to a variety of dyes by pre-treatment or mordanting with a material capable of binding the dyes.

Wool and Silk

Wool and silk fibers are protein substances with both acidic and basic properties. They are destroyed by strong alkali. Strong acid causes hydrolysis, but the process may be controlled to permit dyeing from acidic solutions.

Wool and silk are wetted by water and are dyed with either acid or basic dyes through formation of salt linkages.* They may also be dyed with reactive dyes that form covalent bonds with available amino groups. Mordanting is sometimes used to alter the dyeability of wool and silk.

Cellulose Acetates

Acetylated cellulose fibers differ from cellulose fibers in that they are more hydrophobic and lack large numbers of free hydroxyl groups. The higher the degree of acetylation the more unlike cotton and rayon the acetates become. Strong acid and strong alkali degrade cellulose acetates, although the initial attack is slow under moderate conditions because of the difficulty of wetting the fiber. The triacetate is the most hydrophobic and the most stable.

Dyeing of cellulose acetates is effected with dyes of low water solubility which become dissolved in the fiber, or by occlusion of dyes formed *in situ*.

* This refers to ionic bonds, the forces acting between ions of opposite charges.

Acid, basic, and reactive dyes cannot be used because of the lack of sites for attachment.

Polyamides

Polyamide fibers (nylon) are synthetic fibers possessing properties somewhat like those of wool and silk. They are more hydrophobic, however, with only a limited number of basic or acidic groups. Polyamides are degraded by strong acid but may be dyed from acidic dye baths under controlled conditions.

Polyamide fibers are dyeable near the boiling point of water with acid dyes that form salt linkages with basic sites. Dyeing by this means is limited by the availability of these sites. Dyes like those used on cellulose acetates (i.e., that dissolve in the fiber), or reactive dyes that bond to available amino groups may also be used.

Polyesters

Polyester fibers are synthetic fibers unlike any produced in nature. They are hydrophobic and possess good stability to acid and alkali as a result of this hydrophobicity. They are hydrolyzed under sufficiently drastic conditions, however. Some polyester fibers lack functional groups; others are provided with acidic groups or otherwise modified to make them more hydrophilic.

Unmodified polyester fibers are dyed by solution of dyes in the fiber or, to a limited extent, by occlusion of dyes formed *in situ*. Modified polyester fibers may be dyed in these ways or with dyes selected according to the nature of the sites introduced by the modification. Both unmodified and modified polyester fibers must be dyed under vigorous conditions, often with the assistance of a swelling agent to open up the fiber.

Acrylics

Acrylic fibers are hydrophobic synthetic fibers with excellent chemical stability. They do not resemble any natural product. The only functional groups present are those introduced for the purpose of providing sites for dyeing.

Acrylic fibers are dyed by solution of dyes in the fiber, by occlusion of dyes formed *in situ*, and by formation of salt linkages with dyes capable of attachment to sites provided for that purpose. Basic dyes are used on acrylic fibers bearing sulfonic acid groups, for example.

Vinyls

Vinyl polymers and copolymers make up a class of fiber-forming materials that varies greatly in properties, depending on constitution. Some vinyl fibers are very resistant to degradation by acids. Dyes are selected according to the nature of the specific polymer to be dyed.

Polyolefins

Polyolefin fibers are formed from the products of polymerization of unsaturated compounds of carbon and hydrogen, for example, propylene. They do not absorb water and are chemically quite inert. They can be dyed but are colored best by introducing a colorant into the polymer before the fibers are spun.

Glass Fibers

Glass fibers are used for special purposes, for example where flammable materials cannot be tolerated. They are often colored during manufacture, but can be dyed by special techniques which involve the use of surface coatings that have affinity for dyes.

THE PROPERTIES OF DYES

The properties of dyes may be classified as application properties and end-use properties. Application properties include solubility, affinity, and dyeing rate. End-use properties include hue, and fastness to degrading influences such as light, washing, and bleaching. Dyes are selected for acceptable end-use properties at minimum expense. Involved application procedures are used only when necessary to achieve unusually good results.

It has become common practice to treat dyed textiles with agents designed to improve resistance to shrinking, wrinkling, and the like. These agents frequently alter the appearance and fastness of dyes. Stability to after-treatments must therefore be considered as an important end-use property of dyes.

The amount of dye required to obtain a light shade is usually about 1 per cent of the weight of the fiber; heavier shades may require as much as 8 per cent. These values are very approximate, since dyes differ in color strength and are usually sold in diluted form. These amounts of dye are not sufficient, in most cases, to affect markedly the properties, other than color, of the fiber. Care must be exercised, however, to apply the dye under conditions that do not cause fiber degradation.

Dyes are classified according to application method for the convenience of the dyer. The best classification method available is that used in the Colour Index, a publication sponsored by the Society of Dyers and Colourists (England) and the American Association of Textile Chemists and Colorists.

Acid Dyes

Acid dyes depend on the presence of one or more acidic groups for their attachment to textile fibers. These are usually sulfonic acid groups which serve to make the dye soluble in water. An example of this class is Acid Yellow 36* (Metanil Yellow).

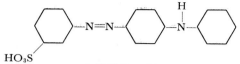

Acid Yellow 36

Acid dyes are used to dye fibers containing basic groups, such as wool, silk, and polyamides. Application is usually made under acidic conditions which cause protonation of the basic groups. The dyeing process may be described as follows:

$$DYE^- + H^+ + FIBER \rightleftarrows DYE^-H^+ — FIBER$$

It should be noted that this process is reversible. Generally, acid dyes can be removed from fibers by washing. The rate of removal depends on the rate at which the dye can diffuse through the fiber under the conditions of washing. For a given fiber, the diffusion rate is determined by temperature, size and shape of the dye molecules, and the number and kind of linkages formed with the fiber.

Chrome dyes (a special kind of acid dye used mainly on wool) possess improved fastness when converted to chromium complexes. A suitable chromium salt is applied to the fiber (1) before the dye, (2) at the same time as the dye, or (3) after the dye. All these methods are satisfactory, but more complicated than is desired. In recent years, manufacturers have made available dyes in which chromium is already a part of the molecule. These dyes are simpler to apply than the older types and, as a consequence, are increasing in importance.

Basic Dyes

Basic dyes become attached to fibers by formation of salt linkages with acidic groups in the fibers. The dyeing process may be regarded as similar to that for the application of acid dyes. In this case, the dye is protonated, or carries an inherently positive group, for example, a quaternary ammonium group. The dyeing process for these two types may be described as follows:

$$FIBER^- + H^+ + DYE \rightleftarrows FIBER^-H^+ — DYE$$

and

$$FIBER^- + DYE^+ \rightleftarrows FIBER^-DYE^+$$

* The dye names used in this chapter are those given in the Colour Index. Trivial names, when well established, are given in parentheses following the Colour Index names.

Typical basic dyes are Basic Brown 1 (Bismarck Brown) and Basic Violet 3 (Crystal Violet).

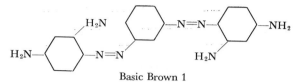

Basic Brown 1

Basic dyes are used primarily on protein fibers, modified acrylic fibers, and mordanted cotton. Application is usually made from mildly acidic dye liquors. Like acid dyes, basic dyes can be removed from fibers by washing under sufficiently drastic conditions.

Direct Dyes

Direct dyes are a class of dyes that become strongly adsorbed on cellulose. They usually bear sulfonic acid groups, but are not considered acid dyes since these groups are not used as a means of attachment to the fiber. Direct dyes are large, flat, linear molecules which can enter the water-swollen amorphous regions of cellulose and orient themselves along the crystalline regions. Common salt or Glauber's Salt is often used to promote dyeing since the presence of excess sodium ions favors establishment of equilibrium with a minimum of dye remaining in the dye bath. Direct Red 28 (Congo Red) is a typical direct dye.

Direct Red 28

Since direct dyes are held in cellulosic fibers by adsorption, the dyeing process is reversible. Unless after-treated with resins and dye fixing agents, direct dyes, as a class, have poor fastness to washing. They are used mainly because they are economical and easy to apply.

A special type of direct dye having free amino groups is designed to be diazotized and coupled (developed) in the fiber. This operation increases the size of the molecules and improves their fastness to washing. An example of this type is Direct Black 17 (Zambesi Black D).

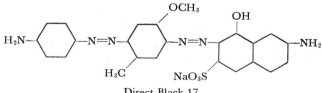

Direct Black 17

These dyes are used primarily to color plain grounds which are later to be printed in a pattern with vat dyes. The sodium hydrosulfite used to reduce the vat dyes destroys the ground color upon contact. Oxidation of the reduced vat dyes then produces two-color effects.

During the application of a "diazotized and developed" dye, the direct dye is first applied in the usual manner. The goods are then passed into a bath containing nitrous acid, where the amino groups are diazotized. Next, the goods are passed through an alkaline solution of beta-naphthol which couples with the diazonium groups to give the final dye.

Sulfur Dyes

Sulfur dyes are insoluble dyes which must be reduced with sodium sulfide before use. In the reduced form they are soluble and exhibit affinity for cellulose. They dye by adsorption, as do the direct dyes, but upon exposure to air they are oxidized to re-form the original insoluble dye inside the fiber. Thus, unlike the direct dyes, they become very resistant to removal by washing.

The exact constitutions of most sulfur dyes are unknown, although the conditions required to reproduce given types are well established. They are fairly cheap and give dyeings of good fastness to washing, as noted above. Their brightness and fastness to bleaching are often inferior, however.

Vat Dyes

Vat dyes, like sulfur dyes, are insoluble. They are reduced with sodium hydrosulfite in strongly alkaline medium to give a soluble form that has affinity for cellulose. This reducing operation was formerly carried out in wooden vats, giving rise to the name vat dye. After the reduced dye has been adsorbed in the fiber, the original insoluble dye is re-formed by oxidation with air or chemicals. The dyeings produced in this way are very fast to washing, and, in most cases, the dyes are designed to be fast to light and bleaching as well. An example of a vat dye is Vat Blue 4 (Indanthrone).

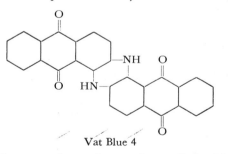

Vat Blue 4

Vat dyes are quite expensive and must be applied with care. They offer excellent fastness when properly selected and are the dyes most often used on cotton fabrics which are to be subjected to severe conditions of washing and bleaching.

It is sometimes impossible to tolerate the strongly alkaline conditions used to reduce vat dyes, for example, when dyeing fibers that are sensitive to alkali. For this reason, and for added convenience, some manufacturers offer soluble vat dyes. These are usually the sodium or potassium salts of the sulfuric esters of reduced vat dyes. When applied to the fiber and subjected to an acid treatment in the presence of an oxidizing agent, they hydrolyze, reverting to the original form of the dye.

Reactive Dyes

Reactive dyes are a relatively new class of dyes that form covalent bonds with fibers possessing hydroxyl or amino groups. One important type of reactive dye contains chlorine atoms that react with hydroxyl groups in cellulose when applied in the presence of alkali. It is believed that an ether linkage is established between the dye and the fiber. An example of this type is the orange azo dye shown below:

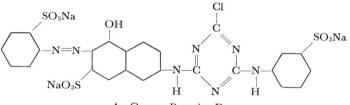

An Orange Reactive Dye

Reactive dyes offer excellent fastness to washing since the dye becomes a part of the fiber. The other properties depend on the structure of the colored part of the molecule and the means by which it is attached to the reactive part.

Disperse Dyes

Disperse dyes, sometimes called acetate rayon dyes, are dyes of low-water solubility which are capable of dissolving in certain textile fibers. They were first introduced for cellulose acetate but are used with a variety of synthetic fibers as well. They are supplied in a very fine state of subdivision to permit their dispersion in water. They dye the fiber in the molecular state, however, and for this reason must possess some solubility in water. Disperse-dye molecules are small and usually bear amino groups. An example is Disperse Violet 1.

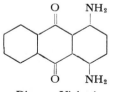

Disperse Violet 1

Since disperse dyes become dissolved in textile fibers, the dyeing process is reversible. Fibers that are swollen easily by water can be dyed with disperse dyes under moderate conditions, but the dyeings have only modest fastness to washing. Fibers that are more difficult to swell must be dyed under more drastic conditions, but offer the advantage that these conditions are not duplicated during normal washing procedures. For example, most polyester fibers must be dyed under pressure or with the use of organic swelling agents. The washing fastness of disperse dyes on these fibers is excellent.

Mordant Dyes

Mordant dyes require a pre-treatment of the fiber with a mordant material designed to bind the dye. The mordant becomes attached to the fiber and then combines with the dye to form an insoluble complex called a "lake." An example of a mordant is aluminum hydroxide that has been precipitated in cotton fiber. This mordant is capable of binding such dyes as Mordant Red 11 (Alizarin) by formation of an aluminum "lake."

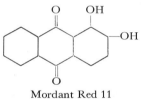

Mordant Red 11

Mordant dyes have declined in importance mainly because their use is no longer necessary. Equal or superior results can be obtained with other classes of dyes at less expense in time and labor.

Azoic Dyes

Azoic dyes are produced inside textile fibers, usually cotton, by azo coupling. The dye is firmly occluded and is fast to washing. A variety of hues can be obtained by proper choice of diazo and coupling components. For example, a bluish-red is produced from diazotized Azoic Diazo Component 1 and Azoic Coupling Component 2 (Naphthol AS).

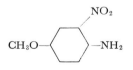

Azoic Diazo Component 1

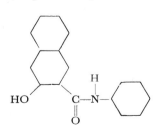

Azoic Coupling Component 2

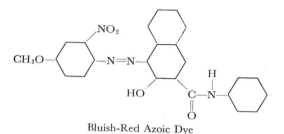

Bluish-Red Azoic Dye

In the usual procedure for the development of azoic dyes, the fiber is first impregnated with an alkaline solution of the coupling component and then treated with a solution of the diazonium compound. Finally, the dyed goods are soaped and rinsed.

The diazonium compound may be produced in the dyehouse by diazotization of the azoic diazo component, or it may be purchased as a stabilized complex ready for use. Examples of stabilized diazonium complexes are the zinc double salts, nitrosamines and diazoamino compounds.

Special techniques have been developed for the use of azoic dyes on synthetic fibers. It is sometimes possible to apply both the diazo component and the coupling component simultaneously from aqueous dispersion and then to treat the goods with nitrous acid to produce the color.

Oxidation Dyes

Oxidation dyes are produced in textile fibers by oxidation of a colorless compound. For example, aniline may be oxidized in cotton with sodium bichromate in the presence of a metal catalyst to produce an aniline black. This is an economical way to produce full black shades. The appearance and fastness of the dyeings may be varied over a wide range by the choice of oxidant, conditions, and catalyst. The exact structures of the aniline blacks are not known.

Ingrain Dyes

Ingrain dyes are produced inside textile fibers. The azoic and oxidation dyes already discussed are examples. In addition, there is a small number of ingrain dyes on the market which do not fall into these classes. One such group, called precursors, is capable of generating the very bright blue dye, copper phthalocyanine, inside cotton fibers. The dyeings are extremely fast to light and washing. The structure of copper phthalocyanine is given elsewhere in this chapter.

THE APPLICATION OF DYES

The process of dyeing may be carried out in batches or on a continuous basis. The fiber may be dyed as stock, yarn, or fabric. No matter how the dyeing is done, the process is always fundamentally the same: dye must be transferred from a bath, usually aqueous, to the inside of the fiber. The basic operations of dyeing include: (1) preparation of the fiber, (2) preparation of the dye bath, (3) application of the dye, and (4) finishing. There are many variations of these operations, depending on the kind of dye. The dyeing process is complicated by the fact that single dyes are seldom used. The matching of a specified shade may require from two to a dozen dyes.

Fiber Preparation

Fiber preparation ordinarily involves scouring to remove foreign materials and ensure even access to dye liquor. Some natural fibers are contaminated with fatty materials and dirt. Synthetic fibers may have been treated with sizing which must be removed. Some fibers may also require bleaching before they are ready for use.

Dye Bath Preparation

Preparation of the dye bath may involve simply dissolving the dye in water, or it may be necessary to carry out more involved operations, such as reducing the vat dyes. Wetting agents, salts, "carriers," retarders, and other dyeing assistants may also be added. "Carriers" are swelling agents which improve the dyeing rate of very hydrophobic fibers such as the polyesters. An example is o-phenylphenol. Retarders are colorless substances that compete with dyes for dye sites and act to slow the dyeing rate. Their use is necessary when overly rapid dyeing tends to cause unevenness in the dyeings.

Dye Application

During application, dye must be transferred from the bath to the fiber and allowed to penetrate. In the simplest cases this is done by immersing the fiber in the bath for a prescribed period of time at a suitable temperature. Unless the dye is unstable, the bath is usually heated to increase the rate of dyeing. To ensure an even uptake of dye, it is desirable to stir the bath. This is done with paddles, by pumping, or by moving the fiber. For continuous dyeing of fabrics, the dye liquor is picked up from a shallow pan, the excess is squeezed out by rollers, and penetration is assured by steaming.

Finishing

The finishing steps for many dyes, such as the direct dyes, are very simple. The dyed material is merely rinsed and dried. Vat dyed materials, on the other hand, must be rinsed to remove reducing agent, oxidized, rinsed again, and soaped before the final rinsing and drying steps are carried out. Generally, the finishing steps must fix the color (if this has not occurred during application) and remove any loose dye from the surface of the fiber. Residual dyeing assistants such as "carriers" must also be removed.

Occasionally, fibers are bleached or otherwise modified after dyeing. When this is to be done, dyes must be carefully selected to assure retention of shade and fastness. Some aftertreatments are intended to improve dye fastness. For example, some dyes are improved in fastness to light by treatment of the dyed goods with a metal salt. Others, especially direct dyes, are improved in fastness to washing by treatment of the goods with resins containing certain quaternary ammonium compounds.

DYEING EQUIPMENT

The equipment used in modern dyehouses varies with the type of dyeing to be done. Stock dyeing is often carried out in large heated kettles made of stainless steel or other corrosion-resistant metal. These kettles can be sealed and used for dyeing at temperatures somewhat above the boiling point of water at atmospheric pressure. Yarns in packages are dyed in closed machines that circulate hot dye liquor through them. Fabrics are dyed in machines that move them through the dye liquor either under tension (jig) or relaxed (beck). Fabrics also are dyed in full width by winding them on a perforated beam through which hot dye liquor is pumped. Some beam dyeing machines are designed to operate under pressure at temperatures as high as 250° F to facilitate dyeing of very hydrophobic fibers. Figure 23.1 shows a beam dyeing machine.

Fabrics may also be treated with dye liquors or pastes continuously, and then steamed or heated in a chamber to cause penetration of the dye. Dyeing of this kind requires a train of equipment. The speed of the operation is limited by the slowest step unless multiple units are available.

In addition to the above, special machines are available to dye textile fibers at any stage during their conversion to finished goods. The principles involved are the same as those outlined in the preceding section, "Application of Dyes."

PRINTING

Printing is a special kind of localized dyeing which produces patterns. Four kinds of printing are recognized: (1) direct, (2) dyed, (3) discharge, and (4) resist. In *direct* printing, a thickened paste of the dye is printed on the fabric to produce a pattern. The fabric is then steamed to fix the dye and finished by washing and drying. *Dyed* printing requires that the pattern be printed on the fabric with a mordant. The entire piece is then placed in a dye bath containing a mordant dye, but only the mordanted areas are dyeable. Washing then clears the dye from the unmordanted areas, leaving the pattern in color.

In *discharge* printing, the cloth is dyed all over and then printed with a substance which can destroy the dye by oxidation or reduction, leaving the pattern in white. When a reducing agent such as sodium hydrosulfite is used to destroy the dye, the paste may contain a reduced vat dye. Finishing the goods by oxidation and soaping then produces the pattern in color. In *resist* printing, certain colorless substances are printed on the fabric. The whole piece is then dyed but the dye is repelled from the printed areas, thus producing a colored ground with the pattern in white.

Printing is most often done with copper rollers etched in the design to be printed. Printing paste is fed constantly to the roller from a trough. A

Figure 23.1. Burlington hy-press dyeing machine, shown open to load. (*Courtesy Burlington Engineering Co., Graham, N. C.*)

scraper then clears the surface of the roller, leaving the dye paste only in the etched areas from which it is transferred to the fabrics.

PIGMENT DYEING AND PRINTING

Pigment dyeing and printing are processes that compete with the more conventional means of dyeing and printing described above. These processes use water-insoluble dyes or pigments which are bound to the surfaces of fabrics with resins. A paste or emulsion containing pigment and resin or resin-former is applied to the fabric. The goods are then dried and cured by heat to produce the finished dyeing or print. During the heating or cure, fabric, resin, and pigment become firmly bonded together. This method of color application is economical and produces good results. It should be noted that the pigment is confined to the surface of the fabric and can be selected without regard for fiber affinity.

NON-TEXTILE USES OF DYES

Substantial quantities of dye are consumed by the paper industry. The most important paper dyes are selected from the direct, acid, and basic groups of textile dyes. The needs of the paper industry are such that it is frequently necessary to select and finish the dyes in a manner different from that employed for textiles.

Natural leather is a protein substance and can be dyed with acid dyes, among others. Finished leather also can be dyed or pigmented, the choice of color type depending on the nature of the finish.

Dyes for many materials such as gasoline, lacquers, inks, and varnishes are selected on the basis of solubility, as well as hue and fastness. It is necessary to modify some dyes to achieve the desired degree of solubility. For example, the solubility in alcohols of many acid dyes is greatly increased by forming the diphenylguanidine salts.

Important and growing markets for dyes are the plastics and metals industries. Dyed anodized aluminum, in particular, is finding increasing use in automotive and architectural applications.

Dyes for foods, drugs, and cosmetics must be chosen with great care to avoid toxic effects. In the United States, dyes are certified by the government when judged safe for such uses. Only the certified dyes may legally be used. This restriction does not apply to natural colors.

PRODUCTION AND USES

Table 23.1 gives the production of synthetic dyes in the United States for the year 1960, arranged according to application class. These figures are taken from the report of the U. S. Tariff Commission.

TABLE 23.1. UNITED STATES PRODUCTION OF COAL-TAR DYES, BY CLASS OF APPLICATION, IN POUNDS, 1960

Disperse Dyes	6,548,000
Acid Dyes	14,306,000
Azoic Dyes	6,910,000
Basic Dyes	6,747,000
Direct Dyes	23,075,000
Fiber-reactive Dyes	291,000
Mordant Dyes	3,975,000
Sulfur Dyes	31,022,000
Vat Dyes	46,574,000
Solvent Dyes	6,479,000
All Other Dyes	9,969,000
TOTAL	155,896,000

RAW MATERIALS FOR THE MANUFACTURE OF DYES

The raw materials for the manufacture of dyes are mainly aromatic hydrocarbons, benzene, toluene, naphthalene, anthracene, pyrene, and others. In the past, these aromatic hydrocarbons came almost exclusively from the distillation of coal tar, but in recent years increasing quantities, especially of benzene and toluene, have become available from petroleum and natural gas. The term "coal-tar dyes," still widely considered synonymous with synthetic dyes, is no longer an entirely correct description.

DYE INTERMEDIATES

The raw materials for dyes are almost never directly useful in dye synthesis. It is necessary to convert them to a variety of derivatives which are in turn made into dyes. These derivatives are called *intermediates.* They are produced by reactions such as nitration, reduction, sulfonation, halogenation, oxidation, and condensation. Most of these reactions lead to the formation of substituted hydrocarbons which are functional in nature, that is, they bear groups capable of undergoing further chemical reaction. The number of dye intermediates actually or potentially available is very large, and the technology of their manufacture is an important part of industrial organic chemistry. Intermediates are used not only for dye manufacture but also for the manufacture of other important products such as pharmaceuticals.

The substitution reactions of aromatic hydrocarbons, in which a hydrogen atom is replaced by another group, frequently lead to the formation of position isomers. Position isomers are compounds which are alike in the groups that they contain but different in the relative positions of these groups, e.g., the two nitrophenols shown in the section on nitration. When position isomers are formed, it is almost always necessary to effect a separation since the isomers differ in properties and lead to different dyes. One of the most difficult problems in the manufacture of dye intermediates is the efficient separation of isomers. A further problem is the control of the relative quantities in which isomers are formed or the discovery of uses for all of them in the event that control is impractical.

The many reactions employed in the manufacture of dye intermediates and the delicate nature of many of the operations make it mandatory that all processes be well planned and controlled. Some of the processes, nitration for example, are inherently dangerous if not properly run. For these reasons, close supervision by technically trained men is the rule in plants where intermediates are made.

In recent years there has been ever increasing emphasis in chemical manufacturing on high standards of uniformity and quality. At the same time, the increasing cost of labor has discouraged the use of numerous manual controls to meet these standards. Consequently, many plants have turned to partly or fully automatic control. Such practice requires advanced kinds of instrumentation which can insure that all process variables are closely controlled.

Because of the large number of compounds that are required, often in limited amounts, most dye intermediates are manufactured in batches. Some of the more fundamental processes can be run continuously, however, with a decided economic advantage. Where continuous production is not justified, the largest practical batches are made to hold the costs of operation to a minimum.

A wide variety of equipment is used for the manufacture of dye intermediates. Reactions such as nitration, sulfonation, and alkaline fusion require the use of corrosion-resistant vessels. Cast-iron, steel, stainless-steel, glass-lined, and enamel-lined vessels are used. The separation of isomeric sulfonated intermediates can often be effected by methods which employ predominantly water systems. Wooden and brick-lined tanks are useful for such operations. Plate-and-frame filter presses, centrifugal filters, and a variety of air and vacuum driers are employed in isolating and drying these intermediates. Others require distillation, or are crystallized from solvents and isolated by filtration on special solvent-type filters. Intermediates in solution can be isolated by spray drying or evaporation of the solvent in a graining bowl.

Nitration

The nitration of aromatic hydrocarbons is a fundamental operation in the manufacture of many dye intermediates. Nitration involves the replacement of one or more ring hydrogen atoms by the nitro ($-NO_2$) group. The nitration of benzene is an example.

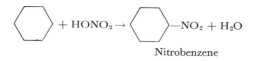

$$\bigcirc + HONO_2 \rightarrow \bigcirc{-}NO_2 + H_2O$$

Nitrobenzene

Nitration of compounds of high reactivity is carried out with nitric acid in water or an organic solvent. Less reactive compounds are nitrated in a combination of nitric and sulfuric acids ("mixed acids"). The sulfuric acid serves as a solvent for the reaction and facilitates nitration by reaction with nitric acid to form the nitronium ion ($-NO_2^+$), generally believed to be the active nitrating agent. It also serves to maintain the strength of the nitrating mixture by combining with the water which is formed. A typical mixed acid consists of 30 per cent nitric acid, 60 per cent sulfuric acid, and 10 per cent water. Since nitric acid is a strong oxidizing agent, nitrations are carried out at low temperatures to avoid destructive side reactions. Some functional groups, such as the amino group, in compounds to be nitrated must be protected against oxidative destruction by acetylation. The acetyl group is removed by hydrolysis when nitration is complete.

When nitrating benzene to nitrobenzene, an excess of nitric acid must be avoided or dinitration will occur. The procedure is to run the "mixed acids" into the benzene, not the converse; this is a general rule when mononitration is desired. About 2,500 pounds of benzene are nitrated in one batch over a period of three to four hours. Heat is evolved during the reaction and is removed by means of cooling coils, or by means of cold water or brine circulated in a jacket surrounding the nitration vessel. Cast iron is used since it is not attacked by "mixed acids." The vessel is agitated to provide good contact between the two layers and to facilitate heat transfer. When the reaction is complete, the agitation is stopped and the nitrobenzene separates as an oil over the acid. This oil is drawn off and agitated with water or dilute alkali to remove residual acid. It may then be distilled if pure nitrobenzene is required. In recent years, continuous vapor-phase nitration methods have been devised. Aqueous nitric acid is used and the water resulting from the reaction is distilled off continuously to keep the nitric acid concentration high enough to be effective. Benzene can be nitrated continuously at about $80°$ C using 61 per cent aqueous nitric acid.

When benzene derivatives are nitrated, isomers of the desired product are obtained in addition to the product itself. For example, nitration of phenol by nitric acid gives ortho nitrophenol and para nitrophenol.

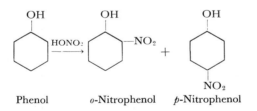

Phenol o-Nitrophenol p-Nitrophenol

The isomeric o- and p-nitrophenols can be separated by steam distillation. The ortho isomer is volatile in steam, while the para isomer is not and therefore remains in the distillation vessel.

Mononitration of anthraquinone at about $50°$ C gives only 1-nitroanthraquinone. At $80–95°$ C dinitration occurs to give a mixture of the 1,5 and 1,8 isomers. These isomers are important as starting materials for the preparation of other intermediates. In some cases the mixture is used; in others isomer separation is necessary.

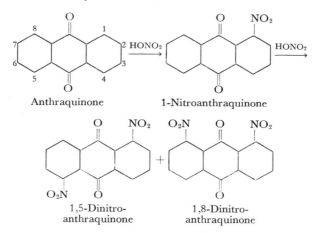

Anthraquinone

1-Nitroanthraquinone

1,5-Dinitro-
anthraquinone

1,8-Dinitro-
anthraquinone

These nitrations are performed in cast-iron or steel vessels with steel agitators. Since the starting materials are solids they are first dissolved in sulfuric acid and then treated with "mixed acids"; the products are also solids.

Reduction

The most common reduction reaction in the manufacture of dye intermediates is the conversion of a nitro compound to the corresponding amine. This reaction is illustrated by the reduction of nitrobenzene to aniline.

$$\langle\ \rangle-NO_2 \xrightarrow{6[H]} \langle\ \rangle-NH_2 + 2H_2O$$

Reduction of nitro compounds is accomplished by: (1) catalytic hydrogenation, (2) iron reduction, (3) sulfide reduction, or (4) zinc reduction in alkaline medium. Generally, where the reaction is carried out on a large scale, the catalytic procedure is best. For small-scale batch operations, chemical reduction may be preferred.

Catalytic hydrogenation requires a catalyst such as nickel, copper, platinum, molybdenum, or tungsten. These catalysts are usually supported on other materials and are especially prepared for the type of reduction to be carried out. Reduction conditions vary widely, depending on the nature of the nitro compound and the catalyst. Reduction may be carried out in solvent, in the vapor phase or in the liquid phase. Aniline can be made by continuous vapor-phase reduction of nitrobenzene at 350–460° C at nearly atmospheric pressure. Some reductions, on the other hand, are run at 1000 to 4000 psi.

Iron reduction is employed on a large scale because of its simplicity. Iron turnings are used in an agitated aqueous system containing a small amount of acid to promote reaction. The over-all reaction is illustrated for nitro-benzene as follows:

$$\langle\bigcirc\rangle\text{—NO}_2 + 2\text{Fe} + 4\text{H}_2\text{O} \xrightarrow{\text{H}^+} \langle\bigcirc\rangle\text{—NH}_2 + 2\text{Fe(OH)}_3$$

The nitrobenzene is placed in a reducer, a vertical cylindrical vessel provided with cover, steam jacket, and agitator. The iron turnings, or powder, and a small amount of hydrochloric acid are added in small portions. A brisk reaction is maintained by means of steam circulated in the jacket of the reducer or blown directly into the charge. A condenser returns to the reducer any vapors that escape. After the nitrobenzene is completely converted to aniline, a strong current of live steam is passed into the charge; a mixture of steam and aniline vapors passes to the condenser and is collected in storage tanks. The bulk of the aniline separates as a lower layer and is drawn off; the water over it still contains aniline, which must be recovered by distilling this "aniline water" again, or by extracting it with nitrobenzene. The iron sludge is washed out of the reducer through a side outlet by flushing. A reducer 6 feet in diameter and 10 feet high takes a charge of 5000 pounds of nitrobenzene in one batch and requires about 10 hours for reduction. The aniline may be redistilled, which renders it water white.

Iron reduction of nitro compounds is also of importance in the naphthalene series. 1-Naphthylamine is made by the reduction of 1-nitro-naphthalene, for example.

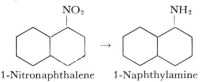

1-Nitronaphthalene   1-Naphthylamine

Sulfide reduction employs sodium sulfide, sodium polysulfide, or sodium hydrosulfide. An important feature of this type of reducing system is its adaptability to bring about stepwise reduction of dinitro compounds. Partial reduction is illustrated with m-dinitrobenzene which can be reduced to m-nitroaniline with sodium sulfide under controlled conditions.

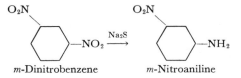

m-Dinitrobenzene   m-Nitroaniline

The sodium sulfide is dissolved in alcohol and placed in a steam-jacketed reducer; the dinitrobenzene is added either in solid form or dissolved in alcohol. The mixture is boiled for two hours; then the alcohol is distilled off and collected for re-use. The *m*-nitroaniline mixed with inorganic salt remains in the reducer. The mass is agitated with water, which dissolves the salt, and is then pumped into a filter press. The press cake of *m*-nitroaniline is washed, and then discharged and dried in a vacuum drier.

Zinc reduction in alkaline aqueous or alcoholic medium is especially useful to bring about bimolecular reduction. This kind of reaction is illustrated by the conversion of nitrobenzene to hydrazobenzene. Rearrangement of hydrazobenzene with acid gives benzidine, an important intermediate for azo dyes.

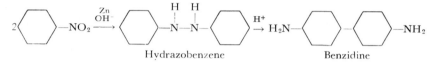

Hydrazobenzene   Benzidine

In a similar way, *o*-nitroanisole is converted to hydrazoanisole and then to *o*-dianisidine.

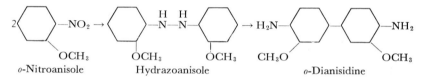

o-Nitroanisole   Hydrazoanisole   *o*-Dianisidine

Amination

The introduction of an amino group into an aromatic nucleus by replacement of another functional group is called amination. This process is to be distinguished from reduction of a nitro group in that one group is totally displaced by another and not simply altered in character.

An example of amination in the benzene series is the conversion of *p*-nitrochlorobenzene to *p*-nitroaniline with ammonia. This reaction may be carried out continuously with 40 per cent aqueous ammonia under 200 atmospheres pressure at 235–240° C.

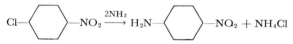

The Bucherer reaction illustrates amination in the naphthalene series. A naphthol is heated with ammonium sulfite or ammonia and alkali metal bisulfite. The result is replacement of the hydroxyl group by an amino group, probably by way of a bisulfite addition product of the keto form of the naphthol.

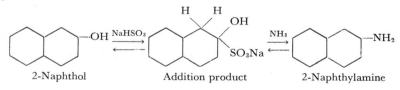

2-Naphthol   Addition product   2-Naphthylamine

The reaction is reversible and may be used to convert naphthylamines to naphthols.

In the anthraquinone series, amination is frequently a convenient means of preparing amines. 1-Aminoanthraquinone-2-carboxylic acid can be made by reaction of 1-nitroanthraquinone-2-carboxylic acid with 15 per cent aqueous ammonia at 130° C. The nitro group is displaced, not reduced. In a similar manner 1-anthraquinonesulfonic acid can be aminated to give 1-aminoanthraquinone or, if desired, ammonia may be replaced by methyl-amine to give 1-N-methylaminoanthraquinone.

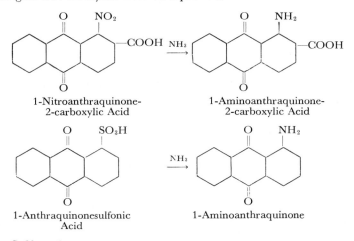

1-Nitroanthraquinone-
2-carboxylic Acid

1-Aminoanthraquinone-
2-carboxylic Acid

1-Anthraquinonesulfonic
Acid

1-Aminoanthraquinone

Sulfonation

The sulfonic acid group ($-SO_3H$) is one of the more common sub-stituents in dye intermediates. It is introduced to render intermediates soluble in water, or to provide a route to other substituents, such as the hydroxyl group which is obtained by subsequent alkaline fusion.

Direct sulfonation is achieved with: (1) strong sulfuric acid, (2) oleum (sulfuric acid plus sulfur trioxide), (3) sulfur trioxide in organic solvent or as a complex, or (4) chlorosulfonic acid. The sulfonation of benzene with sulfuric acid is illustrated by the following equation:

$$\langle \bigcirc \rangle + HOSO_3H \rightarrow \langle \bigcirc \rangle - SO_3H + H_2O$$

The actual sulfonating agent is believed to be the cation, $+SO_3H$. In carrying out this reaction, oleum containing 8 per cent free sulfur trioxide is added slowly to offset the dilution caused by the water formed in the process. The temperature is maintained at 30° C until near the end, when it is raised to 50° C. When reaction is complete, the charge is diluted by running it into water, and the product is precipitated by adding salt. It is isolated by filtration as the sodium sulfonate.

Substitution rules for sulfonation are similar to those for nitration. The groups, $-NO_2$, $-COOH$, and $-SO_3H$ direct the entering group to the meta position.

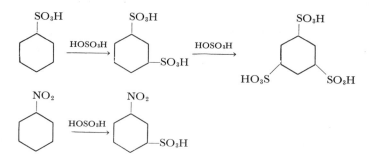

Alkyl groups, for example methyl, direct the entering group predominantly to the ortho and para positions. Usually, a mixture of isomers is formed.

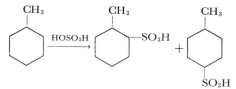

Chlorine is similar to the methyl group in its effect on orientation but gives less of the ortho isomer.

The directing effect of amino groups depends on their basicity. The less basic amines are ortho-para directing. Aniline is an example of this type. More basic amines, for example, dimethylaniline, form salts in acid, which are meta directing.

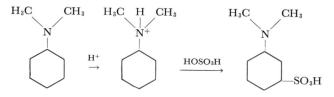

In addition to sulfonation with sulfuric acid or its equivalent, amines may be sulfonated by baking the sulfates at elevated temperatures. This procedure offers the advantage of giving fewer isomers. The baking of aniline sulfate at 260–280° C gives a high yield of the para sulfonic acid.

Indirect sulfonation may be achieved in a number of ways. Sodium bisulfite will often replace a labile functional group with the sulfonic acid group. An example is o-chlorobenzoic acid which is converted to o-sulfobenzoic acid by aqueous sodium bisulfite.

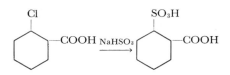

The sulfonation of naphthalene yields a number of isomers. The product obtained may be controlled to some extent by the choice of agent. With any one agent, temperature and time of reaction determine the result. It is rarely possible to obtain a single isomer; effort is directed toward forming a preponderant amount of one isomer. For example, for the monosulfonates, made by direct sulfonation with sulfuric acid, there is formed at 80° C in eight hours, 96 per cent 1-naphthalenesulfonic acid. As the temperature is raised, correspondingly less of this isomer is formed and more of the 2-sulfonic acid. At 150° C, for example, 18 per cent of the 1 isomer is formed and over 80 per cent of the 2 isomer.

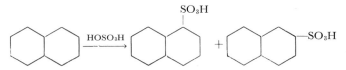

When carrying out this sulfonation, the acid is run into the melted naphthalene to avoid disulfonation. The amount of acid added is the calculated amount for one sulfonic acid group. The water formed during the reaction retards but does not prevent it. Oleum may be added toward the end to hasten the reaction.

The sulfonation of amino and hydroxy derivatives of naphthalene usually leads to a large number of isomers. To avoid isomer formation as much as possible, naphthionic acid is often prepared by baking the sulfate of 1-naphthylamine.

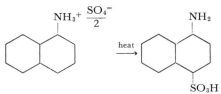

By direct sulfonation of 1-naphthylamine, four of the seven possible 1-naphthylaminesulfonic acids may be formed. The main product under proper conditions is the 1,4 isomer. Direct sulfonation of 2-naphthylamine yields primarily a mixture of 2,5 and 2,8 isomers.

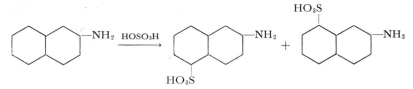

Two important monosulfonic acids resulting from the sulfonation of 2-naphthol are Schaeffer's acid and Crocein acid. At 110° C, Schaeffer's acid is preponderant; at lower temperatures more Crocein acid is formed.

| Schaeffer's Acid | Crocein Acid |

By further sulfonation, two isomeric disulfonic acids are the main products. In the cold, G acid predominates, while at higher temperatures R acid is formed in greater amount. Both isomers are important intermediates for azo dyes.

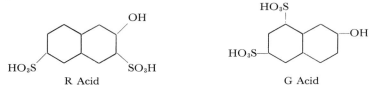

| R Acid | G Acid |

Anthraquinone is sulfonated by suspending it in oleum containing 45 per cent free sulfur trioxide and heating at 150° C for one hour. The resulting melt is run into water and neutralized with sodium hydroxide while still hot. On cooling, the sodium salt of the 2-sulfonic acid separates. Further sulfonation produces a mixture of the 2,6 and 2,7 disulfonic acids.

When anthraquinone is sulfonated in the presence of mercury sulfate, the results differ from those just described. A single sulfonic acid group enters at position 1. Two groups enter to form the 1,5 and 1,8 disulfonic acids. The 1,5 isomer is salted out from the more soluble 1,8 isomer after dilution of the sulfonation mass. The 1,5 and 1,8 disulfonic acids are of great importance for the manufacture of other derivatives which can be made by replacement of the sulfonic acid groups. Examples are the chloro and hydroxyanthraquinones.

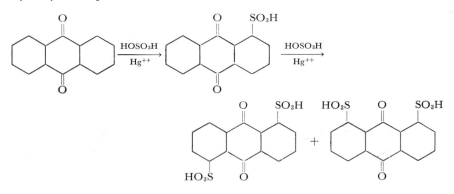

Halogenation

Chlorine is the most widely used of the halogens because it is comparatively economic. Most often, chlorinations are performed by dried chlorine gas, that is, by direct chlorination with or without a catalyst. An alternate procedure consists of generating nascent chlorine *in situ* by the oxidation of a chlorine-containing compound. In a few cases, chlorination may be achieved with reagents such as thionyl chloride, phosphorus oxychloride, phosphorus pentachloride, or sulfuryl chloride.

Chlorination of alkylated aromatic compounds, for example, toluene, can occur either in the aromatic ring or in the side chain. The use of an iron catalyst directs the chlorine to the aromatic ring, probably by inducing formation of the Cl^+ cation as the active agent. Without catalyst, chlorination takes place in the side chain, especially under ultraviolet light; the active agent in this case is believed to be the $Cl \cdot$ radical.

Chlorobenzene is made by passing a stream of dried chlorine into benzene in the presence of ferric chloride; some *p*-dichlorobenzene is formed at the same time.

$$\langle \bigcirc \rangle + Cl_2 \xrightarrow{FeCl_3} \langle \bigcirc \rangle\!-\!Cl + HCl$$

In direct monochlorination reactions, the quantity of chlorine must be carefully controlled to avoid the formation of polychloro compounds.

Chlorination of toluene in the complete absence of iron produces side chain chlorination products; these are benzyl chloride, benzal chloride, and benzotrichloride. The reaction can be controlled to give predominantly one product since the chlorination takes place stepwise. All these compounds are valuable. Benzal chloride is converted to benzaldehyde with calcium carbonate in water, while benzotrichloride gives benzoic acid under the same conditions.

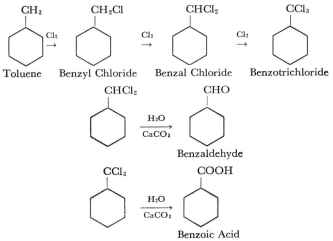

In the naphthalene series, direct chlorination is seldom used. The reaction takes place readily but leads to numerous isomers. In the anthraquinone series, both direct and indirect chlorination are employed. An example of indirect chlorination is the conversion of 1-anthraquinonesulfonic acid to the corresponding chloro compound. This reaction is carried out at approximately 100° C with sodium or potassium chlorate in hydrochloric acid.

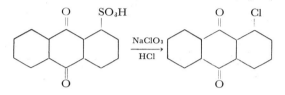

Chlorination of aliphatic compounds is illustrated by the chlorination of acetic acid. One, two, or three of the hydrogen atoms on carbon can be replaced by direct chlorination of the warm liquid in the presence of sulfur.

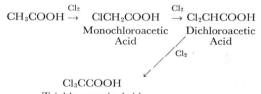

Both fluorine and bromine find some use in the manufacture of dye intermediates, but high cost restricts them to applications where they offer some unique advantage over chlorine.

Alkaline Fusion

Alkaline fusion is an important procedure for the hydroxylation of aromatic compounds. In alkaline fusion, a sulfonic acid group is replaced by a hydroxyl group. This reaction cannot be used when nitro or chloro groups are present but is applicable to amino compounds.

Alkaline fusion is usually carried out with a concentrated solution of sodium hydroxide in a cast-iron pot equipped with a scraping agitator and heated externally. The water is evaporated; then the mass fuses. The reaction temperature is between 190 and 350° C, depending on the reactivity of the sulfonic acid.

Phenol is made by fusing benzenesulfonic acid according to the following equations:

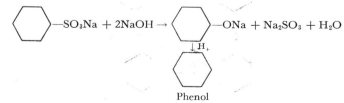

In a similar way, resorcinol is made by fusion of *m*-benzenesulfonic acid.

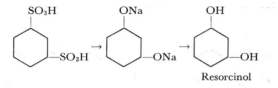

Resorcinol

2-Naphthol is made by fusion of the corresponding sulfonic acid with sodium hydroxide. The naphtholate is treated with carbon dioxide to precipitate the naphthol which is then purified by vacuum distillation.

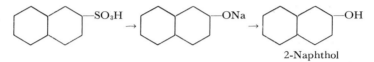

2-Naphthol

1-Naphthol is not made from the sulfonic acid. Instead, 1-naphthylamine sulfate is heated with water at 200° C in a closed vessel. On cooling, 1-naphthol crystallizes out.

For some compounds, the conditions of alkaline fusion are too severe. In such cases the reaction may often be effected in water solution under pressure. Chromotropic acid is prepared from 1-naphthol-3,6,8-trisulfonic acid in 60 per cent sodium hydroxide solution under pressure.

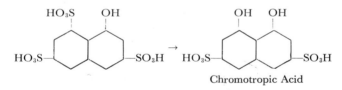

Chromotropic Acid

Sulfonated naphthylamines may be fused without destruction of the amino group. The important azo dye intermediates, H acid and J acid, are made in this way.

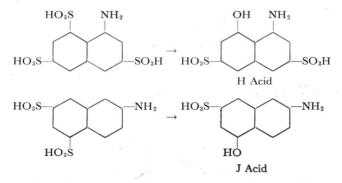

H Acid

J Acid

In the anthraquinone series, 2-anthraquinonesulfonic acid can be converted to the hydroxy compound by heating with calcium hydroxide in water. Alkaline fusion of the same sulfonic acid gives alizarin. The latter reaction is discussed elsewhere in this chapter.

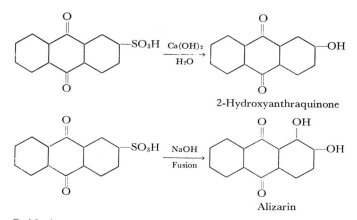

2-Hydroxyanthraquinone

Alizarin

Oxidation

Oxidation may be effected by air in the presence of a catalyst or by a variety of chemical oxidants, such as manganese dioxide and potassium permanganate.

Catalytic vapor-phase oxidation is illustrated by the conversion of naphthalene to phthalic anhydride. This reaction is carried out over a vanadium pentoxide catalyst at 450° C.

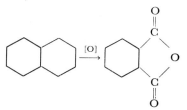

Another route to phthalic anhydride is oxidation of o-xylene, a product of the petroleum industry. The conditions for this reaction are similar to those for naphthalene oxidation, except that the temperature is higher (540° C).

Aniline sulfate can be chemically oxidized with manganese dioxide in sulfuric acid. The product is p-quinone.

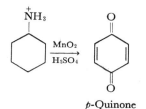

p-Quinone

The use of potassium bichromate in sulfuric acid effects the oxidation of 1-nitro-2-methylanthraquinone to the corresponding carboxylic acid. This reaction illustrates side-chain oxidation, an important route to carboxylic acids.

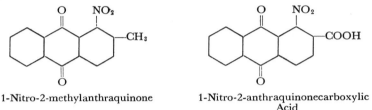

1-Nitro-2-methylanthraquinone   1-Nitro-2-anthraquinonecarboxylic Acid

Other Important Reactions

Condensation. The term condensation describes a variety of reactions which join molecules or parts of the same molecule with elimination of a molecule of water or other low molecular weight substance. An example is the conversion of benzanthrone to dibenzanthronyl, described in detail elsewhere in this chapter.

Addition. An important intermediate, cyanuric chloride, is made by the addition of cyanogen chloride to itself. The reaction is catalyzed by a small amount of free chlorine.

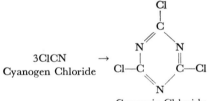

Cyanuric Chloride

Alkylation. Alkylation refers to the introduction of an aliphatic group, such as methyl, into an organic molecule. Alkylation may occur on carbon, nitrogen, oxygen, or sulfur. Of these possibilities, alkylation on nitrogen and oxygen are most important in the manufacture of dye intermediates. A methyl group may be introduced into the amino group of aniline by heating with methyl alcohol under pressure in the presence of a mineral acid.

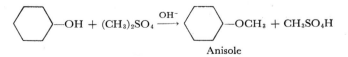

N-Methylaniline

Phenol may be methylated with methyl sulfate in cold alkaline medium to give anisole.

$$\langle\ \rangle\text{—OH} + (CH_3)_2SO_4 \xrightarrow{OH^-} \langle\ \rangle\text{—OCH}_3 + CH_3SO_4H$$

Anisole

Carboxylation. The carboxylic acid group may be introduced by side-chain oxidation as described above. In addition, it may be introduced by direct action of carbon dioxide on certain compounds. When sodium phenolate is treated with carbon dioxide under pressure at about 150° C, sodium salicylate is formed. Acidification of the salicylate gives the free acid which may be purified by vacuum distillation. 2-Hydroxy-3-naphthoic acid, an intermediate for developed azo dyes, is made from sodium 2-naphtholate.

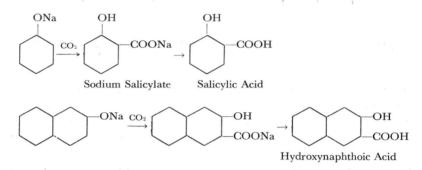

Sodium Salicylate   Salicylic Acid

Hydroxynaphthoic Acid

Sandmeyer Reaction. The replacement of a diazonium group by halogen, nitrile, nitro, sulfhydryl, and other groups in the presence of a cuprous salt, is known as the Sandmeyer reaction. An illustration of the use of this reaction is the preparation of 2-chloro-5-nitrophenol from the corresponding aminophenol.

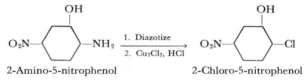

2-Amino-5-nitrophenol   2-Chloro-5-nitrophenol

Cyanoethylation. Reaction of a primary or secondary aromatic amine with acrylonitrile results in N-cyanoethylation. The products are useful intermediates for azo and basic dyes. An example is the cyanoethylation of aniline with cupric sulfate catalyst.

N-Cyanoethylaniline

PRODUCTION OF DYE INTERMEDIATES

Table 23.2 gives the production figures for some important raw materials and intermediates in the United States for 1960. These figures are taken from the report of the U. S. Tariff Commission. It should be remembered that dye intermediates are often used for end-products other than dyes, and that the figures in Table 23.2 do not necessarily correlate with figures on dye production.

THE MANUFACTURE OF DYES

Dyes owe their color to their ability to absorb light in the visible region of the spectrum, between 4000 and 8000 Angstrom units. Absorption is caused by electronic transitions in the molecules and can occur in the visible region only when the electrons are reasonably mobile. Mobility is encouraged by unsaturation and resonance. The main structural unit of a dye, which is always unsaturated, is called the *chromophore*, and a compound containing a chromophore is called a *chromogen*. Any substituent atom or group that

TABLE 23.2. UNITED STATES PRODUCTION OF SOME RAW MATERIALS
AND DYE INTERMEDIATES, IN POUNDS, 1960

Acetanilide	2,321,000
2-Amino-1-naphthalenesulfonic Acid	3,517,000
Aniline	120,243,000
Anthraquinone	4,434,000
o-Benzoylbenzoic Acid	5,258,000
o-Dichlorobenzene	24,678,000
p-Dichlorobenzene	63,973,000
N,N-Dimethylaniline	8,013,000
Dinitrochlorobenzene	5,324,000
Dinitrostilbenedisulfonic Acid	1,967,000
G Acid	1,221,000
Gamma Acid	753,000
H Acid	2,798,000
Hydroxynaphthoic Acid	2,771,000
J Acid	503,000
Benzidine	1,208,000
Benzanthrone	1,283,000
Nitrobenzene	162,308,000
Phthalic Anhydride	401,143,000

increases the intensity of the color is called an *auxochrome*. An auxochrome may also serve to shift the absorption band of a chromophore to a longer wave length, or may play a part in solubilizing the dye and attaching it to fibers.

Dyes are classified according to the type of chromophore that they contain. An example is the azo class, which is characterized by the presence of the —N=N— linkage. A typical chromogen is azobenzene:

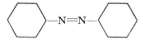

Common auxochromes are hydroxyl, amino, and carboxyl groups.

The hue, strength, and brightness of a dye depend on the entire light-absorbing system, consisting of chromophore and auxochromes, acting together. The nature of these groups and their relative positions in the molecule must be worked out correctly to produce a dye of desired appearance.

In general, for a given type of dye, extension of the unsaturated system and increased opportunities for resonance shifts the absorption of light toward longer wave lengths. Assuming a single main absorption band, the color absorbed progresses across the visible spectrum from violet to purple. As this progression occurs, the light that is not absorbed is reflected and seen by the human eye as the color complementary to that absorbed. The wave lengths absorbed, the corresponding colors, and the observed complementary colors are given below for several major hues.

Wave Length Absorbed Å	Corresponding Color Absorbed	Observed Color
4520	Indigo	Yellow
4500	Blue	Orange
4900	Blue-Green	Red
5300	Yellow-Green	Violet
5900	Orange	Blue
7300	Purple	Green

In addition to securing the desired appearance, it is necessary in dye synthesis to provide the dye with any groups necessary to confer solubility and affinity for textile fibers. It is important also to use only color systems that have the required fastness to light and other degrading influences. Considering that all these properties must be exhibited by one compound, it can readily be understood that the development and manufacture of dyes require a high degree of technical competence in the laboratory and in the plant.

The Colour Index lists 30 chemical classes of dyes. Many of these classes are closely related; others are of relatively minor importance. Only several of the more important classes will be discussed in the following sections of this chapter.

AZO DYES

The azo dye class, one of the most important, includes many hundreds of commercial dyes of various application types. Azo dyes are characterized by the presence of one or more azo ($-N{=}N-$) groups.

The principal method of forming azo dyes involves *diazotization* of primary aromatic amines, followed by *coupling* with hydroxy or amino derivatives of aromatic hydrocarbons or with certain aliphatic keto compounds. Both the aromatic amine, which is diazotized, and the compound to which it is coupled may bear a variety of substituents, such as alkyl, alkoxyl, halogen, sulfonic acid, and others. Because of the large number of compounds that can be combined, often in more than one sequence, the number of possible azo dyes is almost infinite.

Diazotization takes place when nitrous acid (HNO_2) reacts with a primary aromatic amino group in acid medium. Usually sulfuric or hydrochloric acid is used and the nitrous acid is generated from sodium nitrite. The equation for diazotization, using aniline in hydrochloric acid, is as follows:

$$C_6H_5—NH_2 + HNO_2 + H^+Cl^- \rightarrow C_6H_5—N_2^+Cl^- + 2H_2O$$

Diazotization is usually carried out with excess acid to prevent partial diazotization and to inhibit secondary reactions. If the reaction is to proceed easily, the amine must be in solution, or its hydrochloride, if insoluble, must be in a fine state of subdivision. Temperatures of from 0 to 5° C are usually employed for diazotization since diazonium salts are generally unstable. There are exceptions to this, and temperatures of 20° C or higher are occasionally preferred.

The ease of diazotization depends markedly on the basicity of the amine. Extremely weakly basic amines are diazotizable only by special methods.

The coupling reaction with aromatic hydroxy compounds is illustrated with benzene diazonium chloride and phenol.

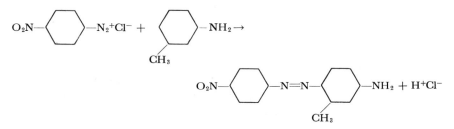

Coupling to phenols, naphthols, and related hydroxy compounds is carried out in alkaline solution. Under alkaline conditions the hydroxy compound is soluble, and coupling is usually rapid. Ordinarily the coupling must be carried out in the cold to prevent decomposition of the diazonium salt.

An example of coupling to an aromatic amine is the reaction of p-nitro-benzenediazonium chloride with m-toluidine.

Couplings to amines are carried out in acid solution in which the amine is soluble. It has been shown, however, that the free amine couples, not the hydrochloride. For this reason coupling proceeds faster near the neutral point where the equilibrium concentration of free amine is highest. It is frequently best to start the reaction at a low pH and then to raise the alkalinity slowly with sodium acetate or soda ash as the reaction proceeds.

It should be noted that in the above examples of coupling the diazonium group is shown entering the position para to the hydroxyl and amino groups. This specificity is characteristic of azo couplings. The diazo group does not enter at random but in certain definite positions. For the benzene derivatives, the attack is always on the position para to the activating group. If this position is blocked, coupling is difficult or impossible.

In naphthalene derivatives, orientation of the entering diazo group is somewhat different. In alpha-naphthol, the attack is at position 4. If 4 is blocked, the diazo group enters at 2. In beta-naphthol, coupling takes place at 1, never at 3 or 4. The same rules apply to the corresponding naphthylamines.

alpha-Naphthol   beta-Naphthol

In the naphthalene series, it is found that the presence of certain substituents, especially the sulfonic acid group, can influence the position of coupling even when not in a directly blocking position. For example, a sulfonic acid group in position 5 of alpha-naphthol causes the coupling to occur predominantly at position 2, rather than 4.

Certain aminonaphthol sulfonic acids couple twice. In this case the place of entry depends on whether the coupling is performed in acid or alkaline solution. If acid, the coupling is ortho to the amino group; if alkaline, it is ortho to the hydroxyl. In the three examples following, the place of entry for acid coupling is marked X, for alkaline coupling Z.

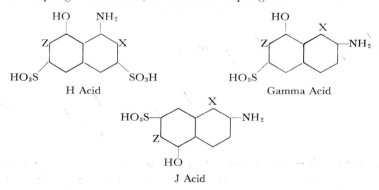

H Acid   Gamma Acid

J Acid

Ortho and para diamines in both the benzene and naphthalene series do not couple at all; only the meta diamines do so.

A generalized procedure for diazotization and coupling as practiced in both laboratory and plant is as follows: Sodium nitrite is added slowly with stirring to an acid solution of the amine in a wooden or brick-lined tub. The tub is not externally cooled but ice is added directly to the amine solution to control the temperature between 0 and 5° C. The progress of the reaction is followed by observing the disappearance of the nitrous acid generated from the sodium nitrite. This is done by spotting the reaction mass on a starch-potassium iodide test paper which turns black when nitrous acid is present. When no more nitrous acid is consumed, the diazotization is judged to be complete. The diazonium compound is not isolated, but is run at once at a slow rate into the alkaline (or acid) solution of the intermediate with which it is to couple. After the addition of the diazonium compound, the batch is stirred for a period varying between a few minutes and three days, until coupling is complete. The solution of the dye is then warmed, and salt (NaCl) is added and allowed to dissolve. On cooling, the dye separates and is filtered. There are a number of variations in procedure. Some dyes are salted hot, some cold, some not at all. Filtration is carried out at a temperature best suited to isolate the dye without inclusion of impurities. As a result of salting, dyes with sulfonic acid groups are always isolated as the sodium sulfonates.

Diazotization and coupling are usually carried out as batch processes because of the limited production required and the necessity of testing the various batches of intermediates that are used. In a few cases, however, continuous diazotization and coupling are practical. When continuous processes are used it becomes necessary to devise a means of isolating the product as rapidly as it is made. Centrifugal filters, spray dryers, and other special apparatus are suitable for this use.

Monoazo Dyes

Monoazo dyes contain the azo $(-N=N-)$ linkage once; the simplest example is aminoazobenzene. This compound is used as a dye for oils, lacquers, and stains under the name Solvent Yellow 1 (Aniline Yellow), and is also an intermediate for other dyes. It is made by coupling benzene-diazonium chloride with aniline in acid medium:

Solvent Yellow 1

To simplify the description of other azo dyes to follow, only the formulas of the dyes will be given, but the place of attack of the diazonium group will be indicated by an asterisk on the diazo nitrogen joined to the coupling component. It will be understood that the diazonium compound was prepared by diazotization of the corresponding amine and that coupling took place on the coupling component with the elimination of a hydrogen ion.

The coupling of benzenediazonium chloride with *m*-phenylenediamine in acid medium gives Basic Orange 2 (Chrysoidine), a dye of limited use on textiles but of importance for coloring paper, leather, and woodstains.

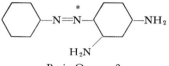

Basic Orange 2

Acid Orange 7 (Orange II) is prepared by coupling diazotized sulfanilic acid with beta-naphthol in basic medium. Acid Orange 7 is useful on textile fibers, such as wool, silk, and nylon, as well as on paper and leather.

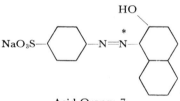

Acid Orange 7

Other acid monoazo dyes of importance are derived from a variety of sulfonated intermediates. Acid Red 26 (Ponceau R) is made from diazotized *m*-xylidine and R-Acid. Acid Red 14 (Azo Rubine) is made from diazotized naphthionic acid and Nevile and Winther's acid. Acid Violet 6 is *p*-aminoacetanilide coupled with chromotropic acid.

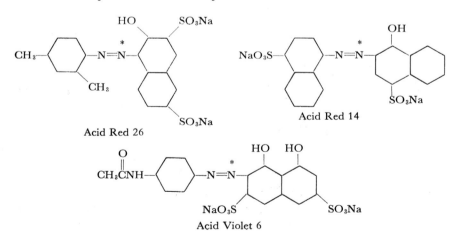

Acid Red 26

Acid Red 14

Acid Violet 6

Mordant Black 17 is an example of a type of dye that shows improved fastness on wool when treated on the fiber with a soluble chromium salt. Reaction occurs between the dye and the chromium ion to form a complex of enhanced fastness to washing and light. The component parts of Mordant Black 17 will be recognized as 1-amino-2-naphthol-4-sulfonic acid and beta-naphthol. Another dye of this type is Mordant Brown 4, which is made by diazotizing picramic acid and coupling it in acid medium with *m*-toluene-diamine.

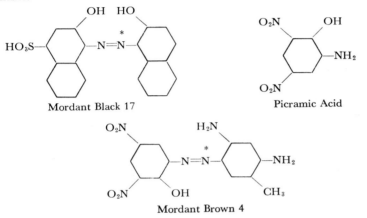

Mordant Black 17   Picramic Acid

Mordant Brown 4

Acid Yellow 23 (Tartrazine) contains the pyrazolone nucleus. It is prepared by coupling diazotized sulfanilic acid with 1-(4'-sulfophenyl)-3-carboxypyrazolone-5, or by heating oxidized tartaric acid (1 mole) with phenylhydrazinesulfonic acid (2 moles). Acid Yellow 23 is useful as a dye for basic fibers, paper, and leather. It is also used as a filter dye in photography.

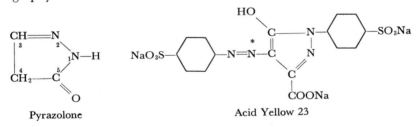

Pyrazolone   Acid Yellow 23

A further example of a pyrazolone dye is Acid Red 38. This dye is the chromium complex of the azo compound made by coupling diazotized 5-nitro-2-aminophenol with 1-(3'-sulfamyl)-3-methylpyrazolone-5. It is used as a dye for wool and nylon. Acid Red 38 has one advantage over dyes such as Mordant Black 17 in that the dyer does not have to form the chromium complex by a separate operation during the dyeing process.

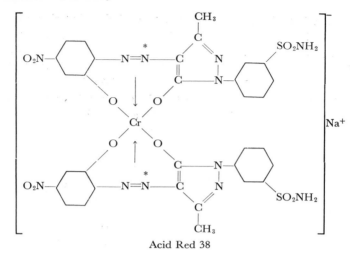

Acid Red 38

Disperse Red 1 is a dye for cellulose acetates, nylon, polyesters, and various plastics. It is prepared by coupling diazotized *p*-nitroaniline with N-ethyl-N-(beta-hydroxyethyl)-aniline in acid medium. It has low solubility in water and is supplied in finely divided form mixed with a dispersing agent.

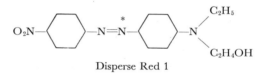

Disperse Red 1

Some insoluble azo dyes are used as pigments. Pigment Yellow 3 (Hansa Yellow 10G) illustrates this type. It is prepared by coupling diazotized 2-nitro-4-chloroaniline with *o*-chloroacetoacetanilide.

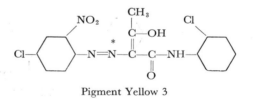

Pigment Yellow 3

A final example of a monoazo dye is the orange reactive dye referred to in an earlier part of this chapter. This dye is prepared by condensing aniline-*m*-sulfonic acid and J Acid with cyanuric chloride under carefully controlled conditions, followed by coupling with diazotized aniline-*o*-sulfonic acid. One chlorine atom remains for reaction with textile fibers bearing hydroxyl or amino groups.

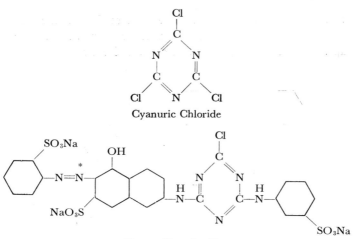

Cyanuric Chloride

Orange Reactive Dye

Disazo Dyes

Disazo dyes contain two azo linkages. They are formed: (1) by the further diazotization and coupling of monoazo dyes containing free amino groups, (2) by the coupling of two moles of diazonium compound to a coupling component that can couple twice, or (3) by the tetrazotization of a diamine followed by coupling to two moles of coupling component. When two moles of diazonium compound or coupling component are used, they may be the same or different in structure.

Acid Red 150 (Cloth Red 2R) is a disazo dye prepared by diazotizing aminoazobenzene and coupling to R Acid.

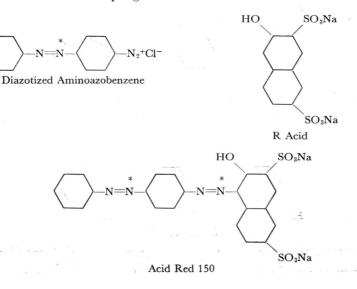

Diazotized Aminoazobenzene

R Acid

Acid Red 150

A more important disazo acid dye is Acid Red 73 (Brilliant Crocein M) which is used to color wool, leather, paper, and anodized aluminum. It is prepared from diazotized aminoazobenzene and G Acid.

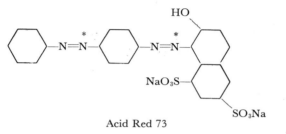

Acid Red 73

Other disazo dyes of this kind are Acid Red 115 (Cloth Red B), which is made by coupling diazotized aminoazotoluene with R Acid, and Acid Black 18. Acid Black 18 will be recognized as having been made by the combination, through diazotization and coupling, of sulfanilic acid, alpha-naphthylamine, and H Acid.

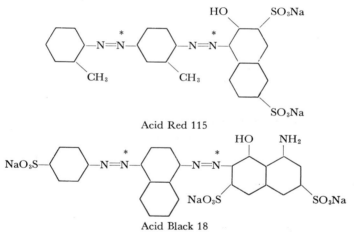

Acid Red 115

Acid Black 18

Solvent Red 27 is a disazo dye used to color gasoline. Its formula indicates that it is made by diazotizing aminoazoxylene and coupling to beta-naphthol.

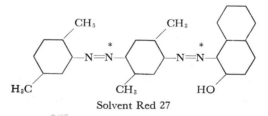

Solvent Red 27

An example of a disazo dye prepared by coupling two different diazonium compounds to a single coupling component is Acid Black 1. This dye is made by coupling diazotized *p*-nitroaniline (acid) and aniline (alkaline) to **H** Acid.

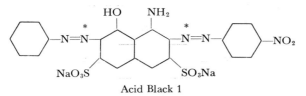

Acid Black 1

Direct Red 28 (Congo Red) is a disazo dye made by coupling tetrazotized benzidine twice with naphthionic acid. This dye is now of limited use on textiles but is an important dye for paper. It is also useful as an indicator since it turns from red to blue in strong acid.

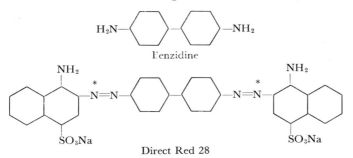

Fenzidine

Direct Red 28

A direct dye of importance is Direct Blue 1 (Sky Blue FF). It is made by coupling tetrazotized *o*-dianisidine twice with Chicago acid. Direct Blue 1 is used as a dye for cellulosic textiles, for paper, and for nylon. It is applied to cellulosic textiles and paper under neutral conditions; it dyes them by adsorption. It is used as an acid dye on nylon and must be applied under acidic conditions.

o-Dianisidine

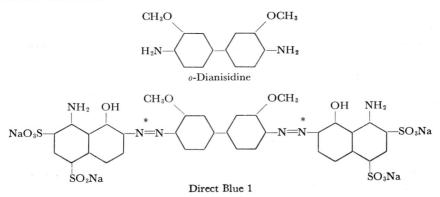

Direct Blue 1

As mentioned above, it is not necessary to couple both diazonium groups of a tetrazotized diamine to the same coupling component. Acid Orange 49 is made by coupling tetrazotized *m*-tolidine with G Acid and with phenol, followed by formation of an ester of the phenol with *p*-toluenesulfonyl chloride. This dye is used on wool, silk, and leather.

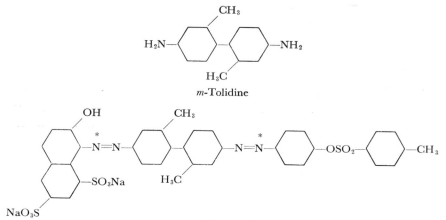

m-Tolidine

Acid Orange 49

The fastness to light of direct dyes is often improved by the formation of copper chelates. Direct Red 83 is the copper complex of the disazo dye prepared by coupling two moles of diazotized 2-aminophenol-4-sulfonic acid to one mole of J Acid urea.

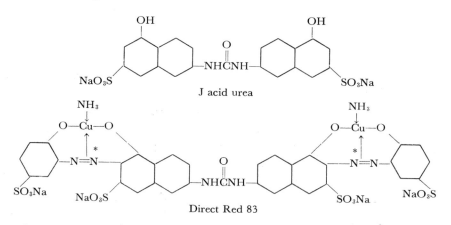

J acid urea

Direct Red 83

Since dyes of this kind are usually made by reacting the coupling product with a cupric salt in aqueous ammonia, ammonia molecules are shown coordinated with the copper in the complex. This position may sometimes be filled by water or by various amines.

A number of important dyes are based on diaminostilbenedisulfonic acid. An example is Direct Yellow 4 (Brilliant Yellow), which is made by coupling tetrazotized diaminostilbenedisulfonic acid twice to phenol. Direct Yellow 4 is an important dye for paper; it is also used as an indicator since it turns red in strong alkali. Reaction of Direct Yellow 4 with ethyl chloride under pressure gives the ethyl ether, Direct Yellow 12 (Chrysophenine). This is an important dye for textiles and paper. Unlike Direct Yellow 4, it is not an indicator.

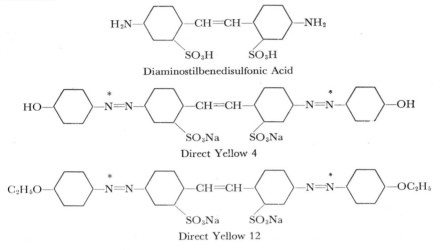

Diaminostilbenedisulfonic Acid

Direct Yellow 4

Direct Yellow 12

Some stilbene azo dyes are prepared by methods other than diazotization and coupling. Direct Orange 61, for example, is prepared by the condensation in alkaline solution of aminoazobenzenesulfonic acid and dinitrostilbenedisulfonic acid. The exact structure of Direct Orange 61 is not known, but the presence of an azo linkage formed by reaction of an amino and a nitro group can be demonstrated.

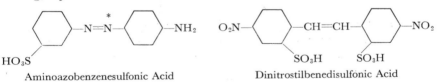

Aminoazobenzenesulfonic Acid

Dinitrostilbenedisulfonic Acid

Polyazo Dyes

Azo dyes can be made with three, four, or more azo linkages. Those with three (trisazo) and four (tetrakisazo) are quite common. An example of an important trisazo dye is Direct Black 38, a dye for cellulose, wool, and silk. Examination of the formula shows that this dye is made from four intermediates: aniline, benzidine, m-phenylenediamine, and H Acid. Benzidine is tetrazotized and coupled first to H Acid. Next aniline is diazotized and coupled to the H Acid also. Finally, the remaining diazonium group of the benzidine is coupled with m-phenylenediamine.

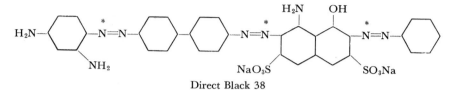

Direct Black 38

MANUFACTURING PROCESSES FOR AZO DYES

The manufacturing process for a typical azo dye may be illustrated with Direct Blue 6 (Direct Blue 2B), an important dye for cotton, viscose, silk, and paper.

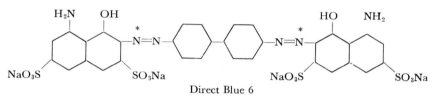

Direct Blue 6

The apparatus required for the manufacture of Direct Blue 6 is shown in Figure 23.2.

Benzidine is suspended in water in a wooden or brick-lined tub (Tub 2) equipped with an agitator. Five moles of hydrochloric acid per mole of benzidine are added, and the whole is brought to a boil by passing in live steam. The required amount of acid is four moles, two per amino group, as indicated earlier in this chapter. The excess of one mole is required to stabilize the tetrazonium salt and prevent side reactions. As soon as the benzidine has dissolved, ice is added and a large part of the benzidine hydrochloride separates as a finely divided solid. Two moles of sodium nitrite, in solution in Tank 1, are run in slowly for about two hours. In the meantime, two moles of H Acid are dissolved in an excess of soda ash in water (Tub 3), and to this the contents of Tub 2 are added with stirring. Enough ice is added to keep the temperature at about 5° C. The dye separates in part as the coupling proceeds. When coupling is complete, the contents of Tub 3 are warmed with steam, and salt is added. After the salt has dissolved, the contents of the tub are allowed to cool, whereupon the dye separates almost quantitatively as the sodium salt.

The suspension of dye is run into a wooden plate-and-frame filter press. The filtrate is tested and if it contains no substantial amount of dye, it is run to the sewer. The filter cake is not washed but merely freed from most of the adhering mother liquor by blowing with compressed air while still in the press. The moist cake is discharged into shallow trays which are placed in a circulating air drier, wherein the moisture is removed at temperatures between 50 and 120° C. Vacuum driers and drum driers may also be used. The dried dye is ground and mixed with a diluent, such as salt, to make it

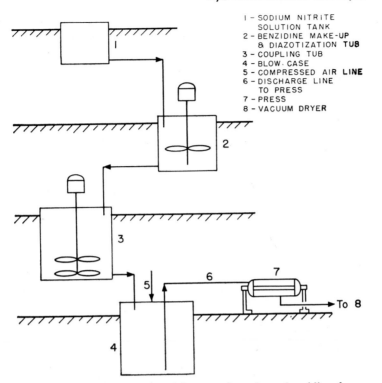

1 – SODIUM NITRITE
    SOLUTION TANK
2 – BENZIDINE MAKE-UP
    & DIAZOTIZATION TUB
3 – COUPLING TUB
4 – BLOW·CASE
5 – COMPRESSED AIR LINE
6 – DISCHARGE LINE
    TO PRESS
7 – PRESS
8 – VACUUM DRYER

Figure 23.2. Schematic diagram for manufacturing a benzidine dye.

equal in color strength to a predetermined standard. Dilution is necessary because batches differ in their content of pure dye; if sold "as is," the user would have to adjust his dyeing recipes for each batch. Uniformity is assured by dilution to a standard strength.

TRIPHENYLMETHANE DYES

Triphenylmethane dyes are characterized by the highly resonance-stabilized chromophore shown below. They are among the strongest and brightest of synthetic dyes, but usually do not exhibit good fastness to light. An exception is found with acrylic fibers, which are dyed in bright light-fast hues by selected triphenylmethane dyes.

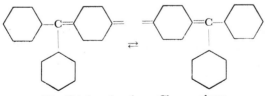

The Triphenylmethane Chromophore

Basic Red 9 (Pararosaniline) is the simplest triphenylmethane dye. It is prepared by the condensation of one mole of *p*-toluidine and two moles of aniline, usually by heating in nitrobenzene which serves as solvent and oxidant. The first product is a colorless carbinol which is converted to the dye with hydrochloric acid.

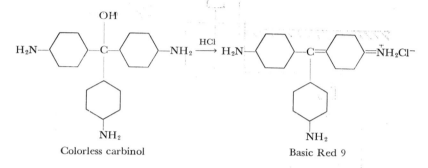

Colorless carbinol   Basic Red 9

Closely related to Basic Red 9 is Basic Violet 14 (Fuchsine). This dye is made by condensing one mole each of aniline, *p*-toluidine, and *o*-toluidine in nitrobenzene. The dye is formed on neutralizing the carbinol with hydrochloric acid.

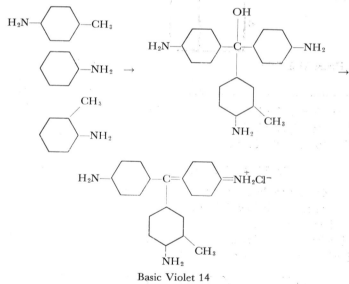

Basic Violet 14

A second method for the synthesis of triphenylmethane dyes is illustrated with Basic Green 4 (Malachite Green). Benzaldehyde (one mole) is condensed with two moles of dimethylaniline to form a leuco base which is oxidized with lead peroxide and treated with hydrochloric acid to give the dye.

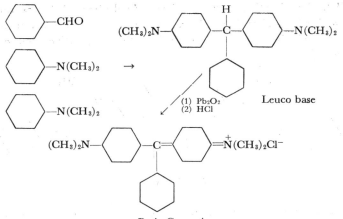

Leuco base

(1) Pb$_2$O$_2$
(2) HCl

Basic Green 4

Basic Green 4 is used as a dye for bast fibers, acrylic fibers, leather, paper, and lacquers. When o-chlorobenzaldehyde is used in place of benzaldehyde, the product is Basic Blue 1, a more alkali-resistant dye which finds use on tannin-mordanted cotton, wool, leather, and paper.

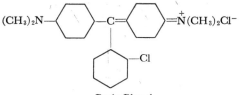

Basic Blue 1

Ketone condensation, a third method of manufacture of triphenylmethane dyes, is illustrated with Basic Violet 3 (Crystal Violet). Michler's Ketone, made by passing phosgene into dimethylaniline, is condensed with dimethylaniline in a solvent using phosphorus oxychloride. A carbinol is formed which is converted to the dye with hydrochloric acid.

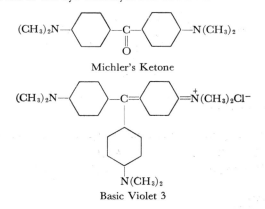

Michler's Ketone

Basic Violet 3

Not all triphenylmethane dyes are basic. Acid Green 3, for example, is a dye for wool, silk, and leather. There are two sulfonate groups in the molecule, one of which forms an inner salt with the positive charge on the chromophore.

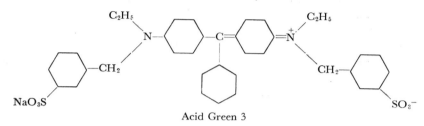

Acid Green 3

Aurin is a triphenylmethane dye containing no nitrogen. It is weakly colored, lacks solubility in water, and has no affinity for fibers. Some of its derivatives, however, with a carboxyl group ortho to one of the hydroxyl groups, are useful as mordant dyes.

Aurin

Closely related to the triphenylmethane dyes are the diphenylmethane dyes. Only one of these, Basic Yellow 2 (Auramine), is important. It is useful on cotton, nylon, silk, wool, leather, and paper. It is sometimes classified as a ketonimine dye since it is the ketonimine hydrochloride of Michler's Ketone.

Basic Yellow 2

XANTHENE DYES

The chromophore of the xanthene dyes is the resonance-stabilized structure below. Acid Yellow 73 (Fluorescein), Acid Red 87 (Eosine), and Basic Violet 10 (Rhodamine B) each represent a series of xanthene dyes.

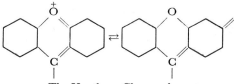

The Xanthene Chromophore

Acid Yellow 73 is made by heating phthalic anhydride (1 mole) and resorcinol (2 moles) in an iron kettle. The temperature is regulated by means of an oil or metal bath and kept at 220° C for seven hours. The melt is dissolved in caustic soda, and the product is precipitated by acidifying. It is a yellow-red powder that fluoresces green-yellow in alkaline solution. The sodium salt is called Uranine and is used to trace underground flow of water.

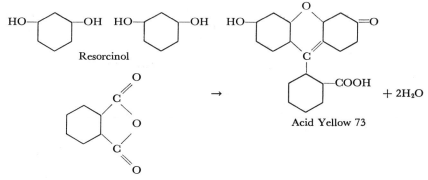

Resorcinol

Phthalic Anhydride

→

Acid Yellow 73

$+ 2H_2O$

When Acid Yellow 73 is dissolved in alcohol and treated, while warm, with bromine, four equivalents are absorbed to form Acid Red 87 (Eosine). This dye is used to a limited extent on wool; its primary uses are for paper and inks.

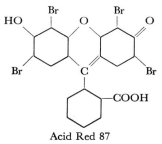

Acid Red 87

Other dyes related to Acid Red 87 are Acid Red 91 (dinitrodibromofluorescein), Acid Red 92 (Phloxine; tetrabromodichlorofluorescein), and Acid Red 95 (Erythrosine; tetraiodofluorescein).

Basic Violet 10 (Rhodamine B) is a dye for bast fibers, mordanted cotton, leather, and paper. It is prepared by condensing phthalic anhydride with *m*-diethylaminophenol and treating with hydrochloric acid. This is the general preparative route for rhodamines.

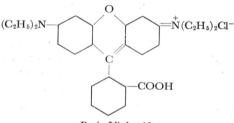

Basic Violet 10

Related to the xanthene dyes are the *acridines, azines, oxazines,* and *thiazines.* Acridine Yellow results from the fusion of *m*-toluenediamine with glycerin and oxalic acid, followed by oxidation with ferric chloride. Basic Orange 15 (Phosphine) is a by-product of the manufacture of Fuchsine, and is an acridine dye.

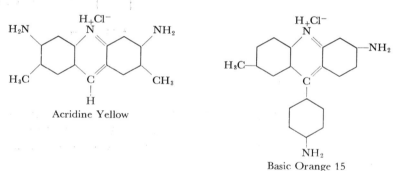

Acridine Yellow

Basic Orange 15

Examples of azine dyes are Safranine B, Basic Red 2 (Safranine T), and Acid Blue 59. The preparation of azine dyes is illustrated with Safranine B. *p*-Phenylenediamine and aniline are reacted to form indamine. Further reaction of indamine with aniline under oxidizing conditions, followed by treatment with hydrochloric acid, gives Safranine B.

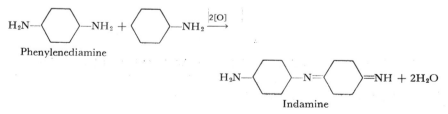

Phenylenediamine

Indamine

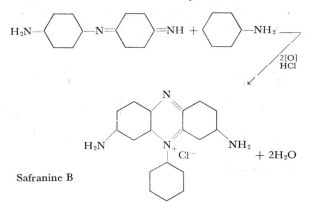

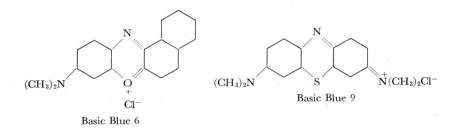

Safranine B

Indamine (above) is an example of a *quinone-imide* dye. Dyes of the indamine type are used in color photography; the dye is formed during development of the film.

Basic Blue 6 (Meldola's Blue) is an oxazine dye. Basic Blue 9 (Methylene Blue) illustrates the thiazine dye class.

Basic Blue 6

Basic Blue 9

ANTHRAQUINONE AND RELATED DYES

Dyes based on anthraquinone and related polycyclic aromatic quinones are of great importance. Many of the most light-fast acid, mordant, disperse, and vat dyes are of this kind. The chromophore is the quinoid group, $\diagdown C{=}O.$

Anthraquinone Acid Dyes

Anthraquinone acid dyes are illustrated by Acid Blue 25, Acid Blue 45, and Alizarin Cyanine Green G (Acid Green 25). These dyes are water-soluble anthraquinone derivatives which are used for dyeing wool, silk, nylon, leather, and paper. The chemistry of this type of dye is shown with Blue 25 as an example. The starting material is 1-aminoanthraquinone which is sulfonated and brominated to give Bromamine acid. Condensation with aniline then yields Acid Blue 25 which is isolated as the sodium salt.

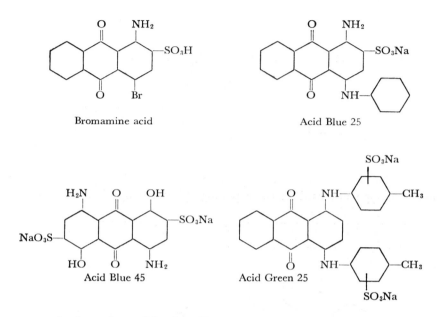

Bromamine acid

Acid Blue 25

Acid Blue 45

Acid Green 25

Anthraquinone Mordant Dyes

Anthraquinone mordant dyes contain groups, such as hydroxyl or carboxyl, which can combine with metal ions. The simplest member of this group, Mordant Red 11 (Alizarin), is 1,2-dihydroxyanthraquinone. When applied to wool with an aluminum mordant it gives the well-known Turkey Red, and when converted to its calcium salt forms a bluish-red powder useful as a pigment.

Mordant Red 11 is made by heating, under pressure, silver salt (sodium anthraquinone-2-sulfonate, so called because of its silvery crystals), caustic soda, potassium chlorate, and water. A steel autoclave is ordinarily used and the temperature is maintained at about 180° C. The resulting melt is blown into water and acidified to decompose the sodium alizarate; the precipitated alizarin is filtered, washed, and standardized as a 20 per cent paste.

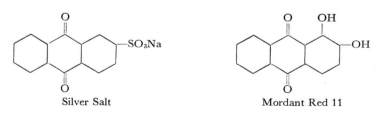

Silver Salt

Mordant Red 11

While Mordant Red 11 is very sparingly soluble in water, the introduction of sulfonic acid groups gives soluble derivatives. The most important water-soluble dye of the alizarin mordant class is Mordant Black 13, a dye primarily for wool. It is made by condensing aniline with 1,2,4-trihydroxyanthra-

Figure 23.3. A plate and frame filter press used for the isolation of intermediates and dyes. (*Courtesy Organic Chemicals Dept., E. I. du Pont de Nemours and Co., Inc.*)

quinone and sulfonating the resulting base. It is applied to wool with a chromium mordant and is quite fast to light and washing.

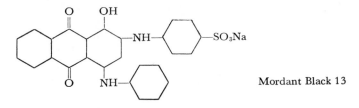

Mordant Black 13

Anthraquinone Disperse Dyes

Disperse Blue 26 illustrates an important group of dyes for cellulose acetates, nylon, and polyesters. It is a dye of low water solubility that must be furnished to the dyer as a fine powder that disperses easily in water. It dyes by dissolving in the fiber.

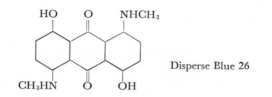

Disperse Blue 26

Anthraquinone Vat Dyes

Many of the best vat dyes are derivatives of anthraquinone or related compounds. A relatively simple dye of this class is Vat Yellow 3, which is made by benzoylation of 1,5-diaminoanthraquinone. It is a yellow pigment that is used as such when properly ground and dried. As a vat dye, it is usually supplied as an aqueous paste. Reduction with sodium hydrosulfite in

Figure 23.4. A low-pressure autoclave used in the manufacture of vat dyes. (*Courtesy Organic Chemicals Dept., E. I. du Pont de Nemours and Co., Inc.*)

Figure 23.5. A jacketed process kettle used in the manufacture of vat dyes and intermediates. (*Courtesy Organic Chemicals Dept., E. I. du Pont de Nemours and Co., Inc.*)

caustic soda solution gives the soluble salt of the hydroquinone, which has affinity for cellulosic fibers. After application to the fiber, the insoluble dye is re-formed by oxidation, as described earlier in this chapter.

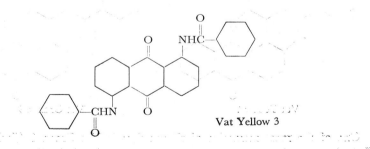

Vat Yellow 3

Perhaps the best known of the anthraquinone vat dyes is Vat Blue 4 (Indanthrone). This attractive dye is made by the fusion of 2-aminoanthraquinone with caustic potash. The fastness to chlorine bleaching of Vat Blue 4 is improved by chlorination. A number of chlorinated indanthrones are in commercial use and make up the most important group of fast vat blues. The preparative route for Vat Blue 4 is outlined below:

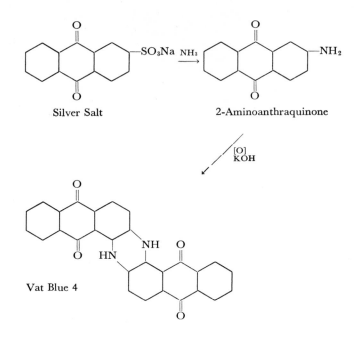

Silver Salt   2-Aminoanthraquinone

Vat Blue 4

Related to Vat Blue 4 are Vat Yellow 1 (Flavanthrone) and Vat Orange 9 (Pyranthrone), as well as other important dyes.

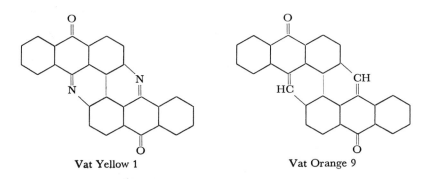

Vat Yellow 1   Vat Orange 9

One of the most attractive of all vat dyes is Vat Green 1 (Jade Green). This dye is a derivative of dibenzanthrone, which is itself a vat dye (Vat Blue 20 or Violanthrone).

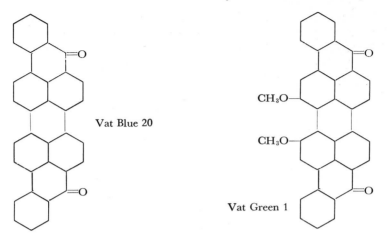

Vat Blue 20

CH_3O-

CH_3O-

Vat Green 1

Anthraquinone vat-dye manufacture is illustrated by the preparation of Vat Blue 20. Phthalic anhydride is condensed with benzene in aluminum chloride to give o-benzoylbenzoic acid which is ring-closed to anthraquinone

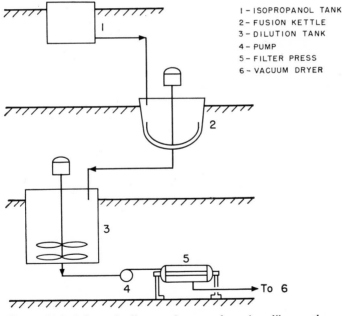

1 – ISOPROPANOL TANK
2 – FUSION KETTLE
3 – DILUTION TANK
4 – PUMP
5 – FILTER PRESS
6 – VACUUM DRYER

To 6

Figure 23.6. Schematic diagram for manufacturing dibenzanthrone.

with sulfuric acid. Treatment of anthraquinone in 82 per cent sulfuric acid with metal powder (iron, copper) and glycerin gives benzanthrone, probably by the series of steps shown below. Condensation of benzanthrone with caustic potash in isobutanol and sodium acetate gives dibenzanthronyl, which undergoes ring-closure to dibenzanthrone upon further heating. The dibenzanthrone usually is dissolved in sulfuric acid and reprecipitated as a paste of fine particle size by dilution with water. The paste is washed free of acid and standardized as Vat Blue 20. The equipment for this series of reactions must be able to resist the strongly corrosive conditions and must be externally heated and cooled. Cast iron, stainless-steel, and enamel-lined closed vessels are used.

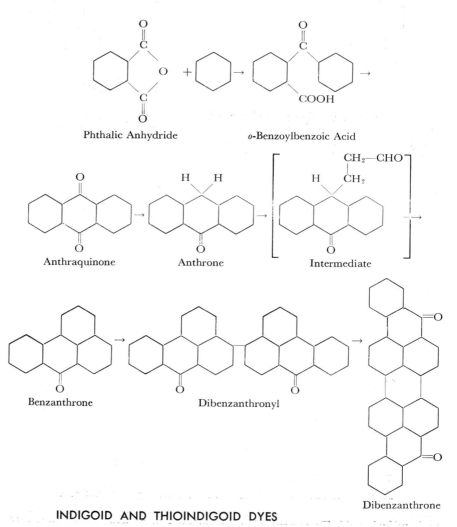

Phthalic Anhydride   o-Benzoylbenzoic Acid

Anthraquinone   Anthrone   Intermediate

Benzanthrone   Dibenzanthronyl   Dibenzanthrone

INDIGOID AND THIOINDIGOID DYES

The parent compound of the indigoid dye class, indigo, has been in use as a vat dye since ancient times. Natural indigo is obtained from a species of plant, Indigofera. It can be reduced by fermentation as well as by the modern method using sodium hydrosulfite and caustic soda. Once reduced, it can be applied to cellulosic fibers and then oxidized by air to produce rich blue dyeings. Natural indigo is no longer important, but large quantities of the synthetic dye are used to produce low-cost blues on cotton. The oxidized form is also used as a pigment. The Colour Index designation for indigo is Vat Blue 1.

A modern synthesis of Vat Blue 1 involves first the preparation of phenylglycine. To a water solution of sodium bisulfite are added formaldehyde, aniline, and sodium cyanide. The nitrile of phenylglycine which is formed is isolated and washed free of sulfite. Warming of the nitrile in an alkaline slurry then gives a solution of phenylglycine as its sodium salt. Ammonia is evolved during this step.

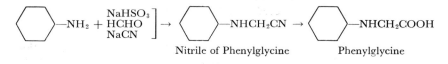

In the second step the phenylglycine salt is condensed by heating with a eutectic mixture of potassium and sodium hydroxides in the presence of sodamide, which removes the water formed. The reaction temperature is 200–220° C. The product, which is formed in high yield, is indoxyl.

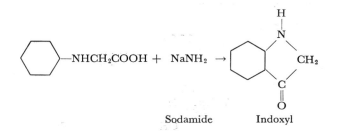

After the fusion step, water is added and air is blown into the alkaline solution of indoxyl. Indigo is formed and separates from solution. It is filtered, washed, and standardized as a paste of about 20 per cent solids.

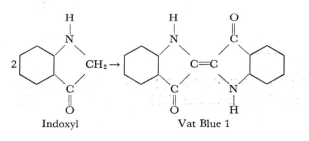

Since very large volumes of indigo are produced, it has been worthwhile to devise continuous processes. Such processes were pioneered by the former I. G. Farbenindustrie in Germany.

Vat Blue 1 is available as a water-soluble salt of the reduced dye. When applied to the fiber and treated with a solution of sodium nitrite or sodium bichromate, it reverts to the insoluble dye.

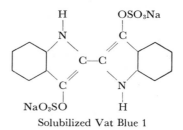

Solubilized Vat Blue 1

Important derivatives of indigo are the chloro and bromo derivatives. Vat Blue 5 is tetrabromoindigo. It is similar to Vat Blue 1 in shade but is considerably brighter. It is made by bromination of indigo in acetic acid.

Vat Red 41 (Thioindigo) is made by the reaction of thiosalicylic acid with chloroacetic acid, followed by fusion with caustic soda and oxidation by air. Thiosalicylic acid is made from anthranilic acid by diazotization and reaction with hydrogen sulfide.

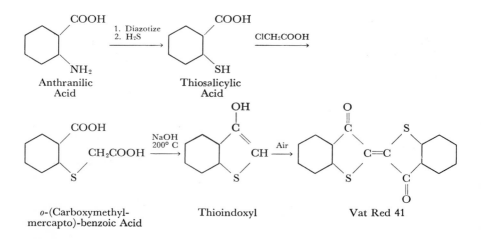

o-(Carboxymethyl-mercapto)-benzoic Acid   Thioindoxyl   Vat Red 41

Vat Red 41 is a dull bluish-red. Many of its derivatives are much more attractive and of greater commercial importance. An example is Vat Orange 5.

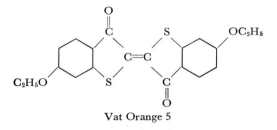

Vat Orange 5

SULFUR DYES

Sulfur dyes are dyes of unknown constitution which can be applied to fibers when reduced with sodium sulfide. Most of them are insoluble in water before reduction. After reduction they are soluble and can be absorbed by fibers and then oxidized to an insoluble form with air. Although structures cannot be written for the sulfur dyes, the methods for reproducing individual types are well established.

m-Diamines (m-toluenediamine for example), fused with sulfur cause the evolution of hydrogen sulfide and produce a melt which yields brown sulfur dyes. Redder shades are obtained by using derivatives of azine, such as the compound below which produces Sulfur Red 6.

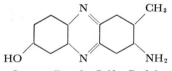

Intermediate for Sulfur Red 6

Blue sulfur dyes are obtained by treating diphenylamine derivatives with sodium polysulfide. Sulfur Blue 7, Sulfur Blue 9, and Sulfur Blue 13 are made from the intermediates below:

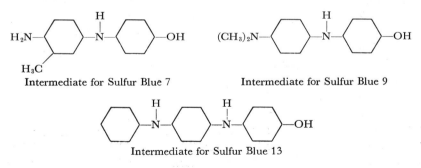

Intermediate for Sulfur Blue 7   Intermediate for Sulfur Blue 9

Intermediate for Sulfur Blue 13

Sulfur Black 1 is prepared by heating m-dinitrophenol with sodium polysulfide. The fusion mass is dissolved in water and blown with air until all the dye has separated. It is then filtered, washed, and dried.

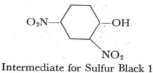

Intermediate for Sulfur Black 1

Vat Blue 43 (Hydron Blue R) is a kind of sulfur dye which, unlike typical sulfur dyes, may be reduced by sodium hydrosulfite without destruction. To prepare Vat Blue 43, carbazole is condensed with *p*-nitrosophenol in sulfuric acid to give an indophenol which is reduced and then fused with polysulfide.

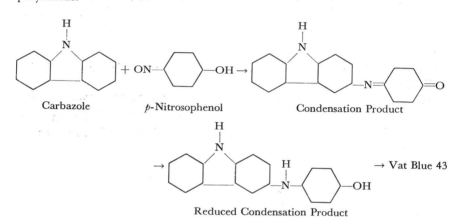

Vat Blue 42 (Hydron Blue G) gives a greener shade than Vat Blue 43. It is prepared by using ethylcarbazole in place of carbazole.

PHTHALOCYANINES

The phthalocyanines constitute an important class of synthetic pigments and dyes. The parent compound is Pigment Blue 16 (Phthalocyanine). One method of preparation involves the fusion of phthalonitrile with cyclo-hexylamine in an inert solvent. The two hydrogen atoms marked with asterisks can be replaced by metals such as copper, nickel, iron, and cobalt. In actual practice, the metal derivatives are not made from the metal-free compound, but are synthesized directly. Pigment Blue 15 (Copper Phthalo-cyanine), for example, is made by the fusion of phthalonitrile with copper metal or a copper salt. An alternative method involves the fusion of phthalic anhydride with urea and a copper salt in the presence of a molybdenum catalyst. Pigment Blue 15 and its polychlorinated derivative, Pigment Green 7, are the most important of the phthalocyanines. They are distinguished by great brilliance, strength and stability, and are used in every field in which colored pigments are used.

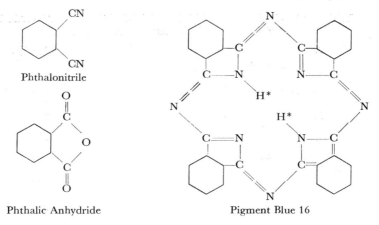

Phthalonitrile

Phthalic Anhydride

Pigment Blue 16

A number of phthalocyanine derivatives can be made by substituting the hydrogen atoms on the benzene rings. Pigment Green 7, mentioned above, is an example. Vat Blue 29 is a partially sulfonated cobalt phthalocyanine. Reduction with sodium hydrosulfite in caustic soda solution converts it to a soluble form that can be applied to textiles and reoxidized to the pigment. The structure of the reduced form is not known.

Direct Blue 86 is copper phthalocyanine which has been sulfonated to the extent of between two and three sulfonic acid groups per molecule. It produces very bright blue-green shades on cotton, viscose, and paper. Solvent Blue 25 is a spirit-soluble derivative of copper phthalocyanine, useful for inks, lacquers, and stains. It is the reaction product of the tetrasulfonyl chloride of copper phthalocyanine with isohexylamine.

PRODUCTION STATISTICS

Table 23.3 gives the production of synthetic dyes in the United States for the year 1960, arranged according to chemical class. These figures are taken from the report of the United States Tariff Commission. As in Table 23.1, it will be noted that the classifications used are not exactly the same as those given in the Colour Index.

NEW DEVELOPMENTS IN DYES

One recent development of importance has already been mentioned. It is the introduction of dyes that react with textile fibers to form covalent bonds. These reactive dyes, as exemplified by the orange reactive dye discussed earlier in this chapter, offer the dyer brightness, ease of application, and near-perfect fastness to washing. In addition to reactive dyes based on cyanuric chloride, trichloropyrimidyl and vinyl-sulfone derivatives are available. Reactive dyes are useful primarily on cotton, viscose, wool, silk, and nylon.

TABLE 23.3. UNITED STATES PRODUCTION OF COAL-TAR DYES,
BY CHEMICAL CLASS, IN POUNDS, 1960

Azo	43,822,000
Anthraquinone	33,891,000
Sulfur or Sulfide	31,022,000
Indigoid	9,526,000
Azoic	6,914,000
Stilbene	8,623,000
Phthalocyanine	487,000
Xanthene	1,216,000
Ketone imine	512,000
Thiazole	355,000
Thiazine	269,000
Oxazine	28,000
Triarylmethane	4,770,000
All Others	14,461,000
TOTAL	155,896,000

Dyes of excellent brightness and fastness have been placed on the market in recent years for the dyeing of acrylic fibers. Some of these are basic azo dyes of a new type. Called diazacyanines, they have great strength because of highly resonance-stabilized structures. The blue dye below is an example:

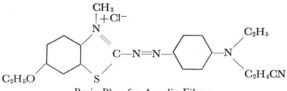

Basic Blue for Acrylic Fibers

A new class of red pigments which rival the phthalocyanines in strength and stability has recently appeared on the market. These pigments are various crystal forms of linear quinacridone.

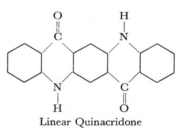

Linear Quinacridone

Earlier in this chapter, under the heading of "Ingrain Dyes," precursors were mentioned that generate phthalocyanines inside cotton fibers. Several products of this kind are now offered. The simplest of these is 1-amino-3-iminoisoindolenine, a water-soluble compound that reacts with a copper salt to form copper phthalocyanine. The other members of this group are condensation polymers of 1-amino-3-iminoisoindolenine which contain bound copper or cobalt. They are applied to textiles and reducing agents to form the metal phthalocyanine. The dyeings produced by these precursors are unexcelled in brightness.

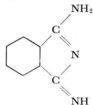

1-Amino-3-iminoisoindolenine

REFERENCES

1. American Association of Textile Chemists and Colorists, *Technical Manual and Year Book,* an annual publication.
2. Fierz-David and Blangey, "Fundamental Processes of Dye Chemistry," translation by Vittum, New York, Interscience Publishers, Inc., 1949.
3. Friedlaender, ed., "Fortschritte der Teerfarbenfabriken," Vols. 1–25, Berlin, Julius Springer, 1888–1942, Vols. 14–25 ed. by Fierz-David.
4. Groggins, ed., "Unit Processes in Organic Synthesis," 4th ed., New York, McGraw-Hill Book Co., 1952.
5. Houben, "Das Anthracene und die Anthrachinone," Leipzig, Thieme, 1929.
6. I. G. Farbenindustrie, FIAT 764 (PB 60946), *Dyestuffs Manufacturing Processes of I. G. Farbenindustrie A. G.,* 1947.
7. I. G. Farbenindustrie, FIAT 1313 (PB 85172), *German Dyestuffs and Dyestuff Intermediates, including Manufacturing Processes, Plant Design, and Research Data,* 1948.
8. Lubs, "The Chemistry of Synthetic Dyes and Pigments," ACS Monograph, New York, Reinhold Publishing Corp., 1955.
9. Society of Dyers and Colourists and American Association of Textile Chemists and Colorists, "Colour Index," Bradford, England, Lund, Humphries and Co., Inc., 1957.
10. Thorpe and Linstead, "The Synthetic Dyestuffs," 7th ed., Cain and Thorpe, London, Charles Griffin and Co., 1933.
11. Venkataraman, "The Chemistry of Synthetic Dyes," New York, Academic Press, 1952.
12. Vickerstaff, "The Physical Chemistry of Dyeing," 2nd ed., London, Oliver and Boyd, 1954.
13. Zollinger, "Chemie der Azofarbstoffe," Basel and Stuttgart, Birkhäuser Verlag, 1958.

24

THE NUCLEAR INDUSTRY

In collaboration with W. K. Eister[*]

INTRODUCTION

Products

THE PRINCIPAL OBJECTIVE of the nuclear industry is the production of energy; radiation and radioisotopes are important by-products. Energy is used by man to increase his productivity and because of increasing population and industrialization, ever-increasing quantities of energy are required[4,19] (Fig. 24.1). Radiation is a special form of energy associated with the nuclear processes of fission, fusion, and radioactive decay. The uses of radiation include tracing chemical and biological reactions, radiography, catalysis of chemical reactions, medical therapy, and energy sources for satellites and buoys. The vast nuclear industrial system begins with exploration and mining of the raw materials, follows with chemical processing of the ore and other materials, fabrication into fuel and other components for nuclear reactors, the production of energy and radiation in nuclear reactors, and follows through with processing of the spent fuel and disposal of by-products and wastes.

The Fission Reaction

The basic raw material of the nuclear industry is uranium. This material, as it occurs in nature, is composed of several isotopes,[†] among which is the only significant naturally occurring fissionable isotope, uranium-235.[14]

* Chemical Technology Division, Oak Ridge National Laboratory.
† 99.28 atom % U^{238}, 0.71 atom % U^{235}, 0.058 atom % U^{234}.

Absorption of a neutron by U^{235} results in a very unstable nucleus which may split into two smaller "fission fragments," with simultaneous release of neutrons and energy. A typical reaction is:

$$_{92}U^{235} + _{0}n^{1} \rightarrow _{92}U^{236} \rightarrow _{35}Br^{89} + _{57}La^{145} + 2.3n + 192 \text{ Mev}$$

The radiant energy is the result of the conversion of mass into energy, and most of the energy is released at the time of fission. A small amount

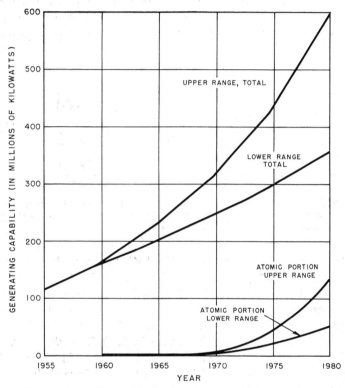

Figure 24.1. Total U. S. electric generating capacity and portion that may be atomic. (*Redrawn from R. McKinney, Peaceful Uses of Atomic Energy, U. S. Government Printing Office, 1956*)

of additional energy, approximately 8 Mev, is subsequently released in the form of β and γ radiations as the fission products undergo a succession of decay processes, resulting finally in stable daughter atoms. If it is assumed that 1 g of U^{235} is fissioned, the total amount of energy produced is approximately

$$\frac{6.02 \times 10^{23} \text{ atoms}}{235 \text{ g}} \frac{200 \text{ Mev}}{\text{atom}} = 5.1 \times 10^{23} \frac{\text{Mev}}{\text{g}}$$

which is equivalent to

$$(5.1 \times 10^{23} \text{ Mev/g})(1.5 \times 10^{-16} \text{ Btu/Mev}) = 7.6 \times 10^{7} \text{ Btu/g}$$

Since 1 ton of bituminous coal will produce 2.8×10^{7} Btu, 1 g of U^{235} may be considered equivalent to about 2.7 tons of coal in available energy content. This energy is generated as heat in the fuel and blanket of the nuclear reactor (Fig. 24.2).

The fission process first came to the attention of the world in 1945 when nuclear bombs were used in the war with Japan. Since that time tremendous resources in time and money have been spent in developing peaceful uses

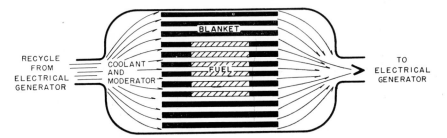

Figure 24.2. Nuclear reactor system. The fissionable material is principally in the fuel section while the fertile material is in the blanket. In many reactors the fissionable and fertile materials are uniformly distributed.

for nuclear energy. Work was begun in 1945 to use nuclear energy in the production of electricity. This objective was realized in 1951 with the Experimental Breeder Reaction in Idaho and in 1953 with the Homogeneous Reactor Experiment at Oak Ridge National Laboratory in Tennessee. Other electric-power-producing reactors were placed in operation in Russia in 1954, in England in 1956, and in France in 1959. The Plowshare program is studying the use of nuclear explosives for excavation of harbors and canals, and the creation of underground heat to extract oil from shale.

The Fusion Reaction

A second important nuclear reaction leading to the production of energy is fusion.[3] In this case, atoms combine to produce a heavier atom, for example, hydrogen isotopes combine to form helium. Again, there is a loss of mass which is converted to energy. A typical fusion reaction is

$$_{1}T^{3} + {}_{1}D^{2} \rightarrow {}_{2}He^{4} + {}_{0}n^{1} + 17.65 \text{ Mev}$$

Extremely high temperatures are required to promote this reaction, and it has been achieved to date only when initiated by a fission bomb explosion. Aggressive research is in progress to develop a device in which to achieve controlled fusion reactions. A major research problem is to develop a "vessel" in which to contain the reaction at the required high temperature. This is being done by a "magnetic bottle," using a very strong magnetic field. Another problem is to maintain the ionized reactant gas free of impurities, which are parasitic poisons; this is solved by carrying out the reactions in high-vacuum systems. A third problem, obtaining the required temperature and particle densities, is being solved by injecting large amounts of energy into the current of ionized gas and magnetically compressing this gas. When the fusion process is achieved, the energy supply for the world may be assured for many centuries; however, it is not yet of technologic significance in the nuclear industry.

Fertile Material

In addition to U^{235}, two other naturally occurring isotopes of major importance to the nuclear industry are U^{238} and thorium-232, known as fertile materials. Their importance lies in the fact that they may be converted to useful fissionable isotopes by neutron irradiation and capture:

$$_{92}U^{238} \xrightarrow{n} {}_{92}U^{239} \xrightarrow[23.5 \text{ m}]{\beta, \gamma} {}_{93}Np^{239} \xrightarrow[2.33 \text{ days}]{\beta, \gamma} {}_{94}Pu^{239}$$

$$_{90}Th^{232} \xrightarrow{n} {}_{90}Th^{233} \xrightarrow[23.3 \text{ m}]{\beta, \gamma} {}_{91}Pa^{233} \xrightarrow[27.4 \text{ days}]{\beta, \gamma} {}_{92}U^{233}$$

Both plutonium-239 and U-233 are fissionable isotopes and may profitably be used to extend the supply of the fissionable material required for nuclear power generation (Table 24.1). The fertile material may be located only

TABLE 24.1. NUCLEAR PROPERTIES OF FISSIONABLE
AND FERTILE MATERIALS*

	σ_{abs}	σ_F	$1 + \alpha$	η	ν
U^{233}	581 ± 7	527 ± 4	1.102 ± 0.005	2.28 ± 0.02	2.51 ± 0.03
U^{235}	694 ± 8	582 ± 6	1.19 ± 0.01	2.07 ± 0.02	2.47 ± 0.03
Pu^{239}	1026 ± 13	746 ± 8	1.38 ± 0.02	2.10 ± 0.02	2.90 ± 0.04
U^{238}	2.71 ± 0.02				
Th^{232}	7.56 ± 0.11				

σ_{abs} = cross section for neutron absorption in barns at a neutron velocity of 2200 meters/sec; one barn = 10^{-24} cm^2

σ_F = cross section for fission in barns at a neutron velocity of 2200 meters/sec

$1 + \alpha = \dfrac{\sigma_{abs}}{\sigma_F}$

η = neutrons emitted/neutrons absorbed

ν = neutrons per atom fissioned

* Neutron Cross Sections, D. J. Hughes and R. B. Schwartz, BNL-325, 7/1/58.

in the blanket region of the reactor, or it may be distributed in both regions (Fig. 24.2).

The Atomic Pile

Controlled nuclear fission was achieved on December 2, 1942 at the University of Chicago by a group of scientists under the guidance of Enrico Fermi. The device in which it was accomplished, then called an "atomic pile," consisted of an ordered pile of graphite and natural uranium cubes and cylinders so arranged that a sustained chain reaction could be obtained and controlled (Fig. 24.3). This chain reaction meant that for every fission

Figure 24.3. Uranium metal fuel from the first atomic pile. This reactor contained 40 tons of uranium oxide along with 6.2 tons of uranium metal. (*ORNL News, 1-01-076*)

event one of the neutrons produced caused a subsequent fission event. Since more than one neutron is produced in fission, some may be absorbed by the fertile isotopes to produce more fissionable isotopes by the processes indicated in the preceding paragraph; others are absorbed by the control rods, structural materials, etc.

Nuclear Reactor Fuel Cycle

The fuel cycle for the nuclear reactor includes three groups of operations (Fig. 24.4). The first group involves uranium and thorium mining, ore milling, feed materials processing, and isotopic separation. Isotopes are now separated on an industrial scale by gaseous diffusion of UF_6, but prior to the birth of atomic energy, isotopic separation was a little-known laboratory curiosity. The second group of operations, fabrication of fuel elements and nuclear reactor operation, includes some chemical steps, but primarily metallurgical and mechanical engineering operations. The third group, operations for recovering the spent fuel, includes chemical operations with the unique problem of processing neutron-irradiated fuels containing large

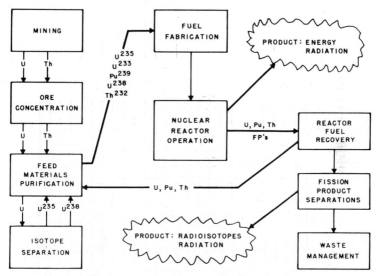

Figure 24.4. Fuel cycle for nuclear power.

amounts of highly radioactive fission products. Fission product separations and radioactive waste management are included in this group.

Nuclear Energy Economics

Considerable effort has been applied to the generation of electric power for civilian applications where nuclear energy must be competitive with energy from other sources (Fig. 24.5). There is a significant demand for electrical energy at costs as high as 1¢ per electrical kw-hr.[23] The fuel cost is about 25 per cent of the final delivered power cost. Therefore, if 1 g of U^{235} produces 1 megawatt-day of heat energy, about $60.00 can be spent for the fuel to produce this amount of energy. The conversion efficiency from thermal to electrical energy is also about 25 per cent; therefore the cost of the fissionable material should be no more than $15.00 per gram. Most of the nuclear material and operating costs are consistent with this objective (Tables 24.2 and 24.3). The higher capital investment in the nuclear power-generating station and the necessity of fuel recycle because of incomplete consumption are two major problems currently preventing the achievement of low-cost electric power from nuclear energy. Unfortunately, the supply of the other nuclear industry products—radioisotopes and

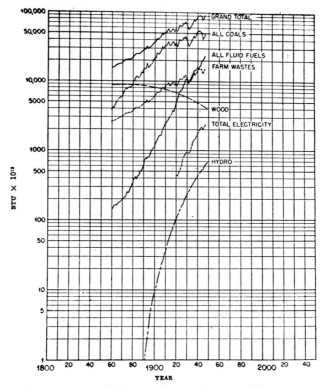

Figure 24.5. Total annual input to the world energy sys-
tem from the major energy sources. (*From P. C. Putnam,
Energy in the Future, Copyright 1953, D. Van Nostrand
Co., Inc., Princeton, N. J.*)

radiation—far exceeds the present demand. Therefore, in the immediate
future at least, the income from these by-products could be only a small
fraction of the total income to a nuclear power industry.

RAW MATERIALS

Uranium and thorium are both relatively abundant in the earth's crust.*
Until the advent of the nuclear reactor, uranium was principally a by-
product of radium, vanadium, and gold mining and its only use was as a
ceramic pigment. Thorium was a by-product of rare earth production and
was used in gas-light mantles. Thorium is believed to be about three times
more plentiful than uranium, but the total known economic reserves of
uranium outside the communist countries are 1,500,000 to 4,000,000 tons

* The uranium concentration in the earth's crust is estimated to be 4 ppm while the
thorium concentration is estimated at 12 ppm. This is the same concentration as zinc,
lead, and tin.

TABLE 24.2. NUCLEAR INDUSTRY MATERIAL PRICES*

Uranium ore, 0.25% U_3O_8, per lb U_3O_8	$ 3.50 †
U_3O_8, 90% mill concentrate, per lb	8.00–11.00 †
UF_4, per kg U	36.25
Uranium metal, per kg U	40.00
UF_6, per kg U	
wt fraction U-235 0.0036 and lower	5.00
0.0050	†6.65
0.0072 (natural)	40.50
0.010	75.75
0.020	220.00
0.030	375.50
0.10	1,529.00
0.20	3,223.00
0.95	16,258.00
Pu metal (price dependent on source and Pu-240 content), per g Pu	12.00–45.00
Thorium ore, 16% Th, per short ton	300.00 ‡
$Th(NO_3)_4$, per lb Th	3.80 ‡
Thorium metal, per lb Th	43.00
U-233 nitrate, per g U^{233}	15.00

* Prices quoted are from OC Doc 54, Classification Guide for Use in the Civilian Application Program, USAEC, 1960, except as otherwise noted.
† From "Atomic Energy Facts," USAEC news letter.
‡ From ASAE-S-4. "Status and Future Requirements for the U-233 Power Reactor Program," D. R. Mash and A. Ottenberg.

TABLE 24.3. NUCLEAR INDUSTRY OPERATING COSTS

Mining, per ton ore	$11.00–20.00 *
Milling, per lb U	7.00–15.00 *
U_3O_8 to $UO_2(NO_3)_2$, per lb U	0.082 †
$UO_2(NO_3)_2$ to UO_3, per lb U	0.023 †
UO_3 to UO_2, per lb U	0.012–0.018 †
UO_2 to UF_4, per lb U	0.124–0.140 †
UF_4 to U metal ingot, per lb U	0.238 †
$UO_2(NO_3)_2$ to UF_6, <5% U-235, per lb U	2.55 ‡
>5% U-235, per lb U	14.55 ‡
$Pu(NO_3)_6$ to Pu metal, per g Pu	1.50 ‡
Fuel fabrication, per kg U-235	962–3960 §
Spent fuel recovery, per kg U	16–2930 ‖
Radioactive liquid waste storage, per gal	0.50–1.50

* From J. C. Johnson, Uranium Production to Match Needs, *Chem. Eng. News*, Dec. 2, 1957, 71–5, Vol. 35, No. 48.
† Direct costs (from C. D. Harrington and A. E. Ruehle, "Uranium Production Technology," D. VanNostrand, New York, 1959) should be doubled to get approximate actual costs.
‡ AEC press release March 12, 1958.
§ Based on ETR plate type fuel and control element costs.
‖ Cost based on daily charge of $15,300 for plant use and two days for plant cleanout from Wash-743, "Summary Report: AEC Reference Fuel Processing Plant."

while known economic thorium reserves are only about 500,000 tons. The smaller thorium reserve reflects the fact that there is still little interest in thorium and consequently little exploration specifically for thorium. Also, the geochemistry of thorium is quite different from that of uranium. The 1959 production in the United States was 33,000 tons of U_3O_8 and about 200 tons of ThO_2.[26]

Uranium

The natural occurrence of uranium in ores falls into two broad economic categories: those from which uranium may be recovered with a market price of $10.00 per pound as U_3O_8; and the very-low-grade uraniferous shale and phosphate deposits which would require an approximate market price of about $50.00.[17] The early known occurrences of uranium were in vein deposits such as the Canadian Great Bear Lake mine, but approximately 90% of all reported reserves are now in sedimentary rocks ranging from pre-Cambrian conglomerates of the South African gold-bearing deposits and Canada to late Tertiary sandstones in the United States.[21]

Extraction from Ore

The uranium is extracted from the ore by grinding, chemical leaching, separation, precipitation, and calcination (Fig. 24.6).[9] The common leaching reagents are sulfuric acid and sodium carbonate, the choice being based

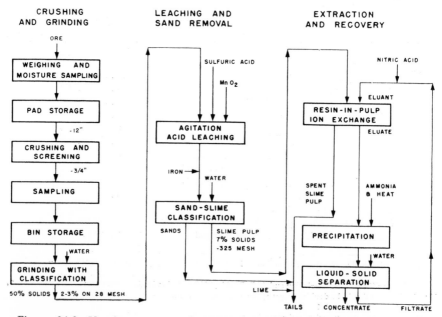

Figure 24.6. Uranium recovery from ore by acid leaching and ion exchange. Uranium Reduction Company, Moah, Utah. (*From J. W. Clegg and D. C. Foley, Uranium Ore Processing, 1958, Addison-Wesley, Reading, Mass.*)

largely on the metallurgical characteristics of the ore. About 70 per cent of the ore is treated by the sulfuric-acid route. In a typical case the ore is ground to —28 mesh for acid leaching and to —200 mesh for carbonate leaching. The uranium is recovered from the leach liquor by three principal processes: solvent extraction, ion exchange, and precipitation. The uranium product in all cases is precipitated, dried, and shipped to feed plants for further processing.

The uranium ore is processed in mills located near the mines. In 1960 there were 25 privately owned mills operating or under construction in the United States, representing a capital investment of $141,820,000, with a processing capacity of 22,100 tons. Since 1943 the USAEC has purchased 126,000 tons of U_3O_8, of which 45,000 tons was produced in the United States.

Processes for Sulfate Liquor. The uranium is recovered from sulfuric acid leach liquor by solvent extraction or ion exchange (Fig. 24.7). The

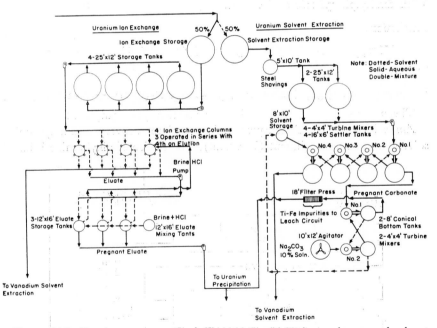

Figure 24.7. Uranium recovery from ore leach liquor by ion exchange and solvent extraction. Shiprock Mill Process of the Kerr-McGee Oil Industries. (*From J. W. Clegg and D. D. Foley, Uranium Ore Processing, 1958, Addison-Wesley, Reading, Mass.*)

solvent extraction process, the simpler and more flexible process, is carried out in mixer-settlers. This flexibility is particularly important when the ore contains other values such as vanadium, found in many Colorado Plateau ores, and thorium, found in the Blind River ore. An outstanding advantage of ion exchange when carried out in the Resin-in-Pulp (RIP) equipment is that it requires considerably less clarification of the feed liquor.

Solvent Extraction Methods. The solvent extraction processes employ either alkyl amines or alkyl phosphate as the solvent.[10] These solvents are best characterized as liquid ion exchange reagents, the amine acting as an anion exchanger and the phosphate as a cation exchanger. Typical reactions with an alkyl tertiary amine solvent are:

Extraction:

$$UO_2(SO_4)_{2(aq)}^= + (R_3NH)_2SO_{4(org)} \rightleftarrows (R_3NH)_2UO_2(SO_4)_{2(org)} + SO_4^=$$

Stripping:

$$(R_3NH)_2UO_2(SO_4)_{2(org)} + 4Na_2CO_{3(aq)} \rightleftarrows$$
$$Na_4UO_2(CO_3)_{3(aq)} + 2R_3N_{(org)} + 2Na_2SO_{4(aq)} + H_2O + CO_2$$

With dialkylphosphoric acid solvent:

Extraction:

$$UO_{2(aq)}^{++} + 2HOOP(OR)_{2(org)} \rightleftarrows UO_2[OOP(OR)_2]_{2(org)} + 2H_{(aq)}^+$$

Stripping:

$$UO_2[OOP(OR)_2]_{2(org)} + 3Na_2CO_{3(aq)} \rightleftarrows Na_4UO_2(CO_3)_3 + 2NaOOP(OR)_2$$

The processes are carried out in mixer-settler type equipment.

Amex Process. The Amex process for uranium recovery uses alkyl amine solvent in a kerosene diluent (Fig. 24.8). The choice of alkyl amine is based

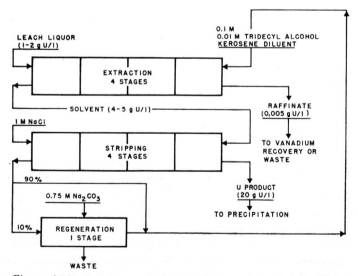

Figure 24.8. Amex process for uranium recovery from sulfuric acid leach liquor.

on extraction power and selectivity, solubility, availability and price, and triisooctylamine represents a reasonable process reagent (Table 24.4). The kerosene diluent is required to control the physical properties of the organic phase.

Dapex Process. The Dapex process for uranium and vanadium recovery uses di-2-ethylhexyl phosphoric acid (D2EHPA) as the active solvent and also uses kerosene as a diluent. Modifying reagents may be added to the

TABLE 24.4. AMINE EXTRACTANT PROPERTIES

Aqueous Phase: 1 M $SO_4^=$, pH 1
Amine concentration in kerosene: 0.1 M
Solvent solubility in 1 M $SO_4^=$, pH 1:

Primary branched amine	50 mg/liter
Secondary amine, medium branched	5
Highly branched	15
Tertiary amine	15

Extraction Coefficients (E_a°)

		Secondary Amine			
Metal Ion	Branched Primary Amine	Straight	Medium Branched	Highly Branched	Tertiary Amine
U(VI)	25	90	110	130	100
Th*	5000	...	5000	10	0.1
V(V)	...	1	1	1	1
V(pH 2)	...	...	20	20	20
Mo(VI)	200	200	200	200	200
Fe(III)	40	0.5	0.5	0.1	0.1
Zr*	50	50	...	50	50
R.E.(III)	20	...	0.01	0.01	0.01
Mg, Ca. Al, Zn, (Fe, Mn, Co, Ni, Cu) (II), V(IX), Cr(III)			<0.01		

* Aqueous phase 0.5 M H_2SO_4.

solvent to increase its extraction power or to increase the solubility of the organic complex in the organic phase (Table 24.5). The flowsheet procedure is quite similar to Amex.

Ion Exchange Methods. Ion exchange for the recovery of uranium in this country is carried out primarily in Resin-in-Pulp equipment developed in the Raw Materials Pilot Plant, Grand Junction, Colorado to eliminate the need for a clear leach liquor. There are several fixed bed ion exchange plants but these were built before the RIP equipment was developed. In the RIP process $-10 + 20$ mesh resin is contained in wire screen baskets which are slowly sloshed up and down in a flowing stream of uranium-bearing leach pulp liquor. The baskets in the Moab plant of the Uranium Reduction Company are $6 \times 6 \times 6$ ft.[22] Each stage contains 4 baskets, and there are 10 sorption and 4 elution stages. The liquor is prepared by leaching ore ground to -28 mesh with sulfuric acid which dissolves about 95 per cent of the uranium, and is only partially clarified by a combination of gravity settlers and hydroclone equipment to remove the $+325$

TABLE 24.5. MODIFYING REAGENTS FOR EXTRACTION OF URANIUM
WITH D2EHPA*

Aqueous solution: 0.5 M $SO_4^=$, pH $= 1$
Organic solvent: 0.1 M D2EHPA $+ 0.1$ M synergistic reagent

Modifying Reagent	E_e° (U)
None	135
Tributyl phosphate	500
Dibutyl phosphonate	1700
Butyl phosphinate	3500
Butyl phosphine oxide (0.05 M)	7000
2-ethylhexanol †	40

* D2EHPA = di-2-ethylhexyl phosphoric acid.
† To increase uranium complex solubility and speed of phase separation.

material. A typical feed to the ion exchange process contains 5 to 10 wt per cent solids.

$$UO_2(SO_4)_3^{4-} + 4RNO_3 \rightarrow R_4UO_2(SO_4)_3 + 4NO_3^-$$

The uranium is sorbed on the resin at a pH of 1.4 to 1.6 and is eluted with a nitrate solution at pH 1.2.

Carbonate Leach Process. The use of sodium carbonate and sodium bicarbonate solutions for leaching uranium ores was one of the first industrial processes for recovering uranium. The chemical reactions are

Oxidation: $2UO_2 + O_2 \rightarrow 2UO_3$
Leaching: $UO_3 + Na_2CO_3 + 2NaHCO_3 \rightarrow Na_4UO_2(CO_3)_3 + H_2O$
Precipitation: $Na_4UO_2(CO_3)_3 + 4NaOH \rightarrow Na_2UO_4 + 3Na_2CO_3 + 2H_2O$
Liquor regeneration: $Na_2CO_3 + NaOH + CO_2 \rightarrow Na_2CO_3 + NaHCO_3$

The alkaline reagent is more specific for uranium than sulfuric acid, and for many ores further purification by ion exchange or solvent extraction is not required. Early disadvantages were the long leaching time and the necessity of clarifying the leach liquor. The leaching time, about 70 hr in air-agitated Pachuca tanks, may be cut to 7 hr by using autoclaves

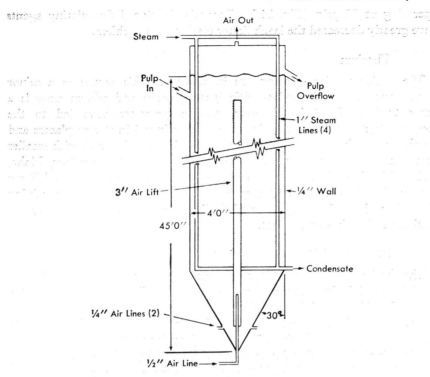

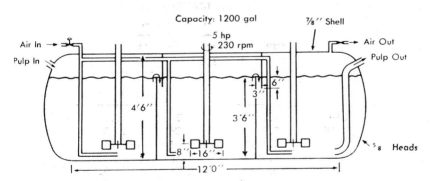

Figure 24.9. Pachuca and autoclave equipment for carbonate leachings of uranium ore. (*From J. W. Clegg and D. D. Foley, Uranium Ore Processing, 1958, Addison-Wesley, Reading, Mass.*)

operating at 50 psig (Fig. 24.9). Recently developed flocculating agents have greatly decreased the leach liquor clarification problem.

Thorium

The major thorium-bearing ore is monazite. This occurs as a minor constituent in granitic and syenitic igneous rocks and seldom exceeds a concentration of 0.1%. However, erosion processes have led to the concentration of this less chemically reactive mineral in stream placers and beach sands. These are located primarily in India and Brazil, with smaller occurrences in many other parts of the world, e.g., in the Carolinas, Idaho, and California.[17] Another source of thorium is the Canadian Blind River ore which, when leached with sulfuric acid, gives a solution containing about 1 g of uranium and 0.2 g of thorium per liter. In this recovery operation thorium is a by-product.

FEED MATERIALS PROCESSING

The feed materials operations are concerned with the preparation of special materials for nuclear reactor components. This includes the fertile and fissionable materials as well as unique materials for use as coolants, moderators and structure. The attention in this chapter is limited to normal uranium and thorium. The technology for plutonium and enriched uranium is similar to that for uranium with special provisions for criticality prevention. Other materials of interest include the neutron moderators such as carbon (graphite), deuterium, and beryllium; neutron poisons such as

TABLE 24.6. THERMAL NEUTRON CROSS SECTIONS* OF TYPICAL NUCLEAR REACTOR MATERIALS, BARNS†

	σ_f	σ_c		
U^{235}	590	108		
U^{233}	520	60		
Pu^{239}	730	300		

	σ_c		σ_c
U^{238}	2.8	B	755
Th^{232}	7.5	Cd	3300
C	0.0032	Hf	105
Be	0.010	Al	0.023
H	0.33	Zr	0.18
D	0.00057	Fe	2.5
Na	0.53	Ni	4.6
K	2.0	Cr	3.1
He	0.007	Xe	35
N	1.9	O	0.0002

*σ_f = cross section for fission; σ_c = cross section for capture.
† 1 barn = 10^{-24} cm².

boron, cadmium, and hafnium; coolants such as sodium, potassium, helium, water (hydrogen and oxygen), air (nitrogen and oxygen) and carbon dioxide (carbon and oxygen); and structural materials such as aluminum, zirconium and stainless steel (iron, chromium and nickel). The nuclear property of interest in all these materials is their cross section for capture of neutrons (Table 24.6).

Uranium Feed Materials

Uranium feed materials operations are concerned principally with the production of uranium metal and uranium (IV) oxide of varying U-235 content.[15] The feed to this operational phase is uranium concentrate from the ore mills and uranium recovered from spent nuclear reactor fuel. The

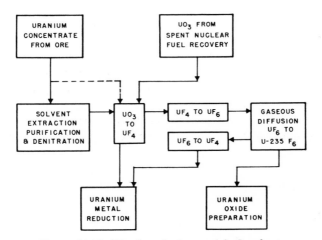

Figure 24.10. Uranium feed materials flowsheet.

chemical operations are uranyl nitrate purification by solvent extraction, denitration to UO_3, hydrogen reduction of UO_3 to UO_2, hydrofluorination of UO_2 to UF_4, reduction of UF_4 to metal by magnesium, fluorination of UF_4 to UF_6, isotopic separation of uranium-235 by gaseous diffusion, and reduction of UF_6 to UF_4, UO_2, and metal after isotopic enrichment (Fig. 24.10). Recovery of scrap material from subsequent fuel fabrication operations is considered a feed materials operation.

The principal feed plants for metal production are located at Weldon Springs, Mo. and Fernald, Ohio. The feed plants for UF_6 production and isotopic separation are located at Oak Ridge, Tennessee and Paducah, Kentucky. These are the property of the United States Government. In addition, there are several other small plants owned and operated by private industry to serve the civilian nuclear power program.

Uranium Solvent Extraction. The solvent extraction feed is the crude uranium concentrate from the mills. The solvent extraction product must meet metal specifications since no significant purification is achieved in the subsequent chemical conversions. The ore concentrate is dissolved in nitric acid and solvent-extracted with tributyl phosphate (TBP) in a kerosene or hexane diluent:

$$UO_{2(aq)}^{++} + 2NO_{3(aq)}^{-} + 2TBP_{org} \rightleftharpoons UO_2(NO_3)_2 \cdot 2TBP_{(org)}$$

This is an easily reversible reaction, directly dependent on the salting ion (NO_3^-) concentration in the aqueous phase. The salting agent is nitric acid.

The extraction is very specific for uranium providing decontamination factors of 10^3 to 10^5. The uranium is extracted into the solvent, leaving most other ions in the aqueous phase; the extract is scrubbed with a small amount of water solution for further purification and the uranium is then stripped from the solvent with sufficient water to give good uranium recovery (Fig. 24.11). The product is an aqueous uranyl nitrate solution.

Uranium Denitration. Denitration of the uranyl nitrate product from solvent extraction involves evaporation followed by calcining. The evaporation is carried out to a final boiling point of 120° to 143° C (9.8 to 12.5 lb U/gal) and the residue is transferred to a stirred pot calciner that is heated to 621° C:

$$UO_2(NO_3)_2 \cdot 6H_2O \xrightarrow[621°\,C]{\Delta} UO_3 + NO_2 + NO + O_2 + 6H_2O$$

Other calciner types in use include the stirred-trough and fluidized-bed, with increasing use of the fluidized bed expected (Fig. 24.12). The type of equipment and processing conditions significantly affect the physical properties of the UO_3 and, therefore, the kinetics of the subsequent reactions in the production of UO_2, UF_4, and metal.

UO_3 Conversion to UF_4. UF_4 is produced from the denitration product UO_3 by reducing to UO_2 with hydrogen and then hydrofluorinating to UF_4:

$$UO_3 + H_2 \xrightarrow{650°\,C} UO_2 + H_2O$$
$$UO_2 + 4HF \xrightarrow{370°-590°\,C} UF_4 + 2H_2O$$

These gas-solid reactions are carried out continuously in stirred-trough or fluidized-bed reactors. The fluidized bed provides better temperature control of the hydrogen reduction reaction and has almost entirely replaced the stirred trough in this step (Fig. 24.13). In the hydrofluorination step,

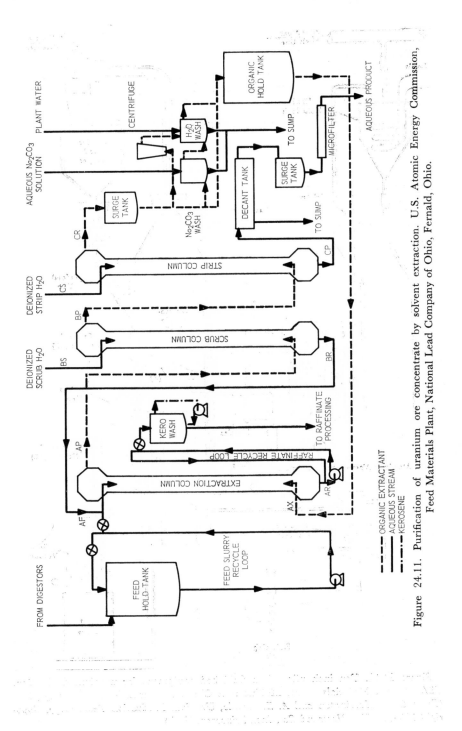

Figure 24.11. Purification of uranium ore concentrate by solvent extraction. U.S. Atomic Energy Commission, Feed Materials Plant, National Lead Company of Ohio, Fernald, Ohio.

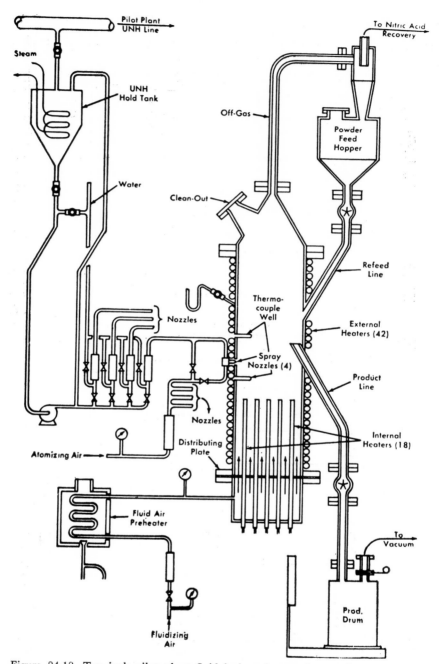

Figure 24.12. Ten inch pilot plant fluid bed equipment for uranium denitration. USAEC Feed Materials Plant, Mallinckrodt Chemical Works, Weldon Springs, Mo. (*From C. D. Harrington and A. E. Ruehle, Uranium Production Technology, Copyright 1959, D. Van Nostrand Co., Inc., Princeton, N. J.*)

the stirred trough still predominates (Fig. 24.14), although the fluidized bed has some economic advantages.

Reduction to Uranium Metal. Uranium metal is produced from UF_4 by reduction with magnesium:

$$UF_4 + 2Mg \rightarrow U \text{ metal} + 2MgF_2 \ (\Delta H_{298} = -83.5 \text{ kcal})$$

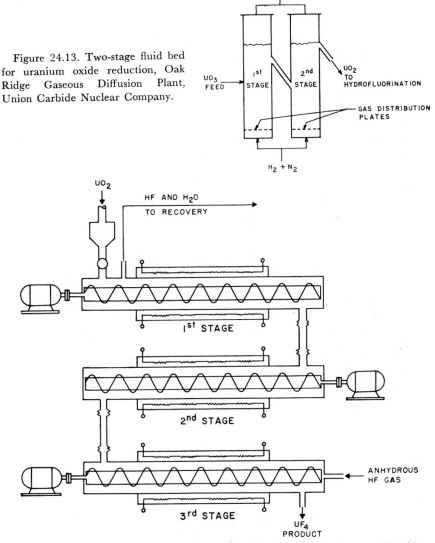

Figure 24.13. Two-stage fluid bed for uranium oxide reduction, Oak Ridge Gaseous Diffusion Plant, Union Carbide Nuclear Company.

Figure 24.14. Continuous stirred bed hydrofluorinator for uranium tetrafluoride production. (*Courtesy National Lead Co. of Ohio*)

This is a batch process, carried out in a steel reactor lined with the reaction by-product, magnesium fluoride (Fig. 24.15). The resulting uranium regulus, called the "derby" or "dingot," is remelted, held at 1454° C in a vacuum furnace to vaporize and remove impurities, and then recast in a graphite mold to produce the ingot. The ingot is fabricated into reactor fuel by extrusion, rolling-mill operations, and machining. The standard reduction process, which produces a 50-lb derby, was scaled up in 1956 to produce a 3000-lb dingot as the result of a Mallinckrodt development. Both reduction procedures are in use today.

GREEN SALT REDUCTION

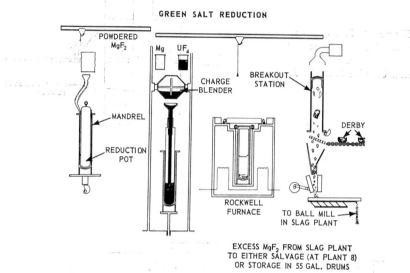

Figure 24.15. Derby process for uranium metal production. U.S. Atomic Energy Commission Feed Materials Plant, National Lead of Ohio.

UF₆ Production. When the reactor fuel is to be enriched in U^{235}, the other isotopes in natural uranium are separated from the U^{235} by gaseous diffusion of UF_6. The UF_6 feed for the gaseous diffusion plant is produced by reacting powdered UF_4 with 25 to 50 per cent excess fluorine introduced into the top of a tower reactor (Fig. 24.16):

$$UF_4 + F_2 \rightarrow UF_6 \ (\Delta H° = -60 \text{ kcal})$$

The reaction vessel temperature is maintained between 460 and 530° C, and the UF_6 product is collected by condensing in a cold-trap at −18° to −48° C.

Alternative Feed Materials Processes

Several alternative methods of uranium tetrafluoride and uranium hexafluoride preparation include the Excer and the fluidized-bed fluorination process. The Excer process, an aqueous process now used by the Japanese, uses ion exchange to convert uranium ore concentrate to uranium tetrafluoride for purification and conversion to UO_2Cl_2, electrolytic reduction, UF_4 precipitation, and drying (Fig. 24.17). Its principal ad-

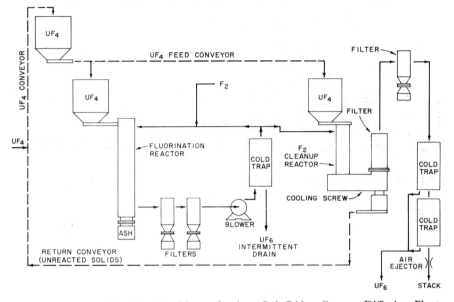

Figure 24.16. Uranium hexafluoride production. Oak Ridge Gaseous Diffusion Plant, Union Carbide Nuclear Co.

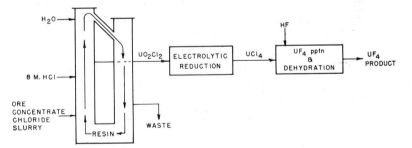

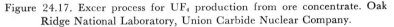

Figure 24.17. Excer process for UF_4 production from ore concentrate. Oak Ridge National Laboratory, Union Carbide Nuclear Company.

vantage is its operational simplicity and less drastic process problems of temperature, atmosphere, and corrosion control.

In the fluidized-bed fluorination process, uranium hexafluoride is produced by direct hydrogen reduction of the uranium ore concentrate, followed by hydrofluorination and fluorination in fluidized beds. Some purification is achieved in each step, with final cleanup by distillation of the UF_6 product. This process eliminates the solvent extraction and denitration steps, but presents problems in fluidized bed operation due to the caking and slagging tendency of the ore concentrate impurities which form low melting fluorides.

Separation of Uranium-235

A unique engineering development in the nuclear industry, aside from the nuclear reactor, is the gaseous diffusion process for separating the uranium isotopes.[2] This phase of the nuclear industry represents 32 per cent, 2.3 billion dollars, of the federal government's capital investment in the nuclear industry. The plants are located at Oak Ridge, Tennessee, Paducah, Kentucky, and Portsmouth, Ohio.

The process is operated at reduced pressure and elevated temperature. The uranium hexafluoride gas flows past a barrier, through which about half is allowed to diffuse by control of the pressure drop across the barrier. The gas passing through the barrier is enriched in U^{235}. The separation is dependent on the difference in diffusion rates of the U^{235} and U^{238} when passing through a permeable membrane, the "diffusion barrier." The difference in diffusion rate is directly related to the molecular weights, and the maximum separation, α, of U^{235} hexafluoride from U^{238} hexafluoride is

$$\alpha = \sqrt{\frac{235 + 6 \times 19}{238 + 6 \times 19}} = 1.0043$$

This is equivalent to the separation across a single theoretical stage from the enriched to the depleted stream. The number of stages required in an ideal cascade[9] is determined from the heads separation factor, β, which is equivalent to the separation gain from the feed to the enriched stream. For U^{235}, $\beta = \sqrt{\alpha} = 1.0021$. The numbers of stages in the stripping and enriching sections are given by

$$N_{stripping} = \frac{\ln X_F(1 - X_W)/(1 - X_F)X_W}{\ln \beta} - 1$$

$$N_{enriching} = \frac{\ln X_P(1 - X_F)/(1 - X_P)X_F}{\ln \beta}$$

where X = the atom fraction, F = the feed fraction, W = the waste fraction and, P = the product fraction. It is apparent that a large number of stages is required for this separation. It is therefore important to taper the plant to minimize the material inventory in the plant. This, in turn, decreases the time required to bring the plant to equilibrium, the capital investment in the plant, and the operating cost.

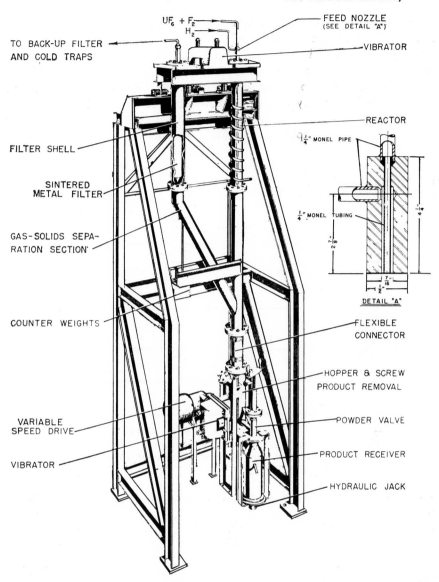

UF$_6$ + F$_2$ →
H$_2$
FEED NOZZLE
(SEE DETAIL "A")
TO BACK-UP FILTER
AND COLD TRAPS
VIBRATOR
REACTOR
$\frac{1}{4}$" MONEL PIPE
FILTER SHELL
SINTERED
METAL FILTER
$\frac{1}{4}$" MONEL TUBING
GAS-SOLIDS SEPA-
RATION SECTION
DETAIL "A"
COUNTER WEIGHTS
FLEXIBLE
CONNECTOR
HOPPER & SCREW
PRODUCT REMOVAL
POWDER VALVE
VARIABLE
SPEED DRIVE
PRODUCT RECEIVER
VIBRATOR
HYDRAULIC JACK

Figure 24.18. Six to four hot wall reactor. (*Courtesy Union Carbide Nuclear Co.,*
Oak Ridge Gaseous Diffusion Plant)

UF$_6$ Reduction to UF$_4$. The UF$_6$ products from gaseous diffusion are
converted back to UF$_4$ by continuous reaction in a tower reactor with 100
per cent excess hydrogen.[15] While the reaction

$$UF_6 + H_2 \rightarrow UF_4 + 2HF \ (\Delta H° = -43.9 \text{ kcal})$$

is exothermic, it is necessary to add energy. This is accomplished by adding 0.05 to 0.08 lb of fluorine per lb of uranium hexafluoride. The reactor wall temperature is maintained at 650° C and the reactor vibrated to prevent the buildup of reaction products on the walls. The UF$_4$ product is collected in a receiver at the bottom of the column (Fig. 24.18). The anhydrous hydrogen fluoride produced as a by-product is recovered for re-use in hydrofluorination.

Conversion to UO$_2$. The production of uranium (IV) oxide for nuclear fuel is particularly important to power reactors which operate at high

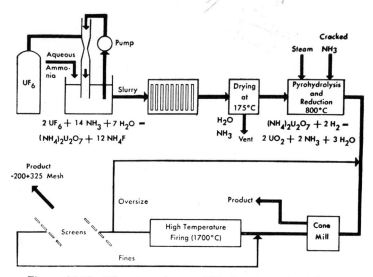

Figure 24.19. UF$_6$ conversion to UO$_2$ by ammonium diuranate precipitation. Feed Materials Plant, Mallinckrodt Chemical Works. [*From C. D. Harrington, Fuel Elements Conference, USAEC Report TID-7546, BK 2, 369 (1957)*.]

temperatures. Uranium(IV) oxide has greater chemical and physical stability than uranium metal, and these factors override the disadvantage of lower neutron economy. To compensate for the loss of neutron economy, it is usual practice to use uranium with a slightly higher U-235 content. The uranium hexafluoride is converted to uranium(IV) oxide by hydrolyzing in an aqueous ammonia solution to precipitate ammonium diuranate which is reduced and calcined to uranium(IV) oxide (Fig. 24.19):

$$2UF_6 + 14NH_3 + 7H_2O \rightarrow (NH_4)_2U_2O_7 + 12NH_4F$$
$$(NH_4)_2U_2O_7 + 2H_2 \rightarrow 2UO_2 + 2NH_3 + 3H_2O$$

The oxide is ground to provide the optimum material for preparation of high-density oxide pellets. Close control of many empirical factors in this operation is necessary to produce a material having the desired properties.

Thorium Feed Material Processing

Thorium is at present essentially a by-product of rare-earth recovery from monazite. The process involves grinding the ore to —200 to —325 mesh followed by leaching with sulfuric acid. The thorium, rare earths, and uranium are recovered by precipitation (Fig. 24.20). The crude thorium

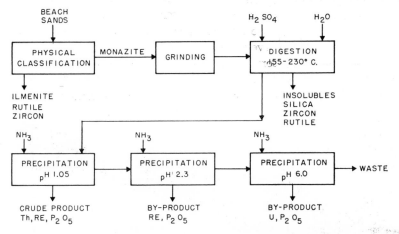

Figure 24.20. Thorium recovery from monazite ore.

product is purified by solvent extraction with tributyl phosphate from a nitric acid solution.

Conversion to Thorium Oxide and Metal. Thorium is usually converted to the oxide for use in a nuclear reactor. The thorium, obtained as $Th(NO_3)_4 \cdot 4H_2O$, is precipitated as the oxalate and calcined to yield ThO_2. The technology of producing thorium metal is not well developed. In the past, thorium oxide was reacted with anhydrous hydrofluoric acid to produce limited amounts of thorium tetrafluoride. This was reduced using calcium metal, with $ZnCl_2$ as a booster, in a dolomite-lined steel bomb to produce a thorium-zinc alloy containing about 2 per cent of zinc. Purification of the thorium metal is difficult and involves de-zincing under vacuum at 1200° C, melting, recasting of the thorium at about 1800° C, and arc-melting for final purification. The reaction of ThO_2 with calcium metal is attractive as an alternate process but has not been completely developed.

THE NUCLEAR REACTOR

Nuclear reactors are classified as burners, converters, and breeders, based on the isotopes used as fuels. The burners are fueled with separated U^{235}, containing insignificant amounts of fertile isotopes, and include most research, test, portable and mobile reactors. Converters use fuel elements containing natural or partially enriched uranium and include the plutonium production reactors at Hanford and Savannah River, as well as the stationary nuclear power reactors now in operation in the United States, Britain, France, and Russia. The fuel material is U^{235}, the fertile material is U^{238}, and Pu^{239} is produced as a by-product fuel material. However, several converter reactors using the U^{235}-Th^{232}-U^{233} conversion cycle will soon be in operation. A breeder is a special type of converter in which more fissionable isotopes are produced than consumed, a condition that is possible because on the average more than two neutrons arise from a fission event. However, breeding is difficult to achieve in practice because of neutron losses by leakage from the reactor, absorption in the reactor materials of construction, absorption in fission products or other isotopes produced as a result of fission or capture, and some non-fission absorption in the fissionable isotopes.

Figure 24.21. N. S. Savannah prototype fuel element. This element contains 164 tubes filled with UO_2 pellets (4.4% U-235). (*Courtesy Atomic Energy Division, The Babcock and Wilcox Co.*)

Breeding was demonstrated in 1951 by the Argonne National Laboratory in the Experimental Breeder Reactor, using a fast neutron flux and the U^{238}-Pu^{239} conversion cycle. Breeding is also the objective of the Homogeneous Reactor, studied at Oak Ridge National Laboratory, which uses a thermal neutron flux and the Th^{232}-U^{233} conversion cycle.

Other systems of reactor classification include: solid or heterogeneous and fluid or homogeneous, based on the physical state of the fuel; the neutron energy in the fission capture process, e.g., fast, intermediate, and thermal; and the type of coolant, e.g., gas, pressurized water, boiling water, organic, and liquid metal. The fuel for the heterogeneous, solid-fuel, nuclear-power reactor is principally in the form of long cylindrical rods or thin plates. The homogeneous fluid-fuel nuclear power reactors have as their fuels aqueous, molten-salt, or molten metal solutions or slurries. The principal advantage of the solid fuel is that the container for the fissionable material is an integral part of the element and is replaced each time the reactor fuel is replaced. One advantage of fluid fuels is lower fabrication

TABLE 24.7. FUEL AND BLANKET ELEMENTS FOR NUCLEAR POWER REACTORS

Reactor	Fuel Shape	Fissionable Material				Fertile Material			Burnup, Mwd/t	Conversion, %
		Type	Wt, kg	Enrichment, %	Clad	Type	Wt, metric tons	Clad		
APS	Rod	U metal	27.5	5	...	...	1.15	SS	...	...
S2W	Plate	U-Zr	...	...	Zr	...	...	...	...	...
PWR	Plate	UO_2	175	0.7	...	...	14.2	Zr	3,000	85
Yankee	Rod	UO_2	685	3	...	...	22.8	SS	8,200	69
NS Savannah	Rod	UO_2	312	4.4	...	...	7.1	SS	7,400	35
CETR	Rod	UO_2	1100	93	...	ThO_2	15.1	SS	18,000	50
EBWR	Plate	U-Zr	82	1.4	...	...	5.7	Zr	10,000	70
Dresden	Rod	UO_2	900	1.5	...	...	60	Zr	10,000	60
Pathfinder	Rod	U-SS	135	93	SS	U-AL*	...	Al	...	...
Humboldt	Rod	UO_2	241	2.1	...	...	13.8	...	15,000	...
EBR I	Rod	U-Zr	52	91	Zr	U	5	SS	0.01	100 ± 4
EBR II	Rod	Fissium	170	47	Zr	U†	28.1	SS	0.12	120
Fermi	Rod	U-Mo	444	47	Zr	...	45.2	SS	0.1	112
SRE	Rod	U	84	2.8	...	...	3.0	SS	3,500	50
Hallam	Rod	U-Mo	948	3	...	...	25.5	SS	3,000	50
OMRE	Plate	U-SS	25.5	93	SS	...	...	...	(12.5%)	...
Calder Hall	Rod	U	910	0.7	...	...	130	Mg	...	...
G2	Rod	U	840	0.7	...	...	120	Mg	...	79
Hinkley Point	Rod	U-Al	2630	0.7	...	...	376	Mg	3,000	85
HRGR	Rod	UO_2	246	2.2	...	...	11.2	SS	10,000	55
HRE	Sol'n	UO_2SO_4	3.6	93	...	...	...	...	...	...

* 1.8% U-235.
† 0.36% U-235.

cost, but the container for fluid fuels is a permanent part of the reactor and must maintain its integrity over the operating life of the reactor.

Heterogeneous Fuel Types

The heterogeneous fuel element is designed to achieve maximum heat transfer from the fuel to the coolant, so that in most cases they resemble shell-and-tube heat exchangers (Fig. 24.21).

Other important considerations in the fabrication of solid fuel elements include heat generation rate, quantity of energy produced, operating tem-

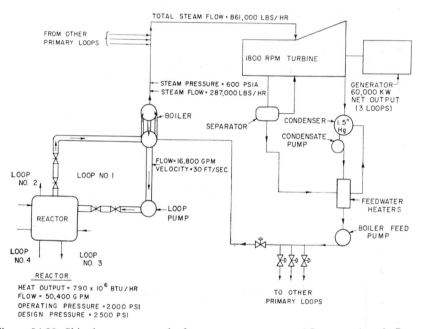

Figure 24.22. Shippingport pressurized water reactor system. (*Courtesy Atomic Power Division, Westinghouse Electric Corp.*)

perature, physical stability, chemical stability, corrosion resistance, fabrication cost, processing cost, and neutron economy. Aside from the British gas-cooled reactors, there are no two power reactors operating, under construction, or seriously proposed in the world using the same fuel elements. In addition, significant changes are being made in succeeding fuel cores for a single reactor. The type most commonly used in pressurized water reactors employs uranium oxide pellets in stainless steel tubes brazed together in bundles (Table 24.7). Zirconium, because of its lower neutron capture cross section, will probably replace stainless steel as soon as fabrication techniques are improved. Uranium-impregnated graphite fuel, expected to permit higher operating temperatures, is being studied for use in gas-cooled reactors.

Power Reactors

The predominant types of nuclear power reactors operating, under construction, and proposed, use pressurized water or gas as the coolant (Table 24.8). Other operating types use liquid sodium or organic coolants. The greatest development effort in the United States is now on the pressurized

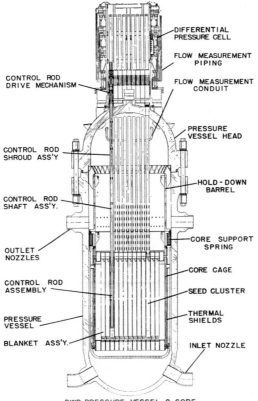

PWR PRESSURE VESSEL & CORE

Figure 24.23. Shippingport pressurized water reactor. Arrangement of core and control elements in the pressure vessel. (*Courtesy Atomic Power Division, Westinghouse Electric Corp.*)

water reactor and it is anticipated that this type will be very important in the development of nuclear power. However, Great Britain has successfully used gas-cooled reactors for the dual purposes of plutonium production and power production.

The conversion factor is also important, and on this basis the Enrico Fermi sodium-cooled reactor is unique. It is the only breeder nuclear power reactor proposed or under construction. However, it will operate only about 50 per cent of the time because the operating life of its fuel load is only

TABLE 24.8. FEATURES OF NUCLEAR POWER REACTORS

Coolant	Reactor	Location	Startup Date	Operation						
				Coolant Outlet Temp., °F	Coolant Inlet Pressure, psig	Energy Production				Time between Shutdowns, weeks
						Therm., Mw	Elec., Mw	Eff., %		
Pressurized water circulating	APS	Russia	1954	518	146	30	5	16.7		8
	S2W	Submarine	1955	...	...	...	...	...		...
	PWR	Shippingport, Pa.	1947	468	585	231	60	26		25
	Yankee	Rowe, Mass.	1960	533	2000	392	110	27		68
	NS Savannah	Ship	1960	...	...	69	22	...		118
	CETR	Indian Point, N. Y.	1961	521	1549	795	255	30		104
Pressurized water boiling	EBWR	Chicago, Ill.	1956	489	...	20	4.5	22.5		...
	Dresden	Morris, Ill.	1959	546	1027	626	180	29		36
	Elk River	Elk River, Minn.	1961	...	...	73	22	29		...
	Pathfinder	Sioux Falls, S. Dak.	1962	825	...	203	62	30.5		24
	Humboldt Bay	Eureka, Calif.	1962	548	...	193	60	31		28
Sodium	EBR-I	NRTS, Idaho	1951	601	13	1.2	0.2	17		...
	EBR-II	NRTS, Idaho	1960	900	57	62.5	17.4	28		16
	SRE	Los Angeles, Calif.	1958	950	6	20	6	28.6		...
	Enrico Fermi	Monroe, Mich.	1961	800	82	300	90	30		1
	Hallam	Hallam, Neb.	1962	945	27	254	76	30		26
Organic	OMRE	NRTS, Idaho	1958	710	200	12	...	...		...
	Piqua	Piqua, Ohio	1962	548	...	45.5	11.4	25		...
Gas	Calder Hall	England	1956	637	115	180	35	19.2		...
	G2	Marcoule, France	1959	740	213	200	32	20		...
	Hinkley Point	England	1962	675	185	980	250	25		...
	HRGR	Peach Bottom, Pa.	1963	1050	315	92	28.5	31		*
Homogeneous	HRE-I, HRT	Oak Ridge, Tenn.	1953	482	1000	1	0.14	14		*

* Refueled while operating.

about one week. Most of the other reactors, including other sodium-cooled systems, operate 26 to 100 weeks before being refueled, and refueling during operation has been proposed in some cases. A common advantage of the sodium- and organic-cooled reactors is that they attain the high temperatures required for efficient electrical generation at low system pressures. However, the chemical stability of these coolants is poor.[7]

Reactor Safety

A very special aspect of nuclear power reactor operation is safety. Power reactors are located near large population centers and accidental release of

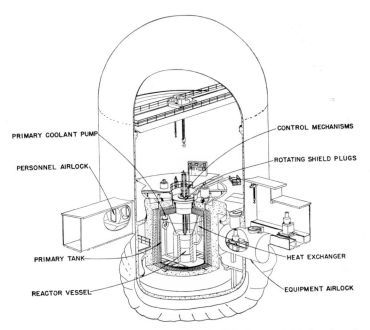

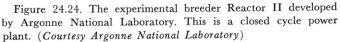

PRIMARY COOLANT PUMP

PERSONNEL AIRLOCK

PRIMARY TANK

REACTOR VESSEL

CONTROL MECHANISMS

ROTATING SHIELD PLUGS

HEAT EXCHANGER

EQUIPMENT AIRLOCK

Figure 24.24. The experimental breeder Reactor II developed by Argonne National Laboratory. This is a closed cycle power plant. (*Courtesy Argonne National Laboratory*)

their contained radioactivity would create public health problems and might contaminate large amounts of economically valuable property. To minimize this possibility, at least two lines of complete containment are required outside the reactor system. All radioactivity is contained in the primary containment zone and all effluents from the system are monitored before discharge. An emergency storage system is provided for contaminated effluents. The secondary containment zone contains no radioactivity under normal conditions, but this zone is so designed that it will contain the maximum credible accident. The primary container is usually a large steel pressure vessel in which the reactor, radiation shield, and coolant system are located. This is surrounded by the secondary container, a building with a controlled ventilation system (Fig. 24.24).

RADIOCHEMICAL PROCESSING

The spent fuel and blanket elements from the nuclear reactor are processed to recover fissionable material, fission products, and, in some cases, other irradiation products.[13] These operations are called "radiochemical processes." The fuel must be removed from the reactor because of the consumption of fissionable material, and both fuel and blanket material must be removed because of the accumulation of neutron-absorbing fission products and physical damage due to corrosion, radiation, and temperature effects. Because of the neutron economy aspects, all fuel factors are optimized to

TABLE 24.9. RECOVERY PROCESSES FOR SPENT NUCLEAR
REACTOR FUEL

Process	Feature	Location
Precipitation		
Bismuth phosphate	Pu recovery by precipitation	Hanford*
Solvent extraction methods		
Redox	Pu and U recovery by MIBK	Hanford
Purex	Pu and U recovery by TBP	Hanford, Savannah River, Oak Ridge,† Windscale, Mol,† Marcoule
Butex	Pu and U recovery by DBC	Windscale
25	U-235 recovery by MIBK	Idaho Falls
TBP-25	U-235 recovery by TBP	Idaho Falls
23	U-233 recovery by MIBK	Oak Ridge*,†
Int-23	U-233 recovery by TBP	Oak Ridge†
Thorex	U-233 and Th recovery by TBP	Oak Ridge†
Dissolution methods		
Sulfex	Stainless steel dissolution in H_2SO_4	
Darex	Stainless steel dissolution in HNO_3—HCl	
Zirflex	Zirconium dissolution in NH_4F	
Zircex	Zirconium dissolution in anhydrous HCl	
Volatility	U-235 recovery by UF_6 sorption	Oak Ridge†
	U-235 recovery by UF_6 distillation	Argonne†
Pyrometallurgy	U and Pu purification by slagging	Idaho Falls†

* Shut down.
† Pilot plant.

achieve maximum performance. For example, little is gained in making the clad adequate for 100 weeks in-pile when the fissionable material is adequate for only 50 weeks, especially since the additional clad material decreases the conversion, i.e., the quantity of fissionable material produced. The plants in which radiochemical processing is carried out are government owned (Table 24.9).

The principal method for processing spent nuclear reactor fuel and blanket recovery is solvent extraction (Fig. 24.25).[10] This method has been

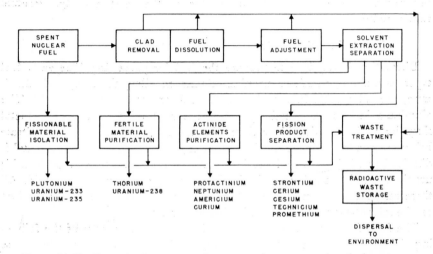

Figure 24.25. General solvent extraction process for spent nuclear fuel recovery.

adapted to the separation of uranium, plutonium, and thorium; other actinide elements, including protactinium, neptunium, americium, and curium; and specific fission products such as strontium, promethium, technetium, cesium, and cerium. The solvent extraction process utilizing tributyl phosphate as the solvent provides single-cycle decontamination factors as high as 10^3 to 10^5, with losses of 0.01 per cent, in relatively simple equipment. Early solvent extraction work employed methyl isobutyl ketone and dibutyl carbitol as solvents. Precipitation processes give decontamination factors of 5 to 100 and entail higher losses. Ion exchange processes occupy a middle ground. Both precipitation and ion exchange procedures are in use, but usually as auxiliaries to solvent extraction. The Bismuth Phosphate precipitation process was originally used for plutonium recovery but has been replaced by solvent extraction; precipitation as the main step in a process is now used principally for separation of fission products and for waste treatment. Other processing techniques now under development include volatility and pyrometallurgy. Neither volatility nor pyrometallurgy has been developed to the point where it can be completely evaluated. Both offer short, simple procedures that in certain situations may provide very significant reductions in the cost of fuel recovery. The high decontamination factors ($\sim 10^8$) obtained by solvent extraction and volatility are required when extensive processing such as return through gaseous diffusion and direct refabrication into nuclear fuel elements by standard metallurgical techniques is necessary, or when the final products are to be removed from the fuel cycle. Pyrometallurgical techniques offer simple recycle processing with decontamination factors (10–100) sufficient for neutron economy but necessitate remote fuel refabrication due to the relatively high residual radioactivity.

Spent Fuel Dissolution

Dissolution is required to prepare the fuel for processing. The early fuel types, containing uranium, uranium-aluminum alloy, thorium, and aluminum, are all soluble in caustic, nitric acid, or catalyzed nitric acid. The aluminum jackets are selectively removed from uranium and thorium metal slugs by sodium hydroxide-sodium nitrate dissolution, the sodium nitrate being present to minimize the formation of hydrogen. The uranium metal is dissolved in nitric acid and thorium metal in fluoride-catalyzed nitric acid; uranium-aluminum alloy is dissolved in mercury-catalyzed nitric acid. All these reagents are compatible with stainless steel and the dissolver product can be solvent-extracted without further treatment.

The fuels for most power reactors will contain one or more of the following materials: stainless steel, zirconium, molybdenum, and graphite. These materials require other dissolvents which are not compatible with stainless steel in most cases. Dissolvents are available for each of these materials, however, and the resulting solution can be readily converted to a solvent-extraction-compatible condition, but there is no experience to indicate which is the most economic. Either sulfuric acid (Sulfex process) or dilute aqua regia (Darex process) may be used to remove stainless steel jackets from uranium or thorium oxide pellet fuels. The Sulfex process has the advantage of low waste volume but the disadvantage of hydrogen evolution. In both cases the uranium in the pellet may be sufficiently soluble or the pellet sufficiently fractured to give excessive losses through solubility or entrainment, and complete dissolution of the core and jacket together may be necessary. Similar problems are faced in applying the Zirflex and Zircex processes to zirconium-containing fuels. Most existing processing plants have head end equipment for just one type of nuclear fuel. However, to achieve minimum processing costs a multipurpose head end system may be required to permit processing many fuel types in a common plant (Fig. 24.26).

The Purex Process. Purex is the major fuel recovery process in use today. It is a solvent extraction process principally applied to irradiated natural uranium fuel for the recovery of uranium and plutonium. The Purex process as it may be applied to the present fuel from the Yankee power reactor is representative of the spent fuel recovery process for nuclear power reactors. The fuel for this reactor was designed to permit 417 days of operation at full power. At the time of discharge from the reactor about 20 per cent of the U-235 will have been consumed and a large number of new materials produced (Table 24.10). The spent fuel will be stored for 160 days (about 20 half-lives of iodine-131) to decrease the discharge of chemically active radioactivity to the atmosphere. As much hardware as possible, e.g., couplings, will be removed before the first chemical operation is started. The

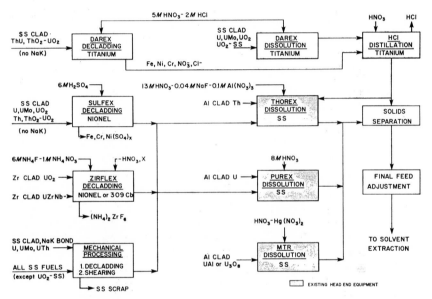

Figure 24.26. Multipurpose nuclear fuel dissolution system.

stainless steel jacket will probably be removed by dissolution in sulfuric acid or dilute aqua regia, thus removing the iron, nickel, and chromium and about 1 per cent of the fission products, e.g., cerium, iodine, krypton, and xenon, that diffused out of the uranium oxide pellets during reactor operation. The UO_2 pellets, being relatively insoluble, will remain in the dissolver.

The declad uranium oxide pellets will be dissolved in nitric acid, releasing the rest of the krypton and xenon and most of the iodine. The resulting dissolver solution might be passed through a scavenging manganese dioxide precipitation for a decontamination factor of 5 to 10 for zirconium, niobium, and ruthenium and, perhaps more important, to clarify the feed for solvent extraction.

In the solvent extraction step, two cycles are required for adequate decon-

TABLE 24.10. APPROXIMATE COMPOSITION OF IRRADIATED UO_2 FUEL

Basis: Yankee Atomic Power Reactor
Fuel: 20,000 kg of 3.4% enriched UO_2
Irradiation: 417 days at 1.6×10^{13} n/cm^2 sec

	Atoms $\times 10^{-23}$*	Half Life
U^{235}	10,320	7.1×10^8 y
U^{236}	780	2.4×10^7 y
U^{237}	0.31	6.75 d
U^{238}	486,000	4.5×10^9 y
Np^{237}	7.78	2.2×10^6 y
Np^{238}	0.007	2.10 d
Np^{239}	34.1	2.33 d
Pu^{238}	0.34	90 y
Pu^{239}	2940	24,300 y
Pu^{240}	329	6600 y
Pu^{241}	40.3	13 y
Am^{241}	0.60	470 y
Cm^{242}	0.05	163 d
Fission Products	5170	
I^{131}	4.4	8.05 d
Xe^{133}	4.1	5.3 d
Kr^{85}	14.9	10.4 y
Ba^{140}	13.9	12.8 d
La^{140}	1.8	40.2 h
Ce^{144}	195	285 d
Cs^{137}	294	30 y
Eu^{154}	0.94	16 y
Eu^{155}	0.08	1.7 y
Nd^{147}	4.9	11.6 d
Pm^{147}	112	2.6 y
Ru^{106}	45.1	1.0 y
Sm^{151}	4.9	80 y
Sr^{90}	269	28 y
Tc^{99}	313	2.1×10^5 y
Zr^{95}	16.9	65 d
Nb^{95}	8.2	35 d
Fe	6170	Stable
Ni	636	Stable
Cr	1610	Stable
O	714	Stable

* At time of reactor shutdown.

tamination. The first cycle removes the major portion of the fission product contaminants and separates the uranium and plutonium (Fig. 24.27). Further separation from fission products is accomplished in the second solvent extraction cycle. The acid raffinate from the second cycle is sometimes used in the first cycle to decrease the quantity of waste (Fig. 24.28). The solvent is tributyl phosphate in a kerosene diluent, as in the purification of uranium from ore concentrate.

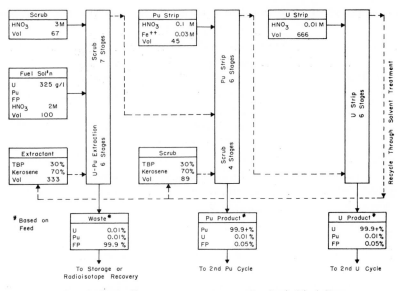

Figure 24.27. Purex process. First solvent extraction cycle.

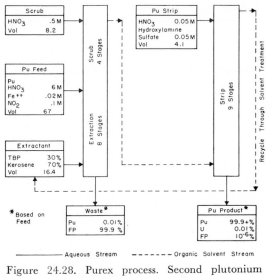

Figure 24.28. Purex process. Second plutonium
solvent extraction cycle.

Other Solvent Extraction Processes. The other solvent extraction procedures for spent reactor fuel recovery are similar in detail to the Purex first- or second-cycle flowsheets. When there is only one product, as in the case of fuel highly enriched in U^{235}, plutonium, or U^{233}, a series of two-column cycles, such as the Purex second cycle, is used. Representative of such procedures are the 25, TBP-25, 23, and Interim-23 processes. When there are two products a three-column cycle, such as the Purex first cycle, is used followed by one or more two-column cycles for each product. Representative of these procedures are the Redox, Butex, Thorex, and Purex processes.

Final Product Treatment. The products from solvent extraction are generally given a final purification treatment, concentrated, and converted to a form suitable for return to fuel fabrication.

Ion exchange is used for final concentration and purification of the plutonium product, both anion and cation exchange having been successfully used for this purpose. At low nitric acid concentration the plutonium is sorbed as a cation along with the cationic impurities and then preferentially eluted. At high nitric acid concentration the plutonium is sorbed as an anion with the cationic impurities passing through.

The uranium final treatment procedures vary considerably. Natural or depleted uranium product is concentrated by evaporation and passed through a silica gel bed for removal of corrosion products and trace amounts of radioactive zirconium and niobium. The uranium-235 product from the 25 process is sent through a final small-scale solvent extraction in glassware for final removal of corrosion products and then evaporated. The U^{233} product from the Thorex process is contaminated with U^{232} which, in turn, has very radioactive decay products; ion exchange is used for concentration and final separation from thorium, zirconium, and niobium, and just before use in metallurgical cycles the U^{233} is solvent extracted to remove the U^{232} decay products.[6]

The thorium product contains Th^{228}, the daughter of U^{232}, whose decay products also constitute a radiation hazard. Long-term storage (~ 10 years) is required to allow the use of direct handling methods for recycle to the reactor. This, plus the limited work done with thorium, accounts for the fact that recycle of thorium is not at present practiced and final treatment of the thorium product has not been defined.

Volatility Process. The Volatility process uses the volatility of uranium hexafluoride for its separation from fission products and fuel structural materials. This process is most applicable to the fused-salt-fueled homogeneous reactor and is under consideration for highly enriched uranium-zirconium alloy fuel (Fig. 24.29).[8] The Oak Ridge process uses hydrofluorination for the dissolution of uranium-zirconium alloy in molten fluoride to produce uranium and zirconium tetrafluoride. The uranium is converted in the salt medium to volatile uranium hexafluoride by reaction with fluorine. The zirconium and a few volatilized fission products, including ruthenium, niobium, iodine, neptunium, and others, follow the uranium to a limited extent. They are separated by absorbing the uranium on a bed of sodium fluoride pellets at 100° C. The uranium hexafluoride is desorbed from the bed with fluorine at 400° C and condensed in a cold trap. In the alternative Argonne volatility process, bromine trifluoride is used for fluorination, and distillation is used instead of absorption. Both processes are in the pilot-plant stage.

Pyrometallurgy Melt Refining Process. The pyrometallurgy melt refining process is being developed specifically for the fuel of fast breeder reactors such as the EBR-II and the Enrico Fermi.[7] This process will use the metallurgical techniques of melting, drossing, and recasting. The removal of neutron poisons by factors of 10 to 100 is sufficient to allow return of the fuel to the reactor, but completely remote operations will be necessary for fuel refabrication. This process is under development at Argonne National Laboratory and a pilot plant will be operated with the EBR-II at the

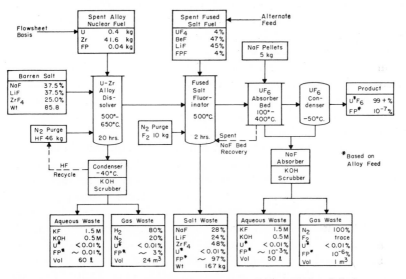

Figure 24.29. Fluoride volatility process. Oak Ridge National Laboratory Pilot Plant.

National Reactor Test Station in Idaho. The fuel is to be melted in a zirconia crucible under an argon atmosphere. This removes the noble gases (krypton and xenon), and certain volatile metallic elements (cadmium and cesium) and iodine, which comprise about 25 per cent of the fission elements. Part of the oxygen from the zirconia reacts to precipitate the alkaline earth and rare earth oxides, about 40 per cent of the fission elements, as a dross. Zirconium, which comprises about 10 per cent of the fission elements, is removed as the insoluble carbide. The noble metals, including molybdenum, technetium, ruthenium, rhodium, palladium, silver and tin, are not removed and represent about 25 per cent of the fission elements. The dross remains in the crucible along with about 10 per cent of the uranium when the uranium is poured off into a second container. The remaining uranium fraction will then be separately processed for recovery, perhaps by solvent extraction.

The uranium product is recast into pins by drawing the molten metal into Vycor glass tubes which are broken off after the metal has cooled. The uranium is then clad for return to the reactor.

Radiochemical Plant Safety. Radiation and nuclear criticality are the chief safety hazards encountered in radiochemical plants and require absolute control. The two principal methods of radiation control are shielding and containment. The radiation shield is generally concrete, and thicknesses up to 7 ft are required.[20] Other common shielding materials are water, iron, and lead. As in the case of nuclear reactors, two lines of containment are required. Nuclear criticality (accumulation of material under conditions leading to a chain reaction) is prevented by controlling the geometry, mass, and concentration. For example, when working with uranium-235 solutions, cylindrical vessel diameters should not exceed 5 in., or the total mass in process should not exceed 500 g, or the concentration in solution should not exceed 10 g/liter. These are very rough approximations, and each individual case must be carefully examined. The principal hazard of a criticality incident in an aqueous process system is the release of neutrons and highly penetrating radiation. It should be mentioned that the energy is released by a boiling-type reaction, not as an explosion. The principal criticality hazard exists in processing fissionable material in unshielded facilities.

Radioisotope Recovery. The chief radioisotopes now used in research and industry are fission products recovered from spent nuclear reactor fuel. The fission product stream from the first cycle of nuclear reactor fuel processing by solvent extraction is the feed to the radioisotopes recovery process. The chemical separations are processed in small plants located at Oak Ridge National Laboratory.[18] Only a small fraction of the fission products produced is recovered since there is relatively little demand. These radioisotopes include strontium-90, technetium-99, ruthenium-106, iodine-131, cesium-137, cerium-144, promethium-147, and europium-155 (Fig. 24.30). For production of some isotopes, special materials may be irradiated in nuclear reactors. For example, sulfur is irradiated to produce phosphorus-32, and nitrogen is irradiated to produce carbon-14. A third group of radioisotopes, the heavy elements produced by neutron capture, include the transuranic elements americium, curium, berkelium, and californium. This group has received relatively little attention because of the small quantities available. They are of considerable research interest and a high flux reactor is planned at Oak Ridge for their production.

Radioactive Waste Management. The final but very important phase to consider is the treatment and disposal of radioactive wastes. The problem of radioactive waste disposal is significant primarily because of the adverse effects of radiation on living organisms.[20,24] The problem exists at all stages of the nuclear industry, from mining, through the nuclear reactors, to the spent fuel processing.[16] In this last stage it becomes most evident because the fission products are found in both the liquid and gaseous media.

TYPICAL CHEMICAL PROCESSES IN .F3 P

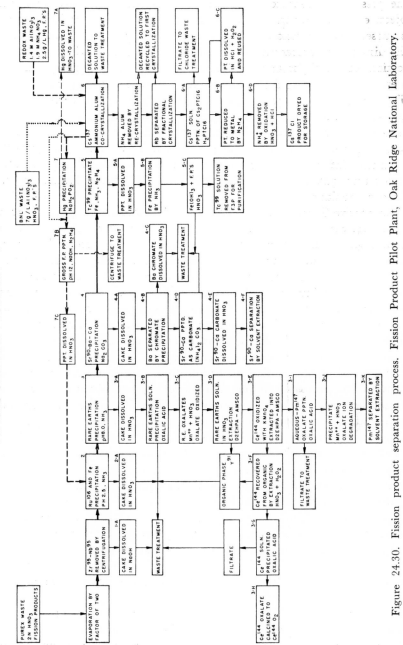

Figure 24.30. Fission product separation process. Fission Product Pilot Plant, Oak Ridge National Laboratory.

The present approach to treatment of radioactive waste has as its primary objectives concentration of the radioactive waste for economic storage and its subsequent conversion to a chemically inert solid for ultimate disposal. The disposal of radioactive waste has as its objective placing the waste in a location completely isolated from man's activities, where it may be monitored to ensure that it stays there and where no event caused by man or nature will cause it to be dispersed into the biologic environment. The cost of this radioactive waste management has been estimated to be about 1 per cent of the over-all cost of the nuclear industry. This cost may be increased as a result of modification of present practices when the anticipated growth of the nuclear industry is realized. These modifications may be required because of increased quantities of radioactivity and the possible location of plants closer to population centers.

Radioactive Gaseous Waste Treatment. The radioactive gas to be treated, is, in most cases, air contaminated with radioactive particulates, but in some cases gaseous iodine, argon, krypton, or xenon may be present. The removal of particulates may involve three stages of cleaning utilizing cyclones, electrostatic precipitators, and filters. In some cases wet scrubbers are used, but their efficiency is of the same order as a cyclone, and a radioactive liquid waste is created in the process. Radioactive argon results from neutron activation in coolant air used for nuclear reactors. Argon removal is not a major problem since it has a short half-life and is chemically inert, and because air cooling is used only on low-power research reactors. Xenon, krypton, and iodine are gaseous fission products and are released when the spent fuel is processed. Iodine is removed by either caustic scrubbing or chemical sorption on a silver-nitrate bed. The silver-nitrate bed minimizes the liquid waste problem. Xenon and krypton may be removed by low-temperature sorption on charcoal or by fluorocarbon scrubbing.

Air cleaning and ventilation of process buildings are vital safety problems to be considered. The control of radioactive contaminated air is achieved by repeating the final stage of cleaning with continuous monitoring of the flow between these two stages. In this manner the final stage can be by-passed for maintenance. Under normal operation the air passing between the final stages meets the specifications for discharge to the environment. A second and more positive method is to place the ventilation system on almost total recycle with only sufficient air discharged to maintain a negative pressure on the container. This requires a tight container and complete cleaning of the air.

Radioactive Liquid Waste Treatment. The radioactive liquid wastes are most often water containing dissolved radioactive salts along with ordinary salts. In the ore processing and feed materials operations, uranium, thorium, and radium are the principal problems. In water-cooled nuclear reactors, neutron-activated impurities such as sodium and corrosion products are a problem. In wastes from spent fuels and separation of radioisotopes, all the fission products plus the trace concentrations of actinide elements are the problems. The liquid wastes are best classified on the basis of the treatment required for their concentration. Low-level wastes might be defined as water from which radioactivity can be removed by simple water-treatment techniques, such as co-precipitation and ion exchange. Co-precipitation is widely used for this purpose and allows most of the ordinary salts to pass on through but removes only 10 to 90 per cent of the activity. Ion exchange has not been widely used but recent studies indicate 50 to 99 per cent removal in similar applications. Intermediate level radioactive wastes are those containing small quantities of principally short-lived isotopes. Such wastes are reduced to the status of low-level wastes by storage for a reasonable period of time, 10 years, for decay, and may then generally be released by methods applicable to the low-level wastes. High-level radioactive wastes may be generally defined as solutions containing large quantities of radioactivity, e.g., those from the first cycles of spent fuel processes. In the treatment and storage of such wastes, water is removed by evaporation and calcination. The control of radioactive-contaminated liquid wastes is achieved by continuously monitoring all liquid effluents leaving the plants. This includes utility and floor drains and sanitary sewers as well as process waste systems. Emergency storage is provided to hold up the plant effluent in the event of excessive radioactive contamination. Most of the radioactivity is contained in the aqueous wastes and is stored in underground tanks. Storage in salt beds, deep wells, or spent gas formations is now being considered.

Radioactive Solid Waste Treatment. Radioactive solid wastes are treated on the basis of their combustibility. They include materials such as paper, wood, plastics, metals, concrete and glass, and equipment such as tanks, motor, valves, pipes and tools. Incinerators have been used successfully for combustible material but the off-gas must be thoroughly cleaned. A wet scrubber is used for cooling and for the primary cleaning; the final cleaning is accomplished by filters. Contaminated equipment is decontaminated with acid, caustic, and complexing reagents. Radioactive solid wastes not amenable to further treatment are buried in the ground. Some of these wastes are dropped in the ocean, but the quantity disposed of in this fashion is relatively small.

REFERENCES

1. American Society of Mechanical Engineers, "Nuclear Reactor Plant Data," Volume 1, McGraw-Hill, 1959.
2. Benedict, Manson, and T. H. Pigford, "Nuclear Chemical Engineering," McGraw-Hill, 1957.
3. Bishop, A. S., "Project Sherwood—The U. S. Program in Controlled Fusion," Addison-Wesley Publishing Co., Reading, Mass., 1958.
4. Brown, H., "The Next Hundred Years," Viking Press, 1957.
5. Brown, K. B., and C. F. Coleman, "Solvent Extraction in Ore Processing," *Process Chemistry*, Volume 2, Progress in Nuclear Energy Series, London, Pergamon Press, 1958.

6. Bruce, F. R., "The Concentration and Purification of Uranium and Plutonium by Ion Exchange," *Ibid.,* Vol. 2, Pergamon Press, 1958.

7. Burris, L., *et al.,* "Developments in Melt Refining of Reactor Fuels," *Ibid.*

8. Cathers, G. I., *et al.,* "Recovery of Uranium from Highly Irradiated Reactor Fuel by a Fused Salt Fluoride-Volatility Process," *Proceedings of the Second United Nations International Conference on the Peaceful Uses of Atomic Energy,* Vol. 17, Geneva, United Nations, 1958.

9. Clegg, J. W., and D. D. Foley, "Uranium Ore Processing," Addison-Wesley Publishing Co., Reading, Mass., 1958.

10. Culler, F. L., Jr., "Reprocessing of Reactor Fuel and Blanket Materials by Solvent Extraction," *Process Chemistry,* Vol. 1, Progress in Nuclear Energy Series, London, Pergamon Press, 1956.

11. Cuthbert, F. L., "Thorium Production Technology," Addison-Wesley Publishing Co., Reading, Mass., 1958.

12. Dietrich, J. P., and W. H. Zinn, "Solid Fuel Reactors," Addison-Wesley Publishing Co., Reading, Mass., 1958.

13. Glasstone, Samuel, "Principles of Nuclear Reactor Engineering," D. Van Nostrand Company, Inc., 1955.

14. Glasstone, Samuel, "Sourcebook on Atomic Energy," 2nd Ed., D. Van Nostrand Company, Inc., 1958.

15. Harrington, C. D., and A. E. Ruehle, "Uranium Production Technology," D. Van Nostrand Company, Inc., 1959.

16. "Industrial Radioactive Waste Disposal, Hearings Before the Special Subcommittee on Radiation of the Joint Committee on Atomic Energy Congress of the United States," Jan. 28, 1959, U. S. Govt. Printing Office, Washington, 1959.

17. Johnson, J. C., "Resources of Nuclear Fuel for Atomic Power," *Proceedings of the Second United Nations International Conference on the Peaceful Uses of Atomic Energy,* Volume 2, Geneva, United Nations, 1958.

18. Lamb, E., *et al.,* "Fission Product Pilot Plant and Other Developments in the Radioisotope Program at Oak Ridge National Laboratory," *Ibid.,* Vol. 20, Geneva, United Nations, 1958.

19. McKinney, R., "Report of the Panel on the Impact of the Peaceful Uses of Atomic Energy," Vol. 1, Washington, D. C., U. S. Government Printing Office, 1956.

20. NBS Handbook 69, "Maximum Permissible Amounts of Radioisotopes in the Human Body and the Maximum Permissible Concentrations in Air and Water," Washington, D. C., U. S. Government Printing Office, June 5, 1959.

21. Nininger, R. D., "Geological Distribution of Nuclear Raw Materials," Proceedings of the Second United Nations International Conference on the Peaceful Uses of Atomic Energy, Volume 15, Geneva, United Nations, 1958.

22. Painter, L. A., and T. F. Izzo, "Operation of the Resin-in-Pulp Uranium Processing Mill at Moab, Utah, *"Proceedings of the Second United Nations International Conference on the Peaceful Uses of Atomic Energy,* Volume 3, Geneva, United Nations, 1958.

23. Putnam, P. C., "Energy in the Future," D. Van Nostrand Company, Inc., 1953.

24. "Radiation Hygiene Handbook," Hanson Blatz, Ed., McGraw-Hill, 1959.

25. "Shippingport Pressurized Water Reactor," Addison-Wesley Publishing Co., Reading, Mass., 1958.

26. U. S. Atomic Energy Commission, "Major Activities in the Atomic Energy Programs January–December 1959," Washington, D. C., U. S. Government Printing Office, 1960.

25

SYNTHETIC ORGANIC CHEMICALS

In collaboration with Dr. William H. Haberstroh*
and Dr. Daniel E. Collins*

SYNTHETIC ORGANIC CHEMICALS are derivative products of naturally occurring materials (petroleum, natural gas and coal) which have undergone at least one chemical reaction such as oxidation, hydrogenation, chlorination, sulfonation, etc.

The volume of synthetic organic chemicals has grown from 17 billion pounds in 1949 to more than 50 billion pounds in 1959. The production for the past decade is shown in Figure 25.1.[171] Much of this phenomenal growth has been due to the replacement of "natural" organic chemicals. Since this replacement is now approaching completion, future growth for synthetic materials will be dictated by the expansion and new developments of organic chemical markets.

Even more spectacular has been the growth of organic chemicals derived from petroleum and natural gas sources (petrochemicals). Output of chemicals from these two sources jumped from 75 tons in 1929 to more than 21 million tons in 1958.[173] It is estimated that chemicals from these raw materials accounted for 57 per cent of the dollar value of all (organic and inorganic) U. S. chemicals in 1959 and 28 per cent of the total tonnage.

More than 2500 organic chemical products are derived principally from petrochemical sources.[174] These are commercially produced from five logical

* Dow Chemical Company, Midland, Mich.

starting points. Consequently this chapter has been subdivided into five major raw material classifications: Methane, Ethylene, Propylene, Butane and Butylenes, and Aromatics.

CHEMICALS DERIVED FROM METHANE

It has been stated that every synthetic organic chemical listed in Beilstein can be made in some way or other starting with methane. This section, however, deals only with the relatively small number which can be made

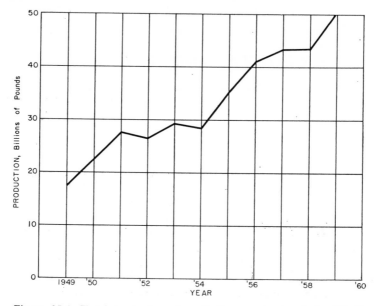

Figure 25.1. Total production of synthetic organic chemicals. (*U. S. Tariff Commission*)

economically and which are useful enough to warrant large volume production. A diagram of the principal materials covered is shown in Figure 25.2. These chemical outlets account for roughly one-half of the country's natural gas production, which totalled more than ten trillion cubic feet in 1960.

Synthesis Gas[77,126]

The most important route for the conversion of methane to petrochemicals is via either hydrogen, or a mixture of hydrogen and carbon monoxide. This latter material is known as "synthesis gas." The manufacture of carbon monoxide-hydrogen mixtures from coal was first established industrially by the well-known water-gas reaction

$$C + H_2O \rightarrow CO + H_2$$

Two important methods are presently used to produce the gas mixture from methane. The first is the methane-steam reaction, where methane and steam at about 900° C are passed through a tubular reactor packed with a promoted iron oxide catalyst. Two reactions are possible, depending on the conditions:

$$CH_4 + H_2O \rightarrow CO + 3H_2$$
$$CO + H_2O \rightarrow CO_2 + H_2$$

The second commercial method involves the partial combustion of methane to provide the heat and steam needed for the conversion. Thus

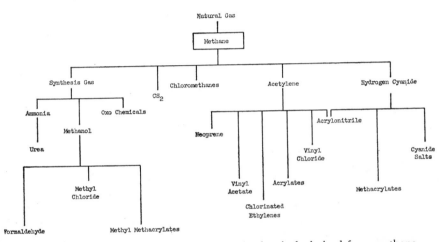

Figure 25.2. Some important synthetic organic chemicals derived from methane.

the reaction can be considered to take place in at least two steps. The combustion step

$$CH_4 + 2O_2 \rightarrow CO_2 + 2H_2O$$

followed by the reaction step

$$CH_4 + CO_2 \rightarrow 2CO + 2H_2$$
$$CH_4 + H_2O \rightarrow CO + 3H_2$$

The process is usually run with nickel catalysts and in the temperature range, 800–1000° C.

The main outlets in the chemical industry for the gas mixtures obtained by the reforming of methane are in the manufacture of ammonia, the methyl alcohol synthesis, and in the Fischer-Tropsch and Oxo reactions.

Ammonia.[44,78,104,138] Ammonia derived from petroleum and natural-gas sources accounts for about 95% of the almost ten billion pounds produced annually. Consequently, it can be termed the number-one petrochemical in volume. Almost three-fourths of the ammonia produced goes into fertilizer, while the remainder is used to produce such chemicals as urea, aniline, hydrogen cyanide, and organic amines.

Detailed descriptions of the ammonia manufacturing processes can be found in Chapter 5.

Methanol.[51,79,145] Before 1926, all American methanol was recovered commercially as a by-product of the wood distillation process (wood alcohol). That year, however, marked the first appearance of German synthetic methanol. Presently less than two per cent of the two billion pounds production comes from wood.

The methyl alcohol synthesis is well known. It resembles the synthesis of ammonia in that the catalysts operate only at high temperature levels, and conversion and equilibrium are greatly assisted by high-pressure operation. The industrial reaction conditions are pressures of 250–350 atmospheres, and temperatures in the range of 300–400° C. The catalysts employed are based on zinc oxide, which is mixed with other oxides to provide temperature resistance. Variations between synthetic methanol plants are quite similar to those between synthetic ammonia plants. In fact, many ammonia operations are designed so that methanol could also be produced in them.

In the past, methanol production has generally paralleled that of its largest end-user, formaldehyde. However, with larger quantities of formaldehyde coming from the hydrocarbon oxidation process, the production of methanol has tended to level off. Other major uses of methanol are in automobile antifreeze, solvents, aviation fuels, and in the synthesis of such materials as methyl amines, methyl chloride, methyl methacrylates, and various methyl esters.

Formaldehyde.[51,79] Formaldehyde may be made from methanol either by catalytic vapor-phase oxidation,

$$CH_3OH + \frac{1}{2}O_2 \text{ (air)} \rightarrow CH_2O + H_2O$$

or by a combination oxidation-dehydrogenation process

$$CH_3OH \rightarrow CH_2O + H_2$$

It can also be produced directly from natural gas, methane, and other aliphatic hydrocarbons, but this process yields mixtures of various oxygenated materials.

Since both gaseous and liquid formaldehyde readily polymerize at room temperature, it is not available in the pure form. It is instead sold as a 37 per cent solution in water, or in the polymeric form as paraformaldehyde ($HO(CH_2O)_nH$, where n is between 8 and 50) or as trioxane ($(CH_2O)_3$).

The largest end use of formaldehyde is in the field of synthetic resins, either as a homopolymer (Delrin), or as a copolymer with phenol, urea, or melamine. It is also reacted with acetaldehyde to produce pentaerythritol ($C(CH_2OH)_4$) which finds use in polyester resins. Two smaller volume users are ethylene glycol and hexamethylenetetramine, the latter being formed by condensation with ammonia.

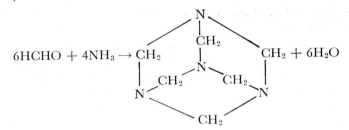

$$6HCHO + 4NH_3 \rightarrow \text{(hexamethylenetetramine)} + 6H_2O$$

Oxo Chemicals.[24,35,119,146] The oxo chemicals are compounds—primarily C_4 and higher alcohols—made by the so-called "oxo" process. This process is a method of reacting olefins with carbon monoxide and hydrogen to produce aldehydes containing one more carbon atom than the olefin, which in turn are converted into alcohols. The earliest reaction studied used

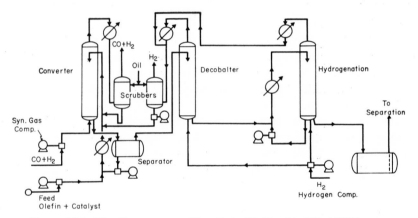

Figure 25.3. The Oxo process. (*Pet. Ref.*, **38**, No. 11, 280 (*1959*), *copyright Gulf Pub. Co.*)

ethylene to produce both an aldehyde and a ketone. Thus the name "oxo," which was adapted from the German "oxierung," meaning ketonization. However, even though other names such as hydroformylation would much more accurately describe the process, the term oxo appears too deeply entrenched to be replaced.

A flow sheet of a typical process is shown in Figure 25.3. The steps involved in the reaction are

$$RCH{=}CH_2 + CO + H_2 \xrightarrow[\substack{250° C}]{\substack{Co \\ 3000 \text{ psi}}} \begin{Bmatrix} RCH_2CH_2CHO \\ RCH(CHO)CH_3 \end{Bmatrix}$$

$$\begin{Bmatrix} RCH_2CH_2CHO \\ RCH(CHO)CH_3 \end{Bmatrix} + H_2 \xrightarrow[\substack{200° C}]{\substack{3000 \text{ psi}}} \begin{array}{l} RCH_2CH_2CH_2OH \\ RCH(CH_2OH)CH_3 \end{array}$$

The cobalt catalyst under these conditions is in the form of dicobalt octacarbonyl and cobalt hydrocarbonyl.

At the present time there is plant capacity in the United States for better than 400 million pounds per year of oxo chemicals. These include such products as normal and iso butanol, propionaldehyde, butyraldehydes, butyronitriles, iso-octyl alcohol, decyl alcohol, tridecyl alcohol, and others. The two major uses for the oxo alcohols are in plasticizers and detergents. Plasticizers consume more than 100 million pounds of the higher alcohols (iso-octyl and decyl), while the tridecyl alcohol is used in the detergents.

Chlorinated Methanes[46,104,139]

The chlorination of methane can be carried out either thermally or photochemically to produce methyl chloride (CH_3Cl), methylene chloride (CH_2Cl_2), chloroform ($CHCl_3$), and carbon tetrachloride (CCl_4). If only a particular one of the chlorinated materials is desired, other methods such as the chlorination of CS_2, or the reaction of methanol with HCl are generally used. These are fairly large volume chemicals, with the 1961 production of carbon tetrachloride alone estimated at 450 million pounds.

Although largely replaced by perchloroethylene in the dry cleaning field, carbon tetrachloride has shown considerable growth as a fire extinguisher and as a raw material for the manufacture of chlorofluorohydrocarbons. Next in volume is methylene chloride which finds use in paint removers, photographic film, and aerosol solvents. Methyl chloride in the past has been used mainly as a catalyst carrier in the low temperature polymerization of butyl rubber, but is now also showing promise as a starting material for silicones. Chloroform is the least used of the four, finding application mainly in the extraction of penicillin and as a raw material for fluorohydrocarbons.

Acetylene

Acetylene is made commercially in two ways; from calcium carbide, or from hydrocarbons. The choice of method is determined mainly by the fact that acetylene cannot be shipped easily, so large users must be at or near the point of origin. The carbide plant in turn must be near a cheap source of electric power, since each pound of carbide requires about 1.5 kw-hr of electricity.

The manufacture of acetylene is described in Chapters 14 and 17. See also references 11, 28, 42, 103, 133 and 136 for more information on this important material.

The largest single use of acetylene is in the metal industry for cutting and welding, but chemical raw material usage is growing rapidly. Some of the major chemicals manufactured, at least in part, from it are neoprene, vinyl chloride, vinyl acetate, chloroethylenes, acrylates, and acrylonitrile. Several others can also be made from acetylene, but are more economically produced from ethylene or propylene.

Vinyl Chloride.[58,86] About 56% of the vinyl chloride produced (or about 500 million pounds) comes from the addition of hydrogen chloride to acetylene. This process involves a mercuric chloride catalyst, and temperatures of about 200° C. Two other important methods are based on the removal of hydrogen chloride from ethylene dichloride; one with high temperature and catalyst, and the other with a caustic treatment. Almost two-thirds of the ethylene dichloride produced is used for this purpose.

All vinyl chloride ends up in plastics. The most important are the homopolymer (PVC), and copolymers with vinylidene chloride (Sarans) or vinyl acetate.

Vinyl Acetate.[57,149] Vinyl acetate is produced by combination of acetylene and glacial acetic acid. This is a catalytic reaction (zinc or mercury compounds), and may be carried out either in the liquid or vapor phase.

$$CH{\equiv}CH + CH_3COOH \rightarrow CH_3COOCH{=}CH_2$$

Approximately 300 million pounds are produced annually, all of which is utilized in the polymeric form. Polyvinyl acetate (PVA) can be found in films and latex paints. It also can be used to produce polyvinyl alcohol (a water-soluble polymer), polyvinyl butyral (for safety-glass), polyvinyl formal, and various copolymers.

Acrylates and Methacrylates[10,34,168,170]

The acrylates are esters of acrylic acid ($CH_2{=}CHCOOR$) with the R generally ranging from methyl to ethylhexyl. The main method of preparation involves reacting a mixture of acetylene, hydrogen chloride, nickel carbonyl, carbon monoxide, and the appropriate alcohol. The carbonyl group in the product ester is derived about 80 per cent from the carbon monoxide, and the remainder from the nickel compound. Other methods involve ethylene cyanohydrin, ketene, or the esterification of acrylic acid.

Methacrylic acid is formed from acetone cyanohydrin in a two step process.

$$\underset{\underset{OH}{|}}{\overset{\overset{CH_3}{|}}{CH_3CCN}} + H_2SO_4 \rightarrow \overset{\overset{CH_3}{|}}{CH_2{=}CCONH_2{\cdot}H_2SO_4} \xrightarrow{H_2O}$$

$$\overset{\overset{CH_3}{|}}{CH_2{=}CCOOH} + NH_4HSO_4$$

While this is the only process currently in operation, reports have been made of a route involving the oxidation of isobutylene to hydroxyisobutyric acid, which in turn is dehydrated to methacrylic acid.

Consumption of methacrylates more than doubled in the five years between 1955 and 1960, and now totals about 120 million pounds. The largest part of this goes into cast sheet, where the clarity and resistance of poly(methyl methacrylate) are desirable. Other uses are in molding powder, latexes, solvent coatings, and copolymers with vinyl acetate and styrene.

Hydrogen Cyanide.[50,144,169] Hydrogen cyanide is prepared, as shown in Figure 25.4, by passing a mixture of air, ammonia, and natural gas over a

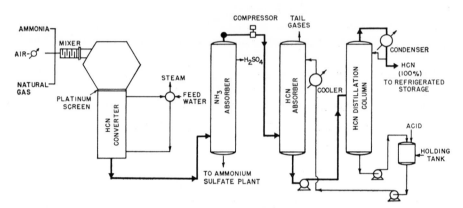

Figure 25.4. The hydrogen cyanide process. [*Ind. & Eng. Chem.*, **51**, *No. 10, 1235 (1959)*.]

platinum catalyst. The converter is operated at a temperature of about 1800° F, and care must be taken to minimize the decomposition of the ammonia and methane, as well as the oxidation of methane to carbon monoxide and hydrogen. The effluent gases are cooled, washed with dilute sulfuric acid, and then passed through a column where the hydrogen cyanide is absorbed in water. This is concentrated by distillation, and an inhibitor added to prevent polymerization. Although all new plants follow the methane-ammonia route, HCN can also be produced from coke-oven gas, from sodium and calcium cyanides, and by the decomposition of formamide.

Safety is a vital consideration in any cyanide plant because of the toxicity of the product. In general, all production is captive to avoid the need for shipment. About one-third of the HCN goes into the production of acrylonitrile, while another third ends up in acrylates and methacrylates. The remainder is used in such products as metal salts and adiponitrile, and as a general-purpose chemical intermediate.

Acrylonitrile.[30,32,43,137] Acrylonitrile (vinyl cyanide) production has grown from about 15 million pounds in 1950 to more than 260 million pounds in 1960. This tremendous growth can be attributed principally to acrylic textile fibers, such as those trademarked Orlon, Acrilan, and Zefran. Smaller uses are in resins, synthetic rubber, solvents, and in intermediates for dyes, pharmaceuticals, and insecticides.

Almost all of the acrylonitrile plants now in production use acetylene and hydrogen cyanide as raw materials. Recently however, interest has been focussed on three processes which produce acrylonitrile from propylene and ammonia in a high-temperature, fluidized-bed reactor. The major difference between these is in the choice of conversion catalyst; one uses silver on silica, another uses oxides of molybdenum, while the third involves bismuth phosphomolybdate. Published estimates[32] indicate a very sizable cost advantage for this type of process over the acetylene-hydrogen cyanide route, and it will undoubtedly replace the older method.

CHEMICALS DERIVED FROM ETHYLENE

Ethylene far surpasses all other hydrocarbons both in volume and in diversity of commercial use. In the whole field of petrochemicals, it is ex-

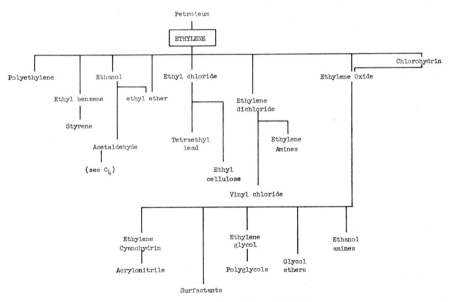

Figure 25.5. Major ethylene derivatives.

ceeded in tonnage only by synthetic ammonia.[18] Consumption of ethylene has grown remarkably in just the last 20 years. In 1940, 300 million pounds were produced, mostly for ethanol and ethylene oxide. The war time demand for styrene, and the postwar impact of polyethylene aided in causing this figure to swell to almost 5 billion pounds in 1960.

The major consumers of ethylene in 1960 are shown in Table 25.1. The volume of at least three of these derivatives, as seen in Table 25.2,[38] is so great that they might well be termed "heavy organic chemicals."[129]

TABLE 25.1. ETHYLENE DERIVATIVES

	Ethylene Consumed (million pounds)	(per cent of total)
Ethylene oxide	1510	30%
Polyethylene	1230	25
Ethanol	1050	21
Ethyl benzene	452	9
Ethyl chloride	365	7
Ethylene dichloride and dibromide	280	6
Others	113	2

Ethylene Oxide

Ethylene oxide was discovered in 1859 by Wurtz, who named it because of certain analogies with inorganic oxides. The method which he used was what is today known as the chlorohydrin process. He considered that direct oxidation was an impossibility, and stated flatly that "ethylene oxide cannot be made by the direct combination of ethylene and oxygen." It took almost eighty years to disprove this statement.[175]

There are two basic processes presently used in the production of ethylene oxide from ethylene; the chlorohydrin process and the catalytic oxidation process.[87] The chlorohydrin process is the older of the two and is based on the addition of hypochlorous acid to ethylene to produce ethylene chlorohydrin,

$$CH_2{=}CH_2 + HOCl \rightarrow CH_2ClCH_2OH$$

which in turn is dehydrochlorinated to produce ethylene oxide.

$$2CH_2ClCH_2OH + Ca(OH)_2 \rightarrow CaCl_2 + 2H_2O + 2CH_2{-}CH_2$$
$$\underset{O}{\diagdown\diagup}$$

A flow sheet of this process is shown in the first part of Figure 25.6. Ethylene, chlorine, and water are fed into the bottom of a large acid-proof brick-lined tower at somewhere below 50° C. The water and chlorine form hypochlorous acid which then reacts rapidly with the ethylene.[49] The dilute solution emerging from the tower contains about 5% chlorohydrin. The major side reaction is the formation of ethylene dichloride. The solution next passes to a hydrolyzer where the chlorohydrin is treated with either slaked lime or caustic soda to produce the oxide.[114] The crude ethylene oxide contains about 10% ethylene dichloride which is removed by distillation.[177] This process accounts for roughly 40% of the oxide plant capacity, but some is used for the production of propylene oxide which has not yet been commercially produced by direct oxidation.

The second important process involves the direct oxidation of ethylene with air in the presence of a silver catalyst.

$$2CH_2{=}CH_2 + O_2 \rightarrow 2CH_2{-}CH_2$$
$$\underset{O}{\diagdown\diagup}$$

A number of processes are available, and a typical one is shown in Figure 25.7. Ethylene, compressed air, and recycle gases are fed to a tubular reactor

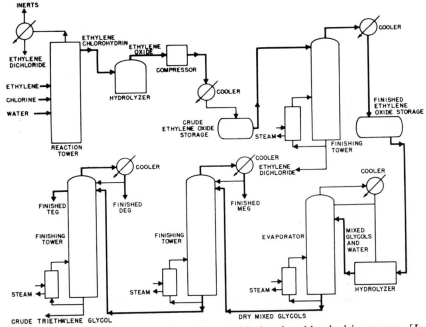

Figure 25.6. Ethylene glycols and ethylene oxide by the chlorohydrin process. [*Ind. & Eng. Chem.*, **51**, *No. 8, 896 (1959)*.]

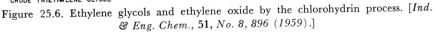
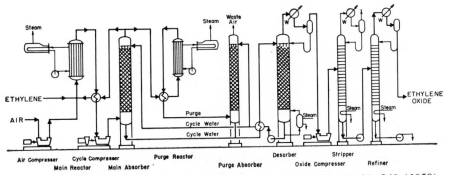

Figure 25.7. Ethylene oxide by direct oxidation. [*Pet. Ref.*, **38**, *No. 11, 248 (1959)*, *copyright Gulf Pub. Co.*]

containing a silver catalyst. The oxygen and ethylene concentrations are maintained at a low level to avoid explosion hazards. The reaction temperature is 250–300° C with a pressure of 120–300 psi. Two competing side reactions which must be minimized are the total combustion of ethylene to carbon dioxide, and the isomerization of ethylene oxide to acetaldehyde.[176]

Recently, interest has been aroused by a modification of the catalytic oxidation process in which oxygen is used in place of air.[142] At the present time, three plants are in operation, accounting for about 8% of the total oxide capacity.

Ethylene oxide is the most important of the olefin oxides. While it can be used directly as a fumigant for foodstuffs (usually mixed with carbon dioxide), it finds its chief outlet as a chemical intermediate.[80] It owes its value to a combination of two types of reactivity; it can combine with chemicals containing a replaceable hydrogen, and it can polymerize to give a polyethenoxy chain. The first is typified in the formation of ethanolamines, while the second occurs in the synthesis of the polyglycols and higher glycol ethers.

The estimated production for 1960 of oxide-derived materials, and the amount of ethylene oxide they consume is shown in Table 25.2.[13]

TABLE 25.2. PRODUCTION OF CHEMICALS FROM ETHYLENE OXIDE*

Product	Output (million lb)	Oxide Requirement (million lb)
Ethylene Glycol	1225	900
Nonionic Surfactants	350	125
Ethanolamines	126	105
Acrylonitrile	245	65
Diethylene Glycol	130	94
Triethylene Glycol	30	24
Glycol ethers	. . .	60
Polyglycols	28	. . .
Others	. . .	67

*Chem. Week, p. 39, April (1959).

Ethylene oxide is expected to continue its present growth trend for at least the next few years. While ethylene glycol will remain the largest end-use, it is in demand for the smaller consumers, such as nonionics, which will probably show the greatest improvement.

Ethylene Glycols. Ethylene glycol can be prepared directly by the hydrolysis of chlorohydrin, but the indirect hydrolysis, via ethylene oxide, is the preferred method. This is shown in the second part of Figure 25.6. The feed stream consists of ethylene oxide (either from the chlorohydrin or direct oxidation process) and water.[178] This mixture is fed under pressure into the reactor vessel at about 100° C.

$$CH_2\overset{\displaystyle O}{\diagdown\diagup}CH_2 + H_2O \rightarrow HOCH_2CH_2OH$$

By the end of the reaction, the temperature has risen to about 170° C. Some diethylene glycol and triethylene glycol are produced by the reaction of ethylene glycol with the oxide. The crude glycols solution is then concentrated in a multiple-effect evaporator. Final separation of the mono-, di-, and triethylene glycols is accomplished by distillation.

Ethylene glycol may also be manufactured by catalytic hydrogenation of an ester of glycolic acid. This acid is produced from the reaction under pressure of carbon monoxide, formaldehyde, and water.[48]

$$CH_2O + CO + H_2O \quad \rightarrow CH_2OHCOOH$$
$$CH_2OHCOOH + ROH \rightarrow CH_2OHCOOR + H_2O$$
$$CH_2OHCOOR + 2H_2 \quad \rightarrow CH_2OHCH_2OH + ROH$$

This is an extremely efficient process, having an overall yield of 80–90%.

The main outlet, by far, for ethylene glycol is as the basic ingredient in permanent-type automotive antifreeze solutions. This accounts for more than 70% of the total production. Other uses are in aircraft de-icing fluids, solvents, hydraulic fluids, and as a plasticizer in cellophane. The chemical reactivity of ethylene glycol is utilized in a series of esters and polyesters. One of the esters is ethylene glycol dinitrate, an essential component in low-temperature dynamites. The most important polyester is that produced from ethylene glycol and terephthalic acid. This is sold both as a fiber and as a film, under the trade marks Dacron and Mylar.

Diethylene glycol has properties similar to those of ethylene glycol. Due to its hygroscopicity, diethylene glycol finds wide use as a tobacco humectant.[15] Triethylene glycol is used as a high-boiling solvent and plasticizer and is showing promise as a drying agent for gases.

Polyethylene glycols are produced by passing ethylene oxide into a small amount of a low molecular weight glycol using a sodium or caustic soda catalyst.[81] Liquid polyglycol products are in the range of molecular weights from 200 to 1000. They are used as plasticizers, dispersants, lubricants, and humectants. Above about 1000 molecular weight, the polyglycols are waxy solids, suitable for use as softening agents, in ointments and cosmetics, and as lubricants.

Nonionic Surfactants. In 1959, nonionics made up approximately 25% of all synthetic detergents produced in the U. S., or more than 300 million pounds.[14] In the years between 1950 and 1959, while the total output of surfactants doubled, nonionics production increased more than sixfold. Behind this rise are two characteristics; most nonionics are liquid, and they have low sudsing power.

There are many nonionic surfactants, but four classes account for more than 80% of the production. These are (1) the alkylphenol-ethylene oxide derivatives, (2) fatty acid-alkanolamine condensates, (3) tall oil-ethylene oxide adducts, and (4) the fatty acid-ethylene oxide adducts. The ethoxylated alkylphenols (primarily nonylphenols) are the largest

Figure 25.8. Ethylene glycol evaporation and finishing. (*Courtesy Dow Chemical Co.*)

group, and go mainly into industrial uses. The alkanolamine condensates are foam stabilizers in various detergent formulations. Tall oil adducts find use in household detergents, chiefly automatic-washer products, because of their low-sudsing properties. The fatty alcohol-oxide adducts are used mainly as light-duty detergents, though some tridecyl adducts are utilized as foam stabilizers. Regardless of which group is emphasized in the future, the surge in nonionics will undoubtedly be an important factor in any increase in ethylene oxide consumption.

Ethanolamines. Ethanolamines are manufactured by reacting ethylene oxide and ammonia. The relative amounts of the three amines will depend primarily on the ammonia/oxide feed ratio.[179]

$$NH_3 \xrightarrow{C_2H_4O} (HOC_2H_4)NH_2 \xrightarrow{C_2H_4O} (HOC_2H_4)_2NH \xrightarrow{C_2H_4O} (HOC_2H_4)_3N$$

The products from the reaction are separated by distillation. During the last few years, each of the amines has in turn been in the greatest demand, so processing flexibility must be maintained.[47]

Monoethanolamine is used primarily in detergents and as an absorbent for acid-gas (H_2S, CO_2) removal. It is to a lesser extent a chemical intermediate for such compounds as ethylene imine.[83] Diethanolamine's major end use is in detergents, but it is also utilized in textiles and as a gas purification agent. Most of the triethanolamine goes into the production of cosmetics and textile specialities.

Isopropanolamines derived from propylene oxide and ammonia are competitive with the ethanolamines, and both are unique in that they are organic compounds and yet strongly alkaline.

Glycol Ethers. In the same way that water reacts with one or more molecules of ethylene oxide, alcohols react to give monoethers of ethylene glycol, with monoethers of diethylene glycol, triethylene glycol, etc., as by-products.[82]

$$ROH + CH_2\overset{\displaystyle O}{\diagup\diagdown}CH_2 \rightarrow ROC_2H_4OH$$

$$+ CH_2\overset{\displaystyle O}{\diagup\diagdown}CH_2 \rightarrow ROC_2H_4OC_2H_4OH$$

$$+ CH_2\overset{\displaystyle O}{\diagup\diagdown}CH_2 \rightarrow ROC_2H_4OC_2H_4OC_2H_4OH$$

Since their commercial introduction in 1926, glycol ethers have become valuable as industrial solvents and chemical intermediates. Because glycol monoethers contain a $-OCH_2CH_2OH$ group, they resemble a combination of ether and ethyl alcohol in solvent properties.[116] The most common alcohols used are methanol, ethanol, and butanol. Principal uses for the glycol ethers are as solvents for paints and lacquers, as intermediates in the production of plasticizers, and as ingredients in brake fluid formulations. The most common trade names are Dowanol, Cellosolve, and Polysolve. Condensation of the monoethers produces glycol diethers which are also useful as solvents.

$$2ROCH_2CH_2OH \xrightarrow{H_2SO_4} ROC_2H_4OC_2H_4OR + H_2O$$

Alcohol-ethylene oxide products have also been developed in which the number of oxide units is considerably higher in order to improve water solubility. Long-chain fatty alcohols are condensed with 10–40 molecules of ethylene oxide to produce detergents for the textile industry. More important are the water soluble alkyl phenyl ethers of the higher polyethylene glycols. Phenols react in the same way as alcohols to give polyglycol ethers. The reaction is rapid, and essentially quantitative. These products are detergents of the same general class as the long chain alcohol-ethylene oxide condensates.

Other Oxide Derivatives. Two other ethylene oxide-derived materials which should be mentioned are acrylonitrile and polyethylene oxide. Hydrogen cyanide adds to ethylene oxide in the presence of a basic catalyst to give ethylene cyanohydrin.

$$\overset{\text{O}}{\overbrace{CH_2\text{——}CH_2}} + HCN \rightarrow HOCH_2CH_2CN$$

This material is then catalytically dehydrated to give acrylonitrile.[84]

$$HOCH_2CH_2CN \rightarrow CH_2\text{:}CHCN + H_2O$$

Even though the production of acrylonitrile is increasing rapidly, it is expected that this process will not expand beyond the single plant which is now using it.[16]

Of recent origin is the interest in the extremely high molecular weight homopolymers of ethylene oxide. These resins, trademarked Polyox, have good water and organic solvent solubility.

Ethanol

Less than ten years ago, synthetic ethanol was the largest consumer of ethylene. Today it is in third place behind ethylene oxide and polyethylene,[17] with a predicted production for 1961 of about 1.9 billion pounds.[105] Just prior to World War II, the fermentation of molasses accounted for about 72% of the ethanol production. Today less than 10% of the ethanol manufactured is made by this route; over 90% is synthesized from ethylene by the esterification-hydrolysis process or by direct catalytic hydration.

The esterification-hydrolysis process, such as that shown in Figure 25.9, is the older of the two, and still accounts for about 80% of the production.[88] This reaction takes place in two steps. The first occurs between sulfuric acid and ethylene at about 75° C in a plate column.

$$3CH_2\text{=}CH_2 + 2H_2SO_4 \rightarrow CH_3CH_2HSO_4 + (CH_3CH_2)_2SO_4$$

The resulting mixture is then diluted in a hydrolyzer to produce the alcohol.

$$CH_3CH_2HSO_4 + H_2O \rightarrow CH_3CH_2OH + H_2SO_4$$

The overall yield is about 90 per cent ethanol and 5–10 per cent diethyl ether. If the emphasis is placed on ether production, the residence time

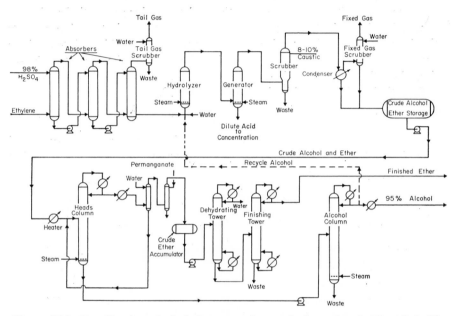

Figure 25.9. Esterification—hydrolysis process for producing ethanol. [*Pet. Ref.,* **38,** *No. 11, 239 (1950), copyright Gulf Pub. Co.*]

in the hydrolyzer is increased, and the alcohol is recycled. The reactions in the hydrolyzer will then include the following:[140]

$$C_2H_5OH + C_2H_5HSO_4 \rightarrow C_2H_5OC_2H_5 + H_2SO_4$$
$$C_2H_5OH + (C_2H_5)_2SO_4 \rightarrow C_2H_5OC_2H_5 + C_2H_5HSO_4$$

The direct hydration process involves a water-ethylene reaction, over a phosphoric acid catalyst, at about 400° C and 1000 psi.

$$C_2H_4 + H_2O \xrightarrow{H_3PO_4} C_2H_5OH$$

This method has the advantage of producing less by-product diethyl ether. Overall yield of ethanol is reported to be better than 97%.[141]

The production of acetalydehyde is the principal use of industrial alcohol, and accounts for about 55% of the total. Other uses are in solvents, synthetic rubber, drugs, and the synthesis of various chemicals, such as acetic acid, ethyl chloride, and ethyl acetate.

Polyethylene

Polyethylene has shown a spectacular rise, accounting for only 4% of the total ethylene consumption in 1950, and almost 25% ten years later. It is anticipated that in about 1967, polyethylene will assume the lead as the number-one ethylene consumer, surpassing ethylene oxide.[39]

Three types of process are currently used to produce polyethylene.[53] The conventional (high pressure) process is by far the oldest, and represents the largest share. The Ziegler (low pressure) and Phillips (intermediate pressure) are more recent processes. They produce a higher density polymer than does the first method.

Polyethylene is covered in detail in Chapter 10.

Ethylbenzene

It has been stated[89] that ethylbenzene and styrene are like grapes and wine in that one exists only for the production of the other. In 1960

TABLE 25.3. PRODUCTION AND SALES OF SOME
HALOGENATED HYDROCARBONS*

Halogenated Aliphatic	Production (1,000 lb)	Sales (1,000 lb)	Sales Value ($1,000)
Ethylene dichloride	1,140,112	354,771	17,423
Vinyl chloride	977,891	329,360	35,817
Ethyl chloride	550,816	210,418	15,730
Trichloroethylene	360,223	302,215	34,950
Perchloroethylene	202,992	185,990	19,604
Carbon tetrachloride	367,847	311,935	25,082
Dichlorodifluoromethane	157,132	151,716	46,830
Trichlorofluoromethane	60,421	. . . .	. . . .
Halogenated hydrocarbons	5,062,926	2,418,958	301,975

* Report of the U. S. Tariff Commission (1959).

they were the fourth largest consumer of ethylene, accounting for about 450 million pounds. In addition to being produced by the alkylation of benzene with ethylene, ethylbenzene is also extracted from C_8 hydrocarbon streams. This source could become more important as the demand for xylenes increases.

Principal uses for styrene are in polystyrene, synthetic rubber, and copolymers with butadiene. For more details see Chapter 10.

Chlorinated Hydrocarbons*

The manufacture of chlorinated hydrocarbons forms an important part of industrial chemistry today. The products are useful as solvents, chemical intermediates, pesticides, monomers, and in many other ways. Table 25.3 shows some of the large volume materials.[172]

* In collaboration with William E. Brown, Dow Chemical Company, Pittsburg, Cal.

Chlorinated derivatives of aliphatic hydrocarbons are usually prepared by one of three general methods: (1) addition of HCl to unsaturated hydrocarbons, (2) addition of chlorine to unsaturated hydrocarbons, or (3) substitution of chlorine for hydrogen in either saturated or unsaturated hydrocarbons. In the last case, hydrogen chloride is a by-product. Examples of the first method are the addition of HCl to ethylene to form ethyl chloride and the addition of HCl to acetylene to form vinyl chloride. Typical of the second method is the addition of chlorine to ethylene to

Figure 25.10. Chlorinated hydrocarbons plant. (*Courtesy Dow Chemical Co.*)

form dichloroethane. The third method of reaction, the direct substitution of chlorine for hydrogen, usually involves a free radical mechanism. The formation of chlorine free radicals occurs spontaneously at temperatures above 250° C and increases with temperature. The formation may also be brought about by the action of actinic light at lower temperatures. These light activated, or photochemical, chlorinations may be carried out in either the gas phase or the liquid phase.[102]

The principal uses for chlorinated hydrocarbons are as solvents, chemical intermediates, and insecticides. Their value as solvents derives from a combination of good solvent power, low flammability, and high vapor density. The latter property is particularly important in vapor degreasing of metal parts, a major use for trichloroethylene and perchloroethylene. Certain of the compounds are of value as chemical intermediates. Thus ethyl chloride is used to make tetraethyl lead, and dichloroethane is used to make vinyl chloride, which in turn is polymerized to polyvinyl chloride.

Ethylene Dichloride. While some ethylene dichloride occurs as a by-product of the chlorohydrin process, the bulk comes from the chlorination of ethylene. About 70 per cent of the ethylene dichloride produced goes into the manufacture of vinyl chloride monomer.[127] Figure 25.11 shows a vinyl

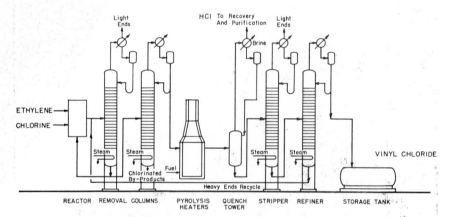

Figure 25.11. Vinyl chloride manufacture. (*Pet. Ref.*, **38**, *No. 11, 306 (1959), copyright Gulf Pub. Co.*)

chloride process starting from ethylene and chlorine with ethylene dichloride as an intermediate. In this process, ethylene and chlorine gas are charged to a reactor containing catalyst and excess dichloride as a solvent. The reaction goes essentially to completion at 50° C and 20 psig. The purified ethylene dichloride is then cracked in direct fired furnaces at about 400° C to produce a mixture containing principally hydrogen chloride, vinyl chloride and unreacted dichloride.[150] This extraction of hydrogen chloride from the dichloride can also be accomplished by treatment with caustic.

Profitable disposal of the HCl has been one of the major restrictions in the growth of this process for making vinyl chloride. Chlorine balance has been achieved in some recent plants by the use of a combined process, where ethylene dichloride is pyrolyzed, and the resulting HCl is then reacted with acetylene to produce additional vinyl chloride.

Most of the remaining ethylene dichloride production goes into the gasoline market, where it serves as a scavenger for tetraethyl lead; i.e., it forms combustible lead compounds during the burning process. It is also used in the synthesis of ethylene diamines by reaction with ammonia.

Ethyl Chloride. About 90 per cent of the ethyl chloride is produced by the addition of hydrogen chloride to ethylene in the presence of an aluminum chloride catalyst.

$$CH_2{=}CH_2 + HCl \xrightarrow{AlCl_3} CH_3CH_2Cl$$

This is a liquid phase reaction, carried out at about 40° C.[90] The remaining production comes from the catalytic reaction of hydrogen chloride with ethanol.

$$CH_3CH_2OH + HCl \xrightarrow{ZnCl_2} CH_3CH_2Cl + H_2O$$

The production of ethyl chloride is closely tied in with that of tetraethyl lead, which consumes almost 85 per cent of the former. It is also used in the production of ethyl cellulose, as a refrigerant, and as an anesthetic.

Tetraethyl lead is made by reacting ethyl chloride with a lead-sodium alloy (about 9 parts lead and 1 part sodium).[54]

$$4NaPb + 4C_2H_5Cl \rightarrow Pb(C_2H_5)_4 + 3Pb + 4NaCl$$

The crude product is purified by vacuum distillation and water washing. It is then blended with ethylene dichloride and ethylene dibromide to make the gasoline antiknock compound. At present, the outlook for tetraethyl lead is somewhat clouded by the advent of tetramethyl lead as a possible substitute.

Chlorinated Solvents. A group of compounds consisting of carbon tetrachloride, trichloroethylene, perchloroethylene, tetrachloroethane, and pentachloroethane comprises the chlorinated solvents.[56] Before World War II carbon tetrachloride dominated the group, but since that time both trichloroethylene and perchloroethylene have become important. While all of these materials are derived from methane, the structural similarity of all except CCl_4 with the ethylene-derived compounds causes their inclusion in this section. The scheme shown below gives an idea of the interrelationship of the five members.

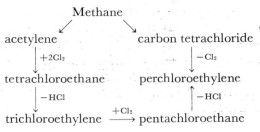

Trichloroethylene, the largest volume solvent, is formed by a two step process. In the first step, acetylene and chlorine are catalytically reacted in the liquid phase to produce tetrachloroethane

$$CH{\equiv}CH + 2Cl_2 \xrightarrow[80°\ C]{SbCl_3\ or\ FeCl_3} CHCl_2CHCl_2$$

In the second step, the tetrachloroethane is dehydrochlorinated either thermally, catalytically, or by reaction with lime. The catalytic method is the most common commercially, and involves a vapor-phase reaction over a bed of barium chloride at about 400–700° F.[148] More than 90%

$$CHCl_2CHCl_2 \rightarrow CHCl{=}CCl_2 + HCl$$

of the trichloroethylene produced is for vapor degreasing of metals, a field in which it has almost completely supplanted carbon tetrachloride.

The other major chlorinated solvent is perchloroethylene. This is made primarily by the pyrolysis of carbon tetrachloride,[147] although it may also be produced by the dehydrochlorination of pentachloroethane. At a temperature of 800–900° C the carbon tetrachloride readily decomposes into perchloroethylene and hexachloroethane.[52] The latter is recycled to produce more perchloroethylene. A modification of this process has been reported in which chlorine and a light hydrocarbon (such as natural gas or LPG) are fed into a chlorination furnace at 900–1200° F. Chlorination takes place readily, producing carbon tetrachloride and perchloroethylene. Undoubtedly the latter is again formed by the pyrolysis of CCl_4.

Most of the perchloroethylene is consumed by the dry-cleaning industry. A relatively small amount is used as a vapor degreasing solvent.

Other Halogenated Hydrocarbons. A considerable amount of ethylene dibromide is made by the addition of bromine to ethylene.[91] It is used as a lead scavenger in anti-knock fluids and as an agricultural fumigant. Smaller uses are as a solvent and in the synthesis of parmaceuticals and dye intermediates.

Fluorocarbons made their first impact on the chemical industry in 1931 with the introduction of *Freon* refrigerants (*Freon* and *Genetron* are the trademarks used by the two largest manufacturers).[7] The next major advance came during World War II with the development of fluorocarbon polymers and non-food aerosol propellents. By 1960, production was estimated at 250 million pounds, of which dichlorodifluoromethane accounted for more than half. The five main compounds today are as follows:

Fluorocarbon—12 (CCl_2F_2) is the most widely used fluorocarbon. It finds application in aerosol propellents, either alone or in combination with other gases, and as a refrigerant.

Fluorocarbon—11 (CCl_3F) is used with fluorocarbon 12 propellent to reduce the pressure in aerosols. It is also widely employed in air conditioning and process water cooling.

Fluorocarbon—22 ($CHClF_2$) is used in small-scale refrigeration and air conditioning units. Tetrafluoroethylene can be produced from this compound.

Fluorocarbon—113 (CCl_2FCClF_2) is used to improve the solvent properties of fluorocarbon 12 propellents. It can be dichlorinated to produce chlorotrifluoroethylene.

Fluorocarbon—114 ($CClF_2CClF_2$) is also used with fluorocarbon 12 propellent, particularly where the aerosol product contains a large amount of water.

In addition to refrigerants and non-food aerosol propellents, fluorocarbons are finding use in plastics, in particular the homopolymers of tetrafluoroethylene and chlorotrifluoroethylene (trademarked *Teflon* and *Kel-F*, respectively). These polymers are specially noted for their temperature resistance and chemical inertness. Also of importance is the elastomer (trademarked *Viton*) produced by the copolymerization of vinylidene fluoride and hexafluoropropylene.

Fluorocarbons find smaller markets as fire extinguishers (bromotrifluoromethane), blowing agents for urethane foams, solvents, and specialty lubricants. Because of the intensification of research in the last few years, it appears almost certain that the application of fluorocarbons will continue to expand. This is particularly true if a propellent can be found that is useful in food aerosols.

CHEMICALS DERIVED FROM PROPYLENE

Propylene as a chemical building block has recently been growing at a greatly accelerated pace. Although propylene was one of the first petroleum raw materials used in chemical manufacture (isopropyl alcohol), it was for many years left behind by rapid developments in ethylene derivatives.

Propylene is available in sufficient quantities to meet vast increases in chemical demand. This is based on an estimated total propylene production of 21 billion pounds per year of which 20 billion pounds comes from refineries and one billion from ethylene plants.[92] Chemical consumption of propylene in 1959 was 2.45 billion pounds, only 12 per cent of this total supply.[164]

A future complication for propylene suppliers will be the requirement of a relatively pure raw material for new derivatives such as polypropylene. This will require added distillation capacity and diversion of a propylene rich stream from polymer gasoline production.

The most important organic chemicals derived from propylene are isopropyl alcohol, dodecene, propylene oxide, nonene, cumene, glycerine and oxo chemicals.

Significant new uses for propylene which have strong growth potential are acrylonitrile and propylene homo- and copolymers.

Isopropyl Alcohol

Isopropyl alcohol is claimed by some to be the first petrochemical.[93] During the latter part of World War I the first isopropanol was manufactured by the Ellis process which was quite similar to the process used today. The flow sheet of Figure 25.13 shows a typical isopropanol process scheme.[122,158]

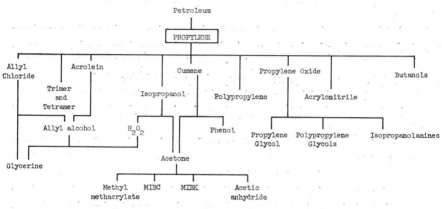

Figure 25.12. Major propylene derivatives.

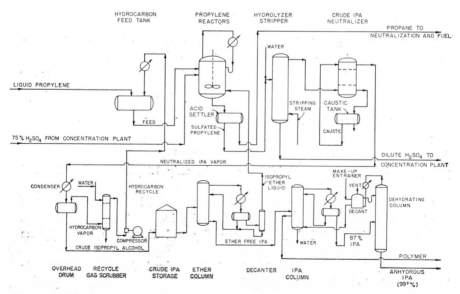

Figure 25.13. Isopropyl alcohol manufacture. (*Pet. Ref.*, **38**, *No. 11, 264 (1959)*, *copyright Gulf Pub. Co.*)

The liquid propylene feed-stock is combined with recycled hydrocarbons and the mixture sulfated at 300–400 psig. The sulfated mixture is then hydrolyzed to the alcohol, stripped from the acid, neutralized with caustic, degassed, distilled from the ether (ether is recycled back to the reactor), distilled to approach the binary azeotrope, and then finished in an azeotropic finishing column with an entrainer such as ethyl ether. The anhydrous product is taken from the bottom of the azeotropic still.

During 1959 some 1.05 billion pounds of propylene were used to produce 1.13 billion pounds of isopropanol.[106,165]

Acetone is the major consumer of isopropyl alcohol. In 1960 it was estimated that about 57% of the isopropanol would go into acetone production.[19] Other significant uses and consumption of isopropanol during 1960 were estimated to be: solvent uses, 15%; chemical manufacture other than acetone, 14%; rubbing alcohol and drugs, 9%; antistalling gasoline and de-icing, 4%; and other miscellaneous outlets including export, 5%.[94]

Acetone. Over 80% of current acetone production comes from isopropanol. By-product acetone from other processes is making inroads into the market and keener competition is expected in the future.

Acetone is made from isopropanol by either dehydrogenation or oxidation. Typical routes for manufacture of acetone from isopropanol are described below:

1. Dehydrogenation is the preferred process when acetone is the prime product.

$$CH_3CHOHCH_3 \rightarrow CH_3\overset{\overset{\displaystyle O}{\|}}{C}CH_3 + H_2$$

Copper, brass or supported zinc is used as the catalyst. This is a high temperature (500° C) low pressure (45 psi) operation leading to a high acetone yield. This process is very similar to that used for producing methyl ethyl ketone from secondary butanol as shown in flow sheet Figure 25.20.

2. Oxidation of isopropyl alcohol with air over a silver or copper catalyst is another route used. Thus:

$$CH_3CHOHCH_3 + \tfrac{1}{2}O_2 \rightarrow CH_3\overset{\overset{\displaystyle O}{\|}}{C}CH_3 + H_2O$$

3. Another, less direct, oxidation route is a liquid phase oxidation through isopropyl alcohol hydroperoxide as an intermediate:

$$2CH_3CHOHCH_3 + O_2 \xrightarrow{H_2O_2} 2CH_3\overset{\overset{\displaystyle OOH}{|}}{C}HCH_3 \xrightarrow{O_2} 2CH_3\overset{\overset{\displaystyle O}{\|}}{C}CH_3 + H_2O_2$$

This reaction is carried out in the liquid phase with oxygen at 100 to 105° C. By this route 25% hydrogen peroxide is produced in 90% yield and acetone is considered the by-product.

4. Acetone is also a by-product of the reaction between isopropanol and acrolein to obtain allyl alcohol.

$$CH_3CHOHCH_3 + CH_2{=}CHCH \rightarrow CH_3\overset{O}{\overset{\|}{C}}CH_3 + CH_2{=}CHCH_2OH$$

The allyl alcohol and hydrogen peroxide from (3) and (4) are both used in a new synthesis of glycerol.

One other process not based on isopropanol generates a significant amount of acetone as a by-product. This is the cumene-phenol process as shown in the reaction below:

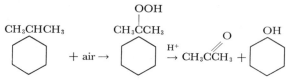

It is estimated[20] that in 1960 acetone end-use was distributed as follows: derivative solvents (methyl isobutyl ketone, methyl isobutyl carbinol, mesityl oxide, diacetone alcohol, hexylene glycol, phorone, and isophorone), 44 per cent; directly as solvent (paint, varnish, lacquer, cellulose acetate, acetylene, miscellaneous), 29 per cent; methyl methacrylate, 14 per cent; drugs, vitamins, and other chemicals such as bisphenol-A, acetyl acetone, and ketene, 12 per cent; and export about 1 per cent.

Isopropanol Derived Chemicals (Other Than Acetone). Leading the chemicals which fall into this category are such materials as isopropyl acetate and xanthates. Materials of this sort provide an outlet for approximately 14% of the isopropanol produced in the U. S.

Isopropyl Alcohol Solvent. A significant amount of isopropanol is used as a solvent for essential and other oils, gums, shellac, rosins and synthetic resins. Isopropanol is an excellent solvent for these materials and thus finds extensive use for compounding or blending numerous incompatible substances.[123] As a component of nitrocellulose lacquer solutions, isopropyl alcohol improves blush resistance and increases solvency in esters and ketones.[124]

Dodecene, Nonene and Cumene

The manufacturing processes for these materials are very similar. The flowsheets of Figures 25.14 and 25.15 show dodecene (tetrapropylene) and nonene (tripropylene) in one and cumene in the other.

When nonene is the desired product, additional fractionation is required, the extent of which is determined by the product specifications.

In the reactor portion of this process, the olefin stock is mixed with benzene (for cumene) or recycle lights (for tetramer). The resulting charge is pumped to the reaction chamber. The catalyst, solid phosphoric acid, is maintained in separate beds in the reactor. Suitable propane quench is provided between beds for temperature control purposes, since the reaction is exothermic.

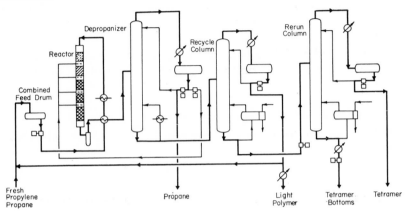

Figure 25.14. Propylene tetramer process. [*Pet. Ref.*, **36**, *No. 11, 278 (1957)*, *copyright Gulf Pub. Co.*]

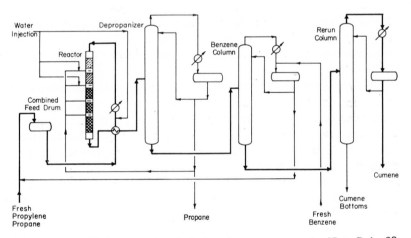

Figure 25.15. Olefin-aromatic alkylation (cumene process). [*Pet Ref.*, **38**, *No. 11, 279 (1959), copyright Gulf Pub. Co.*]

This same process may be used for manufacturing ethylbenzene from ethylene and benzene.

Dodecene[122] is an intermediate for surfactants, going mainly through two routes. One, the largest user, produces dodecyl benzene sulfonate anionic detergents (see process description Chapter 13). The other goes through the oxo process to tridecyl alcohol, which is then converted into a nonionic detergent by the addition of alkylene oxides.

Nonene has two major outlets.[21] The larger one is oxo production of decyl alcohol which is used in the manufacture of esters, etc. for plasticizers. The other significant nonene use is in the manufacture of nonyl phenol, an intermediate for the important series of ethoxylated nonyl phenol nonionic surfactants.

Cumene is used mainly as an intermediate for phenol-acetone manufacture. A relatively small amount of cumene is used to manufacture α-methyl styrene.

Propylene Oxide

Propylene oxide is manufactured entirely by the chlorohydrin route.[22] This process is described under *Ethylene Oxide*. It is difficult to pinpoint capacity, since plants can readily be used for either ethylene or propylene. Production in 1959 is shown as 288 million pounds.[107]

Major uses for propylene oxide are propylene glycol, polypropylene glycols, and isopropanolamines.

Propylene Glycol. Propylene glycol manufacture is carried out with the same process as that used for ethylene glycol. That is, oxide hydrolysis, water removal and product purification.

Propylene glycol is used as an ingredient in hydraulic fluids, as an intermediate in the manufacture of polyesters, and USP-grade is sold for use in cosmetics and as a tobacco humectant. Production in 1959 was 152 million pounds.[166]

Polypropylene Glycols. Polypropylene glycols are prepared commercially by the condensation of propylene oxide. Propylene oxide is added to such starting materials as propylene glycol, glycerine, pentaerythritol, sucrose, sorbitol, etc. depending upon the viscosity, hydroxyl functionality, etc., desired. These starting materials contain a small proportion of sodium hydroxide[117] to act as catalyst.

Polypropylene glycols and polyglycols which are co-condensation products of ethylene and propylene oxide are used as lubricants, as hydraulic fluid components, as mold release agents, and as the polyether portion in polyurethane foam.

Approximately 125 million pounds of polypropylene glycols were produced during 1959. About 90% of these polyols were sold to the polyurethane industry. Use in polyurethanes is growing at a fast pace. For polyurethane uses see *toluene diisocyanate*.

Isopropanolamines. These products are manufactured by processing which is similar to that used for ethanolamines, that is, the reaction of ammonia with propylene oxide.

Likewise, uses for isopropanolamine are closely allied to those of ethanolamines, i.e., in the synthesis of detergents, wetting agents, and dyes.

Oxochemicals

A considerable quantity of propylene is used either directly or indirectly by the producers of oxo alcohols. Estimated 1960 output of oxo alcohols was some 170 million pounds.[95]

The oxo process description is shown under *Methane Chemicals*.

Butyl Alcohols and Aldehydes. Hydroformylation of propylene produces a mixture of n-butyraldehyde and isobutyraldehyde. The aldehyde ratio is approximately 2 to to 1 in favor of n-butyraldehyde, but this ratio may be varied somewhat. The aldehydes may be used separately or the mixed aldehydes may be hydrogenated to the corresponding alcohols (n-butanol and isobutanol) which are then separated.

n-Butyl alcohol is well established as a solvent and as an intermediate for plasticizers and resins. Isobutyl alcohol has many uses similar to those of n-butyl alcohol.

Isobutyraldehyde is used to produce higher molecular weight mono and dihydroxy aldol condensation products such as 2-ethylisohexanol, neopentyl glycol, nonyl alcohol, and 2,2,4-trimethyl-1,3 pentanediol. Isobutyronitrile is made by reacting isobutyraldehyde with ammonia, then dehydrogenating to the nitrile.

Higher Oxo Alcohols. Oxo alcohols of major importance derived from propylene are decyl alcohol (from nonene) and tridecyl alcohol (from dodecene). Uses of these alcohols are described under *Nonene* and *Dodecene*.

One other significant higher oxo alcohol is isooctyl alcohol, derived from a dimer of propylene and butylene. The isooctyl alcohol mixture derived from this oxo reaction contains 26% 4,5-dimethyl-1-hexanol; 13% 3,5-dimethyl-1-hexanol; 18% 3,4-dimethyl-1-hexanol; 17% 3-, and 5-methyl-1-heptanol; and 9% other isomers. Esters of this mixture are used mainly as plasticizers for vinyl chloride resins.

The future of the oxo alcohols depends upon the expansion of the current uses in plasticizers and detergents and the development of other new uses.

Glycerine

Synthetic glycerine (glycerol) is manufactured by two main routes as shown by the chemical reactions below:

1. Epichlorohydrin route:

$$CH_3CH{=}CH_2 + Cl_2 \xrightarrow[\text{15 psig}]{\text{650--950° F}} H_2C{=}CHCH_2{-}\underset{Cl}{|} \xrightarrow[\text{85--100° F}]{\text{HOCl}} CH_2{-}CH{-}CH_2$$
$$\underset{OH}{|}\ \underset{Cl}{|}\ \underset{Cl}{|}$$

$$CH_2{-}CH{-}CH_2 \xrightarrow[\text{<140° F}]{\text{Ca(OH)}_2} CH_2{-}CH{-}CH_2 \xrightarrow{\text{10\% NaOH}} CH_2{-}CH{-}CH_2$$
$$\underset{OH}{|}\ \underset{Cl}{|}\ \underset{Cl}{|} \qquad \underset{O}{\diagdown\ \diagup}\ \underset{Cl}{|} \qquad \underset{OH}{|}\ \underset{OH}{|}\ \underset{OH}{|}$$

2. Acrolein and hydrogen peroxide:

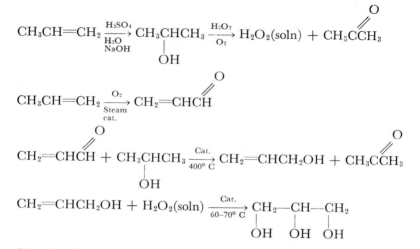

$$CH_3CH{=}CH_2 \xrightarrow[\substack{H_2O \\ NaOH}]{H_2SO_4} CH_3CHCH_3 \xrightarrow[O_2]{H_2O_2} H_2O_2(soln) + CH_3\overset{O}{\overset{\|}{C}}CH_3$$
$$\underset{OH}{|}$$

$$CH_3CH{=}CH_2 \xrightarrow[\substack{Steam \\ cat.}]{O_2} CH_2{=}CH\overset{O}{\overset{\|}{C}}H$$

$$CH_2{=}CH\overset{O}{\overset{\|}{C}}H + CH_3CHCH_3 \xrightarrow[400°\ C]{Cat.} CH_2{=}CHCH_2OH + CH_3\overset{O}{\overset{\|}{C}}CH_3$$
$$\underset{OH}{|}$$

$$CH_2{=}CHCH_2OH + H_2O_2(soln) \xrightarrow[60-70°\ C]{Cat.} \underset{\substack{| \\ OH}}{CH_2}{-}\underset{\substack{| \\ OH}}{CH}{-}\underset{\substack{| \\ OH}}{CH_2}$$

Glycerine by the Epichlorohydrin Process. In the epichlorohydrin process synthetic glycerine is produced in three successive operations; the end products of these are allyl chloride, epichlorohydrin, and finished glycerine, respectively. A flow sheet[157] for this process is shown in Figure 25.16. A portion of the allyl chloride is used to manufacture allyl alcohol and a portion of the epichlorohydrin is used in the manufacture of epoxy resins.

The key reaction in this process is the hot chlorination of propylene which fairly selectively gives substitution rather than the addition reactions. In this chlorination step fresh propylene is first mixed with recycle propylene. This mixture is dried over a desiccant, heated to 650–700° F, then mixed rapidly with chlorine (C_3H_6/Cl_2 ratio = 4:1) and fed to a simple steel tube adiabatic reactor. The effluent gases (950° F) are cooled quickly to 120° F and fractionated. Yield of allyl chloride is 80–85%.

Hypochlorous acid is then reacted with the allyl chloride at 85 to 100° F to form a mixture of dichlorohydrins. The reactor effluent is separated, the aqueous phase returning to make up hypochlorous acid, while the non-aqueous phase containing the dichlorohydrins is reacted with a lime slurry to form epichlorohydrin. Epichlorohydrin is steam distilled out and given a finishing distillation.

Glycerine is formed by the hydrolysis of epichlorohydrin with 10% caustic. Crude glycerine is separated from this reaction mass by multiple effect evaporation to remove salt and most of the water. A final vacuum distillation yields a 99+% product.

Glycerine by Acrolein and Hydrogen Peroxide Process. This process is used to manufacture glycerine, but large amounts of acetone are obtained as a co-product. Basic raw materials consumed are propylene and oxygen.

Glycerine is synthesized in this process by hydroxylation of allyl alcohol with hydrogen peroxide. The flowsheet in Figure 13.18 shows the processing scheme.

Glycerine Uses. An estimated 260 million pounds of glycerine were consumed in 1960.[23] About half of this was obtained from natural sources and the remainder from synthetic manufacture.

Glycerine end-use may be divided as follows: alkyd resins and ester gums, 35 per cent; cellophane, 21 per cent; tobacco, 15 per cent; explosives, 10

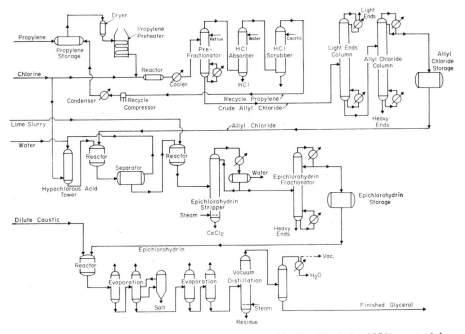

Figure 25.16. Manufacture of glycerol. [*Pet. Ref.*, **38**, No. 11, 252 (1959), *copyright Gulf Pub. Co.*]

per cent; cosmetics and dentifrices, 6 per cent; other drugs and pharmaceuticals, 5 per cent; miscellaneous (food, paper, cork, gaskets, etc.), 8 per cent.

New Propylene Derivatives

Acrylonitrile. Three new processes for manufacturing acrylonitrile from propylene and ammonia are described briefly in the section on chemicals from methane. (See flowsheet Figure 25.17 for a processing scheme.) Based on reports that a propylene-ammonia plant to produce acrylonitrile costs about ⅓ as much as one using the acetylene-hydrogen cyanide process, on an annual-ton basis, one may expect trends in new plant construction to favor the newer processes.

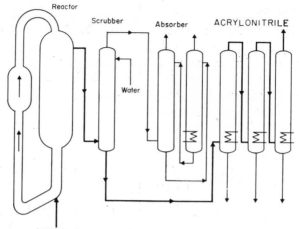

Figure 25.17. Acrylonitrile manufacture from propylene.
[*Chem. Week*, **87**, *No. 4, 39 (1961.)*]

Polypropylene

Polypropylene is a rapidly growing plastic material. It is estimated production will have gone from 20 million pounds in 1959 to 100 million pounds in 1961. However, despite its rapid growth, overcapacity will probably persist for some years. The greatest market potentials for polypropylene appear to be in film, fibers and plastic products.

Polypropylene, allyl chloride, acrolein, and oxo chemicals are demanding new super-pure propylene.[33] This need is due mainly to the sensitivity and, in the case of polypropylene, extreme reactivity of the catalysts used. Also, product quality standards are very high and can be controlled to some extent by raw material purity.

BUTANE AND BUTYLENE CHEMICALS

Consumption of butanes and butylenes in the manufacture of synthetic organic chemicals was more than 3.5 billion pounds in 1960. These materials rank second (behind ethylene) as a raw material for chemical manufacture. However, some 75% goes into the production of one chemical, butadiene. The other significant butyl derivatives are produced from the olefins (*n*-butenes and isobutene) and from hydrocarbon (butane and LPG) oxidation.

n-Butylenes

About 85% of C_4 olefins come from refinery streams. This represents only about 10–15% of the total available in these streams.[96] The remainder comes from dehydrogenation of butane and as by-products of ethylene manufacture.

The basic problem of obtaining C_4 olefins is that of separation. Isobutylene is removed by absorption in 65% sulfuric acid. With isobutylene removed, isobutane and 1-butene are separated from n-butane and the 2-butenes by fractionation. The olefins can then be separated from the paraffin hydrocarbons by extractive distillation (with furfural, actone, etc.). Available today are commercial quantities of 1-butene and 2-butene, 95% pure or higher. The 2-butene is a mixture of the *cis* and *trans* isomers.

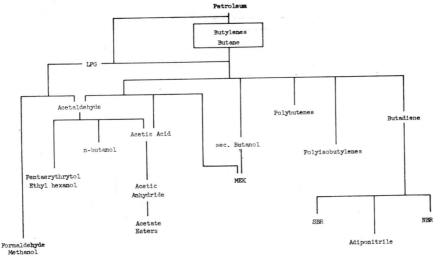

Figure 25.18. Chemicals from butanes, butenes, and LPG.

Butadiene

Butadiene is produced by the dehydrogenation of n-butenes or it may be produced as a co-product with butenes in the dehydrogenation of butane. A flowsheet of the latter processing scheme is shown in Figure 25.19.[152,155] Both are fixed-bed catalytic dehydrogenation processes. Slightly higher yields of butadiene may be obtained from butene, but overall economics, utilization of the resulting product mixture, and feed streams readily available determine the route.

Butadiene production in 1960 was approximately 950,000 short tons.[8] Some 85 per cent of butadiene goes into styrene-butadiene rubber. Other uses are nitrile rubber, 3 per cent; adiponitrile, 4 per cent; high impact polystyrene and paint latexes, 3 per cent; export and miscellaneous uses, 5 per cent.

A promising new outlet is polybutadiene blended with natural rubber about half and half. This is reported to give some improved properties over natural rubber.

For more detail on polymerization, manufacture and uses of butadiene rubber see Chapter 9, "Rubber."

Methyl Ethyl Ketone. The largest end-product chemical use for *n*-butenes is in the manufacture of *sec*-butanol. A mixed feed containing butane and *n*-butenes is contacted with 80 per cent sulfuric acid. Dilution and steam stripping then produces the alcohol. The only important use of *sec*-butanol is the production of methyl ethyl ketone (MEK).

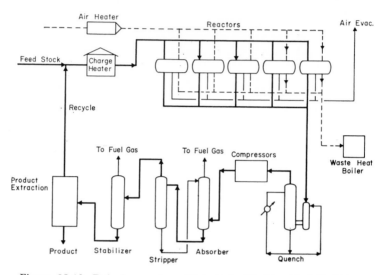

Figure 25.19. Dehydrogenation. [*Pet. Ref.*, **38**, *No. 11, 233 (1959),
copyright Gulf Pub. Co.*]

MEK is obtained by catalytic dehydrogenation of *sec*-butanol. A yield of approximately 75 per cent is obtained in this step. A flow sheet,[160] Figure 25.20, shows an integrated process for producing *sec*-butanol and MEK.

Approximately 85% of MEK is manufactured by the *sec*-butanol route. An alternate route is oxidation of butane.

MEK is used almost wholly as a solvent. Consumption in the U. S. during 1961 was estimated at 235 million pounds, distributed as follows:[27] vinyl resin lacquers, 34 per cent; nitrocellulose lacquers, 28 per cent; other coatings (including acrylic), 6 per cent; lube oil dewaxing, 6 per cent; paint removers and miscellaneous solvent uses, 9 per cent; rubber cement, adhesives, 6 per cent; exports, 5 per cent; other uses (including nonsolvent), 6 per cent.

Oxo Derivatives of *n*-Butenes. Amyl alcohols are produced from *n*-butenes by the oxo process to give approximately a 50-50 mixture of *n*-amyl alcohol and *sec*-amyl alcohol. These alcohols are used as solvents and as intermediates in the manufacture of plasticizers. A mixture of hepenes results from the dimer of propylene and *n*-butylenes (see *nonene* and *dodecene* for process scheme). Oxo processing of this mixture gives isooctyl alcohols. A similar *n*-butylene dimer yields nonyl alcohol by the oxo process. These alcohols are used mainly to make ester plasticizers.

It was estimated that some 65 million pounds of *n*-butene derived oxo alcohols were produced in 1960.

Other interesting chemicals which are derived from *n*-butenes are butylene oxide[108] and maleic anhydride.[6]

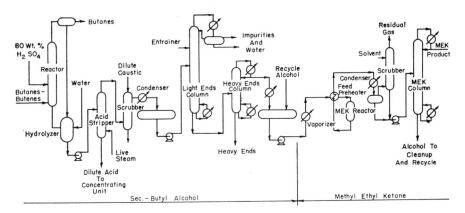

Figure 25.20. Methyl ethyl ketone or acetone. [*Pet. Ref.*, **38**, *No. 11, 272 (1959), copyright Gulf Pub. Co.*]

Polymers and Copolymers. Isotactic polymers of 1-butene are in the development stage and show promise for films because of high tear-resistance and chemical stability.[108]

Copolymers of 1-butene and ethylene or propylene are said to give superior stress cracking and brittleness performance over ethylene or propylene homopolymers. The applications are in such areas as pipe, rope, wire coatings, bottles, and dishes.[108] These copolymer uses are expected to boost the market for *n*-butylenes considerably.

Isobutylene

Isobutylene is more reactive than the *n*-butenes, but many of the compounds formed are quite readily reversible under less than extreme conditions.

About 95% of isobutylene used in the chemical industry goes into di- and triisobutylenes, butyl rubber and other polymers.[98]

t-Butyl Phenols. t-Butyl phenols are formed by the reaction of phenolic compounds with isobutylene using sulfuric acid as catalyst.

These compounds are used as intermediates for bactericides, oil soluble phenol-formaldehyde resins, and antioxidants.[99] Some 35 million pounds of compounds in this class are used annually, requiring about 20 million pounds of isobutylene.[25]

t-**Butyl Alcohol.** The hydration of isobutylene to *t*-butyl alcohol goes readily at mild acid conditions. The alcohol is easily dehydrated under acidic conditions, thus it must be isolated from a dilute acid or neutral system. This property limits the use of this alcohol. Also limiting its use is its relatively high (25.6° C) freezing point. Current (1960) production is approximately 30 million pounds annually.

Isoprene. The Prins reaction between isobutylene and formaldehyde has been used somewhat to produce 4,4-di-methyl-1,3-dioxane as an intermediate. The second step converts this intermediate catalytically to isoprene and formaldehyde.[100] Yields of approximately 76% on formaldehyde and 83% on isobutylene have been reported. Commercial use is still restricted by cost since such materials as butadiene and styrene made on a mammoth scale make competition stiff.

Dimers and Trimers of Isobutylene. A mixture of dimer and trimer of isobutylene is produced by absorbing isobutylene in 60–65% sulfuric acid at 10–20° C, then reacting at 80–100° C for ½ hour.[101]

The main chemical use of the dimer mixture is in the alkylation of phenols to octyl phenols for detergent use. Nonyl alcohol is also produced from this dimer by the oxo process.

Use of diisobutylene is limited by its tendency to thermally depolymerize to isobutylene. Thus, only low temperature reaction conditions can be utilized.

Approximately 100 million pounds of diisobutylene are produced annually.[101]

Polybutenes and Polyisobutylenes.[101] Polymerization of isobutylene can be carried out with such catalysts as boron trifluoride and aluminum chloride. This gives a wide range of polymers—from viscous liquids (called polybutenes) to semi-solid and solid polymers (called polyisobutylenes).

Polybutenes are very stable materials with good oxygen or ozone resistance. These are highly saturated materials which do not set or "dry" on storage or use. Important industrial applications are in caulking and sealing compounds, adhesives, surgical tapes, vibration dampers, electrical insulations and special lubricants. Output of polybutenes in 1960 was estimated at 90 million pounds.[26]

Polyisobutylenes vary from soft, sticky gums to tough, elastic materials. Stability and resistance to chemical attack are excellent. Polyisobutylenes are used as tacky agents for oils to avoid dripping and splattering from bearings and rotating shafts, etc. These materials are also used as a viscosity index improver for oil and hydraulic fluids. Estimated 1960 output of polyisobutylenes was 25 million pounds.[26]

Butyl Rubber.[101] Low temperature copolymerization of isobutylene (98%) and isoprene (2%) produces a solid, rubber-like, vulcanizable polymer. Butyl rubber has unusually low gas permeability and thus has found extensive use in tire inner tubes and pneumatic bags. Chemical variations such as chlorine-containing butyl rubbers have made butyl rubber compatible with SBR and natural rubber for blending purposes. See Chapter 9 for more details.

Output of some 210 million pounds of butyl rubber was estimated for 1960.[26]

Hydrocarbon Oxidation

Oxidation of Propane-Butane (LPG) Mixtures. Liquified Petroleum Gas (LPG) is the name given to a mixture of hydrocarbons consisting primarily of ethane, propane, butane, C_5 (mixed 5-carbon materials), and naptha.[36] About 30% of the 10 billion gallons produced in 1960 was sold to the chemical and rubber industry, an increase of almost 20% over 1959.[9] Nearly two-thirds of the LPG utilized by the chemical industry was consumed by four large-volume petrochemicals; ethylene, propylene, butadiene, and isoprene. It is expected that this use of LPG in the chemical industry will increase during the next few years due to the new pipeline systems which are making it available throughout the country.

One of the smaller but very interesting chemical uses of LPG is the oxidation of butane and butane-propane mixtures.

In 1945, the first major plant for the oxidation of propane and butane was brought on-stream. This was a non-catalytic, vapor phase oxidation which yielded as its principal products formaldehyde, acetaldehyde, and methanol. In addition to these three chemicals, smaller amounts of propionaldehyde, acrolein, ethanol, glycols, and various alcohols and ketones are produced, depending on the nature of the hydrocarbon feed. The number of these products increases with the complexity of the hydrocarbon; propane gives a total of 16 oxygenated compounds, while the oxidation of n-hexane could produce about 60.[130] A few of the possible propane-oxidation reactions are as follows.[128]

$$C_3H_8 + O \rightarrow \text{Acetaldehyde} + CO_2 + H_2O$$
$$\rightarrow \text{Methanol} + \text{Formaldehyde} + CO + H_2O$$
$$\rightarrow \text{Formaldehyde} + \text{Acetaldehyde} + CO + H_2O$$
$$\rightarrow \text{Propionaldehyde} + H_2O$$
$$\rightarrow \text{Ethylene} + \text{Methanol} + CO + H_2O$$

The flowsheet in Figure 25.21 shows the process for the oxidation of a propane and butane mixture. This could be divided into four sections; primary oxidation, formaldehyde concentration, product separation and purification, and secondary oxidation.[156]

In the primary oxidation section the hydrocarbon mixture and compressed air (about a 1:2 ratio) are mixed with a recycle stream and fed into
the reactor at about 100 psig and 700° F (recently, the operation was
switched from air to 95% oxygen). The reactor is a long empty steel tube
in which the temperature rises to about 850° F due to the exothermic nature
of the reaction.[128] The reaction gases are cooled and passed through a
water scrubbing system. The unconverted material is recycled, while the
water solution passes to a separator where dilute formaldehyde is drawn off.

The dilute formaldehyde solution contains about 20–25% formaldehyde
and 10–20% volatile material. This stream is steam stripped and purified

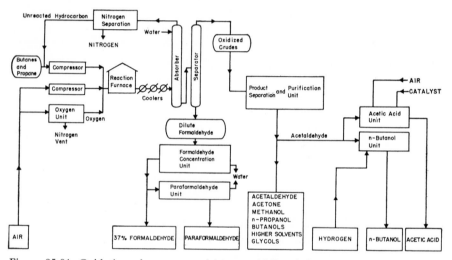

Figure 25.21. Oxidation of propane and butane. (*Oil and Gas J., 115, Sept. 2, 1957*)

to produce a 37% solution (formalin). Some of the formalin is further
processed, essentially by dehydration, to yield paraformaldehyde and
trioxane.

In the first step of the separation and purification section, acetaldehyde is
removed from the crude mixture by fractionation and sent to storage, either
for later sale or further up-grading. The remaining water-crude mixture is
next distilled to separate the acetone and methanol. The remaining material
is hydrogenated and then fractionated to yield propanol, isobutanol, glycols,
and various special solvents. Some of the acetaldehyde undergoes aldoling
to produce *n*-butanol and other materials.

A portion of the acetaldehyde is fed to the secondary oxidation section.
Here it is readily converted by catalytic oxidation to acetic acid.

Oxidation of Butane. Of more recent origin is the catalytic oxidation of
butane, which incidentally emphasizes the trend toward increased product

selectivity in oxidation processes. This employs a liquid-phase, high-pressure (850 psi) oxidation using acetic acid as a diluent, and a metal acetate catalyst.[96] Figure 25.22 shows the flowsheet for this process. From the reactor, the product mixture is passed through coolers, and then through separators where the dissolved gases are released. The major components of the oxidized crude are acetic acid, methanol, acetone, and acetaldehyde.[132] It should be noted that unlike the propane-butane oxidation, this process

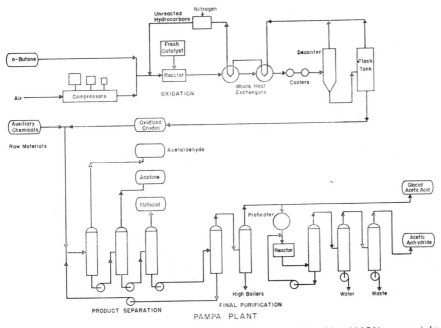

Figure 25.22. Oxidation of butane. [*Pet Ref.*, **38**, *No. 11*, *234* (*1959*), *copyright Gulf Pub. Co.*]

produces no formaldehyde. The separation and purification procedure is similar to that described previously. Part of the acetic acid, which is the major product, is converted in a separate unit at high efficiencies to acetic anhydride. Also connected with this plant are units for producing vinyl acetate, methyl acrylate, and ethyl acrylate.

Reaction conditions in this process can be changed to produce methyl ethyl ketone at the expense of some acetic acid.

Oxidation Products. Most of the chemicals produced by the oxidation of propane and butanes have been described in connection with other methods of preparation. Consequently, methanol, acetone, formaldehyde, propanol, methyl ethyl ketone and others will not be discussed here. Of interest, there remain acetaldehyde, butanol, and related materials.

Acetaldehyde is also produced commercially by the catalytic hydration of acetylene and by the oxidation of ethanol.[40] Recently,[12] announcement was made of a process for the direct oxidation of ethylene to acetaldehyde. This involves reaction of ethylene with either air or oxygen in a solution of cupric and palladium chlorides. Most acetaldehyde is used in the manufacture of other chemicals and never leaves the plant in which it is produced. The most important derivatives are acetic acid, acetic anhydride, butanol, pentaerythritrol, and other aldol products.

Acetic anhydride can be produced by the catalytic oxidation of acetaldehyde.[41] It can also be made from acetic acid (which is also made from acetaldehyde) through an intermediate called ketene.

$$CH_3COOH \rightarrow CH_2{=}C{=}O + H_2O$$
$$CH_3COOH + CH_2{=}C{=}O \rightarrow (CH_3CO)_2O$$

This reaction takes place at high temperatures, and uses a triethylphosphate catalyst. It is also possible to produce ketene from acetone at high temperatures.

$$CH_3COCH_3 \rightarrow CH_2{=}C{=}O$$

It is expected that the future of acetic anhydride will continue to be closely allied with that of its principal user, cellulose acetate.

In addition to being used to make acetic acid and anhydride, some of the acetaldehyde is up-graded to n-butanol by the aldol process.[45] The steps in the reaction are: (1) the acetaldehyde is condensed to aldol, (2) the aldol is dehydrated to crotonaldehyde, and (3) the crotonaldehyde is hydrogenated (180° C, nickel-chrome catalyst) to yield n-butanol.[108]

$$2CH_3CHO \rightarrow CH_3CH(OH)CH_2CHO \rightarrow CH_3CH{=}CHCHO \rightarrow$$
$$CH_3CH_2CH_2CH_2OH$$

The synthetic process for producing butanol has almost completely replaced fermentation, even though in 1944 nearly 80% was made by the latter method. A large user of butanol is the surface coatings industry, where it has found great acceptance as a solvent for lacquers. Other uses are in the manufacture of butyl acetate (also a lacquer solvent), in plasticizers, and in resins.

One of the newest chemicals derived from the hydrocarbon oxidation process is trimethylopropane (TMP). This is also made by an aldol condensation (formaldehyde and butyraldehyde).[5] TMP is used in polyesters for both rigid and flexible polyurethane foams, and shows promise as an ingredient in alkyd resins.

AROMATIC CHEMICALS

Until World War II, coal tar was the only source of basic aromatic raw materials. Since then, petroleum as a source of aromatics has gained rapidly to the point where today 67% of benzene, 89% of toluene, and 97% of xylenes are derived from petroleum. The first petro-naphthalene plant[59] was put on stream as recently as early 1961.

Specific processing methods for obtaining these raw materials from petroleum sources are described in Chapter 14.

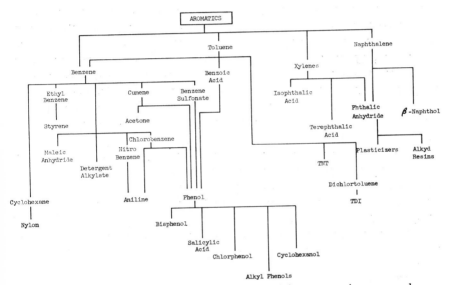

Figure 25.23. Synthetic organic chemicals derived from aromatic compounds.

Benzene, toluene and xylenes are also produced by fractional distillation of light oils obtained from high temperature carbonization of coal, while naphthalene, anthracene and other multi-ring compounds are recovered from tar oils, a high boiling fraction obtained from coal carbonization.[60,131]

Benzene Products

Benzene is the most important aromatic chemical. During 1960 some 473 million gallons were consumed in the United States.[61]

Benzene has a broad end-use pattern. Styrene monomer, phenol, nylon, and maleic anhydride are the major benzene derivatives. These materials appear to be heading for continued growth. Other important benzene outlets are synthetic detergents, aniline, DDT, chlorobenzenes (other than for making phenol), and benzene hexachloride.

Styrene. Styrene manufacture is by far the largest use of benzene. Some 220 million gallons of benzene yielded about 1.75 billion pounds of styrene monomer in 1960.[61] Styrene monomer is made by cracking (dehydrogenating) ethyl benzene (see Chapter 9 for details).

The major uses for styrene are in plastics, rubber, latex paints and coatings, synthetic rubber, polyesters and styrene alkyd protective coatings. In these uses styrene is polymerized as a homopolymer or as copolymers with such materials as acrylonitrile, butadiene, maleic anhydride and glycols. Further details may be found in the chapters on Plastics, Rubber, and Coatings.

Phenol. Synthetic phenol is the second largest market for benzene. Approximately 102 million gallons of benzene were used to manufacture 725 million pounds of phenol in 1960.[1,62] Four different processes are currently used in the U. S. These are sulfonation, chlorobenzene, Raschig, and cumene. Each requires benzene as a raw material. A plant to manufacture phenol from toluene is under construction.[1,62] It is reported that a process to manufacture phenol by the direct oxidation of benzene has been developed and will soon see commercial use.[1] Details of phenol manufacturing processes are given in Chapter 10.

Phenolic Resins. Phenolic resins are the major consumers of phenol and should maintain this position indefinitely. Phenol based epoxy resins are growing rapidly into such uses as adhesives, high strength plastics, coatings and potting compounds. See Chapter 10, "Plastics," for details on phenolic resins.

Bisphenol A. Polycarbonates are a growing new plastic derived from bisphenol A which is in turn obtained from phenol by the following reaction:

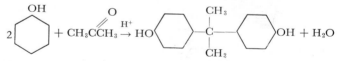

A flow sheet for bisphenol A manufacture is shown in Figure 25.24.

Phenol and acetone in a molar ratio of 3:1 or 4:1 are charged to an acid-resistant stirred bisphenol A reactor. Glass-lined equipment is used ordinarily. A sulfur-containing catalyst is added, then dry HCl gas is bubbled into the reaction mass. The temperature is maintained at 30 to 40° C for 8–12 hours. The product crystallizes from the reaction mixture to form a slurry.

At the end of the reaction, the mixture is water washed and treated with just enough lime to neutralize the free acid. Vacuum and heat are applied to the reaction kettle and water and phenol are distilled separately from the mixture. The batch is finished by blowing the molten product with steam under vacuum at 150° C to remove the odor of the sulfur-containing catalyst.

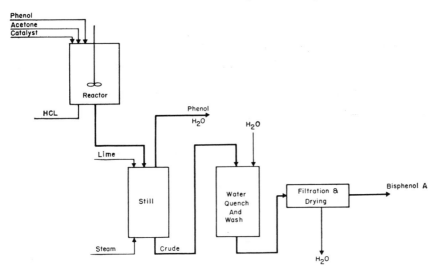

Figure 25.24. Manufacture of bisphenol A. [*Pet. Ref.*, *38, No. 11, 225 (1959)*, *copyright Gulf Pub. Co.*]

Figure 25.25. Bisphenol A plant. (*Courtesy Dow Chemical Co.*)

The molten bisphenol A product is quenched in a large volume of water, filtered, and dried. It is a light tan powder, which may be further purified by recrystallization from solvents.

Other Products from Phenol. Phenol is used extensively in the synthesis of numerous other organic chemicals including aspirin, alkylated phenols, chlorinated phenols (to 2,4D), caprolactam and others. Chemical reactions for some of these materials are shown below:

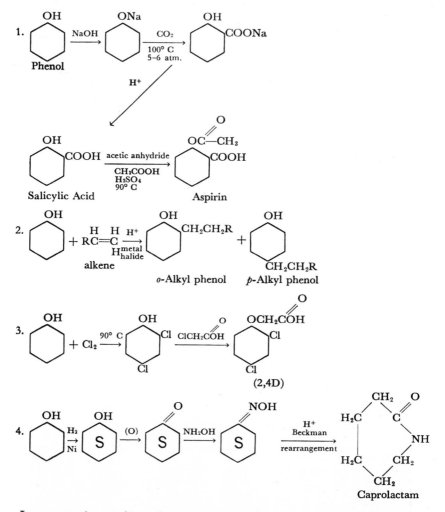

Important by-products from the chlorobenzene process which are now substantial volume chemicals[3] are phenyl phenols, numerous chloro phenols, and Dowtherm A (a eutectic mixture of diphenyl and diphenyl oxide sold as a heat transfer medium).

Nylon. Nylon is the third largest consumer of benzene. During 1960 some 37 million gallons of benzene was used in nylon manufacture yielding about 390 million pounds of nylon.[63] Nylon 66, produced from adipic acid and hexamethylene diamine, is the major current domestic nylon. Nylon 6, derived from caprolactam is gaining rapidly. These intermediates are mainly derived from benzene by various routes. See Chapter 11.

Detergent Alkylate. Alkylbenzene is an intermediate in the manufacture of synthetic detergents. Production during 1960 was approximately 470 million pounds from about 35 million gallons of benzene.[64]

Alkyl benzenes are mostly dodecyl and tridecyl benzene. To make synthetic detergents, propylene polymer is reacted with benzene, fractionated to 350–420° F boiling range, then the resulting alkylate is sulfonated and neutralized, blended with chemical "builders," and flake dried. The following chemical reactions are carried out in the processing:

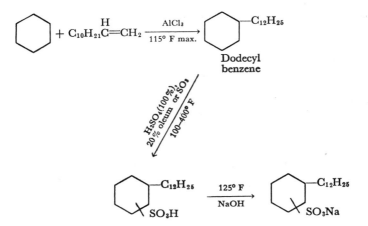

Dodecyl benzene

The manufacture of detergent alkylate is described in Chapter 13, "Soaps and Detergents."

Maleic Anhydride. Maleic anhydride use during 1960 reached approximately 90 million pounds.[65] This was all produced by catalytic oxidation of benzene. The flow sheet (Fig. 25.26) shows the manufacturing process.[159] It has been announced that a new plant will be coming on stream soon using a butylene oxidation route.[65]

Maleic anhydride is used for making polyester resins, alkyd resins, agricultural chemicals, paper-size drying oils, and styrene-maleic anhydride resins. Details on these products may be found in Chapter 10.

DDT (Dichlorodiphenyltrichloroethane). DDT is manufactured from chlorobenzene and chloral:

$$CCl_3CHO + 2C_6H_5Cl \xrightarrow{\text{oleum}} CCl_3CH(C_6H_4Cl)_2 + H_2O$$

Approximately 160 million pounds were produced in 1960.[66] This is a well known insecticide. About 50% of U. S. production is exported to South America and Asia.[66]

Aniline. Some 121 million pounds of aniline were produced from about 13 million gallons of benzene in the U. S. in 1960.[67]

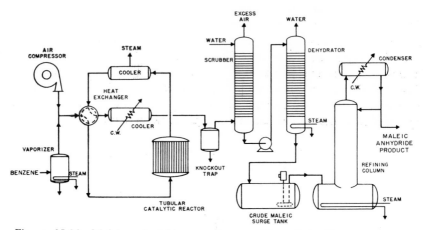

Figure 25.26. Maleic anhydride manufacture. [*Pet. Ref.*, **38**, *No. 11, 265 (1959), copyright Gulf Pub. Co.*]

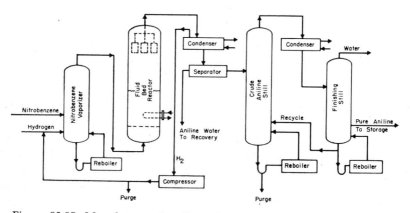

Figure 25.27. Manufacture of aniline. [*Pet. Ref.*, **38**, *No. 11, 224 (1959), copyright Gulf Pub. Co.*]

Aniline is produced in the U. S. by three processes; two start with nitrobenzene as an intermediate, the third starts with chlorobenzene. The chemistry of these processes is shown below and one is exemplified by the flow sheet,[153] Figure 25.27.

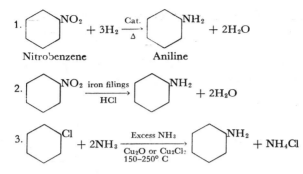

1. Nitrobenzene + $3H_2$ $\xrightarrow[\Delta]{\text{Cat.}}$ Aniline + $2H_2O$

2. NO_2 $\xrightarrow[\text{HCl}]{\text{iron filings}}$ NH_2 + $2H_2O$

3. Cl + $2NH_3$ $\xrightarrow[\substack{Cu_2O \text{ or } Cu_2Cl_2 \\ 150\text{–}250° \text{ C}}]{\text{Excess } NH_3}$ NH_2 + NH_4Cl

About 65% of aniline currently goes into the manufacture of rubber chemicals such as the thiazole derivatives.

Other important aniline uses are in dyes, drugs and veterinary medicines, and photographic chemicals (hydroquinone).

Some Other Benzene Derived Chemicals. Other significant chemicals derived from benzene are mono and dichlorobenzene, nitrobenzene and benzene hexachloride. The chlorobenzenes and nitrobenzene referred to here exclude intermediates for phenol or aniline.

Nitrobenzene is manufactured from benzene and mixed nitrating acids as shown below:

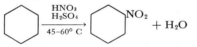

$$\xrightarrow[45\text{–}60° \text{ C}]{\substack{HNO_3 \\ H_2SO_4}} \quad NO_2 + H_2O$$

Nitrobenzene, other than for aniline, is used mainly as a solvent.

Mono and dichlorobenzene are made by two routes—direct chlorination or oxychlorination with HCl and air.[111] Figure 25.28 shows a flowsheet of the Dow process for direct chlorination.

Monochloro benzene is used for manufacture of DDT, sulfur dyes such as sulfur black, drugs, perfumes and numerous solvent applications. *o*-Dichlorobenzene is used mostly as a solvent or cleaner, particularly for metal degreasing. It has utility, when purified and stabilized, as a heat transfer fluid in the temperature range of 150–260° C.[69] *p*-Dichlorobenzene is used extensively in moth protection for wool. Small cakes of *p*-dichlorobenzene are used in the sanitary field. Its vapor pressure and pleasant odor make it highly suitable for this purpose.

Benzene hexachloride is manufactured by the direct addition of chlorine to benzene in the presence of ultraviolet light. Of the five isomers formed only one, the gamma form, is insecticidally active. Commercially, the gamma isomer constitutes about 12% of the product.[110] It is used as an insecticide or a miticide. Some 30 million pounds are marketed annually and production has become quite static.[68]

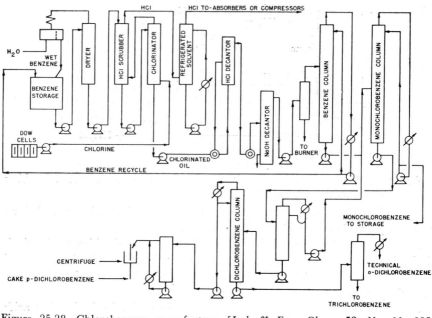

Figure 25.28. Chlorobenzene manufacture. [*Ind. & Eng. Chem.* **52**, *No. 11, 895 (1960).*]

Toluene Products

Approximately 68 million gallons of toluene were consumed in the U. S. in 1960 for chemical manufacture and solvent uses.[69]

Significant chemicals derived from toluene are benzene, toluene diisocyanate, detergents, TNT, benzoic acid, benzaldehyde, benzoyl chloride and phenol.

Benzene is rapidly becoming the most important outlet for toluene because of its availability and because of the rapid development of dealkylation processes. Chapter 14 describes these processes in detail.

Toluene Diisocyanate (TDI). Toluene diisocyanate is manufactured from toluene by the route indicated in the following equations.[55,120]

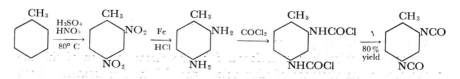

Toluene diamine is dissolved in a high boiling compatible solvent. The solvent mixture (10% amine) is then mixed with phosgene (1.5 to 3.5 lb phosgene per lb diamine) in a reactor held at 20 to 50° C. In this temperature range, the first phosgene unit is reacting.

The resulting slurry is pumped to a second reactor where further reaction with gaseous phosgene is carried out at 185° C. Unreacted phosgene and HCl are vented from the top of the reactor. The final conversion to the diisocyanate occurs in a third vessel where an inert gas is blown through

Figure 25.29. Chlorobenzene plant. (*Courtesy Dow Chemical Co.*)

the solution at 110 to 115° C. The resulting solution of crude TDI is distilled at 2 to 5 mm Hg pressure. The diisocyanate product distills overhead.

Toluene diisocyanate is reacted with polyols or polyesters to make polyurethanes. Only urethane foams have been commercialized at this writing. Flexible polyurethane foams are used for cushioning and padding in automobiles, furniture, carpeting, etc. Semi-rigid urethane foams are used for padding such as crash pads on automobiles. Rigid urethane foams possess excellent thermal insulation properties, thus are used for plastic panels for home construction and in insulation.

Detergents Derived from Toluene. Toluene sodium sulfonate for detergent use is prepared mainly by the use of SO_3 as the sulfonating agent. Some yield loss is incurred due to sulfone formation, but capital investment and operating costs are minimized to overbalance this difficulty.

Toluene sulfonates are used as stabilizers for liquid detergents and as conditioning agents for solid detergents. Some 4 million gallons of toluene were used to produce about 9 million pounds of toluene sulfonate during 1960.[71]

TNT (Trinitrotoluene). Manufacture of TNT[115] is generally carried out by a three stage batch nitration of toluene. Nitrating acids of various combinations of nitric and sulfuric acid are used to obtain maximum yield and efficiency. Strict temperature limitations and rates of heating are observed for safety and product quality. The crude "tri oil" TNT is treated by the Sellite process. This consists of hot and cold water washes, neutralization of free acids, sodium sulfite and sodium hydrogen sulfite treatments, "red water" separation, hot water wash, drying and flaking.

Primarily a military explosive, consumption of TNT is directly influenced by government requirements. TNT requires some 5 million gallons of toluene annually in its manufacture.

Phenol. A new plant to manufacture phenol from toluene is now in the construction stage.[2,72] This plant will use some 5 million gallons of toluene annually if operated at capacity.

The process is a two stage oxidation of phenol. The first step oxidizes toluene to benzoic acid, part of the benzoic acid is oxidized to phenol in the second stage, and unconverted benzoic acid is recycled back to this second stage. Advantages claimed are cheaper raw material, very low by-product generation, and virtually no waste.

Benzyl Chloride. The principal method for producing benzyl chloride[111] consists of chlorinating boiling toluene in darkness until there is a 37.5% increase in weight. The reaction mixture is then treated with mild alkali and distilled.

Benzyl chloride serves as the starting material for many pharmaceuticals, insecticides, perfumes, and dyes. One of the most important uses of benzyl chloride is in the manufacture of benzyl alcohol by reacting with alkalies. Approximately 21 million pounds were produced in 1961.[72]

Vinyl Toluene. Vinyl toluene is produced by a process similar to the one used for styrene, i.e., alkylation to ethyl toluene by Friedel-Crafts reaction between toluene and ethylene, then catalytic dehydrogenation to vinyl toluene.[125] Processing is complicated by the existence of 3 isomers; also, o-vinyl toluene undergoes side reactions in the dehydrogenation and is therefore separated before dehydrogenation.

Vinyl toluene is in many uses a replacement for styrene, in some cases producing a superior product, as in certain types of coatings. During 1960 production of vinyl toluene reached approximately 21 million pounds.

Chemicals from Xylene

Xylene outlets to chemical manufacture and solvent uses totaled approximately 102 million gallons during 1960.[72] For chemical uses, xylene is sold as the separated isomers—ortho, meta and para. Ethyl benzene is also obtained during the separation process. Usual percentages are: ethyl benzene, 21 per cent; para xylene, 18 per cent; meta xylene, 40 per cent; and ortho xylene, 20 per cent.

Ortho xylene in the U. S. is expanding at a very high rate and capacity is expected to reach 680 million pounds in 1961.[73] About 80 per cent of the production will be exported to Japan and Europe where it will be used to make phthalic anhydride. Para xylene is used primarily in the manufacture of terephthalic acid while the only substantial outlet for meta xylene is the manufacture of isophthalic acid.[85] The manufacture of these products is described below.

Phthalic Anhydride from o-Xylene. The flow sheet, Figure 25.30, shows the processing scheme for phthalic anhydride from o-xylene.[162]

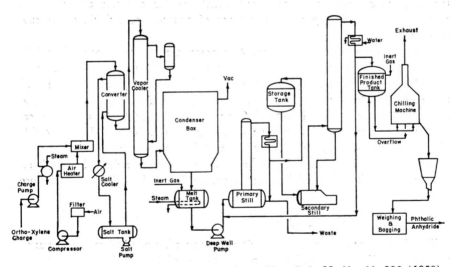

Figure 25.30. Phthalic anhydride from o-xylene. [*Pet. Ref.*, **38**, *No. 11*, 286 (1959), copyright Gulf Pub. Co.]

The vaporized xylene is fed to a mixer where it is contacted with hot air. This mixture then goes to salt cooled fixed-bed converter units where the oxidation reaction to phthalic anhydride and water takes place. The catalyst in the converter tubes is based on vanadium pentoxide (V_2O_5).

Crude phthalic anhydride is condensed out and spent gases are discharged through catalytic incinerating furnaces. The crude, molten phthalic anhydride is distilled batchwise in two vacuum stills in series. Light boilers such as benzoic acid are taken off under vacuum as a heads cut and the purified product is taken as a heart cut from the second still. The product is formed into chips and bagged, or is shipped in steam heated tank cars.

Uses for phthalic anhydride are described in a later section.

Terephthalic Acid. Para xylene is used mainly in the manufacture of terephthalic acid. Terephthalic acid is manufactured by liquid phase oxidation using one of many possible catalysts.[121] The dimethyl ester of terephthalic acid is reacted with ethylene glycol to form polyesters. These polyesters are used to form fibers such as Du Pont's named Dacron and film such as Du Pont's named Mylar. Approximately 140 million pounds of terephthalic dimethyl ester were consumed in the manufacture of polyester resins during 1960.

Isophthalic Acid. The manufacture of isophthalic acid[85] is the only substantial outlet for meta xylene. Processing techniques are very similar to those for converting para xylene to terephthalic acid.

Isophthalic acid is a direct competitor for phthalic anhydride. Superior properties are obtained in certain applications in surface coatings and reinforced plastics. Isophthalic acid can substitute for phthalic anhydride in many other uses during acute shortages of phthalic anhydride or its raw materials.

Products from Mixed Xylenes. A process has recently been placed in operation wherein mixed xylenes are oxidized to mixtures of the dibasic acids.[4] The process is a liquid phase air oxidation involving a heavy metal and some form of bromine as catalyst. Reaction conditions probably include a temperature range of 125–275° C and pressures up to 40 atmospheres. Solid acids are separated from the solvent and catalyst by centrifuging. Acids of high purity and in good yield are reported from this process.

A process for converting diisopropylbenzene to dicarboxylic acids has been reported.[76] Purification of isomers is accomplished in this process before oxidation.

Naphthalene Chemicals

The U. S. supply of naphthalene[74] was approximately 530 million pounds during 1960. The advent of petro-naphthalene will boost this considerably in the next few years. About 80% of the naphthalene produced is converted to phthalic anhydride. The balance goes into β-naphthol, surface active agents, moth balls, tanning agents, and refined naphthalene.

Phthalic Anhydride. Phthalic anhydride is produced by catalytic oxidation of naphthalene. Two major types of processes are available today. One[37] utilizes a fluid bed oxidation reactor while the other[163] utilizes a fixed bed reactor. Both processes utilize naphthalene and air as raw materials, carry out the oxidation under the influence of catalysts, and then finish the product by distillation. The fluid bed process is depicted in Figure 25.31.

Phthalic anhydride is used in the manufacture of plasticizers mainly for vinyl resins. Alkyd resin uses are about equal to that of plasticizers, each consuming about 40% of the phthalic anhydride marketed.

Other substantial outlets for phthalic anhydride are polyesters, dyes, agricultural chemicals, and pharmaceuticals.

Approximately 377 million pounds of phthalic anhydride were produced in the U. S. in 1960.[29,75]

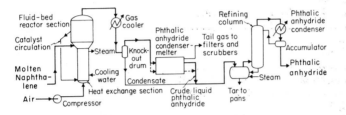

Figure 25.31. Phthalic anhydride by Badger fluid-bed process.
(*Chem. Eng., Dec. 14, 1959.*)

A process for phthalic anhydride derived from *o*-xylene is described in an earlier section.

Other Naphthalene Uses. β-naphthol is the most significant other use for naphthalene, taking some 35 million pounds in 1960. It is manufactured commercially by first making β-naphthalene sulfonic acid.[151] The acid is then fused with caustic, acidified, washed, and vacuum distilled. β-Naphthol has numerous uses in dye, rubber, perfume, and pharmaceutical industries.

Sulfonated naphthalenes are available commercially as surface active agents of various sorts.

A new carbamate insecticide is expected to show substantial growth and could consume 40 to 50 million pounds of naphthalene in the near future.[75]

REFERENCES

1. Angello, L. A., and Williams, W. H., *Ind. and Eng. Chem.*, **52**, No. 11, 894 (1961).
2. Ibid, 895.
3. Ibid, 897.
4. Burney, D. E., et al., *Pet. Ref.*, **38**, No. 6, 186 (1959).
5. *Chem. and Eng. News,* p. 20, Dec. 30 (1957).
6. *Chem. and Eng. News,* p. 21, May 30 (1960).
7. *Chem. and Eng. News,* pp. 92–102, July 18 (1960).
8. *Chem. and Eng. News,* p. 46, Dec. 5 (1960).
9. *Chem. and Eng. News,* p. 22, Dec. 26 (1960).
10. *Chem. and Eng. News,* p. 26, Jan. 16 (1961).

11. *Chem. and Eng. News,* p. 23, Mar. 6 (1961).
12. *Chem. and Eng. News,* p. 52, Apr. 17 (1961).
13. *Chem. Week,* **84,** No. 17, 39 (1959).
14. Ibid, 41–42.
15. Ibid, 42.
16. Ibid, 43–45.
17. Ibid, 48.
18. *Chem. Week,* **84,** No. 19, 80 (1959).
19. *Chem. Week,* **85,** No. 20, 56 (1959).
20. Ibid, 57.
21. Ibid, 59.
22. Ibid, 60.
23. Ibid, 65.
24. *Chem. Week,* **86,** No. 6, 41 (1960).
25. *Chem. Week,* **86,** No. 22, 63 (1960).
26. Ibid.
27. Ibid, 68.
28. *Chem. Week,* **87,** No. 23, 60 (1960).
29. *Chem. Week,* **87,** No. 24, 85 (1960).
30. *Chem. Week,* **88,** No. 4, 28 (1961).
31. Ibid, 39.
32. Ibid, 40.
33. Ibid, 69.
34. Ibid, 81.
35. *Chem. Week,* **88,** No. 10, 84 (1961).
36. *Chem. Week,* **88,** No. 15, 107 (1961).
37. Cronan, C. S., *Chem. Eng.,* **66,** No. 25, 79 (1959).
38. Davenport, C. H., *Pet. Ref.,* **39,** No. 3, 125 (1960).
39. Ibid, 127.
40. Faith, W. L., Keyes, D. B., and Clark, R. L., "Industrial Chemicals," 1–7, New York, John Wiley and Sons, 1957.
41. Ibid, 21–26.
42. Ibid, 31–41.
43. Ibid, 42–46.
44. Ibid, 80–86.
45. Ibid, 184.
46. Ibid, 271–276 and 510–511.
47. Ibid, 334.
48. Ibid, 379.
49. Ibid, 383–387.
50. Ibid, 453–460.
51. Ibid, 505–509.
52. Ibid, 577.
53. Ibid, 617–623.
54. Ibid, 752–755.
55. Ibid, 769.
56. Ibid, 776.
57. Ibid, 794–797.
58. Ibid, 798–803.
59. Fedor, W. S., *Chem. and Eng. News,* **39,** No. 12, 117 (1961).
60. Ibid.

61. Ibid, 120.
62. Ibid, 124.
63. Ibid, 125.
64. Ibid, 128.
65. Ibid, 130.
66. Ibid, 134.
67. Ibid, 132.
68. Ibid, 133.
69. Fedor, W. S., *Chem. and Eng. News*, **39**, No. 13, 132 (1961).
70. Ibid, 133.
71. Ibid, 134.
72. Ibid, 136.
73. Ibid, 140.
74. Ibid, 143.
75. Ibid, 144.
76. Fortuin, J. P., et al., *Pet. Ref.*, **38**, No. 6, 189 (1959).
77. Goldstein, R. F., "The Petroleum Chemicals Industry," 35–40, New York, John Wiley and Sons, 1958.
78. Ibid, 40–43.
79. Ibid, 45.
80. Ibid, 342.
81. Ibid, 346.
82. Ibid, 348.
83. Ibid, 353.
84. Ibid, 357.
85. Gordon, J., *Pet. Ref.*, **40**, No. 2, 141 (1961).
86. Hatch, L. F., *Pet. Ref.*, **37**, No. 11, 214 (1958).
87. Ibid, 217.
88. Ibid, 218.
89. Ibid, 220.
90. Ibid, 222.
91. Ibid, 223.
92. Hatch, L. F., *Pet. Ref.*, **38**, No. 8, 108 (1959).
93. Ibid, 107.
94. Ibid, 110.
95. Ibid, 111.
96. Hatch, L. F., *Pet. Ref.*, **39**, No. 5, 229 (1960).
97. Ibid, 232.
98. Hatch, L. F., *Pet. Ref.*, **39**, No. 6, 207 (1960).
99. Ibid, 208.
100. Ibid, 209.
101. Ibid, 210.
102. Hirschkind, W., *Ind. & Eng. Chem.*, **41**, 2749 (1949).
103. *Ind. & Eng. Chem.*, **59**, No. 9, 983 (1959).
104. Katzen, R., *Pet. Ref.*, **40**, No. 1, 161 (1961).
105. Ibid, 162.
106. Ibid.
107. Ibid.
108. Kirk, R. E. and Othmer, D. F., "Encyclopedia of Chemical Technology," Vol. 2, 678, New York, The Interscience Encyclopedia, Inc., 1952.
109. Ibid, Vol. 3, 661.

110. Ibid, 808.
111. Ibid, 812–817.
112. Ibid, 817–821.
113. Ibid, 824.
114. Ibid, Vol. 5, 906–925.
115. Ibid, Vol. 6, 45.
116. Ibid, Vol. 7, 244–245.
117. Ibid, 259.
118. Ibid, Vol. 9, 237 and 249.
119. Ibid, 699–712.
120. Ibid, Vol. 10, 379.
121. Ibid, 600.
122. Ibid, Vol. 11, 186.
123. Ibid, 189.
124. Ibid.
125. Ibid, Vol. 13, 141.
126. Messing, R. F. and Bradley, J. W., *Chem. Eng.*, **67**, No. 13, 74 (1960).
127. Ibid, 70.
128. Meyer, R. E., *Oil and Gas J.*, **54**, No. 7, 82 (1955).
129. Milledge, A. F., *J. Inst. Pet.*, **46**, 353 (1960).
130. Mitchell, R. L., *Pet. Ref.*, **35**, No. 7, 179 (1956).
131. Nicklaus, G. E., *Chem. Eng.*, **68**, No. 2, 82 (1961).
132. *Oil and Gas J.*, **55**, No. 35, 116 (1957).
133. Patton, J. L., et al., *Pet. Ref.*, **37**, No. 11, 180 (1958).
134. *Pet. Ref.*, **36**, No. 11, 254 (1957).
135. Ibid, 279.
136. *Pet. Ref.*, **38**, No. 11, 201–207 (1959).
137. Ibid, 208–209.
138. Ibid, 212–217.
139. Ibid, 228–231.
140. Ibid., 239.
141. Ibid, 244.
142. Ibid, 248.
143. Ibid, 250.
144. Ibid, 261.
145. Ibid, 266–269.
146. Ibid, 280.
147. Ibid, 283.
148. Ibid, 298.
149. Ibid, 304.
150. Ibid, 306.
151. Ponder, T. C., et al., *Pet. Ref.*, **38**, No. 11, 211 (1959).
152. Ibid, 223.
153. Ibid, 224.
154. Ibid, 225.
155. Ibid, 226.
156. Ibid, 235.
157. Ibid, 252.
158. Ibid, 264.
159. Ibid, 265.
160. Ibid, 272.

161. Ibid, 279.
162. Ibid, 286.
163. Ibid, 287.
164. Ibid, 40, No. 3, 125 (1961).
165. Ibid, 126.
166. Ibid.
167. Robertson, J. M., *Chem. Eng. Prog.*, **56,** No. 12, 64 (1960).
168. Salkind, M., *Ind. Eng. Chem.*, **51,** No. 10, 1232 (1952).
169. Ibid, 1235.
170. Ibid, No. 11, 1328.
171. "Synthetic Organic Chemicals," U. S. Tariff Commission Report (1950–1960 incl).
172. Ibid, 1959.
173. "The Chemical Industry Facts Book," 4th ed., Washington, Mfg. Chemists Assn., Inc., 1959.
174. Ibid.
175. Van Oosten, R. P., *J. Inst. Pet.*, **46,** 347 (1960).
176. Ibid, 350.
177. Weaver, D. G., *Ind. Eng. Chem.*, **51,** No. 8, 894 (1959).
178. Ibid, 897.
179. Ibid, 898.

INDEX

Acetaldehyde, 930
Acetic acid
  by fermentation, 212
  from wood, 588
Acetic anhydride, 930
Acetone, 915, 916, 925
  by fermentation, 190
  from glycerin manufacture, 456, 457
Acetylene, 514, 643, 896
  from calcium carbide, 643
  properties, 624
  transportation, 643
  uses, 642
Acetylsalicylic acid, 719, 734
Acid Black 1, 821
Acid Black 18, 832
Acid Blue 25, 832
Acid Blue 45, 832
Acid Dyes, 784
Acid Green 3, 828
Acid Green 25, 832
Acid number, 324
Acid Orange 7, 816
Acid Orange 49, 822
Acid Red 14, 816
Acid Red 23, 817
Acid Red 26, 816
Acid Red 38, 817, 818
Acid Red 73, 820
Acid Red 87, 829
Acid Red 115, 820
Acid Red 150, 819
Acid Violet 6, 816
Acid Yellow 23, 817

Acid Yellow 73, 829
Acridine Yellow, 830
Acrilan tow, 391
Acrolein, 456
Acrylate esters, 345
Acrylates, 891
Acrylic acid ester, 323
Acrylic fibers
  flow diagram, 389
  polymer manufacture, 388
  spinning, 390 to 392
Acrylonitrile, 899, 906, 921
  manufacture, 345
  production, 122
  synthesis, 122, 123
  uses, 123
Addition polymers, 282
Adipic acid, 323, 380
Aerobic fermentation, 191, 192
Air
  composition, 632
  liquefaction, 629
  rectification, 631
Alcohols from wood, 581
Aldrin, 748
Alizarin, 802
Alkaline fusion, 806
Alkylation, 809, 917
Alkylbenzene sulfonation, 461
Alkylene oxides, 470
Alkylolamides, 471
Alkylphenols, 934
Allyl chloride, 453, 455
Alpha-pinene, 593

Amination, 800
Amino acids, 215
Aminoplast resins, 312
Ammonia
  from coal carbonization, 226
  manufacturing processes, 92, 93, 94, 893
  production, 91
  recovery from soda ash manufacture, 136
  synthesis, 86, 102
  uses, 104, 129, 130
Ammonia converter, 103
Ammonium nitrate
  crystalline forms, 111
  hazards, 111, 112
  in explosives, 684, 686
  production, 111
Ammonium sulfamate, 743
Anderson expeller, 413
Aniline, 936
Animal oils, 399
  fish, 420
  lard, 422
Anionic surfactants, 462–469
Anisole, 800, 809
Anthranilic acid, 840
Anthraquinone, 838
Anthraquinone dyes, 831
Anthrone, 838
Antibiotics
  by fermentation, 198
  chloramphenicol, 205, 206
  chlortetracycline, 206, 207
  erythromycin, 207
  flow diagram, 203
  for plants, 748
  miscellaneous, 208
  oleandomycin, 208
  penicillin, 198
  production, 200, 201
  sales, 709
  streptomycin, 204
  tetracycline group, 206
Antifoam agents, 193
Antimonyl potassium tartrate, 738
Antioxidants, 246
Aramite, 748
Argon, 624, 641, 642
Arsenical compounds, 738
Artificial silk, 351

Aromatic chemicals, 931
  from coal, 236
Ascorbic acid, 720
Aspirin, 719, 934
Atabrine, 716
Atomic pile, 850
Aurin, 828
Azo dyes, 812
  manufacture, 824
Azoic coupling components, 789
Azoic dyes, 789

Bacteria, 181
Basic Blue 1, 827
Basic Blue 6, 831
Basic Blue 9, 831
Basic Brown 1, 786
Basic Dyes, 785
Basic Green, 827
Basic Orange, 816
Basic Orange 15, 830
Basic Red 9, 826
Basic Violet 3, 827
Basic Violet 10, 830
Basic Violet 14, 826
Basic Yellow 2, 828
Beeswax, 425
Beet sugar, 617, 618
Benzal chloride, 805
Benzaldehyde, 805
Benzanthrone, 838
Benzene, 230, 236, 518
  derivatives, 931
Benzene hexachloride, 748, 937
Benzidine, 800, 821
Benzoic acid, 805
Benzotrichloride, 805
Benzyl chloride, 805, 940
Beta-pinene, 593
Bisphenol A, 932
Black powder, 697
Borates, 668, 743
Borax, 668
Boric acid, 668
Brewing, 217
Brines, 127, 666
Bromamine acid, 832
Bromine, 147
Butadiene, 267, 293
  polymers, 245–247
  production, 268

Butane, 922
  oxidation of, 929
2,3-Butanediol, 215
Butane-propane, oxidation, 927
Butanol
  fermentation, 190, 191
  synthetic, 919, 930
Butene copolymers, 925
t-Butyl alcohol, 926
t-Butyl phenols, 925
Butyl rubber, 927
Butylenes, 922

Calcium arsenate, 738
Calcium chloride, 137
Calcium hypochlorite, 177
Cane sugar, 608
  (see Sugar)
Caprolactam, 934
Captan, 749
Carbon black, 760
Carbon dioxide, 644
  properties, 624
  solid, 645
Carbon disulfide, 747
Carbon monoxide shift reaction, 101
Carbon tetrachloride, 911
Carnauba wax, 424
Cascara, 598
Casein plastics, 335
Castor oil, 418
  for soap, 430
  styrenated, 419
Catalyts
  for gasoline, 497–502
  for polymerization, 245, 246
  for sulfuric acid, 75–77
Caustic soda, 158
  by causticizing, 158
  by-products, 173
  electrolytic, 160, 161
  end uses, 173
  lime-soda process, 159
  production, 158
Caustic soda cells
  Allen-Moore, 167
  Billiter, 172
  DeNora, 171
  Dow, 172
  Gibbs, 167
  Griesheim, 167

Caustic soda cells (Cont'd)
  Hargreaves-Bird, 167
  Hochst-Uhde, 171
  Hooker "S," 163
  I. C. I. Wyandotte, 171
  Mathieson, 171
  Mercury, 170, 171
  Nelson, 167
  Solvay, 171
  Sorenson, 171
  Townsend, 163
  Vorce, 167
Cellulose, 356, 524
  acetylation, 371
  alpha, beta, gamma, 356
  derivatives, 332
  formula, 333
  "soda," 358
Cellulose acetate, 367
  blended flake, 375
  delusterants for, 375
  history, 369
  secondary, manufacture, 370
  spinning, 375, 376
  triacetate, 373
  yarn, dope-dyed, 377
Cellulose xanthate, 359, 361
"Cellosolve," 905
Centripure soap process, 434
Ceresan, 749
Charcoal, 584, 585, 590
Chemical industry, 1
  economics, 4
Chemicals, uses, 5
Chinawood oil, 419
Chloramphenicol, 205, 206
Chlordane, 749
Chlorinated hydrocarbons, 908
Chlorinated methanes, 896
Chlorinated solvents, 911
Chlorine
  electrolytic, 173
  gaseous and bleach, 176
  liquid, 174
  nitrosyl process, 174
  shipping, 175
  sources, 173
  uses, 173, 176
Chloroacetic acids, 806
Chlorobenzene, 939
Chloroprene, 252

Chlortetracycline, 206, 207
Chrome dyes, 785
Chrome greens, 762
Chrome yellows, 762
Chromotropic acid, 807
Citric acid, 210
Coal
  analysis, 47
  by-products, 54
  carbonization, 53–55, 221
  carbonization, low temperature, 238
  chemicals, 221, 224, 226, 228
  classification, 40, 41, 43
  coke, 53, 222
  composition, 45
  firing, 48
  gasification, 50, 99, 239
  handling, 221
  hydrogenation, 52
  hydrolysis, 57
  mining, 44
  origin, 38
  oxidation, 57
  preparation, 44
  sintering, 49
  solvent extraction, 57
  utilization, 46
Coal tar
  aromatic chemicals from, 236
  distillation, 232, 233
  naphthalene, 235
  processing, 229, 231
  production, 230
  refining, 234
Cocaine, 718
Coconut oil, 416
  soap, 429
Cod-liver oil, 421
Coke, 53, 222
  gasification, 99
Coke oven gas, 228
  ammonia purification, 236
  ammonia recovery, 226
  H₂S removal, 228, 229
Coke ovens
  chemical recovery, 223
  Koppers-Becker, 225
  types, 224
Coke plant, 227
Colorless carbinol, 826
Condensation polymers, 282, 314
Copper carbonate, 742

Copper naphthenate, 743
Copper oxides, 742
Copper sulfate, 742
Corn oil, 415
Corn products, 608
Corn starch, 620
  hydrolysis, 621
Cottonseed oil, 415
  soap, 430
Cracking, petroleum, 60, 492, 494, 497
Crocein acid, 804
Cryolite, 740
Cumene, 916
Cuprammonium cellulose, 366
Cyanoethylation, 810
Cyanuric chloride, 809
Cyclonite, 693

2,4D, 934
DDT, 749, 935
Decyl alcohol, 919
Delusterants for rayon, 360
Denier, 350
Derby process, 866
Detergent alkylate, 462–464, 935
Dextrose, 621
Diallylphthalate, 323
Diaminostilbenedisulfonic acid, 823
o-Dianisidine, 821
Diazotization, 812
Dibenzanthrone, 838
Dicumyl peroxide, 326
Dicyandiamide, 314
Dihydrostreptomycin, 710, 711
Dipentene, 596
Direct Black 17, 786
Direct Black 38, 824
Direct Blue 1, 821
Direct Blue 6, 824
Direct dyes, 786
Direct Red 28, 786, 821
Direct Red 83, 822
Direct Yellow 4, 823
Direct Yellow 12, 823
Disazo dyes, 819
Disinfectants, 752
Disperse Blue 26, 834
Disperse dyes, 788
Disperse Red 1, 818
Disperse Violet 1, 788
Disproportionation
  in polymerization, 292

Distillation, petroleum, 488, 490, 491
  coal tar, 232, 233
  wood, 583, 587, 589
Ditertiary butyl peroxide, 326
Dithiocarbamates, 749
Dodecene, 916
Dodecyl benzene, 935
"Dowanols," 905
"Dowtherm A," 934
Drugs, sales of, 709
Dry ice, 645
Dye intermediates
  manufacture, 795
  production, 811
Dyes, (see also Pigments)
  application, 790
  equipment, 792
  for various fibers, 784
  manufacture, 811
  non-textile uses, 794
  printing, 792
  production, 794, 843
  properties, 784
  uses, 781
Dynamites, 690

EDNA, 695
Electric generating capacity, U. S., 847
Enamels, 770, 772
Eosine, 829
Epoxy resins
  amine hardeners for, 320
  chemistry, 316, 317
  manufacture, 317
  materials, 319
  production, 315
Erythromycin, 207
Essential oils from wood, 597
Ester interchange, 315
Ethanol, 188, 189, 906
Ethanolamines, 905
Ethylbenzene, 270, 908, 917
Ethyl chloride, 911
Ethyl ether, 717
Ethylene
  chemicals, 899
  manufacture, 515
  purification, 516
Ethylene cyanohydrin, 906
Ethylene dichloride, 910
Ethylene glycols, 902

Ethylene oxide, 900, 902
  adducts, 469
  homopolymers, 906
  surfactants, 470
Ethylene urea, cyclic, 314
Energy, 36, 37, 95
Explosives
  characteristics and uses, 674, 676
  detonation velocity, 684
  initiators, primers, igniters, 696
  propellants, 680, 698
  properties, 675
  table of, 676
  technology, 686

Fats, 399
  butter, 423
  constituents, 400
  consumption, 411
  decolorization, 401
  lard, 423
  oleomargarine, 423
  pressing, 401
  production, 401
  rendering, 401
  soap, 432
  solvent extraction, 401
  splitting, 408
  tallow, 423
Fatty acids
  branched chain, 407
  distillation, 444
  from glycerides, 442, 443
  from tall oil, 445
  production, 446
  purification, 445
  saturated, 402
  soap, 446
  substituted, unsaturated, 406
  Twitchell process for, 443
  unsaturated, 403
  uses, 446
Fatty alcohols, 465
  flow sheet, 467
  production, 465
Fatty alcohol sulfates, 465
Fatty oil deodorizing, 408
Fermentation, 180
  acids, 210
  aerobic, 191
  alcohol, 188
  amino acids, 215

Fermentation (*Cont'd*)
  anaerobic, 188
  anaerobic, alcohol, 188
  anaerobic, butanol-acetone, 190
  antibiotics, 198
  as unit process, 184
  brewing, 217
  equipment, 193
  ketogenic, 213
  media, 186, 196, 201
  microbial nutrition, 182
  microorganisms, 181
  processes, 196
  products, 181
  rates, 187
  steroid transformations, 217
  yields, 186, 197
Fertile material, 849
Fertilizers
  ammoniated superphosphates, 662
  consumption, 663
  history, 660
  mixed, 661
  natural organic, 670
  nitrogen sources, 90, 660
  phosphorus sources, 661
  potassium salts, 663
  potassium sources, 661
  sodium nitrate, 663
  synthetic urea, 671
Fiberboard, 555, 560
Fibers, textile, man-made, 349
  definitions, 350
  elongation, 351
  history, 350
  production, 352
  spinning, 349
  (*see also* Textile fibers)
Fischer-Tropsch process, 51
Fissionable materials, 849
Fission product separation, 885
Fluoride volatility process, 885
Fluorine compounds, insecticides, 739
Fluorocarbons, 912
Formaldehyde, 340, 894
Fourdrinier machine, 550, 552
Fuel elements, 872
Fuels, 36
  reserves, 38
Fumaric acid, 213, 322
Fumigants, 747
Fungi, 181, 182

Fungicides, 741
  classification, 736
  synthetic organic, 748
Furfural process for lube oils, 508

G acid, 804
Gamma acid, 814
Gases, industrial, 623, 624
Gaseous diffusion, 868
Gasoline
  additives, 503
  blending, 61
  by alkylation, 505
  by polymerization, 506
  from petroleum cracking, 493
  increasing octane rating, 504
  motor, 493
  natural, 64, 504
  upgrading by reforming, 500
Glass fibers, 396
Glauber salt, 141, 145, 146
Gluconic acid, 211
Glycerides, hydrolysis, 443
Glycerin
  by fermentation, 454
  crude, 448, 451
  esters, 399
  for dynamite, 451, 452, 454
  from spent soap lye, 450
  manufacture, 919–921
  purification, 451
  supplies, 452
  synthetic (*see* Glycerin, synthetic)
  U.S.P., 451
Glycerin lye, 435
Glycerin stearic acid, 400
Glycerin, synthetic
  acrolein-hydrogen peroxide process, 456
  capacity, 453
  flow diagram, 455
  from formic acid, 456
  from propylene and chlorine, 452
  process description, 454
Glycerol stearates, 399
Glyceryl tristearate, 400
Glycol ethers, 905
Glyodin, 749
Godet, 363
Grease, inedible, 430
Grease, petroleum, 511
Gum turpentine, 594

H acid, 807, 814
Haleite, 695
Halogenated hydrocarbons, 908
Halogenation, 805
Hardboard manufacture, 562
Helium
    occurrence, 640
    production, 640, 641
    properties, 624
Hemicellulose, 525
Herbicides, 743
    organic, 744
    synthetic organic, 751
Hexamethylene tetramine, 112, 113, 341, 895
Holocellulose, 524
Hormones, by fermentation, 181
Hydrazine, 114, 115, 706
    propellant, 704
Hydrazobenzene, 800
Hydrochloric acid, 142–145
Hydrocyanic acid, 747
Hydrogen
    miscellaneous processes for, 627
    molecular forms, 705
    occurrence and manufacture, 625
    production, 96
    properties, 624
    purification, 99
    steam-iron process, 626
    water electrolysis process, 627
    water gas process, 625, 626
Hydrogenation of oils, 425
Hydrogen cyanide, 118–122, 898
Hydrogen peroxide, 456
Hydrophil, 460
Hydrophobe, 460
Hydroxyanthraquinone, 808
Hydroxynaphthoic acid, 810

"Igepon T," 469
Indamine, 830
Indigoid dyes, 838
Indoxyl, 839
Industrial alcohol, 189
Influenza vaccine, 729, 730
Ingrain dyes, 790
Injection molding, 278
Insecticides, 732
    classification, 736
    inorganic compounds, 738
    microbial, 750

Insecticides (Cont'd)
    organic compounds, 744
    phosphates, 750
    regulation, 733
    synthetic organic compounds, 748
Ion exchange, 857
Iron oxide, 761
Isobutylene, 925, 926
Isobutyraldehyde, 919
Isobutyronitrile, 919
Isooctyl alcohol, 919
Isophthalic acid, 942
Isoprene, 926
Isopropanol, 914, 915
Isopropanolamines, 918
Isopropyl acetate, 916
Itaconic acid, 212

J acid, 807, 814
J acid urea, 822
Jordon refiner, 548

2-Ketogluconic, 214
Kojic acid, 212

Lacquers, 773–775
Lactic acid, 211
Lard, 422
Lard oil, 422
Lead arsenate, 739
Lead azide, 697
Lead styphnate, 697
Lebedev process, 269
Leblanc process, 141
Leuco base, 827
Lindane, 748
Linseed oil, 411, 413
Lipids, 400
Litharge, 760
Lithopone, 759
LPG, oxidation, 927
Lubricating oil
    blending, 511
    refining, 506

Maleic anhydride, 322, 344, 935
Mannheim furnace, 138
Melamine, 313, 343
Melt spinning, 382
Mercury fulminate, 696
Methane, 892
    chemicals, 894
    chlorination, 896

Methanol
  from methane, 894
  from wood, 588
Methyacrylates, 897
Methylamines, 123
Methyl bromide, 748
Methyl ethyl ketone, 924
Methyl methacrylate, 341
Methylene bridge, 308
Microbial nutrition, 182–184
Microorganisms, 181
Missile propellants
  (see Propellants)
Mixed xylenes, 942
Monazite ore, 871
Monoazo dyes, 815
Monsavon process, 434
Mordant Black 13, 833
Mordant Black 17, 817
Mordant Brown 4, 817
Mordant dyes, 789
Mordant Red 11, 789, 832

Naphthalene
  derivatives, 803, 942
  from coal tar, 235, 236
  from petroleum, 236, 519
Naphthols, 807, 814
Naphthylamine, 799
Narcotics, 716
Natural gas, 63, 504
Naval stores, 592
  uses, 596
Neat soap, 433
Neosalvarsan, 716
Nicotine, 745
Niter cake, 137, 138
Nitration, 689, 693, 769
Nitric acid, 105
  atmospheric process, 107
  concentration, 109, 110
  high strength, 110
  HOKO process, 108
  manufacture, 105–109
  uses, 110
Nitroalcohols, 124
Nitroanthraquinone, 798
Nitrobenzenes, 796, 799, 937
Nitrogen, 86, 640
Nitrogen fixation
  ammonia (direct synthetic) process, 87
  cyanamide process, 88

Nitrogen fixation (Cont'd)
  cyanide process, 88
  electric arc process, 87
  nitride process, 88
Nitrogen products, synthetic, 86
Nitroglycerin, 689
1-Nitro-2-methylanthraquinone, 809
Nitronaphthalene, 799
Nitroparaffins, 123
  properties, 124
Nitrophenols, 797
Nitrous oxide, 647
Nonene, 916
Nonionic surfactants, 469, 903
  alkylolamides, 471
  block polymers, 471
  ethylene oxide adducts, 469, 470
  polymeric compounds, 470
  sorbitol compounds, 472
  sugar surfactants, 471
Nuclear cross sections, 860
Nuclear energy
  costs, 851, 853
  raw materials, 852
Nuclear fission, 846
Nuclear fusion, 848
Nuclear reactor fuel cycle, 850, 851
Nuclear reactors, 848
  classification, 871
  spent fuel recovery, 878
Nylon, 378, 935
  cold drawing, 384
  history, 378
  manufacture, 379
  melt spinning, 382
  necking down, 383
Nylon 6, 381
Nylon 11, 381

Oleic acid, 469
Oleomargarine, 423
Oleum, 78
Oleyl chloride, 469
Oleyl N-methyltaurate, 469
Oil
  castor, 418
  coconut, 416
  cod-liver, 421
  corn, 415
  cottonseed, 415
  drying, 414, 763
  flaxseed, 414

Oil (*Cont'd*)
  lard, 410
  linseed, 411
  olive, 414
  palm, 415
  peanut, 415
  rape, 419
  seasame, 419
  soybean, 416
  sperm, 410, 424
  tall, 420
  tung, 419
Oils
  adulteration, 410
  animal, 420–422
  constituents, 400
  consumption, 411
  deodorizing of, 408
  fish, 410
  hydrogenation of, 425, 426
  in coatings, 763
  vegetable, 399, 410, 414
  winterizing of, 408
Olive oil, 414
  for soap, 430
Orange reactive dye, 788, 819
Organic chemicals, synthetic,
    production, 891
Ostromislenski process, 270
Oxidation, 808, 927
Oxidation dyes, 790
Oxo chemicals, 895
  from *n*-butenes, 924
Oxygen
  distribution, 636
  gaseous, 634, 635
  Linde-Fränkl process, 637
  liquid, 632
  production, 629
  properties, 624
  separation from air, 633
  transportation, 638
Oxytetracycline, 207

Paint
  application, 776
  emulsion, 767
  epoxy, 769
  fluorescent, 770
  foreign production, 776
  formula, 764
  latex, 767

Paint (*Cont'd*)
  pigments, 755, 764
  types, 763
Palm oil, 415
  soap, 430
Paper
  consumption, 526
  honeycomb cores, 567
  laminates, 564
  materials and equipment for, 555
  modified, 566
  overlay, 566
  process for, 548
  production, 527
  resins in, 565
  stock, 547
Particle board, 562, 563
Peanut oil, 415
Penicillin, 198
  manufacture, 724
  production, 710
Perchloroethylene, 912
Pesticides, 745
  production, 737
PETN, 696
Petrochemicals
  aromatic, 518
  aromatic, dealkylation, 520
  aromatic, purification, 519
  hydrocarbons (*see desired compound*)
  miscellaneous olefins, 518
Petroleum
  composition, 59
  cracking, 60, 492, 494, 497
  crude oil, 59, 478
  discovery, 479
  origin, 57
  platforming, 502, 503
  production, 511, 512
  refining, 60, 488, 489
  reforming, 500
  ultraforming, 502
Petroleum, crude
  classification, 484
  distillation, 488, 490, 491
  nature of, 483
  reserves, 481
  statistics, 482, 483
  transportation, 487
Pharmaceuticals
  antibiotics, 200, 201, 208, 709, 724, 748
  history, 708

Pharmaceuticals (*Cont'd*)
  immunizing biologicals, 728
  preparations, 713
  products, 715
  sulfa drugs, 720
  synthetic medicinals, 712
  vitamins (*see desired compound*)
Phenol, 806, 932, 940
  chlorination (Dow) process, 338
  cumene process, 339
  Raschig process, 339
  sulfonation process, 338
Phenol alcohols, 308
Phenol formaldehyde
  molding powders, 310
  resins, 307–312
Phenolic resins, 932
Phenylenediamine, 830
Phenylglycine, 839
Phosgenation, 315
Phosphate rock
  beneficiation, 652
  deposits, 650
  production, 650
  uses, 649
Phosphates, 658
  uses, 659
Phosphoric acid
  from phosphorus, 657
  wet acid process, 658
Phosphorite, 649
Phosphorus
  compounds, 658
  from electric furnace, 654
Phthalic anhydride, 323, 829, 838, 941
  manufacture, 344, 942
Phthalocyanine blue, 762
Phthalocyanines, 842
Picramic acid, 817
Picric acid, 696
Pigment Blue 16, 843
Pigments (*see also* Dyes)
  applications, 755
  colored, 760
  dispersion in paint, 764
  luminescent, 762
  metallic, 762
  particle size, 774
  production, 761
  rayon, 360
  white, 756
Pigment Yellow 3, 818

Pine oil, 446, 595
Piperidine, 320
Plasticizers, 275
Plastics, synthetic, 274
  addition polymers, 282, 294
  commercial products, table of, 284–291
  condensation polymers, 282, 307
  definition, 274
  extrusion, 278
  fabrication, 276
  film, 279
  injection molding, 278
  manufacturing processes, 294
  organic chemistry of, 281
  physical chemistry of, 280
  plasticizers, 275
  polymer types, 283
  polystyrene crystallites, 281
  testing, 275
  thermoplastic, 276
  thermosetting, 276
  U. S. production, 294, 295
  world production, 296
Plastics, types
  casein, 335
  cellulose, 332–335, 369–375
  condensation polymers, 307
  epoxy resins, 315–322
  molding powders, 302, 310
  phenol-formaldehyde resins, 307
  polycarbonate, 314
  polystyrene, 304
  polyurethanes, 337
  polyvinylbutyral, 336
  silicone, 336
Plutonium, 849
Polio vaccine, 730
Polyazo dyes, 823
Polybutenes, 926
Polycarbonates, 314, 315
Polyester fibers, 386
Polyester resins
  equipment, 325
  raw materials, 322
Polyethylene, 908
  high-pressure process, 327, 330
  low-pressure process, 330
  polymerization, 326
Polyisobutylenes, 926
Polymerization processes, 294
  emulsion, 245, 246, 298
  mass, 297

Polymerization processes (*Cont'd*)
  precipitation, 306
  solution, 303
  suspension, 300
    recipe, 302
Polymers, stereospecific, 259, 292
Polyolefin fibers, 396
Polypropylene, 516, 922, 927
  fibers, 397
Polypropylene glycols, 918
"Polysolve," 905
Polystyrene, 304
Polytetrafluoroethylene, 395
Polyurethanes, 337, 918
Polyvinylbutyral, 336
Potash minerals, 670
Potash salts, 668–670
Potassium salts, 663
Printing dyes, 792
Printing ink, 778
  colored, 780
Propane deasphalting, 508
Propellants, rocket, 680
  liquid bipropellants, 702
  liquid, cryogenic, 705
  liquid monopropellants, 704
  manufacture, 704
  properties, 703
  solid, 700, 704, 705
  specific impulse, 699, 701
Propylene, 516
Propylene chemicals, 913, 914
Propylene glycol, 918
Propylene oxide, 918
Propylene tetramer, 917
Proteins for fibers, 378
Prussian Blue, 762
Purex process, 880, 883
Pulp
  from miscellaneous materials, 545
  from wood, 525
Pyrazolone, 817
Pyrethrum, 746
Pyromellitic dianhydride, 321
Pyrometallurgy for uranium, 885

Quinone, 808

R acid, 804, 819
Radioactive wastes, 886
Radiochemical plant safety, 886
Radiochemical processing, 878

Rape oil, 419
Rare gases, 624, 642
Rayon, 351
  "bright," 359
  cellulose acetate process, 367
  chemical manufacture, 356
  cuprammonium process, 366
  dope dyeing, 360
  nitro process, 366
  pigments for, 360
  spinning, 361, 363, 364
RDX, 693
Reactive dyes, 788
Red lead, 760
Refinery gases, 514
Refining
  coal tar, 234
  petroleum, 60, 488, 489
  sugar, 615
  tall oil, 446
Reserpine, 722
Resins, natural, 275
Resins, synthetic
  aminoplasts, 313
  epoxy, 315
  for coatings, 777, 778
  phenol-formaldehyde, 307
  polyester, 322–326
Resorcinol, 807, 829
Riboflavin, 208, 209
Rocket engines, 698
Rocket propellants
  (*see* Propellants)
Rocket propulsion, 680, 699
Rodenticides, 743, 751
Rosin, 594
Rosin oil, 596
Rotenone, 746
Rubber, 240
  calendering, 264
  compounding, 262
  for automobile tires, 264
  fuel tanks, 267
  GR-S, 240, 241
  mechanical goods, 266
  natural, 256
    drying of, 258
    latex, 257
    synthesis, 260
  oil-extended, 249
  properties, 253
  synthetic, 244

Rubber, synthetic (*Cont'd*)
  butadiene-acrylonitrile, 251
  butadiene-styrene, 244–250
  butyl, 250
  GR-S, 240, 241
  "Hypalon," 255
  polymer structure, 259
  polymerization of, 245, 246
  production capacity, 241
  silicone, 252
  technology, 262
  wear resistance, 248, 249
Ryania, 747

Saccharin, 723
Safranine B, 831
Salt, 126–128
Salt cake, 137
  Laury furnace, 141
  Leblanc process, 141
  Mannheim furnace, 138–140
  synthetic, 141
Salvarsan, 716
Sandmeyer reaction, 810
Schaeffer's acid, 804
Schweizer solution, 366
Seed disinfectants, 742
Sesame oil, 419
Silicone plastics, 366
Silicone polymers, 255
Silver salt, 832
Soap, 428
  batch kettle process, 430
  batch milling, 435
  castor oil, 430
  coconut oil, 429
  cold process, 437
  continuous processing, 433, 436
  cottonseed oil, 430
  crutcher, 437
  end uses, 460
  fatty acids, 442–448
  glycerin, 448–458
  granulated, 438
  laundry, 436
  manufacture, 429
  olive oil, 430
  palm oil, 430
  powder, 438
  raw materials, 429
  sales, 460
  spray drying, 438–442

Soap (*Cont'd*)
  supply, 459
  tallow, 429
  toilet, 435
  toilet, synthetic, 452
  transparent, 438
  types, 428
Soda ash, 129, 132, 134
  materials for, 131
  Solvay process, 129, 130
Soda cellulose, 358, 359
Sodium arsenite, 743
Sodium bicarbonate, calcining, 135
Sodium bisulfite, 155
Sodium carbonate (*see* Soda ash)
Sodium chlorate, 743
Sodium chloride (*see* Salt)
Sodium chlorite, 178
Sodium fluoride, 740
Sodium fluosilicate, 740
Sodium hyposulfite, 156
Sodium nitrate, 663
Sodium phosphates, 475
Sodium silicate, 146
  detergent additive, 475
Sodium sulfate, 475
Sodium sulfate, anhydrous
  (*see* Salt cake)
Sodium sulfide, 148, 149
  production, 152
Sodium thiosulfate (hypo), 152
Solexol process, 418, 421
Soluble castor oil, 418
Solvay process (*see* Soda ash)
Solvent Red 27, 820
Solvent Yellow 1, 815
Sorbitol surfactants, 472
Sorbose, 213
Soybean oil, 416
Sperm oil wax, 424
Spinning, 363
  continuous, 365
  dry, 376
  melt, 382
Spray drying, 438
  countercurrent, 439
  detergents, 438, 466
  soap powder, 441
  variables, 439
Starch, 607, 619
  occurrence, 619
  sources, 607

Steroid transformations, 216
Storax, 598
Streptomycin, 204, 710, 711
Styrene, 270, 339, 932
Sucrose, optical activity, 606
Sugar, 601
　beet, 617
　cane, 608
　　by-products, 619
　　juice clarification, 610
　　juice extraction, 608
　　refining, 615
　chip, 622
　direct consumption, 615
　economics, 603
　flow diagram, 612
　inversion reaction, 607
　production, 604
　surfactants, 471
Sugar cane, 602, 619
Sulfanilimide, 720
Sulfathiazole, 720
Sulfonation, 463, 801
Sulfur
　as fungicide, 741
　as insecticide, 740
　occurrence, 83
　recovery, 84
　transportation, 80
　uses, 85
Sulfur blue dyes, 841
Sulfur dioxide, 748
Sulfur dyes, 787
Sulfuric acid, 66
　anhydrite process, 82
　catalysts, 75
　chamber process, 69
　concentration, 80
　consumption, 82
　contact process, 74–77
　manufacture, 67
　production, 69
　properties, 79
　recovery, 81
Superphosphates, 661
Surfactants
　(see under Synthetic detergents)
Synthesis gas, 97, 892
Synthetic detergents, 460
　amphylotic, 473
　anionic surfactants, 462–469

Synthetic detergents (Cont'd)
　builders and additives, 474, 476, 659
　categories, 460
　cationic surfactants, 474
　end uses, 460
　hydrophil-hydrophobe balance, 460,
　　461
　manufacture, 463
　non-ionic surfactants, 469, 903
　production, 458
　slurry plant, continuous, 465
　supply and disposition, 459
Synthetic fibers
　(see Fibers)

Tall oil, 420, 455, 595
　refining, 446–448
　soaps, 448
　utilization, 449
Tallow, 423
　consumption, 430
　for soap, 429
Tannin, 596
Terphthalic acid, 942
Tetrachloroethane, 912
Tetracycline, 206, 727
Tetryl, 695
Textile fibers, man-made, 349
　"Acrilan," 389
　acrylics, 388–392
　"bright" rayon, 359
　cellulose acetate, 369–378
　crimping, 369
　"Dacron," 386
　dope dyeing, 377
　dry spinning, 376
　"Dynel," 394
　glass, 396
　heat setting, 387
　melt spinning, 382
　nylon, 378–385
　polyester, 386
　polyolefins, 396
　polypropylene, 397
　polytetrafluoroethylene, 395
　prices, 355
　production, 352–354
　protein, 378
　rayon, 356, 357
　"Saran," 394
　spinning, 361
　spun yarn, 368

Textile fibers, man-made (*Cont'd*)
  stereo-regulated, 397
  "Teflon," 395
  "Terylene," 386
  textile operations, 367
  textured yarns, 387
  "Verel," 394
  "Vinyon," 395
  vinyl, 394, 395
Thallous sulfate, 744
Thioindigoid dyes, 838
Thorium, 839, 860, 871
Titanium dioxide, 756
  for rayon, 360
TNT, 692, 940
Toilet soap, 435
Toluene, 54, 230, 518
  derivatives, 938
Toluene diisocyanate, 918, 938
Toluene sodium sulfonate, 940
Topham box, 364
Tranquilizers, 938
Trichloroethylene, 912
Trimethylpropane, 930
Triphenylmethane chromophore, 825
Tung oil, 419
Turkey Red Oil, 418
Turpentine, 596

Ultramarine blue, 762
Uranium, recovery from ore, 854
Uranium-235, 868
Uranium-238, 849
Uranium dioxide, 870
Uranium dioxide fuel, irradiated, 882
Uranium feed materials, 861
Uranium hexafluoride
  manufacture, 866, 867
  reduction to tetrafluoride, 869
Uranium metal, 865
Uranium ore processing
  ion exchange, 857
  leaching equipment, 859
  solvent extraction, 856, 862, 863
  sulfate processes, 855
Uranium tetrafluoride, 862, 867
Urea, 115, 118, 342, 671
  Chemico process, 117
  duPont process, 116
  Inventa process, 117
  Montecatini process, 117
  Pechiney process, 116

Vaccines, 728
Vanillin, 581
Varnish, 770
Varnish resins, 770, 771
Vat dyes, 787
Vat Blue 1, 839
Vat Blue 4, 836
Vat Blue 20, 837
Vat Green 1, 837
Vat Orange 5, 841
Vat Orange 9, 836
Vat Red 41, 840
Vat Yellow 1, 836
Vat Yellow 3, 835
Vegetable oils, 399
Vinegar, 192
Vinyl acetate, 345, 897
Vinyl chloride, 340, 897, 910
Vinyl fibers, 394, 395
Vinyl toluene, 941
Vitamins, 208
  B_{12}, 209
  C, 214, 720, 721
  Riboflavin (B_2), 208
Volatility process, 884

Waste, industrial, treatment, 29–34
Water
  boiler, treatment of, 26
  corrosion by, 15
  drinking, standards for, 20
  hardness, 13
  industrial uses, 10
  industrial waste, 37
  pollution of, 18
  quality, 13
  softening, 23
  sources, 12
  treatment, 19
Water glass, 146
Waxes, 399, 424, 425
Weedkillers, 743
Wet spinning, 361
White arsenic, 743
White lead, 757, 758
Wood
  carbonization, 582, 583, 586
  cellulose from, 356
  chemical analysis, 526
  chemical nature, 524
  chemical pulping, 535

Wood (*Cont'd*)
   compressed, 569
   essential oils from, 597
   explosion process for defibering, 559
   fiberboard, 555
   fire-retardant treatment, 574
   gum turpentine, 594
   hardwood distillation, 583, 587
   hydrolysis, 575
   mechanical pulping, 532, 558
   medicinals from, 598
   naval stores, 592
   occurrence and utilization, 523
   preservation, 569, 572, 574, 752
   pulp and paper, 525
   resin-impregnated, 568
   rosin, 595
   softwoods distillation, 589
   solvent extraction, 525
   steam distillation, 525
   sulphate turpentine, 595
   tannin, 596
   thermal-mechanical pulping, 558
Wood carbonization, chemicals from, 586

Wood hydrolysis
   Bergius-Rheinau process, 577
   Madison process, 578
   pulp production by, 580
   reactions, 576
Wood pulp
   bleaching, 544
   chemical processes for, 535
   cleaning, 541
   preparation of wood, 530
   production, 528, 529
   semichemical, 540–542
   sulphate process, 539
   sulphite process, 536
Wood tars, 584
Wood turpentine, 590, 594

Xanthene chromophore, 829
Xanthene dyes, 528
Xylene, 54, 230, 518
   derivatives, 941

Yeasts, 182

Zinc oxide, 758